D1281259

Encyclopedia
of
Fluid Mechanics

VOLUME 7

Rheology and
Non-Newtonian Flows

Gulf Publishing Company
Book Division
Houston, London, Paris, Tokyo

Encyclopedia
of
Fluid Mechanics

VOLUME 7

Rheology and Non-Newtonian Flows

N. P. Cheremisinoff, Editor

in collaboration with—

R. Agarwal
J. Berlamont
B. H. Bersted
A. F. Borghesani
M.-J. Brekner
J. F. Céspedes B.
R. P. Chhabra
J. T. Chung
Y. Cohen
R. Darby
D. DeKee
J. F. Dijksman
A. Duduković
K. Funatsu
E. R. Harrell

S. L. Harris
C. R. Huang
T. Kajiwara
D. M. Kalyon
W. Kozicki
A. K. Kulshreshtha
C. Kuroda
P. J. R. Leblans
M. F. Letelier S.
G. H. Michler
N. Nakajima
A. Nakayama
K. Ogawa
V. O. Popadić
M. B. Powley

E. P. W. Savenije
H. A. Schneider
B. J. R. Scholtens
D. H. Sebastian
A. V. Shenoy
J. Stastna
K. Takahashi
P. N. Tandon
M. N. Tekić
C. Tiu
P. H. T. Uhlherr
G. Verreet
K. C. Wilson

Encyclopedia of Fluid Mechanics

VOLUME 7

Rheology and Non-Newtonian Flows

Library of Congress Cataloging-in-Publication Data

(Revised for vol. 7)

Encyclopedia of fluid mechanics.

Includes bibliographies and indexes.
Contents: v. 1. Flow phenomena and measurement—
v. 2. Dynamics of single-fluid flows and mixing—[etc.]
— v. 7. Rheology and non-Newtonian flow.
1. Fluid mechanics—Dictionaries. I. Cheremisinoff,
Nicholas P.
TA357.E53 1986   620.1′06   85-9742

Series ISBN 0-87201-492-4

ISBN 0-87201-540-8

CONTENTS

SECTION II: SLIPPAGE AND DRAG PHENOMENA

SECTION III: POLYMER RHEOLOGY AND PROCESSING

CONTRIBUTORS TO THIS VOLUME

R. Agarwal, Department of Mathematics, Harcourt Butler Technological Institute, Kanpur, India.

J. Berlamont, Laboratorium Voor Hydraulica, Katholieke Universiteit te Leuven, Heverlee, Belgium.

B. H. Bersted, Amoco Chemicals Company, Naperville, Illinois, USA.

A. F. Borghesani, Dipartimento diFisica "G. Galilei" Universita di Padova and G.N.S.M./C.I.S.M., Padova, Italy.

M.-J. Brekner, Research and Development Informationstechnik-Division, Hoechst AG, Kalle Wiesbaden, Federal Republic of Germany.

J. F. Céspedes B., Department of Mechanical Engineering, University of Santiago, Chile, Casilla 10233, Santiago, Chile.

N. P. Cheremisinoff, Exxon Chemical Company, Linden, New Jersey, USA.

R. P. Chhabra, Department of Chemical Engineering, Indian Institute of Technology, Kanpur, India.

J. T. Chung, Haake Buchler Instruments, Inc., Saddle Brook, New Jersey, USA.

Y. Cohen, Department of Chemical Engineering, University of California, Los Angeles, California, USA.

R. Darby, Department of Chemical Engineering, Texas A&M University, College Station, Texas, USA.

D. DeKee, Department of Chemical Engineering, University of Windsor, Windsor, Ontario, Canada.

J. F. Dijksman, Philips Research Laboratories, Eindhoven, The Netherlands.

A. Duduković, Institute for Petrochemistry, Gas, Oil and Chemical Engineering, Faculty of Technology, University of Novi Sad, Novi Sad, Yugoslavia.

K. Funatsu, Department of Chemical Engineering, Kyushu University, Fukuoka, Japan.

E. R. Harrell, BF Goodrich Company, Technical Center, Avon Lake, Ohio, USA.

S. L. Harris, Department of Chemical Engineering, Clarkson University, Potsdam, New York, USA.

C. R. Huang, Department of Chemical Engineering, Chemistry & Environmental Science, New Jersey Institute of Technology, Newark, New Jersey, USA.

T. Kajiwara, Department of Chemical Engineering, Kyushu University, Fukuoka, Japan.

D. M. Kalyon, Department of Chemistry and Chemical Engineering, Stevens Institute of Technology, Castle Point, Hoboken, New Jersey, USA.

W. Kozicki, Department of Chemical Engineering, University of Ottawa, Ottawa, Ontario, Canada.

A. K. Kulshreshtha, Department of Mathematics, Harcourt Butler Technological Institute, Kanpur, India.

C. Kuroda, Research Laboratory of Resources Utilization, Tokyo Institute of Technology, Yokohama, Japan.

P. J. R. Leblans, DSM Research, Geleen, The Netherlands.

M. F. Letelier S., Department of Mechanical Engineering, University of Santiago, Casilla, Santiago, Chile.

G. H. Michler, Wissenschaftliches Forschungs-und Koordinierungszentrum im Kombinat VEB Chemische Werke Buna, Schkopau and Institut fur Festkorperphysik und Elektronenmikroskopie der Akademie der Wissenschaften der DDR, German Democratic Republic.

N. Nakajima, Polymer Engineering Center, University of Akron, Akron, Ohio, USA.

A. Nakayama, Department of Energy and Mechanical Engineering, Shizuoka University, Hamamatsu, Japan.

K. Ogawa, Department of Chemical Engineering, Tokyo Institute of Technology, Tokyo, Japan.

V. O. Popadić, Faculty of Technology, University of Novi Sad, Novi Sad, Yugoslavia.

M. B. Powley, Department of Chemical Engineering, University of Windsor, Windsor, Ontario, Canada.

E. P. W. Savenije, Philips Research Laboratories, Eindhoven, The Netherlands.

H. A. Schneider, Institute of Macromolecular Chemistry, Albert-Ludwigs University of Freiburg, Federal Republic of Germany.

B. J. R. Scholtens, DSM Research, Geleen, The Netherlands.

D. H. Sebastian, Department of Chemical Engineering and Polymer Processing Institute, Stevens Institute of Technology, Castle Point, Hoboken, New Jersey, USA.

A. V. Shenoy, Department of Materials Science and Engineering, University of Florida, Gainesville, Florida, USA.

J. Stastna, Department of Chemical Engineering, University of Windsor, Windsor, Ontario, Canada.

K. Takahashi, Department of Chemical Engineering, Yamagata University, Yonezawa, Japan.

P. N. Tandon, Department of Mathematics, Harcourt Butler Technological Institute, Kanpur, India.

M. N. Tekić, Faculty of Technology, University of Novi Sad, Novi Sad, Yugoslavia.

C. Tiu, Department of Chemical Engineering, Monash University, Clayton, Victoria, Australia.

P. H. T. Uhlherr, Department of Chemical Engineering, Monash University, Clayton, Victoria, Australia.

G. Verreet, Laboratorium Voor Hydraulica, Katholieke Universiteit te Leuven, Heverlee, Belgium.

K. C. Wilson, Department of Civil Engineering, Queen's University at Kingston, Ontario, Canada.

ABOUT THE EDITOR

Nicholas P. Cheremisinoff heads the product development group in the Polymers Technology Division of Exxon Chemical Company. Dr. Cheremisinoff has extensive experience and research interests in multiphase and rheologically complex flows. He received his B.S., M.S., and Ph.D. degrees in chemical engineering from Clarkson College of Technology, and he is a member of a number of professional societies including Tau Beta Pi and Sigma Xi.

in memory

A final acknowledgment belongs to my beloved mother, Louise, whose efforts in no small way contributed to this entire series. Beyond the typing services provided for many of the contributors and meticulous effort of volume indexing, she was and still remains the Editor's major source of inspiration.

PREFACE

This volume of the Encyclopedia is devoted to the subjects of rheology and flow dynamics of non-Newtonian fluids. Although related topics are treated in previous volumes, prior subject coverage was specific to the generic flow topics of those volumes. This work attempts to provide a unified treatment of practical rheology and industrial handling/processing of rheologically complex fluids.

Non-Newtonian behavior is encountered in an overwhelming number of situations throughout nature and in commercial operations. Examples where such behavior occurs are industrial waste flows; process slurry operations; the manufacture of dies, inks, pigments, and paints; polymer and plastics synthesis and fabrication; preparation of cosmetics and health care products; food processing; and even biological phenomena such as blood flow and coagulation. In fact, nature, along with mankind's capitalization of nature in industry, offers many more examples of rheologically complex materials than those described by rigorous Newtonian mechanics. Despite this over-abundance of encounters, our theoretical foundations and process design methodology are largely empirical, and often drawn by analogy from specific fluid studies.

The present work attempts to provide a unified treatment of the subjects starting from an advanced entry level. Fundamental concepts and properties of viscous flow behavior are presented in Volumes 1, 2, 5, and 6 of this series. This volume provides only an overview of basic principles and directs detailed attention to state-of-the-art topics in handling/processing viscous materials. The work is organized into three sections. Section I contains twelve chapters aimed at phenomenological description and establishing theoretical development of non-Newtonian flow behavior. Discussions and modeling of flow regimes in symmetric and non-symmetric flow systems are discussed. The relations between viscous behavior and transport properties are presented. Section II contains five chapters addressing the topics of slippage and drag phenomena. These behaviors are major properties but are often least understood in practical process operations. The final section contains eighteen chapters on characterization, behavior, and processing of polymers and elastomeric materials. Polymer technology is perhaps the most advanced in terms of our understanding of viscous flow properties, and although principles discussed evolved from the study of these materials, concepts and design methodology are general. There are three main themes in this section, namely (1) the relationships between the molecular structure of the fluid and its deformation properties, (2) industrial handling operations, including design methodology, and (3) techniques for assessing and predicting the behavior of viscous materials in industrial processing equipment.

This work represents the efforts of 44 researchers/practitioners from around the world. In addition, it reflects the opinions of scores of colleagues who provided invaluable suggestions and critiques. Deepest gratitude is extended to the contributors and to Gulf Publishing Company whose efforts are presented herein.

Nicholas P. Cheremisinoff

ENCYCLOPEDIA OF FLUID MECHANICS

SECTION I

FLOW DYNAMICS AND TRANSPORT PHENOMENA

CONTENTS

CHAPTER 1

CHARACTERIZATION OF THIXOTROPIC FLUIDS

Ching-Rong Huang

Department of Chemical Engineering, Chemistry & Environmental Science
New Jersey Institute of Technology
Newark, New Jersey, USA

CONTENTS

INTRODUCTION

Rheological Classification of Fluid Behavior

Rheology is the science of deformation and flow of materials in response to stress. A rheological equation describes or relates stress or deformation to flow variables of materials such as strain, shear rate, and time. Fluids can be conveniently classified based on their rheological properties as follows [1, 2]: (a) Newtonian fluids follow the simplest rheological equation of Newton's law of viscosity, the stress being proportional to the shear rate. The flow curve (shear stress vs. shear rate) shows a linear relationship and passes through the origin. (b) Time-independent non-Newtonian fluid exhibits a non-linear relationship between the shear stress and the shear rate, or its flow curve exhibits a yield stress (not passing through the origin), provided its viscosity is not time dependent. Time-independent non-Newtonian fluids have attracted more attention by rheologists than others. More than fifteen rheological equations or models have been proposed to represent the time-independent relation as summarized by Skelland [2]. These equations employ two to five parameters to describe the pseudoplastic (shear thinning) or the dilatant (shear thickening) properties of time-independent non-Newtonian fluids with or without a yield stress. (c) Time-dependent non-

Newtonian fluids display time-dependent behavior in the flow curve in addition to the shear-rate dependency. Therefore, the viscosity of time-dependent non-Newtonian fluids is a function of both the shear rate and the time of shearing. They are usually subdivided into two groups, thixotropic fluids and rheopectic fluids. The former are shear-thickening time-dependent fluids. (d) Viscoelastic fluids possess the viscous property of a liquid and the elastic property of a solid. Thus the rheological properties of viscoelastic fluids are inadequately described by relationships between the shear stress and the shear rate unless the elastic properties of the stress and the strain are included. The simplest rheological equation for viscoelastic fluid is the Maxwell model, which includes two rheological parameters—the viscosity and the rigidity modulus. Various theories of viscoelasticity have resulted in many differential or integral constitutive equations relating the shear stress with shear rate, strain, and time.

History of Thixotropy

"Thixotropy" was introduced by Freundlich in 1928 [3]. He and his co-workers observed that many colloidal solutions show a decreased resistance to flow upon being stirred or shaken and revert to their original resistance after being allowed to stand still [4]. He suggested that this phenomenon was due to the structural change of the colloidal particles—a reversible, isothermal gel-sol transition through mechanical disturbance. This reversible, isothermal, viscosity decrease phenomenon was called thixotropy.

The term "thixotropy" has been in continuous use to the present time by many investigators. However, Freundlich's original definition was not uniformly adhered to. It was sometimes interpreted as pseudoplastic or shear-thinning property without considering the time-dependent behavior. Others used it to represent the non-linear viscoelasticity of fluids, failing to recognize the inelastic property of thixotropic fluids.

Experimental Measurements of Thixotropy

The qualitative detection of thixotropy can be achieved experimentally. Capillary viscometers are not suitable for the study of shear rate and time dependencies of viscosity of thixotropic fluids due to the varying shear rate in the flowing system. Both cone-and-plate type and Couette-type viscometers are commonly used. Common proposed experiments are as follows:

The hysteresis loop. Shear stress is monitored in response to shear-rate variation. The shear rate is linearly increased from zero to a maximum value and then decreased from this maximum value to zero. This experiment, originally employed by Green and Weltman [5], generates a hysteresis loop on the flow curve. The hysteresis loop has been used ever since as one of the characteristic curves for the identification of a thixotropic fluid. This experiment is modified into three other experiments: (a) A multiple hysteresis loop is obtained from the continuation of cycles of the shear-rate increase and decrease [6]. The progressive breakdown of gel-structure of the fluid induced by shear can be observed by the gradual reduction of the area enclosed in hysteresis loops. The enclosed area eventually becomes zero and the flow curve of the fluid behaves as a pseudoplastic fluid. (b) A multiple hysteresis is measured with a finite period of pause between cycles. The pause between cycles will establish the necessary rest time required by the fluid to regain its gel-sol equilibrium condition. (c) Another modified hysteresis loop is obtained. When the shear-rate half cycle reaches the maximum value, it is held at this rate for a period of time before returning to zero.

The stress-decay curve. The time-dependent effect on shear stress at constant shear rate is measured, until a steady-state shear stress is reached. This experiment, First designed by Pryce-Jones with a Couette viscometer, demonstrates the time-dependency of viscosity of various thixotropic fluids [7]. This experimentally observed curve is referred to as the stress-decay curve or the torque-decay curve, and is another characteristic curve of thixotropy fluid. This experiment with a step function of shear rate can be replaced by an alternate experiment with a multiple-step function of shear rates from high to low values. It results in a series of stress-decay curves while shear rates drop instantaneously at different time intervals. Another experiment is often performed that is an extension of the stress-decay experiment. A square wave function is used to replace the step function of the shear rate as the input function. The response of shear stress is observed as its variation with time. The first portion of measurement is the stress-decay curve. The next portion is the stress response to a sudden drop of shear rate to zero. For thixotropic fluids, the stress response is a sudden drop to zero because of its inelastic property. On the other hand, a viscoelastic fluid would show a gradual stress relaxation vs. time caused by its elastic behavior.

The shear rate in response to time at constant shear stress. This experiment, preferred by McMilen for Couette Viscometer in earlier studies of thixotropic fluid, is seldomly used recently.

Currently Accepted Definition of Thixotropy

Based on Freundlich's definition of thixotropy and experimental measurements of thixotropic fluid, the currently accepted definition of a thixotropic fluid includes the following characteristics: (a) a thixotropic fluid is an inelastic viscous liquid with a shear rate and time dependent viscosity; (b) it accompanies an isothermal structural change which is brought about by applying a mechanical disturbance to the fluid; (c) when the mechanical disturbance is removed, the fluid recovers its original equilibrium structure; (d) its flow curve exhibits a hysteresis loop and a stress-decay curve is observed under constant shear rate; (e) it has a yield stress because of the dual gel and sol structure of the fluid.

The rheological classification of a fluid is based on the observation of flow behavior of the fluid under a range of measuring conditions. A thixotropic fluid studied experimentally in a low shear-rate region, i.e., with the corresponding shear stress slightly higher than the yield stress, often exhibits viscoelastic behavior. Therefore, a thixotropic fluid becomes a viscoelastic fluid. Whole human blood behaves like a viscoelastic fluid when the shear rate is lower than approximately 1 sec^{-1}. Blood becomes thixotropic as the shear rate is increased to about 10 sec^{-1}. With further increasing of the shear rate, whole human blood becomes a time-independent pseudoplastic fluid [8–10]. This demonstrates that a fluid can be classified as one type of fluid based on its predominant rheological behavior and may also exhibit certain minor rheological properties of another type of fluid measured at certain shear rates.

QUANTITATIVE CHARACTERIZATION OF THIXOTROPY

Various approaches have been followed by rheologists to obtain a quantitative description of thixotropic fluids. In general, they can be classified into the two following categories.

Phenomenological Approach

In this approach, experimental measurements were taken under conditions of interest to individual investigators. Based on the data, they defined and interpreted thixotropy arbitrarily. Green and Weltman [5, 11] employed the area enclosed in a hysteresis loop measured from paints and printing inks as a measure of the extent of thixotropic breakdown in a cycle. The loop showing the largest area among the group of thixotropic materials of similar shear-rate variation was considered the most thixotropic or to have the highest degree of thixotropy.

Dintenfass, on the other hand, used the stress-decay curve to characterize thixotropy [12, 13]. A thixotropic recovery time was defined as the time required between two equilibrium conditions when the shear rate undergoes a sudden drop to a lower value. Pigment dispersions in organic liquids were studied. Dintenfass found that a critical value of shear rate existed above which the phenomenon of stress-decay disappeared.

Goodeve and Whitfield attempted to define thixotropy by two parameters, the coefficient of thixotropy and the residue of viscosity. Based on the stress-decay curves obtained from various shear rates, they plotted the apparent viscosity with reciprocal shear rate. The coefficient of thixotropy was defined as the slope of the plot. The residue viscosity was defined as the equilibrium value of apparent viscosity after the time-dependent effect wore out. Printing inks with carbon black in mineral oil were used in the study.

Many rheological models of thixotropic fluid were proposed from modification of phenomenological models of time-independent pseudoplastic models. The power law was modified by Sestak et al. [14] to fit the response data of shear stress vs. time with a shear-rate step function. They proposed a modified power law model:

$$\tau = K_0\dot{\gamma}^n - m(K_0 - K_\infty) \int_{-\infty}^{t} e^{-m(t-t')}\dot{\gamma}^n \, dt' \tag{1}$$

with four parameters m, n, K_0, and K_∞.

The Herschel-Bulkley model [15] was modified by Tiu and Boger for thixotropic fluids [16]:

$$\tau = \lambda(\tau_y + K_0\dot{\gamma}^n) \tag{2}$$

with $\dfrac{d\lambda}{dt} = K_1\dot{\gamma}^m(\lambda - \lambda_e)^2$. There are six thixotropic parameters in their equation: τ_y, K_0, K_1, n, m, and λ_e. $\tag{3}$

Usui et al. [17] proposed a thixotropic model based on the Bingham model [18]. In their model, they claimed that the thixotropy of a coal-water mixture was caused by the buildup and breakdown of the yield stress:

$$\tau = \tau_y + \eta\dot{\gamma} \tag{4}$$

$$\frac{d\tau_y}{dt} = \frac{1}{A_1}(\tau_{y\infty} - \tau_y) - \frac{K}{A_2}(\tau_y - \tau_{y0})(2m\dot{\gamma}^2) \tag{5}$$

with parameters m, A_1, A_2, τ_{y0}, $\tau_{y\infty}$, and K.

Similar to the Reiner-Philippoff model [19] that expressed the viscosity of a pseudoplastic fluid in terms of initial and final viscosities, Pinder [20] derived an equation that gave the time dependency of viscosity as follows:

$$\log\frac{(\mu_0 + \mu(t))(\mu_0 - \mu_\infty)}{(\mu(t) - \mu_\infty)(\mu_0 + \mu_\infty)} = \frac{2\mu_\infty}{2.303}k_1 t \tag{6}$$

where $\mu(t)$ = time-dependent viscosity
μ_0, μ_∞ = the initial and final viscosities
k_1 = rate constant

The equation fit the viscosity data for a tetrahydrofuran-hydrogen sulfide hydrate slurry.

Godfrey [21] proposed an equation that characterized the viscosity decay under constant shear rate:

$$\mu(t) = \mu_0 - \sum_{n=1}^{N} \Delta\mu_n(1 - e^{-t/\lambda_n}) \tag{7}$$

and $$\mu_0 = \mu_\infty + \sum_{n=1}^{N} \Delta\mu_n \tag{8}$$

where λ_n are the time-decay constants. Thixotropic fuel oil was used experimentally to provide measurements of the transient viscosity for a range of shear rates from 0.90 to 90 sec^{-1}.

Mercer and Weyman [22] modified the Godfrey model by replacing the time-dependent viscosity with a normalized dimensionless viscosity function:

$$\frac{\mu(t) - \mu_\infty}{\mu_0 - \mu_\infty} = (1 - \varepsilon) \exp\left[-\left(\frac{t}{\lambda_1}\right)^{0.4}\right] + \varepsilon \exp\left(-\frac{t}{\lambda_2}\right) \tag{9}$$

with parameters ε, λ_1, and λ_2 evaluated by fitting the viscosity-decay curve of bentonite-water suspensions.

Theoretical Approach

Many investigators have tried to interpret thixotropy by the theoretical approach. This approach may lead to a rheological equation for thixotropic fluids with parameters of physical meaning. There are four major methods of thixotropic analysis based on different theories. They are presented here.

General Theory of Continuous Mechanics

Harris [23] approached thixotropy directly from the theory of continuum mechanics. For time-dependent, inelastic, viscous thixotropic fluids, the general form of the rheological equation was given as:

$$\tau_{ij} = 2\eta(I_2, I_3 t)\dot{\gamma}_{ij} \tag{10}$$

where I_2 and I_3 are the second and the third invariants of shear rate, respectively.

Harris proposed an integral equation for the viscosity deficit:

$$\eta_0 - \eta(t) = \int_{-\infty}^{t} f[I_2(t'), I_3(t')]M(t - t')\, dt' \tag{11}$$

where η_0 is the undisturbed viscosity and $\eta(t)$ is the viscosity at current time. The invariant $f[I_2(t')I_3(t')]$ is a polynomial in $I_2(t')$ and $I_3(t')$. $M(t - t')$ is the memory function that reflects the effect of the past shear history in the current viscosity.

$$M(t - t') = \int_{0}^{\infty} \frac{R(t'')}{t''} \exp\left(-\frac{t - t'}{t''}\right) dt'' \tag{12}$$

where $R(t'')$ is a viscosity relaxation spectrum defined so that $R(t'')\, dt''$ is the contribution to the current viscosity deficit with relaxation times between t'' and $t'' + dt''$.

In order to demonstrate that this model could generate a viscosity-time decay curve at constant shear-rate flow, Harris assumed particularly that the invariant function $f[I_2(t')I_3(t')]$ takes an exponential form of $I_2(t')$ and a finite pulse function for the viscosity relaxation spectrum $R(t'')$.

In a similar form, Harris also proposed an integral equation to describe the yield stress deficit with respect to time:

$$\tau_{y0} - \tau_y(t) = \int_{-\infty}^{t} g[I_2(t')I_3(t')]N(t - t')\, dt' \tag{13}$$

Fredrickson [24] employed the fluidity (the reciprocal of viscosity) and suggested a rheological equation with the rate of fluidity change expressed in two terms, a term of fluidity decay and a shear-dependent term of fluidity recovery as follows:

$$\tau = \frac{2}{\phi}\dot{\gamma}$$

and

$$\frac{D\phi}{Dt} = -\frac{1}{\lambda_1}(\phi - \phi_0) + 2k_1(\dot{\gamma})^2 \frac{\phi_\infty - \phi}{\phi}$$

where ϕ is the fluidity; $\phi_0 \phi_\infty$ are fluidity at zero shear rate and at steady state, respectively; λ_1 and κ_1 are parameters.

Entangled Molecules

Another approach of thixotropy starts with modeling the breakdown and recovery of physical bonds of long-chained molecules. Eyring et al. [25] assumed that for a thixotropic fluid there exist two kinds of molecules, entangled and disentangled, the former non-Newtonian in nature and the latter Newtonian. They developed a rheological equation for pseudoplastic fluid:

$$\tau = B_1 \dot\gamma + \frac{1}{A_2} \sinh^{-1}(B_2 \dot\gamma) \tag{14}$$

where A_2, B_1, and B_2 are parameters. Their model was later modified by assuming the shifting of equilibrium between entanglement and disentanglement induced by shear. It results in a thixotropic equation for thixotropic fluids [26]:

$$\tau = \frac{(1 - B_3 X)B_1}{A_1} \dot\gamma + \frac{X}{A_3} \sinh^{-1}(B_2 \dot\gamma) \tag{15}$$

with $\quad \dfrac{dX}{dt} = -C_1 X \exp(C_2 \dot\gamma^2) \tag{16}$

where X is the fraction of the entangled units; and A_1, A_2, A_3, B_1, B_2, B_3, C_1 and C_2 are parameters.

Storey and Merrill [27] proposed that viscosity is proportional to the density of links of contact, N, at which two molecules are connected through a bond of energy sufficient to bind the molecules for a short period of time but low enough for the bond to be disrupted by shear stress:

$$\tau = (\mu + A_1 N)\dot\gamma \tag{17}$$

where μ is a Newtonian viscosity if there were no association links; and A_1 is a constant. They further assumed that the rate of destruction of links is linear to shear rate and the rate of reformation is first order with respect to the number of links that have been broken:

$$\frac{dN}{dt} = -k_1 N \dot\gamma + k_2 (N_0 - N) \tag{18}$$

where k_1, k_2, and N_0 are constants.

They demonstrated that amylose and amylopectin (a linear and a highly branched form of macromolecule from starch) are well suited to treatment of their network association model.

Ritter and Govier [28] modified the model of Storey and Merrill with a second order relationship of link formation:

$$\tau = \mu \dot\gamma + \tau_s \tag{19}$$

$$\frac{d\tau_s}{dt} = \frac{k_1(\tau_{s0} - \tau_s)^2}{k(t)} - \frac{k_2 \tau_s}{k(t)} \tag{20}$$

where τ_s = structural stress contributed by the number of network linkage
$\qquad$ $k(t)$ = time-dependent concentration of network structure
$\quad$ k_1, k_2, τ_{s0} = material parameters

Experimental data obtained from Pembina Crude Oil were effectively correlated with their theoretical expression.

Ruckenstein and Mewis [29] analyzed the thixotropic behavior on the basis of the kinetics of breakdown and recovery of structural elements of a multicomponent mixture with various chain lengths. By analogy with polymer rheology, they assumed that the viscosity of the mixture can be expressed as a function of the viscosity of all the components. An equilibrium viscosity and a transient viscosity were derived:

$$\frac{\eta_e}{\eta(0)} = \frac{K}{S_0} \sum_{j=0}^{\infty} (j+1)^{C_1} \left(\frac{N_{0,e}}{K}\right)^{j+1} \tag{21}$$

where η_e = equilibrium viscosity
 $\eta(0)$ = viscosity of the monomer
 S_0 = total number of structural units of the system
 K = twice the value of the ratio of the breakdown and the recovery rate constants
 N_0 = number of unbounded structural units
 C_1 = a constant

For the transient viscosity, it became:

$$\frac{\eta_t}{\eta(0)} = \left(\frac{S_1(t)}{S_0}\right)^2 \sum_{j=1}^{\infty} (j+1)^{C_1} \left[1 - \frac{S_1(t)}{S_0}\right]^j \tag{22}$$

where $S_1(t)$ is the total number of chains that can be evaluated by:

$$\frac{dS_1(t)}{dt} = k_1 \sum_{j=0}^{\infty} jN_j - \frac{k_2}{2} [S_1(t)]^2 \tag{23}$$

where k_1 and k_2 are the breakdown and the recovery rate constants.

Structural Parameter

Thixotropy has been modeled theoretically starting with the viscosity as a function of structural parameter and shear rate, while the structural parameter was expressed as a time-dependent rate equation. Moore [30] proposed a model of thixotropic fluids with the following equations:

$$\tau = (\mu + C_1\lambda)\dot{\gamma} \tag{24}$$

and $$\frac{d\lambda}{dt} = a - (a + b\dot{\gamma})\lambda \tag{25}$$

where λ is the structural parameter and μ, a, b, and C_1, are material parameters.

Cheng and Evans [31] generalized Moore's structural parameter-kinetics and discussed restrictions of these generalized equations. The proposed general form of rheological equations and rate equations of structural parameter were expressed as follows:

$$\tau = \eta(\dot{\gamma}, \lambda)\dot{\gamma} \tag{26}$$

and $$\frac{d\lambda}{dt} = g(\dot{\gamma}, \lambda) \tag{27}$$

in which the viscosity η is a function of shear rate $\dot{\gamma}$ and of structural parameter λ, which is a time-dependent variable.

Based on the observed rheological behavior of thixotropic fluids, Cheng and Evans postulated certain restrictions as follows:

$$\eta(\dot{\gamma}, \lambda) > 0 \tag{28}$$

$$\left(\frac{\partial \tau}{\partial \dot{\gamma}}\right)_{\lambda} > 0 \tag{29}$$

$$\left(\frac{\partial \tau}{\partial \dot{\gamma}}\right)_{\dot{\gamma}} > 0 \tag{30}$$

$$g(\dot{\gamma}, \lambda) = 0, \; \lambda = \lambda_e(\dot{\gamma}) \tag{31}$$

$$g(\dot{\gamma}_e, \lambda) < 1, \; \lambda > \lambda_e(\dot{\gamma}) \tag{32}$$

$$g(\dot{\gamma}_e, \lambda) > 0, \; \lambda < \lambda_e(\dot{\gamma}) \tag{33}$$

$$\left(\frac{\partial g}{\partial \dot{\gamma}}\right)_{\lambda} < 0 \tag{34}$$

They also defined a dynamic equilibrium curve which occurs at $g_e(\dot{\gamma}_e, \lambda_e) = 0$:

$$\tau_e = \eta_e(\dot{\gamma}\lambda_e)\dot{\gamma}_e \tag{35}$$

The above time-independent shear-thinning rheological equation is subject to the following restrictions:

$$\left[\frac{\partial g_e(\dot{\gamma}_e, \lambda_e)}{\partial \lambda_e}\right]_{\dot{\gamma}_e} < 0$$

$$\left[\frac{\partial \tau_e(\dot{\gamma}_e, \lambda_e)}{\partial \dot{\gamma}_e}\right]_{\lambda_e} > 0$$

To illustrate the previous discussion, they employed Moore's model [30] as an example to represent experimental data measured from 6.5% aqueous bentonite suspension.

In a later communication, Cheng [31] presented an alternative form of rheological equation:

$$\frac{d\tau}{dt} = \alpha \frac{d\dot{\gamma}}{dt} + \beta \tag{36}$$

where

$$\alpha = \left(\frac{\partial \tau}{\partial \dot{\gamma}}\right)_{\lambda} \tag{37}$$

$$\beta = \left(\frac{\partial \tau}{\partial \lambda}\right)_{\dot{\gamma}} g(\lambda, \dot{\gamma}) \tag{38}$$

He proposed that thixotropy is characterized by these two material functions, $\alpha(\tau, \dot{\gamma})$ and $\beta(\tau, \dot{\gamma})$, and the functional relationship is to be determined experimentally. The functional restrictions of α and β were also given.

Thermodynamic Approach

From the fundamental characteristic sol-gel transformation of thixotropic fluids, thixotropy can be modeled by the order-disorder transition via the thermodynamic function of entropy.

Huang [33] started his interpretation of thixotropy based on principles of statistical mechanics and irreversible thermodynamics via the state variable of entropy. A thixotropic fluid was considered as an assembly of multi-components including an orderly gel phase and a disorderly sol phase. It is well-known that polymeric materials are capable of developing crystalline structure during calendering or under stress that causes the rearrangement of molecules. Similarly, the molecular arrangement of a thixotropic fluid is affected by shearing. A basis of statistical mechanics is a logarithmic relationship existent between entropy and number of micromolecular states of the assembly. Since the number of micromolecular states is related to the energy and the degree of freedom of molecules, the entropy can be interpreted as a measurement of the order-disorder of the assembly. The order to disorder structural change of gel to sol transformation in a thixotropic fluid would result in the decrease of the entropy of the assembly. A structural arrangement parameter β_{ij} is defined by the following equation for the entropy variation with respect to the change of molecular arrangement:

$$\rho \frac{dS_1}{dt} = -\frac{1}{T} \tau^{ij} \frac{d\beta_{ij}}{dt} \tag{39}$$

where dS_1/dt = specific entropy change due to molecular arrangement
ρ = density
τ^{ij} = stress tensor
β_{ij} = molecular arrangement parameter

From irreversible thermodynamics [34], the entropy balance equation of a homogeneous fluid is:

$$\rho \frac{dS_2}{dt} = -\frac{1}{T} \left[q^i_{,i} + \tau^{ij} \frac{d\gamma_{ij}}{dt} \right] \tag{40}$$

where dS_2/dt = specific entropy change due to conductive heat transfer and viscous dissipation
$q^i_{,i}$ = divergence of heat flux vector
γ_{ij} = strain tensor

The addition of Equations 39 and 40 gives the overall entropy change:

$$\rho \frac{dS}{dt} = -\frac{1}{T} \left[q^i_{,i} + \tau^{ij} \frac{d\gamma_{ij}}{dt} + \tau^{ij} \frac{d\beta_{ij}}{dt} \right] \tag{41}$$

For a thixotropic fluid, it is assumed that the change of molecular arrangement parameter induced by shearing follows the kinetics equation:

$$\frac{d\beta_{ij}}{dt} = -k_1 \beta^{ij} |\dot\gamma^{ij}|^n, \qquad |\dot\gamma^{ij}| > 0 \tag{42}$$

and when the shear is removed, it follows that:

$$\frac{d\beta^{ij}}{dt} = k_2(\beta^{ij}_e - \beta^{ij}), \qquad |\dot\gamma^{ij}| = 0 \tag{43}$$

where $|\dot\gamma^{ij}|$ = absolute value of the shear rate tensor
β^{ij}_e = equilibrium value of the molecular arrangement parameter when the shear is removed and the gel-sol structure regains its equilibrium
k_1 and k_2 = rate constants of structural breakdown and recovery

It led to a rheological equation for isotropic thixotropic fluids expressed in scalar form:

$$\tau - \tau_y = \left[\mu + CA\dot{\gamma}^{n-1} \exp\left(-C \int_0^t \dot{\gamma}^n \, dt \right) \right] \dot{\gamma} \tag{44}$$

The five thixotropic parameters of the equation are lumped parameters defined as follows: C is the kinetic rate constant of structural breakdown in the fluid; n, the order of structural breakdown reaction; A, the coefficient representing of the structural parameter at equilibrium condition; μ, the Newtonian contribution of viscosity; and τ_y, the yield stress.

Equation 44 provided the expression of shear rate and time-dependent viscosity of thixotropic fluid as follows:

$$\eta(\dot{\gamma}, t) = \mu + CA\dot{\gamma}^{n-1} \exp\left(C \int_0^t \dot{\gamma}^n \, dt \right) \tag{45}$$

From the model, Huang also showed that a pseudoplastic fluid—a time-independent, shear-thinning fluid—is a special case of thixotropic fluid that has a short time-dependent behavior. The following is the rheological equation for pseudoplastic fluids:

$$\tau - \tau_y = [\mu + CA\dot{\gamma}^{n-1} \exp(-C\dot{\gamma}^n t_0)]\dot{\gamma} \tag{46}$$

where t_0 is a material parameter indicating the duration of time after which the fluid changes its rheological behavior from thixotropic to pseudoplastic.

With thixotropy quantitatively expressed in Equation 44, rheograms that characterize the rheological behavior of thixotropic fluid can be generated theoretically as follows [35]:

The hysteresis loop. This loop consists of two curves, the up curve and the down curve, which measure the response of shear stress with shear rate increasing linearly from zero to a maximum value and immediately decreasing toward zero. For the up curve, Equation 44 becomes:

$$\tau - \tau_y = \mu\dot{\gamma} + CA\dot{\gamma}^n \exp\left[-\frac{C\dot{\gamma}^{n+1}}{m(n+1)} \right], \tag{47}$$

when $0 \leq t \leq t_1$

where t_1 is the time needed for the shear rate to reach its maximum value and m is the proportionality constant of the shear-rate increase with time. For the down curve, Equation 44 yields:

$$\tau - \tau_y = \mu\dot{\gamma} + CA\dot{\gamma}^n \exp\left\{ -\frac{C}{m(n+1)} \left[2\dot{\gamma}^{n+1}(t_1) - \dot{\gamma}^{n+1} \right] \right\} \tag{48}$$

when $t_1 \leq t \leq 2t_1$

where $\dot{\gamma}(t_1)$ is the maximum value of shear rate of the hysteresis loop at $t = t_1$.

The stress-decay curve. The stress-decay curve measures the transient behavior of the stress vs. time under a constant shear rate. At constant shear rate, Equation 44 becomes

$$\tau - \tau_y = \mu\dot{\gamma} + CA\dot{\gamma}^n \exp(-C\dot{\gamma}^n t) \tag{49}$$

The Huang model (Equation 44) was employed successfully to represent the hysteresis loop and the stress-decay curve of a wide variety of thixotropic fluids, including mixtures of high vacuum grease and silicone oil [36], aqueous montmorillonite clay suspensions [39], latex paints [40], and whole human blood [35, 37]. The significance of this representation is two-fold: (a) The equation is capable of representing simultaneously both experimental rheograms of thixotropic fluid, the hysteresis loop and the stress-decay curve. (b) Thixotropic parameters of the equation, which have their physical meanings, give the quantitative characterization of the thixotropy of a fluid.

THIXOTROPIC FLUIDS

There are a variety of thixotropic fluids. Thixotropy has been observed in colloidal dispersions, organic and inorganic suspensions, and organic solutions. Many time-independent, pseudoplastic fluids have been observed as thixotropic fluids more recently due to advancement and refinement of rotational viscometers—both cone and plate type and the Couette type. Based on their physical and chemical nature, thixotropy fluids can be classified as follows:

Organic Suspensions

Paints, printing inks, and pastes were the most widely studied thixotropic fluids in early years [38, 39]. They are basically an organic liquid dispersed in another liquid which may be water or organic solvents. Surface-active agents are added to stabilize the emulsion or suspension. Pigments and small quantities of other compounds are also used to provide the color and to promote the desired properties of products. For most of the rheological studies of paints and printing inks, flow curves (shear stress-shear rate) at equilibrium conditions were measured. The hysteresis loop was reported occasionally. Even less work has been reported on the interpretation and correlation of performance characteristics of a product with the thixotropy of the fluid via thixotropic parameters. Huang, Fabisiak, and Polston [40] investigated six acrylic-based Lucite experimental wall paints and correlations of their thixotropic properties with performance characteristics were obtained. The hysteresis loop and the stress decay curve for paint samples were measured. Rheological equations developed by Huang (Equations 47–49) were employed to represent these measured curves. The five parameters from the equation were calculated from data to characterize the thixotropy of latex paints. They were compared with a number of important consumer-perceived properties including leveling, sagging, brush-ability, film build-up, color float, and changes in gel structure.

Inorganic Suspensions

Many clay-in-water suspensions were shown to have time-dependent viscosity. Joye and Poehlein [41] studied the stress decay and build-up curve of hectorite clay-water suspension. Structural parameter theory suggested by Cheng and Evans [31] was used to interpret experimental data. The equilibrium flow curve and flow curves with constant structure were obtained from the clay-water suspension system. Pinder [20] showed that tetrahydrofurn-hydrogen sulfide hydrate in water displays thixotropic behavior at very low concentrations. An exponential decay equation (Equation 6) was used to represent the time-dependent viscosity data. The most studied inorganic suspension system was probably bentonite in water. Cheng and Evans [31] used a 6.5% aqueous bentonite suspension to demonstrate their structural parameter theory. In a series of three communications, Weymann et al. reported their studies on Wyoming bentonite suspensions at various concentrations. The first paper [41] reported the simple steady-shear flow of the suspension assuming a Bingham fluid. The second paper [42] was on optical properties. The third paper [22] was on the subject of time-dependent viscosity of the suspension which the authors described by a dimensionless double time decay equation (Equation 9).

Oils

Oil has been considered as a Newtonian fluid. Also it has been suggested by others that certain oils exhibit pseudoplastic behavior. Almost half a century ago, Weltmann [43] demonstrated that many different oils in the viscosity range of 1 to 800 poises are thixotropic at high shear rates. The time-dependent viscosity of fuel oil was interpreted by Godfrey, who employed an equation with two exponential terms to represent his experimental data. Ritter and Govier [28] evaluated the thixotropy of Pembina Crude Oil and interpreted their data with a model based on entangled links between chain molecules. Petrellis and Flumerfelt [44] reported their investigation on time-dependent and equilibrium rheological properties of various crude oils at or below pour points. The structural parameter theory developed by Cheng and Evans [31] was used by them to interpret experimental data. Billington [45] observed thixotropy of wax-containing oils from his experiments which recorded the shear-rate change with time under constant shear-stress conditions. The hysteresis loop and the equilibrium flow curve were observed from dispersions of lithium stearate in lubricating oil by Bauer, Shuster, and Wiberley [46]. Seitzer and Lovell [47] investigated the rheological behavior of waxy crude oils and Utah shale oil. Results showed that waxy crude oil is thixotropic and shale oil can be either thixotropic or rheopectic (antithixotropic), which occurs at lower temperature. They claimed that the rheopectic behavior of shale oil is associated with the high oxygen and nitrogen content of the shale oils. These impurities cause the change of the crystallization of the wax from needles into spherulites, which brings about an increase in rheopexy.

Coal-Water Slurries

The research of synthetic fuels and boiler fuels in recent years has opened the rheological studies of coal-water slurries. The problems of storage, pumping, and atomization of coal-water mixture (CWM) must be solved. A desired CWM should have low viscosity even at high solid content and stability without solid sedimentation during storage. Usui et al. [17] studied the thixotropy of CWM and adopted the Bingham model modified by a time-dependent yield stress to represent their experimental data. Usui and Sano [48] later employed a different phenomenological model for CWM. A proposed structural stress is defined as the difference between shear stress and equilibrium shear stress. The structural stress is then expressed as an exponential function of time.

Foodstuffs

Mustard, mayonnaise, yogurt, margarine, butter, ketchup, tomato juice, and honey are rheologically organic dispersons, colloid suspensions, solutions, or combinations of the above three. Their non-Newtonian flow behavior was summarized by Green [49]. Scott-Blair [50] was one of the first researchers to give a thorough investigation of the rheology of foodstuffs. The three-parameter Herschel-Bulkley model [15] has been used mostly to represent the shear-thinning behavior of foodstuff data [51, 52]. DeKee and Turcotte [53] modified the Herschel-Bulkley model by replacing the shear stress by a series of experimental terms. The time-dependent rheological properties of foodstuffs was recently reported by DeKee, Code, and Turcotte [54]. They added a structural parameter in their previous equilibrium model to interpret time-dependent data taken from yogurt, salad dressing, mayonnaise, and tomato juice.

Whole Blood

Whole blood was considered as a Newtonian fluid in the early nineteenth century when Poiseuille [55] observed blood flow through capillaries. In 1942, Copley [56] proposed that blood exhibits non-Newtonian (shear-thinning) behavior and that it might have a yield stress. The equilibrium rheological properties of whole blood from healthy human subjects were measured by Copley, Huang, and King [57, 58] over a wide range of shear rates from 1,000 down to 0.0009 sec^{-1}. A rheological equation developed by Huang (Equation 46) is proposed to characterize the data. In 1972, Huang et al. [59] reported measurements of a hysteresis loop and a stress-decay curve from whole human blood and thus established that whole human blood is a thixotropic fluid. Based on a thermodynamic model and the dynamic equilibrium between individual red blood cells and rouleaux, Huang et al. [60] demonstrated the quantitative representation of both the hysteresis loop and the stress-decay curve generated from a blood sample. A following paper by Huang and Fabisicak [61] showed that the five thixotropic parameters from the Huang equation (Equation 44) can be used to characterize a blood sample. By comparison of thixotropic parameters of blood among eight apparently healthy human subjects in a blind test, they detected two cases of abnormality of thixotropic parameters. It turned out to be one subject with ulceration colitis and another with pernicious anemia. Experimental and phenomenological studies of thixotropy of whole human blood and red cell suspensions were also reported by Joly, Healy, Bureau and Stoltz in France [62–64] and by McMillan and Utterback in California [65, 66].

CONCLUSION

The study of thixotropic fluids attracts much less attention among rheologists than the other type of time-dependent fluid, viscoelastic fluid, as evidenced by the volume and the depth of publications in the literature. This chapter attempts to summarize important work reported on thixotropy by previous investigators. It starts with redefining thixotropy, which has a time-dependent nature, then discusses the experimental characterization of a thixotropic fluid, and illustrates different approaches to quantitatively interpreting and representing thixotropy.

The theoretical modeling of thixotropy is shown to be started with different disciplines of physics. But it is inevitable to come to the fundamental formulation of the dynamic equilibrium and the transient behavior in gel-sol transformation induced by shearing. The choice of a model or a rheological equation for a thixotropic fluid is not an easy task. One of the most important criteria is that the chosen equation should be able to represent the two basic rheograms of the fluid, the hysteresis loop and the stress-decay curve. Values of thixotropic parameters of the equation then can be used as fingerprints characterizing the fluid quantitatively. They can be used for comparison or for correlation between thixotropy and other applications or performance properties among thixotropic fluids.

The classification of thixotropic fluids based on their chemical nature is also presented. It shows that there are always new classes of thixotropic fluids of interest being discovered and investigated. It also demonstrates that, for most thixotropic fluids, there are gaps to be bridged between industrial researchers and theoretical rheologists. The investigation of thixotropy is in its infant stage. There is still a lot of work to be done.

NOTATION

A	structural parameter at equilibrium condition	$N(t - t')$	memory function
A_1, A_2, A_3	material parameters	N_0	equilibrium density of links
B_1, B_2, B_3	material parameters	N_0, e	number of unbounded structural units
C	kinetic rate constant of structural breakdown	$q^i_{,i}$	divergence of heat flux vector
C_1, C_2	material parameters	$R(t'')$	viscosity relaxation spectrum
$g(\dot{\gamma}\lambda)$	defined function for structural parameter change with time	S	entropy
		S_1	entropy contributed by molecular arrangement
I_2, I_3	second and third invariants of rate of deformation	S_2	entropy of a homogeneous fluid
k_1, k_2	rate constants	S_0	total number of structural units of the system
$k(t)$	time-dependent concentration of network structure	$S_1(t)$	total number of chains of the system
K, K_0, K_1, K_N	material parameters	t	present time
m	material parameter	t', t''	dummy variable of time
$M(t - t')$	memory function	T	temperature
n	material parameter	x	fraction of entangled units
N	density of links		

Greek Symbols

α, β	function defined by Cheng	μ	shear-rate independent viscosity
$\dot{\gamma}$	shear rate		
$\dot{\gamma}_e$	shear rate at dynamic equilibrium	μ_0	viscosity at $t = 0$
		μ_∞	viscosity at large t
$\dot{\gamma}(t_1)$	maximum shear rate of the hysteresis loop at $t = t_1$	ρ	density of the fluid
		τ	shear stress
$\dot{\gamma}_{ij}, \dot{\gamma}^{ij}$	shear rate tensors	τ_{ij}, τ^{ij}	shear-stress tensor
ε	material parameter	τ_e	shear stress at dynamic equilibrium
η	non-Newtonian viscosity		
η_0	undisturbed non-Newtonian viscosity	τ_y	yield stress
		τ_{y0}	equilibrium yield stress
η_e	equilibrium non-Newtonian viscosity	$\tau_{y\infty}$	yield stress at large shear rate
		τ_s	structural stress
η_t	transient non-Newtonian viscosity	τ_{s0}	equilibrium structural stress
		ϕ	fluidity
$\eta(0)$	viscosity of monomer	ϕ_0	fluidity at zero shear rate
λ	structural parameter	ϕ_∞	fluidity at steady-state shear rate
λ_e	equilibrium structural parameter		
λ_n	time-decay constant, $n = 1, 2, 3, \ldots$		

REFERENCES

1. Bird, R. B., Stewart, W. E., and Lightfoot, E. N., *Transport Phenomena*, J. Wiley & Sons, New York, 1960, pp. 10–15.
2. Skelland, A. H. P., *Non-Newtonian Flow and Heat Transfer*, J. Wiley & Sons, New York, 1967, pp. 5–16.
3. Freundlich, H., *Kolloid-Z*, 46 (1928) p. 289.
4. Freundlich, H., *Thixotropy*, Hermann et Cie, Paris, 1935.
5. Green, H., and Weltman, R. N., *Colloid Chem.*, 6 (1946). p. 328.
6. Orosz, P. J., Jr., "Characterization of Thixotropic Materials and Modification of Weissenberg Rheogoniometer," Doctoral Dissertation, New Jersey Institute of Technology, 1974.
7. Pryce-Jones, J., *J. Sci. Instr.*, 18 (1941) p. 39.
8. Thurston, G. B., *Biorheology*, 16 (1979) p. 149.
9. Copley, A. L., Huang, C. R., and King, R. G., *Biorheology*, 10 (1973) pp. 17–22.
10. Huang, C. R., King, R. G., and Copley, A. L., *Biorheology*, 10 (1973) pp. 23–28.
11. Green, H., and Weltman, R. N., *Ind. Eng. Chem. Anal. Ed.*, 18 (1946) pp. 167–72.
12. Dintenfass, L., *Kolloid-Z*, 163 (1959) p. 48.
13. Dintenfass, L., *Rheol. Acta*, 2 (1962) p. 187.
14. Sestak, J., Houska, M., and Zitny, R., *J. Rheology*, 26 (1982) pp. 459–475.
15. Herschel, W. H., and Bulkley, R., *Kolloid-Z*, 39 (1926) p. 291.
16. Tiu, C., and Boger, D. V., *J. Text. Studies*, 5 (1974) p. 329.
17. Usui, H., Sano, Y., Sawada, M., and Hongoh, T., *J. Chem. Eng.*, Japan, 17 (1984), pp. 583–588.
18. Bingham, E. C., *Fluidity and Plasticity*, McGraw-Hill, New York, 1922.
19. Philippoff, W., *Kolloid-Z*, 71 (1935) pp. 1–16.
20. Pinder, K. L., *Can. J. Chem. Eng.*, 42 (1964) pp. 132–138.
21. Godfrey, J. C., *Rheol. Acta*, 12 (1973), pp. 540–545.
22. Mercer, H. A., and Weymann, H. D., *Trans. Soc. Rheo.*, 18 (1974) pp. 199–218.
23. Harris, J., *Rheol. Acta*, 6 (1967) pp. 6–12.
24. Fredrickson, A. G., *AIChE J.*, 16 (1970) p. 436–440.
25. Ree, F. H., Ree, T., and Eyring, H., *Ind. Eng. Chem.*, 50 (1958) pp. 1036–1040.
26. Hahn, S. J., Ree, T., and Eyring, H., *Ind. Eng. Chem.*, 51 (1959) pp. 856–857.

27. Storey, B. T., and Merrill, E. W., *J. Polymer Sci.*, 33 (1958) pp. 361–375.
28. Ritter, R. A., and Govier, G. W., *Can. J. Chem. Eng.*, 48 (1970) pp. 505–513.
29. Ruckenstein, E., and Mewis, J., *J. Colloid and Interface Sci.*, 44 (1973) pp. 532–541.
30. Moore, F., *Trans. Brit. Ceram. Soc.*, 58 (1959)p p. 470–492.
31. Cheng, D. C. H., and Evans, F., *Brit J. Appl. Phys.*, 16 (1965) pp. 1599–1617.
32. Cheng, D. C. H., *Rheol. Acta*, 12 (1973) pp. 228–233.
33. Huang, C. R., *Chem. Eng. J.*, 3 (1972) pp. 100–103.
34. deGroot, S. R., and Masur, P., *Non-Equilibrium Thermodynamics*, Interscience, New York, 1962.
35. Huang, C. R., Siskovic, N., Robertson, R. W., Fabisiak, W., Smithberg, E. H., and Copley, A. L., *Biorheology*, 12 (1975) pp. 279–281.
36. Orosz, Jr., P. J., "Characterization of Thixotropic Materials and Modification of the Weissenberg Rheogoniometer," Doctoral Dissertation, New Jersey Institute Technology, 1974.
37. Huang, C. R., and Fabisiak, W., *Thrombosis Research*, Suppl. II, 8 (1976) pp. 1–7.
38. Fischer, E. K., *Colloidal Dispersions*, John Wiley & Sons, New York, 1950.
39. Weltmann, R. N., *Rheology of Pastes and Paints, in Rheology Theory and Application*, Eirich (ed.), Vol. 3, Acad. Press, New York, 1960.
40. Huang, C. R., Fabisiak, W., and Polston, N. L., "Correlation of Thixotropic Parameters with Application Properties of Latex Paints," presented at Seventh International Congress on Rheology, Gothenberg, Sweden, August 23–27, 1976.
41. Joye, D. D., and Poehlein, G. W., *Trans. Svc. Rheol.*, 15 (1971) pp. 51–61.
42. Weymann, H. D., Chuang, M. C., and Ross, R. A., *Phys. Fluids*, 16 (1973) pp. 775–783.
43. Ross, R. A., Weymann, H. D. and Chuang, M. C., *Phys. Fluids*, 16 (1973) p. 784.
43. Weltmann, R. N., *Ind. Eng. Chem.*, 15 (1943) p. 424–429.
44. Petrellis, N. C., and Flumerfelt, R. W., *Can. J. of Chem. Eng.*, 51 (1973) pp. 291–301.
45. Billington, E. W., *Proc. Phys. Soc.*, 76 (1960) pp. 127–136.
46. Bauer, W. H., Shuster, D. O., and Wiberley, S. E., *Trans. Soc. Rheol.* 4 (1960) pp. 315–334.
47. Seitzer, W. H., and Lovell, P. F., *Soc. Petro. Eng. J.*, 21 (1981) pp. 679–684.
48. Usui, H., and Sano, Y., *J. Chem. Eng.*, Japan, 18 (1985) pp. 519–525.
49. Green, H., *Industrial Rheology and Rheological Structures*, John Wiley & Sons, New York, 1949.
50. Scott-Blair, G. W., *Adv. Food Res. III* (1958) p. 1.
51. Balmaceda, E., Rha, C., and Huang, J., *J. Food Sci.*, 38 (1973) p. 1169.
52. Chevalley, J., *J. Texture Studies*, 6 (1975) p. 177.
53. DeKee, D., and Trucotte, G., *Chem. Eng. Commun.*, 6 (1980) p. 273.
54. DeKee, D., Code, R. K., and Turcotte, G., *J. Rheology*, 27 (1983) pp. 581–604.
55. Poiseuille, J. L., *Compte Rendus*, 11 (1840) pp. 961, 1041; 12 (1841) p. 112.
56. Copley, A. L., Krchma, L. C., and Whitney, M. E., *J. Gen. Physiol.*, 26 (1942) p. 19.
57. Copley, A. L., Huang, C. R., and King, R. G., *Biorheology*, 10 (1972) pp. 17–22.
58. Huang, C. R., King, R. G., and Copley, A. L., *Biorheology*, 10 (1972) pp. 23–18.
59. Huang, C. R., Siskovic, N., Wang, H. H., and Orosz Jr., P. J., "Quantitative Representation of Thixotropy of Human Blood," First International Congress of Biorheology, Lyon, France, Aug. 1972.
60. Huang, C. R., Siskovic, N., Robertson, R. W., Fabisiak, W., Smithberg, E. H., and Copley, A. L., *Biorheology*, 12 (1975) pp. 279–282.
61. Huang, C. R., and Fabisiak, W., *Thrombosis Research*, Suppl. II., Vol. 8, 1 (1976).
62. Healy, J. C., and Joly, M., *Biorheology*, 12 (1975) pp. 335–340.
63. Burrean, M., Healy, J. C., Bourgoin, D., and Joly, M., *Biorheology*, 17 (1980) pp. 191–203.
64. Stoltz, J. F., Gaillard, S., and Guillot, M., *AIChE Symposium Series* No. 182, 74 (1978) pp. 4–9.
65. McMillan, D. E., and Utterback, N., *Biorheology*, 17 (1980) pp. 343–354.
66. McMillan, D. E., Utterback, N., and Baldridge, J. B., *Biorheology*, 17 (1980) pp. 445–454.

CHAPTER 2

LAMINAR AND TURBULENT PIPE FLOWS
OF
NON-NEWTONIAN FLUIDS

Ron Darby

Department of Chemical Engineering
Texas A&M University
College Station, Texas, USA

CONTENTS

INTRODUCTION

A non-Newtonian fluid is any fluid for which the anisotropic (i.e., shear or deviatoric) stresses at constant temperature *cannot* be predicted by Newton's law of viscosity:

$$\tau_{ij} = \mu D_{ij} \tag{1}$$

where μ is the (constant) fluid viscosity and D_{ij} is the local rate of deformation tensor. Most "normal" fluids of simple structure are Newtonian (e.g., gases, water, liquids, mixtures, and solutions composed of relatively small inorganic or organic molecules), and obey Equation 1. However, many fluids of complex structure or composition are "non-Newtonian," such as fluids comprising macromolecules (e.g., solutions or melts of high polymers) or multiphase fluids (e.g., solid suspensions, emulsions, foams, etc.), and these fluids do not obey Equation 1. Examples of the latter range from blood to highly loaded coal slurries, from tomato juice to sewage sludge. Suspensions, slurries, muds, pulps, etc. more concentrated than about 20% solids are usually non-Newtonian, as are emulsions with comparable concentration of the dispersed phase (e.g., mayonnaise, cream, chocolate, cosmetics, etc.).

Non-Newtonian behavior can be manifested in various ways. All of the above fluids exhibit a "non-Newtonian viscosity," i.e., the ratio of the shear stress (τ) to the rate of shear ($\dot{\gamma}$) in a simple shear deformation is not a constant (as for the Newtonian fluid), but is instead dependent upon the magnitude of the shear stress or the shear rate. This ratio, which defines the fluid viscosity, is therefore a function, called the "apparent viscosity" function (η). In addition, polymeric fluids of high molecular weight or chain length, gels, micellular fluids, concentrated suspensions of long fibers, etc. exhibit elastic as well as non-Newtonian viscous properties. The influence of elasticity on the flow behavior of these fluids is most pronounced in non-uniform or unsteady flow situations in which conditions experienced by a fluid element vary either explicitly at a given position, or along the path line followed by the element. Extra stress components are developed in such fluids which may cause them to behave much differently in these flows than inelastic fluids. Examples include die swell, when the fluid exits a tube or orifice; the rod-climbing (Weissenberg) effect, when such fluids climb the rotating shaft of a stirrer; and reverse circulation patterns around rotating bodies. A complete description of the properties of such fluids, and the equations required to describe them, are beyond the scope of this chapter, and more extensive references should be consulted for such information [1–3].

The scope of this chapter is limited to the flow behavior of non-Newtonian fluids in straight pipes and conduits. Furthermore, it primarily focuses on the practical aspects of flow behavior that determine the energy or power required to transport these fluids. Thus, for any fluid in laminar flow, and for inelastic fluids in turbulent flow, a knowledge of the non-Newtonian apparent viscosity function for the fluid is all that is required for this purpose. Only in the case of viscoelastic fluids in turbulent flow (which is locally highly unsteady) will the elastic properties influence the flow behavior. Hence, only those properties that influence the flow behavior in such systems is considered.

RHEOLOGICAL MODELS

Purely Viscous Fluids

Many models have been proposed for representing the viscosity function of non-Newtonian fluids. There are some theoretical arguments that support the form of some of these equations, although most of them are primarily the result of empirical representation of measured data. (Experimental methods are discussed briefly in the next section.) The equation that best represents a given material thus depends not only upon the nature of the behavior of that material, but also the quality and range of viscosity data available for that material. Hence, if viscosity data are available over only a limited range of shear rate, for example, a relative simple equation might be adequate to represent that data. However, if a much wider range of shear rate is covered, a more complex equation might be required to represent the entire range of data.

This chapter makes no attempt at complete generality, in that it does not consider general constitutive equations that are capable of describing all possible rheological behavior of any given fluid. To do so inevitably leads to ever more complex expressions, with increasingly intractable analyses required in order to apply them to situations of practical interest. On the contrary, since we are interested here in engineering applications, considerations will be limited to systems that can be described adequately (at least approximately) by relatively simple expressions, along with appropriate warnings concerning the limitations of such expressions.

Power Law (or Ostwald-deWaele) Model

This is simply the equation of a straight line on a log-log plot of shear stress (τ) or viscosity (η) vs. shear rate ($\dot{\gamma}$). Since most viscosity data can be adequately represented by such a relation over a limited range of shear rate or shear stress (which may cover up to two orders of magnitude, for some fluids), this is the most widely used model for non-Newtonian viscosity. The equation is:

$$\tau = m\dot{\gamma}^n \tag{2}$$

where n is the flow index (the slope of log τ vs. log $\dot{\gamma}$) and m is the consistency parameter. (Note that since τ and $\dot{\gamma}$ are directional, they can be either positive or negative, both having the same sign for the usual definition of stress. Hence, if they are negative for a given system, the Equation 2 would be written with τ and $\dot{\gamma}$ replaced by $-\tau$ and $-\dot{\gamma}$, respectively.) The corresponding apparent viscosity function for this model is:

$$\eta = m\dot{\gamma}^{n-1} \tag{3}$$

Eliminating $\dot{\gamma}$ from Equations 2 and 3 gives a corresponding expression for the viscosity as a function of τ:

$$\eta = m^{1/n}\tau^{(n-1)/n} \tag{4}$$

The two parameters, m and n, must be known in order to determine the viscous behavior of any fluid described by this model. Note that if n = 1, the model reduces to that of a Newtonian fluid, with m = μ. If n < 1, the viscosity decreases with increasing shear rate (or stress), and is thus "shear thinning" (or pseudoplastic). If n > 1, the viscosity increases with shear, and is thus "shear thickening" (or dilatant). Shear-thinning behavior is commonly observed with most non-Newtonian fluids (suspensions, emulsions, polymeric fluids, etc.). Shear-thickening behavior is less common, although it can be observed with highly loaded suspensions of very fine particles (e.g., starch, plaster, etc.) and a few unusual polymeric fluids.

Although this model is very simple and versatile, it has some very serious limitations. For example, for a shear-thinning fluid, as the shear rate (or stress) approaches zero, the predicted apparent viscosity approaches infinity. This is an unrealistic limit, unless the material has a yield stress (which is not included in the model). Likewise, as the shear increases, the predicted viscosity decreases without bound, also an unrealistic limit. Thus, it would be expected that this model would fail for any real material at sufficiently low and/or high shear rates (or stresses). Consequently, applications in which this model must be extrapolated significantly beyond the range of conditions under which the values of m and n were evaluated could lead to significant errors [4]. Nevertheless, because of its simplicity and popularity, it will be considered in the analyses, with the above warning as to its limitations.

Bingham Plastic Model

Many materials, including concentrated suspensions of all types, emulsions (e.g., mayonnaise, cosmetics), paints, inks, foams, foodstuffs, pulps, etc. exhibit plastic behavior; i.e., at sufficiently low stress levels they exhibit behavior representative of solids, in that they will not "flow" at a significant rate unless a certain minimum critical or "yield" stress is exceeded. The simplest expression that represents this characteristic is a linear relation known as the Bingham plastic:

$$\tau = \tau_0 + \mu_\infty \dot{\gamma} \quad \text{for } \tau > \tau_0 \tag{5}$$

$$\dot{\gamma} = 0 \quad \text{for } \tau < \tau_0 \tag{6}$$

where τ_0 is the yield stress, and μ_∞ is the limiting viscosity. The significance of μ_∞ is seen from the corresponding expression for the apparent viscosity function:

$$\eta = \tau_0/\dot{\gamma} + \mu_\infty \tag{7}$$

or $\quad \eta = \mu_\infty/(1 - \tau_0/\tau) \tag{8}$

It is evident that this model represents shear-thinning behavior, and that the viscosity approaches a limiting value of μ_∞ as the shear rate (or stress) increases. The viscosity also approaches infinity as the shear approaches zero, which is appropriate for a plastic material with solid-like properties at "zero shear." Hence, unlike the power law model, both the high and low shear-limiting behavior of this model are realistic, so that application involving extrapolation beyond conditions under which the model parameters were determined should be less critical.

Casson Plastic Model

An equation developed by Casson [5] to describe the plastic properties of suspensions of rod-like particles has been found to provide a better fit to viscosity data for some concentrated suspensions such as printing inks, blood, and other suspensions in which significant associations between the particles occur. The equation is:

$$\tau^{1/2} = \tau_c^{1/2} + (\mu_c \dot{\gamma})^{1/2} \tag{9}$$

and the corresponding expressions for the apparent viscosity as a function of shear rate or shear stress are:

$$\eta = [(\tau_c/\dot{\gamma})^{1/2} + \mu_c^{1/2}]^2 \tag{10}$$

$$= \mu_c \tau/(\tau^{1/2} - \tau_c^{1/2})^2 \tag{11}$$

where τ_c is the yield stress and μ_c is the limiting viscosity, with the same significance as the corresponding Bingham plastic parameters. This model has the same qualitative properties as the Bingham plastic model.

Structural Viscosity Models

Most fluids that do not exhibit a yield stress generally approach Newtonian behavior at very low and very high shear rates (or stresses), and are shear thinning in between. This is typical of polymeric fluids (melts and solutions) and, to some extent, suspensions with moderate loadings of the dispersed phase. Such behavior is described as "structural viscosity," since it is characteristic of a material with a certain degree of structure (e.g., gels), which may be broken down under high shear (shear thinning), but which will recover upon standing or at reduced shear. More than two parameters are required to describe the viscous behavior of such fluids, and a variety of models have been proposed that have this characteristic, typical of which is the Carreau model [6]:

$$\eta = \frac{\eta_0 - \eta_\infty}{[1 + (\lambda\dot{\gamma})^2]^\alpha} + \eta_\infty \tag{12}$$

or $\quad \eta = \frac{\eta_0 - \eta_\infty}{[1 + (\tau/\sigma)^2]^\beta} + \eta_\infty \tag{13}$

where η_0 and η_∞ are the low and high shear-limiting viscosities. The parameter λ is a characteristic time constant (and σ is the corresponding characteristic stress) associated with the transition from low-shear Newtonian to non-Newtonian behavior. These quantities are related by $\lambda = \eta_0/\sigma$. At intermediate shear rates (or stresses), the model reduces to the power law model, and α (or β) is related to the flow index, n, by:

$$n = (1 - 2\alpha) = (1 + 2\beta)^{-1} \tag{14}$$

Other models have been proposed to represent the viscosity of various non-Newtonian materials. Obviously, the more extensive and/or the more complex the behavior it is desired to model, the more extensive the data and the more complex the equation necessary to do this. For practical purposes, data are usually limited in range or scope, and it is often possible to represent a given set of data adequately by more than one model. Also, for engineering purposes, it is desirable to have the simplest possible model that is capable of reasonable representation of the desired performance of the system of interest. For our purpose, prediction of pipe flow behavior, it is usually adequate to use one of the simpler (i.e., two parameter) models, along with appropriate caution not to extrapolate calculated results significantly beyond the range that can be justified by the data used to determine the model parameters.

Some representative data for the viscosity of various non-Newtonian fluids are shown in Figures 1–8. Figures 1 and 2 show the viscosity of suspensions of pulverized lignite in saline water as a

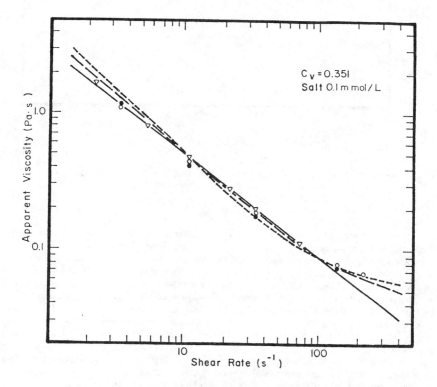

Figure 1. Apparent viscosity of pulverized lignite (35.1% solids by volume) in saline water (0.1 m mol/L salt). Solid line—best fit of Power Law model; short dashes—best fit of Bingham model; long dashes—best fit of Casson model [7].

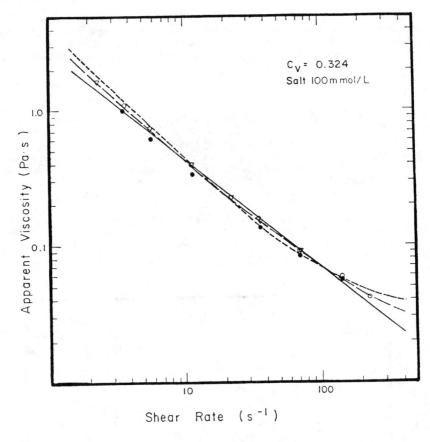

Figure 2. Same as Figure 1, for 32.4% (vol) lignite in 100 m mol/L saline [7].

function of shear rate for a given solids loading and salt concentration [7]. Note that the viscous properties of suspensions depend not only upon the shear rate, but also upon various other parameters such as solids content, particle size and size distribution, the nature and concentration of ionic species, and other parameters that may affect the surface chemistry that influences the interaction between the suspended particles and between the suspended and continuous media. It is also evident that there is no unique model that best represents these viscosity data, as shown by the three different lines through the data. The solid line represents the best fit of the Power Law model to the data, whereas the short dashed line is the best fit of the Bingham Plastic model and the long dashed line is the best fit of the Casson model. Statistically, there is little to choose from between these three models. The dependence of the model parameters upon the solid volume fraction, for a 0.1 molar salt concentration, is shown in Figures 3–5. Similar data for lignite suspensions in methanol are given in References 8 and 9, which also give correlations for the dependence of the model parameters upon solids loading and particle size distribution.

Figure 6 shows the viscosity of dilute solutions of a polyacrylamide (Dow Separan AP-30) in distilled water, which also shows drag reduction in turbulent flow (to be discussed later) [10]. Three polymer concentrations are shown: 500, 250, and 100 wppm. The solid data points are for freshly

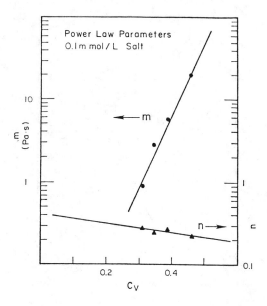

Figure 3. Dependence of Power Law parameters on solids volume fraction for lignite suspensions in 0.1 m mol/L saline [7].

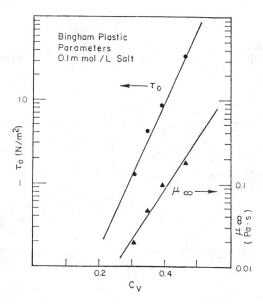

Figure 4. Dependence of Bingham Plastic parameters on solids volume fraction for lignite suspensions in 0.1 m mol/L saline [7].

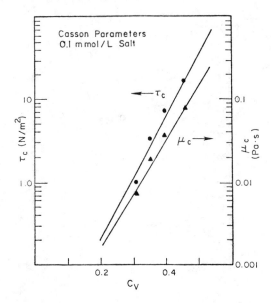

Figure 5. Dependence of Casson model parameters on solids volume fraction for lignite suspensions in 0.1 m mol/L saline [7].

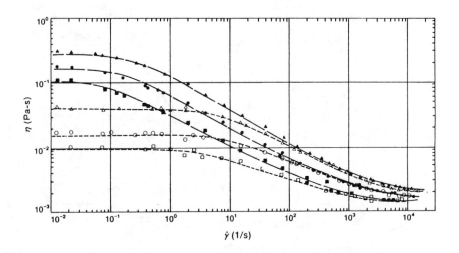

Figure 6. Apparent viscosity of Separan AP-30 polyacrylamide in distilled water. Triangles—500 wppm; circles—250 wppm; squares—100 wppm. Solid symbols—fresh solutions; open symbols—sheared solutions [10].

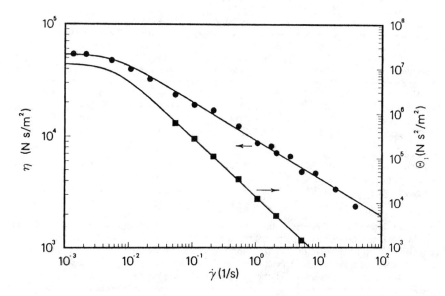

Figure 7. Apparent viscosity and first normal stress difference functions for linear low-density polyethylene sample at 160°C [11].

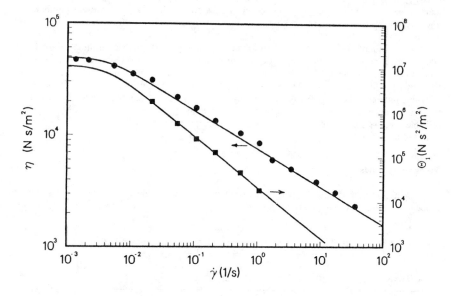

Figure 8. Apparent viscosity and first normal stress difference functions for high-density polyethylene sample at 160°C [11].

Table 1
Values of Structural Viscosity Parameters for Polymer Solutions Shown in Figure 6 [10]

Solution	η_0 (Pa s)	η_∞ (Pa s)	λ (s)	α	n
Fresh					
100 wppm	0.111	0.0013	11.9	0.266	0.468
250 wppm	0.171	0.0014	6.67	0.270	0.460
500 wppm	0.302	0.0017	3.53	0.300	0.400
Sheared					
100 wppm	0.0098	0.0013	0.258	0.251	0.498
250 wppm	0.0169	0.0014	0.106	0.270	0.460
500 wppm	0.0397	0.0017	0.125	0.295	0.410

prepared solutions, and the open points represent shear degraded solutions of the same concentration. The lines through the data points represent the best fit of the structural viscosity equation (Equation 12), and the values of the parameters for each curve are shown in Table 1. The viscosity of such suspensions obviously depends upon polymer concentration; ionic species in solution; various molecular characteristics of the polymer, such as molecular weight, molecular weight distribution and configuration (e.g., number and size of side chains and branches); and shear history.

Figures 7 and 8 show the viscosity of molten polyethylenes at 160°C as a function of shear rate [11]. Also shown on these plots is θ_1, the first normal stress difference for these polymers, which is the stress normal to the plane of shear developed when these polymers are deformed and which is related to their elastic properties. The lines through the viscosity data points represent the best fit of Equation 12, and the resulting values of the parameters are shown in Table 2. Note that the shear rate does not extend to a high enough value to indicate the presence of the high shear limiting viscosity (η_∞), which is typical of polymer melts. The viscosity of molten polymers depends upon many molecular parameters, such as molecular weight, molecular weight distribution, configuration (the size and number of branches), entanglements, temperature, and (for some polymers) shear history.

A comparison of the viscosity functions for suspensions and polymeric fluids indicates distinctive behavior only at very low shear rates. For the suspensions, which exhibit a yield stress, the log-log plot of η vs. $\dot\gamma$ approaches a straight line with a slope of -1 as $\dot\gamma$ (or τ) approaches zero, whereas the polymeric fluids approach Newtonian behavior in this limit. This illustrates the importance of adequate data covering a sufficiently wide range of shear rates, especially at the low end, in order to properly evaluate the rheological character of the fluid.

Table 3 shows some representative viscosity parameters for various non-Newtonian fluids taken from the literature.

Viscoelastic Fluids

Although only the viscous properties of non-Newtonian fluids have been considered so far, the influence of elastic (i.e., viscoelastic) properties upon pipe flow behavior may also be important. In

Table 2
Values of Structural Viscosity Parameters for Polymer Melts Shown in Figures 7 and 8 [11]

Polymer	η_0 (Pa s)	η_∞ (Pa s)	λ (s)	α	n
LDPE (linear)	53,900	0	289	0.171	0.658
HDPE	49,100	0	388	0.171	0.658

Table 3
Model Parameters for Some Non-Newtonian Fluids*

Fluid	Model	Model Parameters	Ref.
Normal Synovial Fluid	Power Law	$m = 6$ "poise"† $n = 0.4$	[12]
Blood	Casson	$\mu_c = 0.0275$ poise $\tau_c = 0.11$ dy/cm^2	[13]
Printing Ink	Casson	$\mu_c = 40$ poise $\tau_c = 400$ dy/cm^2	[5]
Pigment-Plasticizer Dispersions	Bingham	$\mu_\infty = 113$ poise $\tau_0 = 1000$ dy/cm^2	[14]
Molten Chocolate 100°F	Bingham	$\mu_\infty = 20$ poise $\tau_0 = 250$ dy/cm^2	[15]
Tomato Concentrate 90°F, 30% solids	Power Law	$m = 187$ "poise" $n = 0.4$	[16]
Apricot Puree' 80°F, 17.7% solids 77°F, 19% solids	Power Law	$m = 54$ "poise" $n = 0.29$ $m = 200$ "poise" $n = 0.3$	[16] [16]
Applesauce 77°F, 31.7% solids 80°F, 11.6% solids	Power Law	$m = 220$ "poise" $n = 0.4$ $m = 127$ "poise" $n = 0.28$	[16] [16]
Pear Puree' 80°F, 14.6% solids 90°F, 45.8% solids	Power Law	$m = 53$ "poise" $n = 0.38$ $m = 355$ "poise" $n = 0.479$	[16] [16]
Banana Puree' 68°F 75°F 120°F	Power Law	$m = 68.9$ "poise" $n = 0.46$ $m = 107$ "poise" $n = 0.333$ $m = 41.5$ "poise" $n = 0.478$	[16] [16] [16]
Cement Rock in Water 54.3% solids	Power Law ($\dot{\gamma} = 10$–200 s^{-1})	$m = 2.51$ poise $n = 0.153$	[2]
Yellow Clay in Water 23.3% solids	Power Law ($\dot{\gamma} = 1800$–6000)	$m = 5.55$ poise $n = 0.229$	[2]
Polystyrene at 422 K	Power Law ($\dot{\gamma} = 0.03$–3 s^{-1})	$m = 1.6 \times 10^5$ $n = 0.40$	[2]
1.5% CMC in Water	Power Law ($\dot{\gamma} = 10^2$–10^4 s^{-1})	$m = 9.7$ poise $n = 0.40$	[2]

* These values are representative only. The parameter values depend upon the concentration of the dispersed phase and various other conditions.

† The dimensions of m are $[Ft^n/L^2]$. However, it is also equal to the value of the apparent viscosity at $\dot{\gamma} = 1$ s^{-1} (with corresponding viscosity units) and can be interpreted accordingly.

(Continued)

Table 3 (Continued)

Fluid	Model	Model Parameters	Ref.
0.7% CMC in Water	Power Law ($\dot{\gamma} = 10^3\text{--}10^4\ s^{-1}$)	m = 1.5 poise n = 0.5	[2]
3% Polyisobutlyene in Decalin	Power Law ($\dot{\gamma} = 25\text{--}200\ s^{-1}$)	m = 0.94 poise n = 0.77	[2]
0.5% Hydroxyethylcellulose in Water	Power Law	m = 0.84 poise (293 K) n = 0.509	[2]
		m = 0.30 poise (313 K) n = 0.595	[2]
		m = 0.136 poise (333 K) n = 0.645	[2]
1% Poly(ethyleneoxide) in Water	Power Law	m = 0.994 poise (293 K) n = 0.532	[2]
		m = 0.706 poise (313 K) n = 0.544	[2]
		m = 0.486 poise (333 K) n = 0.599	[2]
2% Polyisobutylene in Primol 355	Structural	η_0 = 9230 poise η_∞ = 1.5 poise λ = 191 s α = 0.321 (n = 0.358)	[2]
5% Polystyrene in Aroclor 1242	Structural	η_0 = 1010 poise η_∞ = 0.59 poise λ = 0.84 s α = 0.310 (n = 0.380)	[2]
0.75% Separan-30 in 95/5 Water-Glycerol	Structural	η_0 = 106 poise η_∞ = 0.10 poise λ = 8.04 s α = 0.318 (n = 0.364)	[2]
7% Al soap in Decalin and m-Cresol	Structural	η_0 = 896 poise η_∞ = 0.10 poise λ = 1.41 s α = 0.400 (n = 0.200)	[2]
Polystyrene at 453 K	Structural	η_0 = 1.48 × 10^5 poise η_∞ = 0 λ = 1.04 s α = 0.301 (n = 0.398)	[2]
H-D Polyethylene at 443 K	Structural	η_0 = 89200 poise η_∞ = 0 λ = 1.58 s α = 0.252 (n = 0.496)	[2]
Phenoxy-A at 485 K	Structural	η_0 = 1.24 × 10^5 poise η_∞ = 0 λ = 7.44 s α = 0.136 (n = 0.728)	[2]

steady, fully developed laminar flow, fluid behavior is determined entirely by the viscous properties of the fluid. However, for nonlinear viscoelastic fluids, the viscosity function may also be influenced by the same parameters (i.e., properties) that influence the elasticity. For example, such fluids respond to changing conditions (e.g., deformations) at a finite rate, which can be characterized by a time constant. This time constant may govern the linearity of the viscous response to increasing shear rate, as well as the elastic response to explicitly unsteady processes, so that these properties are not necessarily independent (e.g., λ in Equation 12).

For some viscoelastic fluids (e.g., dilute solutions of very high chain length polymers) in turbulent flow, the elastic properties can have a major effect in terms of drastically reducing the friction loss relative to that exhibited by inelastic fluids under comparable flow conditions. Although the measurement and generalized description of the viscoelastic properties of these fluids is difficult and complex (and beyond the scope of this chapter), it has been shown that for certain strongly drag reducing solutions which exhibit a structural viscosity characteristic, the appropriate rheological parameters that influence drag reduction can be evaluated from this viscosity function, and can be related quantitatively to the degree of turbulent drag reduction for these fluids [17, 18]. Thus, no additional properties or characteristics need be introduced in order to consider both laminar and turbulent pipe flow of such fluids. This will be illustrated subsequently.

MEASUREMENT OF VISCOUS PROPERTIES

The theory underlying the various experimental methods for measuring viscous properties of fluids, independent of the specific character of the fluid, is well established for a variety of geometries [19] and will not be belabored here. We will simply review the working equations needed for proper reduction of laboratory data, for the sake of completeness. This should not be taken lightly, however, because the literature (especially that which accompanies many commercial instruments) abounds with equations that are "recommended" for data reduction, but which in many cases are strictly valid only for Newtonian fluids, or are, at best, crude approximations for use with non-Newtonian fluids. The use of these equations may result in errors which range from negligible, if the fluid is only slightly non-Newtonian, to very significant for highly non-Newtonian fluids. The working equations presented here have been shown to be valid for the geometries considered for any fluid, no matter how nonlinear it may be. Special precautions must be taken, however, to apply proper corrections for end effects, where appropriate. Also, some materials (especially highly loaded suspensions) may exhibit an apparent "slip" at the wall of the viscometer, which must be evaluated and corrected for accordingly in order to obtain a true measure of the deformation of the sample from the measured variable. These effects are specific to the instrument used and the properties of the specific sample, and will not be further elaborated upon here. Refer to the appropriate literature for further discussion of these effects [20, 21, 22].

Tube Flow Viscometry (Poiseuille Flow)

Shear stress (τ) and shear rate ($\dot{\gamma}$) values required to determine the apparent viscosity function ($\eta = \tau/\dot{\gamma}$) may be obtained directly from measurement of pressure drop ($\Delta\phi = \Delta P + \rho g \, \Delta z$) and flow rate (Q) in fully developed tube flow, as follows:

$$\tau = -\Delta\phi R/2L \tag{15}$$

$$\dot{\gamma} = \frac{4Q}{\pi R^3}\left[\frac{3n' + 1}{4n'}\right] = \frac{8V}{D}\left[\frac{3n' + 1}{4n'}\right] \tag{16}$$

where $n' = \dfrac{d \log(-\Delta\phi)}{d \log Q}$ $\tag{17}$

If the fluid obeys the Power Law model, then n' is a constant identical to the flow index n. However, for any other type of non-Newtonian behavior, n' will vary depending on the shear rate (or shear stress). Equation 16 is exact for any type of viscous behavior, and is identical to the exact solution of the momentum equation for a Power Law fluid for constant n.

Cup-and-Bob Viscometry (Couette Flow)

For the cup-and-bob or concentric cylinder (Couette) viscometer, the shear stress in the gap at any distance r from the center is directly related to the developed torque, T, and the length of the (immersed) bob, L, by:

$$\tau = \frac{T}{2\pi L r^2} \tag{18}$$

The shear stress at the bob is thus:

$$\tau_b = \frac{T}{2\pi L R_b^2} \tag{19}$$

The corresponding shear rate at the bob can be determined from the measured torque, T, and angular velocity, Ω, by:

$$\dot{\gamma}_b = \frac{2\Omega}{n'(1 - \beta^{2/n'})} \tag{20}$$

where $\beta = R_b/R_c$ (the ratio of bob to cup radius) and:

$$n' = \frac{d \log T}{d \log \Omega} = \frac{d \log \tau_b}{d \log \Omega} \tag{21}$$

Equation 20 is exact only for a Power Law fluid, i.e., for n' = n (a constant). For other types of fluid behavior, this expression constitutes a "local power law approximation" for the shear rate. Yang and Kreiger [23] have shown that the error resulting from the use of this equation is less than 1% for fluids without a yield stress, and Darby [24] has shown that, for materials with a yield stress, the error depends upon the specific plastic model for the material, the stress at the cup wall relative to the yield stress, and the value of β. The maximum error for the worst possible condition is of the order of 6% for a Bingham material and 2% for a Casson material, although under the vast majority of conditions encountered in practice, the error is 1% or less for these fluids, as well.

There are a variety of other geometries which can be used to measure viscosity (e.g., the cone and plate, the parallel plate or disc and plate, etc.). However, since the tube and cup-and-bob viscometers are by far the most common, we will limit this discussion to these geometries.

LAMINAR TUBE FLOWS

For steady, fully developed flow of an incompressible fluid in a uniform tube, the axial component of the momentum equation reduces to:

$$\tau = \Delta\phi r/2L = -\tau_w r/R \tag{22}$$

where $\tau_w = f\rho V^2/2 = \rho e_f R/2L \tag{23}$

Here, f is the Fanning friction factor, and e_f is the energy dissipated due to friction per unit mass of fluid. This shows that the shear stress is distributed linearly across the tube, which is true for either laminar or turbulent flow. For laminar flow, the stress is determined only by the viscous properties, whereas for turbulent flow, the eddy Reynold's stresses must also be included. For laminar flows, the flow rate can be determined by equating the shear stress—shear rate (e.g., velocity gradient) relation to Equation 22 and integrating to obtain the velocity distribution, then integrating again to obtain the flow rate. An alternate, and more direct method, involves using the continuity principle, by noting that:

$$Q = \int_A v \, dA = \pi \int_0^R 2vr \, dr = \pi \int_0^{R^2} v \, d(r^2)$$

(24)

After integration by parts, this becomes:

$$Q = -\pi \int_A r^2 \, dv = -\pi \int_0^R r^2 \dot{\gamma} \, dr = -\pi \int_0^R \frac{r^2 \tau}{\eta} \, dr = \pi \left(\frac{R}{\tau_w}\right)^3 \int_0^{\tau_w} \frac{\tau^3}{\eta} \, d\tau$$

(25)

Thus a knowledge of the viscosity function, η, as a function of the shear stress, τ, together with Equation 22 for the stress as a function of r, when introduced into Equation 25 enables the flow rate to be evaluated directly for any viscosity model (Newtonian or non-Newtonian).

Newtonian Fluids

For Newtonian fluids, $\eta = \mu$ (constant), and Equation 25 becomes:

$$Q = \frac{-\pi \, \Delta\phi D^4}{128\mu L}$$

(26)

which is the well-known Hagen-Poiseuille equation. Using Equations 22 and 23 to relate $\Delta\phi$ to the friction factor f, this can be written in dimensionless form as:

$$f = 16/N_{Re}$$

(27)

where $N_{Re} = DV\rho/\mu = 4Q\rho/\pi D\mu$ is the Reynolds number. It should be noted that laminar pipe flow of a Newtonian fluid is completely characterized by a single dimensionless quantity, fN_{Re}, which has a value of 16. The density, ρ, appears in the definition of both f and N_{Re} but cancels in the product fN_{Re}. However, the density does influence turbulent flow directly, so it is convenient to retain both f and N_{Re} for comparison with turbulent flow results.

Power Law Fluids

For the Power Law model, η is given in terms of τ by Equation 4, which in turn is related to r by Equation 22. Inserting these expressions into Equation 25 and integrating gives:

$$Q = \frac{\pi n}{3n + 1} \left(\frac{-\Delta\phi}{2Lm}\right)^{1/n} R^{(3n + 1)/n}$$

(28)

which is the Power Law equivalent of the Hagen-Poiseuille equation, and reduces to Equation 26 for n = 1 and m = μ. Using Equation 22 to eliminate $\Delta\phi$, as before, and rearranging to solve for f gives:

$$f = 16/N'_{Re}$$

(29)

where
$$N'_{Re} = \frac{8D^n V^{2-n}\rho}{m}\left(\frac{n}{2(3n+1)}\right)^n \tag{30}$$

is the equivalent Reynolds number for the Power Law fluid. It is defined (arbitrarily) so that Equations 27 and 29 are of identical form. Note that two dimensionless quantities are now required, i.e., fN'_{Re} and n.

Bingham Plastics

Since the Bingham Plastic exhibits a yield stress (τ_0), there will be a region extending from the center of the pipe to $r = R\tau_0/\tau_w = r_0$ which will be undeformed, i.e., will move as a "plug." Thus the total flow rate will include that in the "plug" as well as in the deformed region surrounding the plug, so that Equation 24 can be written:

$$Q = Q_{plug} + \pi \int_{r_0^2}^{R^2} v\, d(r^2) = -\pi \int_{r_0}^{R} r^2 \dot{\gamma}\, dr \tag{31}$$

where the last term results from evaluating the previous integral by parts (the term Q_{plug} cancelling out). Substituting for $\dot{\gamma}$ from Equation 6 gives:

$$Q = -\pi \int_{r_0}^{R} \frac{r^2(\tau + \tau_0)}{\mu_\infty}\, dr = \frac{-\pi}{\mu_\infty} \int_{r_0}^{R}\left(r^2\tau_0 - \frac{r^3\tau_w}{R}\right) dr \tag{32}$$

Evaluating the integral results in the Buckingham-Reiner equation:

$$Q = \frac{\pi R^3 \tau_w}{4\mu_\infty}\left[1 - \frac{4}{3}\frac{\tau_0}{\tau_w} + \frac{1}{3}\left(\frac{\tau_0}{\tau_w}\right)^4\right] \tag{33}$$

This can be rearranged as before by substituting for τ_w in terms of f, and solving for f to give the equivalent dimensionless expression:

$$f = \frac{16}{N_{Re}}\left[1 + \frac{1}{6}\frac{N_{He}}{N_{Re}} - \frac{1}{3}\frac{N_{He}^4}{f^3 N_{Re}^7}\right] \tag{34}$$

where:

$$N_{Re} = \frac{DV\rho}{\mu_\infty} = \frac{4Q\rho}{\pi D\mu_\infty} \quad \text{and} \quad N_{He} = \frac{D^2\rho\tau_0}{\mu_\infty^2} \tag{35}$$

N_{He} is the Hedstrom number. Again, since two rheological parameters are required, the dimensionless solution involves two dimensionless groups, i.e., fN_{Re} and N_{He}/N_{Re}. Note that Equation 34 is implicit in f. However, the last term in the bracket is normally small relative to the other terms, so that a brief iteration using the first two terms as the starting value will converge very rapidly if it is desired to determine f from known values of N_{Re} and N_{He}.

Casson Plastics

A procedure analogous to that above can be followed using the Casson model, Equation 9, with Equation 31 to determine the flow rate as a function of τ_w (i.e., the pressure gradient). The result is:

$$Q = \frac{\pi R^3 \tau_w}{4\mu_c}\left[1 + \frac{4}{3}\left(\frac{\tau_c}{\tau_w}\right) - \frac{16}{7}\left(\frac{\tau_c}{\tau_w}\right)^{1/2} - \frac{1}{21}\left(\frac{\tau_c}{\tau_w}\right)^4\right] \tag{36}$$

In dimensionless form, this becomes:

$$f = \frac{16}{N_{Re}} \left[1 - \frac{N_{He}}{6N_{Re}} + \frac{1}{7} (2fN_{He})^{1/2} + \frac{N_{He}^4}{21f^3 N_{Re}^7} \right] \tag{37}$$

where the Reynolds number and Hedstrom number are defined as in Equation 35, using μ_c and τ_c instead of μ_∞ and τ_0.

Structural Fluids

The structural viscosity model, Equation 12 or 13, is a more general representation of the viscous properties of polymeric fluids, or any shear-thinning fluid which does not exhibit a yield stress. However, it is more complex since it involves four rheological parameters (η_0, η_∞, and λ, α or σ, β). It is convenient to write Equation 13 in dimensionless form, as follows [24a]:

$$\bar{\eta} = \frac{1 - \bar{\eta}_\infty}{[1 + (fN_{Re}N_{We}\bar{\tau}/2)^2]^\beta} + \bar{\eta}_\infty \tag{38}$$

where
$$N_{Re} = \frac{DV\rho}{\eta_0} = \frac{4Q\rho}{\pi D\eta_0}$$

$$N_{We} = \frac{\eta_0 V}{\sigma D}$$

$$\bar{\tau} = \frac{r}{R}$$

$$\bar{\eta} = \frac{\eta}{\eta_0}$$

$$\bar{\eta}_\infty = \frac{\eta_\infty}{\eta_0} \tag{39}$$

N_{We} is the Weissenberg number, which is the ratio of the fluid time constant, $\lambda = \eta_0/\sigma$, to that of the flow, D/V. Equation 25 can be expressed in terms of these dimensionless variables and rearranged to give:

$$fN_{Re} = \frac{4}{I_s(1)}, \quad \text{where } I_s(y) = \int_0^y \frac{x^3}{\bar{\eta}(x)} dx \tag{40}$$

Since $\bar{\eta}$ depends upon fN_{Re}, as well as N_{We}, η_∞, and β (or n), Equation 40 is implicit in fN_{Re}. The solution can be obtained readily by numerical means, and the result is shown in Figure 9 as $[fN_{Re} - (fN_{Re})_\infty]/[(fN_{Re})_{Newt} - (fN_{Re})_\infty]$ vs. N_{We}, for values of $0.4 < n > 1.0$, where $(fN_{Re})_{Newt} = 16$ and $(fN_{Re})_\infty = 16\bar{\eta}_\infty$. For values of N_{We} greater than the order of unity, the polymer molecules in the flow are deformed faster than they can recover, resulting in nonlinear behavior. Actually, as seen from Figure 9, the range of nonlinear behavior depends upon the value of n, but starts as low as $N_{We} = 10^{-2}$.

TURBULENT TUBE FLOWS

For turbulent flows, various semi-empirical models have been used to describe the local momentum transport and velocity distribution due to turbulent eddies. These results have been used to determine overall friction loss in flow fields, including pipe flows. We will not present the details of these analyses here, but will refer the reader to the literature in which they can be found, and will simply present the results in the most generalized and useful form.

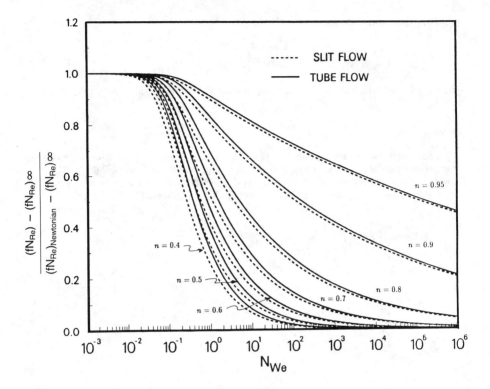

Figure 9. $fN_{Re}/16$ as a function of N_{We} and n for structural viscosity fluid, for $\eta_\infty = 0.01$ (Equation 40) [24a].

Newtonian Fluids

For turbulent flow of a Newtonian fluid in smooth tubes, the classical mixing length theory of Prandtl [25] was applied by von Karman [26], together with the experimental data of Nikuradse, to derive the well-known expression:

$$\frac{1}{\sqrt{f}} = 4.0 \log(N_{Re}\sqrt{f}) - 0.40 \qquad (41)$$

This is implicit in f, but is convenient for determining the flow rate that will result in a given friction loss, since the group $N_{Re}\sqrt{f}$ is independent of flow rate.

For rough surfaces, this expression was modified by Colebrook [27] to include the effect of relative roughness, e/D:

$$\frac{1}{\sqrt{f}} = -4 \log\left[\frac{e/D}{3.7} + \frac{1.255}{N_{Re}\sqrt{f}}\right] \qquad (42)$$

This equation is the basis for the well-known Moody diagram for pipe friction factors, and applies for $N_{Re} > 10^4$.

An equation that is explicit in f, and is valid for all values of N_{Re} in laminar as well as turbulent flow, was developed by Churchill [28]:

$$f = 2\left[\left(\frac{8}{N_{Re}}\right)^{12} + \frac{1}{(A + B)^{3/2}}\right]^{1/12} \tag{43}$$

where $A = \left[2.457 \ln\left(\cfrac{1}{\left(\frac{7}{N_{Re}}\right)^{0.9} + \frac{0.27e}{D}}\right)\right]^{16}$

$$B = \left(\frac{37{,}530}{N_{Re}}\right)^{16}$$

Power Law Fluids

Following the form of the von Karman-Nikuradse equation, Dodge and Metzner [29] derived the following expression for the turbulent flow of a Power Law fluid in a smooth tube:

$$\frac{1}{\sqrt{f}} = \frac{4}{n^{0.75}} \log[N'_{Re} f^{(1 - n/2)}] - \frac{0.4}{n^{1.2}} \tag{44}$$

where N'_{Re} is given by Equation 30. This expression was confirmed by data for non-elastic non-Newtonian fluids over a limited range of N'_{Re} and flow index n.

A more detailed turbulence model (based on the van Dreist modification of the mixing length model) was used by Hanks and Ricks [30] to determine f as a function of N'_{Re} and n by numerical calculations. A comparison of their results with the Dodge-Metzner equation is shown in Figure 10. Also shown in Figure 10 is an empirical fit that incorporates both the Hanks and Ricks results and the theoretical laminar limit (Equation 29), and which is valid for all values of N'_{Re} encompassing laminar as well as turbulent flow [8]. The expression is as follows:

$$f = (1 - \alpha)f_L + \frac{\alpha}{[f_T^{-8} + f_{TR}^{-8}]^{1/8}} \tag{45}$$

where $f_L = \dfrac{16}{N'_{Re}}$,   for $N'_{Re} < N'_{Rec} = 2100 + 875(1 - n)$ \hfill (46)

$$f_T = \frac{0.0682n^{-1/2}}{N'^{1/(1.87 + 2.39n)}_{Re}}, \quad \text{for } 4000 < N'_{Re} < 10^5 \tag{47}$$

$$f_{TR} = 1.79 \times 10^{-4} \exp(-5.24n)N'^{(0.414 + 0.757n)}_{Re} \tag{48}$$

$$\alpha = \frac{1}{1 + 4^{-\Delta}}, \quad \text{where } \Delta = N'_{Re} - N'_{Rec} \tag{49}$$

Although these equations are based upon principles which should be generally valid, they have not been confirmed by comparison with measurements over a wide range of values of N'_{Re} and n. There is also insufficient evidence for the effect of wall roughness upon the friction loss in non-Newtonian tubes. Some workers assume that the ratio of friction loss in rough tubes to that in smooth tubes is the same for non-Newtonian fluids as for Newtonian fluids. However, because the laminar sublayer is generally thicker for non-Newtonian fluids than for Newtonian, the effect of roughness should be smaller. Hence, other authorities neglect the effect of roughness in non-Newtonian flows, which is a practice that we also recommend, as there is some indication that the equations for smooth tubes are conservative.

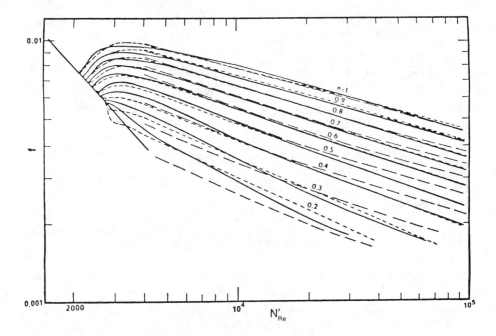

Figure 10. Fanning friction factor vs. Reynolds number and flow index for Power Law fluid. Solid line—Hanks and Ricks [30]; long dashes—Dodge and Metzner [29]; short dashes—Equation 45 [8].

Bingham Plastics

The flow of Bingham plastics in tubes has been studied by a number of people, including Hedstrom [31] and Hanks and Dadia [32]. The latter extended the approach of Hanks and Ricks to the turbulent flow of Bingham plastics in smooth tubes to determine the friction factor as a function of the Reynolds and Hedstrom numbers by numerical solution of the governing equations. The result is shown in Figure 11, which also shows the result of an empirical fit of these curves by Darby and Melson [33]. The difference between these two is virtually imperceptible for values of the Hedstrom number greater than 1,000. The latter expression is:

$$f = [f_L^\beta + f_T^\beta]^{1/\beta} \tag{50}$$

where f_L is the solution to the laminar Buckingham-Reiner equation (Equation 34), and:

$$f_T = 10^a N_{Re}^{-0.193} \tag{51}$$

$$a = -1.378[1 + 0.146 \exp(-2.9 \times 10^{-5} N_{He})] \tag{52}$$

$$\beta = 1.7 + 40,000/N_{Re} \tag{53}$$

N_{Re} and N_{He} are given by Equation 35, as before.

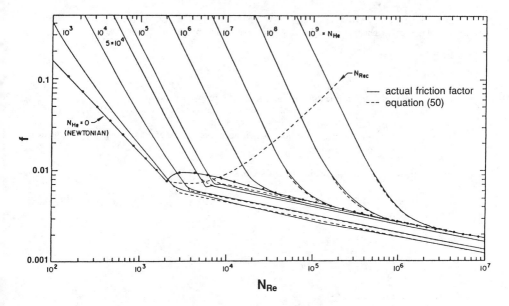

Figure 11. Fanning friction factor as a function of N_{Re} and N_{He} for Bingham plastic. Solid lines—Reference [32]; Dashed lines—Equation 50 [33].

Viscoelastic Fluids—Drag Reduction

Polymeric fluids (e.g., solutions and melts) of sufficiently high chain length exhibit nonlinear viscous properties, as well as marked elastic properties. The stresses resulting from these additional elastic properties can result in flow behavior in non-uniform flows which is markedly different from that exhibited by purely viscous (Newtonian or non-Newtonian) fluids. Die swell, rod climbing, reverse circulation patterns, and the tubeless siphon are but a few examples of "unusual" behavior in laminar flows. Although polymer melts rarely, if ever, encounter turbulent flow conditions, such conditions are not only common but dominant in systems involving polymer solutions. Because of the highly unsteady local nature of turbulence, the elastic properties of such fluids may have a very large effect upon their flow behavior.

In fact, in uniform turbulent flow in tubes, the presence of only a few parts per million of a soluble polymer of sufficiently high molecular weight (e.g., 10^6–10^7) can influence the flow to such an extent as to reduce the friction loss by as much as 80% below that exhibited by the solvent alone at the same flow rate. This drag reduction phenomenon has obvious practical applications, and has been studied extensively by many investigators. Although the phenomenon is not completely understood, one study by Darby and Chang [17] (described in detail by Darby [18]) has resulted in a model for turbulent drag reduction which provides a quantitative relation between measured rheological properties of the polymer solutions and their turbulent friction loss behavior, which correlated well with experimental data. The model is based upon the simple realization that elastic properties store energy rather than dissipating it, as done by viscous properties, so that less energy must be added to the flow from external sources to sustain the turbulence. The details of the model and its derivation are presented in the references cited. Only the results, as modified by Jenkins [34], will be summarized here.

The net result of the analysis is a definition of a generalized friction factor, which accounts for the storage of energy by elastic properties as well as dissipation by viscous properties:

$$f_p = \frac{f_s}{(1 + N_{De}^2)^{1/2}} \tag{54}$$

where f_p = Fanning friction factor for the viscoelastic polymer solution
f_s = Fanning friction factor of the (Newtonian) solvent, evaluated at the flow Reynolds number using the solvent viscosity (N_{Res})
N_{De} = Deborah number for the flow, which accounts for the energy storage by the elastic properties of the solution.

The model gives rise to the following expression for N_{De}:

$$N_{De} = \frac{0.0166 N'_{We} N_{Res}^{3/8} (\mu/\eta_0)^{1/2}}{[1 + (0.0166 N'_{We} N_{Res}^{3/8})^2]^{1/4}} \tag{55}$$

where $N'_{We} = [(1 + N_\lambda^2)^\alpha - 1]^{1/2}$,

$$N_\lambda = \frac{8V\lambda}{D}, \tag{56}$$

$$N_{Res} = \frac{DV\rho}{\mu}$$

The parameters η_0, α, and λ are three rheological parameters, which can be obtained from the apparent viscosity function for the solution (see Equation 12), and μ is the viscosity of the solvent. Although these parameters can, in principle, all be obtained from viscosity data, the parameter λ does, nevertheless, represent a characteristic time of the fluid which is relevant to elastic behavior.

This model was evaluated by comparison with data for polyacrylamide solutions (Dow Separan AP-30) in distilled water, with concentrations of 100, 250, and 500 wppm. Both freshly prepared and shear degraded solutions were tested, in tubes ranging from 2 to 10 mm in diameter [35]. The viscosity functions for these solutions are shown in Figure 6, and the values of the rheological parameters obtained from these data are given in Table 1.

These solutions exhibited as much as 80% drag reduction (i.e., as little as 20% of the friction loss exhibited by pure water at the same value of N_{Res}), for Reynolds numbers up to about 10^5. The best correlation of the data was found by regressing the numerical parameters in Equation 55 to yield the following adjusted form of this equation [34]:

$$N_{De} = \frac{0.0336 N'_{We} N_{Res}^{0.375} (\mu/\eta_0)^{0.296}}{[1 + (0.0077 N'_{We} N_{Res}^{3/8})^2]^{0.262}} \tag{57}$$

The above-referenced data are shown correlated by this equation in Figure 12, in which the solid line is the classical Blasius equation for purely viscous Newtonian fluids in turbulent flow in smooth tubes:

$$f = f_s = \frac{0.0791}{N_{Res}^{1/4}} \tag{58}$$

This classical equation, together with Equation 54 for the modification to the friction factor for energy storage by elastic properties and Equation 57 for N_{De}, is all that is required for the quantitative prediction of drag reduction. The latter contains the rheological parameters of the solution, which can be obtained from viscosity data.

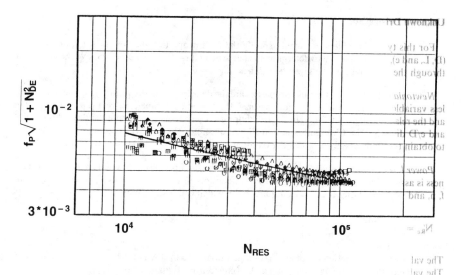

Figure 12. Generalized friction factor for drag-reducing polymer solutions. Solid line is the Blasius equation (Equation 58) for Newtonian fluids ($N_{De} = 0$) in smooth tubes. Data points are for the six solutions shown in Figure 6, in tubes from 2 to 10 mm dia., with N_{De} given by Equation 57 [17, 18, 34, 35].

SOLUTION OF FLOW PROBLEMS

In practice, there are several types of practical pipe flow problems that we might wish to solve. These can be classified as: Unknown Driving Force; Unknown Flow Rate; Unknown Diameter; and Most Economical Diameter. Each of these types of problems can be solved by appropriate application of the macroscopic energy balance (i.e., Bernoulli's equation, with friction) together with the appropriate relation for the friction factor for the particular fluid model of interest. The energy balance equation can be written:

$$DF = e_f \tag{59}$$

where $\quad DF = -\left(\dfrac{\Delta\phi}{\rho} + w\right) \tag{60}$

is the net driving force, which includes the pressure and static head drop ($\Delta\phi = \Delta P + \rho g\,\Delta z$) and pump head ($H = -w/g$) (or any combination thereof), and e_f is the energy dissipated by friction per unit mass of fluid. The Fanning friction factor (Equation 23) is the dimensionless friction loss:

$$f = \frac{e_f D}{2L\rho V^2} = \frac{e_f \pi^2 D^5}{32L\rho Q^2} = \frac{DF\pi^2 D^5}{32L\rho Q^2} \tag{61}$$

which is, in turn, dependent upon the appropriate Reynolds number and either e/D, n, or N_{He}, depending upon the particular fluid. We shall illustrate below the procedure for solving these three types of pipe flow problems for Newtonian, Power Law, and Bingham Plastic fluids. The procedure is independent of whether the flow is laminar or turbulent, since the general relations for f will be used and are valid for either.

Unknown Driving Force

For this type of problem, we would specify the fluid properties, the flow rate (Q), and the pipe (D, L, and e), and would like to determine the net driving force (DF) required to move the given fluid through the given pipe at the given flow rate.

Newtonian. In this case, the fluid properties are the density, ρ, and the viscosity, μ. The dimensionless variables involved are the friction factor, f, the Reynolds number, $N_{Re} = DV\rho/\mu = 4Q\rho/\pi D\mu$, and the relative roughness, e/D. This is straightforward, since we can compute the Reynolds number and e/D directly. The Churchill equation (Equation 43) or the Moody diagram can then be used to obtain the value of f, from which the required net driving force (DF) is found from Equation 61.

Power law. The problem is the same, except that the fluid properties are m, n, and ρ, and roughness is assumed to be unimportant. The three dimensionless quantities involved in this problem are f, n, and N'_{Re}. The latter is given by Equation 30, which can also be written:

$$N'_{Re} = \frac{2^{7-3n}\rho Q^{2-n}}{m\pi^{2-n}D^{4-3n}} \left[\frac{n}{3n+1}\right]^n \tag{62}$$

The value of N'_{Re} is computed from the given quantities, and f is then determined from Equation 45. The value of the net driving force is then determined from Equation 61.

Bingham plastic. The problem is again the same, except that the fluid properties are now τ_0, μ_∞, and ρ, and the effect of wall roughness is neglected. The appropriate dimensionless quantities are now f, N_{Re}, and N_{He}. The values of the Reynolds and Hedstrom numbers can be computed, and Equation 50 is then used to determine f, which in turn determines the driving force from Equation 61, as before.

Unknown Flow Rate

Another common problem is the determination of the flow rate (Q) that would result for a fluid with known properties being transported through a given pipe (D, L, e) with a specified driving force (DF).

Newtonian. The fluid properties are μ and ρ, and the dimensionless quantities are f, N_{Re}, and e/D. However, since the unknown Q appears in the definition of both N_{Re} and f, neither of these can be computed a priori. It is therefore more appropriate to combine the three groups in such a way that the unknown Q appears in only one, which then becomes the dependent variable. A suitable set of groups is

$$N_{Re} = \frac{4Q\rho}{\pi D\mu}, \quad \frac{e}{D}, \quad fN_{Re}^2 = \frac{DF\rho^2 D^3}{2L\mu^2} \tag{63}$$

in which the unknown Q appears only in N_{Re}, and fN_{Re}^2 and e/D can be evaluated from known quantities. If the flow is assumed to be turbulent, these values can be introduced into the Colebrook equation (Equation 42), which gives the value of f. Knowing f and fN_{Re}^2 gives N_{Re}, and hence Q. The assumption of turbulent flow can be checked from the value of the Reynolds number. Alternatively, corresponding values of f, N_{Re}, and e/D determined from the Moody diagram (or the Churchill equation) can be recombined and replotted in the form $N_{Re} = fn(fN_{Re}^2, e/D)$, which can be used to solve this problem directly. Such a plot is shown in Figure 13. This problem can also be solved using Equation 43 by iteration. A value of f is first assumed (0.005) and N_{Re} is determined from the known value of fN_{Re}^2, i.e., $N_{Re} = \sqrt{(fN_{Re}^2)}$. A revised value of f is then calculated from Equation 43, and the procedure is repeated until agreement is obtained.

Power law. The problem is the same as above except the parameters μ and e/D for the Newtonian fluid are now replaced by m and n, and the corresponding dimensionless quantities are f, N'_{Re} (Equa-

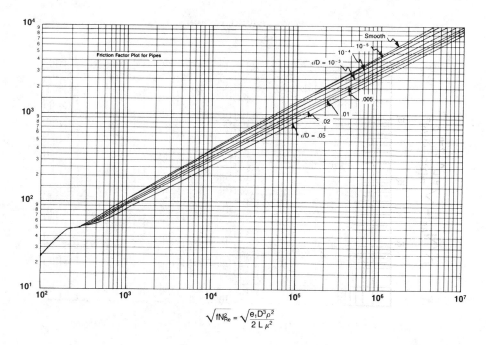

$$\sqrt{fN_{Re}^2} = \sqrt{\frac{e_1 D^3 \rho^2}{2 L \mu^2}}$$

Figure 13. Friction loss plot for solving unknown flow rate problem for Newtonian fluids.

tion 62), and n, which are related by Equation 45. These groups can be combined in such a way that the unknown Q will appear in only one group, N'_{Re}, as follows:

$$N'_{Re} = \frac{2^{7-3n}\rho Q^{2-n}}{m\pi^{2-n}D^{4-3n}}\left[\frac{n}{3n+1}\right]^n,$$

$$N'_{Re}f^{1-n/2} = \left(\frac{DF\pi^2 D^5}{32L}\right)^{1-n/2}\left(\frac{2^{7-3n}\rho}{m\pi^{2-n}D^{4-3n}}\right)\left[\frac{n}{3n+1}\right]^n \tag{64}$$

The group $N'_{Re}f^{1-n/2}$ can be evaluated from given quantities. If the flow is turbulent, this value along with n can be inserted into the Dodge-Metzner equation (Equation 44) to give f and hence Q by Equation 61. Alternatively, corresponding values of f, N'_{Re}, and n can be evaluated from Equation 45 and recombined and replotted in the form $N'_{Re} = fn(n, N'_{Re}f^{1-n/2})$, which can be used to solve this problem directly. Such a plot is shown in Figure 14. An iterative procedure can also be employed using Equation 45. A value of f is assumed (e.g., 0.005) and N'_{Re} is determined from the known value of $N'_{Re}f^{1-n/2}$. This is used to calculate a revised value of f from Equation 45, and the procedure is repeated until successive f values agree.

Bingham plastic. The problem is again the same, except the Newtonian parameters μ and e/D are replaced by the yield stress τ_0 and the limiting viscosity, μ_∞. The governing dimensionless quantities are f, N_{Re}, and N_{He} (Equation 35). As before, the groups are combined so that the unknown Q appears only in one group, i.e., N_{Re}:

$$N_{Re} = \frac{4Q\rho}{\pi D\mu}, \qquad N_{He} = \frac{D^2\rho\tau_0}{\mu_\infty^2}, \qquad fN_{Re}^2 = \frac{DF\rho^2 D^3}{2L\mu_\infty^2} \tag{65}$$

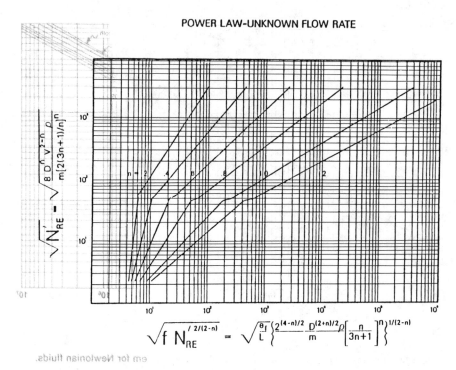

$$\sqrt{f}\, N_{RE}^{\,/\,2/(2-n)} = \sqrt{\frac{g_f}{L}} \left\{ 2^{(4-n)/2}\, \frac{D^{(2+n)/2}\rho}{m} \left[\frac{n}{3n+1} \right]^n \right\}^{1/(2-n)}$$

Figure 14. Friction loss plot for solving unknown flow rate problem for Power Law fluids.

As before, fN_{Re}^2 and N_{He} are known a priori, and N_{Re} (Q) is to be determined. Corresponding values of these groups can be determined using Equation 50, and replotted as $N_{Re} = fn(fN_{Re}^2, N_{He})$ to solve this problem directly. Such a plot is shown in Figure 15. An iterative procedure can also be used with Equation 50. Again, a value for f is initially assumed (e.g., 0.005) and used to determine N_{Re} from $N_{Re} = (fN_{Re}^2/f)^{1/2}$. This is used to calculate f from Equation 50, and the procedure is repeated until agreement is achieved.

Unknown Diameter

A third type of problem frequently encountered is the determination of the pipe diameter (D) which would be required to transport a fluid with known properties at a specified flow rate (Q) with a given driving force (DF). It is assumed that the length of pipe (L) and its surface roughness are also specified.

Newtonian. As before, the appropriate dimensionless quantities are f, N_{Re}, and e/D. Since the unknown D appears in all three of these groups, they may be recombined in the following way so that D appears in only one, N_{Re}:

$$N_{Re}^5 = \frac{4Q\rho}{\pi D\mu}, \quad fN_{Re}^5 = \frac{32DF\rho^5Q^3}{\pi^3 L\mu^5}, \quad N_R = \frac{N_{Re}}{e/D} = \frac{4Q\rho}{\pi\mu e} \qquad (66)$$

Values of fN_{Re}^5 and N_R can be determined from given quantities, and N_{Re} (D) is to be determined. This can be done iteratively, as before, using the Churchill equation (Equation 43). First a value for f is assumed (e.g., 0.005), and $N_{Re} = (fN_{Re}^5/f)^{1/5}$ is determined. Then f is computed from Equation 43, and the procedure repeated until agreement is achieved. Alternatively, corresponding values

BINGHAM PLASTIC-UNKNOWN FLOW RATE

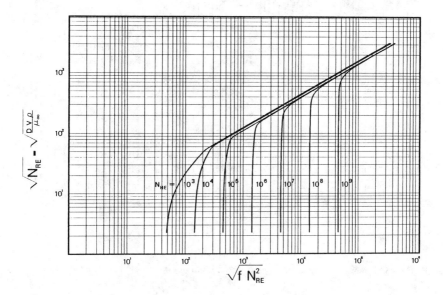

Figure 15. Friction loss plot for solving unknown flow rate problem for Bingham plastic fluids.

of f, N_{Re}, and e/D can be determined using Equation 43, and then recombined and replotted in the form $N_{Re} = fn(fN_{Re}^5, N_R)$ to solve this problem directly. Such a plot is shown in Figure 16.

Power law. The same general procedure can be followed for a Power Law fluid, for which the controlling dimensionless quantities are f, N'_{Re}, and n. These can be combined to give the following equivalent set of groups in which the unknown (D) appears in only one, i.e., N'_{Re}: N'_{Re}, n, and:

$$fN_{Re}^{'5/(4-3n)} = \left(\frac{DF\pi^2}{32LQ^2}\right)\left(\frac{2^{7-3n}\rho Q^{2-n}}{m\pi^{2-n}}\left[\frac{n}{3n+1}\right]^n\right)^{5/(4-3n)} \tag{67}$$

The quantities n and $fN_{Re}^{'5/(4-3n)}$ are known from given values, and N'_{Re} (or f) is to be determined. This can be done iteratively by first assuming a value for f (e.g., 0.005), determining $N'_{Re} = (fN_{Re}^{'5/(4-3n)}/f)^{(4-3n)/5}$, then calculating f from Equation 45 and iterating until agreement is obtained. Alternatively, Equation 45 can be used to determine corresponding values of f, N'_{Re}, and n, which can be recombined and replotted in the form $N'_{Re} = fn(n, fN_{Re}^{'5/(4-3n)})$ to solve this problem directly. Such a plot is shown in Figure 17.

Bingham plastic. As before, the governing dimensionless quantities are f, N_{Re}, and N_{He}. These can be combined into the following equivalent set of groups such that the unknown (D) is in only one group (N_{Re}):

$$N_{Re} = \frac{4Q\rho}{\pi D\mu_\infty}, \quad fN_{Re}^5 = \frac{32DFQ^3\rho^5}{L\pi^3\mu_\infty^5}, \quad N_{Re}^2 N_{He} = \frac{16Q^2\rho^2\tau_0}{\pi^2\mu_\infty^4} \tag{68}$$

The groups fN_{Re}^5 and $N_{Re}^2 N_{He}$ are determined from given quantities, and N_{Re} (D) is to be determined. The usual iterative procedure can be used, i.e., first assume a value for f (e.g. 0.005), calculate

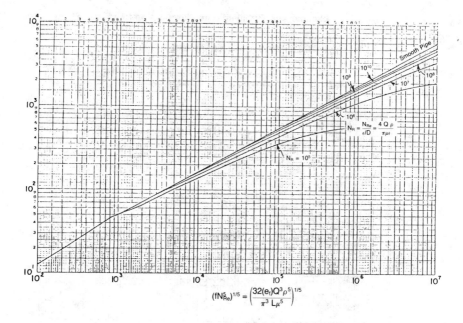

$$(fN_{Re}^5)^{1/5} = \left(\frac{32(e_f)Q^3\rho^5}{\pi^3 L\mu^5}\right)^{1/5}$$

Figure 16. Friction loss plot for solving unknown diameter problem for Newtonian fluids.

POWER LAW-UNKNOWN DIAMETER

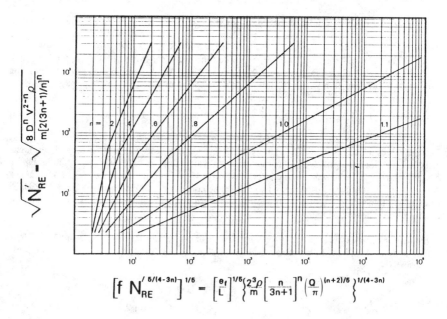

$$\left[f\, N_{RE}^{\prime\, 5/(4-3n)}\right]^{1/5} = \left[\frac{e_f}{L}\right]^{1/5}\left\{\frac{2^3\rho}{m}\left[\frac{n}{3n+1}\right]^n\left(\frac{Q}{\pi}\right)^{(n+2)/5}\right\}^{1/(4-3n)}$$

Figure 17. Friction loss plot for solving unknown diameter problem for Power Law fluids.

BINGHAM PLASTIC-UNKNOWN DIAMETER

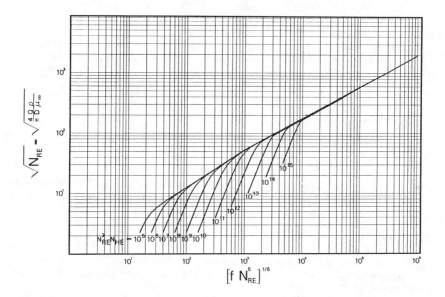

Figure 18. Friction loss plot for solving unknown diameter problem for Bingham Plastic fluids.

$N_{Re} = (fN_{Re}^5)^{1/5}$, then calculate f from Equation 50 and iterate until agreement is achieved. Alternatively, Equation 50 can be used to determine corresponding values of f, N_{Re}, and N_{He} which can then be recombined and replotted in the form $N_{Re} = fn(fN_{Re}^5, N_{Re}^2 N_{He})$ to solve this problem directly. Such a plot is shown in Figure 18.

Economic Optimum Pipe Diameter

A fourth category of problem, which is probably the most frequently used and most practical, is one in which the required flow rate (Q) and fluid properties are specified, but we are free to select both the driving force (DF) (e.g., the pump) and the pipe diameter. The objective is to select the pipe diameter which minimizes the total cost of the system, including both capital and operating costs. For this analysis, we will need additional economic data to evaluate these costs. The analysis given here follows that of Reference 36.

The major costs for a pipeline include the capital costs of the pipe and pump stations and the operating cost of the power to drive the pumps. The capital costs increase as the pipe diameter increases, while the operating cost, which represents the work required to overcome friction, decreases as the diameter increases. Thus, there will be an optimum pipe diameter which minimizes the total cost.

The capital cost of pipe (CCP) increases with increasing pipe diameter according to the relation:

$$\text{Pipe Cost (\$/ft length)} = CCP = a[D(ft)]^p \tag{69}$$

where D is the actual inside diameter, in feet.

The capital cost of pump stations (CCPS) is a linear function of the power rating of the pump station, for stations of 500 hp or more. The actual cost of installed pump stations, in 1980 dollars, is given by the following correlation [36]:

$$\text{Pump Station Cost (\$)} = \text{CCPS} = A + B \text{ hp} \tag{70}$$

where $A = \$172,800$, and $B = \$451/\text{hp}$ for stations of 500 hp or more.

The energy required to move a unit mass of fluid through the pipe is given by DF (Equations 59, 60). We assume here that the fluid enters and leaves the pipeline at the same pressure and that the line is horizontal, so that:

$$DF = e_f = -w \tag{71}$$

The required pumping power is therefore:

$$hp = -w\dot{m}/\eta_e = \frac{32fL\dot{m}^3}{\pi^2 \rho^2 D^5 \eta_e} \tag{72}$$

where η_e is the pump efficiency, and $\dot{m}$ is the mass flow rate of the fluid ($\dot{m} = \rho Q$). Equation 61 relating e_f to the friction factor, f, has been used. The cost of energy (EC) to drive the pumps for a period of time (e.g., one year) is given by:

$$EC = C \text{ hp} \tag{73}$$

where C is the cost per unit energy (e.g., \$/hp-yr).

The total annual cost is the sum of the energy cost plus the amortized capital cost of the pipe and pumps, i.e.:

$$TC(\$/\text{yr}) = X(\text{CCP} \cdot L + \text{CCPS}) + EC \tag{74}$$

where X is the amortization rate, i.e., the reciprocal of the economic lifetime or depreciation period of the pipe and pumps (assumed to be the same). When the cost (Equations 69–73) are introduced into Equation 74, the diameter that minimizes the total cost, i.e., the most economical diameter, D_e, can be found by setting the derivative $d(TC)/dD$ equal to zero and solving for $D = D_e$. The result is:

$$D_e = \left[\left(\frac{BX + C}{apX\eta}\right)\left(\frac{160f\dot{m}^3}{\pi^2 \rho^2}\right)\right]^{1/(p+5)} \tag{75}$$

This is implicit in D_e, however, through the Reynolds number dependence of f. This, in turn, is given by the Churchill equation (Equation 43) for Newtonian fluids, or by Equation 45 or 50 for, respectively, Power Law or Bingham plastic fluids, each of which involves the three basic dimensionless quantities for the fluid of interest.

Newtonian fluids. An explicit relation for D_e can be obtained by solving Equation 75 for f, and combining the result with N_{Re} in a manner which eliminates D_e. This results in the following groups which govern this problem for a Newtonian fluid:

$$fN_{Re}^{p+5} = \left(\frac{4}{\pi}\right)^{p+3} \frac{\rho^2 apX\eta_e\dot{m}^{p+2}}{10(BX + C)\mu^{p+5}}, \quad N_{Re} = \frac{4\dot{m}}{\pi D_e\mu}, \quad N_R = \frac{4\dot{m}}{\pi e\mu} \tag{76}$$

For a given value of p (the exponent in the pipe cost equation), values of f, N_{Re}, and N_R from the Moody diagram or the Churchill equation can be rearranged into equivalent values of fN_{Re}^{p+5}, N_{Re}, and N_R in which the unknown diameter appears in only N_{Re} (which becomes the dimensionless unknown quantity). The result can be plotted in the form shown in Figure 19, which can be used to find N_{Re}, and hence the unknown D_e, directly.

For water in commercial steel pipe, the operating conditions which give rise to the most economical diameter correspond, typically, to a pipe velocity in the range of 6–8 ft/s (2–3 m/s). Thus, a

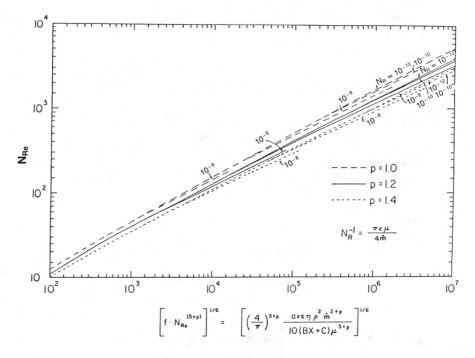

$$\left[f \cdot N_{Re}^{(5+p)} \right]^{1/6} = \left[\left(\frac{4}{\pi} \right)^{3+p} \frac{a \rho X \eta \, \rho^2 \dot{m}^{2+p}}{10 \, (BX + C) \mu^{5+p}} \right]^{1/6}$$

Figure 19. Plot for determining most economical diameter for Newtonian fluids [36].

first approximation for D_e would be the diameter for which the velocity is about 7 ft/s, i.e.:

$$D_e \text{ (in.)} = 0.64 \sqrt{Q \text{ (gal/min)}} \tag{77}$$

An iterative procedure can also be used with Equations 74 and 43 to solve this problem. D_e is first estimated from Equation 77, and used to estimate N_{Re} and e/D. These values are then used to determine f from the Churchill equation (Equation 43) and also from the known value of $f N_{Re}^{p+5}$. An average of these f's is then used to find N_{Re} from $f N_{Re}^{p+5}$, from which a second estimate of D_e and e/D are obtained. The Churchill equation is again used to get f, and the process is repeated until agreement is achieved.

Power law fluids. A similar result can be obtained for a Power Law fluid, by combining the expression for f from Equation 75 with N'_{Re} from Equation 62 to give the following two dimensionless groups which, along with the flow index n, govern this problem:

$$f^{4-3n} N_{Re}^{\prime p+5} = \frac{(52.4)(10^{3n}) 2^{7p-3n(1+p)}}{\pi^{(2+n)(1+p)} m^{5+p}} \left(\frac{a \rho X}{BX + C} \right)^{4-3n} \frac{\rho^{3-p+n(p-1)} \dot{m}^{2(p-1)+n(4-p)}}{[(3n+1)/n]^{n(5+p)}} \tag{78}$$

$$N'_{Re} = \frac{\dot{m}^{2-n} \rho^{n-1} 128}{D^{4-3n} m \pi^{2-n} 2^{3n}} \left(\frac{n}{3n+1} \right)^{n} \tag{79}$$

Equation 45 can be used to determine corresponding values of f and N'_{Re} which, along with various values of p, can be used to determine corresponding values of the above groups. The result is shown in Figure 20, from which N'_{Re}, and hence D, can be determined for this problem. An iterative procedure similar to that for Newtonian fluids can also be used to find D_e, using Equation 78 instead of $f N_{Re}$, and Equation 45 instead of the Churchill equation.

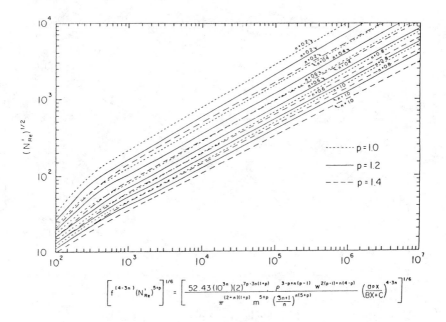

$$\left[f^{(4-3n)} (N'_{Re})^{5+p} \right]^{1/6} = \left[\frac{52.43 (10^{3n})(2)^{7p-3n(1+p)}}{\pi^{(2+n)(1+p)}} \frac{\rho^{3-p+n(p-1)} w^{2(p-1)+n(4-p)}}{m^{5+p} \left(\frac{3n+1}{n} \right)^{n(5+p)}} \left(\frac{a\rho x}{BX+C} \right)^{4-3n} \right]^{1/6}$$

Figure 20. Plot for determining most economical diameter for Power Law fluids [36].

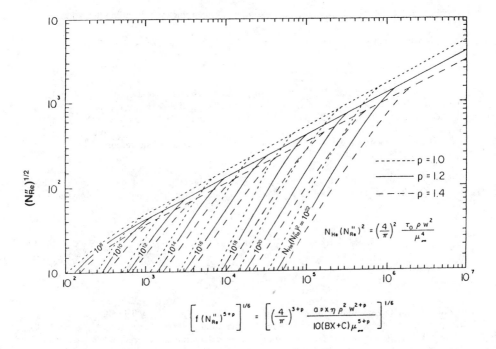

$$N_{He}(N''_{Re})^2 = \left(\frac{4}{\pi} \right)^2 \frac{\tau_0 \rho w^2}{\mu^4_{\sim}}$$

$$\left[f (N''_{Re})^{5+p} \right]^{1/6} = \left[\left(\frac{4}{\pi} \right)^{3+p} \frac{a\rho x \eta \rho^2 w^{2+p}}{10(BX+C) \mu^{5+p}_{\sim}} \right]^{1/6}$$

Figure 21. Plot for determining most economical diameter for Bingham Plastic fluids [36].

Bingham plastics. For Bingham plastics, the governing dimensionless quantities are N_{Re}, N_{He}, and f. As before, combining f from Equation 75 with N_{Re} to eliminate D results in the groups:

$$fN_{Re}^{p+5} = \left(\frac{4}{\pi}\right)^{p+5} \frac{\rho^2 apX\eta\dot{m}^{p+1}}{10(BX+C)\mu_\infty^{p+5}}, \qquad N_{He}N_{Re}^2 = \left(\frac{4}{\pi}\right)^2 \frac{\tau_0\rho\dot{m}^2}{\mu_\infty^4}, \qquad N_{Re} = \frac{4\dot{m}}{\pi D\mu_\infty} \qquad (79)$$

Equation 50 can be used to determine corresponding values of f, N_{Re}, and N_{He} which, along with given values of p, can be recombined to determine values of these groups. The results can be re-plotted, as shown in Figure 21, to determine the unknown N_{Re} (D) for this problem. As for the Newtonian fluid, an iterative procedure can be used to find D_e, using Equation 50 instead of the Churchill equation, and N_{He} instead of e/D.

NOTATION

a   coefficient in pipe cost (Equation 69), $/ft^{p+1}

A   tube cross-sectional area, L^2

B   coefficient in pump cost (Equation 70), $/hp

C   cost per unit of energy (e.g., $/hp-yr or ¢/kwh)

CCP   capital cost of pipe per unit length, $/ft

CCPS   capital cost of pump stations, $

D   tube diameter, L

D_{ij} rate of strain (shear rate) tensor, 1/t

D_e most economical diameter, L

DF   driving force for tube flow per unit fluid mass, FL/M

e   wall roughness, L

e_f energy dissipated by friction per unit fluid mass, FL/M

EC   energy cost per unit time (e.g., $/hp-yr or ¢/kwh)

f   Fanning friction factor (Equation 23) (−)

f_p Fanning friction factor for drag reducing fluids (Equation 54) (−)

f_s Fanning friction factor for Newtonian solvent (−)

hp   power, FL/t

L   tube length (or immersed bob length), L

m   Power Law consistency coefficient $F-t^n/L^2$

$\dot{m}$ mass flow rate, (ρQ), M/t

n   Power Law flow index (−)

n'   slope of $\log(-\Delta\phi)$ vs. $\log(Q)$ (−)

N_{De} Deborah number (Equations 55, 57) (−)

N_{He} Hedstrom number (Equation 35) (−)

N_R roughness number (Equation 66, 76) (−)

N_{Re} Reynolds number, Newtonian (Equation 27, 35) (−)

N_{Re}' Reynolds number, Power Law fluid (Equations 30, 62)

N_{Res} Reynolds number for Newtonian solvent (−)

N_{We} Weissenberg number (Equation 39) (−)

N_{We}' Weissenberg number for drag reducing solutions (Equation 56) (−)

N_λ dimensionless time constant, (Equation 56) (−)

p   exponent in pipe cost (−)

P   pressure, F/L^2

Q   volumetric flow rate, L^3/t

r   distance from tube centerline, L

R   tube radius, L

T   torque in cup-and-bob viscometer, FL

TC   total cost of pipeline per unit time (e.g., $/yr)

V   average velocity in tube, L/t

w   work extracted from fluid per unit mass, FL/M

X   amortization rate for pipeline (1/economic life), 1/t

z   vertical elevation, L

Greek Symbols

α   exponent in structural viscosity (Equation 12) (− 1); coefficient in Equation 45

β   exponent in structural viscosity (Equation 13) (−); ratio of bob-to-cup radii (−)

$\dot{\gamma}$ shear rate in viscometric flow, $1/t$

ρ density, M/L^3

σ characteristics stress for structural viscosity fluid, F/L^2

η viscosity function, non-Newtonian, $F\text{-}t/L^2$

η_e pump efficiency $(-)$

η_0 low shear limiting Newtonian viscosity, $F\text{-}t/L^2$

η_∞ high shear limiting Newtonian viscosity, $F\text{-}t/L^2$

Θ first normal stress difference function, $F\text{-}t^2/L^2$

λ characteristic fluid-time constant, t

μ viscosity (Newtonian), $F\text{-}t/L^2$

μ_c high shear limiting viscosity for Casson plastic, Ft/L^2

μ_∞ high shear limiting viscosity for Bingham plastic, Ft/L^2

τ shear stress component, F/L^2

τ_{ij} deviatoric (shear) stress tensor, F/L^2

τ_c yield stress for Casson plastic, F/L^2

τ_∞ yield stress for Bingham plastic, F/L^2

τ_w wall stress, F/L^2

ϕ combined pressure plus static head, $P + \rho gz$, F/L^2

Ω angular velocity, $1/t$

REFERENCES

1. Bird, R. B., Armstrong, R. C., and Hassager, O., *Dynamics of Polymeric Liquids*, Vol. 1, *Fluid Mechanics*, Wiley (1977).
2. Tanner, R. I., *Engineering Rheology*, Clarendon Press, Oxford (1985).
3. Darby, R., *Viscoelastic Fluids*, Marcel Dekker (1976).
4. Darby, R., *Proced. Ninth Intnl. Tech. Conf. on Slurry Transport.*, Lake Tahoe, Nev., p. 107, March 21–24 (1984).
5. Casson, N., "A Flow Equation for Pigment-Oil Suspensions of the Printing Ink Type," in *Rheology of Disperse Systems*, C. C. Mill (ed), p. 84, Pergamon (1959).
6. Carreau, P. J., *Trans. Soc. Rheol.*, 16, 99 (1972).
7. Darby, R., and Mallett, M. W., *Canad. J. Chem. Eng.*, 59, 341 (1981).
8. Darby, R., "Hydrodynamics of Slurries and Suspensions," Ch. 2 in *Encyclopedia of Fluid Mechanics*, Vol. 5, N. P. Cheremisinoff (ed), Gulf Pub. Co. (1986).
9. Darby, R., *Proced. Fourth Intnl. Tech. Conf. on Slurry Transport.*, Las Vegas, Nev., p. 389, March (1983).
10. Chang, H. D., and Darby, R., *J. Rheol.*, 27(1), 77 (1983).
11. Smith, F. P., and Darby, R., *Poly. Eng. and Sci.*, 16, 46 (1976).
12. Ferguson, J., and Nuki, G., "The Rheology of Synthetic Joint Lubricant," in *The Rheology of Lubricants*, T. C. Davenport (ed), p. 89, Wiley-Halstead (1973).
13. Whitmore, R. L., *Rheology of the Circulation*, p. 16, Pergamon (1968).
14. Bankoff, E., "Some Measurements on Pigment-Plasticizer Dispersions," in *Rheology of Disperse Systems*, C. C. Mill (ed), p. 105, Pergamon, (1959).
15. Steiner, E. H., "The Rheology of Molten Chocolate," in *Rheology of Disperse Systems*, C. C. Mill (ed), p. 167, Pergamon (1959).
16. Heldman, D. R., *Food Process Engineering*, AVI Pub. Co., Westport, Conn. (1975).
17. Darby, R., and Chang, H. D., *AIChE J.*, 30, 274 (1984).
18. Darby, R., "A Generalized Correlation for Friction Loss in Drag Reducing Polymer Solutions," Ch. 33 in *Encyclopedia of Fluid Mechanics*, Vol. 1, N. P. Cheremisinoff (ed), Gulf Pub. Co. (1986).
19. Darby, R., *Viscoelastic Fluids*, Ch. 5, Marcel Dekker (1976).
20. Oldroyd, J. G., *J. Colloid Sci.*, 4, 333 (1949).
21. Oldroyd, J. G., in *Rheology: Theory and Applications*, Vol. 1, F. R. Eirich (ed), p. 653, Academic Press (1956).
22. Hanks, R. W., "Principles of Slurry Pipeline Hydraulics," Ch. 6 in *Encyclopedia of Fluid Mechanics*, Vol. 5, N. P. Cheremisinoff (ed), Gulf Pub. Co. (1986).
23. Yang, T. M. T., and Krieger, I. M., *J. Rheol.*, 22(4), 413 (1978).
24. Darby, R., *J. Rheol.*, 29(4), 369 (1985).
24a. Gaidos, R. E., Darby, R., and Wickern, G., *Canad. J. Chem. Eng.* (in press).

25. Prandtl, L., *Z. angew. Math. Mech.*, 5, 136 (1925).
26. von Karman, T., *Collected Works*, Butterworths, London (1956).
27. Colebrook, C. F., *J. Inst. Civil Engrs.* (*London*), 11, 133 (1938, 39).
28. Churchill, S. W., *Chem. Eng.*, p. 91, Nov. 7 (1977).
29. Dodge, D. W., and Metzner, A. B., *AIChE J.*, 5, 189 (1959).
30. Hanks, R. W., and Ricks, B. L., *J. Hydronautics*, 9, 39 (1975).
31. Hedstrom, B. O. A., *Ind. Eng. Chem.*, 44, 651 (1952).
32. Hanks, R. W., and Dadia, P. H., *AIChE J.*, 17, 554 (1971).
33. Darby, R., and Melson, J. D., *Chem. Eng.*, p. 59, Dec. 28 (1981).
34. Jenkins, R., "Turbulent Drag Reduction Modeling," University Undergraduate Fellows, Project Report, Texas A&M University, April (1986).
35. Chang, H. D., Ph.D. Dissertation in Chemical Engineering, Texas A&M University, (1982).
36. Darby, R., and Melson, J. D., *J. Pipelines*, 2, 11 (1982).

CHAPTER 3

LAMINAR UNSTEADY FLOW OF ELEMENTARY NON-NEWTONIAN FLUIDS IN LONG PIPES

Mario F. Letelier S. and José F. Céspedes B.

Department of Mechanical Engineering
University of Santiago, Chile

CONTENTS

INTRODUCTION

This chapter deals with the analysis of transient laminar flow of some non-Newtonian fluids in long, circular, straight pipes.

Four fluids are considered: Bingham plastics*, viscoelastic fluids of Coleman & Noll-type and of Maxwell-type, and power-law fluids. The choice of constitutive equations has been made essentially by a compromise between physical relevance and analytical convenience.

It is believed that the particular flow cases discussed may give some insight into the characteristically non-Newtonian behavior of the selected substances under unsteady-flow conditions.

For Bingham plastics, Coleman & Noll fluids, and Maxwell fluids an approximate general method of analysis is additionally presented via the one-dimensional approach.

---

* A Bingham plastic is not a fluid, in a strict sense, because of its inherent yield stress. However, for simplicity's sake, the term "fluid" will here be applied to all substances considered.

EQUATIONS OF MOTION

In the following the flow will be assumed laminar, parallel, axisymmetric, incompressible, and isothermal.

The equations of motion, in cylindrical coordinates, are:

continuity

$$\frac{\partial u}{\partial x} = 0 \tag{1}$$

axial momentum

$$\rho \frac{\partial u}{\partial t} + \frac{\tau_{rx}}{r} + \frac{\partial \tau_{rx}}{\partial r} = -\frac{\partial P}{\partial x} \tag{2}$$

radial momentum

$$0 = -\rho g \frac{\partial h}{\partial r} + \frac{1}{r} \left[\frac{\partial}{\partial r} (r\tau_{rr}) + \frac{\partial}{\partial x} (r\tau_{xr}) \right] - \frac{\tau_{\theta\theta}}{r} \tag{3}$$

tangential momentum

$$0 = -\frac{\partial P}{\partial \theta} \tag{4}$$

where   u = axial velocity
x, r, θ, and t = axial, radial, tangential, and time coordinates, respectively
ρ = density
τ_{rx} = axial shear stress
P = p + ρgh = the piezometric pressure
p = pressure
g = acceleration due to gravity
h = a vertical upward-pointing coordinate
τ_{rr} = radial normal stress
and $\tau_{\theta\theta}$ = the tangential normal stress.

The velocity is subject to the no-slip condition, i.e.:

$$u(a, t) = 0 \qquad a = \text{pipe radius} \tag{5}$$

For Newtonian fluids, Equation 3 reduces to:

$$\frac{\partial P}{\partial r} = 0$$

which result is not generally true for non-Newtonians, particularly for viscoelastic fluids. The axisymmetry condition (Equation 4) makes it possible to write Equation 3 as:

$$\frac{\partial P}{\partial r} = \psi(r, t)$$

since the deviatoric part in τ_{rr}, $\tau_{\theta\theta}$, and τ_{xr} should be independent of x. Therefore:

$$P = \int \psi \, dr + \psi_1(x, t)$$

wherefrom $\quad \dfrac{\partial P}{\partial x} = \dfrac{\partial \psi_1}{\partial x}(x, t)$ \hfill (6)

i.e., $\partial P/\partial x$ can at most be a function of x and t. Continuity condition, Equation 1 determines the left hand side of Equation 2 as a function of at most r and t, from which, and considering Equation 6, it is deduced that $\partial P/\partial x$ can only be a function of time, that is:

$$-\frac{\partial P}{\partial x} = \phi(t)$$

It is customary to refer to ϕ as the forcing function of the system, which can depend explicitly on time or implicitly through the velocity of the flow [1].

Non-dimensional variables will be used in the following, viz.:

$$u^* = u/U_0$$

$$r^* = r/a$$

$$t^* = t/T_0 \hfill (7)$$

$$\tau_{rx}^* = \tau^* = \tau/\tau_0; \qquad \tau_0 = \eta \frac{U_0}{a}$$

which, once substituted into Equation 2, yield

$$\Omega \frac{\partial u^*}{\partial t^*} + \frac{\tau^*}{r^*} + \frac{\partial \tau^*}{\partial r^*} = \phi^* \hfill (8)$$

where the unsteadiness number Ω is given by:

$$\Omega = \frac{\rho a^2}{\eta T_0}$$

and $\quad \phi^* = \dfrac{a^2}{\eta U_0} \phi$

In the former, U_0 and T_0 are reference constants, and η is a fluid property constant.

PLASTIC FLOW

Equations

One of the simplest models for plastics is the Bingham model, which has been found useful in the study of flow of slurries, pastes, paints, etc.

The constitutive equation of a Bingham plastic for axisymmetric flow in a circular pipe is:

$$\tau = \tau' - \eta_0 \frac{\partial u}{\partial r} \qquad \tau \geqq \tau'$$

$$\frac{\partial u}{\partial r} = 0 \qquad \tau < \tau'$$

(9)

where τ' is the yield stress, and η_0 is a constant property of the fluid. The dimensionless counterpart of Equation 9 is:

$$\tau^* = N - \frac{\partial u^*}{\partial r^*} \qquad \tau^* \geqq N \qquad \frac{\partial u^*}{\partial r^*} < 0$$

$$\frac{\partial u^*}{\partial r^*} = 0 \qquad \tau^* < N$$

(10)

where $N = \tau' a / \eta_0 U_0$ is the yield number. Here $\eta = \eta_0$ (cf. Equation 7).

After Equation 10 is substituted into Equation 8, the momentum equation is found to be, omitting the asterisks:

$$\Omega \frac{\partial u}{\partial t} - \left(\frac{\partial^2 u}{\partial r^2} + \frac{1}{r} \frac{\partial u}{\partial r} \right) = \phi - \frac{N}{r}$$

(11)

Equation 11 describes the flow in the region where $\partial u / \partial r \neq 0$. For $\tau < N$, a plug-flow zone exists, cf. Figure 1. Equation 11, together with its initial and boundary conditions, defines a velocity field which can be assumed to be valid from the wall (i.e., $r = 1$) up to the cylindrical surface where $\partial u / \partial r = 0$ (i.e., $r = r_0$). The velocity in the plug-flow region is then $u(r_0, t)$ for $r \leqq r_0$.

The function $r_0(t)$ cannot, in general, be determined in closed form, wherefrom some inherent difficulties in the analysis of Bingham plastics arise.

Equation 11 is solved next for the problems of flow establishment under a constant pressure gradient (start-up flow) and transient flow generated by a general instantaneous change of the forcing function.

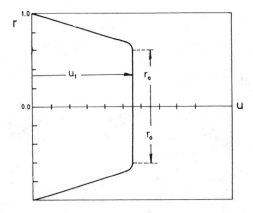

Figure 1. Typical velocity distribution in flow of a Bingham fluid.

Flow Establishment Under a Constant Pressure Gradient

In this problem it is assumed that the fluid is at rest inside the pipe for $t \leq 0$ and is set in motion by an instantaneous pressure gradient applied at $t = 0$, which is kept constant until the flow attains its steady-state velocity. Thus, the flow is analytically characterized by:

$$\phi = \text{constant} \tag{12}$$

$$u(1, 0) = 0 \tag{13}$$

The start-up flow problem has been considered by Atabek [2], Duggins [3], and Mitra [4]. Atabek's contribution is an analytical solution which does not satisfy the initial condition (Equation 13) and presents some undesirable discontinuities [3, 4]. Both Duggins and Mitra present numerical solutions of Equation 11. The analysis presented here is based on the work of Letelier et al. [5].

The solution of Equation 11 can be worked out following essentially the same lines as Szymanski's [6] solution for the start-up problem for a Newtonian fluid. In effect, the velocity field can be expressed by:

$$u(r, t) = \frac{\phi}{4}(1 - r^2) - N(1 - r) + \sum_{n=1}^{\infty} C_n J_0(b_n r) \exp(-b_n^2 t/\Omega) \qquad r_0 \leq r \leq 1 \tag{14}$$

$$u_1(t) = \frac{\phi}{4}(1 - r_0^2) - N(1 - r_0) + \sum_{n=1}^{\infty} C_n J_0(b_n r_0) \exp(-b_n^2 t/\Omega) \qquad 0 \leq r \leq r_0 \tag{15}$$

where u is the velocity in the deformed region, and u_1 is the velocity in the undeformed region. J_0 is the Bessel function of first class and order zero, the C_n's are constant coefficients, and $J_0(b_n) = 0$. The summation term in Equation 14 is the homogeneous solution of Equation 11, while the remaining terms represent the corresponding particular solution, made equal to the ultimate steady-state velocity of the flow for $t \to \infty$. The coefficients C_n are determined through the initial condition, Equation 13; the result is:

$$C_n = \frac{2\phi}{b_n^3 J_1(b_n)} \left[\frac{N/\phi}{J_1(b_n)} \int_0^{b_n} J_0(z)\, dz - 1 \right] \tag{16}$$

Thus Equations 14 and 16 are an exact solution to the equation of motion (Equation 11), which satisfies the boundary and initial conditions. The function r_0 does not come out explicitly and it should be evaluated numerically. However, for small values of N/ϕ, r_0 admits an asymptotic expression of the form:

$$r_0 = \frac{2N}{C_1 b_1^2 e^{-b_1^2 t/\Omega} + \phi} \tag{17}$$

Equation 17 provides a better approximation of the value of r_0 for a given N/ϕ as t increases. For example, if $N/\phi = 0.125$, then the error entailed by Equation 17 is less than 2% for $t/\Omega > 0.4$. Equations 14 and 15 are plotted in Figure 2 for $\phi = 4$ and $N = 0.5$. The velocity for $N = 0$ (i.e., for a Newtonian fluid) is, according to Equation 14:

$$u_N = \frac{\phi}{4}(1 - r^2) - \sum_{n=1}^{\infty} \frac{2\phi J_0(b_n r)}{b_n^3 J_1(b_n)} \exp(-b_n^2 t/\Omega) \tag{18}$$

which is exactly Szymanski's solution to Equation 11 for $N = 0$. Equation 18 is plotted in Figure 3 for $\phi = 4$. The numerical values of the velocity obtained by Duggins [3] show a negligible difference with respect to the analytical values deduced from Equations 14 and 16 for all times and all

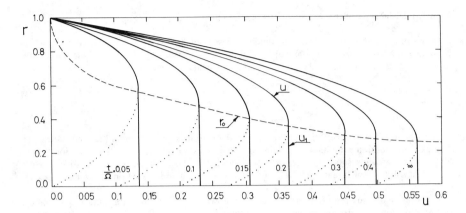

Figure 2. Plastic velocity distribution during start-up for $\phi = 4$, $N = 0.5$; solid line, actual velocity; dotted line, Equation 14 for $r < r_0$.

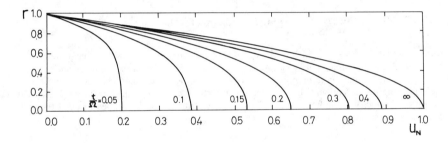

Figure 3. Newtonian velocity distribution during start-up for $\phi = 4$.

values of r. Comparison of Equations 14 and 18, i.e., of plastic vs. Newtonian behavior for equal forcing function ($\phi = 4$), shows that for $N = 0.5$ the velocity in the plastic is greatly reduced. The limit radius r_0 has its maximum value at $t = 0$, and decreases down to its minimum steady-state value $2N/\phi$. The plastic behavior also significantly affects the time of flow establishment, the next subject to be explored.

The spatially averaged velocity U is, in dimensionless nomenclature:

$$U = 2\left[\int_{r_0}^{1} ur\, dr + \int_{0}^{r_0} u_1 r\, dr\right] \tag{19}$$

from which

$$U = \frac{\phi}{8}(1 - r_0^4) - \frac{N}{3}(1 - r_0^3) + \sum_{n=1}^{\infty} \frac{2C_n}{b_n}\left[J_1(b_n) - r_0 J_1(b_n r_0)\right.$$

$$\left. + \frac{b_n}{2} J_0(b_n r_0) r_0^2\right] \exp(-b_n^2 t/\Omega) \tag{20}$$

The Newtonian counterpart of Equation 20 is:

$$U_N = \frac{\phi}{8}\left[1 - \sum_{n=1}^{\infty} \frac{32}{b_n^4} \exp(-b_n^2 t/\Omega)\right] \tag{21}$$

A useful, albeit approximate, form of Equation 20 is obtained, for small N/ϕ, by putting $r_0 = 0$, viz.:

$$U = \frac{\phi}{8} - \frac{N}{3} + \sum_{n=1}^{\infty} \frac{2C_n}{b_n} J_1(b_n) \exp(-b_n^2 t/\Omega) \tag{22}$$

The error entailed by Equation 22 is less than 1% for $t/\Omega > 0.18$, when $N/\phi = 0.125$.

Equations 20 and 21 are depicted in Figure 4 for $\phi = 8$ and $N = 1.2$.

An important characteristic value of the start-up flow is the time of flow establishment, i.e., the time for which $U(te) = 0.99U_\infty$, where U_∞ is the steady-state velocity for $t \to \infty$.

The exact values of t_e for a given N and ϕ must be numerically computed from Equation 20. An approximate explicit expression for t_e can be obtained from Equation 22 in which use is made of the fact that the series is highly convergent for $t \approx t_e$, so that the sum can be replaced by its first term, thus yielding:

$$\frac{t_e}{\Omega} = 0.788 + 0.173 \ln\left\{\frac{1 - 2.832N/\phi}{1 - 2.667N/\phi}\right\} \tag{23}$$

The exact values of t_e and Equation 23 are shown in Figure 5 related to N/ϕ. For $N/\phi = 0.353$, $t_e/\Omega = 0.153$. When N/ϕ is greater than 0.353, Equation 20 predicts a change in the flow charac-

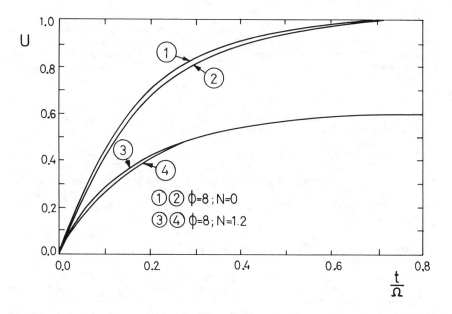

Figure 4. Average velocity during start-up. Curve 1: exact solution, Equation 21; curve 2; approximation, Equation 39; curve 3: exact solution, Equation 20; curve 4: approximation, Equation 39.

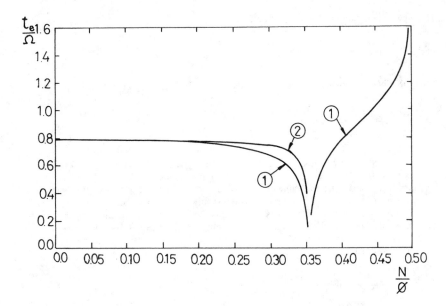

Figure 5. Time of flow establishment for a Bingham fluid during start-up. Curve 1: exact values from Equation 20; curve 2: approximation, Equation 23.

teristics; it is found that for $N/\phi > 0.353$ the velocity has an overshoot; i.e., it attains a maximum value greater than the steady-state one, and afterwards it decreases monotonically to its final value for $\to \infty$. Under these conditions, the definition of the time of flow establishment should be modified, and expressed as:

$$U(t_e) = 1.01 U_\infty \tag{24}$$

As a consequence of Equation 24, t_e greatly increases for larger values of N/ϕ, as illustrated in Figure 5. The complete time-evolution of the average velocity for $N/\phi = 0.4$ is shown in Figure 6. The wall shear stress τ_w is also included in Figure 6, where τ_w is computed from Equation 10 for $r = 1$. The phenomenon of overshoot can be associated with the big inertia of the solid core; the ultimate velocity, on the other hand, is relatively small for $N/\phi > 0.353$. The wall shear stress lags behind the velocity during the overshoot, the equilibrium of forces being established for $t \to \infty$.

The corresponding analysis for a parallel-plates duct leads to similar results. A study of unsteady flow of a Bingham plastic through parallel-plates and circular conduits of related problems can be found in Oldroyd [7].

Flow Establishment Under a General Step Change of Forcing Function

The classical flow situation considered in the previous section is that of an accelerated flow which asymptotically reaches a steady-state flow. It is known [8] that the flow behavior is quite different for decelerated flow of Newtonian fluids, where the values of the time of flow establishment are much bigger compared with those of accelerated flow. An equivalent analysis can be made for Bingham plastics, assuming an initial velocity u_i different from zero, an arbitrary step change of pressure gradient, and an ultimate steady state velocity $u_f \lesssim u_i$. An important analytical simplification results from this more general statement of the flow-establishment problem.

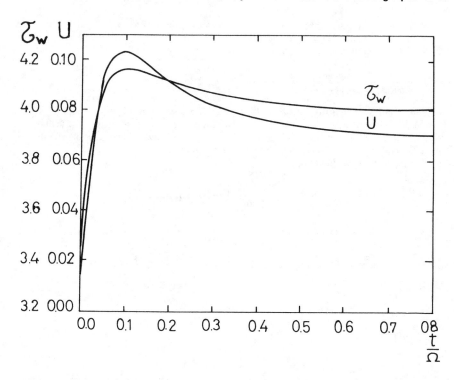

Figure 6. Average velocity and wall shear stress during the overshoot phase in the start-up of a Bingham fluid. $N/\phi = 0.4$.

The momentum equation (Equation 11) and boundary condition (Equation 13) still hold, while time conditions are now:

$$u(r, 0) = u_i = \frac{\phi_i}{4}(1 - r^2) - N(1 - r) \qquad r \geq r_{0i}$$

$$u(r, 0) = \frac{\phi_i}{4}(1 - r_{0i}^2) - N(1 - r_{0i}) \qquad r \leq r_{0i} \tag{25}$$

$$u(r, \infty) = u_f = \frac{\phi_f}{4}(1 - r^2) - N(1 - r) \qquad r \geq r_{0f}$$

$$u_f(r, \infty) = \frac{\phi_f}{4}(1 - r_{0f}^2) - N(1 - r_{0f}) \qquad r \leq r_{0f} \tag{26}$$

where subscripts i and f refer to, respectively, initial and final parameters or functions for steady conditions. In this form, the operating value of ϕ during the unsteady phase of the flow is ϕ_f.

The solution of Equation 11 is again Equations 14 and 15, where the coefficients C_n are given in this case by:

$$C_n = \frac{2(\phi_i - \phi_f)}{b_n^3 J_1(b_n)} \tag{27}$$

which is a very convenient simplification of Equation 16, valid only for $\phi_i > 0$. Thus is found the interesting result that for $\phi_i \neq 0$, the parameter N does not appear in the time-dependent part of the velocity. An approximate expression for r_0 is:

$$r_0 = \frac{2N/\phi_f}{1.602(\phi_i/\phi_f - 1)\exp(-b_1^2 t/\Omega) + 1}$$

valid for small N/ϕ_f. Plots of Equations 14, 15, and 27 are shown in Figures 7 and 8 for accelerated and decelerated flow. The corresponding Newtonian velocity contours are also included. In logical contrast with the behavior of r_0 for $\phi_f > \phi_i$, i.e., for accelerated flow, the limit radius, and hence the plug-flow zone, increases with time for decelerated flow.

The average velocity (Equation 19) takes the form:

$$U = \frac{\phi_f}{8}(1 - r_0^4) - \frac{N}{3}(1 - r_0^3) + \sum_{n=1}^{\infty} \frac{4(\phi_i - \phi_f)}{b_n^4 J_1(b_n)}\left[J_1(b_n) - r_0 J_1(b_n r_0) \right.$$

$$\left. + \frac{b_n}{2} J_0(b_n r_0)r_0^2 \right]\exp(-b_n^2 t/\Omega) \tag{28}$$

The time of flow establishment is defined by:

$$\frac{U(t_e)}{U_f} = 0.99 \qquad \lambda > 1$$

$$\frac{U(t_e)}{U_f} = 1.01 \qquad \lambda < 1 \tag{29}$$

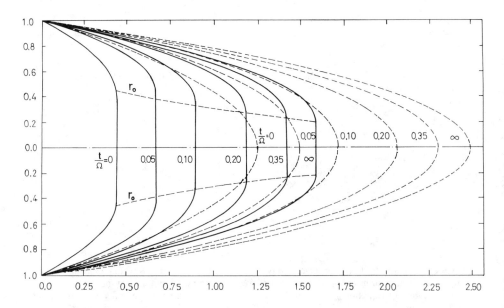

Figure 7. Velocity distribution during accelerated transition between two steady-states. Plastic flow (N = 1, $\phi_i = 5$, $\phi_f = 10$): solid line: Newtonian flow (N = 0, $\phi_i = 10$, $\phi_f = 5$): dashed line.

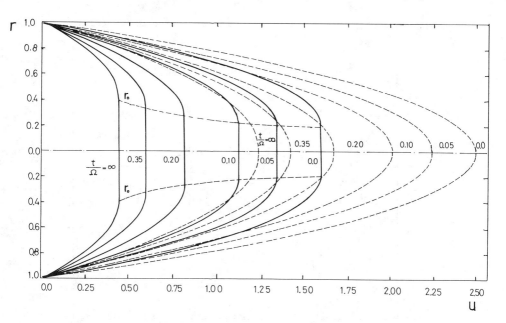

Figure 8. Velocity distribution during decelerated transition between two steady states. Plastic flow (N = 1, $\phi_i = 10$, $\phi_f = 5$): solid line; Newtonian flow (N = 0, $\phi_i = 10$, $\phi_f = 5$): dashed line.

in which $\lambda = U_f/U_i$. The same considerations that led to Equation 23 apply in Equation 28, so that t_e can be expressed explicitly as a function of λ, viz.:

$$\frac{t_e}{\Omega} = 0.788 + 0.173 \ln\left\{\frac{|1 - \lambda|}{\lambda}\right\} \tag{30}$$

Equation 30 is exactly equal to the corresponding formula for a Newtonian fluid [9]. A plot of Equation 30 is shown in Figure 9 together with the exact values of t_e as computed from Equations 28 and 29. It is found that for $\lambda > 1$, Equation 30 yields very accurate values of t_e, while for $\lambda < 1$ it entails some error that increases as $\lambda \to 0$. The structure of t_e for a Bingham plastic indicates that, just as in the case of a Newtonian fluid, the flow requires a long time to become established when the forcing function decreases and λ is small, while for accelerated flow t_e reaches a maximum value of 0.788 for $\lambda \to \infty$.

One-Dimensional Analysis

The complexities associated with the velocity field in the preceding and related problems can be overcome to some extent through the one-dimensional approach. In this approach, the dependent variable in the equations of motion is the average velocity, which is only a function of time. Such method of analysis greatly simplifies the computations in the case of a Newtonian flow [10] as to the average velocity and wall shear stress. A similar procedure can be devised for a Bingham plastic for small N/ϕ. To this end u is expressed by [11]:

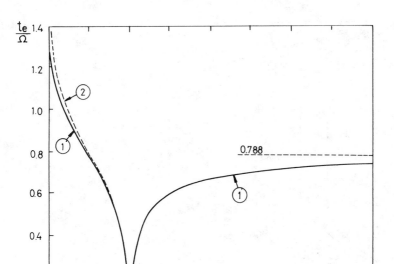

Figure 9. Time of flow establishment for transition flow of a Bingham fluid. Curve 1: exact values from Equation 28; curve 2: approximation, Equation 30.

$$u = -N(1 - r) + A(1 - r^2) + \frac{\Omega}{4^2} \frac{dA}{dt} (1 - r^4) + \cdots \qquad r \geqq r_0 \tag{31}$$

$$u_1 = -N(1 - r_0) + A(1 - r_0^2) + \frac{\Omega}{4^2} \frac{dA}{dt} (1 - r_0^4) + \cdots \qquad r \leqq r_0 \tag{32}$$

where A is a function of time related to the forcing function through:

$$A + \frac{\Omega}{2^2} \frac{dA}{dt} + \frac{\Omega^2}{2^2 4^2} \frac{d^2A}{dt^2} + \cdots = \frac{\phi}{4} \tag{33}$$

Equation 31 is an exact solution of Equation 11 if Equation 33 is satisfied. The average velocity U can be computed as follows:

$$U = 2 \int_0^1 ur \, dr + E(t; N) \tag{34}$$

$$E = 2 \int_0^{r_0} (u_1 - u) r \, dr \tag{35}$$

In this case $E \to 0$ for $N \to 0$. Moreover, from Equation 35 it is possible to demonstrate that E is $0(r_0^2)$, from which it follows that, taking Equation 17 into account, E can be neglected in Equation 34 when $N^2 \ll N$. These considerations lead to an approximate expression for U, independent of r_0, viz.:

$$U = -\frac{N}{3} + \frac{A}{2} + \frac{\Omega}{24}\frac{dA}{dt} + \cdots \tag{36}$$

Equations 33 and 36 can be combined through a general result [12] valid for systems of equations of the type of Equations 33 and 36 and whose derivation is explained in the Appendix to this chapter. In this case it is found that:

$$4\left(U + \frac{N}{3}\right) + \Omega\frac{dU}{dt} + \frac{\Omega^2}{16}\frac{d^2U}{dt^2} + \cdots = \frac{\phi}{2} + \frac{\Omega}{24}\frac{d\phi}{dt} + \cdots \tag{37}$$

which is the momentum equation expressed through U, ϕ, and their derivatives in time; Equation 37 is an approximation valid for any forcing function. In the special case of a constant ϕ, i.e., in the problem of flow establishment, Equation 37 becomes:

$$\left(U + \frac{N}{3}\right) + \frac{\Omega}{2^2}\frac{dU}{dt} + \frac{\Omega^2}{2^2 4^2}\frac{d^2U}{dt^2} + \cdots = \frac{\phi}{4} \tag{38}$$

Its solution, for $U(0) = 0$, is:

$$U = \left(\frac{\phi}{8} - \frac{N}{3}\right)[1 - \exp(-b_1^2 t/\Omega)] \tag{39}$$

whose exact counterpart, as studied in the preceding sections, is Equation 20. Plots of Equation 39 are included in Figure 4 for $N = 0$ and $N = 1.2$. Equation 39 provides a very good approximation for the average velocity for $t/\Omega > 0.2$ when $N/\phi = 0.15$, the error being negligible in the range $0.2 \leq t \leq \infty$. The corresponding convenience of Equations 38 and 39 for $N = 0$ has been discussed elsewhere [1, 13]. The one-dimensional approach presented here is only approximately valid for small N/ϕ. It lacks capacity for predicting velocity overshoot (cf. Figure 9), since its simplified structure cannot reproduce the actual flow behavior for $N/\phi \geq 0.353$, as predicted by the exact solution, Equation 20.

VISCOELASTIC FLOW

Fluid of Coleman & Noll

One elementary model of viscoelastic fluids is given by Coleman & Noll's constitutive relation:

$$\tau = -\eta_1\frac{\partial u}{\partial r} - v_0\frac{\partial^2 u}{\partial t \partial r} \tag{40}$$

Here η_1 and v_0 are constant properties of the fluid, and Equation 40 is a dimensional equation. This is a parallel-flow reduction of the general second-order fluid defined by Coleman & Noll [14]. In this work, and following Ting [15], both η_1 and v_0 will be considered always positive. The Coleman & Noll fluid is presently utilized as a convenient model for describing certain types of viscoelastic flow characteristics [16, 17]. The constitutive law (Equation 40) makes the shear stress dependent both on the radial velocity gradient and on the rate of change of the velocity gradient. This last effect depends on the magnitude of the elastic constant v_0.

The dimensionless version of Equation 40 follows by putting $\eta = \eta_1$ in Equation 7, from which:

$$\tau = -\frac{\partial u}{\partial r} - \beta \frac{\partial^2 u}{\partial t \, \partial r}; \qquad \beta = \frac{v_0}{T_0 \eta_1} \tag{41}$$

in which β is a dimensionless property, gauging the relative elasticity of the fluid.

The basic equation of motion for a fluid of Coleman & Noll is obtained by substituting Equation 41 into Equation 8, whence:

$$\Omega \frac{\partial u}{\partial t} - \left(\frac{1}{r} \frac{\partial u}{\partial r} + \frac{\partial^2 u}{\partial r^2} \right) - \beta \left(\frac{1}{r} \frac{\partial^2 u}{\partial t \, \partial r} + \frac{\partial^3 u}{\partial t \, \partial r^2} \right) = \phi \tag{42}$$

Equation 42 is linear. When $\beta \to 0$, the flow behaves in Newtonian form. For steady flow, i.e., for $\partial u / \partial t = 0$, Equation 42 reduces to the Newtonian steady-state momentum equation, so that the elasticity of the fluid acts only during the unsteady stages of the flow.

Several solutions to Equation 42 have been developed by Ting [15], namely, for generation of flows between two infinite parallel planes by constant tangential surface force, start-up and decay of flow in parallel-plates ducts, and start-up and decay of flow in circular tubes. The method of analysis in these cases is Laplace transforms. McNab [18] solved Equation 42 for the problem of flow establishment by means of the method of separation of variables, and evaluated the average velocity, wall shear stress, and time of flow establishment. This last analysis will be summarized in the following. For a constant forcing function, Equation 42 admits Poiseuille flow as a particular solution, wherefrom [15, 18]:

$$u = \frac{\phi}{4} (1 - r^2) - \sum_{n=1}^{\infty} \frac{2\phi J_0(b_n r)}{b_n^3 J_1(b_n)} \exp\left(-\frac{b_n^2 t}{\Omega + \beta b_n^2} \right) \tag{43}$$

It is seen that the elastic constant β appears in Equation 43 only in the argument of the exponential time-function; Equation 43 is exactly equal to Equation 18 for $\beta = 0$. Equation 43 is illustrated in Figure 10 for $\Omega = 1$ and $\beta = 0.1$. A comparison of Figures 10 and 3 shows that one effect of the elasticity of the fluid is to slow down the flow. For instance, at $t = 0.1$, the velocity at the pipe centerline for the Coleman & Noll fluid is approximately 70% of the corresponding velocity of a Newtonian fluid. This result is clearly explained by the mathematical structure of Equation 43, where a non-zero value of β decreases the factor affecting the time inside the exponential function, hence increasing the time needed to make the transient part of the velocity negligibly small, i.e., to reach its steady-state condition.

The average velocity is:

$$U = \frac{\phi}{8} \left[1 - \sum_{n=1}^{\infty} \frac{32}{b_n^4} \exp\left(-\frac{b_n^2 t}{\Omega + \beta b_n^2} \right) \right] \tag{44}$$

Equation 44 has been plotted in Figure 11 for $\beta = 0.1$ and $\beta = 0.2$, where it is easy to appreciate the retarding effect of the fluid elasticity.

For this fluid an approximate expression of the time of flow establishment can be deduced from Equation 44, use being made of the high convergence of the series for $t \cong t_e$. The outcome of the establishment-in-time condition, i.e., $U(t_e) = 0.99 U(\infty)$, is:

$$\frac{t_e}{\Omega} = 0.788 \left(1 + b_1^2 \frac{\beta}{\Omega} \right); \qquad b_1^2 \cong 5.783 \tag{45}$$

where it is found that t_e increases linearly with β. The value of t_e / Ω for a Newtonian fluid is fixed and equal to 0.788; this value is doubled for a Coleman & Noll fluid when $\beta / \Omega = 0.173$. The wall

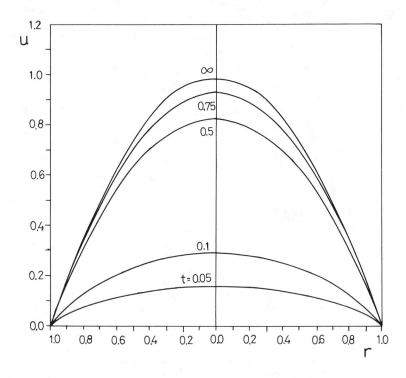

Figure 10. Velocity distribution during start-up of a fluid of Coleman & Noll for $\beta = 0.1$.

shear stress, according to Equations 40 and 43, is:

$$\tau_w = \tau(1, t) = 2 - 8 \sum_{n=1}^{\infty} \left(\frac{1}{b_n^2} - \frac{v_0}{\Omega + v_0 b_n^2} \right) \exp\left(-\frac{b_n^2 t}{\Omega + v_0 b_n^2} \right)$$

The behavior of τ_w is depicted in Figure 12; the wall stress is not zero for $t = 0$, since $\tau(r, t)$ depends on the flow acceleration, cf. Equation 41, which is different from zero at the commencement of the motion.

One characteristic of a Coleman & Noll fluid during the start-up phenomenon is that it cannot predict velocity overshoot. This last, i.e., a momentary increase of the velocity beyond its ultimate steady value, is a common predictive feature of many viscoelastic fluid models (cf. section on Maxwell fluid in this chapter). The incapacity of the Coleman & Noll fluid to produce a velocity overshoot is a consequence of the fact that the exponential argument in Equation 43 is real for all β.

Other related analysis concerning unsteady pipe flow of second order fluids can be found in Markovitz and Coleman [19], Slattery [20], and Waters and King [21].

One-Dimensional Analysis

A series solution for u in Equation 42 is [13]:

$$u = A_2(1 - r^2) + A_4(1 - r^4) + \cdots + A_{2n}(1 - r^{2n}) + \cdots \tag{46}$$

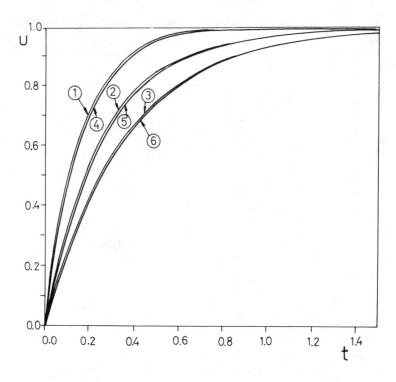

Figure 11. Average velocity during start-up of a fluid of Coleman & Noll. Curve 1: exact solution, Equation 44; Curve 4: approximation, Equation 53; $\beta = 0$. Curve 2: exact solution; curve 5: approximation, Equation 53; $\beta = 0.1$. Curve 3: exact solution; curve 6: approximation, Equation 53; $\beta = 0.2$.

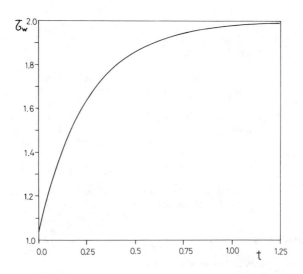

Figure 12. Wall shear stress during start-up of a fluid of Coleman & Noll for $\beta = 0.1$.

where the A_{2n} are functions of time, and the following relationships hold, viz.:

$$4A_2 + (\Omega + 4\beta)\frac{dA_2}{dt} + \Omega\left(\frac{dA_4}{dt} + \frac{dA_6}{dt} + \cdots\right) = \phi \tag{47}$$

$$\Omega\frac{dA_2}{dt} = 16\left(A_4 + \beta\frac{dA_4}{dt}\right)$$

$$\Omega\frac{dA_4}{dt} = 36\left(A_6 + \beta\frac{dA_6}{dt}\right) \tag{48}$$

$$\vdots$$

The A_{2n}, $n > 1$, can be expressed in terms of $A_2 = A$ by means of a series solution for each Equation 48. In this form, e.g. for A_4, it is found that:

$$A_4 = \frac{\Omega}{4^2}\left(\frac{dA}{dt} - \beta\frac{d^2A}{dt^2} + \beta^2\frac{d^3A}{dt^3} - \cdots\right)$$

This procedure allows expression of u in Equation 46 and ϕ in Equation 47 exclusively in terms of A, hence:

$$\phi = \alpha_0 A + \alpha_1\frac{dA}{dt} + \alpha_2\frac{d^2A}{dt^2} + \cdots$$

$$\alpha_0 = 4$$

$$\alpha_1 = (\Omega + 4\beta)$$

$$\alpha_2 = \frac{\Omega^2}{4^2} \tag{49}$$

$$\alpha_3 = \frac{\Omega^2}{4^2}\left(\frac{\Omega}{6^2} - \beta\right)$$

$$\alpha_4 = \frac{\Omega^2}{4^2}\left(\frac{\Omega^2}{6^2 8^2} - 2\frac{\Omega\beta}{6^2} + \beta^2\right)$$

$$\vdots$$

and $$U = 2\int_0^1 ur\,dr = \frac{A_2}{2} + \frac{2}{3}A_4 + \frac{3}{4}A_6 + \cdots$$

wherefrom $$U = \beta_0 A + \beta_1\frac{dA}{dt} + \beta_2\frac{d^2A}{dt^2} + \cdots \tag{50}$$

$$\beta_0 = \frac{1}{2}$$

$$\beta_1 = \frac{2}{3}\frac{\Omega}{4^2}$$

$$\beta_2 = \frac{\Omega}{4^2} \left(\frac{2}{3} \beta - \frac{3}{4} \frac{\Omega^2}{6^2} \right)$$

$$\beta_3 = \frac{\Omega}{4^2} \left(\frac{2}{3} \beta^2 - \frac{3}{2} \frac{\Omega\beta}{6^2} + \frac{4}{5} \frac{\Omega^2}{6^2 8^2} \right)$$

Equations 49 and 50 yield the one-dimensional momentum equation as (cf. Appendix):

$$\alpha_0 U + \alpha_1 \frac{dU}{dt} + \alpha_2 \frac{d^2U}{dt^2} + \cdots = \beta_0 \phi + \beta_1 \frac{d\phi}{dt} + \beta_2 \frac{d^2\phi}{dt^2} + \cdots \tag{51}$$

Form 51 of the momentum equation can be replaced by a more convenient equation, after solving for ϕ in Equation 51, whence:

$$\gamma_0 U + \gamma_1 \frac{dU}{dt} + \gamma_2 \frac{d^2U}{dt^2} + \cdots = \phi \tag{52}$$

The constant coefficients γ_n are combinations of α_n and β_n that can be obtained from the Appendix. The solution to Equation 52 for ϕ = constant, i.e., for the case of flow establishment, is:

$$U = \frac{\phi}{\gamma_0} (1 - e^{-ct}) \tag{53}$$

where c is the dominant root of the characteristic equation associated to Equation 52. The values of c for $\Omega = 1$ and some values of β are:

$\beta = 0.001 \qquad c = 5.75$

$\beta = 0.1 \qquad c = 3.67$

$\beta = 0.2 \qquad c = 2.69$

$\beta = 0.3 \qquad c = 2.12$

Equation 53 has been plotted in Figure 11 for $\beta = 0.1$ and $\beta = 0.2$. The error of Equation 53 is less than 2% for t > 0.25 ($\beta = 0.1$) and for t > 0.05 ($\beta = 0.2$). It is found that the error decreases as β increases. Figure 12 also shows the wall shear stress profile during the start-up of a Coleman & Noll fluid.

Maxwell Fluid

The oldest viscoelastic model of a fluid is that of Maxwell [22]. Its linearity and relative simplicity make this model adequate for the analysis of fluid viscoelastic behavior in many theoretical and practical circumstances [23, 24, 25, 26].

Unsteady pipe-flow of a Maxwellian fluid has been studied by Broer [27] for a pulsating pressure gradient in a circular pipe, similarly by Singh [28] in an annular tube, by Townsend [29] and Puga [30] for the start-up flow, and by Bennis et al. [26] for fluctuating pressure.

As in the previous sections, this one will center on the start-up problem. Puga's [29] analysis will be followed here.

Maxwell's constitutive equation for parallel axisymmetric flow is:

$$\tau + \lambda_0 \frac{\partial\tau}{\partial t} = -\eta_2 \frac{\partial u}{\partial r} \tag{54}$$

where λ and η_2 are material constants for isothermal flow. The dimensionless form of Equation 54 is, for $\eta = \eta_2$:

$$\tau + \tilde{\lambda}\frac{\partial \tau}{\partial t} = -\frac{\partial u}{\partial r}; \quad \tilde{\lambda} = \frac{\lambda_0}{T_0} \tag{55}$$

The elasticity constant $\tilde{\lambda}$ weights the influence that the rate of change of the shear stress τ has on the velocity gradient. If Equation 55 is differentiated with respect to time and the momentum equation (Equation 8) is differentiated with respect to r, it follows that:

$$\frac{\partial \tau}{\partial t} + \tilde{\lambda}\frac{\partial^2 \tau}{\partial t^2} - \frac{1}{r}\frac{\partial \tau}{\partial r} + \frac{\tau}{r^2} - \frac{\partial^2 \tau}{\partial r^2} = 0 \tag{56}$$

i.e., the momentum equation in terms of τ, valid for any forcing function, and where, for simplicity's sake, T_0 has been made equal to $\rho a^2/\eta_1$, so that $\Omega = 1$. For the problem of flow establishment Equation 56 can be conveniently solved by adding the steady-state solution $\phi r/2$ to a solution found by the method of separation variables. Thus:

$$\tau = \sum_{n=1}^{\infty} \{C_{n1}e^{w_{n1}t} + C_{n2}e^{w_{n2}t}\}J_1(b_n r) + \frac{\phi r}{2} \tag{57}$$

The velocity can be obtained by integrating Equation 55, in which τ is Equation 57, viz.:

$$u = \sum_{n=1}^{\infty} \frac{1}{b_n}\{C_{n1}(1 + \tilde{\lambda}w_{n1})e^{w_{n1}t} + C_{n2}(1 + \tilde{\lambda}w_{n2})\}J_0(b_n r) + \frac{\phi}{4}(1 - r^2) \tag{58}$$

where C_{ni}'s are constant coefficients to be determined through the initial conditions $u(r, 0) = 0$ and $\tau(r, 0) = 0$. The parameters w_{n1} and w_{n2} are given by:

$$w_{n1} = \frac{1}{2\tilde{\lambda}}\{(1 - 4\tilde{\lambda}b_n^2)^{1/2} - 1\}$$

$$w_{n2} = -\frac{1}{2\tilde{\lambda}}\{(1 - 4\tilde{\lambda}b_n^2)^{1/2} + 1\} \tag{59}$$

The initial conditions determine C_{n1} and C_{n2} as:

$$C_{n1} = \frac{-2\phi w_{n2}}{b_n^2 J_1(b_n)(w_{n2} - w_{n1})}$$

$$C_{n2} = \frac{2\phi w_{n1}}{b_n^2 J_1(b_n)(w_{n2} - w_{n1})} \tag{60}$$

The exponential arguments w_{n1} and w_{n2}, according to Equation 59, become complex numbers for all $\tilde{\lambda} \neq 0$ when b_n is sufficiently big. This implies that the velocity is pulsating, strictly speaking. However, computations show that only when w_{n1} and w_{n2} become complex for $b_n = b_1$ is the oscillating behavior of the flow numerically noticeable. Therefore, for $\tilde{\lambda} > 1/4b_1^2 = 0.0432$ there is velocity overshoot in the start-up flow problem. For any value of the elastic constant $\tilde{\lambda}$, some of the first terms in the series of Equations 57 and 58 can be evaluated by Equations 58, 59, and 60. When $4\tilde{\lambda}b_n^2 > 1$ and $n \geq N$, Equations 57 and 58 have to be transformed by means of Euler's formula for imaginary exponential arguments for $n \geq N$. This can be done in a straightforward manner, since the imaginary unity cancels out in those and related equations [30].

The time-history of u, after Equation 58, is depicted in Figures 13 and 14, respectively, for $\tilde{\lambda} = 0.025$ and $\tilde{\lambda} = 0.15$.

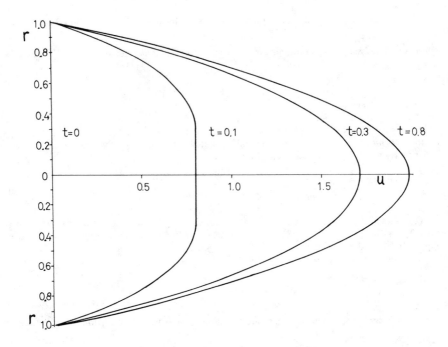

Figure 13. Velocity distribution during start-up of a Maxwell fluid for $\phi = 8$, $\tilde{\lambda} = 0.025$.

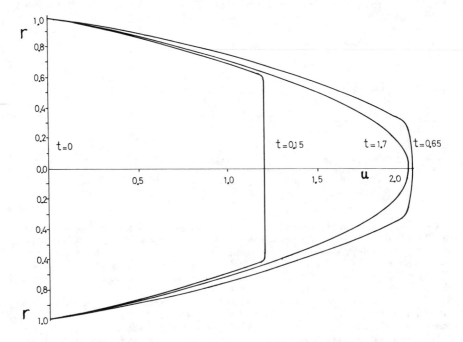

Figure 14. Velocity distribution during start-up of a Maxwell fluid for $\phi = 8$, $\tilde{\lambda} = 0.15$.

The average velocity is:

$$U = 4\phi \sum_{n=1}^{\infty} \frac{w_{n1}(1 + \tilde{\lambda}w_{n2})e^{w_{n2}t} - w_{n2}(1 + \tilde{\lambda}w_{n1}t)e^{w_{n1}t}}{b_n^4(w_{n2} - w_{n1})} + \frac{\phi}{8} \tag{61}$$

which has been plotted in Figures 15, 16, and 17. For $\tilde{\lambda} = 0.035$ (Figure 15) and $\tilde{\lambda} = 0.043$ (Figure 16), U increases monotonically up to its steady-state value, since the oscillating terms in

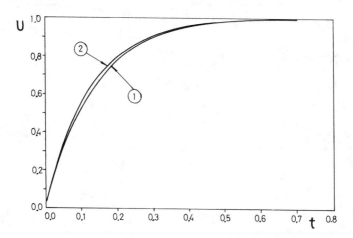

Figure 15. Average velocity during start-up of a Maxwell fluid for $\phi = 8$, $\tilde{\lambda} = 0.035$. Curve 1: exact solution, Equation 58; curve 2: approximation, Equation 72.

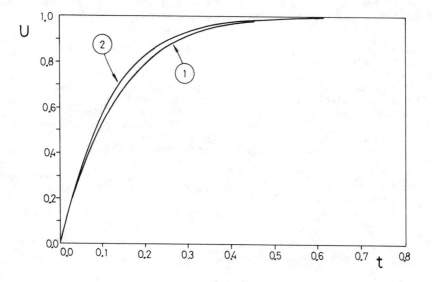

Figure 16. Average velocity during start-up of a Maxwell fluid for $\phi = 8$, $\tilde{\lambda} = 0.043$. Curve 1: exact solution, Equation 61; curve 2: approximation, Equation 72.

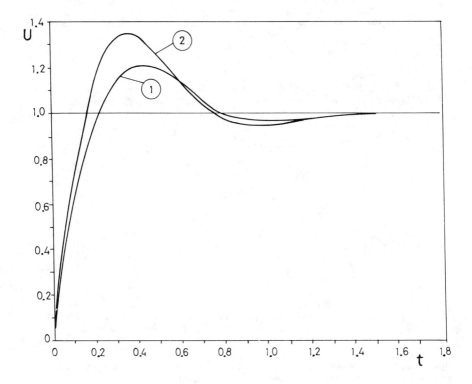

Figure 17. Average velocity during start-up of a Maxwell fluid for $\phi = 8$; $\tilde{\lambda} = 0.15$. Curve 1: exact solution, Equation 61; curve 2: approximation, Equation 73.

Equation 61 are negligible compared to the dominant term. For $\tilde{\lambda} = 0.15$ (Figure 17), the first term of the series in Equation 61 is oscillatory, so that the velocity reaches very fast the steady value but then oscillates with big damping until it decays to its steady-state limit.

The time of flow establishment can be evaluated from Equation 61. In contrast with the results of the previous sections, Equation 61 does not admit a simple analytical approximation for t_e such as Equation 23 or 45. Moreover, t_e varies in a discontinuous form with $\tilde{\lambda}$, depending on the stage of the oscillation of U for which the value $U = U_\infty(1 \pm 0.01)$ is obtained. A numerical computation of t_e from Equation 61 in terms of $\tilde{\lambda}$ is shown in Figure 18.

The expressions for τ (Equation 57), u (Equation 58), and U (Equation 61) converge to their Newtonian limits for $\tilde{\lambda} \to 0$.

The oscillating behavior of viscoelastic fluids during transient stages of flow, such as a start-up motion, is a common predictive feature of many constitutive models [31, 32, 33] and also it is an experimentally verified fact [31, 34].

An important source of information about related problems concerning non-Newtonians is Bird [23]. A good general reference for viscoelastic flow is Zahorski [35].

One-Dimensional Analysis for Maxwellian Fluids

Equation 56 admits a series solution of the form:

$$\tau = A1r + A3r^3 + A5r^5 + \cdots \tag{62}$$

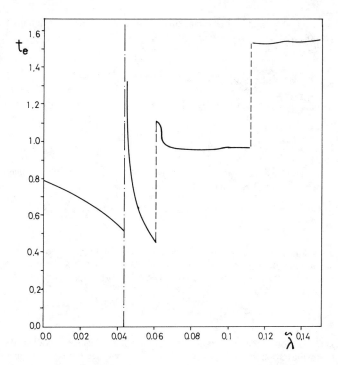

Figure 18. Time of flow establishment for start-up of a Maxwell fluid computed from Equation 61.

provided the functions $A_j(t)$ meet the conditions:

$$\tilde{\lambda}\frac{d^2A_1}{dt^2} + \frac{dA_1}{dt} - 8A_3 = 0$$

$$\tilde{\lambda}\frac{d^2A_3}{dt^2} + \frac{dA_3}{dt} - 24A_5 = 0 \qquad (63)$$

$$\vdots$$

Once the A_j, $j > 1$ in Equation 63 are expressed in terms of $A_1 = A$, and are substituted back in Equation 62, it follows that:

$$\tau = \sum_{n=0}^{\infty} \frac{r^{2n+1}}{4^n n!(n+1)!}\left(1 + \tilde{\lambda}\frac{d}{dt}\right)^n \frac{d^n A}{dt^n} \qquad (64)$$

Equation 64 is put into Equation 55, which, once integrated, yields:

$$u = \sum_{n=0}^{\infty} \frac{1 - r^{2(n+1)}}{2(n+1)4^n n!(n+1)!}\left(1 + \tilde{\lambda}\frac{d}{dt}\right)^{n+1} \frac{d^n A}{dt^n} \qquad (65)$$

The corresponding expression for the forcing function can be obtained after Equations 64 and 65 are put in Equation 8, viz.:

$$\phi = 2A + \sum_{n=0}^{\infty} \frac{1}{2(n+1)4^n n!(n+1)!} \left(1 + \tilde{\lambda}\frac{d}{dt}\right)^{n+1} \frac{d^{n+1}A}{dt^{n+1}} \tag{66}$$

The average velocity is next found by integration of Equation 65, hence:

$$U = \sum_{n=0}^{\infty} \frac{1}{2(n+2)4^n n!(n+1)!} \left(1 + \tilde{\lambda}\frac{d}{dt}\right)^{n+1} \frac{d^n A}{dt^n} \tag{67}$$

Equations 64, 66, and 67 can be written in increasing orders of $d^n A/dt^n$ so that the methods developed in the Appendix apply. Thus, an equation of type:

$$a_0 U + a_1 \frac{dU}{dt} + a_2 \frac{d^2U}{dt^2} + \cdots = \phi \tag{68}$$

can be constructed, in which the a_j's are constant coefficients that depend on $\tilde{\lambda}$ only.

The one-dimensional momentum equation (Equation 68) is now solved for the problem of flow establishment under a constant pressure gradient. The solution to Equation 68, for constant ϕ, is:

$$U = \frac{\phi}{8} + \sum_{n=1}^{\infty} K_n e^{Y_n t} \tag{69}$$

where the Y_n are the roots of the characteristic polynomial of infinite degree associated to Equation 68. As in the previous applications of the one-dimensional momentum equation in this chapter, only the dominant roots of the characteristic equation can be taken into account, whence:

$$U = \frac{\phi}{8} + K_1 e^{Y_1 t} + K_2 e^{Y_2 t} \tag{70}$$

Two roots need be considered in Equation 69, because of the oscillatory behavior of the velocity for $\tilde{\lambda} > 0.0432$. The initial conditions for Equation 70 are:

$$U(0) = 0$$

$$\frac{dU}{dt}(0) = \phi \tag{71}$$

Condition 71 is explained through Equation 8; in effect, integration of Equation 8 across the pipe area yields:

$$\frac{dU}{dt} + 2\tau_w = \phi$$

and, since $\tau(r, 0) = 0$, then the initial wall shear stress τ_w is zero, wherefrom Equation 71 follows. Once the initial conditions are applied to Equation 70, the resulting one-dimensional solution for the average velocity is, for $\phi = 8$:

$$U = 1 - \frac{(Y_2 + 8)e^{Y_1 t} - (Y_1 + 8)e^{Y_2 t}}{(Y_2 - Y_1)} \tag{72}$$

For complex Y_1, Y_2, Equation 72 can be written as:

$$U = 1 - e^{-mt}\{\cos(m\sqrt{\delta - 1}\ t) + \frac{m - 8}{m\sqrt{\delta - 1}}\ \text{sen}(m\sqrt{\delta - 1}\ t)\}$$ (73)

where $\quad m = \dfrac{1}{2\tilde{\lambda}}$

$\qquad \delta = 4\tilde{\lambda}b_1^2$

The roots Y_1, Y_2 converge numerically to w_{11} and w_{12}, as given by Equation 59, if a sufficiently large number of terms in Equation 68 is taken.

Equations 72 and 73 are included in Figures 15, 16, and 17 where it is possible to compare its predictions with those of the exact solution (Equation 61). The error produced by Equations 72 and 73 is less than 2% for $t \geq 0.25$ when $\tilde{\lambda} = 0.035$, for $t \geq 0.3$ when $\tilde{\lambda} = 0.43$, and it is less than 5% for $t \geq 0.5$ when $\tilde{\lambda} = 0.15$.

POWER-LAW FLOW

So far, constitutive equations included in this chapter are linear, either for plastic or viscoelastic fluids. Some non-Newtonian flow behavior demands non-linear models of fluids, the simplest of which is, perhaps, the power-law fluid. This is described, in pipe-flow, by a dimensional equation of the form:

$$\tau = \eta_3\left(-\frac{\partial u}{\partial r}\right)^n$$ (74)

where η_3 and n are constant properties of the fluid. The appropriate dimensionless version of Equation 74 results after defining:

$\eta = \eta_3 U_0^{n-1}/a^{n-1}$, viz.:

$$\tau = \left(-\frac{\partial u}{\partial r}\right)^n$$ (75)

Equations 8 and 75 define a non-linear system of equations that has been solved numerically by several authors for start-up, oscillatory flow, and related problems in rectilinear pipes. Edwards et al. [36, 37] and Balmer and Fiorina [38] solved Equations 8 and 75 by means of finite-difference methods; Gorla and Madden [39] attacked the case of an arbitrary pressure gradient with a variational approach; an approximate analytical solution for the start-up problem was developed by Sestak and Charles [40]; and a useful review of related references appears in Adusumilli and Hill [41]. The characteristics of the velocity profile for steady flow of power-law non-Newtonian, for an ample range of the flow index n, appear in Cheremissinoff [42]. In general, under equal circumstances, the centerline velocity reaches faster a given value the greater is n, during the start-up.

Exact analytical solutions to the system of Equations 8 and 75 seem difficult to obtain for unsteady flow. However, for rational n, a series solution for Equations 8 and 75 can be developed under certain restrictions [43]. The method will be illustrated here for $n = 0.5$. In this case, Equation 75 leads to

$$\frac{\partial u}{\partial r} = -\tau^2$$ (76)

Equation 8, once differentiated with respect to r, is:

$$\Omega \frac{\partial}{\partial t}\left(\frac{\partial u}{\partial r}\right) - \frac{\tau}{r^2} + \frac{1}{r}\frac{\partial \tau}{\partial r} + \frac{\partial^2 \tau}{\partial r^2} = 0 \tag{77}$$

Substitution of Equation 76 into Equation 77 yields:

$$-\varepsilon\tau\frac{\partial \tau}{\partial t} - \frac{\tau}{r^2} + \frac{1}{r}\frac{\partial \tau}{\partial r} + \frac{\partial^2 \tau}{\partial r^2} = 0; \qquad \varepsilon = 2\Omega \tag{78}$$

which is a non-linear momentum equation in terms of the shear stress. When $\varepsilon \to 0$, i.e., for steady flow, Equation 78 has a simple solution given by:

$$\tau = \tau_0 = \frac{\phi r}{2} \tag{79}$$

For relatively small values of ε, some corrections to Equation 79 are found in a simple manner through the method of regular perturbations. To this end τ is expanded as:

$$\tau = \tau_0 + \varepsilon\tau_1 + \varepsilon^2\tau_2 + \cdots \tag{80}$$

and its substitution in Equation 78 generates a system of linear equations for the τ_j, viz.:

$$L\tau_0 = \frac{\partial^2 \tau}{\partial r^2} + \frac{1}{r}\frac{\partial \tau_0}{\partial r} - \frac{\tau_0}{r^2} = 0$$

$$L\tau_1 = \tau_0 \frac{\partial \tau_0}{\partial t}$$

$$L\tau_2 = \tau_0 \frac{\partial \tau_1}{\partial t} + \tau_1 \frac{\partial \tau_0}{\partial t} \tag{81}$$

$$L\tau_3 = \tau_0 \frac{\partial \tau_2}{\partial t} + \tau_1 \frac{\partial \tau_1}{\partial t} + \tau_2 \frac{\partial \tau_0}{\partial t}$$

$$\vdots$$

$L\tau_j$ is a linear differential operator, defined by the first equation in 81. System 81 admits straightforward solutions,

$$\tau_0 = \frac{\phi r}{2}$$

$$\tau_1 = \frac{\phi\dot{\phi}}{60}(r^4 + B_1 r)$$

$$\tau_2 = \frac{\phi^2\ddot{\phi} + 2\phi\dot{\phi}^2}{360}\left(\frac{r^7}{16} + \frac{B_1}{5}r^4 + B_2 r\right) \tag{82}$$

$$\vdots$$

where the dot means derivative with respect to time, and the B_j are constants. The velocity is also expressed in terms of a series in power of ε, i.e.:

$$u = u_0 + \varepsilon u_1 + \varepsilon^2 u_2 + \cdots \tag{83}$$

Combining Equations 76 and 83 there it is found:

$$-\left\{\frac{\partial u_0}{\partial r} + \varepsilon \frac{\partial u_1}{\partial r} + \varepsilon^2 \frac{\partial u_2}{\partial r} + \cdots\right\} = \tau_0^2 + \varepsilon(2\tau_0\tau_1) + \varepsilon^2(\tau_1^2 + 2\tau_0\tau_2) + \cdots \tag{84}$$

from which follow the u_j by integration. The integrals that determine the τ_j from Equation 81 and u_j from Equation 84 involve several constants that are evaluated from the symmetry and boundary conditions, and from Equation 8. This last equation demands that the system:

$$\frac{1}{r}\frac{\partial}{\partial r}(\tau_0 r) = \phi$$

$$\frac{\partial u_0}{\partial t} + \frac{1}{r}\frac{\partial}{\partial r}(2\tau_1 r) = 0$$

$$\frac{\partial u_1}{\partial t} + \frac{1}{r}\frac{\partial}{\partial r}(2\tau_2 r) = 0$$

$$\vdots$$

be satisfied. The final form of the variables, once all constants have been evaluated, is:

$$\tau = \frac{\phi r}{2} + \Omega \frac{\phi\dot{\phi}}{60}(2r^4 - 5r) + \Omega^2 \frac{\phi^2\ddot{\phi} + 2\phi\dot{\phi}^2}{1{,}440}(r^7 - 8r^4 + 16r) + \cdots \tag{85}$$

$$u = \frac{\phi^2}{12}(1 - r^3) + \Omega \frac{\phi^2\dot{\phi}}{180}(-4 + 5r^3 - r^6) + \Omega^2 \left\{\frac{\phi^3\ddot{\phi}}{12{,}960}(37 - 48r^3 + 12r^6 - r^9)\right.$$

$$\left. + \frac{\phi^2\dot{\phi}^2}{3{,}600}(26 - 35r^3 + 10r^6 - r^9)\right\} + \cdots \tag{86}$$

The average velocity is:

$$U = \frac{\phi^2}{20} - \frac{\Omega}{80}\phi^2\dot{\phi} + \frac{7\Omega^2}{8{,}800}(2\phi^3\ddot{\phi} + 5\phi^2\dot{\phi}^2) + \cdots \tag{87}$$

The complexity of the terms in Equations 85, 86, and 87 for large power of Ω increases rapidly. The structure of the velocity, i.e., of Equation 86, is such that convergency can be ensured if ϕ is bounded and Ω is not big. A shortcoming of Equations 86 and 87 is their incapacity to meet arbitrary initial conditions. However, Equations 86 and 87 can satisfy a zero-velocity initial condition if $\phi(0) = 0$. An instance of flow that meets these restrictions is an oscillatory flow, defined by:

$$\phi = \delta_1 \sin t; \quad |\delta_1| \leq 1 \tag{88}$$

since $|\phi| \leq 1$ and $\phi(0) = 0$. Equations 86 and 88 describe, thus, an oscillating flow of a power-law fluid with $n = 0.5$, and in which $u(r, 0) = 0$. Numerical calculations show that for $\Omega = 2.5$ only the first two corrections to the quasi-steady term in Equation 86 are significant. A plot of Equation 86 for $\Omega = 2.5$ and $\delta_1 = 1$ is shown in Figure 19, together with its Newtonian counterpart. There it

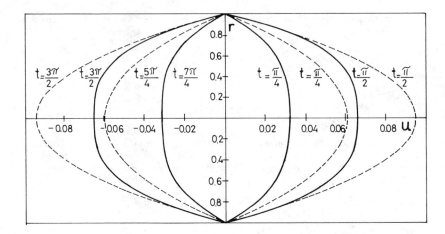

Figure 19. Velocity distribution in oscillatory flow of a power-law fluid for $\phi = \sin t$, $n = 0.5$. Power-law fluid: solid line; Newtonian fluid: dashed line ($u_N/10$).

is seen that the velocity profile is not symmetric in time, since the corrections u_1 and u_2 are not symmetric.

If $n = 1.5$, this method leads to a series for u, in this case, given by:

$$u_0 = \frac{3}{5}\left(\frac{\phi}{2}\right)^{2/3}(1 - r^{5/3})$$

$$u_1 = \frac{2^{5/3}}{1,100}\frac{\dot{\phi}}{\phi^{2/3}}(-8 + 11r^{5/3} - 3r^{10/3})$$

$$u_2 = \frac{1}{66,000}\frac{\ddot{\phi}}{\phi}(129 - 192r^{5/3} + 72r^{10/3} - 9r^5)$$

$$- \frac{1}{363,000}\frac{\dot{\phi}^2}{\phi^2}(607 - 946r^{5/3} + 396r^{10/3} - 57r^5)$$

$$\vdots$$

(89)

which admits forcing functions, e.g., of the form:

$$\phi = 1 \pm \delta_1 \sin t; \qquad |\delta_1| < 1$$

APPENDIX

In the following, the main relationships needed for generating one-dimensional forms of the equations of motion are presented [12].

Let X, Y and Z be functions only of the independent variable s. Further, let X and Y relate to Z through the equations:

$$X = x_0 Z + x_1 \frac{dZ}{ds} + x_2 \frac{d^2 Z}{ds^2} + \cdots$$

(90)

$$Y = y_0 Z + y_1 \frac{dZ}{ds} + y_2 \frac{d^2 Z}{ds^2} + \cdots \tag{91}$$

where x_j and y_j do not depend on s (for the purpose of this chapter, x_j and y_j can be considered constants). Successive differentiation of Equations 90 and 91 with respect to time leads to:

$$y_0 X + y_1 \frac{dX}{ds} + y_2 \frac{d^2 X}{ds^2} + \cdots = x_0 Y + x_1 \frac{dY}{ds} + x_2 \frac{d^2 Y}{ds^2} + \cdots \tag{92}$$

Equation 92 can be solved for X or Y by postulating solutions given by:

$$X = y_0' Y + y_1' \frac{dY}{ds} + y_2' \frac{d^2 Y}{ds^2} + \cdots \tag{93}$$

or

$$Y = x_0' X + x_1' \frac{dX}{ds} + x_2' \frac{d^2 X}{ds^2} + \cdots \tag{94}$$

Once Equation 93 or 94 is substituted into Equation 92, the constants y_j' or x_j' can be determined by putting the coefficients of all orders of the derivatives with respect to s equal to zero. For example, if Equation 93 is substituted into Equation 92, it is found that:

$$y_0 y_0' - x_0 = 0$$

$$y_0 y_1' + y_1 y_0' - x_1 = 0$$

$$y_0 y_2' + y_1 y_1' + y_2 y_0' - x_2 = 0 \tag{95}$$

$$\vdots$$

which system of equations yields the values of the y_j' in this case. Sometimes it is useful to invert a series such as Equation 91, i.e., to express Z in terms of Y and its derivatives with respect to s.

This can be simply achieved by putting $x_0 = 1$, $x_j \geq 0$, $j \geq 1$, so that $X = Z$, wherefrom Equation 95 provides the required constants again, and Equation 93 is the desired inversion of Equation 91.

The momentum equation for a Newtonian fluid is one important source of a series such as Equation 90, which can be combined in order to deduce convenient one-dimensional relations [13]. The equation, for $\Omega = 1$, is:

$$\frac{\partial u}{\partial t} - \left(\frac{\partial^2 u}{\partial r^2} + \frac{1}{r} \frac{\partial u}{\partial r} \right) = \phi(t) \tag{96}$$

A series solution for Equation 96 is:

$$u = A_2(1 - r^2) + A_4(1 - r^4) + A_6(1 - r^6) + \cdots \tag{97}$$

in which the A_j are related by:

$$A_4 = \frac{1}{4^2} \frac{dA_2}{dt} \tag{98}$$

$$A_6 = \frac{1}{4^2 6^2} \frac{d^2 A_2}{dt^2}$$

$$\vdots$$

and
$$A_2 + \frac{1}{2^2}\frac{dA_2}{dt} + \frac{1}{2^2 4^2}\frac{d^2 A_2}{dt^2} + \cdots = \frac{\phi}{4} \tag{99}$$

Equations 98 and 99 reveal that both u and ϕ can be expressed in terms of a single function of time and its derivatives. Once Equation 99 is put to 97, the result is:

$$u = A(1 - r^2) + \frac{1}{4^2}\frac{dA}{dt}(1 - r^4) + \frac{1}{4^2 6^2}\frac{d^2 A}{dt^2}(1 - r^6) + \cdots \tag{100}$$

Series for U and τ in terms of A follow from Equation 100 by, respectively, integration and differentiation with respect to r. Equations 92 and 95 provide, then, the means for constructing many relationships among ϕ, τ, and U, in all of which A does not appear.

Acknowledgments

The financial support of the National Fund for Scientific and Technological Research, and of the Department of Scientific and Technological Research of the University of Santiago are gratefully acknowledged. Special thanks are due to P. Puga and R. McNab for their assistance in the development of analytical and numerical aspects of viscoelastic flow. Last, but not least, thanks are conveyed to R. Castro for his aid in the draftwork and to C. Vega for her typingwork.

NOTATION

a	pipe radius	r_0	limit ratio in Bingham fluids
a_j	constant coefficient for ϕ (Equation 68)	s	independent variable
A_j, A	functions of time	t	time
b_n	roots of J_0	t_e	time of flow establishment
B_j	integration constants (Equation 82)	T_0	reference time
c	dominant root (Equation 52)	u	local velocity
C_n	constant coefficients	u_j	velocity components (Equation 83)
C_{n1}, C_{n2}	constant coefficients (Equation 57)	u_1	velocity of plug-flow zone in Bingham fluids
e	2.7183	U	average velocity
exp( )	exponential function	U_0	reference velocity
E	function defined by Equation 35	U_∞	$U(\infty)$
g	acceleration due to gravity	w_{n1}, w_{n2}	characteristic roots given by Equation 59
h	vertical coordinate		
J_0, J_1	Bessel's functions of the first class	x	axial coordinate
K_n	constant coefficients (Equation 69)	x_j, x_j'	constant coefficients
m	$1/2\tilde{\lambda}$	X	arbitrary function of s
n	flow index in power-law fluids	y_j, y_j'	constant coefficients
N	yield number	Y	arbitrary function of s
p	pressure	Y_n	roots (Equation 68)
P	piezometric pressure	z	dummy variable
r	radial coordinate	Z	arbitrary function of s

Greek Symbols

α_j	coefficients of ϕ (Equation 49)	δ	$4\tilde{\lambda}b_1^2$
β	$v_0/T_0\eta_1$	δ_1	a number equal to or less than unity
β_j	coefficients of U (Equation 50)	ε	2Ω
γ_j	coefficients of momentum (Equation 52)	η	viscosity
		η_0	viscosity of a Bingham fluid

η_1	viscosity of a fluid of Coleman & Noll	ρ	density
η_2	viscosity of a Maxwellian fluid	τ	shear stress, τ_{rx}
η_3	property of a power-law fluid	τ_j	components of τ (Equation 80)
θ	tangential coordinate	τ_0	reference wall shear stress
λ	U_f/U_i	τ'	yield stress of Bingham fluids
λ_0	elasticity constant of a Maxwell fluid	ϕ	pressure gradient or forcing function
$\tilde{\lambda}$	λ_0/T_0	ψ	arbitrary function of r and t
ν_0	elasticity constant of a fluid of Coleman & Noll	ψ_1	arbitrary function of x and t
		Ω	unsteadiness number

Subscripts

i	initial	x	axial
f	final	w	pipe wall
N	Newtonian	θ	tangential
r	radial		

Superscripts

*	dimensionless variables

REFERENCES

1. Letelier S., M. F., "Approaches to Analyzing Unsteady Laminar Flow in Long Pipes," *Encyclopedia of Fluid Mechanics, Vol. 1*, N. P. Cheremisinoff, Ed. Houston: Gulf Publishing Co., 1986, pp. 560–588.
2. Atabek, H. B., "Start-up Flow of a Bingham Plastic in a Circular Tube," ZAMM, Vol. 44, 1964, pp. 332–333.
3. Duggins, R. K., "The Commencement of Flow of a Bingham Plastic Fluid," *Chem. Eng. Science, Vol. 27*, 1972, pp. 1991–1996.
4. Mitra, A. K., "Impulsively Started Flow of a Bingham Plastic in a Tube," Forum on Unsteady Flow, ASME, P. H. Rothe Ed., 1984, pp. 23–25.
5. Letelier S., M. F.; Gutiérrez S., A.; and Céspedes B., J. F.; "Flujo Acelerado de un Plástico de Bingham en Ductos Circulares," Contribuciones, Santiago, Chile, Vol. 76, 1987, pp. 27–34.
6. Szymanski, F. S., "Quelques Solutions Exactes des Équations de l'Hydrodynamique de Fluide Visqueux dans le Cas d'un Tube Cylindrique," *Journal des Mathématiques Pures et Appliqueés, Vol. 11*, Series 9, 1932, pp. 67–107.
7. Oldroyd, J. C., "Rectilinear Plastic Flow of a Bingham Solid IV Non-Steady Motion," *Proc. Cambridge Phil. Society, Vol. 44*, 1948, pp. 214–228.
8. Letelier S., M. F., "Approaches to Analyzing Unsteady Laminar Flow in Long Pipes," *Encyclopedia of Fluid Mechanics, Vol. 1*, N. P. Cheremisinoff, Ed. Houston: Gulf Publishing Co., 1986, pp. 574–575.
9. Letelier S., M. F., "Approaches to Analyzing Unsteady Laminar Flow in Long Pipes," *Encyclopedia of Fluid Mechanics, Vol. 1*, N. P. Cheremisinoff, Ed. Houston: Gulf Publishing Co., 1986, p. 574.
10. Letelier S., M. F., "Approaches to Analyzing Unsteady Laminar Flow in Long Pipes," *Encyclopedia of Fluid Mechanics, Vol. 1*, N. P. Cheremisinoff, Ed. Houston: Gulf Publishing Co., 1986, p. 568.
11. Letelier S., M. F., "Approaches to Analyzing Unsteady Laminar Flow in Long Pipes," *Encyclopedia of Fluid Mechanics, Vol. 1*, N. P. Cheremisinoff, Ed. Houston: Gulf Publishing Co., 1986, p. 567.

12. Letelier S., M. F., "An Approach to the Analysis of Unsteady Parallel Flow in Circular Pipes," Ph.D. thesis presented to the University of Toronto at Toronto, Ontario, Canada, 1979.
13. Letelier S., M. F., and Leutheusser, H. J., "Unified Approach to the Solution of Problems of Unsteady Laminar Flow in Long Pipes," ASME *Journal of Applied Mechanics, Vol. 50*, No. 1, 1983, pp. 8–12.
14. Coleman, B., and Noll, W., "An Approximation Theorem for Functionals, with Applications in Continuum Mechanics," *Archive Rat. Mech. Analysis, Vol. 2*, 1958–59, pp. 197–226.
15. Ting, W., "Certain Non-Steady Flows of Second-Order Fluids." *Archive Rat. Mech. Analysis, Vol. 14*, 1964, pp. 1–26.
16. Chaudhury, T. K., "On Swimming in a Visco-Elastic Liquid," *J. Fluid Mech., Vol. 95*, 1979, pp. 189–197.
17. Bestman, A. R., "Low Reynolds Number Non-Newtonian Flow in Slowly Varying Axisymmetrical Tubes," *Acta Mechanica, Vol. 44*, 1982, pp. 107–119.
18. McNab, R., "Establecimiento de Flujo Laminar de un Fluido de Coleman & Noll en un Ducto Circular," Engineering Thesis, Department of Mechanical Engineering, University of Santiago, Chile, 1987.
19. Markovitz, H., and Coleman, B., "Non-Steady Helical Flows of Second-Order Fluids," *Phys. of Fluids, Vol. 7*, No. 4, 1964, pp. 833–841.
20. Slattery, J. C., "Unsteady Relative Extension of Incompressible Simple Fluids," *Phys. of Fluids, Vol. 7*, No. 2, 1964, pp. 1913–1914.
21. Waters, N. D., and King, M. J. *Rheol. Acta*, 9, 1970, p. 345.
22. Maxwell, J. C., Phil. Trans. Roy. Soc. London Ser. A 157, 1867, pp. 49–88.
23. Bird, R. B., "Useful Non-Newtonian Models." *Annual Review of Fluid Mechanics, Vol. 8*, M. Van Dyke, W. G. Vicenti and J. U. Wehaussen Eds. Palo Alto: Annual Reviews Inc., 1976, pp. 13–34.
24. Phan-Thien, N., "Coaxial-Disk Flow and Flow About a Rotating Disk of a Maxwellian Fluid." *J. Fluid Mech., Vol. 128*, 1983, pp. 427–442.
25. Phan-Thien, N., and Tanner, R. F., "Viscoelastic Squeeze-Film Flows-Maxwell Fluids." *J. Fluid Mech., Vol. 129*, 1983, pp. 265–281.
26. Bennis, S., Bui, R. T., Charette, A., Bellet, D., and Ly, D. P., "Ecoulements Dans un Systéme Viscoélastique." Proceedings of the X Canadian Congress of Applied Mechanics, London, Ontario, Canada, 1985, pp. B-1–2.
27. Broer, L. J. F., *Appl. Sci. Res. A.*, 6, 1956, p. 226.
28. Singh, D., *"Flow of Visco-Elastic Maxwell Fluid Through Concentric Circular Cylinders,"* ZAMM., Vol. 44, 1964, pp. 330–331.
29. Townsend, P., "Numerical Solutions of Some Unsteady Flows of Elastico-Viscous Liquids," *Rheol. Acta*, 12, 1973.
30. Puga M., P., "Flujo Laminar Impermanente de un Fluido Visco-elástico de Maxwell." Engineering Thesis, Department of Mechanical Engineering, University of Santiago, Chile, 1986.
31. Etter, I., and Schowalter, W. R., "Unsteady Flow of an Oldroyd Fluid in a Circular Tube." *Trans. Soc. Rheol*, Vol. 9, 1965, pp. 351–369.
32. Townsend, P., "Numerical Solutions of Some Unsteady Flows of Elastico-Viscous Liquids." *Rheol. Acta*, 12, 1973, pp. 13–18.
33. Randria, P., and Bellet, D., "Theoretical Simulation of Transient Viscoelastic Flows in a Viscoelastic System." *J. of Non-Newtonian Fluid Mechanics*, Vol. 18, 1985, pp. 199–210.
34. Chow, A. W., and Fuller, G. G., "Some Experimental Results on the Development of Couette Flow for Non-Newtonian Fluids" *J. of Non-Newtonian Fluid Mechanics*, Vol. 17, 1985, pp. 233–243.
35. Zahorski, S., *Mechanics of Viscoelastic Fluids*, The Hague: M. Nijhoft, 1982.
36. Edwards, M. F., Nellist, D. A., and Wilkinson, W. L., "Pulsating Flow of Non-Newtonian Fluids in Pipes." *Chem. Eng. Science*, Vol. 27, 1972, pp. 545–553.
37. Edwards, M. F., Nellist, D. A., and Wilkinson, W. L., "Unsteady, Laminar Flows of Non-Newtonian Fluids in Pipes," *Chem. Eng. Science, Vol. 27*, 1972, pp. 295–306.
38. Balmer, R. T., and Fiorina, M. A., "Unsteady Flow of an Inelastic Power-Law Fluid in a Circular Tube," *J. of Non-Newtonian Fluid Mechanics, Vol. 7*, 1980, pp. 189–198.

39. Gorla, R. S. R., and Madden, P. E., "A Variational Approach to Non-Steady Non-Newtonian Flow in a Circular Pipe," *J. of Non-Newtonian Fluid Mechanics, Vol. 15,* 1984, pp. 251–265.
40. Sestak, J., and Charles, M. E., "An Approximate Solution for the Start-up Flow of a Power Law Fluid in a Tube," *Chem. Eng. Science,* Vol. 23, 1968, pp. 1127–37.
41. Adusumilli, R. S., and Hill, G. A., "Transient Laminar Flows of Truncated Power Law Fluids in Pipes," *Canadian Journal of Chemical Engineering,* Vol. 62, 1984, pp. 594–599.
42. Cheremisinoff, N. P., "Properties and Concepts of Single Fluid Flows," *Encyclopedia of Fluid Mechanics, Vol. 1,* N. P. Cheremisinoff Ed. Houston: Gulf Publishing Co., 1986, pp. 277–352.
43. Letelier S., M. F., and Céspedes B., J. F., "An Analytical Method for Pipe-Flow of Power-Law Fluids," Proceedings of the XI Canadian Congress of Applied Mechanics, Alberta, Edmonton, Canada, 1987.

CHAPTER 4

NON-NEWTONIAN FLOW BEHAVIOR OF COAL-FUEL OIL SUSPENSIONS

A. F. Borghesani

Dipartimento di Fisica "G. Galilei"
Università di Padova
and
G.N.S.M./C.I.S.M, Padova, Italy

CONTENTS

INTRODUCTION

The interest in using pulverized coal-fuel oil slurries as substitutes for fuel oils arose many years ago [1, 2]. More recently, the coal-oil technology has received significant thrust by the increased cost of petroleum crude. Further advances in the utilization of coal-oil mixtures as a commercially viable fuel are related to a better knowledge and predictability of the handling characteristics of the coal-oil suspensions.

As a consequence, an accurate knowledge of the rheological properties of such mixtures (known also as COM, an acronym for Coal Oil Mixtures) has become extremely important for the proper design of the operations needed for preparing, transporting, and employing COM [3].

Preparation of the suspensions, bulk tanker storage, mixing, pumping through pipelines, burning in boilers, production of liquid fuels from coal through hydrogenation processes: all these processes of the coal-oil slurry technology require a detailed knowledge of the rheology of COM to be carefully planned and designed [4–8].

COM systems are concentrated suspensions of coal particles in dispersing media. These are typically fuel-oils, but, very recently, more attention has been paid to different liquids, particularly methanol and water, thus giving origin to a self-standing branch of research devoted to Coal-Water Mixtures (CWM or CWF, Coal-Water Fuels).

Like all concentrated suspensions, COM and CWM generally exhibit non-Newtonian behavior. This fact brings about the need not to limit the rheological characterization of the mixtures to a single viscosity measurement, but to fully determine their behavior in response to a shearing action over a given range of shear stresses and shear rates in order to ascertain which rheological model better fits the experimental data [3, 9–13].

The state of affairs is further complicated by the large fluctuations in the chemical and physical nature of the coal and of the dispersing media used. The physical and chemical properties of coal and dispersing media do, indeed, affect the aggregation conditions of the dispersed phase, its inter-action with the liquid one, and hence the stability and the rheology of the suspension. Therefore, almost every suspension has its own history. Its rheological behavior depends on the conditions of preparation, on storage, on aging, and so on. For the same reasons, a review of the state-of-the-art appears more like a casebook than a final assessment of the issue.

In any case, some few rheological models have proven not only useful to fit the data, but also quite general. At the same time, the use of such models allows researchers and engineers to extract fairly general correlations between the several chemico-physical parameters that characterize the mixtures and their rheological behavior, and thus endows them with a powerful tool to make quantitative predictions [14–16].

The present review aims then at stressing out, as much as possible, the general features underlying the rheological characteristics of COM.

To do this, the next two sections will be devoted to recalling some elementary fundamentals of the rheology of non-Newtonian fluids and of the viscometric techniques which are of importance in the field of COM. Then the main body of the experimental findings about COM rheology will be dealt with. Finally, some information on CWM will be given.

FUNDAMENTALS OF THE RHEOLOGY OF NON-NEWTONIAN FLUIDS

Rheology is concerned with the study of the flow properties of fluid substances under the action of shearing forces [17]. The viscous nature of a fluid is due to phenomena of irreversible micro-scopic momentum exchange occurring in the bulk of the fluid. Therefore, it is necessary to apply a shear stress to a fluid in order to get it flowing. The existence of boundary conditions that limit the flow itself (like pipe walls and so on) sets up a velocity gradient in the fluid mass [18, 19].

When describing the steady, laminar, isothermal flow of a homogeneous and isotropic fluid, it is possible to write down a constitutive equation that relates the shear stress applied to the fluid with the shear rate appearing within it.

Referring to Figure 1, one can write

$$\dot{\gamma} \equiv -\frac{\partial v_x}{\partial y} = f(\tau_{xy}) \equiv f(\tau) \tag{1}$$

$\dot{\gamma}$ conventionally denotes the shear rate, i.e., the velocity gradient. Its units are $s^{-1} \cdot \tau_{xy}$, or simply τ, represents the applied stress with units of $Kg\,m^{-1}\,s^{-2} = Pa$, i.e., of a force per unit area.

The functional form of f is still unknown and depends on the particular fluid on hand. For most of the substances of common and scientific interest, f takes on the simple analytical form of direct proportionality, $f(\tau) = \tau/\eta$, and the constitutive Equation 1 becomes

$$\dot{\gamma} = \eta^{-1}\tau \tag{2}$$

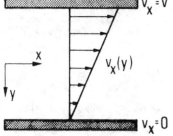

Figure 1. Steady-state velocity profile of a fluid entrained between two flat surfaces. A shear force must be applied to the upper plate in order to maintain it in motion relative to the lower one with velocity V in the x-direction. Because of the fluid viscosity, the force is transmitted through the fluid to the lower plate in such a way that the x-component of the fluid velocity linearly depends on the distance from the lower plate. (It is implicitly assumed, and experimentally verified, that the fluid does not slip at the plate surfaces.)

Such fluids (among which are water, ethanol, and many others) are known as "ideal" or New-tonian fluids. The proportionality coefficient η is named shear viscosity (its units are $\mathrm{Kg\,m^{-1}\,s^{-1}} = \mathrm{Pa \cdot s}$) and it is a unique property of the fluid on hand. The viscosity of these fluids depends on many parameters, particularly on temperature, but it does not depend on the shear rate. So, for a given thermodynamic state of the fluid under study, it is sufficient to perform a single measure-ment of the viscosity η in order to define and to fully characterize the rheological behavior of the fluid over the whole range of shear stresses and shear rates [20].

On the other hand, for a very large class of fluids, including the concentrated suspensions of solids, the analytical form of $f(\tau)$ is not as simple as for the ideal fluids. All such fluids are generally termed as non-Newtonian fluids. In this chapter, we shall focus our attention on the so called "purely viscous" non-Newtonian fluids, i.e., those fluids for which $f(\tau)$ neither contains temporal derivatives of $\dot\gamma$ and τ, nor includes memory effects [21]. Indeed, the rheological models of purely viscous non-Newtonian fluids are well adequate to describe the experimental findings in the COM field. (Up to now, the behavior of Coal-Water Mixtures under the action of an oscillatory shearing force has been reported only very recently in the literature [22, 23].)

For a purely viscous non-Newtonian fluid a viscosity may still be defined as an apparent viscosity, η_a, such that:

$$\eta_a = \tau \dot\gamma^{-1}$$

or, as the slope of the experimental rheograms (shear stress-shear rate curves):

$$\eta = \frac{d\tau}{d\dot\gamma}$$

However, these quantities do now depend on the shear rate, while for a Newtonian fluid they are the same thing (see Figure 2). The non-Newtonian liquids may, therefore, be classified according to the behavior of the viscosity as a function of the shear rate.

Some fluids show an increase of the viscosity with $\dot\gamma$. Others, on the contrary, show a decrease. Some behave like solids until a threshold stress is exceeded, after which they behave like ordinary fluids. In Figure 3 the most commonly observed types of flow behavior are shown in a schematic rheogram.

Curve 1 represents here the ideal rheological behavior. The ratio $\eta = \tau/\dot\gamma$ is constant throughout the whole range of the variables. Curve 2 is representative of a shear thickening liquid for which $d^2\tau/d\dot\gamma^2 > 0$. Its viscosity increases then with the shear rate. On the other hand, curve 3 shows a shear thinning material, whose viscosity decreases with increasing shear rate: $d^2\tau/d\dot\gamma^2 < 0$. Curve 4 exhibits a threshold value of the stress, τ_0, before which the fluid behaves like a solid. This value is also known as yield stress. For stresses larger than τ_0 the fluid starts flowing and its rheogram shows a constant slope, $d\tau/d\dot\gamma$, independent of $\dot\gamma$. Finally, curve 5 combines a shear thinning behavior with a yield stress.

Many rheological models have been proposed to account for the experimental rheograms of the various substances [24]. Probably none of them fits the rheological behavior of a substance over

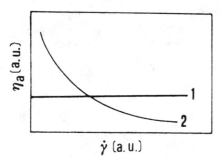

Figure 2. Viscosity-shear rate dependence of a Newtonian fluid (curve 1) and of a non-New-tonian one (curve 2). The Newtonian fluid does not show any dependence of the viscosity on the shear-rate. The non-Newtonian fluid shows, on the contrary, a strong dependence on it. In the particular case here sketched, the viscosity de-creases with the shear rate. In this case it would be more appropriate to speak of an "apparent" viscosity.

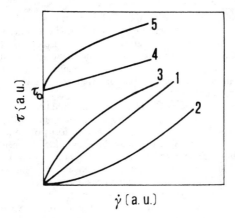

Figure 3. Model rheograms of time-independent fluids. Fluids are classified according to whether they show a yield stress τ_0 (rheograms 4 and 5) or not (rheograms 1 through 3). Rheogram 1 shows a constant slope; therefore its viscosity turns out to be independent of the shear rate; this fluid is Newtonian. Rheogram 2 represents a power-low fluid with flow index $n > 1$. Its apparent viscosity increases with the shear rate: this fluid is a shear thickening one. Rheogram 3 is the rheogram of a power-law fluid with $n < 1$. Its apparent viscosity decreases with $\dot{\gamma}$: this behavior is typical of a shear thinning fluid. Rheogram 4 shows a fluid with yield stress τ_0 and a constant slope for stresses larger than τ_0. This is the case of a Bingham plastic material. Its apparent viscosity decreases with $\dot{\gamma}$ to the limiting value of the plastic viscosity η_B. Finally, rheogram 5 represents the case of a fluid with a yield stress combined with a non linear rheogram. This particular case can be described by means of the generalized Herschel-Bulkley model with a flow index $n < 1$. The apparent viscosity of this fluid decreases with $\dot{\gamma}$: $d^2\tau/d\dot{\gamma}^2 < 0$. This fluid therefore combines a yield stress, typical of a plastic material, with a shear thinning behavior. It is worth recalling that there also exist fluids described by this model with $n > 1$, i.e., they have a shear thickening behavior for $\tau > \tau_0$.

an extended shear rates and shear stresses range. Nevertheless, these models are useful to summarize the experimental data. In Table 1 (Equations 3–7), the flow equations of the rheological models most commonly adopted in the COM literature are shown.

The Newtonian model, Equation 3, is depicted in Figure 3 as curve 1. Liquids behaving like power-law fluids, Equation 4, are represented by curve 2 or curve 3. For these fluids the apparent viscosity is given by:

$$\eta_a = K\dot{\gamma}^{n-1} \tag{8}$$

A shear thickening fluid behavior is obtained if the flow index n is greater than 1. In this case η_a increases with $\dot{\gamma}$. On the other hand, a shear thinning fluid is described by $n < 1$. Hence, its viscosity decreases with $\dot{\gamma}$.

The Bingham plastic model, Equation 5, gives origin to curve 4 of Figure 3. Its apparent viscosity is given by:

$$\eta_a = \frac{\tau_0}{\dot{\gamma}} + \eta_B \tag{9}$$

and decreases to the limiting value η_B as $\dot{\gamma} \to \infty$.

Table 1
Flow Equations for Various Flow Models

Model	Constitutive equations	Eq. #
Newtonian	$\tau = \eta\dot{\gamma}$	3
Bingham plastic	$\tau = \tau_0 + \eta_B\dot{\gamma}$	4
Power law	$\tau = K\dot{\gamma}^n$	5
generalized Herschel-Bulkley	$\tau = \tau_0 + K\dot{\gamma}^n$	6
Casson	$\sqrt{\tau} = \sqrt{\tau_0} + \eta_\infty\sqrt{\dot{\gamma}}$	7

Table 1. τ = shear stress, [Pa]; $\dot{\gamma}$ = shear rate, [s^{-1}]; η = shear viscosity, [Pa·s]; τ_0 = yield stress, [Pa]; η_B = plastic (or Bingham) viscosity, [Pa·s]; n = flow index; K = consistency factor, [Pa·s^n]; η_∞ = high-shear limiting viscosity, [Pa·s]

The generalized Herschel-Bulkley model, Equation 6, is depicted in Figure 3 as curve 5 for n < 1. For this model:

$$\eta_a = \frac{\tau_0}{\dot{\gamma}} + K\dot{\gamma}^{n-1} \qquad (10)$$

Finally, the Casson model, Equation 7, has been reported in Table 1 only for the sake of completeness, but it is not really often used in the COM field [25].

The physical processes that are assumed to be responsible for these various rheological behaviors are quite different from one another [26–33]. Shear thinning behavior, for instance, results from the ability of the dispersed particles to come together to form network-like structures at rest or under low shear. These structures would gradually break down as shear is increased and the particles would then rearrange and reorient themselves in order to lower their resistance to flow. (For instance, an elliptical particle will align its major axis parallel to the flow direction.)

On the other hand, shear thickening behavior may occur in closely packed dispersions when shear introduces irregularities in the packing with bridging effects occurring between particles. The packing conditions may become looser so that the space between particles increases. The liquid is no longer able to fill this space and to efficiently lubricate the particles. Thus, internal friction becomes large and a larger viscosity results. This phenomenon is usually accompanied by an increase of the dispersion volume. However, shear thickening behavior may also occur without any volume changes. For instance, shear may induce particle aggregation that tends to give origin to networks that increase the liquid viscosity [34–38]. Network structures due to particle bridging phenomena are assumed to be responsible for the presence of a yield stress in Bingham plastic materials or in Herschel-Bulkley liquids. In any case, the different rheological behaviors of various substances are determined in a very complicate way by the same variables that affect lyophobic dispersion stability, such as the viscosity, conductivity, and wetting ability of the dispersing medium, the presence of surfactants, the size distribution, shape, and nature of the dispersed particles [24].

Until now, we have considered only the time-independent rheology of non-Newtonian liquids. However, there are liquids which show rheopexy or thixotropy. In the former case there is a reversible increase with time of the viscosity of the liquid under shear and in the latter case the viscosity of a sheared sample decreases with time in a reversible way [39, 40]. Such behaviors are sketched in Figure 4. The thixotropic effect is shown there as curve 1 for a sample exposed first to increasing and then to decreasing shear rates. Owing to the time-decreasing viscosity, the ascending and descending curves do not match and the difference is known as a thixotropic loop. Rheopexy,

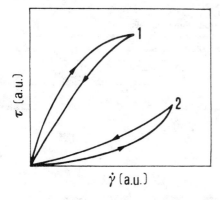

Figure 4. Schematic rheograms of non-Newtonian, time dependent fluids. Rheogram 1 represents the behavior of a thixotropic fluid. The sample is first exposed to increasing and then to decreasing shear rates. Because of the time dependence of its rheological parameters, the two curves do not match, but form a clockwise scanned hysteresis loop, the so-called thixotropic loop. A rheopectic material similarly gives origin to a hysteresis loop, rheogram 2. However, in this case the rheopectic loop is scanned counterclockwise.

shown in Figure 4 as curve 2, similarly gives origin to a rheopectic loop. The area enclosed inside the hysteresis loop is assumed to qualitatively estimate the degree of thixotropy or rheopexy of the sample.

It is sometimes experimentally difficult to distinguish between a thixotropic liquid and a shear thinning one because of the combined shear and time effects during the measurements. Furthermore, measurements made in non steady-state, as is often the case when using rotational viscometers, may produce hysteresis loops because of inertia effects [41].

Finally, when studying the rheology of COM, one has also to take into account irreversibility that occurs as a consequence of the metastable (or, even unstable) nature of the COM. Indeed, COM are subjected to some physical modifications with time. The dispersed phase may coagulate, it may give origin to flocs, or even settle. The liquid phase may evaporate or may be adsorbed in the pores of the coal particles so that the liquid volume fraction is reduced.

As a consequence of these facts, COM must be stabilized against settling, flocculation, oil adsorption, and so on. Stabilization is usually obtained by using chemical additives that, in turn, may drastically modify the rheological properties of the untreated samples. Therefore, COM stability is normally studied in connection with rheology and it will be treated in a later section.

RHEOMETRIC TECHNIQUES AND APPARATUSES

A brief description of the essential features of the viscometers most commonly used in the COM field will give an idea of their performances and capabilities [42–44].

As previously pointed out, one single viscosity measurement at a given shear rate is inadequate to fully characterize the rheological behavior of a non-Newtonian liquid. In fact, it is necessary to carry out measurements in a range of shear rates and shear stresses to deduce the parameters of any rheological models. Furthermore, it may prove convenient to investigate the limiting behavior of the viscosity at low and high shear rates.

To achieve such goals, COM researchers do preferably use three basic viscometer types: capillary (or, extrusion), rotating concentric-cylinder, and cone-and-plate viscometers. Modified versions of such types may also be found in the COM literature. Nevertheless, most of the viscometers fit in one of these classifications.

Capillary Viscometer

In this type of viscometer (see Figure 5a) the liquid is forced to flow through a pipe of length L and diameter D, under the action of a pressure head ΔP. Assuming a laminar and isothermal liquid flow, a pressure gradient uniform throughout the pipe, and negligible end corrections, the fundamental equation of this viscometer can be written as:

$$\frac{8Q}{\pi D^3} = \tau_w^{-3} \int_{0(\tau_0)}^{\tau_w} \tau^2 f(\tau) \, d\tau \tag{11}$$

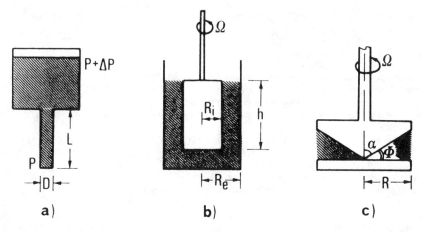

Figure 5. Schematic drawing of the three basic viscometer types. (a) Capillary viscometer: The liquid is forced to flow through the capillary of length L and diameter D by the pressure head ΔP, applied to its free surface in the reservoir. If L/D is small enough, entrance effects (kinetic energy losses) can be neglected. The quantities that are effectively measured are the mass flowrate (hence, the volumetric flowrate if density is known) and the applied pressure. (b) Concentric-cylinder viscometer: The liquid fills the space between the two concentric cylinders. A torque M is applied to the inner one so that it rotates under steady-state conditions at an angular frequency Ω. The exact relationship between M and Ω depends on the rheological model, as well as on the geometric arrangement of the viscometer. (c) Cone-and-plate viscometer: A low-angle inverted cone rotates at an angular frequency Ω against a fixed flat plate. The liquid fills the gap between them. The torque M applied to the cone is recorded and plotted versus Ω. As in the case of the concentric-cylinder viscometer, the exact relationship between Ω and M depends on both the rheological model and the geometrical arrangement of the device.

Q is the volumetric flow rate, τ_w is the shear stress exerted by the liquid on the pipe walls, τ is the shear stress that is exerted on a coaxial cylindrical unit surface of fluid with radius r, and $f(\tau)$ is the constitutive equation of the liquid. The integration limits are $[0, \tau_w]$ for a liquid without yield stress and $[\tau_0, \tau_w]$ for a liquid showing yield stress. Indeed, for $\tau < \tau_0$, one must necessarily have Q = 0.

The volumetric flow rate Q is related to the average fluid velocity V by:

$$Q = \frac{\pi}{4} D^2 V \tag{12}$$

The shear stress on the pipe wall, τ_w, is related to the pressure head ΔP by:

$$\tau_w = \frac{D \, \Delta P}{4L} \tag{13}$$

and therefore, the shear stress, τ, as a function of the pipe radial coordinate r is given by:

$$\tau = \frac{2\tau_w}{D} r \tag{14}$$

By differentiating Equation 11 with respect to τ_w and using Equation 12, one has:

$$\dot{\gamma}_w \equiv f(\tau_w) = \frac{2V}{D} \left[3 + \frac{d \log(8V/D)}{d \log(\tau_w)} \right] \qquad (15)$$

where $\dot{\gamma}_w$ is the shear rate at the boundary and is related to the stress at the walls, τ_w, and to $2V/D$, which can be thought of as an average shear rate. By measuring Q (whence V/D) and ΔP (whence τ_w), one can compute $\dot{\gamma}_w$, and from the relationship between $\dot{\gamma}_w$ and τ_w one can deduce the proper rheological model. In Table 2 the characteristic equations of the capillary viscometer for the different rheological models are shown.

As can be noted by inspection of Equations 16 through 19 (see Table 2), only pure power-law fluids generate linear rheograms with slope 1/n if plotted in a log-log paper. (Newtonian fluids are a special case of pure power-law fluids with n = 1.) Therefore, if rheograms in a double log-log plot are non-linear, the Bingham plastic or the Herschel-Bulkley models have to be adopted. The rheological parameters for any models have to be deduced by performing a least-squares analysis of the experimental data and, therefore, they are determined with large uncertainties unless the experimental data are of very good quality.

This type of viscometer is of great importance for hydraulic engineers who have to design pipelines. In fact, the data obtained with such a viscometer can be immediately used to scale up piping systems [45-50]. From Equations 16 through 19 the pipeline diameter and length can be directly computed for a given pressure drop at any chosen flow rate. Furthermore, in a capillary viscometer shear rates as high as 10^4 s^{-1} can be quite easily obtained and so the limiting behavior at high shear of the liquid of interest may be investigated.

In a continuous-flow apparatus (or recirculation test facility) at high shear rate the onset of turbulence can also be studied and the critical sedimentation velocity of the COM, i.e., the velocity in the turbulent regime beyond which settling of coal powder is greatly reduced, can be determined.

Capillary viscometers prove, therefore, very useful, but there are some drawbacks in their use. First of all, to reduce the influence of the end effects, the ratio L/D must be kept as large as possible [51]. Hence it may be difficult to accurately thermoregulate the fluid sample. Secondly, due to their large viscosity, COM liquids do not normally flow very fast under their own weight. Therefore, in

Table 2
Characteristic Equations of the Capillary Viscometer

Rheological model	Equation	Eq. #
Newtonian	$\dfrac{2V}{D} = \dfrac{8Q}{\pi D^3} = \dfrac{\tau_w}{4\eta}$	16
Plastic	$\dfrac{2V}{D} = \dfrac{8Q}{\pi D^3} = \dfrac{\tau_w}{4\eta_B} \left[1 - \dfrac{4\tau_0}{3\tau_w} + \dfrac{1}{3}\left(\dfrac{\tau_0}{\tau_w}\right)^4 \right]$	17
Power-law	$\dfrac{2V}{D} = \dfrac{8Q}{\pi D^3} = \dfrac{n}{3n+1}\left(\dfrac{\tau_w}{K}\right)^n$	18
gen. Herschel-Bulkley	$\dfrac{2V}{D} = \dfrac{8Q}{\pi D^3} = n\tau_w^{-3}\left(\dfrac{\tau_w - \tau_0}{K}\right)^{1/n}(\tau_w - \tau_0)$ $\times \left[\dfrac{(\tau_w - \tau_0)^2}{3n+1} + 2\tau_0 \dfrac{(\tau_w - \tau_0)}{2n+1} + \dfrac{\tau_0^2}{n+1} \right]$	19

Table 2. V = average fluid velocity, D = capillary diameter, Q = volumetric flowrate, τ_w = shear stress at the capillary walls, η = shear viscosity, η_B = plastic viscosity, τ_0 = yield stress, n = flow index, K = consistency factor.

order to achieve large shear rate values, pressure has to be applied to the liquid-free surface in the reservoir. This does complicate the device design, its thermoregulation, its use, and its maintenance.

Furthermore, in the pipe flow of particle dispersions, effects have been observed like the mechanical exclusion effect and the tubular pinch effect that lead to an effective fluid slip relative to the pipe walls. In fact, these effects result in a lower solid concentration in the fluid closest to the wall so that the volumetric flow rate is increased. Thus, the deduced viscosity turns out to be underestimated. To account for this effective slip several measurements should be made with capillaries of different diameter D but with the same aspect ratio L/D. This is, however, practically impossible and it is not normally done [52–69].

As a consequence of these facts, the capillary viscometer proves not to be a very versatile laboratory instrument. Although the information provided by it is very suitable for engineering applications, rotational viscometers are generally preferred for laboratory needs.

Rotating-Cylinder Viscometer

This viscometer essentially consists of two concentric cylinders. The outer hollow one contains the fluid in which the inner cylinder is immersed. In the first version of this viscometer the inner cylinder is suspended by means of a torsional wire. When the outer cylinder is set into rotation at an angular frequency Ω, the inner cylinder is rotated through an angle θ so that the torque M acting on it can be measured if the characteristics of the torsion wire are known. There have since been many variations on this design: now viscometers are available in which the inner cylinder is rotating and turns out to be the torque-sensing element at the same time (see Figure 5b) [69, 70].

Table 3 (Equations 20–23) reports the characteristic equations for the rotating-cylinder viscometer, obtained by assuming laminar flow, small Reynolds number, and by neglecting end effects corrections. The rheological parameters are obtained by plotting the measured angular frequency Ω versus the torque M applied to the inner cylinder.

This type of viscometer is very convenient for laboratory use because it is more versatile than capillary viscometers. In fact, rotating-cylinder viscometers are very compact, easy to thermoregulate, easy to control via microprocessor. The shear rate range may be easily varied by choosing cylinders of different radii. Moreover, there are commercial viscometers that ensure excellent performances. Rheometric data obtained with rotating-cylinder viscometers, although not immediately

Table 3
Characteristic Equations of the Concentric-Cylinders Viscometer

Rheological model	Equation	Eq. #
Newtonian	$\Omega = \dfrac{M}{4\pi h \eta R_i^2}\left[1 - \left(\dfrac{R_i}{R_e}\right)^2\right]$	20
Plastic	$\Omega = \dfrac{M}{4\pi h \eta_B R_i^2}\left[1 - \left(\dfrac{R_i}{R_e}\right)^2\right] + \dfrac{\tau_0}{\eta_B}\log\left(\dfrac{R_i}{R_e}\right)$	21
Power-law	$\Omega = \dfrac{n}{2}\left(\dfrac{M}{2\pi h K R_i^2}\right)^{1/n}\left[1 - \left(\dfrac{R_i}{R_e}\right)^{2/n}\right]$	22
gen. Herschel-Bulkley	$\Omega = \displaystyle\int_{R_i}^{R_e} r^{-1}\left(\dfrac{M}{2\pi h K r^2} - \dfrac{\tau_0}{K}\right)^{1/n} dr$	23

Table 3. Ω = angular frequency of the inner cylinder; M = torque applied to the inner cylinder; η = shear viscosity; h = immersion height of the inner cylinder; R_i and R_e = radius of the inner and outer cylinders, respectively; η_B = plastic viscosity; τ_0 = yield stress; n = flow index; K = consistency factor.

suitable for scaling up piping systems, can closely approximate industrial processes conditions. As a consequence of these facts, rotating-cylinder viscometers are most commonly used in COM laboratory practice.

Of course, these viscometers have some drawbacks. First, the accessible shear rate range is not as extended as for capillary viscometers. So, the limiting high shear behavior is not easily investigated. Secondly, rotating-cylinder viscometers are drastically affected by the phenomenon of settling. In fact, COM are more or less unstable solid dispersions. If the rheological measurements last for a time longer than the typical settling time of the dispersion (this may be the case for dispersions with a low viscosity suspending medium), settling significantly alters the rheometric results.

Most of the COM rheometric data, however, are obtained with this type of viscometers.

Rotational Cone-and-Plate Viscometer

Finally, we describe the last type of the most commonly used viscometers for measurements in the COM field [71].

In the cone-and-plate viscometer (see Figure 5c), a low angle inverted cone rotates against a flat plate with the liquid sample filling the space between them. If the angular frequency Ω of the rotating cone and the angle ϕ are so small that the non-linear terms in the Navier-Stokes equations can be neglected (we are implicitly assuming creeping flow conditions), and if also the end effects corrections are neglected, the fluid possesses only tangential velocity, v_θ, that linearly increases with the radius r from the center of rotation. The stream-lines lie in horizontal planes parallel to the plate. So, the shear rate turns out to be approximately constant:

$$\dot{\gamma} \approx \frac{\Omega}{\phi} \tag{24}$$

and the fundamental equation of this viscometer is:

$$M = \int_0^{2\pi} \int_0^R r^2 \tau_{\alpha\theta}\big|_{\alpha=\pi/2} \, d\theta \, dr \tag{25}$$

where $\tau_{\alpha\theta}|_{\alpha=\pi/2}$ is the stress acting on the plate surface and M is the torque acting on it. By inserting the proper constitutive equation in Equation 25, one gets the desired relation between the measured quantities Ω and M and the parameters of the rheological model.

This viscometer turns out to be quite versatile. Its most important feature is its extended shear rates-shear stresses range, much larger than that of a concentric-cylinder viscometer. Moreover, it is easy to thermoregulate, and end effect corrections can be made negligible. Unfortunately, for the particular application to COM dispersions, this viscometer presents two major drawbacks.

First of all, the largest particles in the dispersion are forbidden to fill the innermost part of the gap. Indeed, for an angle $\phi \approx \pi/180$ rad, particles larger than 52 μm are confined outside a region of radius ≈ 3 mm from the center of rotation. Since the granulometric distribution of the dispersed solid phase does influence the dispersion viscosity, incorrect results can be obtained. This drawback therefore has to be tackled in advance by using viscometers of suitable radius and aperture angle.

The second major drawback of this viscometer is due to its sensitivity to particles settling, like for the concentric-cylinder viscometer, since settling reduces the effective gap between cone and plate, giving incorrect results. (We recall that settling is not a major drawback for capillary viscometers, if the capillary radius is large enough, if the capillary is set vertically, and if the characteristic settling time is much larger than the characteristic shearing time $\dot{\gamma}^{-1}$). In any case, cone-and-plate viscometers are successfully used in the COM field.

Of the three types of viscometers just described, the concentric-cylinder viscometer is the most frequently used in laboratory testing of COM. Modified versions of this type, where a T-shaped bar is attached to the bottom of the rotating spindle in order to get qualitative information on the vertical concentration gradient and to test the consistency of an eventually present sedimentation bed, have been developed.

For bench scale and pilot plant testing, where, for instance, settling in high flowrate pipelines is of major concern, extrusion viscometers are preferred. Finally, for high accuracy measurements in both the low- and high-shear limits, with particular attention to presence of yield stresses, cone-and-plate viscometers are used.

COM RHEOLOGY

The following section describes the dependence of the parameters of the rheological models on the COM characteristics and on the physical conditions under which COM are tested.

COM Preparation

A Coal-Oil Mixture is obtained by adding a known amount of finely pulverized coal to a fuel oil so that a "homogeneous" mixture results. The fuel oils most commonly used as the liquid base for the mixtures are #2, #4, light #6, and heavy #6 of the standard A.S.T.M. classification scheme. The sulfur content of the oils may be high as well as low [72, 73].

The fuel oils, although some of them may contain a not negligible amount of particulate *per se*, do usually show the rheological behavior of Newtonian liquids in the full temperature range $25°C \leq T \leq 140°C$. (Deviations from a pure Newtonian behavior, if present at all, are shown in the low temperature region.) In the normal temperature range, the oil viscosity is well fitted by the Arrhenius law:

$$\eta = \eta_0 \exp(E^*/RT) \tag{26}$$

where $R = 8.31$ J/mol K is the gas constant, E^* is the activation energy, and η_0 is a constant independent of both T and E^*. The values for E^* are typically of the order of 10 kcal/mol. To get some feeling of the viscosity values of the different types of oils, it is useful to list some of them:

1. A.S.T.M. #2: $\eta \approx 12$ mPa·s at 25°C
2. A.S.T.M. #4: $\eta \approx 12$ mPa·s at 60°C
3. A.S.T.M. light #6: $\eta \approx 200$ mPa·s at 50°C
4. A.S.T.M. heavy #6: $\eta \approx 400$ mPa·s at 50°C

Seldom is the chemical composition of the fuel oils reported, and anyway it does not prove very useful to predict the rheological behavior of the resulting COM. In fact, albeit the chemico-physical nature of the oil is of primary importance in determining its interaction with the coal grains, the chemico-physical structure of the coal grain surface is so largely variable that it is tantalizing to try to find out any definite correlations between the rheology of the mixture and the chemical properties of the oil [74, 75]. On these grounds, from now on we will consider the oil just like a neutral fluid whose only function is to exert the buoyancy force necessary for the coal grains not to settle, to fix the low solid content limit of the mixture viscosity, and to determine to a great extent the heat content of the mixture.

Pulverized coal is obtained by milling processes [76–88]. Coal beneficiation processes, before and/or after milling, reduce the sulfur and ash content of coal. The most typical granulometric size distribution of the pulverized coal, i.e., the distribution of the grain sizes in the sample, is the "industrial granulometric distribution." For this typical distribution, 80% by weight of the coal particles have an equivalent diameter d less or equal to 74 μm. (The equivalent diameter is the diameter of a sphere having the same volume of the coal grain on hand.) It is customary to express the granulometric distribution in terms of the A.S.T.M. mesh. In the previous case it is said that 80% by weight of coal is classified through 200 mesh or, more simply, 80% − 200 mesh. In Figures 6 and 7 the percent differential and the percent cumulative undersize granulometric distributions of a standard industrial size coal, respectively, are shown.

The actual granulometric distribution does depend on the milling and sieving processes. Coal grains as large as 2 mm are occasionally found, but the upper limit of the granulometric distribution

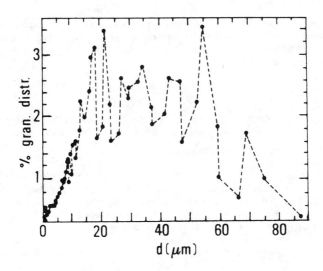

Figure 6. Percent differential granulometric distribution of a typical industrial coal powder.

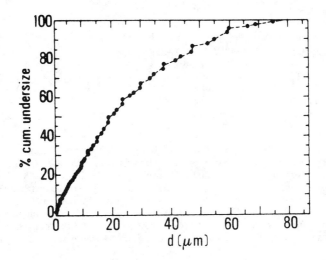

Figure 7. Percent cumulative undersize granulometric distribution of a typical industrial coal powder.

is normally in the range 200–300 μm. Sometimes, for special applications, fine or ultrafine coals are used: 100% by weight through 325 mesh or through 1,250 mesh, respectively (d ≤ 44 μm or d ≤ 10 μm) [89, 90].

For some special applications (e.g., to improve the packing conditions of the solid phase in the COM and to get a significant COM viscosity reduction for a given solid phase content), pulverized coals with multimodal granulometric distributions are used. These are characterized by the presence of several concentration maxima at different equivalent diameters. Such distributions are normally obtained by mixing monomodal coal fractions resulting from subsequent sieving procedures, and, therefore, their production is expensive. In Figures 8 and 9 the percent differential and cumulative undersize granulometric distributions of a bimodal ultrafine coal powder are shown.

Once a coal type and its granulometric distribution are chosen, the mixture with fuel oil is prepared by mixing (mechanically, ultrasonically . . .) them together. The coal concentration normally

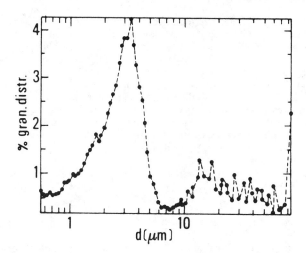

Figure 8. Percent differential granulometric distribution of a bimodal ultrafine coal powder. A sharp maximum is noted in the range 2–5 μm. A second, broader, and less intense one can be noted in the range 10–17 μm.

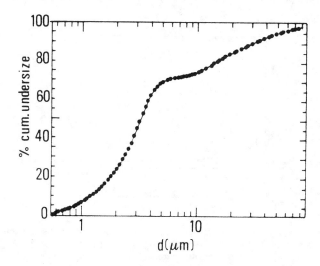

Figure 9. Percent cumulative undersize granulometric distribution of the same bimodal ultrafine coal powder as in Figure 8.

ranges between 10% and 60% by weight. Some additives are also used: surfactants, dispersants to inhibit coal particles clinging, thickeners, and so on. Water (in an amount of a few percent) may also be emulsionated to the oil in order to increase its base viscosity and to loose the coal sediment. As we shall see, such additivation processes do influence the rheology of the resulting mixture.

COM Rheological Properties

Rheological measurements are made on freshly prepared samples and on aged samples as well. In the former case, the COM properties are measured immediately after the preparation of the mixture. Settling phenomena are therefore neglected. In the latter case, however, the properties of mixtures stored for a known while under controlled conditions of temperature and stirring are studied [91]. By so doing, the time evolution of the COM properties may be adequately monitored. Moreover, such aged samples are normally taken at different heights of sedimentation columns so that the influence of settling on the COM rheological properties can be studied (see Figure 10).

The rheological measurements performed on freshly prepared samples as well as on aged ones indicate that the power-law model quite adequately fits the experimental data obtained when using both capillary and rotational viscometers. More sophisticated models, like the *Shangraw-Grim-Mattock* model [92] whose constitutive equation is:

$$\tau = \tau_0 + \eta_\infty \dot{\gamma} + (\tau_\infty - \tau_0)[1 - \exp(-\alpha\dot{\gamma})] \tag{27}$$

where τ_0 = yield stress

τ_∞, η_∞ = high-shear limit values of stress and viscosity

α = a characteristic time of the mixture

give much better fit of the data, but their use is suspicious because the adjustable parameters number is too large. The power-law model, on the contrary, gives satisfactory fit with the minimum number of adjustable parameters.

However, if measurements are carried out at quite low values of shear rate (say $\dot{\gamma} \approx 1 - 10\ \text{s}^{-1}$), researchers do preferentially fit the data with the Bingham plastic model. At low shear rates the solid particles are supposed to transmit the stress through the fluid acting like micropistons, and only at

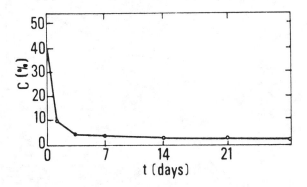

Figure 10. Time dependence of the coal concentration in the top part of a sedimentation column. The data are quite well fitted by a single decreasing exponential: $C \propto \exp -\Gamma t \cdot \Gamma^{-1}$ is the characteristics settling time. It ranges from some tens of minutes to some days depending on many factors, such as base oil viscosity, preparation, storage temperature. It normally turns out that $\Gamma^{-1} \gg \dot{\gamma}^{-1}$, so that viscosity measurements made with a vertically placed capillary viscometer are not substantially affected by settling.

higher shear rates should there be the onset of such relative motions of the particles that give origin to the pseudoplastic (shear thinning) behavior [93–95]. So, the true rheological model should probably incorporate both the limiting properties of a yield stress at low shear as well as a shear thinning behavior at high shear. This, however, would have the drawback of an increased analytical complexity.

The discrepancy in the choice of the rheological models, however, is also due to some experimental facts:

Poor accuracy of the measurements. At low shear the relative error in the stress measurement is larger than at higher shear. If one extrapolates the experimental rheograms down to zero shear rate, the error in the stress intercept may be substantial.

The apparent viscosity of COM. It is much larger (10 to 100 times) than that of pure fuel oils. Thus, the larger slope at low shear enhances the inaccuracy effects on the measurements by leading to an erroneous extrapolation of the yield stress. Continuous flow measurements in a very low shear rate range (say $\dot{\gamma} \approx 10^{-3} - 10^{-2}\,\text{s}^{-1}$) should be desirable, but they are not yet available.

Temperature effects. The thermal conductivity λ of COM is low (a typical figure is $\lambda \approx 0.23\,\text{Wm}^{-1}\,\text{K}^{-1}$.) The heat generated within the liquid by the viscous dissipation of the fluid kinetic energy is therefore poorly dissipated to the thermoregulating bath.

The heat generated in the unit volume by viscous dissipation in a Newtonian liquid is given by [96]:

$$\mathcal{W} \equiv -\dot{E}_k = \frac{1}{2}\eta\dot{\gamma}^2 \tag{28}$$

For highly viscous liquids like COM, and at high shear rates (typically those obtained in a capillary viscometer setup) this heat generation substantially increases the liquid temperature. (For $\eta \approx 0.1\,\text{Pa·s}$ at $\dot{\gamma} = 10^3\,\text{s}^{-1}$, $\mathcal{W} \approx 5 \times 10^4\,\text{Wm}^{-3}$.) The viscosity decreases following the Arrhenius law. The temperature increase may well be of the order of some degrees and the viscosity decrease $\Delta\eta/\eta$ is of some tens %. The net result is that the stress increases with the shear rate less than expected. The liquid therefore resembles a shear thinning liquid and its rheograms may lead to an incorrect yield stress extrapolation.

To conclude this section, it is worth emphasizing that in most of the situations the power-law model is the preferred one because of its larger analytical flexibility in order to fit the experimental rheograms.

Concentration Dependence

The rheological parameters of Coal-Oil Mixtures are greatly dependent on the concentration (by weight or by volume) of the dispersed solid phase. The apparent viscosity is a rapidly increasing function of the solid concentration. The analytical dependence on the concentration turns out to be stronger than exponential.

The first attempt to correlate the relative viscosity of a solid dispersion to the solid concentration was made by Einstein at the beginning of this century [97]. He found that for a very low volume concentration of particles the increase of the mixture viscosity relative to the viscosity of the suspending medium is a hydrodynamic effect. In fact, the fluid velocity field around each particle is largely affected by the particle itself. Assuming a particle volume concentration ϕ low enough to neglect mutual hydrodynamic interference, the suspension can be considered as a homogeneous liquid (on a length scale much larger than the particle dimensions) with an effective viscosity $\eta \neq \eta_0$, where η_0 is the viscosity of the pure liquid. The relative viscosity $\eta_r = \eta/\eta_0$ is given by the so-called Einstein equation:

$$\eta_r = 1 + 2.5\phi \tag{29}$$

Equation 29 is well satisfied only under the condition of very dilute concentration of small rigid spheres $\phi \leq 0.5\%$. (For non-spherical particles the coefficient 2.5 has to be changed accordingly, and, for instance, it has been calculated only for well-defined particle geometries: rods, ellipsoids, dumbbells). If the particle concentration is larger, there is an increasing overlap of the regions of perturbed fluid flow. Non-linear effects contribute then to the kinetic energy dissipation in the fluid, resulting in a further increase of the effective mixture viscosity, which, in turn, no longer depends linearly on ϕ.

Moreover, many other non-hydrodynamical interactions between particles, like electroviscous effects, are effective in influencing the viscosity of an actual mixture. Therefore, Equation 29 can hardly be used in the COM field where the concentration may range well over 20% by volume, where particles haven't got any simple geometrical form, and may be surrounded by an electrical double-layer. At higher than normal solid concentrations, in fact, many other effects and interactions have to be taken into account to describe the concentration dependence of COM.

In an intermediate concentration range, there may be formation of particle doublets, triplets, and so on with a consequent increase of the flow kinetic energy dissipation owing to the relative motions (like rotations) of the particles in such clusters and to particle collisions. At still higher concentrations, there is another energy dissipation mechanism due to the direct friction between particles when crowding is large.

Finally, at the close packing condition, where particles are in intimate contact with each other, the viscosity diverges [98–100]. (This fact corresponds to our intuitive picture that a solid cannot be sheared under normal conditions.) In Figure 11 the plastic viscosity η_B for a COM prepared with a monodispersed coal fraction with median diameter $d \leq 10 \ \mu m$, dispersed in heavy #6 oil is reported as a function of the weight solid concentration at different temperatures. The stronger-than-exponential growth of η_B with the weight concentration C is easily noted [101].

Many analytical formulas to describe the concentration dependence of the mixture relative viscosity have been developed on theoretical as well as empirical grounds. Some of them explicitly include a vertical asymptote for the viscosity at the concentration where particle close packing occurs. Other formulas, on the contrary, try to take into account the hydrodynamic effects of particle doublets formation and the noticeable rearrangement of particles in a highly concentrated sheared suspensions that is then proportional to the probability of a particle being moved from one shear plane to another.

A major drawback of the equations proposed in the literature is the omission of variables other than volume (or mass) fraction. Among the neglected variables are: shear rate, particle size distri-

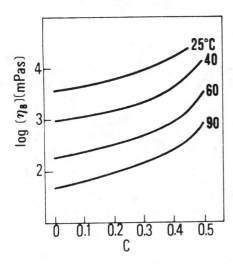

Figure 11. The plastic viscosity η_B of an ultrafine COM prepared by using heavy #6 oil is reported as a function of the solid weight concentration C at different temperatures [101]. η_B is a rapidly increasing function of C. In this logarithmic scale, the behavior of η_B is nearly parabolic. Similar plots are obtained for the consistency factor K of the power-law model.

bution, and several types of surface effects. These parameters are responsible for the discrepancies encountered in COM studies.

There are still other formulas that are derived for monodispersed suspensions and are therefore of relatively small help for COM. Furthermore, each of these formulas contains many adjustable parameters and is therefore of no practical use for engineering applications [102–104].

Very recently, a single adjustable parameter formula has been proposed [105] that reasonably well fits (to within 10–20%) the experimental apparent viscosity vs. concentration data in a concentration range up to 60% by weight at all temperatures. For the plastic viscosity such a formula yields:

$$\eta_B = \eta_0(T) \exp(AC^2) \tag{30}$$

where η_0 = the suspending medium viscosity at temperature T

         C = the concentration by weight of the solid phase

         A = a fitting parameter to be determined by least-squares analysis of the available data

For the consistency index K of the power-law model a similar formula holds true. Equation 30 has been successfully used to analyze literature data. Typical regression results obtained by using Equation 30 are reported in Figure 12.

The parameter A depends on the temperature T as well as on the granulometric distribution of the samples. In any case, its values are restricted to the range $10 \leq A \leq 18$. From an engineering point of view, such a formula proves to be very useful to give a first order evaluation of the viscosity of a COM. In fact, it is sufficient to assume a typical A value, say $A \approx 13$, and to know the base oil viscosity to reasonably well estimate the mixture viscosity without any more information about the properties of the solid phase of the mixture (granulometric distribution, and so on . . .). More refined calculations, however, need a more detailed knowledge of the dependence

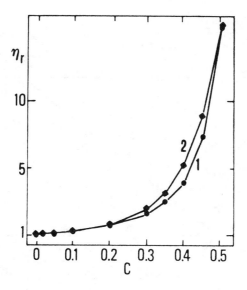

Figure 12. Typical regression analysis result obtained when using Equation 30 to fit the concentration dependence of the COM relative viscosity [105]. Curve 1 represents the experimental data (ultrafine COM with heavy #6 oil at $T = 70°C$) [101]. Curve 2 is the relative viscosity calculated by means of Equation 30 with $A \approx 10.9$.

of the parameter A on temperature and on the granulometric distribution of the pulverized coal [106–122].

A further, very important effect due to the solid concentration is that the amount of solids in the mixture determines, to some extent, the degree of "ideality" of the mixture itself. In other words, such parameters (like the yield stress in the Bingham plastic model or the flow index in the power-law one) do depend on the solid concentration in such a way that their low concentration limits tend to the appropriate values pertaining to the Newtonian model. Indeed, the yield stress τ_0 is such that $\lim_{C \to 0} \tau_0 \approx 0$ with $d\tau_0/dC > 0$, and the flow index has the property that $\lim_{C \to 0} n \approx 1$ with $dn/dC < 0$. It has been found [92] that the yield stress dependence on the solid volume concentration may be expressed by:

$$\tau_0 = \begin{cases} 0, & \text{for } \phi \leq \phi_0 \\ \mathscr{C}(\phi - \phi_0)^3, & \text{for } \phi > \phi_0 \end{cases} \tag{31}$$

where $\mathscr{C}$ is a system-dependent fitting parameter and ϕ_0 is the limiting volume fraction above which the rheological behavior of the system becomes plastic (Figure 13).

To explain this increase of non-ideality with the solid content of the mixtures, it is assumed that the probability for "network-like" structures to be formed increases at increasingly higher solid concentrations. The mechanisms that bring such networks to formation are several, mechanical as well as chemico-physical (colloidal forces, for instance). These network-like structures hinder the free flow of the fluid. To get the liquid flowing, it is therefore necessary to destroy them by applying a shear stress to the system. In such a model, the yield stress τ_0 is the minimum stress necessary to destroy those networks.

On the other hand, the flow index n in the power-law model shows a marked concentration dependence as well. Indeed, it has been found [123] that it is governed by the following equation:

$$n(C) = n_0 \exp(-aC) \tag{32}$$

where   C = weight fraction of solids
         a = fitting parameter
         n_0 = flow index for C = 0 (see Figure 14).

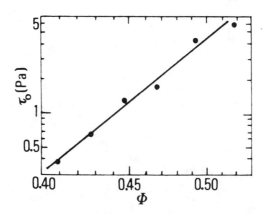

Figure 13. Relationship between the yield stress τ_0 in the generalized Herschel-Bulkley model vs. the coal volume fraction ϕ for a coal-Trimethylphosphate mixture at 25°C [92]. The yield stress is an increasing function of ϕ and is well fitted by Equation 31. Since τ_0 is related to the aggregation conditions of the particles in absence of shear, interparticle forces become progressively stronger at increasingly higher coal concentrations.

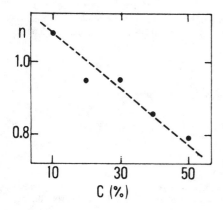

Figure 14. Flow index n vs. coal weight concentration at 100°C for a COM prepared using #6 oil and a coal with standard granulometric distribution [123]. The vertical scale is logarithmic: n depends exponentially on the coal concentration.

Incidentally, it may be observed from Figure 14 that $n_0 \neq 1$. This is ascribed to the particular coal granulometric distribution used. This is very broad in this case with a maximum equivalent diameter $d \approx 2$ mm.

The decrease of the flow index with the solid concentration is ascribed to particle clusters formation at high solid concentration. The liquid phase is entrained in these semi-macroscopic clusters and the particle velocities therein are strongly correlated. This has the consequence that the shear stress to be applied to the fluid to get a defined flow regime increases with the shear rate less rapidly than in a lower solid concentration mixture where particle velocity correlation is lower.

Granulometric Distribution Dependence

In addition to the very pronounced solid concentration dependence of the COM viscosity that may be thought of as a "first order effect," a "second order effect," still dependent on the solid phase characteristics, also affects the COM rheological properties. The granulometric size distribution of the solid phase is responsible for this effect.

It has been experimentally found [33, 124–127] that the finer uniform-sized particles in a bimodal suspension behave as a homoegeneous, uniform fluid toward the coarser particles. For small Reynolds numbers and for a diameter ratio of the two particle kinds larger than ≈ 10, the large spheres encounter a resistance to their motion passing through the suspension of finer particles, as when they pass through a pure liquid of the same viscosity and density as the suspension. The large diameter ratio ensures that the large and small spheres are non-interacting. The viscosity of the monomodal suspension is computed by using the Einstein formula (Equation 29), $\eta_r = 1 + 2.5\phi_1$, where η_r is the viscosity of the suspension relative to that of the suspending medium and ϕ_1 is the solid volume fraction of the fines.

By adding a third fraction of still larger spheres, one can consider the bimodal suspension as a homogeneous fluid, whose relative viscosity increase over that of the monomodal suspension is again calculated by exploiting Equation 29 using the concentration ϕ_2 of the fraction of the original coarser particles [128]. So the relative viscosity of the bimodal suspension to be used to calculate the effect of adding a third fraction of larger spheres is given by:

$$\eta_r = (1 + 2.5\phi_1) \cdot (1 + 2.5\phi_2) \tag{33}$$

By successively adding coarser fractions, each larger than the preceding one by a suitable factor, the calculation of the viscosity of the multicomponent distribution is easily done following the preceding scheme.

It is possible, and desirable, to minimize the resulting relative viscosity with respect to the volume fractions of the multicomponent distribution. It turns out that a minimum viscosity for a given multicomponent system is obtained if the concentration by volume of each granulometric fraction is independent of the diameter of the fraction itself. In mathematical words, it must result in an N-modal multicomponent system:

$$\phi_1 = \phi_2 = \cdots = \phi_N \tag{34}$$

where ϕ_j is the volume concentration of the jth component. ϕ_j is given by:

$$\phi_j = \frac{V_j}{\sum\limits_{k=0}^{j} V_k} \tag{35}$$

where V_k is the volume of the kth component and V_0 is that of the liquid phase [129–131].

Figure 15 shows how the use of multicomponent solid systems improves the concentration dependence of the relative viscosity of a mixture. The maximum viscosity reduction is clearly obtained by using an infinite-modal distribution where $\phi_j \to 0$ and the ratio between successive sphere diameters tends to 1.

It has also been shown [132] that the optimum granulometric size distribution that gives the maximum viscosity reduction for a fixed component number is such that the cumulative percent undersize distribution curve, Y, follows a power law curve of the type:

$$Y = kd^F \tag{36}$$

where k is a constant that depends on the upper diameter cutoff of the distribution, d is the coal grain equivalent diameter, and F is the power law exponent.

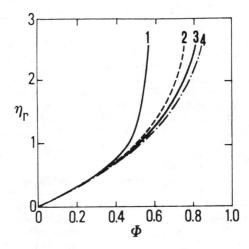

Figure 15. Dependence of the relative viscosity of a dispersion of rigid spheres on the disperse phase concentration for different granulometric distributions [128]. Curve 1: Monomodal distribution; Curve 2: Bimodal distribution; Curve 3: Trimodal distribution; Curve 4: ∞-modal distribution. The use of multimodal granulometric distributions allows one to obtain conditions of higher solids loading at fixed mixture viscosity or to obtain a mixture viscosity reduction at fixed solids concentration.

Such a power law results when the coal size distribution is self-similar. This happens if the solid fraction of the mixture is made up of the union of a number N of non-overlapping solid subfractions, each of which may be ideally obtained from the total solid fraction by operating a scale transformation, i.e., if it is made up of subfractions in which the grain dimensions form a geometrical progression. Starting with fines, coarser fractions are added in such a way that the amount of solid in each fraction is proportional to the amount of undersize already present. The proportionality factor is then the exponent F in Equation 36. By so doing, it results that the void fraction, v, decreases with F: $dv/dF > 0$. It can be shown that F is the fractal dimension of the void distribution [133]. In the limit of $F \rightarrow 0$, one gets a granulometric distribution that completely fills the space.

Several granulometric undersize curves following Equation 36 for different F values are shown in Figure 16. For $F > 1$, the granulometric distribution is relatively rich in larger particles and it is difficult to efficiently pack together large, nearly uniform-sized spheres: the void fraction is then large. For $F < 1$ the percentage of fines is relatively large and the fines can thus fill the voids between the larger particles. The packing condition improves as $F \rightarrow 0$. For $F = 0$ the granulometric distribution is composed by infinitesimal volume fractions $\phi_j \approx 0$, with $\phi_j \approx \phi_i$ for $i \neq j$, and with $d_j \approx d_i$ for $i \neq j$, up to an upper cutoff diameter [134]. Therefore, the granulometric distribution that maximizes the solid concentration in the mixture also improves the mixture viscosity.

The previous distributions are only theoretical ones. In the real world, however, things are not as simple. First of all, the coal grains are not spherical at all but have unpredictable shapes that depend on both coal nature and milling processes. Secondly, electrostatic and colloidal forces between particles inhibit a homogeneous mixing of the different granulometric fractions [134, 135].

Furthermore, milling and sieving costs are very high and, therefore, granulometric distributions with more than three components are practically never encountered. A very good viscosity reduction can be obtained by using an optimized bimodal granulometric distribution. The results obtained for a mixture in which only two coal fractions (with median diameter 37 and 14 μm,

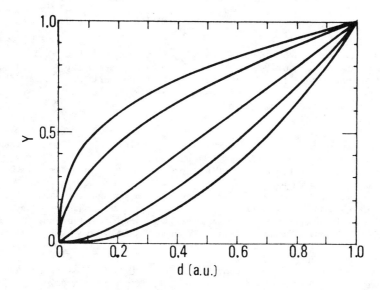

Figure 16. Percent undersize curves for self-similar granulometric distributions following the power-law equation, Equation 36 [132]. The exponent F for the various curves is (from the top) $F = \frac{1}{3}, \frac{1}{2}, 1, 1.5$, and 2.

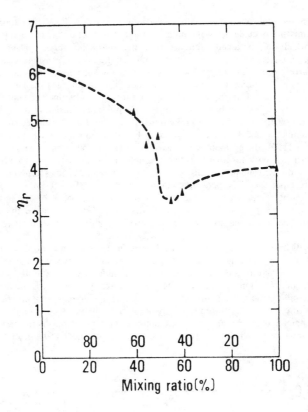

Figure 17. The relative viscosity at 80°C of a light #6 oil, 60% by weight COM, is reported as a function of the mixing ratio of two coal fractions of median diameter 37 and 14 μm, respectively (but with similar granulometric distribution slopes). It can be noted that a significant viscosity reduction of the mixture can be achieved using a bimodal distribution optimized with respect to the relative amount of the two coal fractions [136].

respectively) are mixed in different proportions are shown in Figure 17. Here is reported the dependence of the viscosity of a 60% by weight, bimodal coal-oil suspension on the mixing ratio of the two granulometric fractions. Note that the viscosity can be easily reduced by a factor of ≈2 by only optimizing the relative amounts of the two granulometric fractions [136].

The median size of the coal particles size distribution is also very important in determining the concentration dependence of the COM rheological parameters. If the median particle distribution diameter is small, the large amount of fine and ultrafine particles gives a substantial contribution to the relative viscosity of the mixture because of colloidal effects. For larger median diameters, the colloidal effect contribution becomes less influent with respect to other aforementioned effects (hydrodynamic, crowding, . . .) [137–140].

This median particle size effect is clearly shown in Figure 18 [136]. The relative viscosity of a COM prepared by using a Newtonian Light #6 oil and a standard boiler feed size coal is plotted here as a function of the median particle size at 60°C. The median size of the coal (80% − 200 mesh) is ≈37 μm. The particle distributions with smaller median diameters (27, 21, 14, and ≈9.5 μm, respectively) have been obtained by grinding the original coal for different residence times in such a way that the particle size distribution slope remained practically constant while the median size

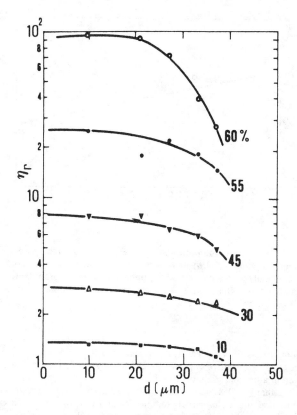

Figure 18. Relative viscosity at 60°C of a light #6 oil COM for several coal concentrations as a function of the median diameter of the coal granulometric distribution [136]. The granulometric distributions used have different median diameter but similar slope. COM prepared with coal granulometric distributions of large median diameter have lower viscosity than COM with smaller median diameter. This effect is more pronounced for the largest concentration COM, and it is ascribed to the lower influence of colloidal forces on particles of large dimensions.

decreased progressively. The decrease of the relative viscosity with the increase of the median size diameter is very striking, particularly for the most concentrated mixture (60% by weight).

A similar effect has been noted by analyzing the dependence of the fitting parameter A of Equation 30 as a function of the median size of the particle size distribution [105]. In Figure 19, A is plotted as a function of the median diameter. Although the data are quite scattered, it can be clearly seen that there is a trend for A to increase with decreasing median diameter size. This means that a COM made with a small median diameter granulometric distribution has a stronger concentration dependence than a COM prepared with a coarser granulometric distribution. This fact is explained by invoking that colloidal forces become more important as the median particle diameter decreases.

To conclude this section on the granulometric distribution effects on the COM rheological parameters, two more facts have to be put into evidence.

The first one is that a COM prepared with a narrow granulometric distribution is more ideal (i.e., it has a flow index closer to 1) than a COM prepared under the same conditions but with

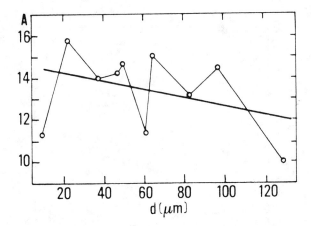

Figure 19. Dependence of the fitting parameter A of Equation 30 on the median granulometric size d of the dispersed phase [105]. A increases with decreasing d. This means that the concentration dependence of the relative viscosity is enhanced by using granulometric distributions with small median diameter. This is ascribed to the increasing influence of the colloidal forces as the particles size decreases.

a broader granulometric distribution. This fact is generally explained by assuming that in a narrow grain distribution COM the relative motions, which are responsible for pseudoplasticity, are less likely to onset than in a broader grain distribution.

The second fact is that a COM, whose median granulometric size is large, is more ideal (yield stress closer to 0 or flow index closer to 1) than a similar COM, whose granulometric distribution has the same slope as the first one but a smaller median diameter [136]. This behavior is clearly pictured in Figure 20, where the concentration dependence of the yield stress in a coal-based suspension is shown, and it may be attributed to the fact that the network structures that give origin to the plastic behavior are due to colloidal forces. If particles are large, the colloidal forces, whose intensity increases only with the square of the particle diameter, are overwhelmed by gravity, whose intensity grows with the third power of the particle diameter.

Temperature Dependence

The temperature dependence of COM viscosity closely resembles that of the base oils. In fact, both the viscosity of the oils and of the COM are well fitted by the Arrhenius law (Equation 26) where the temperature is expressed in degrees Kelvin and E* is the activation energy.

As is to be expected, the activation energy for a COM is slightly less than that of the oils because of the more massive coal particles. The concentration dependence of this activation energy is depicted in Figure 21. Clearly, as the concentration increases the COM viscosity becomes less and less temperature dependent.

On the other hand, the concentration dependence of the COM viscosity is enhanced by a temperature increase. Indeed, it has been found that the fitting parameter A of Equation 30 is such that $dA/dT > 0$: it increase with T. As the Brownian motion of the ultrafine particles (with diameter $d \leq 1$ m) is enhanced by an increase of T, energy dissipation is favored and the viscosity concentration dependence becomes stronger. In Figure 22 the A values for several COM are reported as a function of T. The different slopes of the curves may be attributed to the different granulometric composition of the solid phase [105].

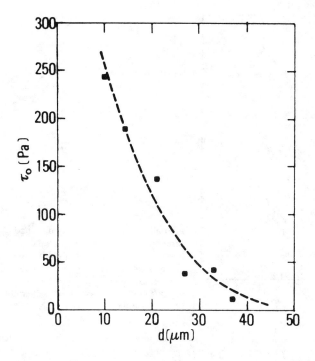

Figure 20. Yield stress of a light #6 oil, 60% concentration COM at 80°C as a function of the median diameter of the granulometric distribution [136]. The yield stress decreases with increasing median diameter as the result of the decreasing influence of the colloidal forces.

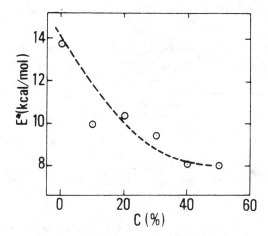

Figure 21. The concentration dependence of the activation energy E^* of COM viscosity. E^* decreases as the solid concentration increases. This means that the viscosity of highly loaded COM is less temperature dependent than that of low concentration COM [139, 140].

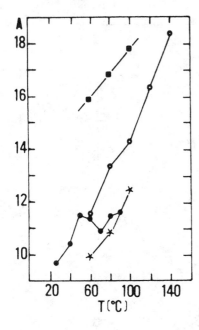

Figure 22. Temperature dependence of the fitting parameter A of Equation 30 for several COM. It turns out that dA/dT > 0; i.e., at high temperature the COM viscosity depends more on the solid concentration than it does at low temperature. The differences between the various curves are ascribed to the different granulometric distributions of the samples [105].

Finally, it has been found that at higher T each mixture behaves more ideally than at lower T. In Figure 23 the flow index n of the pure power-law model of a 50% by weight COM is reported as a function of the temperature. It can be noted that n tends towards 1 as T increases, i.e., to the Newtonian limit. Such a behavior is commonly shared among nearly every COM. This phenomenon has its origin in the decrease of the base oil viscosity with temperature. Indeed, it has been found that, at fixed concentration, particle size distribution, and temperature, COM based on low viscosity oils are more ideal than COM prepared with high viscosity oils.

Stability, Sedimentation, Thixotropy, Aging

In steam generation plants, where the boiler was designed to fire residual oil, COM are potentially attractive as short term means of reducing oil consumption because they can be pumped and

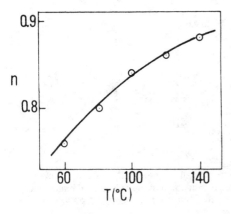

Figure 23. Dependence of the flow index n of the power law model on the temperature T. As T is increased, the flow index tends to 1. COM behave more ideally at high T than they do at low T [139, 140].

handled quite similarly to residual oil, so that no extensive capital expenditures are needed to modify the boiler design. A fundamental requirement for the commercial utilization of COM is that fuel of controlled composition and properties can be produced and delivered on the boiler demand. Unfortunately, the coal variable and heterogeneous nature, the complex nature of the oils and of the chemical additives used, result in a wide variety in type and structure of the COM.

Due to these differences, largely different COM behaviors result, which include rheological properties as well as aggregative and sedimentative stability. These characteristics have practical implications at all stages of COM preparation and handling.

Stability is the primary goal to be achieved for a mixture to be commercially attractive [141–143]. Stability quite generally means that the COM properties do not change during the course of time. In the COM field, distinction is made between sedimentative stability (related to the demixing of the denser solid phase from the lighter liquid phase under the action of the force of gravity) and aggregative stability (that is, related to the interparticle cohesion forces) [144].

COM stabilization techniques may be mechanical as well as chemico-physical [145] and in both cases they strongly influence the COM rheological properties. For this reason, a COM stability investigation is always (or, should always be) made in connection with a rheological study in order to ascertain how COM rheology is modified by stabilization procedures.

One way to obtain a sedimentative stable COM may be to use an ultrafine coal [146]. If the volume fraction of the particles in the micron and in the sub-micron range is large (we have then a *colloidal suspension*), the Brownian motion of the small particles partly inhibits the settling phenomenon. Such a COM, if endowed also with aggregative stability, turns out to be sedimentative-stable. However, ultrafine COM means large viscosity, high non-ideality, and high milling and sieving costs. For more traditional COM, i.e., those in which the coarse particles amount is substantial, sedimentation is not prevented at all by Brownian motion [147].

Sedimentative stability may be obtained by [148–150]:

Enhancing the suspension viscosity. The settling velocity is inversely proportional to the medium viscosity. If this is increased, the settling rate is consequently reduced. To obtain this, the mixture is additivated with "thickeners." On the other hand, a small amount of water (less than 5% by weight) can be emulsionated to the oil. The water-in-oil emulsions have larger viscosities than pure oils have.

To this end, the temperature of a mixture is also effective in preventing (or, in hastening) sedimentation. Indeed, because the COM viscosity is such that $d\eta/dT < 0$, one can store COM at lower temperatures, thus obtaining a reduction of the settling rate.

Increasing the dispersed solid concentration. The mixture viscosity also increases. Furthermore, there is the onset of the "hindered settling" regime, in which each particle offers a mechanical obstacle to the settling of the others [151, 152].

Extended flocs formation. By using suitable chemical additives, extended and loose flocs can be obtained [153]. Formation of these flocs is due to a weak particles aggregation. Then, flocs settle at a lower rate than single particles do because they have a smaller average density. However, there is no longer aggregative stability.

Sedimentation can be mechanically inhibited during pipelining, if the mean flow velocity exceeds a certain threshold velocity that lies well inside the turbulent flow regime. Beyond this threshold velocity, the turbulent eddies have enough energy to efficiently stir and rehomogenize the mixture [3, 154–160].

However, an absolute sedimentative stability is never reached. So, it becomes important to ascertain whether the sedimentation bed is "soft" enough to be easily redispersed. Floc settling gives origin to a relatively soft sedimentation bed. Flocs are, however, weak because of the weakness of the interactions originating them. So, they may be destroyed by compression under their own weight in the sedimentation bed. In any case, it turns out that COM must be endowed with a certain "amount" of aggregative stability. This has to be calibrated so that flocculation is not completely inhibited but, at the same time, it must be such that formation of too compact aggregates is prevented.

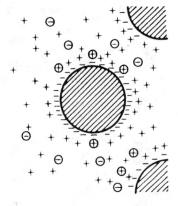

Figure 24. Electrical double-layer around negatively charged particles. The counter-ions are shown as +. $\oplus$ and $\ominus$ are stray ions due to dissolution of inorganic as well as organic matter of coal [161].

To impart aggregative stability to a mixture it is necessary that weak interparticle repulsive forces develop. To achieve this goal there are three basic mechanisms [150]:

A steric hindrance effect. This is due to chemical additives. These normally are organic macromolecules that are selectively absorbed onto the coal grain surface. Part of each organic macromolecule is extended into the liquid phase, forming a protective barrier that prevents clinging of the particles.

Formation of an electrical double-layer. One ion is preferentially adsorbed onto the coal grains and the counter-ions remain in the solution. An electrostatic repulsive force then develops between particles [161] (see Figure 24).

For this mechanism to be effective, a certain amount of water must be present in the mixture. The ions can be directly supplied by the coal grains (which have intrusions, for instance, of soluble inorganic salts), or can be supplied by adding suitable electrolytes to the mixture [162–164].

A preferential orientation of the dispersing medium molecules around the solid particles. This gives origin to solvation spheres around the coal grains.

Due to the interactions that may occur between the liquid media and the dispersed particles, one can pick out three extreme states of suspension of a powder in a single component liquid (for instance, coal in oil without water) as models for the description of an actual mixture [150].

The first type (type 1) is made up of particles which strongly repel each other (at least interacting through a hard-core potential). They retain their individuality and do not aggregate at all. Type 1 suspensions are sedimentative unstable and aggregative stable.

Type 2 suspensions consist of particles which give origin to a three-dimensional network as a result of weak interparticle interactions. The network formation hinders, or even prevents, settling. Thus, type 2 suspensions are sedimentative stable, but, strictly speaking, they are not aggregative stable. From a rheological point of view, network-like structures may give origin to plastic as well as to pseudoplastic behavior, depending on their relative weakness.

The third type of suspension (type 3) is made up of particles that irreversibly flocculate to form large aggregates. Type 3 suspensions are neither sedimentatively nor aggregatively stable. Intermediate suspension states also exist [150].

Weak particle interactions, as for type 2 suspensions, may not be desirable from a rheological standpoint. In fact, flocs may be disrupted under shearing action, but may form again in low shear regions. (For instance, the center of a pipeline is the region of minimum shear stress.) So, clogging may result in such regions. On the other hand, flocs may grow larger by trapping single particles. Or, conversely, flocs can achieve a critical dimension, beyond which they spontaneously break. So, a fluctuating rheological behavior may result.

To modify the interparticle interactions to some extent, and, hence the suspension type and the rheological behavior, addition of a second immiscible liquid is normally required [165, 166]. In coal-oil systems such immiscible liquid is usually water. The complexity of interactions is still larger, but some general parameters that govern the nature of the mixture have been identified [150]:

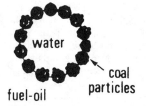

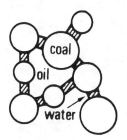

Figure 25. A possible configuration of a water-emulsionated COM. A large amount of small oleophilic particles is arranged at the interface of comparatively larger water droplets, that therefore cannot coalesce [145].

1. The "philicity" of the coal grains.
2. The relative amount of the two liquids.
3. The relative sizes of the emulsionated liquid droplets and the dispersed coal particles.

The "philicity" (oleophilicity/hydrophilicity) nature of the coal particles manifests itself in the relative wettability of the coal in presence of water and oil [167]. Many configurations of the system coal-oil-water may occur.

If the water droplets are large relative to some coal particles and if these are not completely wetted by either water or oil, then the coal particles arrange themselves at the droplet interface. So, they prevent droplet coalescence. If the coal particles are relatively more oleophilic, then the thickness of the layer formed by particles around the droplets is quite large. Thus, coalescence of droplets is better prevented. The settling behavior of particles then depends on that of the water droplets (Figure 25).

If coal particles are hydrophilic, water bridges link the particles. The bridging mechanisms depend on the relative size of particles and droplets and on the hydrophilicity of the coal particles. If these are relatively hydrophilic and larger than the droplets, then they are linked by small water arms. This produces a loose floc structure that is responsible for the plastic behavior of the COM (Figure 26).

On the other hand, if the particles are very hydrophilic and smaller than the droplets, then they may also be included in the water droplets. The configuration that minimizes the free energy of the system in this case is a tight agglomeration. The resulting rheological behavior is highly non-Newtonian, preferably of a power-law fluid. Furthermore, sedimentative stability is hardly achieved in this case [168] (Figure 27).

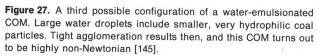

Figure 26. A second possible configuration of a water-emulsionated COM. Large, relatively hydrophilic coal particles are connected by water links. A loose floc structure is produced that endows this COM with yield stress and, perhaps, thixotropy [145].

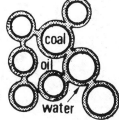

Figure 27. A third possible configuration of a water-emulsionated COM. Large water droplets include smaller, very hydrophilic coal particles. Tight agglomeration results then, and this COM turns out to be highly non-Newtonian [145].

To further modify structure and behavior of COM, surface active agents are added. A surfactant is normally composed of amphiphilic molecules that possess an oleophilic as well as a hydrophilic functional group. In absence of water the orientation of the molecules at the liquid/solid interface depends on the "philicity" of the solid particles. If the particles are more hydrophilic, the molecules of the surfactant are preferentially adsorbed onto the coal grains with the oleophilic group extending in the liquid phase. Particles then become more oleophilic; the resulting mixture is more stable against aggregation but not against settling.

On the other hand, if the particles are more oleophilic, the surfactant molecules are adsorbed onto the coal surface with the hydrophilic group extending into the liquid. The resulting free energy of the system is higher due to the large polarity gradient between particles and liquid [169]. To offset this free energy increase, a second process occurs that lowers the system free energy. It is assumed that the hydrophilic groups interact to form gel-like structures that impart sedimentative stability to the mixture. This is also associated with a rheological plastic behavior and may also give origin to thixotropic behavior.

If, finally, both surfactants and water are added to the suspension, the primary effect of the surfactant is to modify the particles' "philicity" by adsorption onto the coal grain surface. Then, the presence of water may induce bridging of the modified coal or may bring about formation of an emulsion. The emulsifying action of the surfactants themselves has to be further taken into account.

All the previously described phenomena influence the COM rheology. For instance, water bridging generally endows the mixture with a yield stress because the structure has to be destroyed in order to get the fluid flowing. Moreover, as soon as the shear stress is removed, water bridges form again. This fact results in thixotropic behavior of the sample [170].

In the case of an oil-water emulsion with the coal particles at the interface of the droplets, thixotropy turns out not to be important and the mixture is more fluid at low shear rates. The yield stress is therefore considered an indirect estimate of the particle interactions.

Very often COM samples are claimed to be thixotropic. Sometimes, this statement proves to be false because the typical reversibility of the thixotropic phenomenon is lacking. In this case the shearing action has permanently modified the flocs structure. Furthermore, the hysteretic behavior of the rheograms obtained with rotational viscometers may be due to inertial effects associated with their use under non steady-state conditions [41].

In mixtures with a large amount of water, the viscometer shearing action may induce water droplets to coalesce, giving origin to an erratic behavior of the rheograms because of large sample inhomogeneities and to sedimentative instability.

As we have seen, the complexity of the interactions between each component of a mixture is so large that the interpretation of the results and/or the prediction of a mixture to be produced is very

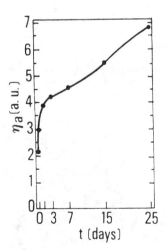

Figure 28. Time dependence of the viscosity of a 60% COM stored at 70°C. This COM is prepared with a coal of median granulometric size d ≈ 36 μm, and with #2 oil additivated with a small amount of tall oil (≈5% by weight). The rapid increase of the viscosity is mainly due to adsorption of the oil into the coal pores, so that the effective volume fraction of the solid phase is larger than the nominal one and the COM viscosity is increased according to the viscosity-concentration relationship [171].

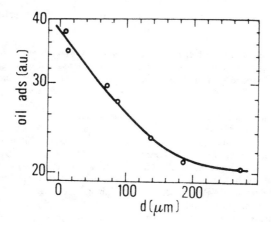

Figure 29. Oil adsorption in the coal pores as a function of the coal grain median diameter at fixed COM solid concentration. As the median granulometric size decreases, the surface area of the solid fraction increases. The pores number also increases and so does oil adsorption [171].

difficult, if not impossible. Each type of coal, even coals of the same rank, have to be treated separately in order to obtain the desired rheological properties and the necessary stability.

To further distress and tantalize COM researchers, COM properties are time-dependent. The coal surface is modified by exposure to free air, so that a surfactant, successfully used with a freshly crushed coal, may prove ineffective with the same coal some days after crushing. The COM rheological properties are also time-dependent. Once a COM is prepared with the proper choice of composition, additives, and so on, even if it should prove perfectly stable against sedimentation and aggregation, its viscosity usually increases with time (see Figure 28). This is due to the fact that oil is progressively adsorbed into the myriad of microscopic pores that are in the coal grains. Such an effect is more pronounced as the mean particle diameter decreases (see Figure 29). By so doing, the effective volume concentration of solid increases and so does the sample viscosity [171].

COAL-WATER MIXTURES

Over the past few years, more attention has been paid to water-based coal liquid fuels. At the very beginning, coal-water mixtures (CWM) were designed to solve the problem of coal powder transportation by pipelining. A CWM is potentially attractive to this end because of the much lower water viscosity relative to that of fuel oils. Indeed, water viscosity is $\approx 10^{-3}$ Pa·s at room temperature. However, if the viscosity of the suspending medium is low, there is the drawback that the settling phenomenon is very pronounced. On the other hand, it would be desirable to directly fire the mixture in boilers without having to transport, to extract, and to waste large amounts of water [172–176].

For both applications (transport and combustion) there is the need to minimize the water content of the mixture, since in the case of direct combustion, energy is lost as latent heat of evaporation and the combustion flame turns out to be unstable. In the case of pipelining, water may be scarce at the preparation plant site, separation of excess water from the mixture at the pipeline terminus is expensive, disposal of excess water poses serious environmental problems, and transportation of this inert material adds to pumping costs [177].

As a first order solution to both problems, the coal content in a CWM has been progressively increased (it is now in the 70%-by-weight range) and flammable liquids (typically, methanol) have been used in connection with or in place of water.

The low viscosity of the suspending medium and the exceptionally high coal concentration have magnified all the problems, and have exaggerated all the phenomena related to the stability and rheology of the COM.

There are several reasons for the higher complexity of the CWM mixtures. First of all, there is the heterogeneous nature of coal, which includes carbonaceous matter as well as inorganic, partly water-soluble matter [178]. Second, is the high solids concentration. (It is worth recalling that coal powder exposed to free air may contain more than 25% by weight of adsorbed water and still remains a moist powder—it is not a liquid!)

In this situation the coal particles are so close together that interparticle forces (hydrodynamic as well as colloidal) are of primary importance in determining CWM stability and rheology. It is of vital importance to use additives that control the relative balance of repulsive and attractive forces, and, hence, the degree and type of flocculation [179, 180]. And it is very important to use additives that cover the coal grain surface with a polymeric film, in order to close the myriad of microscopic pores in which the liquid phase may become adsorbed. In Table 4 the factors affecting the rheology and stability of CWM are schematically summarized.

The procedure to obtain a slurryable CWM is more complicated than for a COM. Each step of the preparation process (crushing, drying, sieving, . . .) has to be optimized. Beneficiation of coal is necessary to lower its specific gravity and to reduce the amount of inorganic water-soluble salts included in the coal. Wet-milling is necessary to facilitate the contacting of coal with additives. Use of multimodal particle size distributions (at least, of an optimized bimodal one as shown in Figures 8 and 9) in order to achieve high loading conditions cannot be given up.

Use of chemical additives is of overwhelming importance. A dispersant is needed to provide reduction of the surface tension between the hydrophobic coal surface and water to allow particles to be wetted and brought into suspension [181]. Settling may be reduced by adding amphiphilic surface active agents that form gel-like structures showing a yield stress and that increase the CWM viscosity. Ionic additives are then added to control the surface charge on the dispersed solid particles. This allows partial determination of the particles packing conditions, to control the collision rate of particles during shearing and hence the viscosity.

Soluble components from mineral matter in coal form acidic solutions in contact with water. To reduce pipeline corrosion, neutralizing agents have to be added that, in turn, control the particle surface charge by modifying the pH of the solution [182].

A second miscible and flammable liquid like methanol can be added to water in order to increase the caloric content of the mixture and to reduce the freezing temperature of the liquid phase. This is a natural choice if coal mines are located in the arctic regions. This liquid may also solve the problem of water scarcity and disposal.

As a consequence of these facts this issue is very complex, and still controversial. We may only quote some general observations.

As a combined effect of the high solid concentration and of the use of additives (dispersing agents as well as gel-like structures forming agents) CWM turn out to be highly non-Newtonian fluids. Their apparent viscosity is a rapidly decreasing function of the shear rate. They possess large yield stress values.

It is considered [183] that the observed differences in their rheological properties and, particularly, in the yield stress values are due to differences in the coal structure. Low rank coals contain a lot of oxygen, so that their surface is highly hydrophilic. Their surface is easily hydrated and spontaneously wetted by water and a hydration shell is formed around each particles. These shells generate gel-network structures because of hydrogen bonding. These structures develop very rapidly and are responsible for the time-independent yield stresses.

On the other hand, high rank coals are richer in carbonaceous matter and therefore the coal surface is more hydrophobic and not spontaneously wetted by water. To disperse such coals, anionic surfactants are commonly used. They increase the surface charge of the particles rather than wetting them by reducing surface tension. No hydration shells are formed and a gel structure is not readily obtained. Such a structure results as a consequence of electrostatic interactions between particles and develops at a much slower rate. This should give origin to a time-dependent yield stress.

The preferred rheological models are the Bingham plastic and the generalized Herschel-Bulkley. If the Bingham plastic model is adopted, large yield stress values result (in the range of tens of Pa). If the pure power-law model is adopted, the flow index usually lies in the range $0.15 < n < 0.6$,

Table 4
Factors Influencing CWM Rheology and Stability

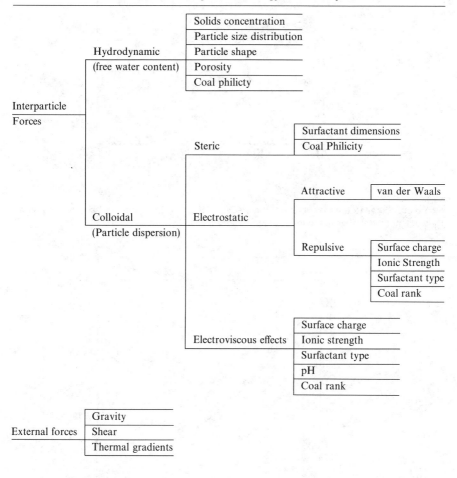

	Hydrodynamic (free water content)	Solids concentration	
		Particle size distribution	
		Particle shape	
		Porosity	
		Coal philicty	
Interparticle Forces		Steric	Surfactant dimensions
			Coal Philicity
	Colloidal (Particle dispersion)	Electrostatic	Attractive — van der Waals
			Repulsive — Surface charge
			Ionic Strength
			Surfactant type
			Coal rank
		Electroviscous effects	Surface charge
			Ionic strength
			Surfactant type
			pH
			Coal rank
External forces	Gravity		
	Shear		
	Thermal gradients		

i.e., in the highly shear thinning behavior region. It also happens that sometimes the apparent viscosity of a sample cannot be fitted at all by one of the simple models previously described (see Figure 30) [184].

Thixotropy (but also rheopexy) is exhibited by CWM because of the gel-structures obtained by using certain additives. However, thixotropy has been claimed as a consequence of the hysteretic loop in non steady-state rheograms obtained with rotational viscometers. Therefore, one must be suspicious of this claim. Reversible gel-sol transition has been detected only in methanol-rich coal-water-methanol mixtures at very low temperatures (T $\leq$ −30°C), during steady-state measurements with a rotating-cylinder viscometer [185].

The CWM viscosity is strongly dependent on the amount of water that is free and able to "lubricate" the coal particles [186]. It is considered that water contained in CWM (i.e., the total water content) is composed of free water and hygroscopic water (i.e., water absorbed in the pulverized coal). For a fixed coal and total water concentration, it is found that the apparent CWM viscosity is a decreasing function of the free water content, as is shown in Figure 31. Conversely, the apparent

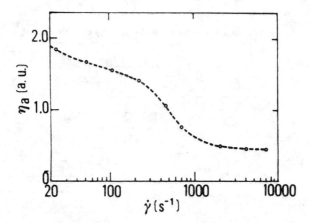

Figure 30. Shear rate dependence of the viscosity of a CWM that cannot be fitted to a single rheological model over the whole range of shear rates [184].

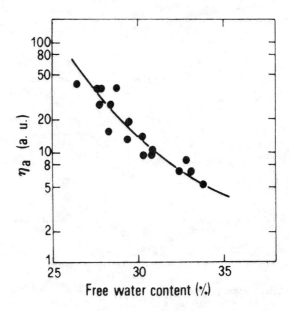

Figure 31. Dependence of the apparent viscosity η_a of a CWM on the free water content of the mixture. The free water content is the amount of water available to "lubricate" the coal particles. Inasmuch as the free water content equals the mixture total water content (i.e., the amount of water absorbed into the pores of the coal particles is negligible), the free water content dependence of η_a is symmetrical to its solid concentration dependence. In fact, as the free water content increases, the solids concentration decreases by the same amount and consequently does η_a, according to the viscosity-solid concentration relationship [186].

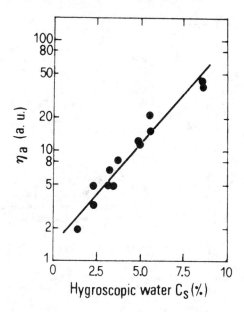

Figure 32. Dependence of the apparent viscosity η_a of a CWM on the hygroscopic water content at fixed total water content of the mixture. Hygroscopic water is practically the amount of water adsorbed into the pores of the coal particles. Its amount is determined by recording the weight loss of coal dried under controlled conditions. The higher the hygroscopic water content, the lower is the free water content and the higher the viscosity. This turns out to exponentially increase with the hygroscopic water content of the CWM [186].

viscosity is an increasing function of the hygroscopic water content as determined by the weight loss of coals dried at 100° after a fixed storage time under controlled temperature and humidity conditions. This case is depicted in Figure 32. The explanation of this fact is self-evident [186].

The coal concentration dependence of the CWM viscosity does not show any qualitative difference from that of COM and it deserves no further comments.

All other parameters being fixed, CWM viscosity depends on the pH of the suspension: the higher the pH, the lower the viscosity [187–189]. This situation is pictured in Figures 33 and 34. It is well known that the pH of the liquid phase controls the adsorption of charged hydroxo complexes onto the dispersed particle surface. The surface charge gets more negative the higher the pH. It has been found that the minimum viscosity is obtained for large and negative ζ-potential values at low ionic strength of the solution. If the electro-kinetic potential ζ is large and the ionic strength of the solution is not too high, the spatial extension of the electrical double-layer around the particles is quite large [190–195]. In this case, there are two competing effects on the CWM apparent viscosity.

First is the hydrodynamic interaction between particles due to the overlap and relative motion of their adjacent electrical double-layers that tends to increase the mixture viscosity. Second is the increased dispersion degree of the particles due to the large repulsive forces between them because of the extended double-layers. The net result is a decrease of the viscosity [187]. Acidic pH does not show such a viscosity reduction because in this case there are no charged hydroxo complexes to be preferentially adsorbed onto the coal surface. The mechanism of viscosity reduction has the drawback that it also reduces the sedimentative stability of CWM.

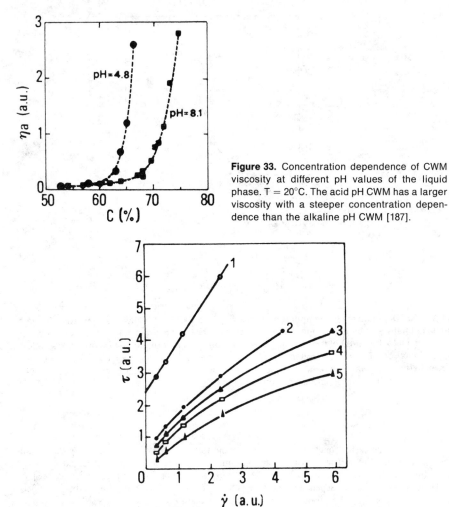

Figure 33. Concentration dependence of CWM viscosity at different pH values of the liquid phase. T = 20°C. The acid pH CWM has a larger viscosity with a steeper concentration dependence than the alkaline pH CWM [187].

Figure 34. Schematic rheograms of 50% coal-water slurries (with 2.5% of gel additive) showing the viscosity reduction effect of different alkaline additives at fairly similar pH values (pH ≈ 7.5–8.5). Rheogram 1: Untreated sample; Rheogram 2: $(NH_4)_2CO_3$; Rheogram 3: Na_3PO_4; Rheogram 4: NaOH; Rheogram 5: Na_2CO_3; (The amount of additives is of the order of 0.1% by weight.) This figure clearly shows that different types of cations have different viscosity reduction capabilities [188].

If the ionic strength is increased beyond a critical concentration that depends on the electrolyte type (and therefore on the cation valence), there is a progressive reduction of the electrical double-layer spatial extension. The hydrodynamic interparticle interaction due to the overlap of the double-layers is similarly reduced, but there is also a drastic reduction of the interparticle repulsive forces, so that their effect in redispersing particles is largely reduced. In this case, the apparent viscosity of a CWM increases rapidly with the electrolyte concentration [187] (Figure 35).

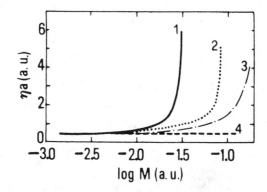

Figure 35. Cations concentration M and cations valence effect on the viscosity of a 71% solid concentration by weight CWM at 20°C.

Curve 1: $AlCl_3$ at pH = 8.1 anionic   dispersant
Curve 2: $CaCl_2$ at pH = 8.1 anionic   dispersant
Curve 3: HCl   at pH = 8.1 anionic   dispersant
Curve 4: $CaCl_2$ at pH = 2.2 non-ionic dispersant

The rapid increase of the CWM viscosity after a threshold electrolyte concentration value is exceeded is due to the large spatial reduction of the electrical double-layer because of the dissolved cations. The coal particles of CWM described by curves 1, 2, and 3 are negatively charged mainly by dissociation of the anionic dispersant adsorbed on the coal particles. The higher the cation valence, the lower the threshold electrolyte concentration at which the surface charge is efficiently screened and the double-layer extension is reduced. No such effect is detected for CWM #4 for which a non-ionic dispersant was used, so that the coal particles are not negatively charged [187].

The pH of the liquid phase and the electrolyte type also influence the solid concentration dependence of the CWM viscosity. At fixed pH, the viscosity of a CWM is lower (and its dependence on the coal concentration is weaker) when an electrolyte is used that upon dissociation supplies OH^- ions. In fact, OH^- ions are preferentially adsorbed onto the coal surface and, therefore, both the surface charge and the ζ potential magnitude increase. In Figure 36 the apparent viscosity of three CWM is reported as a function of the coal concentration for different pH and electrolyte-types conditions. The high-pH CWM has the lowest viscosity. Between the two CWM with acidic pH values, the one additivated with an OH^- containing electrolyte, although it has a lower pH, has the lower viscosity [187].

Furthermore, the pH of the liquid phase influences the CWM viscosity by controlling the degree of dissolution of the coal mineral matter and, hence, the ionic strength of the solution. At low pH, relatively large amounts of metal ions are dissolved. In this way, the extension of the double-layer is reduced and a larger viscosity results. Reduction of the viscosity may be achieved by adjusting the pH of the suspension by addition of selected electrolytes. However, it is reported that pH adjustments may induce changes in the time-dependent rheological behavior of CWM, i.e., from rheopectic to thixotropic [187].

Complete, or partial, substitution of water with flammable liquids introduces yet another variable. Methanol is the most popular flammable liquid used because it may be directly produced by coal liquefaction processes, it can be easily recovered after transportation, and it may be used at the pipeline terminus as raw material to produce fine chemicals. Furthermore, methanol-addicted CWM may be fired without any further modifications [196].

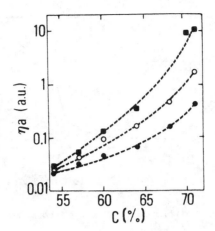

Figure 36. Concentration dependence of CWM viscosity for different pH values of the liquid phase. The lowest curve represents the viscosity of a CWM with alkaline pH ≈ 8. Alkaline pH favors adsorption of negative hydroxo complexes onto the coal surface that becomes negatively charged. Then, electrostatic repulsion between particles improves the dispersion conditions and lowers the viscosity. The middle curve shows the viscosity concentration dependence of a CWM with acid pH ≈ 4.2 obtained by adding CH_3COOH as an electrolyte, while the uppermost curve is for a CWM with acid pH ≈ 4.6, obtained by addition of $AlCl_3$. Albeit the CWM represented by the middle curve has a more acid pH than the uppermost one, its coal surface is more negatively charged because CH_3COOH, upon dissociation, supplies OH^- ions that are preferentially adsorbed on the coal grains. So, its particles are better dispersed because of electrostatic repulsion, and its viscosity turns out to be smaller [187].

Methanol viscosity is ≈ 2 times smaller than water viscosity, but the viscosity of a mixture of them has a maximum of $\approx 1.8 \times 10^{-3}$ Pa·s at 20°C and at a methanol concentration of $\approx 40\%$ by weight. However, the freezing point of a methanol-water mixture is lowered well below 0°C. A 70% coal concentration by weight CWM, whose liquid phase is a 20% by weight of methanol-in-water mixture, freezes at ≈ -13°C. A similar CWM, but with a liquid phase containing 40% of methanol, freezes at ≈ -35°C.

Use of methanol-in-water mixtures evidently makes easier transport operation in the arctic regions. Unfortunately, methanol is not inert against coal particles. Indeed, for low rank coals a relatively high heat of wetting has been experimentally put into evidence [197, 198]. As a consequence, selection of the most suitable additives and prediction of the rheological properties of a coal-water-methanol mixture turn out to be still more complicated. Despite the aforementioned difficulties, research on CWM (with or without methanol) is flourishing and good commercial products are already available on the market.

CONCLUSION

COM and CWM rheology is a very intricate cross-disciplinary issue. Some general properties of such mixtures have been deduced from experiments. The role of the chemical and physical parameters has been clarified to a large extent. Semi-quantitative predictions of the rheological behavior of a mixture are now possible.

Unfortunately, the complex interactions between the solid coal surface and the suspending medium (including additives) and the heterogeneous nature of coal complicate the matter, so that detailed study and characterization of coal systems are needed.

A great deal of basic work is still necessary to better characterize the mixtures and to develop predictive tools for their rheological behavior. Computer simulation studies of the transport coefficients of mixtures of hard spheres of different diameters should help predict how the granulometric distribution influences the rheological behavior of an actual mixture [199].

Rheometric measurements in the high- and low-shear limit, in steady-state as well as under oscillating shear should give valuable information to be compared with computer simulation and generalized hydrodynamic data. Ultrasonic attenuation measurements should also help in investigating interparticle interactions.

From a chemical point of view, the investigation and characterization of the coal grain surface by means of more sophisticated techniques (LEED, ESCA, AUGER, ...) should be implemented in order to get a more detailed knowledge of the coal surface chemistry and its time-dependence, and to better predict the action of different types of additives.

Moreover, studies on coal beneficiation processes should be encouraged and developed to a very high degree, not only because they influence the coal properties, but also because the use of coal-based liquid mixtures has a strong environmental impact.

These time-consuming efforts are both necessary from a commercial point of view and fruitful for the improvement and deepening of scientific and engineering knowledge.

Acknowledgments

The author is indebted to Dr. G. Torzo for critical reading of the manuscript. Thanks are moreover due to Mr. A. Rampazzo of the Padua Division of the Natl. Inst. for Nuclear Physics for the drawings, and to Mr. F. Calvi and Ing. P. Iwanski of Eniricerche for help in updating the references.

REFERENCES

1. Anonym, "Coal-slurry, a New Commodity?," *Mining Eng.*, January 1962, p. 48.
2. Vogel, J. C., and Quass, F. W., "Preliminary Studies of Coal-in-Oil Suspensions," *J. Chem. Met. Min. Soc. of South Africa, 1*, 262 (1941).
3. Wasp, E. J., Kenny, J. P., and Gandhi, R. L., *Solid-Liquid Flow-Slurry Pipeline Transportation* (TransTech Publications, Switzerland, 1977).
4. Berkowitz, N., Moreland, C., and Round, G. F., "The Pipeline Flow of Coal-in-Oil Suspensions," *Can. J. Chem. Eng., 41*, 116 (1963).
5. Elliot, D. E., and Gliddon, B. J., "Hydraulic Transport of Coal at High Concentrations," *Hydro-Transport* 1, I Int. Conf. on the hydraulic transport of solids in pipes, paper G2 (London, 1970).
6. Sharp, A. N., and Gas, E., "Coal by Pipeline," *Coke Gas, 23*, 336 (1961).
7. Roberts, R. N., "Pipelines for Process Slurries," *Chem. Eng., 14*, 125 (1967).
8. Moreland, C., "Viscosity of Suspensions of Coal in Mineral Oil," *Can. J. Chem. Eng., 41*, 24 (1963).
9. Thomas, D. G., "Non-Newtonian Suspensions. Physical Properties and Laminar Transport Characteristics," *Ind. Eng. Chem., 55*(11), 18 (1963).
10. Thomas, D. G., "Non-Newtonian Suspensions. Turbulent Transport Characteristics," *Ind. Eng. Chem., 55*(12), 28 (1963).
11. Skelland, A. H. P., *Non-Newtonian Flow and Heat Transfer*, (J. Wiley and S. Inc., New York 1967).
12. Shaheen, E. I., "Rheological Studies of Viscosities and Pipeline Flow of Concentrated Slurries," *Powder Technology, 5*, 245 (1971/72).
13. Ellis, H. S., P. J. Redberger, and L. H. Bolt, "Transporting Solid Slurries. Basic Principles and Power Requirements," *Ind. Eng. Chem., 55*(8), 18 (1963).
14. Smith, S. R., et al., "Investigation of Coal-Oil Mixtures as Utility Boiler Light-Off Fuel," Proc. II Int. Symp. on Coal-Oil Mixtures Combustion, Danvers (MA), 27–29 Nov. 1979, Ed. Pittsburgh Energy and Technology Center (PETC, 1980), vol. I.
15. Dooher, J. P., et al., "Feasibility Study of Using a Coal/Oil/Water Emulsion and Coal/Oil Mixtures as Clean Liquid Fuels," Proc. II Int. Symp. on Coal-Oil Mixtures Combustion, (PETC, 1980), vol. II.

16. Miyazaki, T., et al., "Utilization of Fine Coal-Oil Mixtures (COM) for Injection to Blast Furnaces (Injection to Experimental Blast Furnace)," ibid., vol. I.

17. Bird, R. B., Stewart, W. E., Lightfoot, E. N., *Transport Phenomena*, chap. 1, pp. 12–27, (J. Wiley & S., Inc. New York, 1960).

18. Landau, L., Lifsits, E. M., *Mecanique des Fluides*, chap. 2, pp. 62–124, (MIR, Moscou, 1971).

19. *Encyclopaedic Dictionary of Physics*, pp. 643–648 (Pergamon Press, Oxford, 1962).

20. Pierce, P. E., and Schoff, C. K., "Rheological Measurements," in Kirk-Othmer *Encyclopedia of Chemical Technology*, Vol. 20, p. 259 (J. Wiley & S., New York, 1982).

21. Jinescu, V. V., "The Rheology of Suspensions," *Int. Chem. Eng.*, *14*(3), 397 (1974).

22. Alessandrini, A., Lapasin, R., and Torriano, G., "Rheological Properties of Coal Suspensions," Proc. II Conference of European Rheologists, Prague, June 17–20, 1986.

23. Szymanski, J. K., and Mansour, N. A., "Rheological Transient Model of Dense Coal/Water Suspensions," Proc. VII International Symposium on Coal Slurry Fuels Preparation and Utilization, May 21–24, 1985, New Orleans, ed. Pittsburgh Energy and Technology Center (PETC, 1985).

24. Frisch, H. L., and Simha, R., "The Viscosity of Colloidal Suspensions and Macromolecular Solutions," *Rheology*, ed. F. R. Eirich, vol. 1, p. 525, (Academic Press, New York, 1956).

25. Darby, R., "Rheological Properties of Methacoal Suspensions Formulated from Texas Lignite," Final Report to DoE (PETC), August 1979.

26. Papenhuijzen, J. M. P., "The Role of Particle Interactions in the Rheology of Dispersed Systems," *Rheol. Acta*, *11*, 73 (1972).

27. Ackermann, N. L., and Shen, H. T., "Rheological Characteristics of Solid-Liquid Mixtures," *AIChE Journal*, *25*(2), 327 (1979).

28. Krieger, I. M., "Rheology of Monodisperse Lattices," *Advances in Colloid and Interface Sci.*, *3*, 111 (1972).

29. Van der Poel, C., "On the Rheology of Concentrated Dispersions," *Rheol. Acta*, *1*(2–3), 198 (1958).

30. Quemada, D., "Rheology of Concentrated Disperse Systems and Minimum Energy Dissipation Principle. II. A Model for Non-Newtonian Shear Viscosity in Steady Flows," *Rheol. Acta*, *17*, 632 (1978).

31. Quemada, D., "Rheology of Concentrated Disperse Systems and Minimum Energy Dissipation Principle. III. General Features of the Proposed Non-Newtonian Model. Comparison with Experimental Data," *Rheol. Acta*, *17*, 643 (1978).

32. Thomas, D. G., "Heat and Momentum Transport Characteristics of Non-Newtonian Aqueous Thorium Oxide Suspensions," *AIChE Journal*, *6*(4), 631 (1960).

33. Fidleris, V., and Whitmore, R. L., "The Physical Interaction of Spherical Particles in Suspensions," *Rheol. Acta*, *1*(4–6), 573 (1961).

34. Churchill, St. W., and Churchill, R. U., "A General Model for the Effective Viscosity of Pseudoplastic and Dilatant Fluids," *Rheol. Acta*, 14, 404 (1975).

35. Takano, M., Goldsmith, H. L., and Mason, S. G., "The Flow of Suspension through Tubes. VII. Rotation and Deformation of Particles in Pulsatile Flow," *J. Colloid Interface Sci.*, 23, 248 (1965).

36. Blair, G. W. Scott, "An Equation for the Flow of Blood, Plasma and Serum through Glass Capillaries," *Nature*, *183*, 613 (1959).

37. Krieger, I. M., and Dougherty, T. J., "A Mechanism for Non-Newtonian Flow in Suspensions of Rigid Spheres," *Trans. Soc. Rheol.*, *3*, 137 (1959).

38. Maron, S. H., Fok, S. M., "Rheology of Synthetic Latex. V. Flow Behavior of Low-Temperature GR-S Latex," *J. Colloid Sci.*, *10*, 482 (1961).

39. Brown, J. P., and Pinder, K. L., "Time Dependent Rheology of Artificial Slurries," *Can. J. Chem. Eng.*, *49*, 38 (1971) 3636.

40. Bauer, W. H., and Collins, E. A., "Thixotropy and Dilatancy," *Rheology*, ed. F. R. Eirich, vol. 4, p. 423 (Academic Press, New York 1976).

41. Pollice, U., et al., *Rheol. Acta*, *21*, 201 (1982).

42. Oka, S., "The Principles of Rheometry," *Rheology*, ed. F. R. Eirich, vol. 3, pp. 17–80, (Academic Press, New York, 1967).

43. Bird, R. B., Stewart, W. E., and Lightfoot, E. N., *loc. cit*, chap. 2, pp. 42–47.
44. Skelland, A. H. P., *loc. cit.*, chap. 2, pp. 27–49, chap. 3, pp. 68–82, chap. 4, pp. 109–126, and chap. 5, pp. 157–176.
45. Bowen, R. Le Baron, Jr., "Interpreting and Converting Data," *Chem. Eng.*, *68*(9), 131 (1961).
46. Bowen, R. Le Baron, Jr., "Determining End of Laminar Region," ibid., *68*(6), 127 (1961).
47. Bowen, R. Le Baron, Jr., "Designing Turbulent Flow Systems," ibid., *68*(7), 143 (1961).
48. Bowen, R. Le Baron, Jr., "How to Handle Slurries," ibid., *68*(8), 129 (1961).
49. Bowen, R. Le Baron, Jr., "Turbulent Flow—A Historical Review," ibid., *68*(7), 147 (1961).
50. Bowen, R. Le Baron, Jr., "Best Methods for Obtaining Flow Data," ibid., *68*(8), 119 (1961).
51. Bogue, D. C., "Entrance Effects and Prediction of Turbulence in Non-Newtonian Flow," *Ind. Eng. Chem.*, *51*(7), 874 (1959).
52. Mooney, M., "Explicit Formulas for Slip and Fluidity," *J. of Rheology*, *2*, 210 (1931).
53. Severs, E. T., and Austin, J. M., "Flow Properties of Vinyl Chloride Resin Plastisols," *Ind. Eng. Chem.*, *46*(11), 2369 (1954).
54. Bowen, R. Le Baron, Jr., "Designing Laminar Flow Systems," *Chem. Eng.*, *68*(6), 243 (1961).
55. Rabinowitsch, B., *Z. Physik, Chem.* (Leipzig) *145A*, 1 (1929).
56. Alves, G. E., Boucher, D. F., and Pigford, R. L., "Pipe-Line Design for Non-Newtonian Solutions and Suspensions," *Chem. Eng. Prog.*, *48*(8), 385 (1952).
57. Chong, J. S., Christiansen, E. B., and Baer, A. D., "Rheology of Concentrated Suspensions," *J. Appl. Polymer Sci.*, *15*, 2007 (1971).
58. Hedstroem, B. O. A., "Flow of Plastic Materials in Pipes," *Ind. Eng. Chem.*, *44*(3), 651 (1952).
59. Hanks, R. W., and Pratt, D. R., "On the Flow of Bingham Plastic Slurries in Pipes and Between Parallel Plates," *Soc. Petroleum Eng. Journal*, Dec. 1967, p. 342.
60. Metzner, A. B., and Reed, J. C., "Flow of Non-Newtonian Fluids. Correlation of the Laminar, Transition, and Turbulent-Flow Regions," *AIChE Journal*, *1*(4), 434 (1955).
61. Krieger, I. M., and Maron, S. H., "Direct Determination of the Flow Curves of Non-Newtonian Fluids," *J. Appl. Phys.*, *23*, 147 (1952).
62. Seshadri, V., and Sutera, S. P., "Concentration Changes of Suspensions of Rigid Spheres Flowing through Tubes," *J. Colloid and Interface Sci.*, *27*(1), 101 (1968).
63. Segrè, G., and Silberberg, A., "Radial Particle Displacements in Poiseuille Flow of Suspensions," *Nature*, *189*, 209 (1961).
64. Segrè, G., and Silberberg, A., "Behavior of Macroscopic Rigid Spheres in Poiseuille Flow," *J. Fluid Mech*, *14*, 115 (1962) and ibid., 14, 136 (1962).
65. Repetti, R. V., and Leonard, E. F., "Segrè-Silberberg Annulus Formation: A Possible Explanation," *Nature*, *203*, 1346 (1964).
66. Denson, C. D., and Christiansen, E. B., "Particle Migration in Shear Fields," *AIChE Journal*, *12*, 589 (1966).
67. Oiknine, C., Azelvandre, F., "Scott Blair and Fahraeus-Lindqvist Effect," *Rheol. Acta*, *14*, 51 (1975).
68. Maude, A. D., and Whitmore, R. L., "The Wall Effect and the Viscometry of Suspensions," *Brit. J. Appl. Phys.*, *7*, 98 (1956).
69. Eveson, G. F., Whitmore, R. L., and Ward, S. G., "Use of Coaxial-Cylinder Viscometers and Capillary-Tube Viscometers for Suspensions," *Nature*, *166*, 1074 (1950).
70. Sweeny, K. H., and Geckler, R. D., "The Rheology of Suspensions," *J. Appl. Phys.*, *25*(9), 1135 (1954).
71. Bird, R. B., Stewart, W. E., and Lightfoot, E. N., *loc. cit.*, chap. 3, pp. 69–107.
72. Stokes, C. S., and Cherry, N. H., "The Production of Stable Coal-Oil Mixtures Using High Power Mechanical Mixing Devices," Proc. II Int. Symp. on coal-oil mixtures combustion, (PETC, 1980), vol. II.
73. Adams-Viola, M., et al., "Characterization of the Various Types of COM and its Implication for Utilization and Specifications of Formulations," Proc. III Int. Symp. on coal-oil mixtures combustion, Orlando (Fa), 1–3 April 1981, (PETC, 1981), vol. II.
74. Ekmann, J. M., and Bienstock, D., "The Role of Coal and Oil Characteristics on the Stability of Coal-Oil Mixtures," Proc. II Int. Symp. on Coal-Oil Mixtures Combustion, (PETC, 1980), vol. II.

75. Veal, C. J., Wall, D. R., and Groszek, A. J., "Stable Coal/Fuel Oil Dispersions," ibid., vol. I.
76. Austin, L. G., "Introduction to the Mathematical Description of Grinding as a Rate Process. A review," *Powder Technology*, 5, 1 (1971/72).
77. Carta, M., "Quelques examples d'application de procedes electriques et magnetiques a l'elimination de la pyrite contenue dans le charbon," *Industrie Minerale, les Techniques*, January 1982, p. 43.
78. Carta, M., "Progressi e prospettive della separazione elettrica dei minerali," *L'industria mineraria*, October 1972, p. 505.
79. Beddow, J. K., "Dry Separation Techniques," *Chem. Eng.*, 88(8), 70 (1981).
80. Noyes Data Corp., "Coal Cleaning Technology," (Park Ridge, NJ, 1981).
81. Tsai, S. C., "Fundamentals of Coal Beneficiation and Utilization," (Elsevier Publishing Co., New York, 1982).
82. Hirama, T., et al., "Effect of the Size Distribution of Coal on Fluidized-Bed Combustion," *Int. Eng. Chem.*, 24(3), 502 (1984).
83. Kempton, A. G., "Removal of Pyrite from Coal by Conditioning with Thiobacillum Ferro-oxidans Followed by Oil Agglomeration," *Hydrometallurgy*, 5, 117 (1980).
84. Mitchell, R. S., and Glustoker, H. J., "Mineralogy of Ash of Some American Coals. Variations with Temperatures and Source," *Fuel*, 56, 91 (1976).
85. Huffman, G. P., Huggins, F. E., and Dunmyre, G. R., "Investigation of the High-Temperature Behavior of Coal Ash in Reducing and Oxidizing Atmospheres," *Fuel*, 60, 585 (1981).
86. Stallman, J. J., and Neavel, R. C., "Technique to Measure the Temperature of Agglomeration of Coal Ash," *Fuel*, 59, 584 (1980).
87. Borio, R. W., and Narciso, R. R., Jr., "The Use of Gravity Fractionation Techniques for Assessing Slagging and Fouling Potential of Coal Ash," *Trans. ASME*, 101, 500 (1979).
88. Kosmack, D. A., and Huffman, G. P., "Correlation Between Ash-Fusion Temperatures and Ternary Equilibrium Phase Diagrams," *Fuel*, 60, 577 (1981).
89. Klimpel, R. R., and Austin, L. G., "Determination of Selection-for-Breakage Functions in the Batch Grinding Equation by Non Linear Optimization," *Ind. Eng. Chem. Fundam.*, 9(2), 230 (1970).
90. Austin, L. G., Luckie, P. T., and Klimpel, R. R., "Solutions of the Batch Grinding Equation Leading to Rosin-Rammler Distributions," *Trans. Soc. Min. Eng. AIME*, 252, 87 (1972).
91. Cherry, N. H., "The Application to Plant Operation of Laboratory Practices Used in the Characterization of Coal Oil Mixtures," Proc. III Int. Symp. on Coal-Oil Mixtures Combustion, (PETC, 1981), vol. II.
92. Alessandrini, A., Kikic, I., and Lapasin, R., "Rheology of Coal Suspensions," *Rheol. Acta*, 22, 500 (1983).
93. Sabadell, A. J., "Survey of Commercial Instrumentation for the Continuous Measurements of Viscosity and Coal Content of Coal-Oil Mixtures, Proc. I Int. Symp. on coal-oil mixtures combustion, (PETC, 1978), p. 242.
94. Gradishar, Faith, Hedrick, "Laminar Flow of Oil-Coal Suspensions," *AIChE Journal*, 39, 201 (1943).
95. Covey, G. H., and Stanmore, B. R., "Rheological Behavior of Victorian Brown Coal," *Fuel*, 59, 123 (1980).
96. Landau, L., and Lifsits, E. M., *loc. cit.*
97. Einstein, A., "Eine neue Bestimmung der Moleküldimensionen," *Ann. Phys.*, 19, 289 (1906).
98. Ghassemzadeh, M. R., and Carmi, S., "Rheological Study of Coal-Oil Mixtures," *Rheol. Acta*, 20, 198 (1981).
99. Ghosh, A. K., and Bhattacharya, S. N., "Rheological Study of Black Coal-Oil Suspensions," *Rheol. Acta*, 23, 195 (1984).
100. Munro, J. M., et al., "A Characterization of the Rheological Properties of Coal-Fuel Oil Slurries," *AIChE Journal*, 25(2), 355 (1979).
101. Papachristodoulou, G., and Trass, O., "Rheological Properties of Ultrafine Coal-Oil Mixtures," Proc. III Int. Symp. on coal-oil mixtures combustion, Orlando (Florida), 1–3 April 1981, (PETC, 1981), vol. II.
102. Rutgers, Ir. R., "Relative Viscosity of Suspensions of Rigid Spheres in Newtonian Liquids, *Rheol. Acta*, 2, 202 (1962).

103. Rutgers, Ir. R., "Relative Viscosity and Concentration," *Rheol. Acta*, *2*(4), 305 (1962).
104. Allen, S. J., and Kline, K. A., "The Effects of Concentration in Fluid Suspensions," *Trans. Soc. Rheol.*, *12*(3), 457 (1968).
105. Borghesani, A. F., "Concentration-Dependent Behavior of the Shear Viscosity of Coal-Fuel Oil Suspensions," *Rheol. Acta*, 24, 189 (1985).
106. Rejek, U., and Franke, F. H., "Viscosity and Transportation Characteristics of Coal-Oil Slurries," Proc. III Int. Symp. on Coal-Oil Mixtures Combustion, (PETC, 1981) vol. II.
107. Jeffrey, D. J., and Acrivos, A., "The Rheological Properties of Suspensions of Rigid Particles," *AIChE Journal*, *22*(3), 417 (1976).
108. Eilers, H., "Die Viskosität von Emulsionen hochviskoser Stoffe als Funktion der Konzentration," *Kolloid-Z.*, *97*(3), 313 (1941).
109. Robinson, J. V., "The Viscosity of Suspensions of Spheres. III. Sediment Volume as a Determining Parameter," *Trans. Soc. Rheol.*, *1*, 15 (1957).
110. Williams, P. S., "Flow of Concentrated Suspensions," *J. Appl. Chem.*, *3*, 120 (1953).
111. Eyring, H., Henderson, D., Stover, B. J., Eyring, E. M., "Statistical Mechanics and Dynamics," p. 460, (J. Wiley and S. Inc., New York 1964).
112. Manley, R. St. J., and Mason, S. G., *Can. J. Chem. Eng.*, *33*, 763 (1955).
113. Manley, R. St. J., and Mason, S. G., "Particles Motion in Sheared Suspensions. II. Collisions of Uniform Spheres," *J. Colloid Sci.*, *7*, 354 (1952).
114. Ford, T. F., *J. Phys. Chem.*, *64*, 1168 (1960).
115. Happel, J., "Viscosity of Suspensions of Uniform Spheres," *J. Appl. Phys.*, *28*, 1288 (1957).
116. Thomas, D. G., "Transport Characteristics of Suspensions. VIII. A Note on the Viscosity of Newtonian Suspensions of Uniform Spherical Particles," *J. Colloid Sci.*, *20*, 267 (1965).
117. Guth, E., Simha, R., *Kolloid-Z.*, *74*, 266 (1936).
118. Saito, N., *J. Phys. Soc.* (Japan), *5*, 4 (1950).
119. Quemada, D., "Rheology of Concentrated Disperse Systems and Minimum Energy Dissipation Principle. I. Viscosity-Concentration Relationship." *Rheol. Acta*, *16*, 82 (1977).
120. Mooney, M., "The Viscosity of Concentrated Suspensions of Spherical Particles," *J. Colloid Sci.*, *6*, 162 (1951).
121. Vand, V., "Viscosity of Solutions and Suspensions. I," *J. Phys. Chem. & Colloid Chem.*, *52*, 277 (1948).
122. Vand, V., "Viscosity of Solutions and Suspensions. II," *J. Phys. Chem. & Colloid Chem.*, *52*, 300 (1948).
123. Cen, K. F., et al., "Experimental Investigation of Preparation and Handling of COM in Zhejiang University," Proc. III Int. Symp. on coal-oil mixtures combustion, (PETC, 1981), vol. II.
124. Ting, A. P., and Luebbers, R. H., "Viscosity of Suspensions of Spherical and Other Isodimensional Particles in Liquids," *AIChE Journal*, *3*(1), 111 (1957).
125. Roscoe, R., "The Viscosity of Suspensions of Rigid Spheres," *Brit. J. Appl. Phys.*, *3*, 267 (1952).
126. Ward, S. G., and Whitmore, R. L., "Studies of the Viscosity and Sedimentation of Suspensions. Part I: The Viscosity of Suspensions of Spherical Particles," *Brit. J. Appl. Phys.*, *1*, 286 (1950).
127. Robinson, J. V., "The Viscosity of Suspensions of Spheres. II. The Effect of Sphere Diameter," *J. Phys. & Colloid Chem.*, *55*, 455 (1951).
128. Farris, R. J., "Prediction of the Viscosity of Multimodal Suspensions from Unimodal Viscosity Data," *Trans. Soc. Rheol.*, *12*(2), 281 (1968).
129. Probstein, R. F., and Sengun, M. Z., "Viscosity Prediction of Highly Concentrated Polymodal Coal-Water Slurries," Proc. VII Int. Symp. on coal slurry fuels preparation and utilization, (PETC, 1985).
130. Henderson, C. B., and Scheffee, R. S., "The Optimum Particle-Size Distribution of Coal for Coal-Water Slurries," Preprints Vol. 28, No. 2, Div. of Fuel Chem., Am. Chem. Soc., (1983).
131. Yucel, O., and Dabak, T., "Determination of Particle Size Distribution of Coal-Water Mixtures for Optimum Stability and Hydraulic Handling Characteristics," Proc. VII Int. Symp. on coal slurry fuels preparation and utilization, (PETC, 1985).
132. Andreasen, A. H. M., and Andersen, J., "Über die Beziehung zwischen Kornabstufung und Zwischenraum in Produkten aus lösen Körnern . . . ," *Kolloid-Z.*, *50*, 217 (1930).
133. Mandelbrot, B. B., *The Fractal Geometry of Nature* (W. H. Freeman & Co., New York, 1977).

134. Westman, A. E. R., and Hugill, H. R., "The Packing of Particles," *J. Am. Ceramic Soc., 13,* 767 (1930).
135. Rajagopal, E. S., "Effect of Particle Size and Interfacial Film on the Viscosity of Disperse Systems," *Z. Phys. Chem., 23,* 342 (1960).
136. Papachristodoulou, G., Boghossian, H., and Trass, O., "Rheological Properties of Coal-Oil-Mixtures. Effect of Particle Size Distribution," Proc. IV Int. Symp. on coal-slurry combustion, (PETC, 1982), vol. I.
137. Rukin, E. I., et al., "Influence of the Grain-Size Composition of Coal on the Properties of Acqueous Coal Suspensions," *Khim. Tverdogo Topliva, 11*(1), 66 (1977).
138. Smit, P. P. A., "The Effect of Filler Size and Geometry on the Flow of Carbon Black Filled Rubber," *Rheol. Acta, 8,* 277 (1969).
139. Girardi, E., and Passarini, N., "Rheology of Coal-Oil Mixtures," Proc. III Int. Symp. on coal-oil mixtures combustion, (PETC, 1981), vol. I.
140. Passarini, N., et al., Rheology, Stability, and Combustion of Coal-Oil Mixtures," Proc. IV Int. Symp. on coal-slurry combustion, (PETC, 1982), vol. I.
141. Meyer, W. C., "Stabilization of Coal/Fuel Oil Slurries," Proc. II Int. Symp. on coal-oil mixtures combustion, (PETC, 1980), vol. II.
142. Marlow, B. J., and Rowell, R. L., "Stability and Rheology of Coal-Oil Mixtures and Coal Water Mixtures," Proc. II Int. Symp. on coal-oil mixtures combustion, (PETC, 1980), vol. II.
143. Botsaris, G. D., "Stability and Instability of Coal-Oil Mixtures Fuels. Some Practical Considerations," *Alternative Energy Sources,* p. 3341, (Hemisphere Publishing Corp., Washington D.C., 1978).
144. Kugel, R. W., "The Determination of Coal-Oil Mixture Stability," Proc. I Int. Symp. on coal-oil mixtures combustion, (PETC, 1978), p. 300.
145. Yamamura, M., Yamashita, T., and Igarashi, T., "Studies on the Stabilization of COM," Proc. II Int. Symp. on coal-oil mixtures combustion, (PETC, 1980), vol. II.
146. Cochran, J. W., "Progress in Developing Ultrafine Coal-Oil Mixtures," Proc. II Int. Symp. on coal-oil mixtures combustion, (PETC, 1980), vol. II.
147. Ferrini, F., et al., "Shear Viscosity of Settling Suspensions," *Rheol. Acta, 18,* 289 (1979).
148. Adams-Viola, M., Botsaris, G. D., and Glazman, Y., "The Sedimentation of Coal in Oils. The Effect of the Viscosity and Composition of the Oil," *AIChE Journal, 28*(3), 392 (1982).
149. Moreland, C., "Settling Velocities of Coal Particles," *Can. J. Chem. Eng., 41,* 108 (1963).
150. Botsaris, G. D., et al., "Characterization and Structural Studies of the Various Types of COM," Proc. II Int. Symp. on Coal-Oil Mixtures Combustion, (PETC, 1980) vol. II.
151. Zimmel, Y., "Theory of Hindered Sedimentation of Polydisperse Mixtures," *AIChE Journal, 29*(4), 669 (1983).
152. Thomas, D. G., "Transport Characteristics of Suspensions. VII. Relation of Hindered-Settling Floc Characteristics to Rheological Parameters," *AIChE Journal, 9*(3), 310(1963).
153. Thomas, D. G., "Transport Characteristics of Suspensions. III. Laminar Flow Properties of Flocculated Suspensions," *AIChE Journal, 7*(3), 431(1961).
154. Shook, C. A., and Daniel, S. M., "A Variable Density Model of the Pipeline Flow of Suspensions," *Can. J. Chem. Eng., 47,* 196 (1969).
155. Shook, C. A., and Daniel, S. M., "Flow of Suspensions of Solids in Pipelines. Part I: Flow with a Stable Stationary Deposit," *Can. J. Chem. Eng., 43,* 56 (1965).
156. Shook, C. A., et al., "Flow of Suspensions in Pipelines. Part II: Mechanism of Particle Suspension," *Can. J. Chem. Eng., 46,* 238 (1968).
157. Thomas, D. G., "Transport Characteristics of Suspensions. VI: Minimum Transport Velocity for Large Particle Size Suspensions in Round Horizontal Pipes," *AIChE Journal, 8*(3), 373 (1962).
158. Thomas, D. G., "Transport Characteristics of Suspensions. II. Minimum Transport Velocity for Flocculated Suspensions in Horizontal Pipes," *AIChE Journal, 7*(3), 423 (1961).
159. Im, K. H., and Chung, P. M., "Particulate Deposition from Turbulent Parallel Streams," *AIChE Journal, 29*(3), 498 (1983).
160. Oroskar, A. R., and Turian, R. M., "The Critical Velocity in Pipeline Flow of Slurries," *AIChE Journal, 26*(4), 551 (1980).

161. Pieranski, P., "Colloidal Crystals," *Contemp. Phys.*, *24*(1), 25 (1983).
162. Coburn, T. T., "Evaluation of Stable Emulsions of Coal," Proc. II Int. Symp. on Coal-Oil Mixtures Combustion, (PETC, 1980), vol. II.
163. Elton, G. A. H., "Electroviscosity. III. Sedimentation Phenomena in Ionic Liquid," *Proc. Roy. Soc.* (London), *197A*, 568 (1951).
164. Hedrick, J. E., Andrews, A. C., and Sutherland, J. B., "Electrostatic Charges on Coal Particles in Oil," *Ind. Eng. Chem.*, *33*(8), 1055 (1941).
165. Carty, R. H., and Coburn, T. T., "Coal/Oil/Water Mixture Stability," Proc. II Int. Symp. on coal-oil mixtures combustion, (PETC, 1980), vol. I.
166. Adiga, K. C., et al., "Rheology of Coal Slurries in No. 2 Oil and Ethanol Blends. Effect of Water," *Rheol. Acta*, *22*, 402 (1983).
167. Foster, E. P., et al., "Rheological Properties of Solvent Refined COM," Proc. II Int. Symp. on coal-oil mixtures combustion, (PETC, 1980), vol. II.
168. Aikens, A. C., and Ekmann, J. M., "The Effect of Coal Particle Size on Settling Behavior of Coal-Oil Mixtures," Proc. III Int. Symp. on coal-oil mixtures combustion, (PETC, 1981), vol. II.
169. Erdògan, M. E., "Polar Effects in the Apparent Viscosity of a Suspension," *Rheol. Acta*, *9*, 434 (1970).
170. Bauer, W. H., and Collins, E. A., "Thixotropy and Dilatancy," *Rheology*, ed. F. R. Eirich, vol. 4, p. 423 (Academic Press, New York 1976).
171. Maeda, S., Takeshita, T., and Kanamori, S., "New Additive for Low-Viscosity COM and New Parameter of Coal for Predicting COM-Viscosity," Proc. VII Int. Symp. on coal slurry fuels preparation and utilization, (PETC, 1985).
172. Goedde, E., "Möglichkeiten des Transports von Kraftswerkkohle durch pipelines unter Verwendung von Methanol als Traegerfluessigkeit," *Tech. Mitt. Krupp Forsch. Ber.*, *39*, 23 (1981).
173. Anonym, "Coal-Water Slurries," *Chem. Eng.*, *90*(10), 15 (1983).
174. Anonym, "Coal-Water Slurries," *Chem. Eng.*, *90*(6), 14 (1983).
175. Johnson, E. P., "Payoff Time is Near for Coal-Water Slurries," *Chem. Eng.*, *89*(1), 11 (1982).
176. Belyagin, G. N., Ko'zmin, G. V., and Dzhundubaev, A. K., "Stability and Rheological Properties of Acqueous Suspensions of the Brown Coal of the Agulak Deposit of the Kirghiz SR," *Khim. Tverdogo Topliva*, *14*(1), 126 (1980).
177. Pohl, J. H., "Correlation of the Spray Characteristics of Coal-Water Fuels," Proc. VII Int. Symp. on coal slurry fuels preparation and utilization, (PETC, 1985).
178. Aoki, K., "Pretreatment of Coal for Coal-Water Slurries," Proc. IV Int. Symp. on coal-slurry combustion, (PETC, 1982), vol. I.
179. Reich, I., and Vold, R., "Flocculation-Deflocculation in Agitated Suspensions. I: Carbon and ferric oxide in water," *J. Phys. Chem.*, *63*, 1497 (1959).
180. Watz, D., "Die Bildung verschiedener grossen Flocken aus einer Kohle-Wasser Suspension," *Glueckaufforschungshefte*, 30. Jahrgang, *H6*, 303 (1969).
181. Williams, J. A., Akoto, W. O., and Tagoe, C. C., "Effect of Selected Additives on the Stability and Rheology of Coal-Water Mixtures," Proc. VII Int. Symp. on coal slurry fuels preparation and utilization, (PETC, 1985).
182. Sastri, V. S., Hoey, G. R., and Whalley, B. J. P., "Review of the Effects of Corrosion Inhibitors in Coal-Water Slurry Pipelines," *Can. Met. Quart.*, *18*, 435 (1979).
183. Morgan, M. E., et al., "A Study of the Yield Stress of CWF," Proc. VII Int. Symp. on coal slurry fuels preparation and utilization, (PETC, 1985).
184. Goodman, R. M., Mathiesen, M. M., and Persson, J. E., "Coal-Water Fuels—Development of Commercially Meaningful Specifications," Proc. VII Int. Symp. on coal slurry fuels preparation and utilization, (PETC, 1985).
185. Borghesani, A. F., *ASSORENI Report* #6974 (1982), unpublished.
186. Seki, M., Kiyama, K., and Nishino, J., "Effects of Coal Property and Additive on the Rheological Characteristics of Coal Water Mixtures," Proc. VII Int. Symp. on coal slurry fuels preparation and utilization, (PETC, 1985).
187. Kaji, R., et al., "Effect of Ions on the Rheology of CWM," Proc. VII Int. Symp. on coal slurry fuels preparation and utilization, (PETC, 1985).

188. Shook, C. A., and Nurkowski, A., "The Effect of Some Alkalyne Additives on the Viscosity of Coal-Water Slurries," *Can. J. Chem. Eng.*, *55*, 510 (1977).
189. Street, N., "Effect of a Polyanion on the Rheology of a Kaolinite Suspension," *J. Colloid Sci.*, *12*, 1 (1957).
190. Poreh, M., et al., "Drag Reduction in Hydraulic Transport of Solids," *J. of the Hydraulic Division*, Proc. A.S.C.E., *HY 4*, 904 (1970).
191. Viswanathan, K., and Mari, B. P., "Hold-Up Studies in the Hydraulic Conveying of Solids in Horizontal Pipelines," *AIChE Journal*, *30*(4), 682 (1984).
192. Televentos, Y., et al., "Flow of Slurries of Coarse Particles at High Solids Concentrations," *Can. J. Chem. Eng.*, *57*, 255 (1979).
193. Zubkova, Yu. N., "Influence of Inorganic Electrolytes on the Electrokinetic Potential of Hard Coals," *Khim. Tverdogo Topliva*, *14*(1), 80 (1980).
194. Butler, Conway, James, "The Effect of Salts on Polyelectrolyte Interactions . . . ," Trans. Faraday Soc., *50*, 612 (1954).
195. Reizes, Horsley, "Variation in the Head Loss Gradient in Laminar Slurry Pipe Flow Due to Changes in the Zeta Potential," *S. Afr. Mech. Eng.*, *28*, 307 (1978).
196. Narain, C., "Coal-Fluid Gel Process," *J. Min. Met. and Fuels*, *4*, 79 (1980).
197. Glansville, J. O., and Wightman, J. P., "Wetting of Powdered Coals by Alkanol-Water Solutions and Other Liquids," *Fuel*, *59*, 557 (1980).
198. Lynch, L. J., and Webster, D. S., "Effect of Thermal Treatment on the Interaction of Brown Coal and Water: a NMR Study," *Fuel*, *61*, 271 (1982).
199. Ballone, P., "Additive and Non-Additive Hard Sphere Mixtures. Monte Carlo Simulation and Integral Equation Results," *Mol. Phys.*, *59*(2), 275 (1986).

CHAPTER 5*

RHEOLOGY AND NON-NEWTONIAN BEHAVIOR
OF SEA AND ESTUARINE MUD

G. Verreet and J. Berlamont

Laboratorium Voor Hydraulica
Katholieke Universiteit te Leuven
Heverlee, Belgium

CONTENTS

INTRODUCTION

Mud is defined as a natural cohesive suspension containing clay minerals, non-clay minerals, organic matter, and a subordinate sand and silt fraction in water. The heterogeneous composition includes colloidal (1 nm $-$ 1 μm) and non-colloidal ($>$1 μm) particles, in a wide range of mineralogical and chemical compositions (surface reactive/non-reactive; environmentally stable/unstable). In the considered marine and estuarine environment, these fine particles are flocculated to form flocs and aggregates. The cohesion between the particles and flocs is the essential factor determining the complex material behavior.

The mud flocs can concentrate in a static suspension near the bottom, to form "fluid mud" ([16]: fluid mud 10–170 g/l; [19]: 10–480 g/l; [60]: 3–300 g/l). The transition from a suspension with single flocs to a bed structure (cohesive boundary [60]) is not sharp and depends on many variables. An omnivalent definition of this material in the gap between fluid and soil mechanics is difficult.

Mud is present in many estuarine and coastal reaches where it is very often trapped for a long time due to tidal action. Its appearance as fluid mud can persist for a sufficiently long time to be considered a specific material. Its appearance can be altered into a settled bed by self-weight consolidation, or by resuspension (erosion). The former process is a special case of rheological behavior that is excluded from the present discussion.

---

* Dedicated to the memory of Johan van Goethem, 27, our dear departed colleague, friend, and collaborator on mud rheology. He died in a car crash while we were preparing this chapter.

RHEOLOGICAL MODELS AND RESEARCH METHODOLOGY

Theoretical Background of Suspension Rheology

The most elaborate analyses of suspension behavior deal with ideal systems of dilute, non-flocculated, monodisperse particles [7, 49, 64], for which theoretical calculations agree with experimental data. However, extension of the results of this fundamental approach to exactly the opposite, i.e., non-ideal, concentrated, flocculated, polydisperse systems, is far from being completed.

In the absence of a decisive theoretical conclusion as to the most appropriate method of description, different rheological models have been applied to mud.

It is common knowledge that the kinetics of particle and floc aggregation/disaggregation by the action of shear and its time and shear-rate dependency are very important. Nevertheless, most researchers up to now have used a pragmatic approach, assuming applicability of simplified, easy-to-handle, time-independent operational models. Depending on the practical purposes of the research, such approximations may be most useful.

Time-dependency is difficult to assess; measuring, for instance, material "history" parameters ("structures") is one of the great challenges of mud research.

Time-Independent Models

Types of basic models of rheological behavior of mud in laminar flow, the equivalent equations, and some definitions are summarized in Figure 1 and Table 1. Discussions of the theory of these types of flow can be found in [11] and [71].

Deviation from Newtonian behavior has been reported to occur for mud at a concentration of 10 g/l dry solids [72] or 80 g/l for kaolinite (a mud-like material) [27]. The dilute suspensions below these limits are not considered further here [74].

The *shear-thinning* (or *pseudoplastic*) curve can almost intuitively be related to the flow of a suspension (fluid-supported units, no structural strength) in which the deformable flow units re-adjust themselves by the action of shear in the higher energy environment, causing the apparent viscosity to decrease with increasing $\dot\gamma$.

Williams and James [72] and Parker and Kirby [61] apply this model to mud suspensions. In the opinion of Kirby [34], mud showing some kind of Bingham plastic behavior (Figure 1), thus having a framework with a definite strength, must be considered to be bed material and no longer

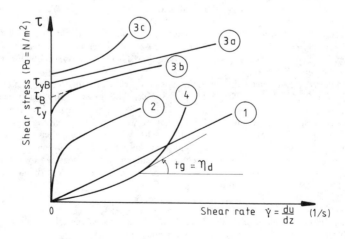

Figure 1. Model response curves (rheograms). See Table 1 for explanation.

Table 1
Rheological Behavior of Mud

Model	Curve	Equations	Material Type	Reference
NEWTONIAN	1	$\tau = \eta \dfrac{du}{dz}$	dilute suspensions	
		$\eta_r = 1 + 2.5\phi$	spherical particles	15
		$\eta_r = \exp[2.5\phi/(1 - k_1\phi)]$		54
SHEAR THINNING (Pseudoplastic)	2	$\tau = m\left(\dfrac{du}{dz}\right)^n \quad n < 1$	flocculated clay slurries	
		$\eta_a = m\left(\dfrac{du}{dz}\right)^{n-1}$		
GENERALIZED BINGHAM	3	$\tau = \tau_0 + \eta_B\left(\dfrac{du}{dz}\right)^n$ $\quad$ if $|\tau| \geq \tau_0$ $\quad$ with $\dfrac{du}{dz} = 0 \quad$ if $|\tau| < \tau_0$		
BINGHAM PLASTIC	3a	$\tau = \tau_{yB} + \eta \dfrac{du}{dz}$		
SHEAR THICKENING (Dilatant)	4	$\tau = k\left(\dfrac{du}{dz}\right)^n \quad n > 1$	concentrated defloccated clay slurries	3
VISCOELASTIC (Voigt solid, Kelvin body)		$\tau = G\gamma + \mu\dot{\gamma}$		45

Symbols

τ = shear stress	m = pseudoplastic viscosity	ϕ = solids volume fraction
η = dynamic viscosity	$\tau_0 = \tau$ at $\dot{\gamma} = 0$	n = flow index
η_s = dynamic viscosity of medium	τ_{yB} = true Bingham plastic yield stress	k = shear-thickening analog of m
$\eta_r = \dfrac{\eta}{\eta_s}$ = relative viscosity	τ_y = yield stress (see fig. 3)	k_1 = constant
$\eta = \dfrac{d\tau}{d\dot{\gamma}}$ = differential viscosity	τ_B = 'Bingham' yield stress	G = rigidity modulus or shear modulus
	γ = shear deformation	
$\eta_a = \dfrac{\tau}{\dot{\gamma}}$ = apparent viscosity	$\dot{\gamma}$ = shear rate	

a (fluid mud) suspension. Although this is conceptually a very clear distinction, some problems remain. The first problem is a clear methodological distinction between both types of flow. Further, the development in time of a particular structure in the static suspension, without density increase, can drastically alter low-shear rheological behavior, changing a liquid into a solid without even a macroscopically observable event. The reverse, a liquefaction following a slight mechanical agitation, can also occur.

The choice between shear-thinning and generalized Bingham behavior is important for cases in which the initiation of mud movement and low shear effects in general are of primordial importance. For high shear rate problems, the discussion is of rather academic value.

Michaels and Bolger [51], Hunter and Nicol [29], Firth and Hunter [20], and Williams [73] analyze shear-thinning flow by means of the energy dissipation processes involved (viscous flow, particle interactions). This type of analysis includes particle, floc, and aggregate characteristics, such as surface electrokinetic properties.

Selection of the *generalized Bingham plastic* (Figure 1, curve 3) model is based on the consideration that a flocculated suspension can be a loose particle structure starting from a very low solids content. The original Bingham (visco-) plastic concept has been extended so as to include materials with a yield stress (see Table 1) and shear-thinning (or shear-thickening) properties as well.

Although reported measurements are not always conclusive as to the exact nature of the type of flow observed, the generalized Bingham model has been widely used since the beginning of systematic cohesive sediment research [35, 46, 52, 57, 62] because of its simplicity [8].

Shear-thickening behavior is not a common phenomenon in mud. The increase of the apparent viscosity with increasing shear rate in a limited shear-rate interval has been observed [9, 18, 69].

Time Dependency

The term "thixotropy" is attributed to the phenomenon of continuous decrease of apparent viscosity with time under constant shear and the subsequent recovery of viscosity when the flow is discontinued [48]. Analogously, it is applied for such changes in the elastic modulus or yield stress [2].

The experimentally determined rheogram can show a hysteresis loop for increasing or decreasing $\dot{\gamma}$; this is called thixotropy as well. Thixotropy is not only the shear-softening effect, but also the recovery of (a part of) the initial strength after resting. Figure 2 shows the different aspects of the phenomenon, related to three possible methods of its determination [47].

Its presence is ascribed to the dynamics of the internal structure: the evolution of the continuous particle network if it is present, or the rearrangement of flocs and aggregates in the suspension.

Although it is an essential variable in the complete description of fluid mud behavior, no quantifying parameters or generally accepted experimental procedures that would allow the comparison of different muds are known.

Thixotropy means the disappearance of a unique relation between $\dot{\gamma}$ and τ. Although fluid muds could be considered to have an optimum potential for structural change (related to the product of particle density and particle mobility), the error introduced by neglecting thixotropy is unknown.

Viscoelastic Model

A viscoelastic material has properties of liquids (dissipation of viscous energy by means of flow) and of solids (storage of elastic energy, for a limited time). Metha and Maa [45] have investigated viscoelastic properties of mud. At present, only limited data exist on this subject.

Methodological Approach

Accurate measurements generally require sensitive and complex apparatus. However, the object of study in its natural conditions is not prone to detailed and controlled measurement of relevant rheological and related parameters.

In situ rheological testing of mud is a hazardous enterprise, from which it is difficult to obtain meaningful results. Studies concerned with the determination of the "nautical depth" of navigation

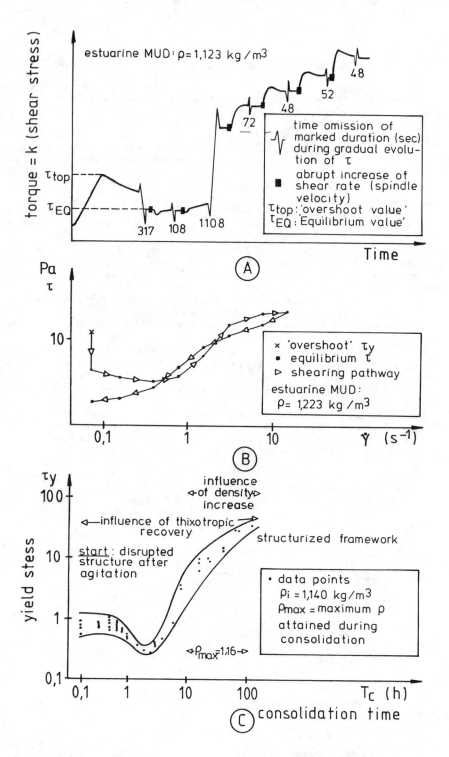

Figure 2. (A) Experimentally recorded rheogram (abbreviated) showing transient (time-dependent) mud behavior. (B) Experimentally recorded rheogram showing complex hysteresis loop ($\dot{\gamma}$ up-curve vs. $\dot{\gamma}$ down-curve). (C) Experimental data on thixotropic recovery of yield stress at different consolidation times T_c (duration of rest).

channels have used the resistance encountered by a rotating propeller (related to the dynamic viscosity, empirically related to a Bingham yield value) as a pertinent way to determine the possible keel clearance of vessels [44, 53]. Total comparison of the uncontrolled measurements in the real situation with the controlled data obtained in an artificial laboratory environment is still to be made.

Observation in nature or experimental research into mass movement of mud on submerged slopes, such as turbidity currents [12, 13, 17, 65], can yield results regarding rheology and related phenomena (equilibrium slopes, resuspension, types and kinetics of free flow, etc.). The possibility, however, of obtaining strict rheological data is limited due to the geometrical complexity of the flow, which makes it less suited for the fundamental study of material properties.

The type of rheological test equipment employed for mud in a *laboratory* situation depends on the state of the material, the rheological model assumed, and the required accuracy. An advanced discussion on rheometry can be found in [70].

Tube-type viscometers (capillary tubes) were used in the studies of Einstein and Krone [16], enabling them to derive a τ_B value and differential (Bingham) viscosities. Tube viscometers are not very sensitive, but can be useful when the suspension is heterogeneous and contains, for instance, coarse materials. It is common in the study of sewage sludges [10].

In a *vane-type viscometer* one can measure the torque(proportional to the shear stress) at different rotational speeds (related to shear rate). It is not clear whether the flow geometry allows accurate deduction of stress and viscosity data [9, 63]. It has advantages in the determination of a yield stress [55].

Coaxial rotating cylinder viscometers (Couette flow) are most widely used [19, 27, 36, 41, 54, 62, 75]. Popular commercial types available include the Brookfield and the Haake rotoviscometer, each with different extensions. Flow conditions, such as the form of the rotating body, geometry, and inner or outer cylinder turning and/or measuring, can change. Measurements at discrete $\dot{\gamma}$ or at continuously changing $\dot{\gamma}$ can also make a difference.

This variety in apparatus results in different operational definitions of the "yield stress" (Figure 3). A true yield stress (also static shear; F.: *rigidité initiale*) is a static property of a material. A non-zero definite low shear rate has to be applied in order to make a measurement ("no-flow" condition approximation). Tadros [66] prefers to call these τ_0 "apparent yield values."

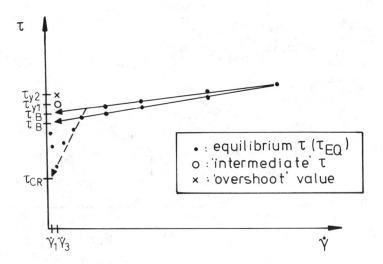

Figure 3. Different operational definitions of yield stress. τ_B: down-curve intercept; τ_{y1}: initiation of movement yield stress (generally $\tau_{y1} < \tau_{y2}$); τ_{y2}: overshoot; τ_{CR}: critical yield stress or pseudoplastic yield value.

Procedures for measuring apparent yield value include (Figure 3):

- O-back extrapolation (τ_B) of the linear portion of the rheogram on the up-curve [62] or the down-curve [74] (thixotropy).
- Stress value at observed initiation of movement at the lowest possible deformation rate of the apparatus [41].
- "Overshoot technique" [50]: maximum stress value (Figure 2A) at the lowest applicable rate of shear deformation [69].
- Measurement of the residual torque after application of shear [45, 51].
- O-back extrapolation of τ-increase in low region: "critical yield stress" or "pseudoplastic yield value" [30, 57, 58].

None of these techniques delivers sufficient proof for the physical presence of a yield stress. Laboratory observation of static slopes of layered mud depositions (no-gravity flow on non-zero slopes) indicates that a yield stress can be a physical reality [6]. The assumption of the shear-thinning model results in very high differential viscosities in the low shear-rate range, which are likewise flow inhibitors.

The determination of the remaining part of the rheogram is less controversial. However, for sedimentological purposes, experimental shear rates exceeding $50 \, s^{-1}$ are thought to be unnecessary.

The differential viscosity is obviously a function of the shear rate in the low-$\dot\gamma$ range; single values are, therefore, not always very meaningful. The viscosity curve can be derived from the measurements. For higher shear rate ($> 20 \, s^{-1}$), viscosity mostly tends to a constant value.

James et al. [33] have proposed a technique for the investigation of viscoelastic properties of mud. A miniature vane is combined with an applied stress rheometer. It avoids excessive structural disruption of the material, thus approaching static measurements.

COASTAL AND ESTUARINE MUDS—SPECIFIC PROPERTIES AND BEHAVIOR

Reported Behavior

Most data in the literature are obtained from case studies on single materials, used in laboratory set-ups. Comparative research, such as that from Migniot [52], is rather scarce. Since methodologies vary widely, comparisons between different results remain qualitative.

It is notable that several authors [9, 18, 69] observed a rheological behavior more complex than that of the described models. A minimum equilibrium shear stress is found at a low shear rate, after application of the lowest initial shear rate, followed by a sharp increase [18] (see example in Figure 2B).

The well-known relation between the yield stress and the solids concentration of the mud offers the most straightforward opportunity to evaluate the wide range of mud materials. Table 2 lists some of the published results.

Sediment Properties Affecting Rheology

A comprehensive, quantitative evaluation of the many interfering variables that affect the rheological behavior of mud is lacking.

Compositional parameters and the way in which the particles and components are organized determine how the suspension flows. Mineralogy, chemistry, and biology intervene.

Flocculation

The fact that the solid particles stick together (flocculation, aggregation) to build primary flocs and higher order aggregates is considered to be the most important parameter.

Table 2
Mud Materials

Material	Model Equation	Parameter Value	Measuring System	Reference
mud	$\tau_B = k \cdot T_s$	$k = 0.0058$ $10 < T_s < 90$ g/l	tube	35
Thames mud	$\tau_B = k \cdot T_s^P$	$p = 2.5; k = 4.3 \ 10^{-6}$ $15 < T_s < 120$ g/l	rotational viscometer	36
different muds	$\tau_{y1} = k \cdot T_s^P$	$4 < p < 5$	rotational viscometer	52
Rotterdam mud id.	(data-curve) $\tau_y = k \cdot T_s^P$ $\tau_B = \exp(D \cdot T_s + k)$	 $p = 4.6; k = 4.5 \ 10^{-11}$ $D = 0.01893 \ m^3/kg$ $k = -2.8402$	rotational viscometer	23 24 in 67
Zeebrugge mud	$\tau_y = k_1 \cdot T_s^P$	$p = 5.6$	rotational viscometer	41
Rotterdam & Brisbane mud	shear-thinning τ_B down-extrapolation $\tau_B = k \cdot T_s^P$ (numerical data)	B: $p = 2.79$; $k = 1.18 \ 10^{-6}$ R: $p = 3.03$; $k = 3.84 \ 10^{-7}$		72
Scheldt mud	$\tau_{CR} = k \cdot T_s^P$ (numerical data)	$p = 6.0$	cone and plate	30
Zeebrugge mud	$\tau_y = k \cdot T_s^P$ S: % $< 63 \ \mu m$	$\log k = 0.035 \ S - 17.3$ $0 < S < 77\%$ $p = 5.6$	rotational viscometer	43
mud (general)	generalized Bingham $\tau_B = k \cdot T_s^P$	$3 < p < 4$	not reported	63
Brazilian continental shelf mud	$\tau_y = k \cdot T_s^P$	$p = 1$	rotational viscometer	19
Belgian coast: Ostend 1 Ostend 2 Zeebrugge Nieuwpoort 1 Nieuwpoort 2 Kallo Antwerp 1 Antwerp 2	$\tau_y = k \cdot T_s^P$	 $p = 3.1; k = 1.4 \ 10^{-7}$ $p = 3.4; k = 6.2 \ 10^{-8}$ $p = 3.1; k = 8 \ 10^{-8}$ $p = 2.3; k = 9.3 \ 10^{-6}$ $p = 2.4; k = 2 \ 10^{-6}$ $p = 5.0; k = 1.3 \ 10^{-12}$ $p = 5.5; k = 8.6 \ 10^{-15}$ $p = 3.6; k = 6.2 \ 10^{-9}$	rotational viscometer	(1)

(1) unpublished results 1986 – Hydraulics lab., K. U. Leuven

The specific type of particle attachment and the state of flocculation depend on the type of clay minerals and colloids, the ionic strength, the type and amount of cations, pH, and organic matter (including micro-organisms). More information on the complex electrokinetic phenomena involved can be found in [28, 31, 68, 74].

Ambient fluid properties

Salinity. Early workers have recognized the influence of salinity (cation concentration proportional to ocean water distribution) on floc-settling velocity. It was concluded that salt flocculation was completed in a low salinity region: 1 g/l [39], 2 g/l [52] (also depending on particle concentration), or 2 to 10 g/l [38]. This suggests that a constant cohesion can be assumed above 3 g/l salts.

However, the relative cation abundance (Na, K, Ca, Mg) is not constant in an estuarial transition zone. Arulanandan [1] introduced the SAR (Sodium Absorption Ratio) concept to take this into account:

$$SAR = \frac{Na^+(+K^+)}{[\frac{1}{2}(Ca^{++} + Mg^{++})]^{1/2}} \quad \text{(molar concentrations)}$$

For pure clays (kaolinite, illite, montmorillonite) characterized by their CEC (Cation Exchange Capacity), a low SAR (<2) means aggregation by divalent ions, while a high SAR (20–30) can bring about dispersion in low-ionic-strength waters, affecting, for instance, the critical erosive stresses of sediments.

Yong et al. [75] studied the complex interaction of the type of anion, clay mineralogy, salt concentration, and solids concentration for dispersive clays. The differences are described in terms of net attraction or repulsion on the level of the particles and the primary flocs. Each different set of circumstances gives rise to a particular rheological behavior.

For coastal muds with only small salinity variations, salt flocculation can be assumed to be constant.

Estuarine muds are very often mixtures of nearby marine material and riverine suspension load. The latter is heavily altered by the salinity shock found in the transition zone (that can be accompanied by a "turbidity maximum"). The original hypothesis that salt flocculation is responsible for the trapping of this sediment is disputed by more recent findings about the behavior of organic matter in an estuary [17]. But even if salts should not be the main cause for particle aggregation in an estuary, they surely prevent deflocculation.

pH. Most natural mud suspensions are buffered (calcium-carbonate system) at near-neutral basic values. Artificial change can be drastic: Acid pH causes more intense particle attachment and high shear stresses, while bases bring about deflocculation. pH changes have an influence not only on the flocculation process, but also on the stability of several chemical components (destruction, solubility). The effects are hard to separate in an experimental analysis. For a kaolinite clay at 20 mass % the change from pH = 7.0 to 5.0 means a doubling of the τ_B, while a change to pH = 8.0 halves the τ_B [62].

Apart from exceptional microenvironments, the natural influence of pH is negligible.

Eh. Oxygen depletion by biological consumption rapidly turns suspensions anoxic. They become favorable habitats for methane-producing bacteria. The reducing environments lead to alteration of iron-colloids and metal precipitations. Presence of gas leads to a strength reduction of sediment and suspension; the influence of other effects is unquantified.

Solid Particle Properties

A broad spectrum of minerals and mineraloids makes up the solid content in mud. Clay minerals from terrigenic and marine (partly authigenic) sources form the bulk; detrital carbonates (biogenic skeleton material), chemical precipitates (Fe, Al, Si colloids), and a zoo of living and non-living organic matter (bacteria, algae, plant remains, etc.) travels along. Silt and sand particles (quartz, feldspars) can be incorporated into the flocs. Pure terrigenic clay minerals are often used as mud-model materials in research, because they are easier to handle, as in sampling and storage. The organic content of natural muds is sensitive to the environment. Gas development in a model, for instance, can spoil the test. The surface properties of the clays in mud are altered by the other materials present. Therefore, more research is needed to see how far the analogy goes.

Inert materials, such as sand grains (quartz), do not take an essential part in the cohesion. For an equal bulk density, mud yield-stress decreases with an increase of such "balast" materials.

Clay Minerals

Parameters for the description of clay particle properties are: mineralogy, granulometry, specific surface (O_s), cation exchange capacity (CEC), morphology, and crystallinity. Electrostatic charge density is a combination of O_s and CEC. Most of the parameters are interrelated.

The rheological behavior of suspensions of the different types of clay minerals (most frequently illite, kaolinite, and montmorillonite) in relatively pure forms has been studied for industrial applications. Norton et al. [56] first mentioned that the yield point of a kaolinite suspension is proportional to the cube of its solids content. Ornsby and Marcus [59], in their study on different kaolinites and different particle size fractions, found a positive relation between the "pseudoplastic viscosity" (or power-law constant k) and the CEC and O_s. Crystallinity was evaluated as unimportant for the viscosity. Particle size was found to be of primary importance in controlling viscous and plastic properties.

Flegmann et al. [21] and Godwin [26] describe the influence of the ionic environment on kaolinite particle aggregation and its subsequent rheological behavior.

Montmorillonites are the finest clays with a very high water-swelling capacity. The comparative experiments of Einsele [14] show that montmorillonite (bentonite) has, for a given water content (or void ratio), a higher shear strength (determined with a vane test), as compared with illite or kaolinite. Foster et al. [22] showed the influence of different cations on the rheology of dilute montmorillonite suspensions. In mono-electrolytic systems, increasing shear strength was found in the order Ca < K < Na < Li. Considered to be an effect of different swelling, these results are in agreement with the discussion of cohesive soil erosion in [1].

Different types of clay do not intermix at random, but form specific arrangements, as reported by Yong et al. [75] for the edge (kaolinite)-face (illite) aggregation. Rheological parameters are, therefore, not necessarily proportional interpolations of the properties of the pure minerals. Lannicelli and Millmann [40] found, at continuous addition of montmorillonite, the viscosity of kaolinite to increase sharply above a montmorillonite content of 5%.

Mixtures of kaolinite and fine quartz [32] show a gradual decrease of flow resistance (shear stress, plastic viscosity) with increasing quartz content.

The clay-mineral mixtures in mud suspensions are source-dependent (types of soils, geological substratum) and can vary within an estuary due to mixing from different origins. Krone and Einstein [39] and Migniot [52] give some qualitative information on the relative amounts of different clays in mud.

Migniot [52] states that the elements with the smallest diameters seem to have the highest yield points, but no further analysis is made of the influence of different clay mineralogies. Bulk properties, such as granulometry, O_s, and CEC, are easier to measure accurately than the exact relative amounts of the different clays. The strength of the primary aggregates of five fine sediments was related to CEC by Krone [37, 38]: $\tau_B = 3.92 + 0.8447$ (CEC), CEC measured on the fraction $< 10\ \mu m$.

On the basis of experimental work on estuarial and coastal muds, Verreet et al. [69] proposed (for particles of the same "population" or location) a relation of the form:

$$\tau_y = k_1 \left[T_s \times \% \ \text{fr} < 1\ \mu m \right]^{n_1}$$

or $\tau_y = k_2 \left[T_s \times 0_s \right]^{n_2}$, with O_s in m^2/g, T_s solids content in kg/m^3

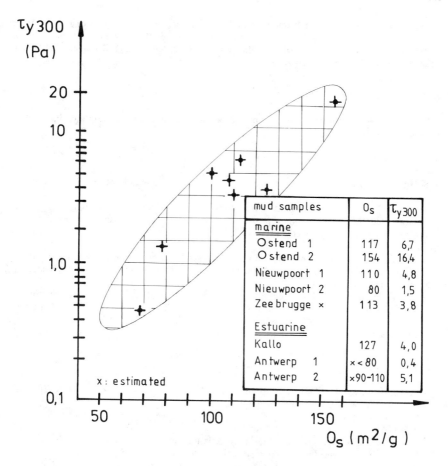

Figure 4. Relation of yield stress (at high solids concentration of 300 g/l) with specific surface (O$_s$) of dry solids of different Belgian estuarine and coastal muds.

The "fineness" of the material influences the potential number of particle and floc bonds in a suspension. This effect of "fineness" (measured as specific surface) is illustrated for different natural muds through the yield stress at a solids concentration of 300 g/l in Figure 4.

The very finest, colloidal, fraction ($\ll 1~\mu$m) in mud seems to have a great influence on mud rheology [69]. These colloids include clay minerals, chemical precipitates, coatings (Fe, Al, Si-oxides, hydroxides), and organic matter.

Organic matter

Organic matter (bacteria, polysaccharides) influences [25] or determines [17] flocculation of suspended matter in estuaries. Introduction of bacteria in a stable clay suspension can be enough to cause flocculation (Faas, pers. comm. 1985). Microorganisms and their products are the main cause for aggregate stability in soils [42]. Bennett et al. [5] did not find any conclusive influence of organic matter on geotechnical properties of submarine sediments below 5% TOC; they suggested a further, more selective study of different groups of organic matter and their possible influence. Verreet et al.

[69] propose that an analytical distinction should be made between particle-surface active ("humic" and "fulvic" compounds) and less particle-surface active types of organic matter (apolar lipoidal matter and residual "humine"). Many indications exist of the rheological influence of organic "gluing" materials, but no systematic study of the specific subject has been undertaken yet.

RELATED/SIMILAR MATERIALS

Study of the fundamental properties of mud suspensions can benefit from the knowledge of related materials, such as:

- Pure clay suspensions for industrial (paper, ceramics) or engineering (drilling muds, slurry walls) purposes.
- Sludges from process industries (tailings, organic sludges) or domestic waste-water treatment.

The pure clays are less complex in composition, allowing a more sensitive analysis of different variables. Often, the physico-chemical properties of the fluid medium are substantially different due to artificial pH, salt, or polymer concentration [4]. These modifications restrict relevance for natural muds.

Parallelism extends to research methodologies. Geotechnical properties of the ultimately deposited bed materials (pelitic sediments) are a function of many of the same variables that influence fluid mud, such as clay mineralogy.

On the other hand, several other disciplines may benefit from a better knowledge of mud properties and behavior. Examples are the understanding of the mechanism of the consolidation of mud deposits for optimum use of dredge spoil sites (fast consolidation), the dewatering of sludges from water treatment plants, and the performance of dredging equipment.

REFERENCES

1. Arulanandan, K., "Fundamental Aspects of Erosion of Cohesive Soils," *Journal of the Hydraulics Division*, ASCE, Vol. 101, HY5, 1975, pp. 635–639.
2. Bauer, W. H., and Collins, E. A., "Thixotropy and Dilatancy," *Rheology: Theory and Applications* (4), Eirych (ed.), 1967, pp. 423–459.
3. Beazley, K. M., "Viscosity—Concentration Relations in Deflocculated Kaolin Suspensions," *Journal of Colloid and Interface Science*, Vol. 41, 1972, pp. 105–115.
4. Beazley, K. M., "Industrial Aqueous Suspensions," *Rheometry: Industrial Applications*, K. Walters (ed.), Research Study Press, John Wiley New York, 1980.
5. Bennett, R. H., et al., "Interrelationships of Organic Carbon and Submarine Sediment Geotechnical Properties," *Marine Geotechnology*, Vol. 6, no. 1, 1985, pp. 61–98.
6. Berlamont, J., et al., "A Permanent Mud Pumping Installation as an Alternative for Local Maintenance Dredging," Preprinted Proceedings 21st IAHR Congress, Melbourne Australia, Vol. 4.
7. Brenner, H., "Suspension Rheology," *Progress in Heat and Mass Transfer*, R. Schowalter (ed.), Vol. 5, Pergamon Press, 1972, pp. 89–129.
8. Chen, C., "On Frontier Between Rheology and Mudflow Mechanics," Proceedings Conference on Frontiers of Hydraulic Engineering, Bangkok, 1983, pp. 113–118.
9. Clanton, M. L., "Application of Rate Process Theory to Erosional Parameters of a Deep Sea Pacific Sediment," University of Rhode Island, Ph.D. thesis, 1980, 148 pp.
10. Colin, F., "Characterisation of the Physical State of Sludges," *Methods of Characterisation of Sewage Sludge*, Casey et al (eds.), D. Reidel Publ. Co., 1984, pp. 78–105.
11. Crochet, M. J., Davies, A. R., and Walters, K., "Numerical Simulation of Non-Newtonian Flow," Elsevier, 1984, pp. 352.
12. Dangeard, L., Larsonneur, C., and Migniot, C., "Les courants de turbidité, les coulées boueuses et les glissements: résultats d'experiences," *Comptes Rendus de l'Académie des Sciences*, Paris, t. 261, 1965, pp. 2123–2126.

13. Dott, R. J., "Dynamics of Subaqueous Gravity Depositional Processes," Bulletin American Association of Petroleum Geologists (AAPG), Vol. 47, 1963, pp. 104–128.
14. Einsele, G., et al., "Mass Physical Properties, Sliding and Erodibility of Experimentally Deposited and Differently Consolidated Clayey Muds," Sedimentology, Vol. 21, 1974, pp. 339–372.
15. Einstein, A., "Eine neue Bestimmung der Moleküldimensionen," Ann. Physik, Vol. 19, 1906, pp. 289–306.
16. Einstein, H. A., and Krone, R. B., "Experiments to Determine Modes of Cohesive Sediment Transport in Salt Water," Journal of Geophysical Research, Vol. 67, no. 4, 1962, pp. 1451–1461.
17. Eisma, D., "Flocculation and De-flocculation of Suspended Matter in Estuaries," Netherlands Journal of Sea Research, Vol. 20, no. 2/3, 1986, pp. 183–199.
18. Faas, R. W., "Rheological Characteristics of Rappahannock Estuary Muds, Southeastern Virginia U.S.A.," Spec. Publs. int. Ass. Sediment., Vol. 5, 1981, pp. 505–515.
19. Faas, R. W., "Time and Density-Dependent Properties of Fluid Mud Suspensions, NE Brasilian Continental Shelf, Geo-Marine Letters, Vol. 4, 1984, pp. 147–152.
20. Firth, B. A., and Hunter, R. J., "Flow Properties of Coagulated Colloidal Suspensions, I. Energy Dissipation in the Flow Units," Journal of Colloid and Interface Science, Vol. 57, no. 2, 1976, pp. 248–256.
21. Flegmann, A., Goodwin, J., and Ottewill, R., "Rheological Studies on Kaolinite Suspensions," Proceedings British Ceramic Society, no. 13, 1969, pp. 31–45.
22. Foster, W., Savins, J., and Waite, J., "Lattice Expansion and Rheological Behavior relationships in Water-Montmorillonite Systems," Clays and Clay Minerals, National Conference Proceedings, Vol. 3, 1954.
23. Gemeentewerken Rotterdam, "Bepaling van het max. leidingdebiet van slib bij gegeven opvoerhoogte," report 103.05-R7807, 1978, pp. 16.
24. Gemeentewerken Rotterdam, "Weerstand van slib in persleidingen," report 103.05-R7906.
25. Gibbs, R. J., "Effect of Natural Organic Coatings on the Coagulation of Particles," Environmental Science and Technology, Vol. 17, no. 4, 1983, pp. 237–240.
26. Goodwin, J., "Rheological Studies on the Dispersion of Kaolinite Clays," Transactions and Journal of the British Ceramic Society, Vol. 70, no. 2, 1970, pp. 65–70.
27. Hanack, S., and Stefan, H., "Strömungen von Tonsuspensionen mit einem hohen Feststoffgehalt," Mitteilung vom Institut für Wasserbau und Wasserwirtschaft TU Berlin, no. 67, 1968, pp. 67.
28. Hiemenz, P. C., "Principles of Colloid and Surface Chemistry," Marcel Dekker Inc., New York, 1977, pp. 516.
29. Hunter, R. J., and Nicol, S. K., "The Dependence of Plastic Flow Behaviour of Clay Suspensions on Surface Properties," Journal of Colloid and Interface Science, Vol. 28, no. 2, 1968, pp. 250–259.
30. HRS, "River Scheldt Surge Barrier—Study of Estuary Sediments," Hydraulics Research Station Wallingford, Report EX928, 1980.
31. Ives, K. J. (ed.), The Scientific Basis of Flocculation, Sijthoff and Noordhoff Publ., 1978, pp. 369.
32. James, A. E., and Williams, D. J. A., "Flocculation and Rheology of Kaolinite/Quartz Suspensions," Rheologica Acta, Vol. 21, 1982, pp. 176–183.
33. James, A. E., Williams, D. J. A., and Williams, P. R., "Small Strain, Low Rate Rheometry of Cohesive Sediments," Abstracts International Symposium Physical Processes in Estuaries, Nl., 1986, pp. 144–145.
34. Kirby, R., "Fluid Mud Layers in Estuaries," Abstracts International Symposium Physical Processes in Estuaries, Nl., 1986.
35. Krone, R. B., "Flume Studies of the Transport of Sediment in Estuarial Shoaling Processes," University of California, Berkeley, 1962.
36. Krone, R. B., "A Study of Rheological Properties of Estuarial Sediments," University of California, Berkeley, 1963.
37. Krone, R. B., "Engineering Interest in the Benthic Boundary Layer," The Benthic Boundary Layer, McCave (ed.), Plenum Press, 1976, pp. 143–156.
38. Krone, R. B., "Advances in Knowledge of Fine Sediment Transport Processes in Estuaries," presented at third International Symposium on River Sedimentation, Jackson, Mississippi, 1986.
39. Krone, R. B., and Einstein, H. A., "Modes of Sediment Behavior and Selection of Harbor

Design and Maintenance Techniques for Minimum Shoaling in Estuaries," Proceedings of the 8th Conference on Coastal Engineering, 1963, pp. 331–338.

40. Lannicelli, J., and Millman, N., "Relation of Viscosity of Kaolin-Water Suspensions to Montmorillonite Content of Certain Georgia Clays", Clays and Clay Minerals, Proceedings of the 14th national conference, 1966, pp. 347–354.

41. LCHF, "Etude rhéologique des vases de Zeebrugge," raport Laboratoire Central d'Hydraulique de France, 1978.

42. Lynch, J. M., and Bragg, E., "Microorganisms and Soil Aggregate Stability," *Advances in Soil Science*, B. A. Stewart (ed.), Vol. 2, Springer Verlag Berlin, 1985, pp. 134–171.

43. Malherbe, B., Bastin, A., and De Potter, B., "Physical Properties of Sand and Mud Sediments," Symposium Engineering in Marine Environment, K. VIV (ed.), Belgium, 1982, pp. I 17–23.

44. Malherbe, B., Dewolf, P., and Paquot, B., "Nautical Bottom Research and Survey for Optimization of Maintenance Dredging in Mud Areas," *Advances in Underwater Technology, Ocean Science and Offshore Engineering*, Vol. 6, *Oceanology*, Proceedings of Oceanology International 86, U.K., 1986, pp. 427–441.

45. Mehta, A. J., and Maa, P. Y., "Waves over Mud: Modeling Erosion," Proceedings Third International Conference on River Sedimentation, Jackson Ms. U.S.A., 1986, pp. 588–601.

46. Mei, C. C., and Liu, K. F., "A Non-Newtonian Model for the Motion of a Fluid-Mud under Shallow Water Waves," Abstracts International Symposium Physical Processes in Estuaries, Nl., 1986, pp. 146–148.

47. Mercer, H. A., and Weymann, H. D., "Time-Dependent Behavior of Thixotropic Suspensions," *Rheologica Acta*, Vol. 13, 1974, pp. 413–417.

48. Mewis, J., "Thixotropy—A General Review," *Journal of Non-Newtonian Fluid Mechanics*, Vol. 6, 1979, pp. 1–20.

49. Mewis, J., "Suspension Rheology," *Rheological Measurements of Polymers and Suspensions*, University of Minnesota, 1983.

50. Mewis, J., and Spaull, A. J. B., "Rheology of Concentrated Dispersions," *Advances in Colloid and Interface Science*, Vol. 6, 1976, pp. 173–200.

51. Michaels, A. S., and Bolger, J. C., "The Plastic Flow Behaviour of Flocculated Kaolin Suspensions," *I and EC Fundamentals*, Vol. 1, 1962, pp. 153–162.

52. Migniot, C., "Etude des propriétés physiques de différents sédiments très fins et de leur comportement sous des actions hydrodynamiques," *La Houille Blanche*, Vol. 23, 1968, pp. 591–620.

53. Migniot, C., "Mesures des characteristiques mécaniques des vases déposées dans les chenaux de navigation," XVIIIe *Journées de l'Hydraulique*, Société Hydrotechnique de France, communication I-13, 1984.

54. Mooney, M., "The Viscosity of a Concentrated Suspension of Spherical Particles," *Journal of Colloid Science*, Vol. 6, 1951, pp. 162–170.

55. Nguyen, Q. D., and Boger, D. V., "Yield Stress Measurements for Concentrated Suspensions," *Journal of Rheology*, Vol. 27, no. 4, 1983, pp. 321–349.

56. Norton, F., Johnson, A., and Lawrence, W., "Fundamental Study of Clay, VI. Flow Properties of Kaolinite-Water Suspensions," *Journal of the American Ceramic Society*, 1944, p. 149.

57. Odd, N., "Mathematical Modeling of Mud Transport in Estuaries," International Symposium Physical Processes in Estuaries, NI., 1986, 26 pp.

58. Ohtsubo, K., and Muraoka, K., "Resuspension of Cohesive Sediments by Currents," Proceedings of the 3rd International Symposium on River Sedimentation, Jackson Ms U.S.A., 1986, pp. 1680–1689.

59. Ormsby, W., and Marcus, J., "Flow Properties of Aqueous Suspensions Containing Kaolin of Varying Degrees of Crystallinity," *Journal of the American Ceramic Society*, Vol. 50, 1966, pp. 190–195.

60. Parker, W. R., "On the Observation of Cohesive Sediment Behaviour for Engineering Purposes," *Estuarine Cohesive Sediment Dynamics*, A. J., Mehta (ed.), Springer Verlag, 1986, pp. 270–289.

61. Parker, W. R., and Kirby, R., "Time-Dependent Properties of Cohesive Sediment Relevant to Sedimentation Management—European Experience," *Estuarine Comparisons*, V. S. Kennedy (ed.), Academic Press, 1982, pp. 573–589.

62. Pazwash, H., and Robertson, J. M., "Fluid-Dynamic Consideration of Bottom Materials," *Journal of the Hydraulics Division*, ASCE, Vol. HY9, 1971, pp. 1317–1329.
63. Périgaud, C., "Mécanique de l'érosion des vases," *La Houille Blanche*, no. 7/8, 1983, pp. 501–512.
64. Russel, W. B., "Review of the Role of Colloidal Forces in the Rheology of Suspensions," *Journal of Rheology*, Vol. 24, no.3, 1980, pp. 287–317.
65. Stefan, H., "High Concentration Turbidity Currents in Reservoirs," Proceedings International Association for Hydraulic Research, 15th Congress, Istanbul, Turkey, 1973, pp. 341–352.
66. Tadros, T. F., "Concentrated Dispensions, II: An Industrial Viewpoint," *Science and Technology of Polymer Colloids*, Poehlein et al. (eds.), Vol. 2 Nijhoff Publ., 1983.
67. Van Damme, P. M., "Slibgedrag in een natuurlijk milieu (literatuuronderzoek)," thesis TH Delft, June 1982.
68. Van Olphen, H., *An Introduction to Clay Colloid Chemistry*, Interscience, 1963.
69. Verreet, G. et al., "Relations Between Physico-Chemical and Rheological Properties of Fine-Grained Muds," Proceedings 3rd International Symposium on River Sedimentation, Jackson, Mississippi, 1986, pp. 1637–1646.
70. Walters, K., *Rheometry*, Chapman and Hall, London, 1975, 278 pp.
71. Wilkinson W.L., *Non-Newtonian Fluids, Fluid Mechanics, Mixing and Heat-Transfer*, Pergamon Press, 1960.
72. Williams, D. J. A., and James, A. E., "Rheology of Brisbane and Rotterdam Mud," Department of Chemical Engineering, University College of Swansea, Swansea N. K., 1978.
73. Williams, D. J. A., "Rheology of Cohesive Suspensions," *Estuarine Cohesive Sediment Dynamics*, A. J. Mehta (ed.), Springer Verlag, 1986, pp. 110–125.
74. Yariv, S., and Cross, H., *Geochemistry of Colloid Systems*, Springer Verlag, 1979, 450 pp.
75. Yong. R.N., et al., "Interparticle Action and Rheology of Dispersive Clays," *Journal of the Geotechnical Engineering Division*, ASCE, Vol. 105, no. GT 10, 1979, pp. 1193–1209.

CHAPTER 6

VELOCITY AND VELOCITY GRADIENT IN TURBULENT VISCOELASTIC PIPE FLOW

Chiaki Kuroda

Research Laboratory of Resources Utilization
Tokyo Institute of Technology
Yokohama, Japan

and

Kohei Ogawa

Department of Chemical Engineering
Tokyo Institute of Technology
Tokyo, Japan

CONTENTS

INTRODUCTION

The work given for shearing motion of viscoelastic fluids, such as most polymer solutions or melted polymers, is not preserved as completely as elastic materials and is not dissipated as wholly as viscous fluids, because both elastic and viscous properties coexist as rheological properties in the fluids. The viscoelastic fluids show some characteristic flow phenomena which are not observed in normal viscous fluids, and the drag reduction in turbulent pipe flow (Toms phenomenon [1]), discussed in this chapter, is a well-known, unique phenomenon and is effective for practical usage.

This drag reduction phenomenon has been studied extensively from different viewpoints, and many things have been noticed, e.g., wall shear stress in connection with flow rate, pipe diameter, polymer concentration, etc. [2–8], turbulent flow mechanism based on measurements of velocity fluctuations [9–16], and modeling of the relation between the flow mechanism and the origin of drag reduction [17–23]. Further examples of review papers are listed in the references [24–28]. Despite these many works, the following common problems have heretofore remained:

1. Sufficient discussions for relatively high concentration polymer solutions, which clearly have non-Newtonian and elastic properties, have not been given, since drag reduction can be observed even in very dilute solutions and studies have been conducted mainly in dilute polymer solutions.
2. A relationship between a characteristic of turbulent viscoelastic flow and a basic rheological property has not been sufficiently investigated.
3. There have been few papers [29] about the velocity gradient fluctuation at the wall, which must be closely connected with the turbulent dissipation of the mechanical energy, though there has been much research on the wall shear stress and the velocity near the wall.

Our discussion of turbulent viscoelastic pipe flow in this chapter is based on the experimental investigation [30] of the connection between the turbulent flow mechanism of polymer solutions in a circular pipe and basic rheological properties, i.e., the non-Newtonian viscosity and the shear elasticity.

RHEOLOGICAL PROPERTIES OF TEST FLUIDS

A water-solution of polyacrylamide (PAA) is a well-known viscoelastic fluid for research. The polymer used was PAA, Separan AP-30 manufactured by Bokusui Brown & Co., Ltd., and its average molecular weight was estimated as 4×10^6 g/g-mol by using the equation of Collinson [31] based on the intrinsic viscosity.

Test polymer solutions contained two electrolytes, $K_3Fe(CN)_6$ and $K_4Fe(CN)_6$, each of 3.0×10^{-3} mol/liter and a supporting electrolyte KCl of 1.0×10^{-1} mol/liter, which were necessary for the electrochemical technique used for measuring velocity fluctuations and velocity gradient fluctuations.

The degradation of polymer solutions by adding electrolytes was already pointed out [32], and was also reconfirmed by the authors. Moreover, another novel effect discovered of electrolytes on rheological properties will be mentioned later.

Viscous Properties

The viscous property of the test fluids is often considered to be Newtonian, since very dilute polymer solutions are used in many studies on drag reduction. Most polymer solutions, however, show non-Newtonian viscous properties more or less except the case of very small shearing velocity [33], and the non-Newtonian viscous property seems to be natural, especially in turbulent flow with large shearing velocity. Figure 1 shows some examples of flow curves obtained by the method of Krieger and Maron [34] with a capillary viscometer. The effect of electrolytes on the viscous property is clearly observed; however, any flow curve of the PAA solutions used can be approximately expressed by the power-law model as far as the present test condition of shear is concerned:

$$\tau = K\dot{\gamma}^n \tag{1}$$

where K is the pseudo-plastic viscosity and n is the power-law exponent. In the laminar pipe flow

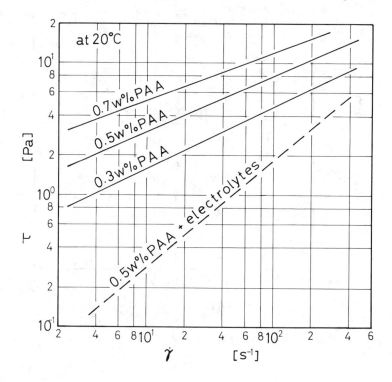

Figure 1. Some examples of flow curves.

of power-law fluids, the following relation between the flow rate Q and the pressure drop ΔP is derived:

$$Q = \frac{n\pi}{3n + 1}\left(\frac{\Delta P}{2KL}\right)^{1/n} R^{(3n + 1)/n} \tag{2}$$

where L is the axial length of the measured section and R is the inner pipe radius (R = D/2). The values of rheological constants K and n can be obtained from the relation between Q and ΔP in the test pipe used as shown in Figure 2.

Elastic Properties

The modulus of shear elasticity G, which is measured with a Schwedoff rheogonimeter, is used to express the elastic property of the test fluids concretely. The relation between G and the weight concentration C is shown in Figure 3. The value of G increases proportionally to the approximate cube of C and decreases greatly by adding electrolytes.

Degradation by Elapsed Time

Viscoelastic properties are changed greatly by adding electrolytes as previously mentioned. Also in this study, it was found that there was a certain relation between the progress of degradation and

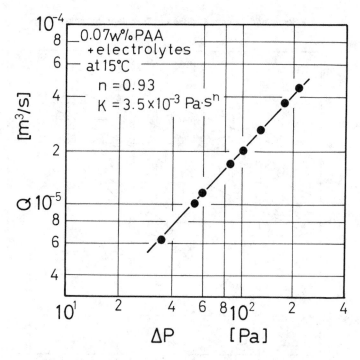

Figure 2. A relation between Q and ΔP in laminar condition.

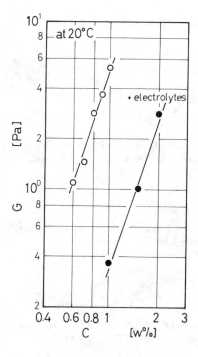

Figure 3. Modulus of shear elasticity G.

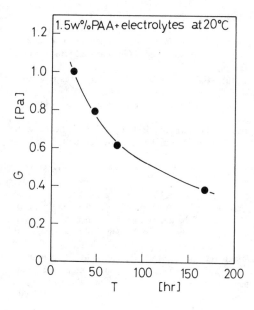

Figure 4. Decrease of G by degradation.

the elapsed time T after addition of electrolytes. Namely, the degradation proceeds as the increase of T even if the test solutions settle down without shearing motion. Such degradation can be concretely detected as the decrease of G, as shown in Figure 4. On the other hand, viscous properties hardly ever change with the elapsed time as listed in Table 1. Though the explanation of such phenomena based on the detailed molecular model is not clear, it is sure from the practical viewpoint that the effect of elastic properties on the flow behavior of polymer solutions can be investigated by using the test fluids of different values of T.

Table 1
Viscous Properties of Test Fluids

C [w%]	n [−] K [Pa·sⁿ]	T 24	48	[hr] 72	168	240	ave.
0.01	n	0.97	0.98	1.00	0.99	1.00	0.99
	K × 10³	1.8	1.6	1.5	1.5	1.4	1.6
0.03	n	0.97	0.95	0.95	0.97	0.96	0.96
	K × 10³	2.5	2.6	2.4	2.3	2.4	2.5
0.05	n	0.95	0.95	0.94	0.93	0.94	0.94
	K × 10³	3.3	3.2	3.3	3.5	3.4	3.3
0.07	n	0.95	0.91	0.92	0.93	0.94	0.93
	K × 10³	3.2	3.9	3.8	3.5	3.2	3.5
0.10	n	0.85					
	K × 10²	1.2					

EXPERIMENTAL PROCEDURE

Two circular pipes made of acrylic resin, 10.0 mm and 23.5 mm in inner diameter D, were used for measurements of $\dot{\gamma}_w$ and U, respectively. The test fluid was lifted up into a head tank without using a pump and flowed down through the test pipe.

The wall shear stress τ_w was evaluated from the axial pressure drop ΔP, which was measured by using an electric pressure transducer.

Both the axial velocity and the axial velocity gradient at the pipe wall were measured by electrochemical techniques [35–37].

The velocity fluctuations were measured by using a platinum spherical electrode with the diameter of 0.5 mm. The following empirical relation exists between the diffusion-limited current i_d through the electrode and the velocity U:

$$U = k_1 i_d^{m_1} \tag{3}$$

where k_1 and m_1 are experimental constants that depend on the shape of electrodes and the properties of test fluids. The values of these constants should be determined by calibration; however, only the value of m_1 for Newtonian fluids has been confirmed to be 2. Such probes were fixed at six radial positions with the distance of 2 mm, and the axial velocities at those points were measured simultaneously. All the data were recorded on magnetic tapes and treated statistically by a computer.

The velocity gradient fluctuations at the pipe wall were measured by a platinum electrode, 0.35 mm in diameter, which was plugged in the wall and its surface was flush with the wall surface. The following empirical relation exists between the diffusion-limited current i_d and the velocity gradient $\dot{\gamma}_w$, as well as the case of measurement of velocity:

$$\dot{\gamma}_w = k_2 i_d^{m_2} \tag{4}$$

where k_2 and m_2 are also experimental constants which should be evaluated by calibration. However, the value of m_2 for Newtonian fluids has been confirmed to be 3.

PRESSURE DROP AND FRICTION FACTOR

Figure 5 shows some examples of the relation between the pressure drop ΔP and the flow rate Q. These results were obtained by using the test fluids of a uniform weight concentration C and different elapsed time T. Because viscous properties are almost the same for these test fluids, all of the data in laminar conditions are on a unique line. In turbulent conditions, ΔP takes a smaller value than that of the solvent (water) even in the case of constant Q, and it means the phenomena of drag reduction. The degree of drag reduction declines with the increase of T, and therefore the decrease of the modulus of shear elasticity G with time is considered to have great effects on the decline of drag reduction.

Based on the above-mentioned results, the relationship between the friction factor f and the Reynolds number Re is investigated:

$$f = \frac{\Delta P \cdot D}{2\rho U_{av}^2 L} \tag{5}$$

$$Re = \frac{\rho U_{av}^{2-n} D^n}{K\{(3n + 1)/4n\}^n 8^{n-1}} \tag{6}$$

The above Reynolds number is defined on the basis of the theoretical laminar velocity distribution of the power-law fluid so that the relation of $f \cdot Re = 16$ holds in laminar conditions. As shown in Figure 6, the relation of $f \cdot Re = 16$ is experimentally confirmed. In turbulent conditions, all results for the test fluids at 24 hr after preparation fall on a unique curve regardless of the concentration.

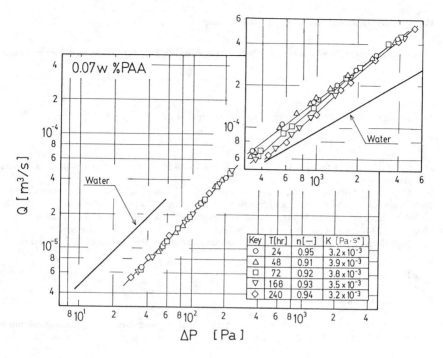

Figure 5. Relations between Q and ΔP.

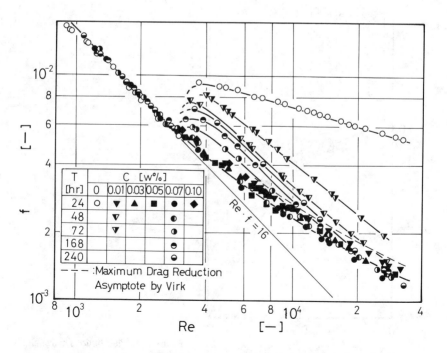

Figure 6. Relations between f and Re.

That is to say, regardless of viscoelastic properties, there is a following maximum drag reduction asymptote:

$$f^{-1/2} = 20.2 \log \text{Re} \cdot f^{1/2} - 33.6 \tag{7}$$

This asymptote is a little different from the following universal one by Virk [28]:

$$f^{-1/2} = 19.0 \log \text{Re} \cdot f^{1/2} - 32.4 \tag{8}$$

and one of its causes is thought to be that the Reynolds number Re for power-law fluids is defined as expressed in Equation 6.

The transition from laminar flow to turbulent flow occurs gradually on the maximum drag reduction asymptote, and sometimes such slow transition is treated as early turbulence [3, 4, 16]. On the other hand, the relation between f and Re changes with the elapsed time T and the transition occurs more suddenly. This tendency can be seen in other test solutions and it suggests that the change of the modulus of shear elasticity G has great effects on the process of flow transition.

TURBULENT VELOCITY

Mean Velocity Profile

Some examples of distributions of the axial mean velocity $\overline{U}_z$ from laminar to turbulent condition are shown in Figure 7. A solid line shows the laminar velocity distribution of a power-law fluid,

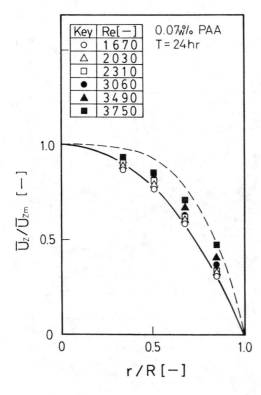

Key	Re[−]
○	1 6 7 0
△	2 0 3 0
□	2 3 1 0
●	3 0 6 0
▲	3 4 9 0
■	3 7 5 0

0.07wt% PAA
T = 24 hr

Figure 7. $\overline{U}_z$ distributions in transitional condition.

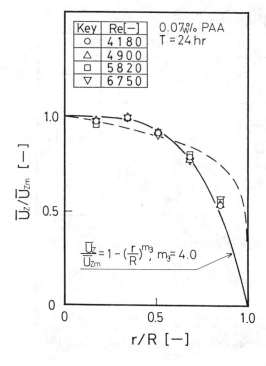

Figure 8. $\bar{U}_z$ distributions in fully developed turbulent condition.

expressed as follows:

$$\overline{U_z/U_{zm}} = 1 - (r/R)^{(n+1)/n} \tag{9}$$

where $\overline{U_{zm}}$ is the maximum axial velocity at the center. On the other hand, a broken line shows the fully developed turbulent velocity distribution obtained experimentally. The change of velocity distribution with Re seems to be speedy near the pipe wall with the increase of Re, and it may be due to the condition of turbulence generation.

Figure 8 shows a unique distribution of $\overline{U_z}$ in the fully developed turbulent condition. A solid line shows the following approximate relation:

$$\overline{U_z/U_{zm}} = 1 - (r/R)^{m_3} \tag{10}$$

and a broken line is drawn by the $\frac{1}{7}$ power-law relation which is an approximate expression of turbulent velocity distributions of Newtonian fluids.

Two characteristics of mean velocity profiles of turbulent viscoelastic flow are the flatter distribution in the central region of the pipe and the smaller velocity gradient near the pipe wall, as reported in previous papers [11]. The value of the index m_3 in Equation 10 decreases with the increase of viscoelasticity and the difference between Equations 9 and 10 becomes small.

Axial Velocity Fluctuation and Laminar-Turbulent Transition

The signals of axial velocity fluctuations u_z, which were measured at six positions in the radial direction simultaneously, are compared. Some examples at the center axis and near the pipe wall are shown in Figures 9 and 10. Figure 9 shows the results for the test fluid of C = 0.05 w% at

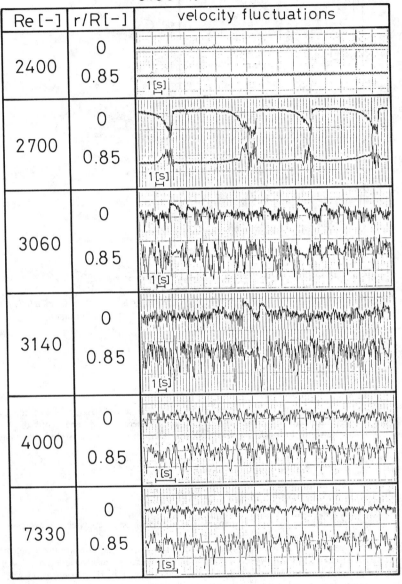

Figure 9. Signals of u_z at C = 0.05 w% and T = 240 hr.

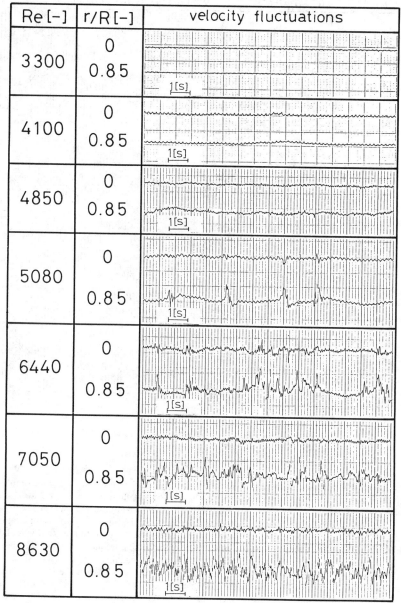

Re [-]	r/R [-]	velocity fluctuations
3300	0 0.85	
4100	0 0.85	
4850	0 0.85	
5080	0 0.85	
6440	0 0.85	
7050	0 0.85	
8630	0 0.85	

0.10w% PAA (T=24hr)

Figure 10. Signals of u_z at C = 0.1 w% and T = 24 hr.

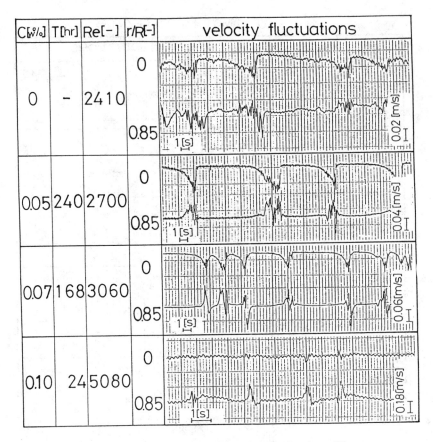

Figure 11. Comparison of u_z signals in transitional condition.

T = 240 hr, whose elastic property weakens and the f − Re relation is not on the maximum drag reduction asymptote. Figure 10 shows the results for the test fluid of C = 0.1 w% at T = 24 hr, whose f − Re relation is just on the maximum drag reduction asymptote and the laminar-turbulent transition occurs gently. Particularly in the central region, the laminar condition is maintained up to larger Re. By comparing turbulent signals in Figure 9 with those in Figure 10, it is found that the change in high-frequency signals is characteristic. That is, high-frequency turbulent eddies seem to be suppressed by elastic effects [24]. Figure 11 shows the signals in the transitional condition. In Newtonian pipe flow, large-amplitude disturbances appear suddenly in the laminar-turbulent transition region [38]. In the case of the test fluids of C = 0.05 w% and 0.07 w% in Figure 11, similar large-amplitude disturbances appear almost simultaneously at r/R = 0 and 0.85. On the other hand, in the case of test fluids which show a gentle transition in the f − Re relation as seen at C = 0.1 w%, no large-amplitude disturbances appear up to large Re and simultaneously at r/R = 0 and 0.85. Such characteristics of large-amplitude disturbances can be clearly confirmed by using contour line maps of axial velocity, as shown in Figures 12 and 13, which are drawn with simul-taneously-measured data at six radial positions.

0.05$_w$% PAA , Re = 2700, T = 240hr

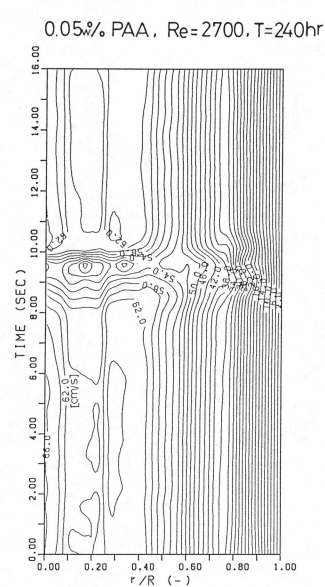

Figure 12. Contour line map of U_z at C = 0.05 w%, Re = 2,700, and T = 240 hr.

The relationship between the intensity of axial velocity fluctuation u'_z ($= (\overline{u_z^2})^{1/2}$) and Re is investigated. Figure 14 shows the results for water and the test fluid of C = 0.1 w% at T = 24 hr. At every radial position, the value of u'_z/U_z increases first, comes to a maximum value, and decreases with Re. Its changing curve is gentler for the polymer solution than for water, and such a characteristic

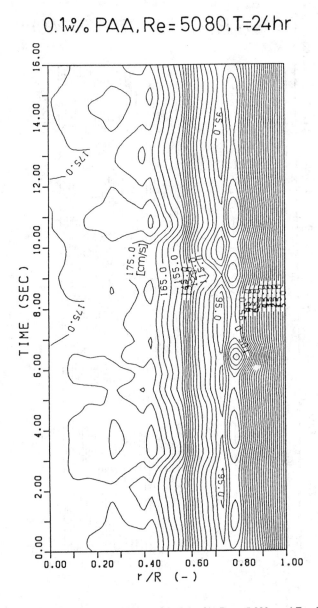

0.1w% PAA, Re = 5080, T=24hr

Figure 13. Contour line map of U_z at C = 0.1 w%, Re = 5,080, and T = 24 hr.

is considered to be connected with the above-mentioned gradual laminar-turbulent transition. Observing the shape of the curve that takes a maximum value, it is possible to define the laminar-turbulent transitional region of Re even for the test fluid that shows no sudden transition in the f — Re relation; e.g., it can be determined as Re = 3,500 ~ 7,500 for this test fluid. As such the

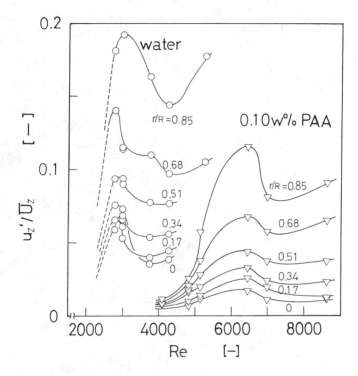

Figure 14. Relations between relative intensity of u_z and Re.

transitional region of Re can be considered to move to the higher Re range as the viscoelasticity increases.

VELOCITY GRADIENT AT THE WALL

Mean Velocity Gradient at the Wall

Figure 15 shows some measured values of the mean velocity gradient at the pipe wall in turbulent conditions. Though the above data are concerned with the test fluid of constant concentration, the value of $\bar{\gamma}_w$ increases with the increase of the elapsed time T; i.e., the decrease of the elastic modulus G. In this case, viscous properties are almost unchangeable and the condition of constant Re means that the flow rate Q is constant. This suggests that the distribution of $\overline{U}_z$ near the pipe wall is changeable with the degree of drag reduction, as mentioned in the previous section.

Velocity Gradient Fluctuation at the Wall

Figure 16 shows some measured values of the intensity (the root-mean-square value) of velocity gradient fluctuations at the pipe wall $\dot{\gamma}'_w$. The value of $\dot{\gamma}'_w$ increases with T in the same way as the

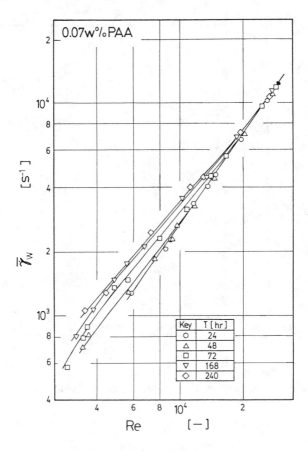

Figure 15. Relations between $\bar{\dot{\gamma}}_w$ and Re.

case of the mean velocity gradient. In Figure 17, the results of some conditions are rearranged as the relative intensity $\dot{\gamma}'_w/\bar{\dot{\gamma}}_w$. The relations for all test fluids at $T = 24$ hr can be expressed by one unique curve, which is connected with the maximum drag reduction asymptote, independent of the concentration C. As T increases, the curve separates from the above unique one and approaches that of water. Such results are also like the $f - \text{Re}$ relation. By comparing the signals of velocity gradient fluctuations for each test fluid at $T = 24, 48, 72, 168,$ and 240 hr, it is found that not only the whole amplitude but also the ratio of high-frequency signals increases with T. An example of fluctuating signals is shown in Figure 18. Such changes in velocity gradient fluctuations are considered to be closely connected with the change in the elastic modulus G.

A Model of Energy Dissipation

Most of the mechanical energy dissipation in pipe flow is controlled by the structure of shear flow near the wall, and therefore much research on drag reduction deals with the turbulence structure near the wall. The thickened laminar sublayer model by Seyer and Metzner [21], the elastic sublayer model by Virk [23], and the damping factor model by Mizushina et al. [19] are well-known models of drag reduction.

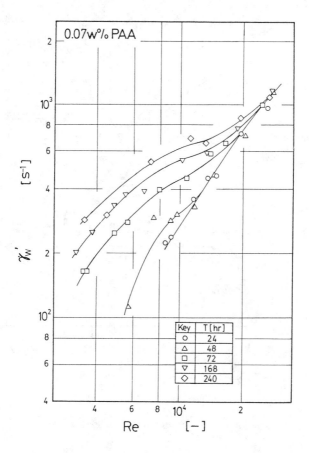

Figure 16. Relations between $\dot{\gamma}'_w$ and Re.

In this section, the relation between drag reduction and velocity gradient fluctuations at the pipe wall, which are connected with velocity fluctuations in the viscous sublayer [29], is investigated by modeling on the basis of Newtonian flow.

The dissipation rate of mechanical energy in Newtonian pipe flow is generally expressed as follows:

$$\Delta P \cdot Q = \mu \int_v \left\{ \left(\frac{\partial \overline{U}_z}{\partial r} \right)^2 + \frac{\overline{\partial u_j}}{\partial x_i} \frac{\partial u_j}{\partial x_i} \right\} dV \tag{11}$$

When $\bar{\gamma}_w$ and $\dot{\gamma}'_w$ are used as characteristic quantities of the mean velocity gradient and the velocity gradient fluctuation respectively, Equation 11 is assumed to be rewritten as follows:

$$\Delta P \cdot Q = \mu V(F_1 \bar{\gamma}_w^2 + F_2 \dot{\gamma}_w'^2) \tag{12}$$

$$\frac{\Delta P \cdot Q}{\bar{\gamma}_w^2 \mu V} = F_1 + F_2(\dot{\gamma}_w'^2 / \bar{\gamma}_w^2) \tag{13}$$

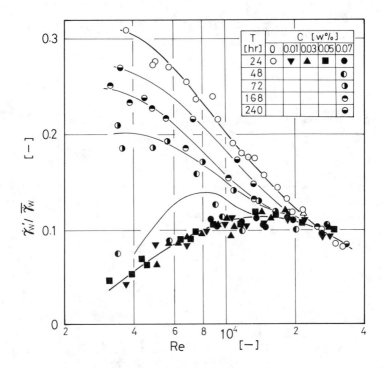

Figure 17. Relations between relative intensity of $\dot{\gamma}_w$ and Re.

where F_1 and F_2 are unknown functions. Substituting the following quantities into Equation 13:

$$\bar{\dot{\gamma}}_w = \frac{\Delta P \cdot R}{2\mu L}, \qquad Q = \pi R^2 U_{av}, \quad V = \pi R^2 L \tag{14}$$

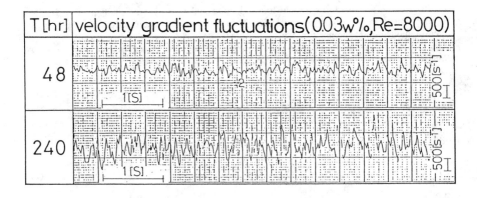

Figure 18. Change of $\dot{\gamma}_w$ signals with T.

the following relation is obtained:

$$\frac{4\mu U_{av} L}{\Delta P \cdot R^2} = F_1 + F_2(\dot{\gamma}_w'^2/\bar{\dot{\gamma}}_w^2) \tag{15}$$

Assuming that the flow condition is laminar, the pressure loss can be expressed as follows:

$$\Delta P_L = \frac{8\mu U_{av} L}{R^2} \tag{16}$$

and therefore Equation 15 is transformed into the following equation:

$$\frac{\Delta P_L}{\Delta P} = 2F_1 + 2F_2(\dot{\gamma}_w'^2/\bar{\dot{\gamma}}_w^2) \tag{17}$$

$$\frac{f_L}{f} = 2F_1 + 2F_2(\dot{\gamma}_w'^2/\bar{\dot{\gamma}}_w^2) \tag{18}$$

If the above relation is applicable to the case of laminar flow, the value of $2F_1$ should be unity and finally the following relation is obtained:

$$\frac{f - f_L}{f} = -2F_2(\dot{\gamma}_w'^2/\bar{\dot{\gamma}}_w^2) \tag{19}$$

On the basis of the above-mentioned discussion of Newtonian pipe flow, it is estimated that there is also a certain quantitative relation between $(f - f_L)/f$ and $\dot{\gamma}_w'^2/\bar{\dot{\gamma}}_w^2$ for viscoelastic pipe flow. Concerning the test fluids of constant C at variable T, which have different elastic properties, $(f - f_L)/f$ is uniformly proportional to $(\dot{\gamma}_w'^2/\bar{\dot{\gamma}}_w^2)^{0.38}$, except the data on the maximum drag reduction asymptote. An example is shown in Figure 19 for a test solution of C = 0.07 w%. The following

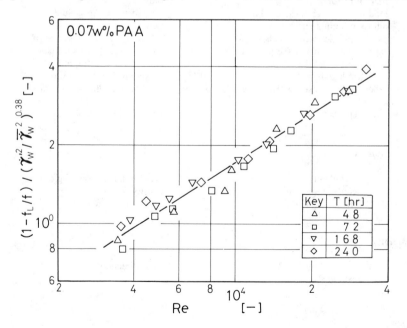

Figure 19. An expression of energy dissipation model.

empirical equation was assumed in developing this figure:

$$\frac{f - f_L}{f} = A \ Re^a (\overline{\dot{\gamma}_w'^2}/\overline{\dot{\gamma}_w^2})^{0.38} \tag{20}$$

where A and a are empirical constants dependent on C. However, the index of $(\overline{\dot{\gamma}_w'^2}/\overline{\dot{\gamma}_w^2})$ takes a constant value of 0.38 independent of C, and it is considered to show a characteristic of the viscoelastic flow behavior.

CONCLUSION

By utilizing the experimental fact that the elastic property of polymer solutions changes with elapsed time after preparation by the effect of electrolytes, the influence of the elasticity on turbulent viscoelastic pipe flow was discussed experimentally. The characteristics, which are seen in fluctuations of axial velocity and axial velocity gradient at the pipe wall and in drag reduction in the laminar-turbulent transition region, are affected significantly by the elastic property, and they are closely related to each other.

NOTATION

A, a	empirical constant (Equation 20)	ΔP	pressure drop, Pa
C	weight concentration, w%	Q	flow rate, m^3/s
D	inner diameter of pipe, m	R	inner radius of pipe, m
F_i	unknown functions (Equation 12)	Re	Reynolds number (Equation 6)
f	friction factor	r	radius, m
G	modulus of shear elasticity, Pa	T	elapsed time of test fluid after preparation, s
i_d	diffusion-limited current, A		
K	pseudo-plastic viscosity, $Pa \cdot s^n$	U	velocity, m/s
k_i	experimental constants (Equations 3 and 4)	U_{av}	cross-sectional average velocity, m/s
		$\overline{U}_z$	axial mean velocity, m/s
L	axial test length, m	$\overline{U}_{zm}$	maximum $\overline{U}_z$ at center axis, m/s
m_i	experimental constants (Equations 3, 4, and 10)	u_z	axial velocity fluctuation, m/s
		u_z'	root-mean-square value of u_z, m/s
n	power-law exponent	V	volume of test section, m^3

Greek Symbols

$\dot{\gamma}$	velocity gradient, 1/s	μ	Newtonian viscosity, kg/m s
$\dot{\gamma}_w'$	root-mean-square value of velocity gradient fluctuation at wall, 1/s	ρ	density, kg/m^3
		τ	shear stress, Pa

Subscripts

L	laminar condition	z	axial direction
w	wall position		

Superscript

—	time-mean value

REFERENCES

1. Toms, B. A., Proc. 1st Int. Rheology Congress, Part 2, North Holland, 135 (1948).
2. Berman, N. S., *Physics of Fluids, 20*, S168 (1977).
3. Forame, P. C., R. J. Hansen, and Little, R. C., *AIChE J., 18*, 213 (1972).
4. Hansen, R. J., R. C. Little, and Forame, P. C., *J. Chem. Eng. Japan, 6*, 310 (1973).
5. Little, R. C., and Wiegard, M., *J. Appl. Polymer Sci., 14*, 409 (1970).
6. Oliver, D. R., and Bakhtiyarov, S. I., *J. Non-Newtonian Fluid Mechanics, 12*, 113 (1983).
7. Seyer, F. A., and Metzner, A. B., *Canadian J. Chem. Eng., 45*, 121 (1967).
8. Virk, P. S., and Baher, H., *Chem. Eng. Sci., 25*, 1183 (1970).
9. Berner, C., and Scrivener, O., "Viscous Flow Drag Reduction," *Progress in Astronautics and Aeronautics, 72*, 290 (1980).
10. Logan, S. E., *AIAA J., 10*, 962 (1972).
11. Nicodemo, L., D. Acierno, and Astarita, G., *Chem. Eng. Sci., 24*, 1241 (1969).
12. Patterson, G. K., J. Chosnek, and Zakin, J. L., *Physics of Fluids, 20*, S89 (1977).
13. Rollin, A., and Seyer, F. A., *Canadian J. Chem. Eng., 50*, 714 (1972).
14. Rudd, M. J., *Nature, 224*, 587 (1969).
15. Rudd, M. J., *J. Fluid Mech., 51*, 673 (1972).
16. Zakin, J. L., C. C. Ni, and Hansen, R. J., *Physics of Fluids, 20*, S85 (1977).
17. Gustavsson, L. H., *Physics of Fluids, 20*, S120 (1977).
18. Hoffmann, L., and Schümmer, P., *Rheol. Acta 17*, 98 (1978).
19. Mizushina, T., H. Usui, and Yoshida, T., *J. Chem. Eng. Japan, 7*, 162 (1974).
20. Schümmer, P., and Thielen, W., *Chem. Eng. Commun., 4*, 593 (1980).
21. Seyer, F. A., and Metzner, A. B., *AIChE J., 15*, 426 (1969).
22. Shaver, R. G., and Merrill, E. W., *AIChE J., 5*, 181 (1959).
23. Virk, P. S., *J. Fluid Mech., 45*, 417 (1971).
24. Berman, N. S., *Encyclopedia of Fluid Mechanics* (Cheremisinoff, ed.), Vol. 1, Ch. 32, Gulf Publishing (1986).
25. Berman, N. S., *Ann. Rev. Fluid Mechanics, 10*, 47 (1978).
26. Sellin, R. H. I., J. W. Hoyt, and Scrivener, O., *J. Hydraulic Res., 20*, 29 (1982).
27. Sellin, R. H. I., J. W. Hoyt, J. Pollet, and Scrivener, O., *J. Hydraulic Res., 20*, 235 (1982).
28. Virk, P. S., *AIChE J., 21*, 625 (1975).
29. Fortuna, G., and Hanratty, T. J., *J. Fluid Mech., 53*, 575 (1972).
30. Ogawa, K., and Kuroda, C., *Canadian J. Chem. Eng., 64*, 497 (1986).
31. Collinson, E., F. S. Dainton, and McNaughton, G. S., *Trans. Faraday Soc., 53*, 489 (1957).
32. Frommer, M. A., A. F. Lavy, and Kraus, M. A., *J. Colloid and Interface Sci., 48*, 165 (1974).
33. Darby, R., *Encyclopedia of Fluid Mechanics*, Vol. 1, Ch. 33, Gulf Publishing (1986).
34. Krieger, I. M., and Maron, S. H., *J. Appl. Phys., 23*, 147 (1952).
35. Ito, S., K. Ogawa, and Yuhara, T., *Kagaku Kogaku, 37*, 698 (1973).
36. Mizushina, T., *Advances in Heat Transfer, 7*, 87 (1971).
37. Ranz, W. E., *AIChE J., 4*, 338 (1958).
38. Ito, S., K. Ogawa, and Urushiyama, S., *J. Chem. Eng. Japan, 4*, 128 (1971).

CHAPTER 7

THE FLOW OF NEWTONIAN AND NON-NEWTONIAN LIQUIDS THROUGH ANNULAR CONVERGING REGIONS*

J. F. Dijksman and **E. P. W. Savenije**

Philips Research Laboratories
Eindhoven, The Netherlands

CONTENTS

INTRODUCTION

An annular convergent region is the space between two conical surfaces the axes of which coincide. In general, the apices of both cones do not coincide. An example of such a geometrical set-up is shown in Figure 1. In order to describe the flow through such a region either a cylindrical or a spherical coordinate system can be used. As the apices of the cones are apart the definition of the conical surfaces is not trivial. As a consequence, the solution of the equations governing the fluid flow through the region between the cones is cumbersome. This chapter presents a coordinate system that can be used for the problems stated such that the boundaries of the domain of interest are coordinate surfaces. For this so-called special toroidal coordinate system we derive a set of differential operations involving the nabla operator similar to the ones given for the rectangular, cylindrical, spherical, and bipolar coordinate systems in [1] and [2].

---

* Apart from minor changes in text and numbering of references this chapter was originally published as: Dijksman, J. F., and Savenije, E. P. W., "The flow of Newtonian and non-Newtonian liquids through annular converging regions," *Rheologica Acta* 24:105–118 (1985). Reproduction with kind permission of Steinkopff Verlag Dortmund, FRG.

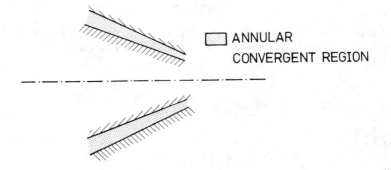

□ ANNULAR
CONVERGENT REGION

Figure 1. Annular convergent region.

Using the special toroidal coordinate system we will give solutions for a selection of fluid flow problems such as:

- Flow through a slightly tapered wire-coating die
- Flow through a narrow annular convergent channel
- Extended cone-and-plate flow

The last section discusses some more complicated examples such as the flow of a generalized Newtonian liquid through an axisymmetric wire-coating head, and the pressure built up in a conical pump filled with either a Newtonian or a viscoelastic liquid. In order to keep the analysis simple we confined the discussion to isothermal flow of Newtonian and generalized Newtonian liquids. It is assumed that these fluids are incompressible. Also considered are flows for which the Reynolds number, defined as the ratio of inertia to viscous forces, is small. In that case disturbances of the fully developed flow profile are rapidly damped [3]. When there are no rapid changes in the flow geometry, it can be expected that at any instant and at any place there exists a fully developed flow.

THE SPECIAL TOROIDAL COORDINATE SYSTEM

Let OXYZ be a rectangular coordinate system. (See Figure 2). In the OXY plane a circle with fixed radius "a" around O is defined. The angular position of a plane through the OZ axis is given

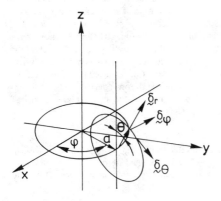

Figure 2. The special toroidal coordinate system.

by the angle φ. In such a plane circles with radius r are defined around the intersection of this plane and the circle with radius a. The position of a point on this circle with radius r is measured by θ. The line $\theta = 0$ is perpendicular to the OXY plane. A point P in space is defined by its special toroidal coordinates (r, θ, φ). The coordinate surfaces are:

- Planes φ = constant through the OZ axis.
- Toroids r = constant, that have the circle with radius a in the OXY plane as center line.
- Cones θ = constant. All these cones run through the circle with radius a. Their apices are on the OZ axis.

Berger and Talbot [4] have employed the special toroidal coordinate system to analyze extensively the flow of Newtonian and non-Newtonian liquids through curved pipes. The special toroidal coordinate system has been used by Chang [5] for the description of the electromagnetic field caused by a circular antenna and by Lewin [6] for the calculation of the radiation from curved dielectric slabs and fibers. The special toroidal coordinate system has been employed by Clark and Reissner [7] for their analysis of the mechanical behavior of pipe bends. A similar coordinate system has been used by Pearson and March [8] for the description of the flow of a liquid in the gap between a plate and a cone, the apex of which is at a certain distance above the plate surface [8, 9]. In Reference 10 the analysis of the flow through an axisymmetric wire-coating head has been discussed using the special toroidal coordinate system.

In Figure 2 the unit vectors $\underline{\delta}_r$, $\underline{\delta}_\theta$, $\underline{\delta}_\varphi$ are indicated. It is clear that these unit vectors constitute a local orthogonal coordinate system.

The special toroidal coordinates (r, θ, φ) are related to the rectangular coordinates (x, y, z) by

$$x = (a + r \sin \theta) \cos \varphi$$

$$y = (a + r \sin \theta) \sin \varphi \tag{1}$$

$$z = r \cos \theta$$

The relations between the unit vectors $\underline{\delta}_r$, $\underline{\delta}_\theta$, $\underline{\delta}_\varphi$ and $\underline{\delta}_x$, $\underline{\delta}_y$, $\underline{\delta}_z$ are:

$$\underline{\delta}_r = (\sin \theta \cos \varphi)\underline{\delta}_x + (\sin \theta \sin \varphi)\underline{\delta}_y + (\cos \theta)\underline{\delta}_z$$

$$\underline{\delta}_\theta = (\cos \theta \cos \varphi)\underline{\delta}_x + (\cos \theta \sin \varphi)\underline{\delta}_y + (-\sin \theta)\underline{\delta}_z$$

$$\underline{\delta}_\varphi = (-\sin \varphi)\underline{\delta}_x + (\cos \varphi)\underline{\delta}_y + (0)\underline{\delta}_z$$

$$\underline{\delta}_x = (\sin \theta \cos \varphi)\underline{\delta}_r + (\cos \theta \cos \varphi)\underline{\delta}_\theta + (-\sin \varphi)\underline{\delta}_\varphi \tag{2}$$

$$\underline{\delta}_y = (\sin \theta \sin \varphi)\underline{\delta}_r + (\cos \theta \sin \varphi)\underline{\delta}_\theta + (\cos \varphi)\underline{\delta}_\varphi$$

$$\underline{\delta}_z = (\cos \theta)\underline{\delta}_r + (-\sin \theta)\underline{\delta}_\theta + (0)\underline{\delta}_\varphi$$

Note that the unit vectors $\underline{\delta}_r$, $\underline{\delta}_\theta$, and $\underline{\delta}_\varphi$ all have unit length.
The nabla operator is given by:

$$\underline{\nabla} = \underline{\delta}_r \frac{\partial}{\partial r} + \underline{\delta}_\theta \frac{1}{r} \frac{\partial}{\partial \theta} + \underline{\delta}_\varphi \frac{1}{a + r \sin \theta} \frac{\partial}{\partial \varphi} \tag{3}$$

With respect to the special toroidal coordinate system a vector $\underline{v}$ is defined as:

$$\underline{v} = v_r \underline{\delta}_r + v_\theta \underline{\delta}_\theta + v_\varphi \underline{\delta}_\varphi \tag{4}$$

and a tensor $\underset{\approx}{\pi}$ as:

$$\underset{\approx}{\pi} = \pi_{rr}\underset{\sim}{\delta}_r\underset{\sim}{\delta}_r + \pi_{r\theta}\underset{\sim}{\delta}_r\underset{\sim}{\delta}_\theta + \cdots + \pi_{\varphi\varphi}\underset{\sim}{\delta}_\varphi\underset{\sim}{\delta}_\varphi \tag{5}$$

where $\underset{\sim}{\delta}_r\underset{\sim}{\delta}_r, \underset{\sim}{\delta}_r\underset{\sim}{\delta}_\theta, \ldots, \underset{\sim}{\delta}_\varphi\underset{\sim}{\delta}_\varphi$ are unit dyads [1, 2].

A summary of differential operations involving the nabla operator in special toroidal coordinates (r, θ, φ) is given in Appendix A. The components of the equation of motion in terms of the stress tensor and the components of the equation of motion for a Newtonian liquid with constant density and viscosity are given in Appendix B.

Note that when the radius "a" equals zero, the special toroidal coordinate system becomes the spherical coordinate system. For the case that a tends to infinity, the special toroidal coordinate system becomes identical to the cylindrical coordinate system (with $a\varphi = z$ being the axis of symmetry).

FLOW THROUGH A SLIGHTLY TAPERED WIRE-COATING DIE

Consider the flow of a viscous liquid through a convergent die in which a core moves concentrically at a constant speed. The core has a circular cross section whose dimensions are constant. The hole in the die has a conical shape and the axis of the cone coincides with that of the core. (See Figure 3.) The questions are:

● What is the pressure drop needed to maintain a certain volume rate of flow through the die?
● What are the magnitude and the direction of the stresses exerted by the fluid on the core?

The volumetric flow rate and the core speed determine the ultimate thickness of the layer on the core. By integrating the stresses acting on the core we can calculate the total force exerted by the fluid on the core. In order to use the special toroidal coordinate system to describe the flow through the die we state the following (see Figure 4):

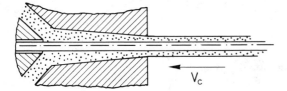

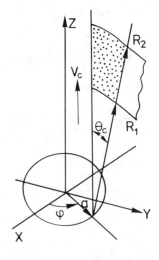

Figure 3. Geometry of wire-coating die and core.

Figure 4. Flow region defined with respect to the special toroidal coordinate system.

- Radius a is equal to the core radius.
- The circle with fixed radius a is the intersection of the skin of the core and the cone describing the inside of the die. The skin of the core is given by $\theta = 0$, the cone by $\theta = \theta_c$.
- Liquid enters the die through the surface $r = R_2$, $0 \leq \theta \leq \theta_c$, $0 \leq \varphi < 2\pi$.
- Liquid leaves the die through the surface $r = R_1$, $0 \leq \theta \leq \theta_c$, $0 \leq \varphi < 2\pi$.

The volume rate of flow Q and the core speed V_C determine the radius of the wire r_w:

$$Q = \pi(r_w^2 - a^2)V_C \tag{6}$$

(The core speed V_C is positive in the Z direction.)

In the case where θ_c is small compared with unity and the length of the die is long compared with the cross-sectional gap dimensions it is convenient to introduce the following scaling:

$$
\begin{array}{ll}
v_r = Vv_r^* & v_\theta = \theta_c Vv_\theta^* \\[6pt]
r = Lr^* & \theta = \theta_c \theta^* \\[6pt]
a = \theta_c La^* & p = P_0 p^* \\[6pt]
\sin\theta \approx \theta & \cos\theta \approx 1 \\[6pt]
Q = 2\pi\theta_c L^2 Vq^* & V = |V_C|
\end{array}
\tag{7}
$$

A convenient choice for the length scale L is the difference of R_2 and R_1. P_0 is a characteristic pressure for the wire-coating process, say 100 bar. The geometry is axisymmetric. As long as the inflow and outflow take place in an axisymmetric way the flow is assumed to be axisymmetric as well.

Substituting Equation 7 into the components of the equation of motion for a liquid with constant density and viscosity and keeping only the leading terms gives:

$$\beta \frac{dp^*}{dr^*} = \frac{1}{r^{*2}} \frac{\partial^2 v_r^*}{\partial\theta^{*2}} + \frac{1}{r^*} \frac{1}{a^* + r^*\theta^*} \frac{\partial v_r^*}{\partial\theta^*} \tag{8}$$

where $\quad \beta = \theta_c^2 \dfrac{P_0 L}{\mu V} \tag{9}$

The solution of Equation 8 must satisfy the following boundary conditions:

$$
\begin{array}{ll}
r^* = R_1^* & p^* = p_a^* \\[6pt]
\theta^* = 0 & v_r^* = -1 \\[6pt]
\theta^* = 1 & v_r^* = 0.
\end{array}
\tag{10}
$$

The value of p_a is equal to the ambient pressure when the die is the end of the wire-coating device. (Note that for converging wire-coating dies the value of V_C is negative!)

The solution for v_r^* reads:

$$v_r^* = -1\left[1 - \ln\left(1 + \frac{r^*}{a^*}\theta^*\right) \Big/ \ln\left(1 + \frac{r^*}{a^*}\right)\right]$$

$$+ \beta\frac{dp^*}{dr^*}r^{*2}\left[\frac{\theta^{*2}}{4} + \frac{1}{2}\frac{a^*}{r^*}\theta^* - \left(\frac{1}{4} + \frac{1}{2}\frac{a^*}{r^*}\right)\frac{\ln\left(1 + \frac{r^*}{a^*}\theta^*\right)}{\ln\left(1 + \frac{r^*}{a^*}\right)}\right] \tag{11}$$

The pressure gradient is unknown at this stage. The volume rate of flow through any coordinate plane r = constant must be equal to Q. Performing the integration and solving for dp*/dr* gives:

$$\frac{dp^*}{dr^*} = \left[q^* + r^*\left(a^* + \frac{r^*}{2}\right) - \frac{1}{4}\frac{a^{*2}}{\ln\left(1 + \frac{r^*}{a^*}\right)} - \frac{1}{2}\frac{(a^* + r^*)^2}{\ln\left(1 + \frac{r^*}{a^*}\right)}\left\{\ln\left(1 + \frac{r^*}{a^*}\right) - \frac{1}{2}\right\}\right] \Bigg/$$

$$r^{*3}\beta\left[\frac{1}{4}a^* + \frac{1}{16}r^* + \frac{1}{4}\frac{a^{*2}}{r^*} - \frac{1}{8}\frac{a^{*2}}{r^*}\frac{\frac{1}{2} + \frac{a^*}{r^*}}{\ln\left(1 + \frac{r^*}{a^*}\right)} - \frac{\left(\frac{1}{2} + \frac{a^*}{r^*}\right)(a^* + r^*)^2\left\{\ln\left(1 + \frac{r^*}{a^*}\right) - \frac{1}{2}\right\}}{4r^*\ln\left(1 + \frac{r^*}{a^*}\right)}\right]$$

(12)

It is clear that the pressure profile consists of a part coming from the moving core (a drag flow causing a pressure rise) and a part coming from the pressure-driven flow, inducing a pressure drop. The solution of Equation 12 that satisfies the condition at the outlet can be found by numerical calculation.

The force required to move the core is obtained by integration of the shear stresses acting on the skin of the core:

$$\frac{F}{2\pi\mu VL} = -\int_{R_1^*}^{R_1^* + 1}\left[\frac{1}{\ln\left(1 + \frac{r^*}{a^*}\right)} + \beta\frac{dp^*}{dr^*}r^{*2}\left\{\frac{1}{2}\frac{a^{*2}}{r^{*2}} - \frac{\frac{1}{2} + \frac{a^*}{r^*}}{2\ln\left(1 + \frac{r^*}{a^*}\right)}\right\}\right]dr^*$$

(13)

The simplest fluid model that takes into account the shear thinning behavior of, e.g., a molten thermoplastic material is given by:

$$\underset{\approx}{\tau} = -\eta(\dot{\gamma})\underset{\approx}{\dot{\gamma}}$$

(14)

$$\eta(\dot{\gamma}) = m\dot{\gamma}^{n-1}$$

where $\underset{\approx}{\tau}$ is the extra stress tensor and $\underset{\approx}{\dot{\gamma}}$ the rate-of-strain tensor. The scalar $\dot{\gamma}$ is related to the second scalar invariant of the rate-of-strain tensor. m and n are constants [1]. Carrying out the scaling procedure given by Equation 7 on the components of the rate-of-strain tensor (given in Appendix A) we find that:

$$\underset{\approx}{\dot{\gamma}} = \frac{V}{\theta_c L}\begin{bmatrix} 2\theta_c\frac{\partial v_r^*}{\partial r^*} & \frac{1}{r^*}\frac{\partial v_r^*}{\partial \theta^*} + \theta_c^2(\quad) & 0 \\[2mm] & 2\theta_c\left(\frac{v_r^*}{r^*} + \frac{1}{r^*}\frac{\partial v_\theta^*}{\partial \theta^*}\right) & 0 \\[2mm] \text{symmetric} & & 2\theta_c\frac{v_\theta^* + \theta^* v_r^*}{a^* + r^*\theta^*} \end{bmatrix}$$

(15)

When θ_c is sufficiently small, the components $\dot{\gamma}_{r\theta}$ and $\dot{\gamma}_{\theta r}$ dominate. Consequently the leading components of the stress tensor are:

$$\tau_{r\theta} = \tau_{\theta r} = -\eta(\dot{\gamma})\frac{1}{r}\frac{\partial v_r}{\partial \theta}$$

(16)

and the shear rate $\dot{\gamma}$ becomes:

$$\dot{\gamma} = \sqrt{\frac{1}{2}(\dot{\gamma}_{rr}^2 + \dot{\gamma}_{\theta\theta}^2 + \dot{\gamma}_{\varphi\varphi}^2) + \dot{\gamma}_{r\theta}^2} \approx \left| \frac{1}{r} \frac{\partial v_r}{\partial \theta} \right| \qquad (17)$$

Examination of the order of magnitude of each of the terms constituting the components of the equation of motion shows that the influence of the dominating shear stress is even enlarged by a factor of $1/\theta_c$ with respect to the other ones. To leading order, components of the equation of motion are:

$$\beta \frac{\partial p^*}{\partial r^*} \approx \frac{1}{r^{*2}} \frac{1}{a^* + r^*\theta^*} \frac{\partial}{\partial \theta^*} \left[(a^* + r^*\theta^*)\eta^*(\dot{\gamma}^*) \frac{\partial v_r^*}{\partial \theta^*} \right]$$

$$\frac{1}{r^*} \frac{\partial p^*}{\partial \theta^*} \approx 0 \qquad (18)$$

where $\beta = \theta_c^2 \dfrac{LP_0}{\eta_0 V}$

$$\eta_0 = m_0 \left(\frac{V}{L\theta_c} \right)^{n-1} \qquad (19)$$

$$\eta^*(\dot{\gamma}^*) = \left| \frac{1}{r^*} \frac{\partial v_r^*}{\partial \theta^*} \right|^{n-1} = \dot{\gamma}^{*n-1}.$$

The solution of Equation 18 that satisfies the boundary conditions of Equation 10 is given by:

$$v_r^* = \beta r^{*2} \frac{dp^*}{dr^*} \left\{ I(r^*, \theta^*) - \frac{I(r^*, 1)}{II(r^*, 1)} II(r^*, \theta^*) \right\} + \left\{ \frac{II(r^*, \theta^*)}{II(r^*, 1)} - 1 \right\} \qquad (20)$$

The functions $I(r^*, \theta^*)$ and $II(r^*, \theta^*)$ are given by:

$$I(r^*, \theta^*) = \int_0^{\theta^*} \frac{a^*\zeta + \frac{1}{2}r^*\zeta^2}{(a^* + r^*\zeta)\{\dot{\gamma}(r^*, \zeta)\}^{n-1}} d\zeta$$

$$II(r^*, \theta^*) = \int_0^{\theta^*} \frac{d\zeta}{(a^* + r^*\zeta)\{\dot{\gamma}(r^*, \zeta)\}^{n-1}} \qquad (21)$$

The requirement that the flow through any surface r = constant must equal Q leads to the pressure gradient:

$$\frac{dp^*}{dr^*} = \frac{q^* - \int_0^1 r^*(a^* + r^*\theta^*) \left\{ \dfrac{II(r^*, \theta^*)}{II(r^*, 1)} - 1 \right\} d\theta^*}{\beta r^{*3} \int_0^1 (a^* + r^*\theta^*) \left\{ I(r^*, \theta^*) - \dfrac{I(r^*, 1)}{II(r^*, 1)} II(r^*, \theta^*) \right\} d\theta^*} \qquad (22)$$

The local value of the shear rate equals:

$$\dot{\gamma}^*(r^*, \theta^*) = \left| \frac{1}{r^*} \frac{\beta r^{*2} \dfrac{dp^*}{dr^*} \left\{ \left(a^*\theta^* + \dfrac{1}{2} r^*\theta^{*2} \right) II(r^*, 1) - I(r^*, 1) \right\} + 1}{II(r^*, 1)(a^* + r^*\theta^*)} \right|^{1/m} \qquad (23)$$

As the solution of the set of equations depends on the solution of the velocity field, the final result has to be obtained by iteration. Here a Picard scheme is used. For a certain value of r^* start with a guess for the velocity field, e.g., the Newtonian profile (see Equations 11 and 12). Then the functions I and II can be calculated. After calculating the local pressure drop from Equation 22, a new guess of the velocity profile can be made, and so on.

THE FLOW THROUGH A NARROW ANNULAR CONVERGENT CHANNEL

The domain of calculation is the region between two conical surfaces, the axes of which coincide. In this region a special toroidal coordinate system is defined, as shown in Figure 5. In the case considered, the circle with radius a is the intersection of the two cones. The inner cone is given by $\theta = \theta_0$, and the outer cone by $\theta = \theta_0 + \theta_c$. The coordinate φ runs from 0 to 2π. The areas through which the fluid enters the conical annular region and leaves it are, respectively:

$$r = R_1, \qquad \theta_0 \leq \theta \leq \theta_0 + \theta_c, \qquad 0 \leq \varphi < 2\pi$$

$$r = R_2, \qquad \theta_0 \leq \theta \leq \theta_0 + \theta_c, \qquad 0 \leq \varphi < 2\pi$$

Clearly the advantages of this particular coordinate system are:

- the conical surfaces and the entrance and exit areas are coordinate planes, which fact simplifies the expressions for boundary conditions.
- a wide variety of shapes can be considered. It is obvious that by changing the values of θ_0, θ_c, R_1 and R_2 the shape of the convergent annular channel can be altered. Changing a is another possible way of altering the geometry. It is even possible to use negative values of a, as shown in Figure 6.

When using all these possibilities the domain of calculation must be chosen in such a way that each point from this domain is defined by a unique set of coordinates r, θ, φ. Moreover, singular points must be excluded (for a > 0 all the points r = 0 and $0 \leq \varphi < 2\pi$ are singular, while for a < 0 all the points on the rotation axis OZ are singular).

In this chapter we restrict our attention to cases where:

- θ_c lies in the neighborhood of $\pi/4$ rad
- θ_c is small compared with unity
- the flow is axisymmetric

The first two remarks imply that a kind of lubrication approximation can be used, for which only the component of the velocity in the r direction is significant. Although the geometry is axisymmetric, the flow is axisymmetric only if the inflow and outflow take place in an axisymmetric way.

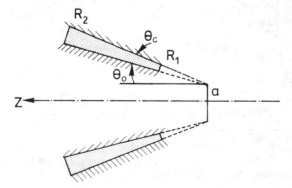

Figure 5. An annular convergent region defined with respect to the special toroidal coordinate system.

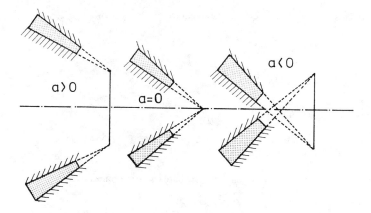

Figure 6. An ensemble of annular convergent regions, the boundaries of which can be described by coordinate surfaces of the special toroidal coordinate system.

We assume that this will be the case. In order to investigate the relative magnitude of the terms of the components of the equation of motion for a fluid with constant density and viscosity with respect to each other, the following scaling of the variables is used ($\theta_c \ll 1$):

$$v_r = Vv_r^* \qquad\qquad v_\theta = \theta_c Vv_\theta^*$$

$$r = Lr^* \qquad\qquad \theta^* = \frac{\theta - \theta_0}{\theta_c}$$

$$a = La^* \qquad\qquad p = P_0 p^* \tag{24}$$

$$Q = 2\pi\theta_c VL^2 q^*$$

For the scaling quantities V and P_0 we may take the mean velocity at the exit opening and a rough indication of the pressure loss, respectively. (V and P_0 are positive numbers). The length scale L is equal to the difference of R_2 and R_1. Comparison of the scaled components of the equation of motion in the r^* direction and θ^* direction leads to the conclusion that the component of the scaled pressure gradient vector in the θ^* direction is two orders of magnitude smaller than the component in the r^* direction. So it can safely be assumed that the pressure p^* is a function of r^* alone. The component of the equation of motion in the r^* direction simplifies to:

$$\beta \frac{dp^*}{dr^*} = \frac{1}{r^{*2}} \frac{\partial^2 v_r^*}{\partial\theta^{*2}} \tag{25}$$

where $\quad \beta = \theta_c \dfrac{P_0 L}{\mu V} \tag{26}$

The solution of this equation, which satisfies the boundary conditions $v^*(r^*, 0) = 0$ and $v_r^*(r^*, 1) = 0$, reads:

$$v_r^* = \frac{1}{2}\beta r^{*2}\frac{dp^*}{dr^*}(\theta^{*2} - \theta^*) \tag{27}$$

As the flux Q is known, the dp^*/dr^* can be found from:

$$q^* = r^*(a^* + r^* \sin \theta_0) \int_0^1 v_r^* \, d\theta^*$$

$$= -\frac{1}{12} \beta r^{*3}(a^* + r^* \sin \theta_0) \frac{dp^*}{dr^*}. \tag{28}$$

After some rearrangement we get:

$$\frac{dp^*}{dr^*} = -\frac{12q^*}{\beta} \frac{1}{r^{*3}(a^* + r^* \sin \theta_0)}. \tag{29}$$

For a given pressure at the exit, the entrance pressure can be obtained from:

$$\Delta p^* = p_2^* - p_1^* = -12 \frac{q^*}{\beta} \int_{R_1^*}^{R_1^* + 1} \frac{dr^*}{r^{*3}(a^* + r^* \sin \theta_0)}. \tag{30}$$

The final result is:

$$\Delta p^* = -12 \frac{q^*}{\beta} \left[\frac{\sin^2 \theta_0}{a^{*3}} \ln \left\{ \frac{R_1^* + 1}{R_1^*} \frac{a^* + R_1^* \sin \theta_0}{a^* + (R_1^* + 1) \sin \theta_0} \right\} \right.$$

$$\left. + \frac{\sin \theta_0}{a^{*2}} \left(\frac{1}{R_1^* + 1} - \frac{1}{R_1^*} \right) - \frac{1}{2a^*} \left(\frac{1}{(R_1^* + 1)^2} - \frac{1}{R_1^{*2}} \right) \right] \tag{31}$$

The solutions given are valid as long as:

- for $a \geq 0$: $R_1^* \neq 0$
- for $a < 0$: $a^* + R_1^* \sin \theta_0 \neq 0$

Substitution of the solution for v_r^* in the equation of continuity reveals that v_θ^* must be zero. (Consequently, the analysis presented above is identical to the one that starts with the postulate $\underline{v} = (v_r, 0, 0)$.) From the equation of continuity it follows directly that $v_r = f(\theta)/(r(a + r \sin(\theta)))$. Combination of Equations 27 and 29 yields:

$$v_r^* = -6q^* \frac{\theta^{*2} - \theta^*}{r^*(a^* + r^* \sin \theta_0)} \tag{32}$$

When a tends to zero the expression for Δp^*, Equation 31, is:

$$\Delta p^* = \frac{4a^*}{\beta} \left\{ \frac{1}{(R_1^* + 1)^3} - \frac{1}{R_1^{*3}} \right\} \frac{1}{\sin \theta_0}. \tag{33}$$

In the following we shall consider the isothermal flow of a shear thinning liquid through a convergent annular channel. Following the same scaling procedure as at the beginning of this section it appears that the only significant components of the stress tensor are $\tau_{r\theta}$ and $\tau_{\theta r}$, the value of which is given by:

$$\tau_{r\theta} = \tau_{\theta r} = -m \dot{\gamma}^{n-1} \dot{\gamma}_{r\theta}, \tag{34}$$

where the shear rate $\dot{\gamma}$ can be approximated by:

$$\dot{\gamma} \approx |\dot{\gamma}_{r\theta}| = \left| \frac{1}{r} \frac{\partial v_r}{\partial \theta} \right| \tag{35}$$

Substitution of these expressions in the r component of the equation of motion and retaining only the leading terms we get (scaled variables):

$$\beta \frac{dp^*}{dr^*} = \frac{1}{r^*} \frac{\partial}{\partial \theta^*} \left| \frac{1}{r^*} \frac{\partial v_r^*}{\partial \theta^*} \right|^{n-1} \frac{1}{r^*} \frac{\partial v_r^*}{\partial \theta^*} \tag{36}$$

where
$$\beta = \theta_c^2 \frac{P_0 L}{m \left(\frac{V}{L\theta_c} \right)^{n-1} V} \tag{37}$$

The boundary conditions for Equation 36 are symmetric with respect to $\theta^* = \frac{1}{2}$. Furthermore, we notice that the solution of Equation 36 is symmetric with respect to $\theta^* = \frac{1}{2}$. Using this and integrating once we obtain:

$$\beta r^* \frac{dp^*}{dr^*} \left(\theta^* - \frac{1}{2} \right) = \left| \frac{1}{r^*} \frac{\partial v_r^*}{\partial \theta^*} \right|^{n-1} \frac{1}{r^*} \frac{\partial v_r^*}{\partial \theta^*} \tag{38}$$

In order to obtain the solution for Equation 38 that satisfies the no-slip conditions along the walls, we must distinguish between several cases. Because of symmetry we confine the analysis to $\theta \leq \theta^* \leq \frac{1}{2}$, $R_1^* \leq r^* \leq R_2^*$. In that region when Q is positive it holds that:

- v_r^* is positive
- dp^*/dr^* is negative
- $dv_r^*/d\theta^*$ is positive

On removing the absolute signs from Equation 38 we get:

$$\left(\frac{1}{r^*} \frac{\partial v_r^*}{\partial \theta^*} \right)^n = -\beta r^* \frac{dp^*}{dr^*} \left(\frac{1}{2} - \theta^* \right) \tag{39}$$

Both sides of the Equality 39 are positive, and therefore manipulations with the "Power Law Index" are allowed. The solution of Equation 39 that satisfies the no-slip condition at $\theta^* = 0$ reads:

$$v_r^* = -\left(-\beta r^* \frac{dp^*}{dr^*} \right)^{1/n} r^* \frac{n}{n+1} \left[\left(\frac{1}{2} - \theta^* \right)^{(n+1)/n} - \frac{1}{2}^{(n+1)/n} \right] \tag{40}$$

The volume rate of flow through a coordinate plane $r^* = $ constant equals:

$$q^* = \left(-\beta r^* \frac{dp^*}{dr^*} \right)^{1/n} \frac{2n}{2n+1} \left(\frac{1}{2} \right)^{(2n+1)/n} r^{*2}(a^* + r^* \sin \theta_0) \tag{41}$$

from which expression we can deduce the local pressure drop:

$$\frac{dp^*}{dr^*} = -\frac{1}{\beta r^*} \left\{ \frac{q^*}{r^{*2}(a^* + r^* \sin \theta_0) \frac{2n}{2n+1} \left(\frac{1}{2} \right)^{(2n+1)/n}} \right\}^n \tag{42}$$

For a given pressure at $r^* = R_1^*$, the pressure P_2^* at $r^* = R_2^*$ can be found by numerical evaluation of:

$$\Delta p^* = \int_{R_1^*}^{R_1^*+1} \frac{dp^*}{dr^*} dr^* \tag{43}$$

The velocity distribution in terms of the volume rate of flow is given by:

$$v_r^* = -\frac{q^*}{r^*(a^* + r^* \sin \theta_0)} \frac{2n + 1}{2(n + 1)} 2^{(2n + 1)/n} \left[\left(\frac{1}{2} - \theta^* \right)^{(n + 1)/n} - \frac{1^{(n + 1)/n}}{2} \right] \tag{44}$$

In the same way, expressions for the case where Q is negative can be found:

$$v_r^* = \left(\beta \frac{dp^*}{dr^*} r^* \right)^{1/n} r^* \frac{n}{n + 1} \left[\left(\frac{1}{2} - \theta^* \right)^{(n + 1)/n} - \frac{1^{(n + 1)/n}}{2} \right] \tag{45}$$

$$q^* = -\left(\beta r^* \frac{dp^*}{dr^*} \right)^{1/n} \frac{2n}{2n + 1} \left(\frac{1}{2} \right)^{(2n + 1)/n} r^{*2}(a^* + r^* \sin \theta_0) \tag{46}$$

$$\frac{dp^*}{dr^*} = \frac{1}{\beta r^*} \left\{ \frac{-q^*}{r^{*2}(a^* + r^* \sin \theta_0) \dfrac{2n}{2n + 1} \left(\dfrac{1}{2} \right)^{(2n + 1)/n}} \right\}^n \tag{47}$$

Equation 44 is similar in both cases. The shear rate at the wall is given by:

$$\dot{\gamma}_w^* = \frac{2(2n + 1)}{n} \frac{q^*}{r^*(a^* + r^* \sin \theta_0)} \tag{48}$$

EXTENDED CONE-AND-PLATE FLOW

To obtain the viscometric data of a viscoelastic fluid, a cone-and-plate or a parallel plate rheometer is often used [11]. Most of the cone-and-plate rheometers are able to fix the cone at a certain distance from the plate surface. In that way a geometry is obtained that can be considered as an intermediate form with regard to the conventional cone-and-plate and plate-plate geometries. The so-called extended cone-and-plate geometry with respect to the special toroidal coordinate system is shown in Figure 7. The plate surface is defined by $\theta = \pi/2$, and the cone surface by $\theta = \theta_0$.

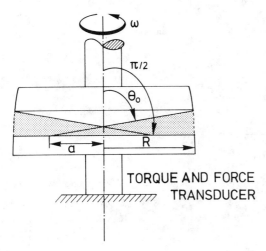

Figure 7. The extended cone-and-plate geometry.

It should be noted that the value of a, the radius of the fixed circle, is negative! The components of the equation of motion are:

$$-\frac{\partial p}{\partial r} - \left\{ \frac{\partial \tau_{rr}}{\partial r} + \frac{\tau_{rr} - \tau_{\theta\theta}}{r} + \frac{\tau_{rr} - \tau_{\varphi\varphi}}{a + r \sin \theta} \sin \theta \right\} = 0$$

$$-\frac{1}{r}\frac{\partial p}{\partial \theta} - \left\{ \frac{1}{r}\frac{\partial \tau_{\theta\theta}}{\partial \theta} + \frac{\tau_{\theta\theta} - \tau_{\varphi\varphi}}{a + r \sin \theta} \cos \theta \right\} = 0 \tag{49}$$

$$\frac{1}{r}\frac{\partial \tau_{\theta\varphi}}{\partial \theta} + 2\frac{\tau_{\theta\varphi} \cos \theta}{a + r \sin \theta} = 0,$$

where $\underset{\approx}{\pi} = p\underset{\approx}{\delta} + \underset{\approx}{\tau}$ are the components of the total stress tensor [1]. As θ_0 is close to $\pi/2$ the components of the equation of motion can be approximated by:

$$-\frac{\partial p}{\partial r} - \left\{ \frac{\partial \tau_{rr}}{\partial r} + \frac{\tau_{rr} - \tau_{\theta\theta}}{r} + \frac{\tau_{rr} - \tau_{\varphi\varphi}}{a + r} \right\} = 0$$

$$\frac{1}{r}\frac{\partial p}{\partial \theta} - \frac{1}{r}\frac{\partial \tau_{\theta\theta}}{\partial \theta} = 0 \tag{50}$$

$$\frac{1}{r}\frac{\partial \tau_{\theta\varphi}}{\partial \theta} = 0.$$

From the last expressions it follows that:

$$\tau_{\theta\varphi} = \tau_{\theta\varphi}(r), \qquad \pi_{\theta\theta} = p + \tau_{\theta\theta} = \pi_{\theta\theta}(r). \tag{51}$$

When the height of the gap is very small compared with the radii of the cone and the plate, the only non-zero component of the velocity vector is the component in the φ direction v_φ. It is assumed that v_φ is a linear function of the coordinate in the gap height direction. This assumption is valid as long as the inertia forces can be left out of account [12] and the flow remains stable [13, 14]. Consequently we have:

$$v_\varphi \approx \omega(a + r)\frac{\xi}{\xi_0}, \tag{52}$$

where we have introduced a new variable ξ according to:

$$\xi = \frac{\pi}{2} - \theta; \qquad \xi_0 = \frac{\pi}{2} - \theta_0. \tag{53}$$

The only non-zero component of the rate-of-strain tensor is given by:

$$\dot{\gamma}_{\theta\varphi} = -\frac{1}{r}\frac{\omega(a + r)}{\xi_0}. \tag{54}$$

The equation relating the shear stress to $\dot{\gamma}_{\theta\varphi}$ reads:

$$\tau_{\theta\varphi} = -\eta(\dot{\gamma})\dot{\gamma}_{\theta\varphi} \tag{55}$$

where $\dot{\gamma}$ is the shear rate, which is equal to the absolute value of $\dot{\gamma}_{\theta\varphi}$. Integration of the shear stress over the plate surface yields the total torque exerted by the fluid on the plate:

$$M = 2\pi \int_{-a}^{-a+R} \eta(\dot{\gamma})\dot{\gamma}(a + r)^2 \, dr \tag{56}$$

For a = 0 (the cone-and-plate geometry) the shear rate is constant throughout the gap and the integration can be performed easily:

$$M = \frac{2}{3} \pi \frac{\omega}{\xi_0} R^3 \eta(\dot{\gamma}) \tag{57}$$

For a ≠ 0 we have, using as new integration variable $\dot{\gamma} = -\omega(a + r)/\xi_0/r$:

$$M = -2\pi \frac{a^3(-a + R)}{R} \int_0^{\dot{\gamma}_{-a+R}} \frac{\dot{\gamma}_{-a+R}}{\left(\dot{\gamma} - \frac{-a + R}{R}\dot{\gamma}_{-a+R}\right)^4} \eta(\dot{\gamma})\dot{\gamma}^3 d\dot{\gamma}. \tag{58}$$

To deduce the viscosity as a function of the shear rate from a series of measurements is not trivial. When the viscosity is known, however, Equation 58 can be used to check, e.g., whether the fluid is degraded during a series of measurements with different tip distances. For the case where a tends to minus infinity, we obtain the well-known parallel plate result:

$$\eta(\dot{\gamma}_{RIM}) = \frac{1}{2\pi R^3} \frac{M}{\dot{\gamma}_{RIM}}\left(3 + \frac{\partial \ln M}{\partial \ln \dot{\gamma}_{RIM}}\right). \tag{59}$$

The measurement of the normal stress differences runs as follows:
By definition we have:

$$\pi_{\varphi\varphi} - \pi_{\theta\theta} = N_1$$
$$\pi_{\theta\theta} - \pi_{rr} = N_2 \tag{60}$$

Substitution of these definitions in the r component of the equation of motion results in:

$$\frac{\partial \pi_{rr}}{\partial r} = \frac{N_2}{r} + \frac{N_1 + N_2}{a + r} \tag{61}$$

$$\pi_{rr} = -\int_r^{-a+R} \left[\frac{N_2}{r} + \frac{N_1 + N_2}{a + r}\right] dr \tag{62}$$

On using this result, together with the definition of the second normal stress difference, we obtain:

$$\pi_{\theta\theta} = N_2 + \pi_{rr} = N_2 - \int_r^{-a+R} \left[\frac{N_2}{r} + \frac{N_1 + N_2}{a + r}\right] dr \tag{63}$$

By integration of $\pi_{\theta\theta}$ over the plate surface we obtain the total force exerted by the fluid on the plate:

$$F = 2\pi \int_{-a}^{-a+R} N_2(a + r)\, dr - \pi \int_{-a}^{-a+R} (a + r)^2 \left\{\frac{N_2}{r} + \frac{N_1 + N_2}{a + r}\right\} dr \tag{64}$$

The two limiting cases are:

$$a = 0 \text{ (cone-and-plate)} \qquad F = -\frac{1}{2}\pi R^2 N_1$$

$$a \to -\infty \text{ (plate-and-plate)} \qquad F = -\pi \int_{center}^{rim} (N_1 - N_2)r'\, dr' \qquad (r' = a + r) \tag{65}$$

Thus, using the cone-and-plate set-up directly we obtain N_1, while the result coming from the parallel plate configuration contains information on both N_1 and N_2. Looking at the general formula (Equation 64) we see that by increasing the distance between the cone tip and the plate surface we increase the influence of N_2 in the measured value of total force. On changing the integration variable we get:

$$\frac{F}{\pi a^2 \xi_0^2 \omega} = -\int_0^{\dot{\gamma}_{-a+R}} (N_1 - N_2) \frac{\dot{\gamma}}{(\omega + \xi_0 \dot{\gamma})^3} \, d\dot{\gamma} + \int_0^{\dot{\gamma}_{-a+R}} N_2 \frac{\xi_0}{\omega} \frac{\dot{\gamma}^2}{(\omega + \xi_0 \dot{\gamma})^3} \, d\dot{\gamma} \qquad (66)$$

Differentiation with respect to $-a\xi_0$ (the distance between cone tip and plate surface) results in:

$$\frac{\partial}{\partial(-a\xi_0)} \frac{F}{\pi a^2 \xi_0^2 \omega} = \left\{ (N_1 - N_2) - \frac{\xi_0}{\omega} \dot{\gamma}_{-a+R} N_2 \right\} \frac{R^2}{\omega(-a\xi_0)^3} \qquad (67)$$

which is identical to the expression given by March and Pearson [8].

By using the special toroidal coordinate system we have been able to present the theory of the cone-and-plate flow, the extended cone-and-plate flow and the parallel plate flow in one single framework.

SOME MORE COMPLICATED EXAMPLES

By using the special toroidal coordinate system, we have shown that a solution of the equations governing fluid flow in a number of quite complicated geometries is feasible.

By connecting several regions to each other it is possible to solve even more complicated problems such as the flow through axisymmetric wire-coating heads and the pressure built-up in conical pumps. An example of a wire-coating head is shown in Figure 8. Note that this geometry is nearly equal to the one discussed by Caswell and Tanner [15, Figure 1].

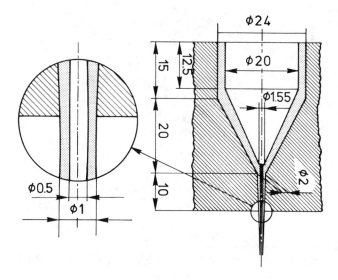

Figure 8. Cross section of a wire-coating head.

In Figure 9, the division of such a flow geometry into the "elements" discussed in earlier sections is depicted. The "elements" are numbered starting at the exit. The dimensions of the "elements" are given in Table 1, using the conventions given earlier.

The solution for the equations governing flow through the annular inflow region, "element" 4, can be found in textbooks [1, 2].

The type of the "element" is indicated by the sequence of the sections of this chapter (3 = Flow through a Slightly Tapered Wire-Coating Die; 4 = Flow through a Narrow Annular Convergent Channel).

The speed of the wire is equal to 1 m/s. The radius of the coated wire, r_w, measured directly after the exit, is equal to 0.5 mm. At the exit we assume that the pressure in the fluid is equal to the ambient pressure. The fluid processed is polyethylene (LDPE at 180°C) the viscosity of which is given by [16, 17]:

$$\eta(\dot{\gamma}) = 10^4 \dot{\gamma}^{-0.6} \; \text{Pa·s} \tag{68}$$

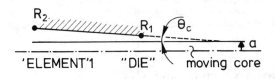

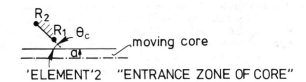

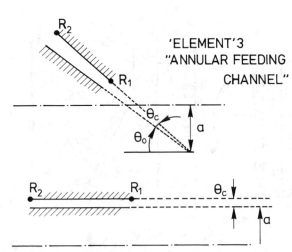

Figure 9. Division of the wire-coating head into "elements."

Table 1
Dimensions of Elements

Element number	Type of element	a [mm]	R_1 [mm]	R_2 [mm]	θ_0 [deg]	θ_c [deg]
1	3	0.25	5.004	15.004	—	2.86
2	3	0.25	1	3.5	—	28.80
3	4	−8.25	21	41.25	25	3.8

Starting at the exit we first analyze the flow through "element" 1. The pressure at the entrance of "element" 1 will be the exit pressure of "element" 2, and so on. At the interfaces between the "elements" we prescribe continuity of the volumetric flow rate. We have been able to compare our results with those obtained by using the finite element program package POLYFLOW developed by Crochet and co-workers [18, 19]. The mesh used is shown in Figure 10. From the set of results we present here the pressure distribution, the shear stress distribution along the skin of the core and the velocity distribution at several places in the die (element 1). (See Figures 11, 12, and 13). The similarity of the results of the analytic approach and the finite element calculations is striking. It should be emphasized, however, that the geometry of the wire-coating head considered, in fact consists of a chain of narrow channels. For such a geometry one could expect a lubrication-type of approximation to give reasonable results. From the results shown it is clear that in regions such as the place where the core enters the wire-coating head and the exit of the die, the conditions for the applicability of the lubrication approximation are violated.

Another example that can be analyzed quite easily by using the special toroidal coordinate system is the conical pump (see Figure 14.) A conical pump consists of a conically shaped bob that rotates concentrically in a converging part of a tube. (We have referred here to the set-up mentioned in [1], Figure 3Q3). The annular convergent region is filled with either a Newtonian liquid or a viscoelastic

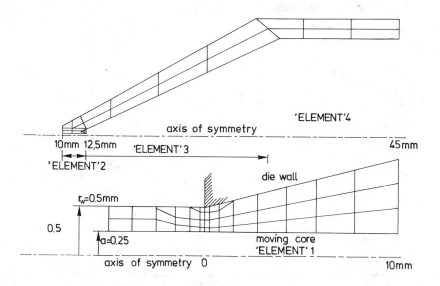

Figure 10. Finite element mesh used for the numerical simulation of the flow of a shear thinning liquid through a wire-coating head.

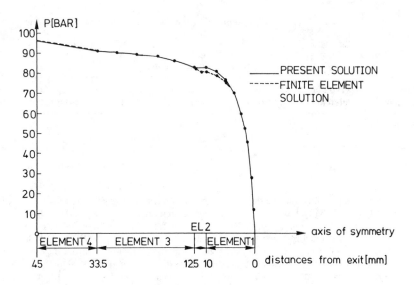

Figure 11. Pressure distribution in the wire-coating head. The pressure is indicated with respect to the position along the axis of symmetry. The origin is located at the exit.

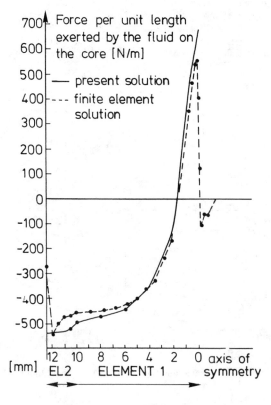

Figure 12. The distribution of the force per unit length exerted by the fluid on the skin of the core indicated with respect to the position along the axis of symmetry.

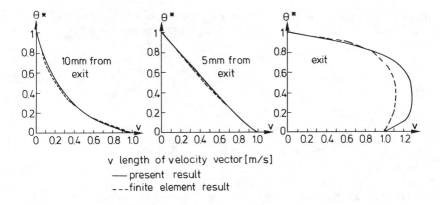

v length of velocity vector [m/s]
—— present result
---- finite element result

Figure 13. Velocity distribution in "element" 1, the die.

liquid. The cylindrical channels are filled with an immiscible Newtonian liquid. We will treat the case where the ends of the cylindrical channels are closed, so there will be no net axial flow.

When θ_c is sufficiently small, the only non-zero component of the velocity vector is v_φ, whose value is given by:

$$v_\varphi = \omega(a + r \sin \theta_0) \frac{\theta_0 + \theta_c - \theta}{\theta_c}. \tag{69}$$

In order to obtain an impression about the behavior of a Newtonian liquid, we substitute in the Navier-Stokes equation (for the components of this equation see Appendix B of this chapter). The result reads:

$$\rho \frac{v_\varphi^2 \sin \theta}{a + r \sin \theta} = \frac{\partial p}{\partial r},$$

$$\rho \frac{v_\varphi^2 \cos \theta}{a + r \sin \theta} = \frac{1}{r} \frac{\partial p}{\partial \theta}. \tag{70}$$

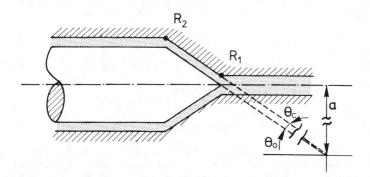

Figure 14. Cross section of a conical pump. In order to have a smooth entrance and exit, a somewhat different set-up is shown compared with the one discussed in [4].

As θ_c is small, the component of the pressure gradient in the direction is one order of magnitude smaller than the component in the r direction. Averaging the component of the pressure gradient in the r direction gives:

$$\frac{d\bar{p}}{dr} = \frac{1}{\theta_c} \int_{\theta_0}^{\theta_0 + \theta_c} \frac{\partial p}{\partial r} \, d\theta = \frac{1}{3} \rho\omega^2 (a + r \sin \theta_0) \sin \theta_0 \tag{71}$$

from which we derive:

$$\Delta p = \int_{R_1}^{R_2} \frac{d\bar{p}}{dr} \, dr = \frac{1}{3} \rho\omega^2 \left[a(R_2 - R_1) + \frac{1}{2} (R_2^2 - R_1^2) \sin \theta_0 \right] \sin \theta_0 \tag{72}$$

The pressure in the cylindrical annular channel is higher than in the tube.

For the case where the annular convergent region is filled with a viscoelastic material, we proceed as follows: Leaving out of account the stresses associated with the convective transport of momentum, the components of the equilibrium equation expressed in terms of the components of the total stress tensor $\underline{\pi} = p\underline{\delta} + \underline{\tau}$ are:

$$\frac{\partial \pi_{rr}}{\partial r} = \frac{N_2}{r} + (N_1 + N_2) \frac{\sin \theta}{a + r \sin \theta}$$

$$\frac{1}{r} \frac{\partial \pi_{\theta\theta}}{\partial \theta} = N_1 \frac{\cos \theta}{a + r \sin \theta} \tag{73}$$

where N_1 and N_2 are given by:

$$N_1 = \pi_{\varphi\varphi} - \pi_{\theta\theta} = -\psi_1(\dot{\gamma})\dot{\gamma}^2$$

$$N_2 = \pi_{\theta\theta} - \pi_{rr} = \alpha\psi_1(\dot{\gamma})\dot{\gamma}^2 \tag{74}$$

The factor α is assumed to be a constant whose value lies between 0 and 0.3 [1]. In the case where θ_c is small, the shear rate $\dot{\gamma}$ is a function of r only. Consequently the normal stress differences N_1 and N_2 are likewise functions of r only. In cases where θ_0 lies in the region halfway between 0 and $\pi/2$, again the component of the pressure gradient in the r direction dominates. We remove the dependence of π_{rr} and θ by the averaging procedure given in Equation 71. On integrating $\partial\bar{\pi}_{rr}/\partial r$ with respect to r we get:

$$\bar{\pi}_{rr} = \int_{R_1}^{r} \left\{ \frac{N_2}{r} + \frac{N_1 + N_2}{a + r \sin \theta_0} \sin \theta_0 \right\} dr + \bar{\pi}_{rr}(R_1) \tag{75}$$

and finally:

$$\Delta\bar{p} = \bar{\pi}_{rr}(R_2) - \bar{\pi}_{rr}(R_1) = -\int_{R_1}^{R_2} \psi_1 \dot{\gamma}^2 \frac{\sin \theta_0}{a + r \sin \theta_0} \left\{ 1 - \alpha \left(\frac{a}{r \sin \theta_0} + 2 \right) \right\} dr \tag{76}$$

This result shows some remarkable features. When $a = 0$ for the values of α known, the pressure in the tube will be higher than in the cylindrical annular region. When $a < 0$, this pressure difference will be amplified; while on the other hand, a positive value of a will have a reducing effect.

When ψ_1 is known as a function of the shear rate, a set of conical pumps with different values of a could be used to determine the value of α, provided that α is a constant.

The case $a = 0$ and $\theta_0 = \pi/2$ has been discussed by Van Es [20].

APPENDIX A

Summary of Differential Operations Involving the V Operator in Special Toroidal Coordinates (r, θ, φ)

$$\nabla \cdot \underline{v} = \frac{1}{r(a + r\sin\theta)}\frac{\partial}{\partial r}\{r(a + r\sin\theta)v_r\} + \frac{1}{r(a + r\sin\theta)}\frac{\partial}{\partial\theta}\{(a + r\sin\theta)v_\theta\} + \frac{1}{a + r\sin\theta}\frac{\partial v_\varphi}{\partial\varphi}$$

$$\nabla^2 S = \frac{1}{r(a + r\sin\theta)}\frac{\partial}{\partial r}\left\{r(a + r\sin\theta)\frac{\partial S}{\partial r}\right\} + \frac{1}{r(a + r\sin\theta)}\frac{\partial}{\partial\theta}\left\{(a + r\sin\theta)\frac{1}{r}\frac{\partial S}{\partial\theta}\right\} + \frac{1}{(a + r\sin\theta)^2}\frac{\partial^2 S}{\partial\varphi^2}$$

$$\underline{\underline{\tau}}:\nabla\underline{v} = \tau_{rr}\frac{\partial v_r}{\partial r} + \tau_{r\theta}\left(\frac{1}{r}\frac{\partial v_r}{\partial\theta} - \frac{v_\theta}{r}\right) + \tau_{r\varphi}\frac{1}{a + r\sin\theta}\left(\frac{\partial v_r}{\partial\varphi} - v_\varphi\sin\theta\right) + \tau_{\theta r}\frac{\partial v_\theta}{\partial r} + \tau_{\theta\theta}\left(\frac{v_r}{r} + \frac{1}{r}\frac{\partial v_\theta}{\partial\theta}\right)$$

$$+ \tau_{\theta\varphi}\frac{1}{a + r\sin\theta}\left(\frac{\partial v_\varphi}{\partial\varphi} - v_\varphi\cos\varphi\right) + \tau_{\varphi r}\frac{\partial v_\varphi}{\partial r} + \tau_{\varphi\theta}\frac{1}{r}\frac{\partial v_\varphi}{\partial\theta}$$

$$+ \tau_{\varphi\varphi}\frac{1}{a + r\sin\theta}\left(v_\theta\cos\theta + v_r\sin\theta + \frac{\partial v_\varphi}{\partial\varphi}\right)$$

$$[\nabla S]_r = \frac{\partial S}{\partial r} \qquad [\nabla S]_\theta = \frac{1}{r}\frac{\partial S}{\partial\theta} \qquad [\nabla S]_\varphi = \frac{1}{a + r\sin\theta}\frac{\partial S}{\partial\varphi}$$

$$[\nabla \times \underline{v}]_r = \frac{1}{r}\frac{\partial v_\varphi}{\partial\theta} + \frac{v_\varphi\cos\theta}{a + r\sin\theta} - \frac{1}{a + r\sin\theta}\frac{\partial v_\theta}{\partial\varphi}$$

$$[\nabla \times \underline{v}]_\theta = \frac{1}{a + r\sin\theta}\frac{\partial v_r}{\partial\varphi} - \frac{\partial v_\varphi}{\partial r} - \frac{v_\varphi\sin\theta}{a + r\sin\theta}$$

$$[\nabla \times \underline{v}]_\varphi = -\frac{1}{r}\frac{\partial v_r}{\partial\theta} + \frac{\partial v_\theta}{\partial r} + \frac{v_\theta}{r}$$

$$[\nabla \cdot \underline{\underline{\tau}}]_r = \frac{\partial\tau_{rr}}{\partial r} + \frac{1}{r}\frac{\partial\tau_{\theta r}}{\partial\theta} + \frac{1}{a + r\sin\theta}\frac{\partial\tau_{\varphi r}}{\partial\varphi} + \frac{\tau_{rr} - \tau_{\theta\theta}}{r} + \frac{\tau_{rr} - \tau_{\varphi\varphi}}{a + r\sin\theta}\sin\theta + \frac{\tau_{\theta r}\cos\theta}{a + r\sin\theta}$$

$$[\nabla \cdot \underline{\underline{\tau}}]_\theta = \frac{\partial\tau_{r\theta}}{\partial r} + \frac{1}{r}\frac{\partial\tau_{\theta\theta}}{\partial\theta} + \frac{1}{a + r\sin\theta}\frac{\partial\tau_{\varphi\theta}}{\partial\varphi} + \frac{\tau_{r\theta} + \tau_{\theta r}}{r} + \frac{\tau_{r\theta}\sin\theta}{a + r\sin\theta} + \frac{(\tau_{\theta\theta} - \tau_{\varphi\varphi})\cos\theta}{a + r\sin\theta}$$

$$[\nabla \cdot \underline{\underline{\tau}}]_\varphi = \frac{\partial\tau_{r\varphi}}{\partial r} + \frac{1}{r}\frac{\partial\tau_{\theta\varphi}}{\partial\theta} + \frac{1}{a + r\sin\theta}\frac{\partial\tau_{\varphi\varphi}}{\partial\varphi} + \frac{\tau_{r\varphi}}{r} + \frac{(\tau_{r\varphi} + \tau_{\varphi r})\sin\theta}{a + r\sin\theta} + \frac{(\tau_{\theta\varphi} + \tau_{\varphi\theta})\cos\theta}{a + r\sin\theta}$$

$$[\nabla^2\underline{v}]_r = \frac{\partial^2 v_r}{\partial r^2} + \frac{1}{r}\frac{\partial v_r}{\partial r} - \frac{v_r}{r^2} + \frac{\partial v_r}{\partial r}\frac{\sin\theta}{a + r\sin\theta} - \frac{v_r\sin^2\theta}{(a + r\sin\theta)^2} + \frac{1}{r^2}\frac{\partial v_r}{\partial\theta} + \frac{1}{r}\frac{\partial^2 v_r}{\partial\theta}\frac{\cos\theta}{a + r\sin\theta}$$

$$+ \frac{1}{(a + r\sin\theta)^2}\frac{\partial^2 v_r}{\partial\varphi^2} - \frac{2}{r^2}\frac{\partial v_\theta}{\partial\theta} - \frac{v_\theta\cos\theta}{r(a + r\sin\theta)} - \frac{v_\theta\cos\theta\sin\theta}{(a + r\sin\theta)^2} - 2\frac{\sin\theta}{(a + r\sin\theta)^2}\frac{\partial v_\varphi}{\partial\varphi}$$

$$[\nabla^2\underline{v}]_\theta = \frac{\partial^2 v_\theta}{\partial r^2} + \frac{1}{r}\frac{\partial v_\theta}{\partial r} - \frac{v_\theta}{r^2} + \frac{\sin\theta}{a + r\sin\theta}\frac{\partial v_\theta}{\partial r} - \frac{v_\theta\cos^2\theta}{(a + r\sin\theta)^2} + \frac{1}{r^2}\frac{\partial^2 v_\theta}{\partial\theta^2} + \frac{1}{r}\frac{\cos\theta}{a + r\sin\theta}\frac{\partial v_\theta}{\partial\theta}$$

$$+ \frac{1}{(a + r\sin\theta)^2}\frac{\partial^2 v_\theta}{\partial\varphi^2} + \frac{2}{r^2}\frac{\partial v_r}{\partial\theta} + \frac{v_r\cos\theta}{r(a + r\sin\theta)} - \frac{v_r\sin\theta\cos\theta}{(a + r\sin\theta)^2} - \frac{2\cos\theta}{(a + r\sin\theta)^2}\frac{\partial v_\varphi}{\partial\varphi}$$

$$[\nabla^2 \underline{v}]_\varphi = \frac{\partial^2 v_\varphi}{\partial r^2} + \frac{1}{r}\frac{\partial v_\varphi}{\partial r} + \frac{\sin\theta}{a + r\sin\theta}\frac{\partial v_\varphi}{\partial r} - \frac{v_\varphi}{(a + r\sin\theta)^2} + \frac{1}{r^2}\frac{\partial^2 v_\varphi}{\partial\theta^2} + \frac{\cos\theta}{r(a + r\sin\theta)}\frac{\partial v_\varphi}{\partial\theta}$$

$$+ \frac{1}{(a + r\sin\theta)^2}\frac{\partial^2 v_\varphi}{\partial\varphi^2} + \frac{2\sin\theta}{(a + r\sin\theta)^2}\frac{\partial v_r}{\partial\varphi} + \frac{2\cos\theta}{(a + r\sin\theta)^2}\frac{\partial v_\theta}{\partial\varphi}$$

$$[\underline{v} \cdot \nabla \underline{w}]_r = v_r\frac{\partial w_r}{\partial r} + v_\theta\left(\frac{1}{r}\frac{\partial w_r}{\partial\theta} - \frac{w_\theta}{r}\right) + \frac{v_\varphi}{a + r\sin\theta}\left(\frac{\partial w_r}{\partial\varphi} - w_\varphi\sin\theta\right)$$

$$[\underline{v} \cdot \nabla \underline{w}]_\theta = v_r\frac{\partial w_\theta}{\partial r} + v_\theta\left(\frac{w_r}{r} + \frac{1}{r}\frac{\partial w_\theta}{\partial\theta}\right) + \frac{v_\theta}{a + r\sin\theta}\left(\frac{\partial w_\theta}{\partial\varphi} - w_\varphi\cos\theta\right)$$

$$[\underline{v} \cdot \nabla \underline{w}]_\varphi = v_r\frac{\partial w_\varphi}{\partial r} + \frac{v_\theta}{r}\frac{\partial w_\varphi}{\partial\theta} + \frac{v_\varphi}{a + r\sin\theta}\left(\frac{\partial w_\varphi}{\partial\varphi} + w_\theta\cos\theta + w_r\sin\theta\right)$$

$$\{\nabla\underline{v}\}_{rr} = \frac{\partial v_r}{\partial r}$$

$$\{\nabla\underline{v}\}_{r\theta} = \frac{\partial v_\theta}{\partial r}$$

$$\{\nabla\underline{v}\}_{r\varphi} = \frac{\partial v_\varphi}{\partial r}$$

$$\{\nabla\underline{v}\}_{\theta r} = \frac{1}{r}\frac{\partial v_r}{\partial\theta} - \frac{v_\theta}{r}$$

$$\{\nabla\underline{v}\}_{\theta\theta} = \frac{v_r}{r} + \frac{1}{r}\frac{\partial v_\theta}{\partial\theta}$$

$$\{\nabla\underline{v}\}_{\theta\varphi} = \frac{1}{r}\frac{\partial v_\varphi}{\partial\theta}$$

$$\{\nabla\underline{v}\}_{\varphi r} = \frac{1}{a + r\sin\theta}\left(\frac{\partial v_r}{\partial\varphi} - v_\varphi\sin\theta\right)$$

$$\{\nabla\underline{v}\}_{\varphi\theta} = \frac{1}{a + r\sin\theta}\left(\frac{\partial v_\theta}{\partial\varphi} - v_\varphi\cos\theta\right)$$

$$\{\nabla\underline{v}\}_{\varphi\varphi} = \frac{1}{a + r\sin\theta}\left(v_\theta\cos\theta + v_r\sin\theta + \frac{\partial v_\varphi}{\partial\varphi}\right)$$

$$\{\underline{v} \cdot \nabla\underline{\underline{\tau}}\}_{rr} = (\underline{v} \cdot \nabla)\tau_{rr} - \frac{v_\theta}{r}(\tau_{\theta r} + \tau_{r\theta}) - \frac{v_\varphi\sin\theta}{a + r\sin\theta}(\tau_{r\varphi} + \tau_{\varphi r})$$

$$\{\underline{v} \cdot \nabla\underline{\underline{\tau}}\}_{r\theta} = (\underline{v} \cdot \nabla)\tau_{r\theta} + \frac{v_\theta}{r}(\tau_{rr} - \tau_{\theta\theta}) - \frac{v_\varphi\sin\theta}{a + r\sin\theta}\left(\frac{\cos\theta}{\sin\theta}\tau_{r\varphi} + \tau_{\varphi\theta}\right)$$

$$\{\underline{v} \cdot \nabla\underline{\underline{\tau}}\}_{r\varphi} = (\underline{v} \cdot \nabla)\tau_{r\varphi} - \frac{v_\theta}{r}\tau_{\theta\varphi} + \frac{v_\varphi\sin\theta}{a + r\sin\theta}\left(\frac{\cos\theta}{\sin\theta}\tau_{r\theta} - \tau_{\varphi\varphi} + \tau_{rr}\right)$$

$$\{\underset{\sim}{v} \cdot \underset{\approx}{\nabla \tau}\}_{\theta r} = (\underset{\sim}{v} \cdot \underset{\sim}{\nabla})\tau_{\theta r} + \frac{v_\theta}{r}(\tau_{rr} - \tau_{\theta\theta}) - \frac{v_\varphi \sin \theta}{a + r \sin \theta}\left(\tau_{\theta\varphi} + \frac{\cos \theta}{\sin \theta}\tau_{\varphi r}\right)$$

$$\{\underset{\sim}{v} \cdot \underset{\approx}{\nabla \tau}\}_{\theta\theta} = (\underset{\sim}{v} \cdot \underset{\sim}{\nabla})\tau_{\theta\theta} + \frac{v_\theta}{r}(\tau_{r\theta} + \tau_{\theta r}) - \frac{v_\varphi \sin \theta}{a + r \sin \theta}(\tau_{\theta\varphi} + \tau_{\varphi\theta})\frac{\cos \theta}{\sin \theta}$$

$$\{\underset{\sim}{v} \cdot \underset{\approx}{\nabla \tau}\}_{\theta\varphi} = (\underset{\sim}{v} \cdot \underset{\sim}{\nabla})\tau_{\theta\varphi} + \frac{v_\theta}{r}\tau_{r\varphi} + \frac{v_\varphi \sin \theta}{a + r \sin \theta}\left\{\tau_{\theta r} + \frac{\cos \theta}{\sin \theta}(\tau_{\theta\theta} - \tau_{\varphi\varphi})\right\}$$

$$\{\underset{\sim}{v} \cdot \underset{\approx}{\nabla \tau}\}_{\varphi r} = (\underset{\sim}{v} \cdot \underset{\sim}{\nabla})\tau_{\varphi r} - \frac{v_\theta}{r}\tau_{\varphi\theta} + \frac{v_\varphi \sin \theta}{a + r \sin \theta}\left(\tau_{rr} - \tau_{\varphi\varphi} + \frac{\cos \theta}{\sin \theta}\tau_{\theta r}\right)$$

$$\{\underset{\sim}{v} \cdot \underset{\approx}{\nabla \tau}\}_{\varphi\theta} = (\underset{\sim}{v} \cdot \underset{\sim}{\nabla})\tau_{\varphi\theta} + \frac{v_\theta}{r}\tau_{\varphi r} + \frac{v_\varphi \sin \theta}{a + r \sin \theta}\left\{\tau_{r\theta} + (\tau_{\theta\theta} - \tau_{\varphi\varphi})\frac{\cos \theta}{\sin \theta}\right\}$$

$$\{\underset{\sim}{v} \cdot \underset{\approx}{\nabla \tau}\}_{\varphi\varphi} = (\underset{\sim}{v} \cdot \underset{\sim}{\nabla})\tau_{\varphi\varphi} + \frac{v_\varphi \sin \theta}{a + r \sin \theta}\left\{\tau_{r\varphi} + \tau_{\varphi r} + (\tau_{\theta\varphi} + \tau_{\varphi\theta})\frac{\cos \theta}{\sin \theta}\right\}$$

where the operator $(\underset{\sim}{v} \cdot \underset{\sim}{\nabla}) = v_r \dfrac{\partial}{\partial r} + v_\theta \dfrac{1}{r}\dfrac{\partial}{\partial \theta} + \dfrac{v_\varphi}{a + r \sin \theta}\dfrac{\partial}{\partial \varphi}$

APPENDIX B

Components of the Equation of Motion and the Navier-Stokes Equation in the Special Toroidal Coordinate System

In terms of $\underset{\approx}{\tau}$:

$$\rho\left(\frac{\partial v_r}{\partial t} + v_r\frac{\partial v_r}{\partial r} + \frac{v_\theta}{r}\frac{\partial v_r}{\partial \theta} + \frac{v_\varphi}{a + r \sin \theta}\frac{\partial v_r}{\partial \varphi} - \frac{v_\theta^2}{r} - \frac{v_\varphi^2 \sin \theta}{a + r \sin \theta}\right)$$

$$= \rho g_r - \frac{\partial p}{\partial r} - \left\{\frac{\partial \tau_{rr}}{\partial r} + \frac{1}{r}\frac{\partial \tau_{\theta r}}{\partial \theta} + \frac{1}{a + r \sin \theta}\frac{\partial \tau_{\varphi r}}{\partial \varphi} + \frac{\tau_{rr} - \tau_{\theta\theta}}{r} + \frac{\tau_{rr} - \tau_{\varphi\varphi}}{a + r \sin \theta}\sin \theta + \frac{\tau_{\theta r}\cos \theta}{a + r \sin \theta}\right\}$$

$$\rho\left(\frac{\partial v_\theta}{\partial t} + v_r\frac{\partial v_\theta}{\partial r} + v_\theta\frac{1}{r}\frac{\partial v_\theta}{\partial \theta} + \frac{v_\varphi}{a + r \sin \theta}\frac{\partial v_\theta}{\partial \varphi} + \frac{v_\theta v_r}{r} - \frac{v_\varphi^2 \cos \theta}{a + r \sin \theta}\right)$$

$$= \rho g_\theta - \frac{1}{r}\frac{\partial p}{\partial \theta} - \left\{\frac{\partial \tau_{r\theta}}{\partial r} + \frac{1}{r}\frac{\partial \tau_{\theta\theta}}{\partial \theta} + \frac{1}{a + r \sin \theta}\frac{\partial \tau_{\varphi\theta}}{\partial \varphi} + \frac{\tau_{r\theta} + \tau_{\theta r}}{r}\right.$$

$$\left. + \frac{\tau_{r\theta}\sin \theta}{a + r \sin \theta} + \frac{(\tau_{\theta\theta} - \tau_{\varphi\varphi})\cos \theta}{a + r \sin \theta}\right\}$$

$$\rho\left(\frac{\partial v_\varphi}{\partial t} + v_r\frac{\partial v_\varphi}{\partial r} + \frac{v_\theta}{r}\frac{\partial v_\varphi}{\partial \theta} + \frac{v_\varphi}{a + r \sin \theta}\frac{\partial v_\varphi}{\partial \varphi} + \frac{v_\varphi v_r \sin \theta}{a + r \sin \theta} + \frac{v_\theta v_\varphi \cos \theta}{a + r \sin \theta}\right)$$

$$= \rho g_\varphi - \frac{1}{a + r \sin \theta}\frac{\partial p}{\partial \varphi} - \left\{\frac{\partial \tau_{r\varphi}}{\partial r} + \frac{1}{r}\frac{\partial \tau_{\theta\varphi}}{\partial \theta} + \frac{1}{a + r \sin \theta}\frac{\partial \tau_{\varphi\varphi}}{\partial \varphi} + \frac{\partial \tau_{r\varphi}}{r}\right.$$

$$\left. + \frac{(\tau_{r\varphi} + \tau_{\varphi r})\sin \theta}{a + r \sin \theta} + \frac{(\tau_{\theta\varphi} + \tau_{\varphi\theta})\cos \theta}{a + r \sin \theta}\right\}$$

For a Newtonian liquid with constant density ρ and viscosity μ:

$$\rho\left(\frac{\partial v_r}{\partial t} + v_r\frac{\partial v_r}{\partial r} + \frac{v_\theta}{r}\frac{\partial v_r}{\partial \theta} + \frac{v_\varphi}{a + r\sin\theta}\frac{\partial v_r}{\partial \varphi} - \frac{v_\theta^2}{r} - \frac{v_\varphi^2\sin\theta}{a + r\sin\theta}\right)$$

$$= \rho g_r - \frac{\partial p}{\partial r} + \mu\left[\frac{\partial^2 v_r}{\partial r^2} + \frac{1}{r}\frac{\partial v_r}{\partial r} - \frac{v_r}{r^2} + \frac{\sin\theta}{a + r\sin\theta}\frac{\partial v_r}{\partial r} - \frac{v_r\sin^2\theta}{(a + r\sin\theta)^2} + \frac{1}{r^2}\frac{\partial^2 v_r}{\partial\theta^2}\right.$$

$$+ \frac{1}{r}\frac{\partial v_r}{\partial\theta}\frac{\cos\theta}{a + r\sin\theta} + \frac{1}{(a + r\sin\theta)^2}\frac{\partial^2 v_r}{\partial\varphi^2} - \frac{2}{r^2}\frac{\partial v_\theta}{\partial\theta} - \frac{v_\theta\cos\theta}{r(a + r\sin\theta)} - \frac{v_\theta\cos\theta\sin\theta}{(a + r\sin\theta)^2}$$

$$\left. - 2\frac{\sin\theta}{(a + r\sin\theta)^2}\frac{\partial v_\varphi}{\partial\varphi}\right]$$

$$\rho\left(\frac{\partial v_\theta}{\partial t} + v_r\frac{\partial v_\theta}{\partial r} + \frac{v_\theta}{r}\frac{\partial v_\theta}{\partial\theta} + \frac{v_\varphi}{a + r\sin\theta}\frac{\partial v_\theta}{\partial\varphi} + \frac{v_\theta v_r}{r} - \frac{v_\varphi^2\cos\theta}{a + r\sin\theta}\right)$$

$$= \rho g_\theta - \frac{1}{r}\frac{\partial p}{\partial\theta} + \mu\left[\frac{\partial^2 v_\theta}{\partial r^2} + \frac{1}{r}\frac{\partial v_\theta}{\partial r} - \frac{v_\theta}{r^2} + \frac{\sin\theta}{a + r\sin\theta}\frac{\partial v_\theta}{\partial r} - \frac{v_\theta\cos^2\theta}{(a + r\sin\theta)^2} + \frac{1}{r^2}\frac{\partial^2 v_\theta}{\partial\theta^2}\right.$$

$$+ \frac{1}{r}\frac{\cos\theta}{a + r\sin\theta}\frac{\partial v_\theta}{\partial\theta} + \frac{1}{(a + r\sin\theta)^2}\frac{\partial^2 v_\theta}{\partial\varphi^2} + \frac{2}{r^2}\frac{\partial v_r}{\partial\theta} + \frac{v_r\cos\theta}{r(a + r\sin\theta)}$$

$$\left. - \frac{v_r\sin\theta\cos\theta}{(a + r\sin\theta)^2} - \frac{2\cos\theta}{(a + r\sin\theta)^2}\frac{\partial v_\varphi}{\partial\varphi}\right]$$

$$\rho\left(\frac{\partial v_\varphi}{\partial t} + v_r\frac{\partial v_\varphi}{\partial r} + \frac{v_\theta}{r}\frac{\partial v_\varphi}{\partial\theta} + \frac{v_\varphi}{a + r\sin\theta}\frac{\partial v_\varphi}{\partial\varphi} + \frac{v_\varphi v_r\sin\theta}{a + r\sin\theta} + \frac{v_\theta v_\varphi\cos\theta}{a + r\sin\theta}\right)$$

$$= \rho g_\varphi - \frac{1}{a + r\sin\theta}\frac{\partial p}{\partial\varphi} + \mu\left[\frac{\partial^2 v_\varphi}{\partial r^2} + \frac{1}{r}\frac{\partial v_\varphi}{\partial r} + \frac{\sin\theta}{a + r\sin\theta}\frac{\partial v_\varphi}{\partial r} - \frac{v_\varphi}{(a + r\sin\theta)^2} + \frac{1}{r^2}\frac{\partial^2 v_\varphi}{\partial\theta^2}\right.$$

$$\left. + \frac{\cos\theta}{r(a + r\sin\theta)}\frac{\partial v_\varphi}{\partial\theta} + \frac{1}{(a + r\sin\theta)^2}\frac{\partial^2 v_\varphi}{\partial\varphi^2} + \frac{2\sin\theta}{(a + r\sin\theta)^2}\frac{\partial v_r}{\partial\varphi} + \frac{2\cos\theta}{(a + r\sin\theta)^2}\frac{\partial v_\theta}{\partial\varphi}\right]$$

NOTATION

a	radius of fixed circle	β	parameter
r, θ, φ	special toroidal coordinate	ΔP	pressure drop
$\underline{\delta}_r, \underline{\delta}_\theta, \underline{\delta}_\varphi$	unit vectors of special toroidal coordinate system	μ	dynamic viscosity
		$\underset{\approx}{\dot\gamma}$	rate-of-strain tensor
$\underline{\delta}_x, \underline{\delta}_y, \underline{\delta}_z$	unit vectors of rectangular coordinate system	$\underset{\approx}{\tau}$	extra stress tensor
		$\dot\gamma$	shear rate
$\underline\nabla$	nabla operator	m, n	"Power Law" constants
$\underline{v}$	velocity vector	$I(r^*, \theta^*), II(r^*, \theta^*)$	functions
$\underset{\approx}{\pi}$	total stress tensor	θ_0	angle to define conical surface
	$\underset{\approx}{\pi} = p\underset{\approx}{\delta} + \underset{\approx}{\tau}$		
$\underline{\delta}_r\underline{\delta}_r, \underline{\delta}_r\underline{\delta}_\theta, \underline{\delta}_\varphi\underline{\delta}_\varphi$	unit dyads	ζ	variable $\zeta = \dfrac{\pi}{2} - \theta$
θ_c	angle between conical surfaces	ω	angular velocity
Q	volume rate of flow	M, F	torque, force
r_w	wire radius	R_1, R_2	positions on conical surface
V_c	core speed		
P_0, L, V	scaling quantities (pressure, length, velocity)		

Barred symbols refer to mean values.
Symbols with asterisks are dimensionless.

N_1, N_2	first and second normal stress difference	α	ratio between second and first normal stress coefficient
ρ	density		
ψ_1	first normal stress coefficient		

REFERENCES

1. Bird, R. B., Armstrong, R. C., and Hassager, O., *Dynamics of Polymeric Liquids*, John Wiley & Sons 1977.
2. Bird, R. B., Stewart, W. E., and Lightfoot, E. N., *Transport Phenomena*, John Wiley & Sons 1960.
3. Winter, H. H., *Advances in Heat Transfer, 1977*: 205–268.
4. Berger, S. A., and Talbot, L., *Ann. Rev. Fluid Mech., 15*: 461–512 (1983).
5. Chang, H-T., *Appl. Phys. 3*: 149–154 (1974).
6. Lewin, L., *IEEE Transactions on Microwave Theory and Techniques, Vol. MTT-22, No 7*: 718–727 (1974).
7. Clark, R. A., and Reissner, E., *Advances in Applied Mechanics, Vol. II*, Academic Press, 93–122 (1950).
8. March, B. D., and Pearson, J. R. A., *Rheol. Acta, Heft 7, Band 4*: 326–331 (1968).
9. Jackson, R., and Kaye, A., *Brit. J. Appl. Phys., Vol. 17*: 1355–1360 (1966).
10. Dijksman, J. F., *Proceedings of the International Workshop Elongational Flows*, La Bresse, January 1983: 12.1–12.4.
11. Walters, K., *Rheometry*, Chapman and Hall, 1975.
12. Schrag, J. L., *Transactions of the Society of Rheology 21*:3: 399–413 (1977).
13. Hutton, J. F., *Rheol. Acta 8*: 54 (1969).
14. Tanner, R. I., and Keentok, M., *Journal of Rheology, 27*(1): 47–57 (1983).
15. Caswell, B., and Tanner, R. I., *Polymer Engineering and Science, Vol. 18, No. 5*: 416–421 (1978).
16. Meissner, J., *Pure and Appl. Chem., 42*: 551–612 (1975).
17. Chen, I-Jen, and Bogue, D. C., *Transactions of the Society of Rheology, 16*:1: 59–78 (1978).
18. Crochet, M. J., and Keunings, R., *Journal of Non-Newtonian Fluid Mechanics, Vol. 10, no. 3 + 4*: 339–356 (1982).
19. Crochet, M. J., and Walters, K., *Ann. Rev. Fluid Mech., 15*: 241–260 (1983).
20. Van Es, H. E., *Rheologica Acta 13*: 905–909 (1974).

CHAPTER 8

PARAMETRIC MODELING OF FLOW GEOMETRIES IN NON-NEWTONIAN FLOWS

W. Kozicki

Department of Chemical Engineering
University of Ottawa
Ottawa, Canada

C. Tiu

Department of Chemical Engineering
Monash University
Clayton, Australia

CONTENTS

INTRODUCTION

Many engineering problems are concerned with the flow of fluids in channels of complex geometry. The boundary conditions for these flow situations are usually so complicated that it is often not possible to obtain analytical solutions by solving the equations of motion, even for the simple Newtonian fluids. Although numerical solutions are now more readily available with the advancement of personal computers, many solutions or software packages are either too time-consuming or expensive for practical usage. It remains a great challenge for rheologists and engineers to seek simplified methods, using idealized mathematical models with respect to flow geometry as well as fluid model, to solve the complex flow problems.

In this chapter, a simple and general geometric parameter method of modeling the steady, fully developed laminar flow of any time-independent fluid in a channel of arbitrary cross section is introduced. The method is based on a generalization of the Rabinowitsch-Mooney analysis for flow in circular tubes and a similar result for the parallel-plate (slit) geometry. The surface effects encountered in many non-Newtonian fluid systems, including polymer solutions, biological fluids, mineral suspensions, and other particulate systems, in flow channels are incorporated in the analysis. For engineering applications the method normally requires only the knowledge of two geometric parameters, characterizing the flow geometry; and a shear stress-shear rate or viscosity function, representing the viscous behavior of the fluid. The geometric parameters evaluated for a variety of flow channels are presented. A refined geometric parameter method, making use of an infinite number of geometric coefficients, is shown to improve the accuracy of the prediction, as well as providing a firm basis for the two parameter technique.

The generality of the method is demonstrated for the flow of purely viscous and viscoelastic fluids in closed conduits and open channels of arbitrary but axially uniform cross section. Applications are also made to the expansion/contraction problem associated with non-Newtonian liquid jets emerging from a capillary die of arbitrary cross section and to the flow of purely viscous fluids in packed beds or porous media.

Engineering flow data are conveniently represented in the form of Fanning friction factor vs. Reynolds number plots. The generalized Reynolds number defined for non-Newtonian fluids in circular tube flow is extended to non-circular conduits and open channels by incorporating the respective geometric parameters. It is shown that all existing friction factor-Reynolds number correlations, both laminar and turbulent, for non-Newtonian flow in circular pipes are directly applicable to non-circular cross-sectional channels. The relationship between the friction factor and Reynolds number for porous media flow consistent with various packed bed models is also presented.

POISEUILLE OR CIRCULAR TUBE FLOW

The flow behavior of a fluid in a channel can be described by solving the equations of motion in conjunction with an appropriate constitutive equation representing the rheological characteristics of the fluid. The stress field, however, can be determined from the equations of motion without assuming a particular rheological equation for the fluid. This is shown below for the steady, fully-developed, laminar flow of a fluid in a circular tube. The equations of motion in cylindrical coordinates are:

r-*component*

$$
\rho \left(\frac{\partial u_r}{\partial t} + u_r \frac{\partial u_r}{\partial r} + \frac{u_\theta}{r} \frac{\partial u_r}{\partial \theta} - \frac{u_\theta^2}{r} + u_z \frac{\partial u_r}{\partial z} \right)
$$
$$
= -\left[\frac{1}{r} \frac{\partial}{\partial r} (r\pi_{rr}) + \frac{1}{r} \frac{\partial \pi_{r\theta}}{\partial \theta} - \frac{\pi_{\theta\theta}}{r} + \frac{\partial \pi_{rz}}{\partial z} \right] \tag{1}
$$

θ-component

$$\rho\left(\frac{\partial u_\theta}{\partial t} + u_r\frac{\partial u_\theta}{\partial r} + \frac{u_\theta}{r}\frac{\partial u_\theta}{\partial \theta} + \frac{u_r u_\theta}{r} + u_z\frac{\partial u_\theta}{\partial z}\right)$$

$$= -\left[\frac{1}{r^2}\frac{\partial}{\partial \theta}(r^2\pi_{r\theta}) + \frac{1}{r}\frac{\partial \pi_{\theta\theta}}{\partial \theta} + \frac{\partial \pi_{\theta z}}{\partial z}\right] \qquad (2)$$

z-component

$$\rho\left(\frac{\partial u_z}{\partial t} + u_r\frac{\partial u_z}{\partial r} + \frac{u_\theta}{r}\frac{\partial u_z}{\partial \theta} + u_z\frac{\partial u_z}{\partial z}\right) = -\left[\frac{1}{r}\frac{\partial}{\partial r}(r\pi_{rz}) + \frac{1}{r}\frac{\partial \pi_{\theta z}}{\partial \theta} + \frac{\partial \pi_{zz}}{\partial z}\right] \qquad (3)$$

where π_{ij} represents the ij-component of the total stress tensor, which is defined as the sum of the ij-component of the momentum flux or stress tensor τ_{ij}, and the hydrostatic potential P by:

$$\pi_{ij} = \tau_{ij} + \delta_{ij}P \qquad i, j = r, \theta, z \qquad (4)$$

Here δ_{ij} is the Kronecker delta with the values $\delta_{ij} = 1$ for $i = j$ and $\delta_{ij} = 0$ for $i \neq j$. The potential P is defined by the relation $\nabla P = \nabla p - \rho g$ and for an incompressible fluid is given by $P = p + \rho g h$, where h is the elevation relative to a horizontal reference plane. As seen from Equation 4, a negative normal stress component τ_{ii} (deviatoric stress) denotes a tensile stress, while a positive τ_{ii} implies a compressive stress.*

For steady, fully-developed laminar flow in a circular tube, Equations 1, 2, and 3 reduce to:

r-component

$$\frac{\partial \pi_{rr}}{\partial r} + \frac{\pi_{rr} - \pi_{\theta\theta}}{r} = 0 \qquad (5)$$

θ-component

$$\frac{\partial \pi_{\theta\theta}}{\partial \theta} = 0 \qquad (6)$$

z-component

$$\frac{1}{r}\frac{\partial}{\partial r}(r\tau_{rz}) = -\frac{\partial P}{\partial z} \qquad (7)$$

Since the axial potential gradient $\partial P/\partial z$ is constant for fully-developed flow, Equation 7 may be integrated from $r = 0$ to $r = r$ to yield:

$$\tau_{rz} = \frac{r}{2}\left(-\frac{\partial P}{\partial z}\right) = \frac{r}{2}\left(-\frac{\Delta P}{L}\right) \qquad (8)$$

---

* In many treatises on fluid mechanics a different sign convention is used for the stress tensor. Equation 4 may also be defined as $\pi_{ij} = \tau_{ij} - \delta_{ij}P$, where a tensile stress is positive and a compressive stress is negative. For a detailed discussion of the sign convention, refer to Bird et al. [1].

Equation 8, for the wall condition, becomes:

$$\tau_w = \frac{R}{2}\left(-\frac{\Delta P}{L}\right) \tag{9}$$

The combination of Equations 8 and 9 yields a linear variation of shear stress from zero at the centerline to τ_w at the pipe wall:

$$\tau_{rz}/\tau_w = r/R \tag{10}$$

Integration of Equation 5, expressed in terms of the deviatoric stresses, from $r = 0$ to $r = r$ at a particular z, yields:

$$\tau_{rr} + \int_0^r (\tau_{rr} - \tau_{\theta\theta})d \ln r = 0 \tag{11}$$

The total stress components, defined by:

$$\pi_{rr} = \tau_{rr} + P \tag{12}$$

$$\pi_{zz} = \tau_{zz} + P \tag{13}$$

are therefore given by:

$$\pi_{rr} = P(z) - \int_0^r (\tau_{rr} - \tau_{\theta\theta})d \ln r \tag{14}$$

and:

$$\pi_{zz} = (\tau_{zz} - \tau_{rr}) + P(z) - \int_0^r (\tau_{rr} - \tau_{\theta\theta})d \ln r \tag{15}$$

The advantage of using the potential P instead of the hydrostatic pressure p in the above development lies in the fact that the former varies only with the spatial coordinate in the direction of flow, in this case $P = P(z)$; whereas, in general, $p = p(r, \theta, z)$. Equations 8, 14, and 15 define the stress field for the steady, fully-developed laminar flow of a fluid in a circular tube.

For an inelastic (purely viscous) fluid, $\tau_{zz} = \tau_{rr} = \tau_{\theta\theta} = 0$; Equations 14 and 15 both reduce to:

$$\pi_{rr} = \pi_{zz} = P(z) \tag{16}$$

Characterization of Surface Effects

It is generally recognized that the flow of polymer solutions in conduits, packed beds, and porous media may be influenced by various surface effects at the solid-fluid interface. These may include polymer adsorption, gel-formation, and polymer depletion in a thin layer adjacent to the solid surface. The latter phenomenon has been attributed variously to steric effects between the polymer molecules and the solid surface, separation due to polymer alignment in the wall region, and to stress-induced polymer diffusion away from the solid surface. Although the detailed analysis of these phenomena, which may occur to varying extents in a specific flow situation depending upon the polymer-solvent system, nature of solid surface, flow configuration, and flow conditions, lies outside the scope of the present subject matter, it is nevertheless desirable to account for them in the representation of the flow characteristics.

In steady uniform laminar tubular flow with a surface effect, the velocity gradient near the wall may be represented by:

$$\frac{du}{dy} = f(\tau_{rz}) + g(\tau_{rz}, y) \tag{17}$$

where $y = R - r$ is the normal distance from the wall; $f(\tau_{rz})$ is the characteristic function of shear stress obtained by solving the shear stress-shear rate relationship (fluid model equation) for the shear rate, $f(\tau_{rz}) = \gamma_{rz} = \tau_{rz}/\eta$; and $g(\tau_{rz}, y)$ is a correction function applied to $f(\tau_{rz})$ in the wall region, where the viscous characteristics deviate from the homogeneous behavior ascribed to the bulk of the fluid.

Integration of Equation 17 beyond the region of anomalous flow produces:

$$u = \int_0^y f(\tau_{rz})\, dy + \int_0^\delta g(\tau_{rz}, y)\, dy \tag{18}$$

where the upper limit y originally appearing in the second term on the right side has been replaced by δ, the thickness of the anomalous zone, since $g(\tau_{rz}, y) = 0$ for $y \geq \delta$. At the wall condition, $y = 0$, Equation 18 yields a finite velocity, which is designated the effective velocity at the wall:

$$u_w = \int_0^\delta g(\tau_{rz}, y)\, dy \tag{19}$$

The velocity distribution for tubular flow in the presence of an anomalous surface effect may thus be represented by the usual expression for flow without a surface effect supplemented by the effective velocity at the wall.

A positive u_w is referred to as an effective velocity of slip at the wall. If the slip is attributed to polymer depletion in the wall region, one may evaluate an effective solvent layer thickness manifesting the slip velocity. Thus, for a thin pure solvent layer at the wall in which any variation of τ_{rz} from τ_w is negligible, $du/dy = \tau_w/\mu_s$ and Equation 17 gives:

$$g(\tau_{rz}, y) = \frac{\tau_w}{\mu_s} - f(\tau_{rz}) = \tau_w\left(\frac{1}{\mu_s} - \frac{1}{\eta_w}\right) \tag{20}$$

where μ_s is the solvent viscosity and η_w is the non-Newtonian viscosity of the bulk solution evaluated at the wall shear stress.

Substituting for $g(\tau_{rz}, y)$ in Equation 19 results in the solvent layer thickness as follows:

$$\delta_s = \frac{u_w}{\tau_w}\left(\frac{1}{\mu_s} - \frac{1}{\eta_w}\right)^{-1} \tag{21}$$

If the anomalous zone comprises a thin polymer adsorption-gel formation layer, then $du/dy = 0$ in this region, and Equation 17 gives $g(\tau_{rz}, y) = -\tau_w/\eta_w$. Substitution in Equation 19 yields the thickness δ_a of the polymer adsorption-gel formation zone as follows:

$$\delta_a = -\frac{u_w\eta_w}{\tau_w} \tag{22}$$

It is seen that a polymer adsorption-gel formation phenomenon is consistent with a negative effective velocity at the wall.

Rabinowitsch–Mooney Equation

In the following, we set out to derive the general equation relating the volumetric flow rate Q or average velocity $\langle u \rangle$ in a pipe to the shear stress at the wall τ_w, for the steady uniform laminar flow of a non-Newtonian fluid exhibiting a surface effect.

The volumetric flow rate is given by:

$$Q = 2\pi \int_0^R u\, r\, dr \tag{23}$$

or by:

$$Q = \pi \int_0^R r^2 \left(-\frac{du}{dr} \right) dr \tag{24}$$

after integration by parts, using the boundary condition $u = 0$ at $r = R$.
Substitution for $(-du/dr)$ in accordance with Equation 17 and utilization of Equation 10 leads to:

$$Q = \pi \left[\frac{R^3}{\tau_w^3} \int_0^{\tau_w} \tau^2 f(\tau)\, d\tau + \int_{R-\delta}^R r^2 g(\tau_{rz}, y)\, dr \right] \tag{25}$$

where the dummy variable τ_{rz} has been replaced by τ in the first integral in Equation 25. In the current discussion and in the presentation which follows relating to rectilinear flows, τ may be interpreted as the magnitude of the shear stress given by $\tau = \eta \gamma$ where γ is the shear rate defined in terms of the second invariant of the rate of deformation tensor $\boldsymbol{\gamma}$ by $\gamma = +\sqrt{[\frac{1}{2}(\boldsymbol{\gamma} : \boldsymbol{\gamma})]}$ and η is the non-Newtonian viscosity representable as a function of γ or τ determined by the fluid model equation. In the case of a purely viscous non-Newtonian fluid, the shear stress τ is related to the second invariant of the stress tensor $\boldsymbol{\tau}$ by $\tau = +\sqrt{[\frac{1}{2}(\boldsymbol{\tau} : \boldsymbol{\tau})]}$. This expression may also be used for evaluation of τ for the rectilinear flow of a viscoelastic fluid if the normal stress terms are disregarded in the summation given by $\boldsymbol{\tau} : \boldsymbol{\tau} = \sum_i \sum_j \tau_{ij}\tau_{ji}$, that is, the summation is carried out for $i \neq j$. This corresponds to considering the viscoelastic fluid as a purely viscous fluid in the evaluation of τ. It can be shown that the latter summation is also a scalar invariant.

For a thin anomalous zone, $\delta/R \ll 1$, r inside the second integral in Equation 25 may be replaced by R, producing:

$$\langle u \rangle = \frac{R}{\tau_w^3} \int_0^{\tau_w} \tau^2 f(\tau)\, d\tau + \int_0^\delta g(\tau_{rz}, y)\, dy \tag{26}$$

which, using Equation 19, finally yields:

$$\frac{8\langle u \rangle}{D} = \frac{8u_w}{D} + \frac{4}{\tau_w^3} \int_0^{\tau_w} \tau^2 f(\tau)\, d\tau \tag{27}$$

Notice that the same result could have been obtained directly by using the boundary condition $u = u_w$ at the wall consistent with Equation 19 and a homogeneous fluid across the entire cross section, instead of the boundary condition $u = 0$ as in Equation 24. The latter analysis thus justifies this alternative approach, which will be used in subsequent developments, as well as delineating the underlying assumptions inherent in the development of Equation 27.

Assuming the effective velocity at the wall due to a surface effect is a function only of the wall shear stress, Equation 27 indicates a plot of $8\langle u \rangle/D$ vs. $1/D$ at constant τ_w should be linear, with slope equal to $8u_w$. Thus, repeating this procedure for different τ_w, u_w may be evaluated as a function of τ_w, which may then be used to determine $8(\langle u \rangle - u_w)/D$ vs. τ_w from experimental data.

This procedure for evaluation of the effective velocity at the wall, which implies u_w is independent of the tube diameter D, is in concordance with Oldroyd's analysis [2]. More recently, it has been observed [3–5] that u_w may vary with tube diameter as well as with wall shear stress and solute concentration. Further, it was indicated that in a polymeric system both polymer adsorption-gel formation (negative effective velocity at the wall) and polymer depletion (positive effective velocity of slip) phenomena may occur simultaneously. The relative extents depend upon the polymer-solvent system, nature of solid surfaces, flow configuration, and flow conditions. The procedure for evaluating the effective wall velocity when the two phenomena are involved is inherently more complicated. Although the subject matter is beyond the scope of this chapter, it is worth noting a recent paper [5] proposing a superposition model for evaluation of the two effects in capillary flow.

Equation 27, rewritten in the form:

$$\frac{8(\langle u \rangle - u_w)}{D} = \frac{4}{\tau_w^3} \int_0^{\tau_w} \tau^2 f(\tau) \, d\tau \tag{28}$$

points to a unique relationship between $8(\langle u \rangle - u_w)/D$ and τ_w, which is a function only of the fluid model, represented by $f(\tau)$. Equation 28 may therefore be differentiated with respect to τ_w, utilizing the Leibnitz formula for differentiating an integral, to obtain:

$$\gamma_w = f(\tau_w) = \frac{1}{4} \tau_w \frac{d[8(\langle u \rangle - u_w)/D]}{d\tau_w} + \frac{3}{4} \left[\frac{8(\langle u \rangle - u_w)}{D} \right] \tag{29}$$

which is the Rabinowitsch-Mooney equation extended to include the effective velocity at the wall. The equation is utilized subsequently in the formulation of flow in ducts of arbitrary cross-sectional geometry.

Equation 29 may be rearranged to:

$$\gamma_w = \left(\frac{3n' + 1}{4n'} \right) \left[\frac{8(\langle u \rangle - u_w)}{D} \right] \tag{30}$$

where n' is defined by:

$$n' = \frac{d \ln \tau_w}{d \ln[8(\langle u \rangle - u_w)/D]} \tag{31}$$

It is evaluated as the slope of the tangent to the curve obtained in a log-log plot of τ_w vs. $8(\langle u \rangle - u_w)/D$. For a power law fluid, $f(\tau) = (\tau/K)^{1/n}$, Equation 27 gives:

$$\tau_w = K \left(\frac{3n + 1}{4n} \right)^n \left[\frac{8(\langle u \rangle - u_w)}{D} \right]^n \tag{32}$$

and the flow curve is therefore linear with n' equal to n. In the case of a Newtonian fluid, the plot is linear with a slope of unity. Further, as seen from Equation 30, the quantity $8(\langle u \rangle - u_w)/D$ for steady uniform laminar flow of a Newtonian fluid in a tube gives the shear rate at the wall, referred to simply as the shear rate. For a Newtonian fluid the effective velocity at the wall u_w is normally zero. For non-Newtonian fluids for which the actual relationship is described by Equation 30, $8(\langle u \rangle - u_w)/D$ is termed the apparent shear rate.

Equation 30 finds application in capillary tube viscometry in determination of the shear stress-shear rate relationships of non-Newtonian fluids.

FLOW BETWEEN PARALLEL PLATES (SLIT FLOW)

Consider the steady, laminar, fully-developed flow of a time-independent fluid between two parallel plates of infinite extent separated by the distance H; the relevant velocity component corresponds to the axial velocity $u = u(x)$, which is a function of the normal distance x from the mid-plane.

The shear stress distribution for the flow in the z-direction yielded by the z-component of the equations of motion in Cartesian coordinates is given by:

$$\tau_{xz} = \tau_w \left(\frac{x}{H/2} \right) \tag{33}$$

where $\tau_w = \frac{H}{2} \left(-\frac{\Delta P}{L} \right) \tag{34}$

The volumetric flow rate is determined by integrating the velocity over the flow cross section of width W:

$$Q = 2W \int_0^{H/2} u \, dx \tag{35}$$

Integration by parts, using the boundary condition $u = u_w$ at $x = H/2$, in the presence of a surface effect, gives:

$$Q = 2W \left[\frac{u_w H}{2} + \int_0^{H/2} x \left(-\frac{du}{dx} \right) dx \right] \tag{36}$$

Substitution of $f(\tau_{xz}) = -du/dx$ and introduction of Equation 33 yields $\langle u \rangle = Q/WH$ as follows:

$$\langle u \rangle = u_w + \frac{H}{2\tau_w^2} \int_0^{\tau_w} \tau_{xz} f(\tau_{xz}) \, d\tau_{xz} \tag{37}$$

or

$$\frac{4(\langle u \rangle - u_w)}{H} = \frac{2}{\tau_w^2} \int_0^{\tau_w} \tau f(\tau) \, d\tau \tag{38}$$

This equation may be differentiated with respect to τ_w, recognizing that $4(\langle u \rangle - u_w)/H$ is uniquely related to τ_w for a given fluid model, to obtain after rearrangement:

$$\gamma_w = f(\tau_w) = \frac{1}{2} \tau_w \frac{d[4(\langle u \rangle - u_w)/H]}{d\tau_w} + \left[\frac{4(\langle u \rangle - u_w)}{H} \right] \tag{39}$$

or, after further rearrangement:

$$\gamma_w = \left(\frac{2n' + 1}{2n'} \right) \left[\frac{4(\langle u \rangle - u_w)}{H} \right] \tag{40}$$

where, for this flow geometry:

$$n' = \frac{d \ln \tau_w}{d \ln[4(\langle u \rangle - u_w)/H]} \tag{41}$$

Equation 39 is the analogous equation for slit flow to the Rabinowitsch-Mooney equation derived previously for flow in pipes. These equations are central to the analysis which follows.

FLOW IN DUCTS OF ARBITRARY CROSS SECTION

The flow behavior of Newtonian fluids in non-circular channels has been studied extensively, while the subject of non-Newtonian flow in similar channels remains relatively unexplored despite its importance in many industrial applications. The relative scarcity of analytical solutions to this type of flow problem is due primarily to mathematical difficulties resulting from either the nonlinearity attributed to the fluid model equation or the complexity of boundary conditions in solving the equations of motion. Nevertheless, a number of analytical and semi-analytical solutions for purely-viscous non-Newtonian fluids have appeared in the literature over the last 2–3 decades.

The problem of fully developed laminar axial flow of power law and Bingham plastic fluids in concentric annuli was first studied by Fredrickson and Bird [6]; Hanks and Larsen [7] extended the solution for power law fluids to non-integer values of the reciprocal of the flow behavior index n. McEachern [8] presented a similar solution for Ellis fluids. Using a variational method, Schechter

[9] obtained the fully-developed velocity profiles and the corresponding friction factors for the laminar flow of a power law fluid in rectangular ducts having aspect ratios from 0.25 to 1.0. Wheeler and Wissler [10] applied an over-relaxation method to solve the same problem. Analytical solutions for flow of power law fluids through elliptical and triangular ducts have been presented by Mizushina [11] and Mitsuishi et al. [12]. Theoretical and experimental studies of power law fluids flowing in the entrance region of annular and rectangular ducts have also been carried out [13–20].

Several analyses for fully developed laminar flow in ducts of arbitrary cross section are available. Kozicki et al. [21] proposed a general method utilizing geometric parameters to characterize the flow geometry and a function of shear stress determined by the fluid model equation for prediction of flow rate as a function of potential gradient for any time-independent fluid flowing in complex geometries. Miller [22] introduced a single shape factor obtained from the product of friction factor and Reynolds number to characterize a particular flow channel. However, the method has been shown [23] to be invalid for fluids exhibiting a yield stress, and for power law fluids with a flow behavior index much less than unity. Lenk [24] presented a series of papers on the flow of polymer melts, represented by the purely viscous power law model, in dies of different geometries. Liu [25] recently employed the Galerkin finite-element method to solve the flow of power law fluid in ducts of unusual cross section.

The subject of non-Newtonian fluids in turbulent flow through non-circular ducts has received scant attention. Kozicki et al. [21] suggested the direct use of the Dodge-Metzner equation since the effect of geometry has been reported to be insignificant in turbulent flow. Kostic and Hartnett [26] modified this recommendation, proposing instead that the generalized Reynolds number proposed by Kozicki et al. incorporating the geometric parameters replace the generalized Reynolds number in the original Dodge-Metzner correlation. A recent experimental study in a square duct [27] showed excellent agreement with the modified correlation.

In the characterization of non-Newtonian flow in non-circular ducts we make use of the fact that the Rabinowitsch-Mooney equation (Equation 29) for pipe flow and the corresponding expresssion for non-Newtonian flow in slits (Equation 39) are represented by the single equation:

$$\gamma_w = f(\tau_w) = a\tau_w \frac{d[2(\langle u \rangle - u_w)/R_h]}{d\tau_w} + b \left[\frac{2(\langle u \rangle - u_w)}{R_h} \right] \tag{42}$$

where the hydraulic radius R_h is defined as:

$$R_h = \frac{\text{cross-sectional area to flow}}{\text{wetted perimeter of conduit}} = \frac{1}{4} \times \text{equivalent diameter } (D_e) \tag{43}$$

For a circular duct, $R_h = D/4$, or the equivalent diameter D_e is equal to the actual diameter; and for a slit, $R_h = H/2$, where H is the slit separation. The shear stress at the wall τ_w for both flow geometries is given by:

$$\tau_w = R_h \left(-\frac{\Delta P}{L} \right), \tag{44}$$

as seen from Equations 9 and 34.

The coefficients a and b are the "geometric parameters" with the values $\frac{1}{4}$ and $\frac{3}{4}$ for a circular duct and $\frac{1}{2}$ and 1.0 for parallel plates, respectively. $f(\tau_w)$ is the function determined by the fluid model evaluated for the argument τ_w and yielding the shear rate γ_w at the wall.

The generalization to flow of an arbitrary fluid model in a straight conduit of arbitrary cross-sectional geometry is represented by:

$$f(\bar{\tau}_w) = a\bar{\tau}_w d \frac{[2(\langle u \rangle - \bar{u}_w)/R_h]}{d\bar{\tau}_w} + b \left[\frac{2(\langle u \rangle - \bar{u}_w)}{R_h} \right] \tag{45}$$

where $\bar{u}_w$ and $\bar{\tau}_w$ denote the contour-integrated average values of u_w and τ_w, which in general are not constant along the wetted perimeter, given by:

$$\bar{u}_w = \frac{1}{c} \oint_c u_w \, ds \qquad (46)$$

$$\bar{\tau}_w = \frac{1}{c} \oint_c \tau_w \, ds = R_h \left(\frac{-\Delta P}{L} \right) \qquad (47)$$

The latter equality follows from a momentum balance on a length L of the conduit. Referring to Figure 1, since the net force due to the normal stress τ_{zz} is zero in steady uniform flow, the force in the direction of flow exerted by the fluid on the wall of the conduit is given by:

$$F = L \oint_c \tau_w \, ds = A(p_0 - p_L) + \rho gAL \cos \theta$$
$$= A[p_0 - p_L + \rho g(h_0 - h_L)]$$
$$= A(P_0 - P_L)$$

Therefore:

$$\frac{1}{c} \oint_c \tau_w \, ds = \frac{A}{c} \frac{(P_0 - P_L)}{L} = R_h \left(-\frac{\Delta P}{L} \right)$$

and the equality is proved.

Rearrangement of Equation 45 yields the following expression for the average shear rate at the wall for laminar flow in non-circular ducts:

$$f(\bar{\tau}_w) = \frac{a + bn^*}{n^*} \left[\frac{2(\langle u \rangle - \bar{u}_w)}{R_h} \right] \qquad (48)$$

$$\text{where} \quad n^* = \frac{d \ln \bar{\tau}_w}{d \ln[2(\langle u \rangle - \bar{u}_w)/R_h]} \qquad (49)$$

Using the boundary condition $2(\langle u \rangle - \bar{u}_w)/R_h = 0$ at $\bar{\tau}_w = 0$, Equation 45 integrates to:

$$\frac{2(\langle u \rangle - \bar{u}_w)}{R_h} = \frac{1}{a} \bar{\tau}_w^{-\xi} \int_0^{\bar{\tau}_w} \tau^{\xi - 1} f(\tau) \, d\tau \qquad (50)$$

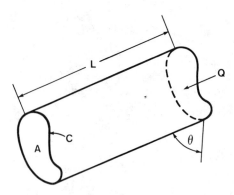

Figure 1. Schematic diagram of a flow channel of arbitrary cross section.

where an aspect factor $\xi = b/a$ has been introduced. For a fluid exhibiting a yield stress τ_y, the lower integration limit in Equation 50 becomes τ_y, and the shear stress function $f(\tau)$ refers to the viscous characteristics of the fluid for $\tau \geq \tau_y$. Equation 50 may also be expressed in terms of the non-Newtonian viscosity function by making the substitution $f(\tau) = \tau/\eta$ to obtain:

$$\frac{2(\langle u \rangle - \bar{u}_w)}{R_h} = \frac{1}{a} \bar{\tau}_w^{-\xi} \int_0^{\bar{\tau}_w} \frac{\tau^\xi}{\eta} \, d\tau \tag{51}$$

Equations 50 and 51 are equivalent and the actual equation used in an application is determined by the form of the analytical expression describing the viscous characteristics of the fluid. Equation 50 may also be rewritten in the following form utilizing flow data obtained with circular tubes, as given by Equation 30, directly in the determination of the non-circular flow characteristics:

$$\frac{2(\langle u \rangle - \bar{u}_w)}{R_h} = \frac{1}{a} \bar{\tau}_w^{-\xi} \int_0^{\bar{\tau}_w} \bar{\tau}_w^{\xi-1} \left(\frac{3n'+1}{4n'}\right) \left[\frac{8(\langle u \rangle - \bar{u}_w)}{D}\right] d\bar{\tau}_w \tag{52}$$

For a fluid whose behavior in the mainstream is given by the Newtonian expression, $\eta = \mu$ or $f(\tau) = \tau/\mu$, Equations 50 and 51 reduce to:

$$\frac{2(\langle u \rangle - \bar{u}_w)}{R_h} = \frac{\bar{\tau}_w}{\mu(a+b)} \tag{53}$$

The analogous expression for non-Newtonian flow in non-circular ducts may be represented by:

$$\frac{2(\langle u \rangle - \bar{u}_w)}{R_h} = \frac{\bar{\tau}_w}{\eta_R(a+b)} \tag{54}$$

Equation 54 defines the Rabinowitsch viscosity, η_R. Combination of Equation 54 with Equations 50 and 51 yields η_R as follows:

$$\eta_R = \frac{\bar{\tau}_w^{1+\xi}}{(1+\xi) \int_0^{\bar{\tau}_w} \tau^{\xi-1} f(\tau) \, d\tau}$$

$$= \frac{\bar{\tau}_w^{1+\xi}}{(1+\xi) \int_0^{\bar{\tau}_w} \frac{\tau^\xi}{\eta} \, d\tau} \tag{55}$$

While the non-Newtonian viscosity η is a function only of the shear stress or shear rate for a time-independent fluid, the Rabinowitsch viscosity η_R depends on the fluid model $f(\tau)$, the flow geometry (through ξ), as well as on the contour-integrated average wall shear stress $\bar{\tau}_w$. For a Newtonian fluid, $\eta_R = \mu$.

The same considerations used in generalization of the average velocity may be followed to obtain an analogous expression for the maximum velocity [21]:

$$\frac{2(u_m - \bar{u}_w)}{R_h} = \frac{1}{a\bar{\tau}_w} \int_0^{\bar{\tau}_w} f(\tau) \, d\tau \tag{56}$$

This equation may be verified for the circular tube for which $a = \frac{1}{4}$ and $R_h = D/4$, using Equations 10, 18, and 19 with the appropriate variable transformations.

Table 1 presents the maximum and average velocity expressions for duct flow of a number of fluid models including Newtonian, Ostwald-deWaele (power-law), Bingham plastic, Ellis, etc. The wall effect term $\bar{u}_w$ is usually significant for tubes in the capillary range. The expressions in Table 1 all reduce to the circular and parallel plate results with the geometric parameters (a, b) given by

Table 1
Average and Maximum Velocity Expressions for Various Fluid Models [43]

Fluid Model	$2(\langle u \rangle - \bar{u}_w)/R_h$	$2(u_m - \bar{u}_w)/R_h$
Newtonian $\eta = \mu$	$\dfrac{\bar{\tau}_w}{\mu}\left(\dfrac{1}{a+b}\right)$	$\dfrac{\bar{\tau}_w}{2a\mu}$
Ostwald-de Waele (Power Law) $\eta = K\gamma^{n-1}$	$\left(\dfrac{\bar{\tau}_w}{K}\right)^{1/n}\left(\dfrac{n}{a+bn}\right)$	$\left(\dfrac{\bar{\tau}_w}{K}\right)^{1/n}\left[\dfrac{n}{a(1+n)}\right]$
Bingham Plastic $\eta = \eta_B\left[\dfrac{\tau}{\tau - \tau_y}\right]$ for $\tau \geq \tau_y$ $\eta = \infty$ for $\tau < \tau_y$	$\dfrac{\bar{\tau}_w}{a\eta_B}\left[\dfrac{1}{1+\xi} - \dfrac{\chi}{\xi} + \dfrac{\chi^{1+\xi}}{\xi(1+\xi)}\right]$ where $\chi = \tau_y/\bar{\tau}_w$	$\dfrac{\bar{\tau}_w}{2a\eta_B}[1 - 2\chi + \chi^2]$
Ellis $\eta = \eta_0[1 + (\tau/\tau_{1/2})^{\alpha-1}]^{-1}$	$\dfrac{\bar{\tau}_w}{a\eta_0}\left[\dfrac{1}{1+\xi} + \dfrac{\phi^{\alpha-1}}{\alpha+\xi}\right]$ where $\phi = \bar{\tau}_w/\tau_{1/2}$	$\dfrac{\bar{\tau}_w}{2a\eta_0}\left[1 + \dfrac{2\phi^{\alpha-1}}{\alpha+1}\right]$
Meter* $\eta = \eta_\infty + \dfrac{\eta_0 - \eta_\infty}{1 + (\tau/\tau_m)^{\alpha-1}}$	$\dfrac{\bar{\tau}_w}{a\eta_0}\sum_{j=0}^{\infty}\left[\dfrac{1}{j(\alpha-1)+1+\xi}\right.$ $\left. + \dfrac{\psi^{\alpha-1}}{(j+1)(\alpha-1)+1+\xi}\right]\psi_1^j$ where $\psi = \bar{\tau}_w/\tau_m$ $\psi_1 = [-(\eta_\infty/\eta_0)(\psi)^{\alpha-1}]$	$\dfrac{\bar{\tau}_w}{a\eta_0}\sum_{j=0}^{\infty}\left[\dfrac{1}{j(\alpha-1)+2} + \dfrac{\psi^{\alpha-1}}{j(\alpha-1)+\alpha+1}\right]\psi_1^j$
Reiner-Rivlin $\eta = \mu_0\left(1 + \sum_{q=1}^{k} b_q\tau^{2q}\right)^{-1}$	$\dfrac{\bar{\tau}_w}{a\mu_0}\sum_{q=0}^{k}\dfrac{b_q\bar{\tau}_w^{2q}}{(2q+1)+\xi}$	$\dfrac{\bar{\tau}_w}{2a\mu_0}\sum_{q=0}^{k}\dfrac{b_q\bar{\tau}_w^{2q}}{q+1}$
Rabinowitsch $\eta = \mu_0(1 + b_1\tau^2)^{-1}$	$\dfrac{\bar{\tau}_w}{a\mu_0}\left[\dfrac{1}{1+\xi} + \dfrac{b_1\bar{\tau}_w^2}{3+\xi}\right]$	$\dfrac{\bar{\tau}_w}{2a\mu_0}\left[1 + \dfrac{b_1\bar{\tau}_w^2}{2}\right]$

* The relationships presented are for η_∞ much smaller than η_0 [30].

$(\frac{1}{4}, \frac{3}{4})$ and $(\frac{1}{2}, 1)$, respectively. Geometric parameters for other non-circular conduits are given in the subsequent table.

For a Newtonian fluid for which $\bar{u}_w = 0$, which includes pure solvents and most homogeneous non-polymeric liquids, Equation 51 or 53 and Equation 56 simplify to:

$$\frac{2\langle u \rangle}{R_h} = \frac{1}{(a+b)} \frac{\bar{\tau}_w}{\mu} \tag{57}$$

and

$$\frac{2u_m}{R_h} = \frac{1}{2a} \frac{\bar{\tau}_w}{\mu} \tag{58}$$

These two equations provide the means for evaluating the parameters a and b utilizing average and maximum velocity data for rectilinear flow of a Newtonian fluid. Geometric parameters evaluated in this manner are tabulated in Table 2 for a variety of cross-sectional shapes shown in Figure 2. The sources of the Newtonian analytical and experimental results used in the evaluations are

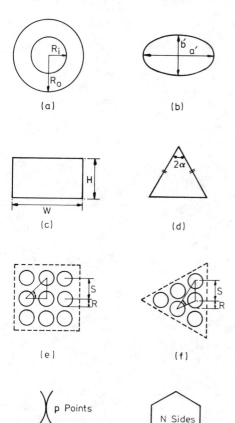

(a)

(b)

(c)

(d)

(e)

(f)

(g)

(h)

Figure 2. Schematic representation of various flow channels: (a) annulus; (b) ellipse; (c) rectangle; (d) isosceles triangle; (e) square array of cylinders; (f) triangular array of cylinders; (g) star-shaped duct of p points; (h) regular polygon of N sides. (Reproduced with permission from *Developments in Plastics Technology*—2, A. Whelan and J. L. Craft, Editors, Copyright 1985, Elsevier Applied Science Publishers, Ltd.)

Table 2
Geometric Parameters For Closed Conduits [21, 28]

Geometry	Configuration	a	b
Circular Tubes	—	0.2500	0.7500
Parallet Plates (Slit)	—	0.5000	1.0000
Concentric Annuli [31]	$k = R_i/R_0$		
	0.00	0.2500	0.7500
	0.01	0.3768	0.8751
	0.03	0.4056	0.9085
	0.05	0.4217	0.9263
	0.07	0.4331	0.9383
	0.10	0.4455	0.9510
	0.20	0.4693	0.9737
	0.30	0.4817	0.9847
	0.40	0.4890	0.9911
	0.50	0.4935	0.9946
	0.60	0.4965	0.9972
	0.70	0.4983	0.9987
	0.80	0.4992	0.9994
	0.90	0.4997	1.0000
	1.00	0.5000	1.0000
Elliptical Ducts [32]	$\beta = b'/a'$		
	0.00	0.3084	0.9253
	0.10	0.3018	0.9053
	0.20	0.2907	0.8720
	0.30	0.2796	0.8389
	0.40	0.2702	0.8107
	0.50	0.2629	0.7886
	0.60	0.2575	0.7725
	0.70	0.2538	0.7614
	0.80	0.2515	0.7546
	0.90	0.2504	0.7510
	1.00	0.2500	0.7500
Rectangular Ducts [32]	$E = H/W$		
	0.000	0.5000	1.0000
	0.020	0.4806	0.9795
	0.100	0.4132	0.9097
	0.125	0.3951	0.8911
	0.167	0.3673	0.8639
	0.200	0.3472	0.8446
	0.250	0.3212	0.8182
	0.333	0.2867	0.7817
	0.500	0.2439	0.7276
	0.750	0.2178	0.6866
	1.000	0.2121	0.6766

(Continued)

indicated in Table 2. Analytical expressions for a and b in terms of the respective aspect ratios used to specify the geometric configurations are available [21, 28].

Figures 3 and 4 show comparisons of the flow rate—pressure drop predictions by the geometric parameter method with analytical and numerical evaluations based on application of the equations

Table 2 (Continued)

Geometry	Configuration	a	b
Isosceles Triangular Ducts [32]	2α		
	10°	0.1547	0.6278
	20°	0.1693	0.6332
	40°	0.1840	0.6422
	60°	0.1875	0.6462
	80°	0.1849	0.6438
	90°	0.1830	0.6395
Arrays of Cylinders			
(i) Infinite (Open-boundary) [33]			
(a) Square	S/2R		
	1.00	—	—
	1.05	0.1310	0.5521
	1.10	0.1810	0.7368
	1.20	0.2471	1.0196
	1.50	0.4474	1.4107
	2.00	0.7891	1.7288
	4.00	2.0174	3.3397
(b) Triangular	1.00	0.0789	0.3271
	1.05	0.1818	0.7851
	1.10	0.2658	1.0074
	1.20	0.3895	1.1699
	1.50	0.6080	1.3319
	2.00	0.8642	1.5973
	4.00	1.9829	3.0046
(ii) Finite (enclosed) [34]			
(a) Square	1.07	0.2334	0.9672
	1.23	0.3812	1.5107
	1.47	0.6062	1.9457
	2.00	1.1486	2.5164
(b) Triangular	1.11	0.3026	1.1137
	1.27	0.5555	1.5233
	1.51	0.8057	1.7574
	2.06	1.2310	2.2484
Star-Shaped Ducts [35]	P		
	3	0.0792	0.3272
	4	0.0871	0.3258
	5	0.0910	0.3237
	6	0.0933	0.3217
	8	0.0958	0.3185
Regular Polygonal Ducts [35]	N		
	4	0.2121	0.6771
	5	0.2245	0.6966
	6	0.2316	0.7092
	8	0.2391	0.7241

of motion. The predicted results for power law fluids flowing in concentric annuli agree to within 2% of the solution provided by Fredrickson and Bird [6] over a wide range of aspect ratio $0.25 \leq k \leq 1.0$, and for n ranging from 0.1 to 4.0 (Figure 3). Similar agreement has been reported [21, 28] for Bingham plastic, Ellis and Rabinowitsch fluids based on comparisons with analytical

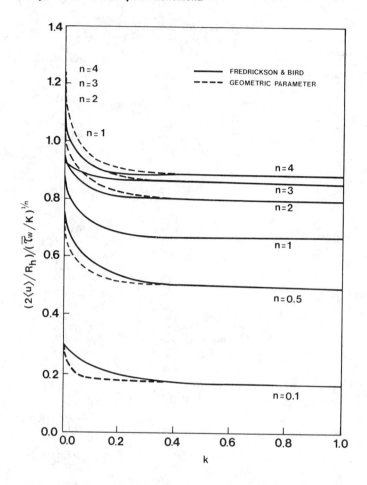

Figure 3. Comparison of geometric parameter method prediction with solution by Fredrickson and Bird [6] for power law flow in concentric annuli. (Reproduced with permission from W. Kozicki et al. [21], Copyright 1966, Pergamon Press, Ltd.)

solutions given by Fredrickson and Bird [6], McEachern [8] and Rotem [29], respectively. At lower values of the annulus aspect ratio k, larger discrepancies between the predictions and the analytical solutions are observed. This has been attributed to the asymmetric stress distributions along the inner and outer cylinders of the annulus.

Figure 4 presents the flow curves plotted as dimensionless pressure drop for the flow of power law fluids in rectangular ducts as a function of the aspect ratio E. The predicted results agree within 5% over the entire range of values reported by Schechter [9] and by Wheeler and Wissler [10].

The predictions for the flow of power law fluids in equilateral triangular ducts agree will with the correlation developed by Mitsuishi, et al. [12], with a maximum discrepancy of less than 10% over the entire range of flow rates [28]. Similar agreement has been found [28] for the flow of power law fluids in isosceles triangular ducts and in elliptical conduits in comparisons with the solutions of Mizushina et al. [11].

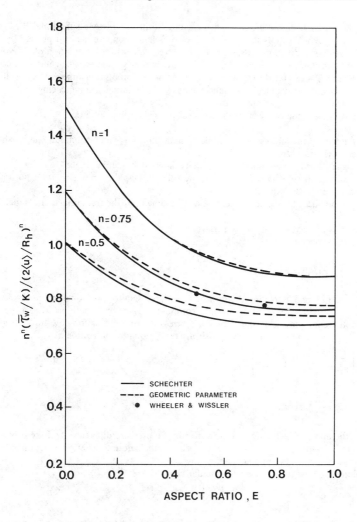

Figure 4. Comparison of prediction for power law flow in rectangular ducts [9, 10]. (Reproduced with permission from W. Kozicki et al. [21], Copyright 1966, Pergamon Press, Ltd.)

FLOW IN OPEN CHANNELS

The flow of Newtonian fluids, in particular water, in a variety of open channels has been studied at length by a number of investigators [36, 37]. For example, Straub et al. [37] have presented some analytical solutions for the flow of Newtonian fluids through various cross-sectional open channels along with experimental data. However, the literature appears to be lacking in information on flow through open channels of non-Newtonian fluids, despite their great importance in polymer processing, including textile fiber, industries. The gravity flow of non-Newtonian fluids has been solved only for some very special cases [38–42], mainly along an inclined plane. Astarita, et al. [41] performed an analysis of flow along an inclined surface for the general case of a fluid exhibiting slip at the wall and of unspecified rheological properties. Matsuhisa and Bird [42] also presented the analytical expression for flow of an Ellis fluid along an inclined plane.

In the following we direct our attention to the development of a formulation of gravity flow of a non-Newtonian fluid in an open channel of arbitrary flow geometry. The same technique used for closed conduits is extended to flow in constant cross section open channels. The flow in a semi-circular channel and down an inclined plane will be examined initially, commencing with an analysis of flow in a semi-circular open channel.

The assumptions made concerning the physical problem are as follows:

1. The fluid is an incompressible, non-Newtonian fluid for which a unique relationship exists between the shear stress and shear rate.
2. Isothermal, steady, one-dimensional, gravity, laminar flow takes place.
3. An effective slip velocity is involved at the solid surface that may vary with position along the periphery of the section.
4. There is no shear stress, hence, zero velocity gradient, at the free surface in contact with the gas.
5. No ripples or waves form on the surface.
6. The solid surface is smooth.

Flow in a Semi-Circular Channel

Referring to Figure 5, depicting the flow in an inclined semi-circular open channel, the relevant component of the equations of motion is the z-component, given by Equation 3. Under the assumed conditions, the equation yields the same shear-stress distribution as for flow through a circular tube, shown by Equations 7–10. The wall shear stress, Equation 9, written as:

$$\tau_w = \frac{R}{2}\left[\frac{-\Delta p}{L} + \rho g\frac{(h_0 - h_L)}{L}\right] \tag{59}$$

becomes $\tau_w = \dfrac{R}{2}\rho g \cos\theta$ (60)

where θ is the angle of inclination to the vertical. The pressure difference Δp is zero between the upstream and downstream sections of the open channel. Equation 60 gives τ_w in terms of the relevant physical variables in open channel flow.

The volumetric flow rate in the semi-circular channel is:

$$Q = \pi \int_0^R ur\, dr \tag{61}$$

Integration by parts, using the boundary condition $u = u_w$ at $r = R$ allowing for surface effects, gives:

$$Q = \frac{\pi R^2}{2}\left[u_w + \frac{1}{R^2}\int_0^R r^2\left(-\frac{du}{dr}\right)dr\right] \tag{62}$$

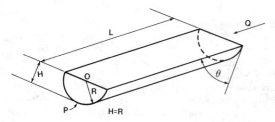

Figure 5. Flow in a semi-circular open channel.

Substituting $f(\tau_{rz}) = -du/dr$ and changing the position coordinate r to τ_{rz}, using Equation 10, results in the following after replacement of τ_{rz} by τ:

$$\frac{8(\langle u \rangle - u_w)}{D} = \frac{4}{\tau_w^3} \int_0^{\tau_w} \tau^2 f(\tau) \, d\tau \tag{63}$$

As seen by comparison of Equations 63 and 28, the steady uniform laminar flow of non-Newtonian fluids in semi-circular open channels and circular tubes is represented by the same equation relating the quantity $8(\langle u \rangle - u_w)/D$ to the shear stress at the wall τ_w. Furthermore, the Rabinowitsch-Mooney equation, Equation 29, derived for circular tubes from Equation 28, also applies to the gravity flow of non-Newtonian fluids in semi-circular channels.

In view of the latter result, Equation 38 for rectilinear flow between parallel plates also describes the gravity flow of a non-Newtonian fluid down an inclined plane, where H/2 denotes the perpendicular distance (depth) from the fluid surface to the plane. Equation 39 is also the analog to the Rabinowitsch-Mooney equation for gravity flow down an inclined plane. From Equation 34, the wall shear stress for the gravity flow problem is given by:

$$\tau_w = \frac{H}{2}\left(-\frac{\Delta P}{L}\right) = \frac{H}{2}\rho g \cos\theta \tag{64}$$

Flow in Open Channels of Arbitrary Cross Sections

The extended Rabinowitsch equation for semi-circular open channels (Equation 63) and the analogous equation for the inclined plane (Equation 39) are also both represented by Equation 42, same as in the case of the circular tubes and slits. The geometric parameters for the semi-circular open channel and inclined plane, i.e., a = 0.25, b = 0.75; and a = 0.50, b = 1.00, are also the same as for the circular tube and slit, respectively. The wall shear stress for the two open channels is given by:

$$\tau_w = R_h\left(\frac{-\Delta P}{L}\right) = R_h \rho g \cos\theta \tag{65}$$

The generalization to flow in open channels of arbitrary cross section is also the same as for closed conduits, which is given by Equation 45. The contour-integrated average values of u_w and τ_w are replaced by the average values integrated along the wetted perimeter, i.e.:

$$\bar{u}_w = \frac{1}{p}\int_p u_w \, ds \tag{66}$$

and $$\bar{\tau}_w = \frac{1}{p}\int_p \tau_w \, ds = R_h \rho g \cos\theta \tag{67}$$

The last equality follows from a momentum balance on a length L of the flow channel. Since the net force due to the normal stress τ_{zz} in steady uniform flow and pressure difference is zero, the force in the direction of flow exerted by the fluid on the channel wall is given by:

$$F = L\int_p \tau_w \, ds = \rho g A L \cos\theta$$

Hence $$\frac{1}{p}\int_p \tau_w \, ds = R_h \rho g \cos\theta$$

Since Equation 45 applies to closed conduits and open channels of arbitrary cross section, the integrated expression (Equation 50) and related equations (Equations 51 and 52) also apply to both flow types. The average and maximum velocity expressions presented in Table 1 for various fluid models are valid for open channel flow as well. Finally, since the generalized maximum velocity, Equation 56, is applicable to open channels also [43], the geometric parameters may be evaluated by the technique used for closed conduits utilizing average and maximum velocity data for Newtonian flow.

Geometric parameters for various open channels are presented in Table 3. In the case of the rectangular, triangular, and semi-elliptical open channels, the analytical solutions for Newtonian flow given by Straub et al. [37] were used for evaluation of a and b. Analytical expressions for the

Table 3
Geometric Parameters for Open Channels

Channel Geometry	Configuration	a	b
Semi-circular	—	0.2500	0.7500
Flat-Plate	—	0.5000	1.0000
Semi-elliptical	$\beta = b'/a'$	same as elliptical ducts in Table 1	
Rectangular	$E = H/W$	same as rectangular ducts in Table 1 with H equal to twice the liquid depth	
90° Triangular (Symmetrical) [37]		0.2122	0.6765
60° Triangular (Symmetrical) [37]		0.2009	0.6831
Open-circular [44]	H/D		
	0.00	0.222	0.750
	0.01	0.224	0.750
	0.05	0.232	0.751
	0.10	0.238	0.752
	0.15	0.242	0.753
	0.20	0.245	0.753
	0.25	0.247	0.753
	0.30	0.248	0.752
	0.35	0.249	0.751
	0.40	0.250	0.751
	0.45	0.250	0.750
	0.50	0.250	0.750
	0.55	0.250	0.750
	0.60	0.250	0.751
	0.65	0.251	0.753
	0.70	0.253	0.757
	0.75	0.256	0.762
	0.80	0.262	0.768
	0.85	0.273	0.775
	0.90	0.289	0.785
	0.95	0.296	0.808
	0.98	0.287	0.820
	0.99	0.278	0.814
	1.00	0.250	0.750

geometric parameters are available elsewhere [43]. Values of a and b for open circular channels in Table 3 were obtained by Sestak [44].

The same agreement observed with closed conduits obtained by reflecting the solid boundary in the free surface might be expected to apply to the corresponding open channels, since the analytical solutions for the open channels for these cases are derived from the solutions for the closed conduits [37].

FRICTION FACTOR-REYNOLDS NUMBER RELATIONSHIPS

The Fanning friction factor for steady, fully-developed flow of a non-Newtonian fluid exhibiting a wall effect in an open or closed conduit is defined by:

$$f = \frac{2\bar{\tau}_w}{\rho(\langle u \rangle - \bar{u}_w)^2} \tag{68}$$

Substitution for $\bar{\tau}_w$ by the following relationship in terms of the Rabinowitsch viscosity η_R given by Equation 54:

$$\bar{\tau}_w = \frac{2(a + b)\eta_R(\langle u \rangle - \bar{u}_w)}{R_h} \tag{69}$$

produces the laminar flow relation:

$$f = \frac{16}{Re^*} \tag{70}$$

where $$Re^* = \frac{4R_h(\langle u \rangle - \bar{u}_w)\rho}{(a + b)\eta_R} \tag{71}$$

For a circular tube, $R_h = D/4$ and $(a + b) = 1$, the Reynolds number reduces to $Re^* = D(\langle u \rangle - \bar{u}_w)\rho/\eta_R$. For a Newtonian fluid for which $\eta_R = \mu$, $\bar{u}_w = 0$, Equation 71 gives:

$$Re^* = \frac{4R_h\langle u \rangle \rho}{(a + b)\mu} \tag{72}$$

Equation 49 suggests the tangent to the flow curve depicting a log-log plot of $\bar{\tau}_w$ vs. $[2(\langle u \rangle - \bar{u}_w)/R_h]$ can be represented by the equation:

$$\bar{\tau}_w = K^* \left[\frac{2(\langle u \rangle - \bar{u}_w)}{R_h} \right]^{n^*} \tag{73}$$

which defines the fluid consistency K^*.

When this expression is substituted in Equation 68, one obtains the laminar $f - Re^*$ relation in Equation 70, with Re^* given by:

$$Re^* = \frac{R_h^{n^*}(\langle u \rangle - \bar{u}_w)^{2 - n^*}\rho}{2^{n^* - 3}K^*} \tag{74}$$

Note that n^*, K^*, and Re^*, defined here for arbitrary cross sections in closed conduit and open channel flow, correspond to n', K', and Re', originally defined by Metzner and Reed [45] for non-Newtonian flow in circular tubes without the wall effect. The equivalence of the Reynolds numbers given by Equations 71 and 74 may be verified using the power law model.

Equation 51 may be utilized to express n* and K* in terms of the non-Newtonian viscosity η of the fluid and the aspect factor ξ:

$$n^* = \frac{\eta_w \int_0^{\tau_w} (\tau^\xi/\eta)\,d\tau}{\bar\tau_w^{1+\xi} - \xi\eta_w \int_0^{\tau_w} (\tau^\xi/\eta)\,d\tau} \tag{75}$$

$$K^* = a^{n^*}\bar\tau_w^{1+\xi n^*}\left[\int_0^{\tau_w} (\tau^\xi/\eta)\,d\tau\right]^{-n^*} \tag{76}$$

Table 4 presents the Reynolds number Re* and flow behavior index n* for the same fluid models as in Table 1. For a power law fluid, n* is equal to the flow behavior index n and for a Newtonian fluid n* = 1. The Reynolds number expression for the power law fluid may be readily verified by substituting K* in Equation 74 by the relation:

$$K^* = \left(\frac{a + bn}{n}\right)^n K \tag{77}$$

which is evaluated using Equation 76.

For a circular tube, $a = \frac{1}{4}$, $b = \frac{3}{4}$, the power law expression for K* reduces appropriately to $K' = [(3n + 1)/4n]^n K$ and Re* similarly simplifies to $Re' = D^n\langle u\rangle^{2-n}\rho/8^{n-1}K'$ as given by Metzner and Reed [45] for the case $\xi = 0$.

Fanning friction factors for fully-developed laminar flow of aqueous Carbopol and Separan solutions in a square duct evaluated by Hartnett et al. [27] as a function of the Reynolds number Re* may be seen in Figure 6. The Reynolds numbers were evaluated using the Re* expression for the power law fluid in conjunction with the values 0.1561 and 0.7326 for a and b. These values correspond to the refined solution [46] presented in the last section of this chapter and usually result in improved agreement. The experimental results are in excellent agreement with the prediction f = 16/Re* for a wide range of the power law indices. Although there is experimental evidence for secondary flow in rectangular channels, especially in the case of viscoelastic fluids, the measurements by Hartnett et al. with aqueous Separan solutions indicate that such secondary flows have little, if any, influence on the pressure drop in laminar flow through a square channel.

By analogy with Newtonian flow [31], it was proposed [21, 43] that the friction factor for turbulent flow of a purely viscous non-Newtonian fluid in closed conduits and open channels of arbitrary cross section may be evaluated by the direct use of the Dodge-Metzner equation [47] for pipes:

$$1/\sqrt{f} = (4.0/n'^{0.75}) \log(Re' f^{(2-n')/2}) - 0.4/n'^{1.2} \tag{78}$$

Recast in terms of n*, Re*, and the geometric parameters, this equation becomes:

$$1/\sqrt{f} = (4.0/n^{*0.75}) \log(Re^* f^{(2-n^*)/2}) - 0.4/n^{*1.2} + 4.0n^{*0.25} \log[4(a + bn^*)/(1 + 3n^*)] \tag{79}$$

Recently, Kostic and Hartnett [26] recommended that the original Dodge-Metzner equation be modified for turbulent flow of power law fluids in non-circular channels by replacing Re' by Re*. This suggestion is consistent with the finding by Jones [48] that all turbulent friction factor data for Newtonian fluids in rectangular channels could be predicted by the equation for circular tubes using a new Reynolds number Re+. The latter expression is yielded by Re* written for a Newtonian fluid.

The expression proposed by Kostic and Hartnett for turbulent flow of a power law fluid in non-circular conduits is as follows:

$$1/\sqrt{f} = (4.0/n^{0.75}) \log(Re^* f^{(2-n)/2}) - 0.4/n^{1.2} \tag{80}$$

Table 4
Reynolds Number and n* for Various Fluid Models[‡] [43]

Fluid Model	Re*	n*
Newtonian	$$\dfrac{4R_h\langle u\rangle\rho}{\mu(a+b)}$$	1
Ostwald-de Waele (Power Law)	$$\dfrac{R_h^n(\langle u\rangle - \bar{u}_w)^{2-n}\rho}{2^{n-3}K\left(\dfrac{a+bn}{n}\right)^n}$$	n
Bingham Plastic	$$\dfrac{4R_h(\langle u\rangle - \bar{u}_w)\rho}{a\eta_B}\left[\dfrac{1}{1+\xi} - \dfrac{\chi}{\xi} + \dfrac{\chi^{1+\xi}}{\xi(1+\xi)}\right]$$ where $$A_1 = \left[\dfrac{1-\chi^{1+\xi}}{1+\xi} - \dfrac{\chi(1-\chi^\xi)}{\xi}\right]$$	$$\dfrac{A_1}{1-\chi-\xi A_1}$$
Ellis	$$\dfrac{4R_h(\langle u\rangle - \bar{u}_w)\rho}{a\eta_0}[A_2 + A_3]$$ where $A_2 = \dfrac{1}{1+\xi}$, $A_3 = \dfrac{\phi^{\alpha-1}}{\alpha+\xi}$	$$\dfrac{A_2+A_3}{A_2+\alpha A_3}$$
Meter	$$\dfrac{4R_h(\langle u\rangle - \bar{u}_w)\rho}{a\eta_0}\sum_{j=0}^{\infty}[A_4+A_5]\psi_1^j$$ where $A_4 = \dfrac{1}{j(\alpha-1)+1+\xi}$ $A_5 = \dfrac{\psi^{\alpha-1}}{(j+1)(\alpha-1)+1+\xi}$	$$\dfrac{\displaystyle\sum_{j=0}^{\infty}[A_4+A_5]\psi_1^j}{\displaystyle\sum_{j=0}^{\infty}[j(\alpha-1)+1][A_4+A_5]\psi_1^j}$$
Reiner-Rivlin	$$\dfrac{4R_h(\langle u\rangle - \bar{u}_w)\rho}{a\mu_0}\sum_{q=0}^{k}A_q$$ where $A_q = \dfrac{b_q\bar{\tau}_w^{2q}}{(2q+1)+\xi}$	$$\dfrac{\displaystyle\sum_{q=0}^{k}A_q}{\displaystyle\sum_{q=0}^{k}(2q+1)A_q}$$
Rabinowitsch	$$\dfrac{4R_h(\langle u\rangle - \bar{u}_w)\rho}{a\mu_0}\left[\dfrac{1}{1+\xi} + \dfrac{b_1\bar{\tau}_w^2}{3+\xi}\right]$$	$$\dfrac{\dfrac{1}{1+\xi}+\dfrac{b_1\bar{\tau}_w^2}{3+\xi}}{\dfrac{1}{1+\xi}+\dfrac{3b_1\bar{\tau}_w^2}{3+\xi}}$$

[†] Same symbols as defined in Table 1.

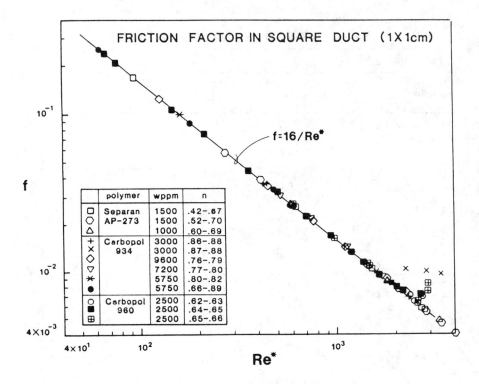

Figure 6. Friction factor-Reynolds number plot for laminar flow of aqueous polymer solutions in a square duct. (Reproduced with permission from J. P. Hartnett et al. [27], Copyright 1986, John Wiley & Sons, Inc.)

Figure 7 shows a friction factor plot of the pressure drop measurements for turbulent flow of aqueous Carbopol solutions in a square duct carried out by Hartnett et al. [27] which are in agreement with the latter equation.

Values of the critical Reynolds number Re_c^* for Newtonian flow through annuli predicted by Hanks [49] from the stability parameter vary from a value of 2,100 for pipe flow to a value of 1,870 for flow between parallel plates corresponding to a variation in aspect ratio k from zero to unity. For Newtonian flow in rectangular ducts, the critical Reynolds numbers fall in the vicinity of 2,000 over a wide range of aspect ratio E [28]. This suggests that the same criteria established for the existence of laminar flow of a non-Newtonian fluid for circular conduits by Dodge and Metzner [47] or by evaluation of the stability parameter [49, 50] might be applied tentatively for non-circular ducts.

Straub et al. [37] found that the friction factor expression for turbulent flow of Newtonian fluids through smooth open channels at low Reynolds number was the same as for closed conduits. Measurements of Re_c^* conducted by Straub et al. for Newtonian flow in rectangular channels over a range of E = H/W varied from 2,000 to more than 3,000. The critical Reynolds number for non-Newtonian flow in circular tubes should therefore be useful as a qualitative indication of the transition point for open channel flow.

A method for predicting the transition point and friction factor in turbulent flow of viscoelastic fluids in non-circular channels based on a technique developed by Meter [51] for pipe flow of

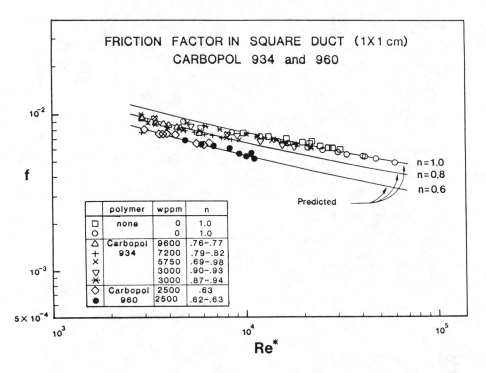

Figure 7. Experimental vs. predicted f-values for turbulent flow of aqueous Carbopol solution in a square duct. (Reproduced with permission from J. P. Hartnett et al. [27], Copyright 1986, John Wiley & Sons, Inc.)

aqueous Natrosol hydroxyethylcellulose is available [21]. The difficulty in prediction of the turbulent flow characteristics of viscoelastic fluids relates to the fact that a universal correlation for circular tubes which is valid for all viscoelastic fluids is still to be developed.

Example 1: Flow of a Power Law Fluid in Various Closed Conduits

A power law fluid whose rheological parameters are $n = 0.716$ and $K = 0.304 \text{ Ns}^n/\text{m}^2$ is flowing with an average velocity of 1.524 m/s (5 ft/s) in various ducts whose cross sections are:

1. Concentric-annular, $k = 0.406$, $R_0 = 26.3 \times 10^{-3}$ m
2. Circular
3. Rectangular, $E = 0.5$
4. Elliptical, $\beta = 0.5$
5. Isosceles triangular, $\alpha = 20$

Using the geometric parameter method, calculate the potential gradient required to sustain the flow in these flow channels, all of which have the same hydraulic radius as the concentric annulus. Calculate also the Reynolds number for each case to ensure that the flow is laminar. The density of the fluid may be taken as 1,000 kg/m^3.

Solution

1. For a concentric annulus with k = 0.406, the geometric parameters taken from Table 2 are:
   a = 0.4893   b = 0.9917
   ξ = b/a = 2.027
   The hydraulic radius is:

$$R_h = \frac{R_0(1 - k)}{2} = 7.81 \times 10^{-3} \text{ m}$$

The relevant flow equation for a power law fluid in Table 1 is:

$$\frac{\bar{\tau}_w}{K} = \left[\frac{a(1 + \xi n)}{n}\left(\frac{2\langle u \rangle}{R_h}\right)\right]^n, \text{ assuming } \bar{u}_w = 0.$$

Substituting in the equation:

$$\frac{\bar{\tau}_w}{K} = \left[\frac{0.4893(1 + 2.027 \times 0.716)}{0.716} \times \frac{2(1.524)}{0.00781}\right]^{0.716}$$

$$= 103.7 \text{ s}^{-n}.$$

Hence $\bar{\tau}_w = R_h\left(-\frac{\Delta P}{L}\right) = 103.7 \times 0.304$

$$= 31.52 \text{ N/m}^2$$

and $\left(-\frac{\Delta P}{L}\right) = \frac{31.52}{0.00781} = 4035 \text{ N/m}^3.$

This value of $(-\Delta P/L)$ compares with 4,006 N/m² determined from the numerical solution of Fredrickson and Bird [6].
The generalized Reynolds number is calculated as:

$$Re^* = \frac{R_h^n \langle u \rangle^{2-n} \rho}{2^{n-3} K \left(\frac{a + bn}{n}\right)^n} = 573$$

Therefore, the flow is laminar.
Following the same procedure for the other flow geometries, the results are as follows:

2. Circular tube, a = 0.2500, b = 0.7500
   $(-\Delta P/L)$ = 2,986 N/m³
         Re* = 774
3. Rectangular duct, E = 0.5, a = 0.2439, b = 0.7276
   $(-\Delta P/L)$ = 2,925 N/m³
         Re* = 790
4. Elliptical duct, β = 0.5, a = 0.2629, b = 0.7886
   $(-\Delta P/L)$ = 3,095 N/m³
         Re* = 747
5. Isosceles triangular duct α = 20, a = 0.1840, b = 0.6422
   $(-\Delta P/L)$ = 2,586 N/m³
         Re* = 894

Example 2: Flow of Bingham Fluid Down an Inclined Open-Rectangular Channel

Calculate the flow rate for a Bingham fluid, with density 1,700 kg/m³ and rheological parameters $\tau_y = 26.5$ N/m² and $\eta_B = 2.787 \times 10^{-2}$ Pa.s, flowing down an inclined open-rectangular channel which makes an angle of 4° with the horizontal plane. The channel width is 0.10 m and the depth of the liquid is 0.05 m. Determine the Reynolds number.

Solution

For an open rectangular channel with W = 0.10 m and H = 2 × liquid depth = 0.10 m:

$$E = H/W = 1.0$$

The corresponding geometric parameters are:

$$a = 0.2121, \qquad b = 0.6766, \qquad \xi = b/a = 3.19$$

The hydraulic radius is given by:

$$R_h = \frac{HW/2}{H + W} = 0.025 \text{ m}$$

The wall shear stress is evaluated as:

$$\bar{\tau}_w = R_h \left(\frac{-\Delta P}{L} \right) = R_h \rho g \cos \theta$$

$$= 0.025 \times 1700 \times 9.81 \times \cos 86$$

$$= 29.1 \text{ N/m}^2$$

The flow rate-shear stress relationship for a Bingham fluid from Table 1 is:

$$\frac{2\langle u \rangle}{R_h} = \frac{\bar{\tau}_w}{a\eta_B} \left[\frac{1}{1+\xi} - \frac{1}{\xi} \left(\frac{\tau_y}{\bar{\tau}_w} \right) + \frac{1}{\xi(1+\xi)} \left(\frac{\tau_y}{\bar{\tau}_w} \right)^{1+\xi} \right]$$

Substituting the relevant numerical values in the above equation gives:

$$\langle u \rangle = 0.228 \text{ m/s}$$

The volumetric flow rate is therefore:

$$Q = \langle u \rangle A = 0.228 \times 0.05 \times 0.10 = 1.14 \times 10^{-3} \text{ m}^3/\text{s}$$

The corresponding Reynolds number is:

$$Re^* = \frac{4R_h \langle u \rangle \rho}{a\eta_B} \left[\frac{1}{1+\xi} - \frac{1}{\xi} \left(\frac{\tau_y}{\bar{\tau}_w} \right) + \frac{1}{\xi(1+\xi)} \left(\frac{\tau_y}{\bar{\tau}_w} \right)^{1+\xi} \right]$$

$$= 24.2$$

Therefore, the flow is laminar.

EXPANSION-CONTRACTION BEHAVIOR OF NON-CIRCULAR JETS

Liquid jets have been the subject of considerable experimental and theoretical investigation because of their importance in certain processing and manufacturing industries. Much of the earlier activity was also prompted by theoretical considerations as to the rheological behavior exhibited by the fluids when extruded. Gaskins and Philippoff [52] suggested the measurement of the expansion of a jet of fluid issuing from a capillary (the Barus or Merrington effect) provided a convenient means for measuring normal stresses at high shear rates. Subsequently, Harris [53, 54] pointed out that the thrust of the jet is the primary quantity required for determination of the normal stress. Metzner and colleagues [55–58] developed analyses for use in evaluation of the normal stress from measurements of the thrust of the jet or jet diameter and conducted extensive experimental measurements of normal stresses. Much of the past work in this area has been reported by Middleman [59] and Metzner et al. [55–58].

In the development which follows, we present a generalization of the analysis of jet swelling pertaining to viscoelastic fluids for jets of arbitrary cross-sectional shape. Aside from the practical value of the result, the problem is of fundamental interest because of its generality. The effect of the anomalous behavior at the solid-fluid interface in the die, which may have a significant influence on the result, will be accounted for by inclusion of the wall effect term [60, 61].

We consider steady, laminar, isothermal flow of a fluid stream which emerges from a die of arbitrary cross-section. The effects of surface tension, gravity, and drag of air on the emerging jet are assumed negligible. Further, the velocity profile in the exit plane is assumed to correspond to the fully developed profile in the die. Analyses for circular jets which include surface tension effects are available [62–64].

The relationship obtained when the net thrust of the fluid issuing from a die is equated to the difference between the momentum flux of the fluid leaving the die and the tensile stresses exerted on the fluid at the exit section of the die is given by:

$$T = \iint \rho u^2 \, dA + \iint \pi_{11} \, dA = \rho \langle u^2 \rangle A + \langle \pi_{11} \rangle A \tag{81}$$

The expression for the thrust of the jet evaluated at a section sufficiently far downstream for the velocity profile to be flat and all normal stresses to have completely relaxed is $T = A_j \rho u_j^2$ which, combined with the continuity equation $A_j \rho u_j = A \rho \langle u \rangle$, yields:

$$T/A = \rho(A/A_j)\langle u \rangle^2 \tag{82}$$

It is seen that a simple analysis of the extrusion problem in terms of T/A also suffices for the determination of the behavior in terms of the area ratio A/A_j.

By subtracting $\bar{u}_w$ from u then adding $\bar{u}_w$, Equation 81 may be rewritten as follows:

$$T_w = \rho \langle (u - \bar{u}_w)^2 \rangle + \langle \pi_{11} \rangle \tag{83}$$

where T_w denotes:

$$T_w = T/A - 2\rho \bar{u}_w (\langle u \rangle - \bar{u}_w) - \rho \bar{u}_w^2 \tag{84}$$

Next we will derive an important relationship by first considering the circular and slit geometries. The result is then generalized to arbitrary cross-sectional shapes also involving the contour-averaged quantities by invoking the same procedure used in the development of the generalized Rabinowitsch-Mooney equation.

Making the substitution $f(\tau) = -du/ds'$, where for the two reference geometries s' is the position variable, r in the case of the circular tube or x in the case of parallel plates, in Equation 50 gives:

$$\frac{2(\langle u \rangle - \bar{u}_w)}{R_h} = -\frac{1}{a\bar{\tau}_w \xi} \int_0^{\bar{\tau}_w} \tau^{\xi-1}(d\tau/ds') \, du = (-\bar{\tau}_w^{1-\xi}/aS) \int_0^{\bar{\tau}_w} \tau^{\xi-1} \, du \tag{85}$$

The last equality uses the relation $d\tau/ds' = \bar{\tau}_w/S$, where S is the characteristic length, R, for the circular tube or H/2 for parallel plates.
Integration of Equation 85 by parts gives:

$$\frac{2(\langle u \rangle - \bar{u}_w)}{R_h} = -\frac{\bar{u}_w}{aS} + (\xi - 1)\frac{\bar{\tau}_w^{1-\xi}}{aS}\int_0^{\bar{\tau}_w} u\tau^{\xi-2}\,d\tau \tag{86}$$

Setting $S = R_h/2a$, where a equals $\frac{1}{4}$ and $\frac{1}{2}$ for the circular tube and for parallel plates, respectively, in Equation 86 results in:

$$\langle u \rangle = (1/A)\iint u\,dA = (\xi - 1)\bar{\tau}_w^{1-\xi}\int_0^{\bar{\tau}_w} u\tau^{\xi-2}\,d\tau \tag{87}$$

Equation 87 may be considered equivalent to Equation 50 and to define an operator which averages a point function, in this case the velocity, over the flow cross section. Application of the averaging operation to Equation 83 leads to:

$$\frac{\bar{\tau}_w^{\xi-1}T_w}{\xi - 1} = \rho\int_0^{\bar{\tau}_w}(u - \bar{u}_w)^2\tau^{\xi-2}\,d\tau + \int_0^{\bar{\tau}_w}\pi_{11}\tau^{\xi-2}\,d\tau \tag{88}$$

This equation is of the form $T_w = f(\bar{\tau}_w, R_h, \xi)$. Taking the partial derivative with respect to $\bar{\tau}_w$ yields:

$$(-\pi_{11})_w = \frac{\rho}{\bar{\tau}_w^{\xi-2}}\left(\frac{\partial I'}{\partial\bar{\tau}_w}\right) - T_w\left[1 + \frac{1}{(\xi-1)}\frac{\partial\ln T_w}{\partial\ln\bar{\tau}_w}\right] \tag{89}$$

where I' is the integral:

$$I' = \int_0^{\bar{\tau}_w}(u - \bar{u}_w)^2\tau^{\xi-2}\,d\tau \tag{90}$$

Differentiating I' with respect to $\bar{\tau}_w$ with the help of the equation (equivalent to Equation 56 with $u = u_m$ at $\tau = 0$) for the local velocity:

$$u - \bar{u}_w = \frac{R_h}{2a\bar{\tau}_w}\int_\tau^{\bar{\tau}_w} f(\tau)\,d\tau \tag{91}$$

and Equation 48 for $f(\bar{\tau}_w)$ results in [61]:

$$\frac{\partial I'}{\partial\bar{\tau}_w} = \frac{\bar{\tau}_w^{\xi-2}R_h^2}{2(\xi-1)}\left[\frac{\xi n^* + 1}{n^*}\right]\left[\frac{2(\langle u \rangle - \bar{u}_w)}{R_h}\right]^2 - \frac{2}{\bar{\tau}_w}\int_0^{\bar{\tau}_w}(u - \bar{u}_w)^2\tau^{\xi-2}\,d\tau \tag{92}$$

Substituting for $\partial I'/\partial\bar{\tau}_w$ in Equation 89, utilizing Equation 49 defining n^*, yields the following equivalent expressions for evaluation of $(-\pi_{11})_w$ from viscoelastic jet data as a function of $\bar{\tau}_w$:

$$(-\pi_{11})_w = \rho(\langle u \rangle - \bar{u}_w)^2\left[\frac{2(\xi n^* + 1)}{n^*(\xi - 1)} - 2\int_0^1\left(\frac{u - \bar{u}_w}{\langle u \rangle - \bar{u}_w}\right)^2\left(\frac{\tau}{\bar{\tau}_w}\right)^{\xi-2}d\left(\frac{\tau}{\bar{\tau}_w}\right)\right]$$
$$-T_w\left[1 + \frac{1}{n^*(\xi - 1)}\frac{\partial\ln T_w}{\partial\ln[2(\langle u \rangle - \bar{u}_w)/R_h]}\right] \tag{93}$$

or $\quad (-\pi_{11})_w = \frac{2\rho(\langle u \rangle - \bar{u}_w)^2}{(\xi - 1)}\left[\xi + \frac{1}{n^*} - A_r'\right] - T_w\left[1 + \frac{1}{(\xi - 1)}\frac{\partial\ln T_w}{\partial\ln\bar{\tau}_w}\right] \tag{94}$

Equation 93 is of the same form and reducible to the result of Shertzer and Metzner [58] for circular jets on setting $\xi = 3$ and $\bar{u}_w = 0$. The latter equation, which is in a convenient form for application purposes, contains A_r', defined as:

$$A_r' = \frac{\langle (u - \bar{u}_w)^2 \rangle}{(\langle u \rangle - \bar{u}_w)^2}$$

(95)

The quantity $(\xi + 1/n^*)$ in Equation 94 is found with the help of Equation 75 to be given by the following general expression applicable to an arbitrary fluid model:

$$\left(\xi + \frac{1}{n^*} \right) = \frac{\bar{\tau}_w^{\xi} f(\bar{\tau}_w)}{\int_0^{\tau_w} \tau^{\xi - 1} f(\tau) \, d\tau}$$

(96)

For a power law fluid, it is given simply by $(\xi + 1/n)$, and for an Ellis fluid for which $f(\tau) = (\tau/\eta_0)[1 + (\tau/\tau_{1/2})^{\alpha - 1}]$, this becomes:

$$\left(\xi + \frac{1}{n^*} \right)_{\text{Ellis}} = \frac{1 + (\bar{\tau}_w/\tau_{1/2})^{\alpha - 1}}{\dfrac{1}{1 + \xi} + \dfrac{1}{\alpha + \xi} (\bar{\tau}_w/\tau_{1/2})^{\alpha - 1}}$$

(97)

Determination of the Die to Jet Area Ratio

Equations 81 and 82 can be combined to obtain the ratio of the cross-sectional area of the die to that of the issuing jet:

$$A_r = A/A_j = \frac{\langle u^2 \rangle}{\langle u \rangle^2} + \frac{\langle \pi_{11} \rangle}{\rho \langle u \rangle^2}$$

(98)

Equation 98 may be expanded, as was done previously, to include the term $\bar{u}_w$, characterizing the wall effect in the die to yield:

$$A_r = A_r'(1 - u_r)^2 + 2u_r - u_r^2 + \frac{\langle \pi_{11} \rangle}{\rho \langle u \rangle^2}$$

(99)

where $u_r = \bar{u}_w/\langle u \rangle$. It is seen that A_r' is equal to A_r for a fluid not exhibiting surface effects along the contour of the die and without normal stresses.

The quantity $\langle \pi_{11} \rangle$ may be evaluated with the help of the area averaging operation defined in Equation 87, utilizing π_{11} vs. τ data for the geometry in question. In the absence of such data, one might use π_{11} versus τ for circular jets when available as a first approximation.

The following expression for A_r' is readily found with the help of Equations 50, 87, and 91:

$$A_r' = \frac{(\xi - 1)\bar{\tau}_w^{\xi - 1} \int_0^{\tau_w} \tau^{\xi - 2} \, d\tau \left[\int_\tau^{\tau_w} f(\tau) \, d\tau \right]^2}{\left[\int_0^{\tau_w} \tau^{\xi - 1} f(\tau) \, d\tau \right]^2}$$

(100)

By performing successive interchanges in the order of integration [61], this equation may be expressed as:

$$A_r' = \frac{2\bar{\tau}_w^{\xi - 1} \int_0^{\tau_w} f(\tau) \, d\tau \int_0^{\tau} \tau^{\xi - 1} f(\tau) \, d\tau}{\left[\int_0^{\tau_w} \tau^{\xi - 1} f(\tau) \, d\tau \right]^2}$$

(101)

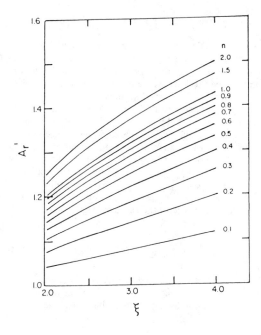

Figure 8. Plot of A_r' vs. the geometric aspect factor ξ for power law fluids with n as parameter. (From W. Kozicki and C. Tiu [61].)

For a power law fluid, this gives:

$$(A_r')_{\text{power law}} = \frac{2(1 + \xi n)}{2 + n(1 + \xi)} \tag{102}$$

The extremum value for A_r' is unity at $n = 0$. This value of n corresponds to infinite pseudoplasticity, i.e., a flat velocity profile or plug flow which is in agreement with the result expected intuitively.

Figure 8 shows a plot of A_r' vs. ξ for power law fluids, with n as parameter. The abscissa spans the aspect factor range covered by the geometries represented.

For an Ellis fluid, A_r' is given by:

$$(A_r')_{\text{Ellis}} = 2 \left[\frac{\alpha + \xi}{2\alpha + \xi + 1} \left(\frac{\bar{\tau}_w}{\tau_{1/2}} \right)^{2(\alpha - 1)} + \frac{(\alpha + \xi)(\alpha + 2\xi + 1)}{(1 + \xi)(\alpha + \xi + 2)} \left(\frac{\bar{\tau}_w}{\tau_{1/2}} \right)^{\alpha - 1} \right.$$
$$\left. + \frac{(\alpha + \xi)^2}{(1 + \xi)(3 + \xi)} \right] \Bigg/ \left[\left(\frac{\bar{\tau}_w}{\tau_{1/2}} \right)^{\alpha - 1} + \frac{\alpha + \xi}{1 + \xi} \right]^2 \tag{103}$$

It can be verified that the result obtained for a Newtonian fluid, $\alpha = 1$, agrees with the corresponding result yielded by Equation 102 for $n = 1$.

Plots of A_r' vs. the aspect factor ξ for Ellis fluids at α equal to 2 and 3, with the ratio $\bar{\tau}_w/\tau_{1/2}$ as parameter, are presented elsewhere [61]. These show A_r' decreasing with an increase in $\bar{\tau}_w/\tau_{1/2}$, in contrast with the behavior for power law fluids where A_r' is independent of the shear stress $\bar{\tau}_w$.

ENTRANCE AND EXIT CORRECTIONS: SHORT DUCTS

In the development of Rabinowitsch-Mooney equations for laminar tube and other cross-sectional channel flows, the flow field is assumed to be fully developed, i.e., $u_1 = u_1(x_2)$ only. Unfortunately, in many real systems, such as in extrusion through a short die, the fluid is not fully developed because the fluid enters the duct from some other region, and the velocity field must rearrange itself from its configuration in the upstream region. The axial distance over which this occurs is known as the entrance region.

Theoretical analysis of the entry problem is quite difficult because the dynamic equations involve both u_1 and u_2 as functions of x_1 and x_2. These equations are nonlinear, and no rigorous analytical solution is possible. However, numerical solutions and several approximate analytical solutions using linearization, perturbation, and boundary layer techniques are available in the literature.

From a practical point of view, perhaps the question to answer is, "under what circumstances does one need to consider the entrance and exit effects, and how does one correct for these effects?" As a general guide, the entrance and exit effects can be ignored if the tube or die length-to-diameter ratio is large, say over 200. Otherwise, one must consider these effects, and apply a so-called "Bagley end correction method" [65]. Bagley carried out extrusion experiments using various circular dies of decreasing L/D ratio and obtained different flow curves for the same polymer melts. A plot of ΔP vs. L/D for a particular apparent shear rate $8\langle u \rangle/D$ yielded a straight line with an intercept on the negative L/D axis. The value of the intercept e is equal to an extra dimensionless length L_e/D in fully developed flow, accounting for the extra losses in the entrance and exit regions. This value must be added to the nominal tube or die length to give the effective length. The true wall shear stress is then calculated as:

$$\tau_w = \frac{\Delta P}{4(L/D + e)} \tag{104}$$

In principle, the Bagley end correction method may be extended to dies of non-circular cross section using the hydraulic radius R_h or equivalent diameter $D_e = 4R_h$ in place of the diameter D, and with $\bar{\tau}_w$ replacing τ_w. Note that the method is applicable only in the absence of surface effects.

FLOW IN PACKED BEDS AND POROUS MEDIA

The subject of non-Newtonian flow through porous media has received considerable attention, due in large part to its important industrial applications. In the earlier work, Sadowski and Bird [66, 67] carried out extensive studies of the flow of fluids described by the Ellis and power law models through beds packed with beads. Christopher and Middleman [68] modified the Blake-Kozeny equation for the Ostwald-de Waele (power law) fluids. McKinley et al. [69] extended Darcy's law to non-Newtonian flow by considering the porous medium as a capillary with equivalent radius proportional to the square root of the ratio of permeability to porosity. In a related study, Hassel and Bondi [70] developed a correlation to describe the flow of a highly viscous non-Newtonian fluid (rubber cement) through packed beds. Reviews of the literature that has accumulated in the area of non-Newtonian flow in packed beds and porous media have been presented by Savins [71] and, more recently, by Kemblowski and Michniewicz [72].

In the following analysis we are primarily concerned with the flow of purely-viscous non-Newtonian fluids in packed beds and porous media. Unlike the flow in a straight channel where simple shear or viscometric flow prevails, the flow channels in a packed bed are convergent-divergent and highly tortuous. Hence, the generalized Rabinowitsch equation is not expected to be valid for viscoelastic fluids. An abnormally large flow resistance or pressure drop has been observed for the flow of high molecular weight polymer solutions through packed beds. Correlations have been proposed [66, 67, 73, 74] using various elastic parameters to account for the deviation from the purely viscous behavior. The treatment of viscoelastic and extensional flows in packed beds and porous media is beyond the scope of this chapter.

The flow of a non-Newtonian fluid in an isotropic porous medium or packed bed may be represented as follows, depending upon the physical model [75] assumed for the porous medium or bed:

Blake model

$$\frac{\langle u \rangle - \bar{u}_w}{R_h} = \frac{(1 + \xi)}{k_i} \bar{\tau}_w^{-\xi} \int_0^{\bar{\tau}_w} \tau^{\xi - 1} f(\tau) \, d\tau \tag{105}$$

Blake-Kozeny model

$$\frac{\langle u \rangle - \bar{u}_w}{R_h} = \frac{(1 + \xi_0)}{k_0} \left(\frac{\bar{\tau}_w}{T_{BK}} \right)^{-\xi_0} \int_0^{\bar{\tau}_w/T_{BK}} \tau^{\xi_0 - 1} f(\tau) \, d\tau \tag{106}$$

Kozeny-Carman model

$$\frac{(\langle u \rangle - \bar{u}_w) T_{KC}}{R_h} = \frac{(1 + \xi_0)}{k_0} \left(\frac{\bar{\tau}_w}{T_{KC}} \right)^{-\xi_0} \int_0^{\bar{\tau}_w/T_{KC}} \tau^{\xi_0 - 1} f(\tau) \, d\tau \tag{107}$$

In the Blake model, the bed is envisaged as a bundle of straight tubes of complicated cross section with an average hydraulic radius R_h. In Equation 105, ξ and k_i denote the aspect factor $\xi = b/a$ and the Kozeny constant, defined in terms of the geometric coefficients for the bed by $k_i = 2(a + b)$. The void velocity and the effective velocity at the particle surface are related to the respective superficial velocities by the Dupuit [76] equation $\langle u \rangle = q/\varepsilon$ and the analogous equation $\bar{u}_w = q_w/\varepsilon$. The average wall shear stress is evaluated as $\bar{\tau}_w = R_h(-\Delta P/L)$, where the hydraulic radius of a packed bed or porous medium is given by $R_h = \varepsilon/(1 - \varepsilon)S_0$; S_0 is the specific surface of the particles, which defines the particle diameter $D_p = 6/S_0$. Strictly, for packed bed flows, $R_h = \varepsilon D_p/[6(1 - \varepsilon) + 4(D_p/D_c)]$, where D_c is the diameter of the column. The latter accounts for the surface area of the confining column and is seen to reduce to the usual expression only when $(D_p/D_c) \ll 1$.

The Blake-Kozeny model portrays the bed or porous medium as a bundle of tangled tubes with an effective length greater than the length of the bed. The average wall shear stress for the flow channels is therefore given by $R_h(-\Delta P/L_e)$ or by $\bar{\tau}_w/T_{BK}$, where T_{BK} denotes the tortuosity of the channels in the Blake-Kozeny model. The cross-sectional shape of the channels is characterized by $\xi_0 = b_0/a_0$ and $k_0 = 2(a_0 + b_0)$ where ξ_0 and k_0 denote the aspect factor and shape factor, respectively, of the tortuous channels.

The Kozeny-Carman model also regards the bed as a bundle of tortuous tubes, as in the Blake-Kozeny representation. However, the effect of the tortuosity on the average velocity in the channels is also evaluated, as shown on the left side of Equation 107. For this reason, the Kozeny-Carman expression may be considered to represent a more accurate portrayal of non-Newtonian flow in a bed comprising tortuous tubes.

For an Ellis fluid defined by $1/\eta = (1/\eta_0)[1 + (\tau/\tau_{1/2})^{\alpha - 1}]$, the foregoing equations become:

Blake

$$\langle u \rangle - \bar{u}_w = \frac{\bar{\tau}_w R_h}{k_i \eta_0} \left[1 + \frac{1 + \xi}{\alpha + \xi} \left(\frac{\bar{\tau}_w}{\tau_{1/2}} \right)^{\alpha - 1} \right] \tag{108}$$

Blake-Kozeny

$$\langle u \rangle - \bar{u}_w = \frac{\bar{\tau}_w R_h}{T_{BK} k_0 \eta_0} \left[1 + \frac{1 + \xi_0}{\alpha + \xi_0} \left(\frac{\bar{\tau}_w}{\tau_{1/2} T_{BK}} \right)^{\alpha - 1} \right] \tag{109}$$

Kozeny-Carman

$$\langle u \rangle - \bar{u}_w = \frac{\bar{\tau}_w R_h}{T_{KC}^2 k_0 \eta_0} \left[1 + \frac{1 + \xi_0}{\alpha + \xi_0} \left(\frac{\bar{\tau}_w}{\tau_{1/2} T_{KC}} \right)^{\alpha - 1} \right] \tag{110}$$

Equation 108 yields the expression developed by Sadowski and Bird [66, 67] for Ellis fluid flow in packed beds on setting $\bar{u}_w = 0$ (no surface effect), $\xi = 3$, and $k_i = 5.0$. The latter value of the Kozeny constant corresponds to the universally accepted value for randomly packed beds of spheres or granular particles based on studies conducted with Newtonian fluids. The value of 3 for ξ is the same value found for elliptical and circular conduits.

In Equations 108–110, the quantities in the brackets all approach unity in the limit as $\bar{\tau}_w$ approaches zero, yielding:

$$\text{Blake:} \quad \langle u \rangle - \bar{u}_w = \frac{\bar{\tau}_w R_h}{k_i \eta_0} \tag{111}$$

$$\text{Blake-Kozeny:} \quad \langle u \rangle - \bar{u}_w = \frac{\bar{\tau}_w R_h}{T_{BK} k_0 \eta_0} \tag{112}$$

$$\text{Kozeny-Carman:} \quad \langle u \rangle - \bar{u}_w = \frac{\bar{\tau}_w R_h}{T_{KC}^2 k_0 \eta_0} \tag{113}$$

which correspond to Newtonian flow characterized by the lower limiting viscosity η_0.

Equations 111 and 113 yield the following relationship between the tortuosity, Kozeny constant, and shape factor k_0:

$$k_i = T_{KC}^2 k_0 \tag{114}$$

Similarly, Equations 111 and 112 give:

$$k_i = T_{BK} k_0 \tag{115}$$

Substitution of these results in the appropriate Equations 109 and 110 results in:

$$\text{BK:} \quad \langle u \rangle - \bar{u}_w = \frac{\bar{\tau}_w R_h}{k_i \eta_0} \left[1 + \frac{1 + \zeta}{\alpha + \zeta} \left(\frac{\bar{\tau}_w}{\tau_{1/2} T_{BK}} \right)^{\alpha - 1} \right] \tag{116}$$

$$\text{KC:} \quad \langle u \rangle - \bar{u}_w = \frac{\bar{\tau}_w R_h}{k_i \eta_0} \left[1 + \frac{1 + \zeta}{\alpha + \zeta} \left(\frac{\bar{\tau}_w}{\tau_{1/2} T_{KC}} \right)^{\alpha - 1} \right] \tag{117}$$

where the substitution $\zeta_0 = \zeta$ has been made since the same value of 3 has been used for ζ_0 and ζ in published work. This is due to the fact that most expressions in the literature were derived for circular flow channels. It has also been demonstrated by Miller [22] that the final expression for a power law fluid is relatively insensitive to the value of ζ over a relatively wide range.

Although Equations 116 and 117 are of the same form, their difference arises from the different values assumed by T_{KC} and T_{BK} and the different values assigned to the Kozeny constant, in Equations 114 and 115. Thus, following Carman [77], the Kozeny constant k_i equals 5.0 and $T_{KC} = \sqrt{2}$. The k_0 value yielded by Equation 114 is 2.5, which corresponds to elliptically shaped flow channels with a ratio of minor to major axis in the order of 0.1. Kemblowski and Michniewicz [72] have successfully predicted the flow of molten polypropylene using the Kozeny-Carman equation for power law fluids, and Shirato [78, 79] utilized the same equation in non-Newtonian filtration.

The data of Christopher and Middleman [68] for power law fluids were used to corroborate the Blake-Kozeny equation using $k_i = \frac{25}{6}$ and $k_0 = 2.0$ (circular channels). Substituting these values in Equation 115 yields $T_{BK} = \frac{25}{12}$. Kemblowski and Michniewicz [72] point out that this value is higher than the maximum value of $\pi/2$ and is a result of the over-simplified portrayal of the capillary model leading to Equation 115. The value of $\frac{25}{6}$ for the Kozeny constant k_i is also inconsistent with the generally accepted value of 5.0 [77] for Newtonian fluids. The same may be said [72, 77] about the prediction by the Ergun equation in the viscous flow regime on which the former value is based.

In the limit as $\bar{\tau}_w$ becomes large, Equations 108, 116, and 117 simplify to:

$$\text{B:} \quad \langle u \rangle - \bar{u}_w = \frac{\bar{\tau}_w R_h}{k_i \eta_0} \frac{(1 + \zeta)}{(\alpha + \zeta)} \left(\frac{\bar{\tau}_w}{\tau_{1/2}} \right)^{\alpha - 1} \tag{118}$$

BK: $\langle u \rangle - \bar{u}_w = \dfrac{\bar{\tau}_w R_h}{k_i \eta_0} \dfrac{(1 + \xi)}{(\alpha + \xi)} \left(\dfrac{\bar{\tau}_w}{\tau_{1/2} T_{BK}} \right)^{\alpha - 1}$ (119)

KC: $\langle u \rangle - \bar{u}_w = \dfrac{\bar{\tau}_w R_h}{k_i \eta_0} \dfrac{(1 + \xi)}{(\alpha + \xi)} \left(\dfrac{\bar{\tau}_w}{\tau_{1/2} T_{KC}} \right)^{\alpha - 1}$ (120)

These equations yield the following relationships between the evaluations of the shear stress parameter, at the same flow rate, in the non-Newtonian regimes:

$$(\bar{\tau}_w)_{KC} / (\bar{\tau}_w) = T_{KC}^{1 - 1/\alpha}$$ (121)

$$(\bar{\tau}_w)_{KC} / (\bar{\tau}_w)_{BK} = (T_{KC} / T_{BK})^{1 - 1/\alpha} [(k_i)_{KC} / (k_i)_{BK}]^{1/\alpha}$$ (122)

where $(k_i)_{KC} = (k_i)_B$.

For a bed tortuosity $T_{KC} = \sqrt{2}$ and flow behavior index $\alpha = 2$, the Kozeny-Carman model predicts a pressure drop 18.9% higher than the Blake model for the same flow rate. On the other hand, letting $(k_i)_{KC} = 5.0$, $(k_i)_{BK} = \frac{25}{6}$, $T_{KC} = \sqrt{2}$, and $T_{BK} = \frac{25}{12}$, for the same α, leads to a pressure drop prediction by the Blake-Kozeny method 10.8% higher than by the Kozeny-Carman method and 31.7% higher than by the Blake method. It is seen that the Kozeny-Carman equation gives a prediction that falls between the Blake and Blake-Kozeny values. The same numerical discrepancies between the values provided by the three models would apply to a power law fluid with n = 0.5.
For a Newtonian fluid, $\alpha = 1$, Equations 108–110 reduce to Equations 111–113, with the right sides multiplied by the factor 2. The Newtonian expressions yielded by the Blake and Kozeny-Carman equations, which use $k_i = 5.0$, are in agreement with the generally accepted result. The Blake-Kozeny result differs due to the use of the value $k_i = \frac{25}{6}$ for the Kozeny constant. This value corresponds to the laminar asymptote of the Ergun equation and as originally pointed out by Carman [77] differs from the generally accepted value.
All the equations, Equations 105–107, for the three bed models and their features may be represented by the following single equation in terms of the aspect factor ξ and the Kozeny constant k_i:

$$\frac{\langle u \rangle - \bar{u}_w}{R_h} = \frac{(1 + \xi)T}{k_i} \left(\frac{\bar{\tau}_w}{T} \right)^{-\xi} \int_0^{\bar{\tau}_w/T} \tau^{\xi - 1} f(\tau) \, d\tau$$ (123)

where T and k_i are given as follows. Blake model: T = 1, $k_i = 5.0$; BK model: $T = T_{BK} = 25/12$, $k_i = T_{BK} k_0 = \frac{25}{6}$; and KC model: $T = T_{KC} = \sqrt{2}$, $k_i = T_{KC}^2 k_0 = 5.0$.
For a Newtonian fluid, Equation 123 reduces to:

$$\frac{\langle u \rangle - \bar{u}_w}{R_h} = \frac{\bar{\tau}_w}{k_i \mu}$$ (124)

which is the basis for the definition of the Darcy viscosity for non-Newtonian flow in packed beds and porous media as follows:

$$\frac{\langle u \rangle - \bar{u}_w}{R_h} = \frac{\bar{\tau}_w}{k_i \eta_D}$$ (125)

Combination of Equations 123 and 125 yields the following expression for the Darcy viscosity:

$$\eta_D = \frac{(\bar{\tau}_w / T)^{1 + \xi}}{(1 + \xi) \int_0^{\bar{\tau}_w / T} \tau^{\xi - 1} f(\tau) \, d\tau}$$ (126)

For the Blake model, T = 1, this reduces to the expression (Equation 55) for the Rabinowitsch viscosity η_R for non-Newtonian flow in straight conduits, which is obtained directly as a function of $\bar{\tau}_w$ by capillary viscometry.

Differentiation of Equation 123 with respect to $\bar{\tau}_w/T$ yields the shear rate for flows through packed beds and porous media as follows:

$$\gamma_w = f(\bar{\tau}_w/T) = \frac{k_i(\xi n^* + 1)}{(1 + \xi)Tn^*}\left(\frac{\langle u \rangle - \bar{u}_w}{R_h}\right) \tag{127}$$

where n^* is defined as in Equation 49.

Equation 127 yields the following relationships between the shear rates for the respective bed configurations, at the same $(\langle u \rangle - \bar{u}_w)/R_h$:

$$(\gamma_w)_B = 2.5(\gamma_w)_{BK} = \sqrt{2}(\gamma_w)_{KC} \tag{128}$$

As in the previous comparisons, the predicted wall shear rate based on the Kozeny-Carman model is intermediate between the Blake and Blake-Kozeny predictions, i.e., $(\gamma_w)_B > (\gamma_w)_{KC} > (\gamma_w)_{BK}$.

For the power law fluid, $f(\tau) = (\tau/K)^{1/n}$, Equation 123 becomes:

$$\frac{\langle u \rangle - \bar{u}_w}{R_h} = \frac{n(1 + \xi)T}{k_i(1 + n\xi)}\left(\frac{\bar{\tau}_w}{KT}\right)^{1/n} \tag{129}$$

For the cases considered, this gives:

B: $$\frac{\langle u \rangle - \bar{u}_w}{R_h} = \frac{4n}{5(3n + 1)}\left(\frac{\bar{\tau}_w}{K}\right)^{1/n} \tag{130}$$

BK: $$\frac{\langle u \rangle - \bar{u}_w}{R_h} = \frac{4n}{2(3n + 1)}\left(\frac{\bar{\tau}_w}{KT_{BK}}\right)^{1/n} \tag{131}$$

KC: $$\frac{\langle u \rangle - \bar{u}_w}{R_h} = \frac{\sqrt{2}(4n)}{5(3n + 1)}\left(\frac{\bar{\tau}_w}{KT_{KC}}\right)^{1/n} \tag{132}$$

The data of Sadowski and Bird [66, 67] for a power law fluid is described [75] by Equation 130 with $\bar{u}_w = 0$. Equation 131 for $k_i = \frac{25}{6}$ and $T_{BK} = \frac{25}{12}$, with $\bar{u}_w = 0$, corresponds to the equation of Christopher and Middleman [68] for power law flow in packed beds. Savins [71] in a comprehensive review paper compares the agreement obtained by these two equations with experimental data. Kemblowski and Michniewicz [72], in a more recent review, demonstrated the success of Equation 132 in predicting the flow of molten polypropylene in a packed bed.

Figure 9 presents experimental results obtained by Tiu et al. [80] for a Methocel solution in viscometric and packed bed flows, with $\bar{u}_w = 0$. Comparing the Blake model for a power law fluid given by Equation 130 with the corresponding tabular flow equation (see Table 1), at a constant value of the shear stress parameter $\bar{\tau}_w$, the respective $2(\langle u \rangle - \bar{u}_w)/R_h$ data should be separated by a simple shift factor $k_i/2 = 2.5$, which is confirmed by the data. The flow behavior of a power law fluid in a given packed bed model is thus readily predictable from viscometric data.

The Darcy law expression for flow of a non-Newtonian fluid in an isotropic porous medium follows from the relations $\bar{\tau}_w = R_h|-\nabla P|$, $\langle u \rangle = q/\varepsilon$ (Dupuit equation), $\bar{u}_w = q_w/\varepsilon$ and Equation 125, as follows:

$$q - q_w = -(k/\eta_D)\,\nabla P \tag{133}$$

where k is the permeability:

$$k = \frac{\varepsilon R_h^2}{k_i} = \frac{\varepsilon^3 D_p^2}{36k_i(1 - \varepsilon)^2} \tag{134}$$

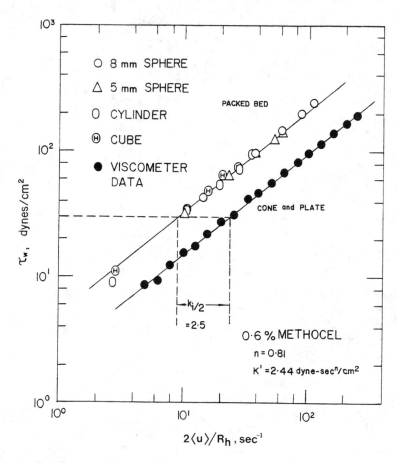

Figure 9. Comparison of wall shear stress parameter vs. apparent shear rate for packed bed and viscometer data [80].

Evaluation of Surface Effects

Equation 123 rewritten in the form:

$$\frac{\langle u \rangle}{R_h} = \frac{\bar{u}_w}{R_h} + \frac{(1 + \xi)T}{k_i} \left(\frac{\bar{\tau}_w}{T}\right)^{-\xi} \int_0^{\tau_w/T} \tau^{\xi - 1} f(\tau) \, d\tau \qquad (135)$$

suggests a procedure similar to that used in conduit flow for evaluation of surface effects in non-Newtonian flow through packed beds. Assuming $\bar{u}_w$ is a function only of $\bar{\tau}_w$, a plot of the flow data in the form of $\langle u \rangle / R_h$ vs. $1/R_h$, at constant $\bar{\tau}_w$, should be linear with slope equal to $\bar{u}_w$. By repeating the analysis at different $\bar{\tau}_w$, one may evaluate $\bar{u}_w$ as a function of $\bar{\tau}_w$. The procedure assumes the parameters characterizing the geometry and the tortuosity are unchanged when the hydraulic radius R_h of the bed is altered by changing the particle size. This requires that the porosity of the bed be fixed.

Friction Factor-Reynolds Number Relation in Porous Media Flow

The behavior depicted by Equation 125 corresponds to a bed friction factor:

$$f = \frac{D_p(-\Delta P/L)}{2\rho(q - q_w)^2} \tag{136}$$

with a Reynolds number dependence given by:

$$\frac{2f\varepsilon^3}{1 - \varepsilon} = \frac{36k_i}{Re_p^*} \tag{137}$$

where $\quad Re_p^* = \dfrac{D_p(q - q_w)\rho}{\eta_D(1 - \varepsilon)} \tag{138}$

In terms of the indices n* and K*, defined as in Equations 49 and 73 for flow in conduits or open channels, the expression for Re_p^* is:

$$Re_p^* = \frac{6k_i R_h^{n*}(\langle u \rangle - \bar{u}_w)^{2-n*}\rho}{2^{n*}K^*} \tag{139}$$

Combination of Equations 49 and 73 with Equation 123 yields the following relations for evaluation of n* and K* for packed bed and porous media flow:

$$n^* = \frac{\eta'_w \int_0^{\bar{\tau}_w/T} (\tau^\xi/\eta)\, d\tau}{(\bar{\tau}_w/T)^{\xi+1} - \xi\eta'_w \int_0^{\bar{\tau}_w/T} (\tau^\xi/\eta)\, d\tau} \tag{140}$$

where n'_w is η evaluated at $\bar{\tau}_w/T$, and:

$$K^* = \bar{\tau}_w \left[\frac{2(1 + \xi)T}{k_i}\left(\frac{\bar{\tau}_w}{T}\right)^{-\xi} \int_0^{\bar{\tau}_w/T} \frac{\tau^\xi}{\eta}\, d\tau \right]^{-n*} \tag{141}$$

In view of the similarity of the expression for n* with Equation 75, Table 4 giving n* for various fluid models may also be used directly for determination of n* in flow through packed beds or porous media. One needs only to replace $\bar{\tau}_w$ in the table with $\bar{\tau}_w/T$. For a power law fluid, n* = n and K* = $KT[k_i(1 + n\xi)/2n(1 + \xi)T]^n$. The expressions for the void velocity $\langle u \rangle$ in packed-bed or porous-media flow of non-Newtonian fluids may similarly be derived from the average velocity expressions in Table 1 by replacing $\bar{\tau}_w$ with $\bar{\tau}_w/T$ and 1/a with $2(1 + \xi)T/k_i$, in the latter expressions. It is noticed that the numerator on the right side of Equation 137 is 180 for the case $k_i = 5.0$ and 150 for beds represented by the Blake-Kozeny model consistent with the Ergun equation. A formulation in which the numerator on the right side of Equation 137 is 180 for all values of the Kozeny constant is also available [81]. For operation in the viscous regime, Re_p^* should be less than 5–10.

Anisotropic Porous Media

To account for the anisotropy and particle migration in a compressible porous medium such as a filter cake, Darcy's law may be represented [82] in the expanded form:

$$\eta_D \cdot (q - er - q_w) = -k \cdot \nabla P \tag{142}$$

where r is the superficial particle velocity and e = $\varepsilon/(1 - \varepsilon)$ the local void ratio introduced by Tiller and Shirato [83]. A mapping tensor Φ may be defined by:

$$\nabla P = -\Phi \cdot (q - er - q_w) \tag{143}$$

such that the Darcy viscosity tensor is given by $\boldsymbol{\eta}_D = \mathbf{k} \cdot \boldsymbol{\Phi}$. For an isotropic medium for which $\mathbf{k} = k\mathbf{I}$ and $\boldsymbol{\Phi} = \phi\mathbf{I}$, this gives $\boldsymbol{\eta}_D = k\phi\mathbf{I}$ which, when substituted in the general Darcy law, produces a result in accord with Equation 133, for $\phi = \eta_D/k$.

It can be shown [82] that the cake permeability and Darcy viscosity in non-Newtonian filtration are each symmetric tensors as a result of the colinearity of the potential gradient and the $(\mathbf{q} - \mathbf{er} - \mathbf{q}_w)$ vector during the cake formation. For an orthogonal (Cartesian) reference frame with one of the principal axes, designated the x-axis, aligned along the direction of the filtration, Darcy's law becomes:

$$\begin{pmatrix} \eta_{Dx} & 0 & 0 \\ 0 & \eta_{Dy} & 0 \\ 0 & 0 & \eta_{Dz} \end{pmatrix} \begin{pmatrix} q_x - er_x - q_{wx} \\ q_y - er_y - q_{wy} \\ q_z - er_z - q_{wz} \end{pmatrix} = - \begin{pmatrix} k_x & 0 & 0 \\ 0 & k_y & 0 \\ 0 & 0 & k_z \end{pmatrix} \begin{pmatrix} \dfrac{\partial P}{\partial x} \\ \dfrac{\partial P}{\partial y} \\ \dfrac{\partial P}{\partial z} \end{pmatrix} \qquad (144)$$

which leads to the equations:

$$q_j - er_j - q_{wj} = -\frac{k_j}{\eta_{Dj}}\frac{\partial P}{\partial x_j} \qquad j = x, y, z \qquad (145)$$

where the respective components of the permeability and Darcy viscosity are given by:

$$k_j = \varepsilon R_{hj}^2/k_{ij} = \varepsilon^3/k_{ij}S_{0j}^2(1 - \varepsilon)^2 \qquad (146)$$

$$\eta_{Dj} = \frac{(\bar{\tau}_{wj}/T_j)^{1 + \xi_j}}{(1 + \xi_j)\displaystyle\int_0^{\bar{\tau}_{wj}/T_j} \tau^{\xi_j - 1}f(\tau)\, d\tau} \qquad (147)$$

and where $\bar{\tau}_{wj} = R_{hj}(\partial P/\partial x_j)$. Since the cake permeability is isotropic in a plane normal to the x-direction, $k_y = k_z$.

In one-dimensional filtration in which the cake is deposited on a planar septum, Equation 145 becomes:

$$q - er - q_w = -(k/\eta_D)\, dP_x/dx \qquad (148)$$

This equation is the basis for the analysis of non-Newtonian filtration [81, 82, 84, 85].

IMPROVED PARAMETRIC CHARACTERIZATION OF FLOW GEOMETRIES

In the foregoing, a method was described for prediction of non-Newtonian flow in open or closed conduits utilizing 2 geometric parameters (a, b) for characterization of the flow cross-section. The same technique was applied to purely viscous, inelastic flow in packed beds and porous media and to a viscoelastic jet issuing from a die of arbitrary cross section. Surface effects were accounted for by inclusion of a term denoting the effective velocity of the fluid at the solid boundary.

The agreement obtained with the available analytical results and experimental data for duct flow was generally satisfactory with a maximum deviation of less than 5% for a broad range of fluid models and flow geometries including rectangular, triangular, and elliptical ducts and concentric annuli over a wide range of aspect ratios. In the aspect ratio range $0 \leq k \leq 0.2$ for annuli, however, the deviations from the analytical evaluations were somewhat greater with the maximum deviations observed with power law fluids, as shown in Figure 3. Perhaps of greater immediate concern is the marked reduction in the efficacy of the existing methods of correlation of packed bed and porous media flow data observed with viscoelastic fluids. Since highly viscoelastic fluids are also highly non-Newtonian (i.e., shear-thinning), the accurate evaluation of viscoelastic effects in the flow of such fluids through packed beds and porous media is contingent upon having an accurate means of characterization of purely viscous flow in arbitrary geometries.

The representation of steady, fully-developed laminar flow of non-Newtonian fluids in open or closed conduits of arbitrary cross section is based on the generalization given by Equation 45 of Equation 42 for circular tubes and slits. The generalized equation does not provide for interaction in the general case with second and higher derivatives of $2(\langle u \rangle - \bar{u}_w)/R_h$ with respect to $\bar{\tau}_w$. A more general formulation may therefore be achieved by the following generalization in terms of a basic differential equation of infinite order, which is postulated to characterize the flow of non-Newtonian fluids in conduits of arbitrary cross-sectional shape:

$$f(\tau) = \varepsilon_0 \omega + \varepsilon_1 \tau \frac{d\omega}{d\tau} + \varepsilon_2 \tau^2 \frac{d^2\omega}{d\tau^2} + \cdots + \varepsilon_i \tau^i \frac{d^i\omega}{d\tau^i} + \cdots \tag{149}$$

For brevity, the apparent shear rate $2(\langle u \rangle - \bar{u}_w)/R_h$ is denoted by ω and the average wall shear stress $\bar{\tau}_w$ by τ. The ε_i are the new geometric parameters which characterize the shape of the flow cross section. In general, an infinite number of geometric parameters ε_i are required, in contrast with the 2 parameters a and b used originally. For the simple circular and slit cross sections, the geometric parameters are $\varepsilon_0 = \frac{3}{4}$, $\varepsilon_1 = \frac{1}{4}$, $\varepsilon_{i>1} = 0$; and $\varepsilon_0 = 1$, $\varepsilon_1 = \frac{1}{2}$, $\varepsilon_{i>1} = 0$, respectively, and Equation 149 reduces to Equation 42 or 45. Also, for Newtonian fluids, $d^i\omega/d\tau^i = 0$ for $i > 1$ and Equation 149 again reduces to Equation 45, which governs the flow of Newtonian fluids.

A general procedure for obtaining an analytical solution to Equation 149 has been developed [46]. It is based on a perturbation technique utilizing the assumption $\varepsilon_{i>1}^2 < 1$ and the boundary condition $\omega = 0$ at $\tau = 0$. One begins by representing the solution to the i-th order differential equation obtained by truncating Equation 149 at the i-th term:

$$f(\tau) = \varepsilon_0 \omega_i + \varepsilon_1 \tau \frac{d\omega_i}{d\tau} + \varepsilon_2 \tau^2 \frac{d^2\omega_i}{d\tau^2} + \cdots + \varepsilon_i \tau^i \frac{d^i\omega_i}{d\tau^i} \tag{150}$$

as a power series in the coefficient ε_i:

$$\omega_i = \sum_{j=0}^{\infty} \omega_{ij}(\tau)\varepsilon_i^j \qquad \omega_{ij}(0) = 0 \quad \text{for all j} \tag{151}$$

The coefficients ω_{ij} of the ε_i^j are functions of τ to be evaluated. The boundary condition $\omega_i = 0$ at $\tau = 0$ will be satisfied if a solution given by Equation 151 can be found satisfying the condition $\omega_{ij}(0) = 0$ for all j. Substitution of Equation 151 in Equation 150 yields an equation when expanded and equating coefficients of like powers of ε_i, leads to a set of differential equations of $(i-1)$-th order to be solved recursively for the functions ω_{i0}, ω_{i1}, ω_{i2}, etc. The function ω_{i0} is given by $\omega_{i0} = \omega_{i-1}$, where ω_{i-1} is the solution to the differential equation, Equation 150, of order $(i-1)$. The problem of obtaining the solution ω_i to the i-th order differential equation has thus been transformed into one of obtaining the solutions to the equations of order $(i-1)$.

A solution to Equation 149 is therefore sought by stepwise integration, beginning with the second order differential equation:

$$f(\tau) = \varepsilon_0 \omega_2 + \varepsilon_1 \tau \frac{d\omega_2}{d\tau} + \varepsilon_2 \tau^2 \frac{d^2\omega_2}{d\tau^2} \tag{152}$$

The functions ω_{2j} comprising the solution ω_2 are given by [46]:

$$\omega_{20} = \omega_1 = \varepsilon_1^{-1}\tau^{-\xi} \int_0^\tau \tau^{\xi-1} f(\tau) \, d\tau \tag{153}$$

$$\omega_{21} = -\varepsilon_1^{-1}\tau^{-\xi} \int_0^\tau \tau^{\xi+1} \frac{d^2\omega_{20}}{d\tau^2} \, d\tau \tag{154}$$

$$\omega_{2j} = -\varepsilon_1^{-1}\tau^{-\xi} \int_0^\tau \tau^{\xi+1} \frac{d^2\omega_{2(j-1)}}{d\tau^2} d\tau \qquad (155)$$

where the aspect factor $\xi = \varepsilon_0/\varepsilon_1$.

Substitution of the ω_{2j} expressions in Equation 151 yields the solution ω_2 to Equation 152. The solution ω_3 to the third order truncated equation is obtained similarly from $\omega_{30} = \omega_2$ and the other ω_{3j} functions which are readily evaluated [46]. One can obtain ω_4 and subsequent higher order solutions in a similar fashion. Usually, the solutions ω_i and ω can be deduced by inspection of the expressions for ω_2 and ω_3.

Application to Various Fluid Models

For the Ostwald-de Waele (power law) fluid represented by $f(\tau) = (\tau/K)^s$, Equations 153–155 become:

$$\omega_{20} = \frac{1}{\varepsilon_0 + \varepsilon_1 s}\left(\frac{\tau}{K}\right)^s \qquad (156)$$

$$\omega_{21} = -\frac{s(s-1)}{(\varepsilon_0 + \varepsilon_1 s)^2}\left(\frac{\tau}{K}\right)^s \qquad (157)$$

$$\omega_{2j} = \frac{(-1)^j s^j(s-1)^j}{(\varepsilon_0 + \varepsilon_1 s)^{j+1}}\left(\frac{\tau}{K}\right)^s \qquad (158)$$

The solution ω_2 to Equation 152 for the power law fluid obtained by substitution of these functions in Equation 151, with i = 2, is given by:

$$\omega_2 = \frac{(\tau/K)^s}{\varepsilon_0 + \varepsilon_1 s}\sum_{j=0}^\infty \left[\frac{-s(s-1)\varepsilon_2}{\varepsilon_0 + \varepsilon_1 s}\right]^j \qquad (159)$$

This may be expressed in closed form by:

$$\omega_2 = \frac{(\tau/K)^s}{\varepsilon_0 + \varepsilon_1 s}\left[1 + \frac{s(s-1)\varepsilon_2}{\varepsilon_0 + \varepsilon_1 s}\right]^{-1} = \frac{(\tau/K)^s}{\varepsilon_0 + \varepsilon_1 s + \varepsilon_2 s(s-1)} \qquad (160)$$

which follows from Equation 159 for $|s(s-1)\varepsilon_2/(\varepsilon_0 + \varepsilon_1 s)| < 1$.

Similarly, setting $\omega_2 = \omega_{30}$, one can determine the solution ω_3 to the truncated third order equation, Equation 150, and in the same way obtain ω_4, ω_5, etc. The functions ω_3 and ω_i are as follows:

$$\omega_3 = \frac{(\tau/K)^s}{\varepsilon_0 + \varepsilon_1 s + \varepsilon_2 s(s-1) + \varepsilon_3 s(s-1)(s-2)} \qquad (161)$$

$$\omega_i = \frac{(\tau/K)^s}{\varepsilon_0 + \varepsilon_1 s + \varepsilon_2 s(s-1) + \cdots + \varepsilon_i s(s-1)\cdots(s-i+1)} \qquad (162)$$

By inspection, the solution ω to the untruncated differential equation, Equation 149, representing the flow of power law fluids in channels of arbitrary cross section, is given by:

$$\frac{(\tau/K)^s}{\omega} = \varepsilon_0 + \varepsilon_1 s + \varepsilon_2 s(s-1) + \cdots + \varepsilon_i s(s-1)\cdots(s-i+1) + \cdots \qquad (163)$$

The solution for power law fluids possesses interesting and useful mathematical properties. Assigning $s = 1/n$ the values $0, 1, 2, \ldots$, the right side of Equation 163 becomes $\varepsilon_0, \varepsilon_0 + \varepsilon_1, \varepsilon_0 + 2\varepsilon_1 + 2\varepsilon_2, \ldots$, respectively. Thus, for s an integer, the number of geometric parameters retained in the general solution is finite and increases with an increase in the non-Newtonian character of the fluid being given by $s + 1$. Equation 163 for s integral may be represented by:

$$\frac{(\tau/K)^s}{\omega} = \sum_{j=0}^{s} \frac{\varepsilon_j s!}{(s-j)!} = \sum_{j=0}^{s} \varepsilon_j \binom{s}{j} j! \tag{164}$$

which is also the solution ω_s to the truncated differential equation of order s, Equation 150 with $i = s$. To illustrate this, for a power law fluid with $n = \frac{1}{3}$, $s = 3$, and Equation 163 or 164, gives:

$$\frac{(\tau/K)^3}{\omega} = \varepsilon_0 + 3\varepsilon_1 + 6\varepsilon_2 + 6\varepsilon_3 \tag{165}$$

which corresponds to Equation 161 with $s = 3$.

The simplicity of the results yielded by Equations 163 and 164 for $s = 0, 1, 2 \ldots$ can be used to determine the geometric parameters. If analytical or experimental data are available relating τ/K to ω for the flow of a power law fluid in a conduit, ε_0 can be obtained directly from the flow characteristics for $s = 0$ as the quantity $(\tau/K)^s/\omega$. Knowing ε_0, ε_1 may then be computed from the flow characteristics for $s = 1$. With ε_0 and ε_1 known, ε_2 may be determined from the data for $s = 2$, and so on. Since the geometric parameters are independent of the fluid, they can be used to predict the flow of other fluid models in the same geometry.

The following general relationship describing the flow of an Ellis fluid, $f(\tau) = (\tau/\eta_0)[1 + (\tau/\tau_{1/2})^{\alpha-1}]$, in conduits of arbitrary cross section is yielded by Equation 149 [146]:

$$\omega = \frac{\tau}{\eta_0} \left[\frac{1}{\varepsilon_0 + \varepsilon_1} + \frac{1}{\varepsilon_0 + \varepsilon_1 \alpha + \varepsilon_2 \alpha(\alpha - 1) + \cdots + \varepsilon_i \alpha(\alpha - 1) \cdots (\alpha - i + 1) + \cdots} \left(\frac{\tau}{\tau_{1/2}} \right)^{\alpha-1} \right] \tag{166}$$

For $\alpha = 2$, Equation 166 simplifies to:

$$\omega = \frac{\tau}{\eta_0} \left[\frac{1}{\varepsilon_0 + \varepsilon_1} + \frac{1}{\varepsilon_0 + 2\varepsilon_1 + 2\varepsilon_2} \left(\frac{\tau}{\tau_{1/2}} \right) \right] \tag{167}$$

The number of geometric parameters utilized in conjunction with this fluid model is $(\alpha + 1)$. The dependence of the required geometric parameters on the integer value of an appropriate flow behavior index is a general property of the solutions for all the fluid models investigated. For α integral, Equation 166 can be represented as follows:

$$\omega = \frac{\tau}{\eta_0} \left[\frac{1}{\varepsilon_0 + \varepsilon_1} + \frac{1}{\displaystyle\sum_{j=0}^{\alpha} \varepsilon_j \binom{\alpha}{j} j!} \left(\frac{\tau}{\tau_{1/2}} \right)^{\alpha-1} \right] \tag{168}$$

This equation is also the Ellis fluid solution of the differential equation obtained on setting $i = \alpha$ in Equation 150 [46].

The average velocity-potential drop relationship for the flow of a Rabinowitsch fluid, $f(\tau) = (\tau/\mu_0)(1 + b_1\tau^2)$, can be derived from Equation 166 or 168 by setting $\alpha = 3$, $\eta_0 = \mu_0$, and $\tau_{1/2} = 1/\sqrt{b_1}$, which yields:

$$\omega = \frac{\tau}{\mu_0} \left[\frac{1}{\varepsilon_0 + \varepsilon_1} + \frac{b_1\tau^2}{\varepsilon_0 + 3\varepsilon_1 + 6\varepsilon_2 + 6\varepsilon_3} \right] \tag{169}$$

Four geometric parameters suffice to characterize the flow geometry with this fluid model.

Meter [51] proposed a 4-parameter fluid viscosity function containing a lower limiting viscosity η_0, an upper limiting viscosity η_∞, the shear stress τ_m at which the viscosity is 0.5 $(\eta_0 + \eta_\infty)$, and an additional parameter α:

$$\eta = \eta_\infty + \frac{\eta_0 - \eta_\infty}{1 + (\tau/\tau_m)^{\alpha - 1}} \tag{170}$$

The Peek-McLean and Reiner-Philippoff models are special cases [30, 51] of the Meter model corresponding to $\alpha = 2$ and $\alpha = 3$, respectively.

For a large class of fluids, including concentrated polymer solutions, $\eta_\infty \ll \eta_0$ and the Meter model can be rewritten [51]:

$$\frac{\eta_0}{\eta} = [1 + (\tau/\tau_m)^{\alpha - 1}] \sum_{j=0}^{\infty} \left[-\left(\frac{\eta_\infty}{\eta_0}\right)\left(\frac{\tau}{\tau_m}\right)^{\alpha - 1} \right]^j \tag{171}$$

which is valid for $[(\tau/\tau_m)^{\alpha - 1}(\eta_\infty/\eta_0)] \ll 1$.

The general solution to Equation 149 for a Meter fluid represented by Equation 171 is [30]:

$$\omega = \frac{\tau}{\eta_0} \sum_{j=0}^{\infty} \left[\frac{1}{M_j} + \frac{(\tau/\tau_m)^{\alpha - 1}}{N_j} \right]\left[-\left(\frac{\eta_\infty}{\eta_0}\right)\left(\frac{\tau}{\tau_m}\right)^{\alpha - 1} \right]^j \tag{172}$$

where M_j and N_j are given by:

$$M_j = \varepsilon_0 + \varepsilon_1 p + \cdots + \varepsilon_i p(p - 1) \cdots (p - i + 1) + \cdots \tag{173}$$

$$N_j = \varepsilon_0 + \varepsilon_1 r + \cdots + \varepsilon_i r(r - 1) \cdots (r - i + 1) + \cdots \tag{174}$$

where $p = j(\alpha - 1) + 1$ $\tag{175}$

$$r = j(\alpha - 1) + \alpha \tag{176}$$

When the exponent α is an integer, p and r are also integers and M_j and N_j each reduce to a series with a finite number of terms, expressed in terms of binomial coefficients as follows:

$$M_j = \sum_{k=0}^{p} \varepsilon_k \binom{p}{k} k! \tag{177}$$

$$N_j = \sum_{k=0}^{r} \varepsilon_k \binom{r}{k} k! \tag{178}$$

For $\eta_\infty = 0$, the Meter model reduces to the Ellis fluid model and it can be verified that Equation 172 similarly reduces to Equation 166 for Ellis fluid flow in an open or closed conduit. For details on the development of the above equations and for equations for other fluid models, including the Reiner-Rivlin general model, refer to the original papers [30, 46].

Evaluation of Geometric Parameters

The analytical solution of Fredrickson and Bird [6] for power law flow with integral values of the reciprocal of the flow behavior index in concentric annuli was utilized in evaluation of the geometric parameters ε_i, using the relationship:

$$\sum_{j=0}^{s} \varepsilon_j \frac{s!}{(s - j)!} = \frac{(1 + k)(s + 2)}{4\gamma(s, k)} \tag{179}$$

where $\gamma(s, k)$ denotes the function of s and aspect ratio k available in tabular form [6]. At the infinite dilatancy ($n = \infty$, $s = 0$) condition, corresponding to a triangular velocity profile, Equation 179 gives $\varepsilon_0 = (1 + k)/2\gamma(0, k) = 1.0000$. For a Newtonian fluid, $n = s = 1$, one obtains $\varepsilon_0 + \varepsilon_1 = 3(1 + k)/4\gamma(1, k)$, which yields ε_1 as a function of k:

$$\varepsilon_1 = \frac{3(1 + k)}{4\gamma(1, k)} - 1.0000 \tag{180}$$

Similarly, for $s = 2$, Equation 179 becomes:

$$\varepsilon_0 + 2\varepsilon_1 + 2\varepsilon_2 = \frac{(1 + k)}{\gamma(2, k)} \tag{181}$$

which yields ε_2 as a function of k. Subsequent parameters are obtained in the same manner.

Geometric parameters ε_i for concentric annuli are presented as a function of the aspect ratio in Table 5. The primary parameters ε_0 and ε_1 have different values from the binary parameters b and a of the original method, which were evaluated from average velocity and maximum velocity data for Newtonian fluids. Although the sums $(\varepsilon_0 + \varepsilon_1)$ and $(b + a)$ are equal numerically, the ratios $\varepsilon_0/\varepsilon_1$ and b/a differ due to the fact that ε_0 is unity for all aspect ratios.

The results of Schechter [9] and Wheeler and Wissler [10] for power law flow in rectangular ducts presented in terms of the friction factor and Reynolds number, as a function of the aspect

Table 5
Refined Geometric Parameters for Concentric Annuli*

$k = R_i/R_0$	ε_0	ε_1	ε_2	ε_3	ε_4	ε_5
0.01	1.0000	0.2519	−0.02304	0.01220	−0.00359	0.000769
0.10	1.0000	0.3964	−0.01690	0.00438	−0.00073	0.000208
0.20	1.0000	0.4430	−0.01205	0.00198	−0.00042	0.000101
0.30	1.0000	0.4664	−0.00783	0.00130	−0.00024	0.000060
0.40	1.0000	0.4801	−0.00506	0.00085	−0.00012	0.000030
0.50	1.0000	0.4881	−0.00268	0.00045	−0.00005	0.000011
0.60	1.0000	0.4937	−0.00159	0.00025	−0.00002	—
0.70	1.0000	0.4970	−0.00087	0.00012	—	—
0.80	1.0000	0.4987	−0.00033	0.00005	—	—
0.90	1.0000	0.4997	−0.00011	—	—	—
1.00	1.0000	0.5000	—	—	—	—

$k = R_i/R_0$	ε_6	ε_7	ε_8	ε_9	ε_{10}
0.01	−0.000132	0.0000191	−0.00000239	0.00000026	−0.00000003
0.10	−0.000036	0.0000104	−0.00000060	0.00000004	—
0.20	−0.000016	0.0000045	−0.00000020	0.00000001	—
0.30	−0.000007	0.0000019	−0.00000005	—	—
0.40	−0.000002	0.0000006	—	—	—
0.50	—	—	—	—	—
0.60	—	—	—	—	—
0.70	—	—	—	—	—
0.80	—	—	—	—	—
0.90	—	—	—	—	—
1.00	—	—	—	—	—

* Evaluated from numerical data for power law fluids of Fredrickson and Bird [6]. Reproduced with permission from W. Kozicki and C. Tiu [46], Copyright 1971, The Canadian Society for Chemical Engineering.

Table 6
Refined Geometric Parameters for Rectangular Ducts*

E	ε_0	ε_1	ε_2	ε_3
0.0	1.0000	0.5000	—	—
0.25	0.8730	0.7665	−0.0140	−0.0036
0.50	0.7967	0.1749	−0.0046	−0.0016
0.75	0.7424	0.1620	−0.0035	0.0026
1.00	0.7326	0.1561	−0.0108	0.0001

* Evaluated from the solutions of Schechter [9] and of Wheeler and Wissler [10] for pseudoplastic (power law) fluids. Reproduced with permission from W. Kozicki and C. Tiu [46], Copyright 1971, The Canadian Society for Chemical Engineering.

ratio E and flow behavior index n, were used in evaluation of the geometric parameters for rectangular channels:

$$\sum_{j=0}^{s} \varepsilon_j \frac{s!}{(s-j)!} = \frac{(f \cdot Re)^s}{\left[\dfrac{4(1+E)}{E}\right]^{1+s}} \tag{182}$$

Geometric parameters ε_i for rectangular conduits are presented in Table 6. The evaluations extend only to ε_3, corresponding to the range of n covered by the available data.

Evaluations of ε_i for elliptical and triangular geometries are not available. The original first order prediction method in terms of the geometric parameters a and b gives excellent agreement [21, 28] with published results for these geometries.

Comparisons with Predictions

For a detailed discussion of the accuracy of the predictions by the refined geometric parameter method, refer to the original papers [30, 46]. Since their data were utilized in evaluation of the ε_i, the predictions for flow of pseudoplastic power law fluids in concentric annuli agree with the results of Fredrickson and Bird [6]. It should be noted that Fredrickson and Bird's evaluations have been shown by Vaughn and Bergman [86] to disagree with experimental data in the region of low shear rates because of the deviation of the flow from power law behavior. Figure 10 compares the predictions by the refined method using only the primary geometric parameters ε_0 and ε_1 with interpolated values of Fredrickson and Bird [6] for annular flow of dilatant fluids with n > 1. The first-order approximation using only ε_0 and ε_1 is seen to give excellent agreement with the results of Fredrickson and Bird. The maximum deviation is now less than 1%, compared with a maximum disagreement of 10% at k = 0.01 by the original 2-parameter method. Since the simplified expression in terms of the primary parameters ε_0 and ε_1 is the same as the original expression which uses a and b, the significant improvement is due to the use of the primary parameters ε_0 and ε_1 in place of the previous parameters a and b.

The agreement is excellent in comparisons of Ellis fluid annular flow with the solutions obtained by McEachern [8] for $\alpha = 2$ and 3 [46]. The same agreement is observed between the present prediction of Rabinowitsch fluid flow in concentric annuli utilizing four geometric parameters and the solution of Rotem [29].

The original solution in terms of the parameters a and b was shown to give a good representation of non-Newtonian flow in rectangular conduits, with a maximum disagreement with analytical and experimental data of less than 5%. The new geometric parameters ensure a higher accuracy in prediction of non-Newtonian flow through rectangular ducts, as corroborated by the recent data of Hartnett et al. [27] seen in Figure 6.

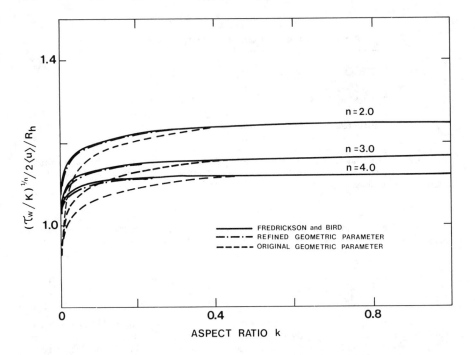

Figure 10. Comparisons of improved and original geometric parameter method with solution of Fredrickson and Bird [6] for a dilatant fluid. (Reproduced with permission from W. Kozicki and C. Tiu [46], Copyright 1971, The Canadian Society for Chemical Engineering).

In summary, the refined geometric parameter method gives excellent predictions of non-Newtonian rectilinear flow in conduits when using the number of geometric parameters ε_i determined by the non-Newtonian character of the fluid, and also when using only the primary parameters ε_0 and ε_1 corresponding to the first-order solution. The latter result indicates that the accuracy of the prediction by the original 2-parameter method can be significantly improved by using ε_0 and ε_1 in place of b and a, when available. It also provides a firm basis for the use of the 2-parameter method for characterization of flow geometries and for applying the technique to packed bed and porous media flows of time-independent fluids.

Friction Factor—Reynolds Number Considerations

The following analysis is confined to rectilinear flow in open or closed conduits. The extension to flow in packed beds or porous media is straightforward.

The friction factor is defined by:

$$f = \frac{2\bar{\tau}_w}{\rho(\langle u \rangle - \bar{u}_w)^2} = \frac{16(\tau/\omega)}{4R_h\rho(\langle u \rangle - \bar{u}_w)} \tag{183}$$

and the Reynolds number is defined in accordance with the following relationship, resulting in laminar flow:

$$Re^* = \frac{16}{f} = \frac{4R_h\rho(\langle u \rangle - \bar{u}_w)}{(\tau/\omega)} = 2\rho\tau R_h^2\left(\frac{\omega}{\tau}\right)^2 \tag{184}$$

This Reynolds number definition which yields a single relationship for laminar flow, $f = 16/Re^*$, which is applicable to all fluid models and all shapes of cross section, also results in a critical Reynolds number marking the transition to turbulent flow in the range 1,800–3,000 for most geometries.

For the Meter fluid model, the Reynolds number expressions become:

$$Re^* = \frac{4R_h\rho(\langle u \rangle - \bar{u}_w)}{\eta_o} \cdot \Delta \tag{185}$$

and

$$Re^* = \frac{2\rho\tau_m R_h^2}{\eta_o^2}\left(\frac{\tau}{\tau_m}\right)\cdot \Delta^2 \tag{186}$$

respectively, where the interaction parameter Δ for the Meter model is the summation with respect to the index j in Equation 172. The approximate expressions for Δ for other fluid models are readily determined as $\Delta = \eta_o(\omega/\tau)$, from the corresponding general solutions.

Equation 185 contains the usual grouping of terms associated with a Reynolds number, whereas Equation 186 contains an expression corresponding to the quantity $D^2\tau_m\rho/\eta_o^2$ employed by Meter [51] in a similar connection involving the flow of a non-Newtonian polymer solution in a circular conduit. It is noted that Equation 186 contains only τ, whereas Equation 185 requires a knowledge of both τ and ω (or $\langle u \rangle - \bar{u}_w$). Hence, the explicit Reynolds number expressions for individual fluid models (e.g., Equations 185 and 186) are difficult to use. It is simpler to calculate ω for the particular fluid model assuming laminar flow, which can then be verified by calculation of the Reynolds number using the defining equation, Equation 184. For the case of viscoelastic fluid flow in non-circular conduits in which secondary flow effects are negligible, the existence of laminar flow can be established by evaluation of the friction factor, Equation 183, in accordance with the procedure developed by Meter [51] for circular conduits.

Example 3: Prediction of Flow of Ellis and Meter Fluids in an Annulus Using Refined Geometric Coefficients

A 0.3% aqueous solution of hydroxyethyl cellulose, high viscosity grade, is flowing in a concentric annulus with aspect ratio $k = 0.1$ and hydraulic radius $R_h = 2.30 \times 10^{-3}$ m. Compute the average velocity when the potential gradient (pressure gradient in horizontal flow) is 8,700 N/m³ using:

(a) The Ellis model representation of the viscosity function ($\eta_o = 0.023$ Pa.s, $\tau_{1/2} = 9.20$ Pa and $\alpha = 2$).

(b) The viscosity function given by the general Meter model ($\eta_o = 0.023$ Pa.s, $\tau_m = 7.80$ Pa, $\alpha = 2$ and $\eta_\infty = 0.00120$ Pa.s).

The applicable values of the geometric coefficients are: $\varepsilon_0 = 1.0000$, $\varepsilon_1 = 0.3964$, $\varepsilon_2 = -0.01690$, $\varepsilon_3 = 0.00438$, $\varepsilon_4 = -0.00073$, $\varepsilon_5 = 0.000208$, $\varepsilon_6 = -0.000036$.

Solution

(a) *The rigorous Ellis fluid solution for* $\alpha = 2$ *is given by:*

$$\omega = \frac{\tau}{\eta_o}\left[\frac{1}{\varepsilon_0 + \varepsilon_1} + \frac{\tau/\tau_{1/2}}{\varepsilon_0 + 2\varepsilon_1 + 2\varepsilon_2}\right]$$

Now, $\tau = \bar{\tau}_w = R_h\left(-\frac{\Delta P}{L}\right) = 2.30 \times 10^{-3} \times 8{,}700 = 20.0$ Pa

Therefore, $\omega = \dfrac{2(\langle u \rangle - \bar{u}_w)}{R_h} = \dfrac{20.0}{0.023}\left[\dfrac{1}{1.3964} + \dfrac{20.0/9.20}{1 + 2(0.3964) - 2(0.0169)}\right] = 1{,}700$ s^{-1}

and, neglecting surface effects ($\bar{u}_w = 0$):

$$\langle u \rangle = \frac{1,700}{2} \times 2.30 \times 10^{-3} = 1.954 \text{ m/s.}$$

The corresponding simplified solution, in terms of the primary coefficients, is:

$$\omega = \frac{\tau}{\eta_0} \left[\frac{1}{\varepsilon_0 + \varepsilon_1} + \frac{\tau/\tau_{1/2}}{\varepsilon_0 + 2\varepsilon_1} \right]$$

yielding $\langle u \rangle = 1.930$ m/s, which compares favorably with the previous value.

(b) For a Meter fluid with $\alpha = 2$ (Peek-McLean model), we use the solution given by [30]:

$$\omega = \frac{\tau}{\eta_0} \sum_{j=0}^{\infty} \left[\frac{1}{M_j} + \frac{\tau/\tau_m}{N_j} \right] \left[-\left| \frac{\tau}{\tau_m} \right| \left(\frac{\eta_\infty}{\eta_0} \right) \right]^j$$

where $M_j = \sum_{k=0}^{j+1} \varepsilon_k \binom{j+1}{k} k! = \sum_{k=0}^{j+1} \varepsilon_k \frac{(j+1)!}{(j+1-k)!}$

and $N_j = \sum_{k=0}^{j+2} \varepsilon_k \binom{j+2}{k} k! = \sum_{k=0}^{j+2} \varepsilon_k \frac{(j+2)!}{(j+2-k)!}$

Evaluations of M_j and N_j for $j = 0$ to 4 are given in Table 7.

Since $\tau = 20.0$ Pa, $\dfrac{\tau}{\tau_m} = \dfrac{20.0}{7.80} = 2.565$ and $\dfrac{\tau}{\eta_0} = \dfrac{20.0}{0.023} = 870 \text{ s}^{-1}$

Also, $\left(\dfrac{\tau}{\tau_m} \right) \left(\dfrac{\eta_\infty}{\eta_0} \right) = 2.565 \times \dfrac{0.0012}{0.023} = 0.134$

Table 7
Tabulation of the Quantities M_j and N_j^*

j	M_j	$\left(\dfrac{1}{M_j}\right)_{calc.}$
0	$\varepsilon_0 + \varepsilon_1$	0.7161
1	$\varepsilon_0 + 2\varepsilon_1 + 2\varepsilon_2$	0.5685
2	$\varepsilon_0 + 3\varepsilon_1 + 6\varepsilon_2 + 6\varepsilon_3$	0.4730
3	$\varepsilon_0 + 4\varepsilon_1 + 12\varepsilon_2 + 24\varepsilon_3 + 24\varepsilon_4$	0.4048
4	$\varepsilon_0 + 5\varepsilon_1 + 20\varepsilon_2 + 60\varepsilon_3 + 120\varepsilon_4 + 120\varepsilon_5$	0.3516

j	N_j	$\left(\dfrac{1}{N_j}\right)_{calc.}$
0	$\varepsilon_0 + 2\varepsilon_1 + 2\varepsilon_2$	0.5685
1	$\varepsilon_0 + 3\varepsilon_1 + 6\varepsilon_2 + 6\varepsilon_3$	0.4730
2	$\varepsilon_0 + 4\varepsilon_1 + 12\varepsilon_2 + 24\varepsilon_3 + 24\varepsilon_4$	0.4048
3	$\varepsilon_0 + 5\varepsilon_1 + 20\varepsilon_2 + 60\varepsilon_3 + 120\varepsilon_4 + 120\varepsilon_5$	0.3516
4	$\varepsilon_0 + 6\varepsilon_1 + 30\varepsilon_2 + 120\varepsilon_3 + 360\varepsilon_4 + 720\varepsilon_5 + 720\varepsilon_6$	0.3069

Substituting these values in the above equation gives:

$$\omega = 870[2.174 - 1.782(.134) + 1.511(0.134)^2 - 1.307(0.134)^3 + 1.139(0.134)^4 - \cdots]$$
$$= 1,703 \text{ s}^{-1}$$

and an average velocity of 1.959 m/s, which is in excellent agreement with the previous rigorous result. This is as expected, since the viscosity curves for the two fluid models in the shear stress range up to 20.0 Pa are essentially the same. It provides an excellent check of the Meter fluid solution required for prediction of the flow characteristics in the shear stress range approaching the upper limiting viscosity η_∞. The simplicity of the calculation in part (a) shows the advantage of using the Ellis model solution in the low and intermediate shear stress range.

The corresponding simplified solution in terms of the primary coefficients for $\alpha = 2$ is given by:

$$\omega = \frac{\tau}{\eta_o} \sum_{j=0}^{\infty} \left[\frac{1}{\varepsilon_0 + \varepsilon_1(j+1)} + \frac{\tau/\tau_m}{\varepsilon_0 + \varepsilon_1(j+2)} \right] \left[-\left(\frac{\tau}{\tau_m}\right)\left(\frac{\eta_\infty}{\eta_o}\right) \right]^j$$

$$= 870[2.146 - 1.729(0.134) + 1.449(0.134)^2 - 1.247(0.134)^3 + 1.095(0.134)^4 - \cdots]$$
$$= 1,685 \text{ s}^{-1}$$

which yields $\langle u \rangle = 1.938$ m/s (compared with 1.930 in the previous approximation).

The concordance with the Ellis model results and the accuracy of the approximation using just the primary coefficients is noteworthy.

Evaluating the Reynolds number:

$$\text{Re}^* = 2\rho\tau R_h^2 \left(\frac{\omega}{\tau}\right)^2 = 2(1,000)(20.0)(0.0023)^2 \left(\frac{1,700}{20.0}\right)^2 = 1,530$$

which indicates laminar flow. For a viscoelastic polymer solution, we require the friction factor evaluated as:

$$f = \frac{16}{\text{Re}^*} = \frac{16}{1,530} = 0.01046$$

assuming laminar flow. The corresponding turbulent flow friction factor is 0.0049 [51]. Since the former value lies above the value determined by the turbulent flow friction factor curve, we conclude the flow is laminar.

NOTATION

a, b	original geometric parameters	b_q	parameters in Reiner-Rivlin model, $q = 1, 2 \ldots k$; $q = 1$ reduces to Rabinowitsch model
a_0, b_0	geometric parameters in Blake-Kozeny and Kozeny-Carman bed models		
a', b'	major and minor axes in an elliptical duct	c	contour of flow conduit
A	cross-sectional area of flow channel or die	D	pipe diameter; with subscript e denotes equivalent diameter
A_j	cross-sectional area of liquid jet	D_p	particle or packing diameter
A_r	A/A_j, area ratio	e	$\varepsilon/(1-\varepsilon)$, local void ratio; L_e/D, Bagley end correction factor
A_r'	velocity ratio defined by Equation 95	E	H/W, aspect ratio of rectangular duct
		f	friction factor

F   force

g   acceleration due to gravity

h   elevation relative to a horizontal datum

H   height of rectangular duct or distance separating two parallel plates; liquid depth in open circular channel

k R_i/R_0, annular aspect ratio; permeability defined by Equation 134

k_i $2(a + b)$, Kozeny constant

k_0 shape factor in Blake-Kozeny and Kozeny-Carman bed models

K   fluid consistency coefficient in power law model

K^* consistency index defined by Equation 73

K' consistency index defined for circular pipe flow

L   length of flow channel; subscript e denotes equivalent length

n   flow behavior index in power law model

n^* index defined by Equation 49

n' index defined for circular pipe flow, Equation 31

N   number of sides in regular polygonal conduit

p   wetted perimeter; pressure; points of contact in star-shaped conduit; function defined by Equation 175

P $p + \rho gh$, hydrostatic potential

q $\varepsilon\langle u\rangle$, superficial average velocity

q_w $\varepsilon\bar{u}_w$, superficial effective velocity at the wall

Q   volumetric flow rate

r   radial position; function defined by Equation 176

r   superficial particle velocity; with subscript i denotes velocity component

R   pipe radius; with subscript i or o denotes inner or outer radius of an annulus

R_h hydraulic radius

Re*   Reynolds number defined by Equation 71, 74, or 184

Re_p^* Reynolds number defined by Equation 138 or 139

Re' Reynolds number for circular pipe flow

s   position variable along the contour of flow channel; reciprocal of flow behavior index in power law model, $1/n$

s' position variable from the axis or plane of symmetry for circular tube and parallel plates

S $R_h/2a$, characteristic length; distance between centers of two cylinders (Figure 2)

S_0 surface area per unit volume of solids

T   thrust; tortuosity

T_w function defined by Equation 84

t   time

u   axial velocity

u_i velocity component

u_j velocity of liquid jet at its fully relaxed state

$\langle u\rangle$ average velocity

u_m maximum velocity

u_w effective velocity at the wall; an over-bar denotes the average quantity along the contour or wetted perimeter

u_r $\bar{u}_w/\langle u\rangle$, velocity ratio

W   width of flat plate or rectangular channel

y $R - r$, distance measured from tube wall

z   axial coordinate

Greek Symbols

α index in Ellis and Meter models; half vertex angle of an isosceles triangular duct (Figure 2)

β b'/a', aspect ratio of elliptical duct

Δ $\eta_0(\omega/\tau)$, interaction parameter

δ thickness of anomalous zone; subscripts a and s denote adsorption and solvent zones, respectively

γ magnitude of shear rate

ε porosity

ε_i geometric coefficients defined in the refined method; $i = 1, 2 \ldots$

η non-Newtonian viscosity

η_B plastic viscosity in Bingham model

η_D Darcy viscosity defined by Equation 125

η_R Rabinowitsch viscosity defined by Equation 54

η_0, η_∞ lower and upper limiting viscosity

θ angle of inclination to the vertical

μ Newtonian viscosity; subscript s denotes solvent viscosity; subscript o denotes Reiner-Rivlin or Rabinowitsch parameter

ζ b/a or $\varepsilon_0/\varepsilon_1$, aspect factor; subscript o refers to channels in Blake-Kozeny and Kozeny-Carman models

π total stress tensor; subscript ij denotes component

ρ density

τ deviatoric stress tensor; subscript ij denotes component

τ magnitude of shear stress

$\tau_{1/2}, \tau_m$ parameters in Ellis and Meter models, respectively

τ_y yield stress in Bingham model

Φ mapping tensor defined by Equation 143

ω $2(\langle u \rangle - \bar{u}_w)/R_h$

Functions

$f(\tau \text{ or } \tau_{rz})$ function of shear stress characterizing the viscous flow behavior of the fluid, denoting velocity gradient

$g(\tau_{rz}, y)$ correction function due to a surface effect

$\gamma(s, k)$ annular function defined by Fredrickson and Bird [6]

Subscripts

i, j   indices denoting 1, 2; x, y; or r, θ

w   conditions at the wall

BK   Blake-Kozeny bed model

KC   Kozeny-Carman bed model

REFERENCES

1. Bird, R. B., Armstrong, R. C., and Hassager, O., *Dynamics of Polymeric Liquids: Volume I-Fluid Mechanics*, John Wiley, N.Y. (1977) p. 5.
2. Oldroyd, J. G., "The Interpretation of Observed Pressure Gradients in Laminar Flow of Non-Newtonian Liquids Through Tubes," *J. Colloid Sci.*, Vol. 4 (1949) pp. 333–342.
3. Jastrzebski, Z. D., "Entrance Effects and Wall Effects in an Extrusion Rheometer During the Flow of Concentrated Suspensions," *Ind. Engng. Chem. Fundls.*, Vol. 6 (1967) pp. 445–454.
4. Kozicki, W., et al., "Anomalous Effects in Laminar Capillary Flow of Polymer Solutions," *Chem. Engng. Sci.*, Vol. 25 (1970) pp. 41–52.
5. Kozicki, W., Hsu, C. J., and Pasari, S. N., "Evaluation of Polymer Adsorption-Gel Formation and Slip in Polymer Solution Flows," Proc. of 35th Canadian Chem. Engng. Conf. Vol. 1, Calgary (1985) pp. 116–121.
6. Fredrickson, A. G., and Bird, R. B., "Non-Newtonian Flow in Annuli," *Ind. Engng. Chem.*, Vol. 50 (1958) pp. 347–352.
7. Hanks, R. W., and Larsen, K. M., "The Flow of Power-Law Non-Newtonian Fluids in Concentric Annuli," *Ind. Engng. Chem. Fundls.*, Vol. 18 (1979), pp. 33–35.
8. McEachern, D. W., "Axial Laminar Flow of a Non-Newtonian Fluid in an Annulus," *AIChE J.*, Vol. 12 (1966) pp. 328–332.
9. Schechter, R. S., "On the Steady Flow of a Non-Newtonian Fluid in Cylinder Ducts," *AIChE J.*, Vol. 7 (1961) pp. 445–448.
10. Wheeler, J. A., and Wissler, E. H., "The Friction Factor-Reynolds Number Relation for the Steady Flow of Pseudoplastic Fluids Through Rectangular Ducts" *AIChE J.*, Vol. 11 (1965) pp. 207–216.
11. Mizushina, T., Mitsuishi, N., and Nakamura, R., "On the Flow of Power Model Fluid in Elliptic Tube," *Kaguku Kogaku* (*Chem. Engng. Japan*), Vol. 28 (1964) pp. 648–652.
12. Mitsuishi, N., Kitayama, Y., and Aoyagi, Y., "Non-Newtonian Flow in Non-Circular Ducts," *Kaguku Kogaku* (*Chem. Engng. Japan*), Vol. 31 (1967) p. 570.

13. Tiu, C., and Bhattacharya, S. N., "Flow Behavior of Power-Law Fluids in the Entrance Region of Annuli," *Can. J. Chem. Engng.*, Vol. 51 (1973) pp. 47–54.

14. Bhattacharya, S. N., and Tiu, C., "Development Pressure Profile for Non-Newtonian Flow in an Annular Duct," *AIChE J.*, Vol. 20 (1974) pp. 154–158.

15. Tiu, C., and Bhattacharya, S. N., "Developing and Fully Developed Velocity Profiles of Power-Law Fluids in an Annulus," *AIChE J.*, Vol. 20 (1974) pp. 1140–1144.

16. Curr, R. M., Sharma, D., and Tatchell, D. G., "Numerical Prediction of Some Three-Dimensional Boundary Layers in Ducts," *Computer Methods in Appl. Mech. and Engng.*, Vol. 1 (1972) pp. 143–158.

17. Liu, J., and Shah, V. L., "Numerical Solution of a Casson Fluid Flow in the Entrance of Annular Tubes," *Appl. Sci. Res.*, Vol. 31 (1975) pp. 213–222.

18. Salem, E., and Embaby, M. H., "Theoretical and Experimental Investigations of Non-Newtonian Fluid Flow Through Non-Circular Pipes," *Appl. Sci. Res.*, Vol. 33 (1977) pp. 119–139.

19. Chandrupatla, A. R., and Sastri, V. M. K., *Numerical Methods in Laminar and Turbulent Flow*, Pentech Press (1978) p. 547.

20. Tachibana, M., Kawabata, N., and Genno, H., "Steady Laminar Flow of Power-Law Fluids in the Inlet Region of Rectangular Ducts," *J. of Rheol.*, Vol. 3 (1986) pp. 517–538.

21. Kozicki, W., Chou, C. H., and Tiu, C., "Non-Newtonian Flow in Ducts of Arbitrary Cross-Sectional Shapes," *Chem. Engng. Sci.*, Vol. 21 (1966) pp. 665–679.

22. Miller, C., "Predicting Non-Newtonian Flow Behavior in Ducts of Unusual Cross Section," *Ind. Engng. Chem. Fundls.*, Vol. 11 (1972) pp. 524–528.

23. Hanks, R. W., "Prediction of Non-Newtonian Flow Behavior in Ducts of Non-Circular Cross Section," *Ind. Engng. Chem. Fundls.*, Vol. 13 (1974) pp. 62–68.

24. Lenk, R. S., "Rheology and Die Design," Chap. 6, *Developments in Plastics Technology-I*, Whelan, A., and Dunning, D. J., ed., Appl. Science Publishers (1982).

25. Liu, T. J., "Fully Developed Flow of Power-Law Fluids in Ducts," *Ind. Engng. Chem. Fundls.*, Vol. 22 (1983) pp. 183–186.

26. Kostic, M., and Hartnett, J. P., "Predicting Turbulent Friction Factors of Non-Newtonian Fluids in Non-Circular Ducts," *Int. Comm. Heat and Mass Transfer*, Vol. 11 (1984).

27. Hartnett, J. P., Kwack, E. Y., and Rao, B. K., "Hydrodynamic Behavior of Non-Newtonian Fluids in a Square Duct," *J. of Rheol.*, Vol. 30(S) (1986) pp. S45–S59.

28. Tiu, C., Kozicki, W., and Phung, T. Q., "Geometric Parameters for Some Flow Channels," *Can. J. Chem. Engng.*, Vol. 46 (1968) pp. 389–393.

29. Rotem, Z., "Non-Newtonian Flow in Annuli," *Trans. ASME: J. Appl. Mech.*, Vol. 84E (1962) pp. 421–424.

30. Kozicki, W., and Tiu, C., "Flow of Complex Fluids in Open and Closed Conduits, Packed Beds and Porous Media," *Can. J. Chem. Engng.*, Vol. 51 (1973) pp. 359–363.

31. Bird, R. B., Stewart, W. E., and Lightfoot, E. N., *Transport Phenomena*, John Wiley, N.Y. (1960).

32. Lundgren, T. S., Sparrow, E. M., and Starr, J. B., "Pressure Drop Due to the Entrance Region in Ducts of Arbitrary Cross Section," *Trans. ASME: J. Basic Engng.*, Vol. 86D (1964) pp. 620–626.

33. Sparrow, E. M., and Loeffler, A. L., "Longitudinal Laminar Flow Between Cylinders Arranged in Regular Array," *AIChE J.*, Vol. 5 (1959) pp. 325–330.

34. Galloway, L. R., and Epstein, N., "Longitudinal Flow Between Cylinders in Square and Triangular Arrays in a Tube with Square-Edge Entrance," Proc. on Transport Phenomena, AIChE-I. Chem. E. Symp. Series No. 6, London (1965) 6:3.

35. Shih, F. S., "Laminar Flow in Axisymmetric Conduits by a Rational Approach," *Can. J. Chem. Engng.*, Vol. 45 (1967) pp. 285–294.

36. Chow, V. T., *Open Channel Hydraulics*, McGraw-Hill, N.Y. (1959) pp. 24–29.

37. Straub, L. G., Silberman, E., and Nelson, H. C., "Open-Channel Flow at Small Reynolds Numbers," *Trans. ASCE*, Vol. 123 (1958) pp. 685–714.

38. Severs, E. T., and Austin, J. M., "The Thermal Incline: A Means of Measuring Viscosities of Plastisols at Elevated Temperatures," *Trans. Soc. Rheol.*, Vol. 1 (1957) pp. 191–202.

39. Pasley, R. R., and Slibar, A., "Flow of an Imcompressible Viscoplastic Layer," *Trans. Soc. Rheol.*, Vol. 2 (1958) pp. 255–262.
40. Hoffman, R. D., and Myer, R. R., "Flow Down an Inclined Plane," *Trans. Soc. Rheol.*, Vol. 4 (1960) pp. 119–129.
41. Astarita, G., Marrucci, G., and Palumbo, G., "Non-Newtonian Gravity Flow Along Inclined Plane Surfaces," *Ind. Engng. Chem. Fundls.*, Vol. 3 (1964) pp. 333–339.
42. Matsuhisa, S., and Bird, R. B., "Analytical and Numerical Solutions for Laminar Flow of the Non-Newtonian Ellis Fluid," *AIChE J.*, Vol. 11 (1965) pp. 588–595.
43. Kozicki, W., and Tiu, C., "Non-Newtonian Flow Through Open Channels," *Can. J. Chem. Engng.*, Vol. 45 (1967) pp. 127–133.
44. Sestak, J., "Flow of Non-Newtonian Fluids in Open Circular Channels," *Can. J. Chem. Engng.*, Vol. 52 (1974) pp. 670–672.
45. Metzner, A. B., and Reed, J. C., "Flow of Non-Newtonian Fluids-Correlation of the Laminar, Transition, and Turbulent-flow Regions," *AIChE J.*, Vol. 1 (1955) pp. 434–440.
46. Kozicki, W., and Tiu, C., "Improved Parametric Characterization of Flow Geometries," *Can. J. Chem. Engng.*, Vol. 49 (1971) pp. 562–569.
47. Dodge, D. W., and Metzner, A. B., "Turbulent Flow of Non-Newtonian Systems," *AIChE J.*, Vol. 5 (1959) pp. 189–204.
48. Jones, O. C., "An Improvement in the Calculation of Turbulent Friction in Rectangular Ducts," *J. Fluid Engng.*, Vol. 98 (1976) pp. 173–181.
49. Hanks, R. W., "The Laminar-Turbulent Transition for Flow in Pipes, Concentric Annuli, and Parallel Plates," *AIChE J.*, Vol. 9 (1963) pp. 45–48.
50. Ryan, N. W., and Johnson, M. M., "Transition from Laminar to Turbulent Flow in Pipes," *AIChE J.*, Vol. 5 (1959) pp. 433–435.
51. Meter, D. M., "Tube Flow of Non-Newtonian Polymer Solutions: Part I. Laminar Flow and Rheological Models; Part II. Turbulent Flow," *AIChE J.*, Vol. 10 (1964) pp. 878–884.
52. Gaskins, F. H., and Philippoff, W., "Behavior of Jets of Viscoelastic Fluids," *Trans. Soc. Rheol.*, Vol. 3 (1959) pp. 181–203.
53. Harris, J., "Flow of Viscoelastic Liquids from Tubes," *Nature*, Vol. 190 (1961) p. 993.
54. Harris, J., "The Measurement of a Normal Stress Effect Using a Tube Viscometer," Proc. 4th Int. Cong. on Rheol., Part 3, E. H. Lee, ed., J. Wiley, N.Y. (1965) pp. 417–428.
55. Metzner, A. B., et al., "A Method for the Measurement of Normal Stresses in Simple Shearing Flow," *Trans. Soc. Rheol.*, Vol. 5 (1961) pp. 133–147.
56. Metzner, et al., "Dynamic of Fluid Jets: Measurement of Normal Stresses at High Shear Rates," IUTAM Int. Symp. on Second Order Effects in Elasticity, Plasticity and Fluid Dynamics, Haifa (1962) pp. 650–667.
57. Ginn, R. F., and Metzner, A. B., "Normal Stresses in Polymeric Solutions," Proc. 4th Int. Cong. on Rheol., Part 2, E. H. Lee ed., J. Wiley, N.Y. (1965) pp. 583–601.
58. Shertzer, C. R., and Metzner, A. B., "Measurement of Normal Stresses in Viscoelastic Materials at High Shear Rates," Proc. 4th Int. Cong. on Rheol., Part 2, E. H. Lee, ed., J. Wiley, N.Y. (1965) pp. 603–618.
59. Middleman, S., "Profile Relaxation in Newtonian Jets," *Ind. Engng. Chem. Fundls.*, Vol. 3 (1964) pp. 118–122.
60. Kozicki, W., and Tiu, C., "Expansion-Contraction Behavior of Non-Newtonian Jets," *Chem. Engng. Sci.*, Vol. 23 (1968) pp. 1165–1172.
61. Kozicki, W., and Tiu, C., "Expansion-Contraction Behavior of Non-Newtonian Jets," Chem. Engng. Prog. Symp. Series, Vol. 65, No. 91 (1969) pp. 75–81.
62. Middleman, S., and Gavis, J., "Expansion and Contraction of Capillary Jets of Newtonian Liquids," *Phys. Fluids*, Vol. 4 (1961) pp. 355–359; pp. 963–971.
63. Slattery, J., and Schowalter, W. R., "Effect of Surface Tension in the Measurement of Average Normal Stress at the Exit of a Capillary Tube Through an Analysis of the Capillary Jet," *J. Appl. Polym. Sci.*, Vol. 8 (1964) pp. 1941–1947.
64. Fredrickson, A. G., *Principles and Applications of Rheology*, Prentice-Hall, N.J. (1964) pp. 214–221.

65. Bagley, E. B., "End Corrections in the Capillary Flow of Polyethylene," *J. Appl. Phys.*, Vol. 28 (1957) pp. 624–627.
66. Sadowski, T. J., and Bird, R. B., "Non-Newtonian Flow Through Porous Media. I. Theoretical," *Trans. Soc. Rheol.*, Vol. 9, Part II (1965) pp. 243–250.
67. Sadowski, T. J., "Non-Newtonian Flow Through Porous Media. II. Experimental," *Trans. Soc. Rheol.*, Vol. 9 Part II (1965) pp. 251–271.
68. Christopher, R. H., and Middleman, S., "Power-Law Flow Through a Packed Tube," *Ind. Engng. Chem. Fundls.*, Vol. 4, No. 4 (1965) pp. 422–426.
69. McKinley, R. M., et al., "Non-Newtonian Flow in Porous Media," *AIChE J.*, Vol. 12, No. 1 (1966) pp. 17–20.
70. Hassel, H. L., and Bondi, A., "Mixing of Viscous Non-Newtonian Fluids in Packed Beds," *AIChE J.*, Vol. 11, No. 2 (1965) pp. 217–221.
71. Savins, J. G., "Non-Newtonian Flow Through Porous Media," *Ind. Engng. Chem.*, Vol. 61, No. 10 (October 1969) pp. 18–47.
72. Kemblowski, Z., and Michniewicz, M. A., "A New Look at the Laminar Flow of Power Law Fluids Through Granular Beds," *Rheol. Acta*, Vol. 18, No. 6 (1979) pp. 730–739.
73. Marshall, R. J., and Metzner, A. B., "Flow of Viscoelastic Fluids Through Porous Media," *Ind. Engng. Chem. Fundls.*, Vol. 6 (1967) pp. 393–400.
74. Sheffield, R. F., and Metzner, A. B., "Flow of Nonlinear Fluids Through Porous Media," *AIChE J.*, Vol. 22 (1976) pp. 736–744.
75. Kozicki, W., Hsu, C. J., and Tiu, C., "Non-Newtonian Flow Through Packed Beds and Porous Media," *Chem. Engng. Sci.*, Vol. 22 (1967) pp. 487–502.
76. Dupuit, A. J. E. J., *Etudes Théoriques et Pratiques sur le Mouvement des Eaux* (1863).
77. Carman, P. C., *Flow of Gases Through Porous Media*, Academic Press, N.Y. (1956).
78. Shirato, M., et al., "Constant Pressure Filtration of Power-Law Non-Newtonian Fluids," *J. Chem. Engng. Japan*, Vol. 10 (1977) pp. 54–60.
79. Shirato, M., Aragaki, T., and Iritani, E., "Analysis of Constant Pressure Filtration of Power-Law Non-Newtonian Fluids," *J. Chem. Engng. Japan*, Vol. 13 (1980) pp. 61–66.
80. Tiu, C., Quinn, B. W., and Uhlherr, P. H. T., "Flow of Non-Newtonian Fluids Through Beds of Various Packing Geometries," Proc. 5th Australasian Conf. in Hydraulic and Fluid Mech., Christchurch, N.Z. (1974) p. 411.
81. Kozicki, W., "Recent Developments in Filtration of Non-Newtonian Fluids," Filtration Symposium Nagoya (1986) pp. 121–129.
82. Kozicki, W., Rao, A. R. K., and Tiu, C., "Filtration of Polymer Solutions," *Chem. Engng. Sci.*, Vol. 27 (1972) pp. 615–625.
83. Tiller, F. M., and Shirato, M., "The Role of Porosity in Filtration: VI. New Definition of Filtration Resistance," *AIChE J.*, Vol. 10 (1964) pp. 61–67.
84. Kozicki, W., "Filtration in Non-Newtonian Media," Proc. World Cong. III of Chem. Engng., Vol. 3, Tokyo (1986) pp. 134–137.
85. Kozicki, W., "Filtration in Non-Newtonian Media," Chap. 23, *Encyclopedia of Fluid Mechanics*, Vol. 6, N. P. Cheremisinoff, ed., Gulf Publishing Co. (1986) pp. 965–985.
86. Vaughn, R. D., and Bergman, P. D., "Laminar Flow of Non-Newtonian Fluids in Concentric Annuli," *Ind. Engng. Chem. Proc. Des. Dev.*, Vol. 5 (1966) pp. 44–47.

CHAPTER 9

HYDRODYNAMICS OF BUBBLES AND DROPS IN RHEOLOGICALLY COMPLEX LIQUIDS

R. P. Chhabra

Department of Chemical Engineering
Indian Institute of Technology
Kanpur, India

CONTENTS

INTRODUCTION

Numerous chemical and processing engineering operations involve relative motion between bubbles or drops and a continuous phase. Examples of such flows include gas-liquid contacting (particularly bubble columns), fermentation, liquid-liquid extraction, activated sludge processes, emulsion polymerization, and production of paints and liquid detergents. Obviously, an adequate understanding of the hydrodynamical aspects of bubble and drop motion is a prerequisite to understanding and rationalizing the other transport processes (heat and mass transfer) with or without chemical reactions. Indeed, considerable efforts have been expended in exploring and understanding the fluid mechanics of such two phase systems. The resulting voluminous literature has been summarized in an excellent treatise of Clift et al. [28], and in a number of review papers [32, 34–36, 53, 87]. A quick perusal of the book of Clift et al. [28] reveals that our understanding of the behavior of bubble or drop motion in Newtonian continuous phases is adequate, and a coherent picture has emerged.

In recent years, there has been a recognition of the fact that not all materials of industrial importance exhibit Newtonian behavior; indeed, fermentation broths, paints and detergents, and the intermediate products of emulsion polymerization, etc., display complex rheological behavior, as pointed out by Mashelkar [68], Blanch and Bhavaraju [14], Kemblowski and Kristiansen [62], and others [78].

In comparison to the state-of-the-art of bubble or drop motion in Newtonian continuous phases, the fluid mechanics of non-Newtonian liquids involving the motion of bubbles or drops is in an elementary stage. While the pragmatic importance of such flows has already been emphasized, even from a purely fundamental point of view, the motion of a single bubble or drop constitutes an

Table 1
Summary of Investigations Concerning the Motion of Bubbles and Drops in Non-Newtonian Media

Investigator	Nature of Work	Details of the Study	Fluid Model Used	Comments
Acharya et al. [3]	Experimental	Air/aqueous solutions of CMC, PEO and PAA	Power law	Data on bubble shapes, volume-velocity, and drag coefficient
Acharya et al. [4]	Experimental	Drops of $C_2H_4Br_2$, C_6H_5Cl, $C_6H_5NO_3$ in aqueous solutions of CMC, PEO and PAA	Power law	Shape and terminal velocity measurement
Aiba et al. [5]		Gas bubbles	Power law	Mass transfer studies
Ajayi [6]	Theoretical	Fluid spheres	Oldroyd fluid model	Expressions for drag coefficient and shape of fluid spheres.
Astarita [7]	Theoretical	Gas bubbles	Maxwell fluid model	Qualitative results on the role of viscoelasticity
Astarita and Appuzzo [8]	Experimental	Bubbles rising in aqueous solutions of CMC, carbopol and ET 497	Power law	Velocity-volume data and shapes of bubbles
Barnett et al. [9]	Experimental	Bubbles moving in aqueous solutions of CMC	Power law and Ellis fluid	Shapes of bubbles and mass transfer data
Bhavaraju et al. [11]	Theoretical	Single bubble and swarms of bubbles	Power law and Bingham plastic	Drag coefficient and mass transfer study
Bisgaard and Hassager [13]	Experimental	Air bubbles moving in aqueous solutions of Polyacrylamide	—	Flow visualization and measurement of axial velocity component
Calderbank et al. [18]	Experimental	CO_2 bubbles in aqueous solutions of Polyox	Power law	Shape of bubbles, velocity-volume and mass transfer data
Carreau et al. [20]	Experimental	—	—	Velocity-volume data for bubbles in viscoelastic fluids

Reference	Type	System	Model	Description
Chhabra [22]	Theoretical	Swarms of bubbles	Power law	Lower bound on drag coefficient
Chhabra and Dhingra [23]	Theoretical	Newtonian fluid spheres	Carreau fluid model	Upper and lower bounds on drag coefficient
Dang et al. [29]	Theoretical	Bubbles	Power law	Mass transfer accompanied by Chemical reaction
Dekee et al. [30]	Experimental	Bubbles moving in aqueous solutions of CMC and PAA	Power law	Data on velocity-volume and coalescence in viscoelastic fluids
Fararoui and Kintner [31]	Experimental	Drops of nitrobenzene and tetrachloroethane in aqueous solutions of CMC	Power law	Data on shapes and drag coefficients
Grace [38]	—	—	—	A brief review of the information available in this area
Gummalam and Chhabra [41]	Theoretical	Swarms of spherical bubbles	Power law	Upper and lower bound on terminal velocity
Gummalam, Harayan and Chhabra [42]	Theoretical	Swarms of spherical bubbles	Carreau fluid model	Upper and lower bound on drag coefficient
Gürkan and Wellek [43]	Theoretical	Fluid spheres	Power law	Mass transfer in creeping flow
Hassager [47]	Theoretical	Single bubble	Rivlin-Ericksson fluid model	Effect of the two normal stress differences on the shape of bubbles
Hassager [48]	Experimental	Air bubble in separan solution	—	Reported the presence of a oscillating negative wake behind a bubble
Hirose and Moo-Young [49]	Theoretical	Single bubble	Power law	Solved linearized equations of motion to obtain expressions for drag coefficient and Sherwood number
Jarzebski and Malinowski [51, 52]	Theoretical	Swarms of bubbles and drops	Power law	Analyzed steady flow using linearization method and variational principles. Also studied transient motion

Table 1 (Continued)
Summary of Investigations Concerning the Motion of Bubbles and Drops in Non-Newtonian Media

Investigator	Nature of Work	Details of the Study	Fluid Model Used	Comments
Kawase and Hirose [54]	Semi-theoretical	Drops in non-Newtonian medium	Power law	Empirical correlation for drag coefficient
Kawase and Ulbrecht [58]	Theoretical	Fluid spheres	Power law	Expressions for drag coefficient and Sherwood number in creeping flow
Kawase and Ulbrecht [57]	Theoretical	Bubble	Power law	Explained the discontinuity in volume-velocity data via a combination of viscous and surface tension effects
Kawase and Ulbrecht [59]	Theoretical	Drops	Power law	Considered the effect of surfactants on the terminal velocity of liquid drops
Kawase and Moo-Young [55]	Theoretical	Bubbles	Carreau and Ellis fluid models	Approximate expressions for drag coefficient
Leal et al. [63]	Experimental	Bubbles in aqueous solutions of Separan AP-30	No specific fluid model used	Attempted to explain the discontinuity in volume-velocity data
Macedo and Yang [65]	Experimental	Air bubbles in aqueous solutions of Separan AP-30	Power law	Drag coefficient data
Marrucci et al. [57]	Experimental	Drops in non-Newtonian media	Power law	Drag coefficient data
Mhatre and Kintner [69]	Experimental	Drops of nitrobenzene and carbontetrachloride in aqueous solutions of sodium carboxymethyl cellulose and Lytron 890	Power law	Shapes and drag coefficient data

Reference	Type	System	Fluid model	Description
Mitsuishi et al. [70]	Experimental	Air bubble and drops (CCl_4) in aqueous solutions of CMC and PEO	Sutterby fluid model	Empirical expression for drag coefficient
Mohan [72]	Theoretical	Newtonian fluid sphere	Power law	Upper bound on drag coefficient
Mohan et al. [73]	Experimental	Drops in aqueous solutions of PEO, PAM and CMC	Power law	Terminal velocity and drag coefficient data
Mohan and Raghuraman [74]	Theoretical	Fluid spheres	Ellis fluid model	Numerical results on drag coefficient at intermediate values of Reynolds number
Mohan and Venkateswarlu [77]	Theoretical	Fluid spheres	Ellis fluid model	Lower bound on drag coefficient of
Mohan and Venkateswarlu [75, 76]	Theoretical	Newtonian fluid spheres	Power law and Ellis fluid model	Employed variational principles to obtain upper and lower bounds on drag coefficients in creeping flow
Moo-Young and Hirose [79]	Theoretical	Bubble	Maxwell fluid	Mass transfer study
Moo-Young et al. [80]	Theoretical	—	—	Mass transfer characteristics in creeping flow
Nakano and Tien [81]	Theoretical	Newtonian fluid spheres	Power law	Employed a combination of variational and Galerkin method to obtain an upper bound on drag coefficient of a fluid sphere in creeping flow
Nakano and Tien [82]	Theoretical	Newtonian fluid spheres	Power law	Extended their previous work to the intermediate values of Reynolds number
Philippoff [83]	Experimental	Air bubbles rising through time-dependent fluids	—	Bubble shapes
Schafermeyer et al. [88]	Experimental	Droplets	—	Mass transfer data

Table 1 (Continued)
Summary of Investigations Concerning the Motion of Bubbles and Drops in Non-Newtonian Media

Investigator	Nature of Work	Details of the Study	Fluid Model Used	Comments
Shirotsuka and Kawase [91]	Theoretical	Fluid spheres	Both phase assumed to be power law type fluids	Drag coefficient and mass transfer characteristics
Shirotsuka and Kawase [92]	Theoretical	Droplet moving in a viscoelastic fluid	—	Highlighted the role of fluid elasticity on the drag coefficient
Tiefenbruck and Leal [95]	Theoretical	Solid sphere and gas bubbles	Oldroyd fluid model	Numerical results on the detailed kinematics of flow fields
Wagner and Slattery [96]	Theoretical	Non-Newtonian droplet moving in a viscoelastic fluid	3rd order Coleman-Noll	Approximate expressions for drag and shape
Warshay et al. [97]	Experimental	—	—	Wall effects and shape of fluid spheres
Wellek and Gürkan [98]	Theoretical	Fluid spheres	Power law	Obtained Sherwood number as a function of n and Re for high Reynolds number flow
Wellek and Huang [99]	Theoretical	Fluid spheres	Power law	Obtained Sherwood number in creeping flow regime
Wilkinson [100]	Experimental	Droplets	—	A tail behind the drops was observed
Yamanaka and Mitsuishi [101]	Experimental	Air bubbles and CCl_4 drops in aqueous solutions of CMC and PEO	Sutterby fluid model	Drag coefficient-Reynolds number data
Zana and Leal [102, 103]	Experimental and theoretical	CO_2 gas bubbles moving in aqueous solutions of Separan AP-30	Oldroyd fluid model	Mass transfer characteristics and the relevance of viscoelasticity

interesting example of a strongly non-viscometric flow wherein major macroscopic differences are observed from its Newtonian counterpart.

This chapter aims to provide a comprehensive review of the information that has become available during the past three decades. It should be pointed out however, that the ensuing discussion is restricted to the situations where there is a relative motion between the dispersed and continuous phases. Neither the formation of bubbles (or drops) nor the growth or decay of a stationary bubble or drop is considered here; these aspects have been adequately covered in other references [46, 84, 90]. Furthermore, the consideration is limited to the case of non-Newtonian continuous phase, whereas the dispersed phase is always assumed to be Newtonian in character.

A brief summary of the investigations pertaining to the motion of bubbles or drops in non-Newtonian media is presented in Table 1. An examination of the contents of this table suggests that the research efforts have been directed at elucidating the following four aspects of the problem:

1. Shapes of bubbles and drops.
2. Velocity-volume (or size) relationship.
3. Terminal velocity or drag coefficient measurements as functions of the relevant physical and kinematic parameters.
4. Mass transfer characteristics.

Each of the above-mentioned phenomena will now be dealt with in great detail. We further divide the presentation of information into two categories, viz., single bubbles or drops, and ensembles of drops or swarms of bubbles

BEHAVIOR OF SINGLE BUBBLES AND DROPS

Shape Regimes

A number of investigators [3, 4, 8, 9, 18, 31, 67, 69, 71, 83, 97] have reported the shapes of bubbles and drops moving in non-Newtonian fluids. It is now generally agreed that qualitatively dissimilar shapes are obtained for drops moving in Newtonian and non-Newtonian liquids. Typical shapes of drops in Newtonian and non-Newtonian liquids, as observed and reported by Fararoui and Kintner [31], are drawn in Figure 1; similar results have been reported by other investigators. For a Newtonian drop moving in another Newtonian fluid, the distortion from spherical shape gradually progresses to spheroidal to oblate ellipsoidal, as the drop size increases. Further increase in drop size results in a flattened rear surface of the drop, which eventually folds in as a depression

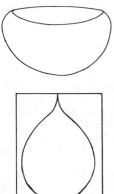

Figure 1. Comparison of drop shapes in Newtonian and non-Newtonian liquids. Top: Drop of nitrobenzene + tetrachloroethane in corn syrup (d = 3.06 cm, U = 1.5 cm/sec). Bottom: Drop of water in caster oil (d = 2.12 cm, U = 1.52 cm/sec). (Replotted from [31].)

in very large drops. Depending upon the physical properties of the continuous phase and drop liquid, a different sequence of changes in shape has been observed for drops falling through non-Newtonian continuous phase. For a drop size such that the surface forces are overcome by the viscous forces, the shape changes from spherical to ovate with increasing drop size. Further increase in drop size will result in tear drop shape with trailing filament. Finally, for very large drops, the ratio of vertical to horizontal diameters decreases, and the rear surface begins to fold inward. Mohan [71] has presented good photographs of the shapes of drops in non-Newtonian polymer solutions. This sequence of shape transitions is qualitatively consistent with the analyses of Ajayi [6] and Wagner and Slattery [96].

Likewise, numerous researchers [3, 8, 9, 18] have visually observed the shapes of bubbles rising in shear thinning and viscoelastic type non-Newtonian liquids. The salient features are: at very low values of Reynolds number, the surface tension forces tend to maintain the spherical shape, which undergoes gradual transition to tear shape, oblate spheroidal, and finally spherically capped. This is essentially the same sequence as that observed in the case of gas bubbles in Newtonian liquids.

No description of the shapes of drops and bubbles in rheologically complex liquids would be complete without mentioning the two "weird" effects which are not seen in the fluid mechanics of Newtonian continuous phase. The first one concerns the motion of a drop in a non-Newtonian liquid. Wilkinson [100] reported the presence of a "long tail" attached to a drop, and the other phenomenon is the so-called "negative wake" behind a gas bubble. Furthermore, Hassager [48] reported the presence of circulation currents in the wake. As of now, no physical explanation has been attempted for either of these observations.

All studies concerning the shapes of drops and bubbles have been qualitative in nature, and also entail a degree of inherent arbitrariness and subjectivity. Although it is evident that the shape of a bubble or drop is likely to have significant bearing on the calculations of the rates of transfer process, as conjectured by Barnett et al. [9] and Calderbank et al. [18], no attempt has been made to seek quantitative information.

At this stage it is instructive to consider the following dimensionless groups, which are likely to exert some influence in governing the shapes of bubbles and drops:

1. Reynolds number, $\mathrm{Re} = \dfrac{\rho_c U_D d_d}{\mu_c}$

2. Eötvös number, $E_o = \dfrac{\Delta\rho\, g d_d^2}{\sigma}$

3. Morton number, $M = \dfrac{g\mu_c^4 \Delta\rho}{\rho_c^3 \sigma}$

4. Viscosity ratio, $X_E = \dfrac{\mu_d}{\mu_c}$

5. Density ratio, $\gamma = \dfrac{\rho_d}{\rho_c}$

where the subscripts c and d denote the continuous and dispersed phases, respectively, and the symbols are defined in the notation. As pointed out by Grace [38], some other dimensionless groups are currently in use, but these can be obtained by suitable rearrangements of the five groups listed above. For instance, the commonly used drag coefficient can be obtained by combining E_o, Re, and M numbers. It is also obvious that not all dimensionless groups would always be important. For example, for the case of a bubble rising through a liquid, $X_E \approx 0$; $\gamma \approx 0$; and $\Delta\rho$ may be approximated as ρ_c.

Based on the use of these dimensionless groups, Grace et al. [40] constructed a so-called "shape regime map," which has been found to be quite satisfactory for Newtonian fluid particles moving in another Newtonian liquid. Further refinements to the map of Grace et al. [40] have been suggested by Bhaga and Weber [10] and by Grace et al. [39].

Intuitively, it appears that these dimensionless groups, with suitable modifications for the non-Newtonian properties, should also be useful in quantitative description of the shapes observed in non-Newtonian continuous phases, though additional groups may be needed while dealing with viscoelastic types of non-Newtonian liquids [102]. However, sufficient information is presently not available to pursue this line of approach. Acharya et al. [3] have provided some tentative empirical correlations, which purport to quantify the shapes of bubbles observed in viscoinelastic and visco-elastic liquids.

Volume-Velocity Relationship

Among the various phenomena that are exhibited by gas bubbles and liquid drops moving in non-Newtonian media, perhaps the most striking is the occurrence of an "abrupt" transition in terminal velocity when measured as a function of size, particularly in the case of gas bubbles. For example, Astarita and Appuzzo [8], who were the first to note this phenomenon, found a six-to ten-fold increase in bubble velocity at the critical bubble volume for an air bubble in a 0.5% aqueous solution of a commercial polymer J-100. Since then, similar results have been reported by Calderbank et al. [18], Leal et al. [63], and Acharya et al. [3] for a wide variety of test liquids. However, no such discontinuity was reported by Macedo and Yang [65] and Dekee et al [30]. Nor is this effect observed for dissolving gas bubbles [102]. Figure 2 shows the typical results for gas bubbles moving in a non-Newtonian continuous phase (aqueous solutions of ET 497), where indeed a sudden six fold increase is evident in the bubble velocity.

Similarly, numerous investigators have studied the analogous situation of Newtonian drops moving in non-Newtonian media. Not all authors have presented the corresponding results on volume-velocity; Mhatre and Kintner [69], Warshay et al. [97], Fararoui and Kintner [31], and Mohan [71] have all reported a steep, but not abrupt, change in the terminal velocity of Newtonian drops moving in non-Newtonian media. Data plotted in Figure 3 exemplify this behavior.

It is to be expected that this change in size-velocity relationship would play a significant role in controlling the rates of transport processes, e.g., mass and heat transfer. Therefore, a complete understanding of this phenomenon is desirable.

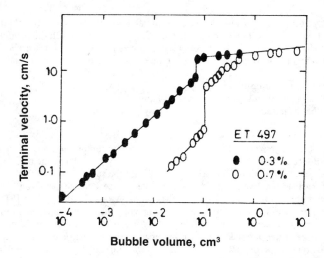

Figure 2. Typical bubble velocity—bubble volume data for air bubbles rising through aqueous solutions of ET497 [8].

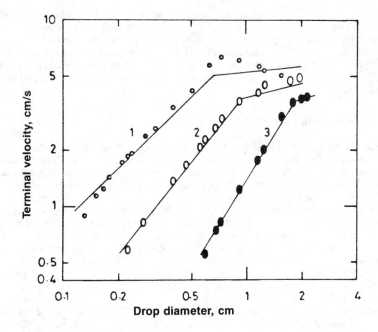

Figure 3. Typical drop velocity—drop size data for aniline drops moving in Newtonian and non-Newtonian liquids. (1) water; (2) 0.5% sodium alignate solution; (3) 10% CMC solution. (Data replotted from [71].)

In the case of drops motion, the change in terminal velocity is so small and the transition so gradual that it has not caused much concern, whereas the peculiarity (both the magnitude and the abruptness of change) in the case of gas bubbles continues to intrigue the researchers. Pertaining to the abrupt transition in volume-velocity data, there are three basic questions one may ask:

1. Why does the transition occur?
2. At what value of the bubble volume does it happen?
3. What is the magnitude of the change in velocity?

We shall take up these issues one by one.

It is now generally agreed that the transition is a manifestation of the change of boundary condition at the surface of the bubble [3, 8, 102]. At low values of the volume, the bubble behaves like a rigid sphere, i.e., the condition of "no-slip" is satisfied at the surface; and with an increase in volume, the fluid particle acts like a bubble with a mobile surface, and the condition of "no-shear" is satisfied at the bubble surface. Based on this hypothesis, Astarita and Appuzzo [8] showed that the slope of log (velocity) against log (volume of bubble) data should be equal to $(n + 1)/3n$ for gas bubbles rising in power law liquids. Indeed, they found that there was close correspondence between the values of the power law index n obtained from viscometric data and those extracted from log (velocity) — log (volume) plots. The match was particularly impressive for purely shear thinning liquids; and the correspondence was very poor for viscoelastic liquids, although Acharya et al. [3] reported a perfect agreement between the values of n obtained by the two methods for viscoelastic as well as viscoinelastic continuous phases. Astarita and Appuzzo [8] cited this as a proof in favor of their thesis for the change in velocity. However, a more rigorous and direct test of the notion (that the discontinuity is due to the change in boundary conditions) was provided by the experiments of Leal et al. [63], who measured the terminal velocities of gas bubbles (in the no-slip range) and of glass spheres of comparable sizes in an aqueous solution of Separan AP-30. They found that after correcting for the density difference, the terminal velocities of glass spheres were *precisely equal* to those of gas bubbles as long as the latter were smaller than the critical size. Thus, there is no doubt or confusion regarding the question of why the transition occurs.

Now we turn our attention to the prediction of the critical volume or size of the bubble at which the transition takes place. Evidently, a priori calculation of the critical size would help delineate the flow regime for a given bubble moving in a liquid of known rheology and physical properties. Acharya et al. [3] and Kawase and Ulbrecht [57] have recently reviewed the literature on this aspect of the phenomenon, and have proposed a criterion based on the analysis of Bond and Newton [17] and of Levich [64], originally developed for the surfactant free fluid spheres moving in Newtonian media. According to these theories, the critical radius of the bubble is given by:

$$R_c = \left(\frac{\sigma}{\Delta\rho g}\right)^{1/2} \tag{1}$$

In the case of gas bubbles, the density difference term $\Delta\rho$ can be approximated as ρ_c. Indeed, Acharya et al. [3] found that the agreement between the critical radii calculated using Equation 1 and those observed experimentally was as good as can be expected. The range of rheological properties covered by Acharya et al. [3] and others [8, 18, 63, 102] showing good correspondence is truly remarkable. It is tempting to conclude that the rheology plays no role in governing the critical size at which the transition occurs. This is somewhat surprising. Furthermore, perhaps other reasons for the success of Equation 1 are that the polymer solutions used to date do not have surface tensions too different from that of pure water, nor do the densities of such polymer solutions deviate significantly from that of water.

Kawase and Ulbrecht [57] extended the analysis of Schechter and Farley [89] to include power model liquids as continuous phases, and suggested that the bubble will behave as a rigid sphere when the surface tension gradient at the particle surface is given by:

$$\alpha = -R^2 g \,\Delta\rho\, \frac{n(n+2)}{(7-4n)}\left[\left(\frac{2}{3}\right)^n \frac{n(-8n^2+4n+13)}{(-22n^2+29n+2)} - 1\right] \tag{2}$$

This equation offers the key to the understanding of the interaction between the surface tension gradient (α), the shear dependent viscosity of the continuous phase (n), the bubble size (R), and the density difference ($\Delta\rho$) in the mechanism of the velocity transition. The existing information on the bubble motion is such that quantitative comparisons between experiments and Equation 2 are not yet possible.

And now to the final question of the estimation of the magnitude of change in the velocity. Perhaps this is the most difficult exercise in this problem. It is appropriate to recall that a bubble moving in a Newtonian liquid undergoes a jump of 50% in the terminal velocity when the transition takes place from no slip condition to "shear free" surface; i.e., all other things being equal, in the shear free zone, a bubble has 1.5 times the terminal velocity in "no-slip" regime. This directly follows from the analyses of Hadamard and Rybczynski (e.g., see Clift et al. [28]) for fluid spheres and that of Stokes for rigid spheres. Since the magnitude of jump in the velocity of a bubble in non-Newtonian media is *always* greater than the factor of 1.5, this must imply that the extra jump is attributable to the rheological characteristics of the continuous phase. Zana and Leal [102] were probably the first ones to examine this phenomenon quantitatively. They carried out a systematic numerical study, and concluded that the use of the shear dependent viscosity alone explains only about 30% of the change observed in the velocity of a bubble, and one must invoke the fluid viscoelasticity to explain the remaining 70% of the magnitude of change. They added weight to their intuitive assertion by performing an order-of-magnitude analysis wherein they observed that the presence of even a small degree of fluid viscoelasticity (essentially the primary normal stress difference) was sufficient to acount for the large observed jumps in the velocity, as reported by Astarita and Appuzzo [8].

On the other hand, in most experimental studies relating to the bubble motion, aqueous solutions of high molecular weight polymers including Separan AP-30, Polyox WSR-301, and Carboxymethyl cellulose have been used as continuous media. Most such solutions are known to exhibit both shear dependent viscosity as well as viscoelasticity (measured as primary normal stress difference), whence the deviations in the bubble behavior from their Newtonian counterpart are due to the combined effects of shear thinning and viscoelasticity. It is not at all possible to isolate the contributions of these two non-Newtonian effects. From an experimental point of view, it is now possible to examine the role of fluid elasticity in the near absence of shear thinning by using the so-called Boger fluids [16]; such fluids were employed by Chhabra et al. [27] to elucidate the influence of elasticity on the drag coefficient of a sphere. At this stage, therefore, it is not possible to predict a priori the magnitude of change in the terminal velocity for a given gas-liquid system.

This section may thus be concluded by reiterating that the reasons for the abrupt change in the terminal velocity are satisfactorily understood, and a priori prediction of the critical size at which the transition takes place is also possible. However, the calculation of the magnitude of the change in velocity is not yet possible.

Drag Coefficient—Reynolds Number Relationship

In situations involving the relative motion between single bubbles or drops and a continuous phase, the quantity of primary interest is the terminal rise (or fall) velocity as a function of the pertinent variables, e.g., rheology, bubble size, etc. This information is conveniently expressible in terms of the usual Reynolds number and drag coefficient in conjunction with other dimensionless groups involving interfacial tension, viscosity ratio, etc. In the case of non-Newtonian ambient fluids, the rheological model parameters give rise to additional dimensionless groups, such as Ellis number and Weissenberg number.

In the mechanics of non-Newtonian liquids, it is customary to divide the fluid response into two components, viz., shear thinning and viscoelasticity. Whereas such a distinction may not be strictly justifiable on scientific grounds, it often does provide a reasonable understanding of the problem. Therefore, this sub-division of fluid behavior is adopted here. We, however, begin by presenting a terse discussion of the drag coefficient-Reynolds number relationships for drops and bubbles moving in Newtonian ambient fluids. This, in turn, facilitates the presentation of results for non-Newtonian media.

Newtonian Continuous Phase

From a theoretical standpoint, the problem is rather complex, since two equations of motion (one for each phase) have to be solved simultaneously. General solutions are therefore not possible. For the idealized case of a spherical fluid sphere, with clean interface moving slowly (under creeping flow) in an infinite extent of another immisicible Newtonian fluid, Hadamard and Rybczynski (e.g., see Clift et al. [28]) presented the following result:

$$C_D = \frac{24}{Re} Y \tag{3}$$

$$\text{and} \quad Y = \frac{2 + 3X_E}{3 + 3X_E} \tag{4}$$

where C_D is the usual drag coefficient; Re is the Reynolds number ($\rho_c U_d d_d / \mu_c$), and X_E is the ratio of the viscosity of the dispersed phase to that of the continuous phase. Evidently, for a gas bubble rising through a liquid, $X_E \ll 1$ and Equation 4 yields $Y = 2/3$; whereas for a solid sphere, $X_E \gg 1$ and the value of Y approaches unity as expected. Equations 3 and 4 are expected to hold for Re $\ll 1$. Typical comparisons between experiments and the predictions of Equations 3 and 4 are shown in Figures 4-6, covering the complete range of the values of X_E, i.e., solid spheres, gas bubbles, and

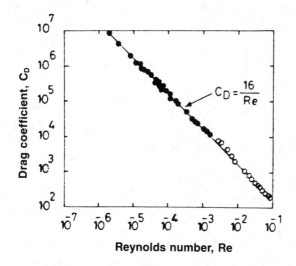

Figure 4. Drag coefficient—Reynolds number relationship for fluid spheres moving in jelly. ($\bigcirc$) drop ($\mu_c = 60.9$ P); ($\ominus$) drop ($\mu_c = 3,065$ P); ($\oplus$) air bubble ($\mu_c = 3,065$ P). (Replotted from [101].)

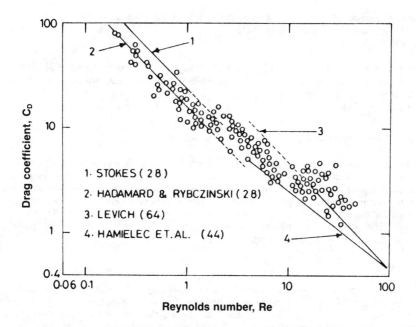

Figure 5. Typical drag coefficient—Reynolds number data for CO_2 bubbles in a 21% aqueous sucrose solution [50].

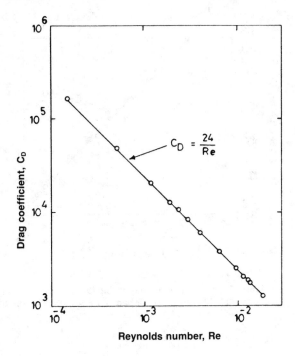

Figure 6. Typical drag coefficient—Reynolds number data for solid spheres moving in a Newtonian corn syrup. (Redrawn from [27].)

liquid droplets. Numerous workers [1, 44, 85, 86] have sought approximate numerical solutions to the governing equations and have reported the values of drag coefficient as a function of Reynolds number and other variables. These as well as other related studies have been adequately summarized by Clift et al. [28].

Shear Thinning Continuous Phase—Creeping Flow Region

A shear thinning fluid is characterized by an apparent viscosity (shear stress divided by shear rate) which decreases with increasing shear rate and exhibits constant viscosities both in the limits of zero and infinite shear rates. Such a behavior has been illustrated by Boger [15]. Numerous models of varying complexity which purport to fit the experimental data on steady shear stress-shear rate are available in the literature. Excellent descriptions of these models are available [12, 93]. One of the simplest, and perhaps the most widely used, non-Newtonian fluid model is the so-called power law fluid model. In steady shear, it is written as:

$$\tau = m(\dot{\gamma})^n \tag{5}$$

where m and n are respectively known as the fluid consistency and fluid-flow behavior index. For a shear thinning fluid, n < 1. Although the limitations of Equation 5 are rather well known, it continues to be used as a starting point for theoreticians to keep the mathematical complexity at a tractable level. Even when the power law model is used to represent the shear thinning behavior of an ambient liquid involving the motion of bubbles or drops, the relevant governing equations are hopelessly complex, and are not amenable to exact analysis. Consequently, numerous workers, as listed in Table 1, have obtained results with varying degrees of approximations. Some [22, 23, 41, 42, 51, 70, 72–77, 81] have used the well known variational principles [94] whereas others [11, 49, 52, 55, 58, 96] have resorted to some kind of linearization of the governing equations, and perturbation methods. In most cases, the creeping flow has been considered, and the results have been expressed as a correction factor X, which now becomes a function of the power law index (n). For a power law fluid, Equation 3 is rewritten as:

$$C_D = \frac{24}{Re_{PL}} YX \tag{6}$$

$$Re_{PL} = \frac{\rho_c U_d^{2-n} d_d^n}{m_c} \tag{7}$$

$$X_E = \frac{\mu_d}{m_c \left(\dfrac{U_d}{d_d}\right)^{n-1}} \tag{8}$$

and $X = X(n)$ \hfill (9)

Clearly, for a Newtonian continuous phase, X = 1. The application of variational principles [94] yield supper and lower bounds on the value of X, and generally the use of arithmetic average is suggested. Whereas, the analyses based on perturbation schemes or linearization techniques yield closed-form expressions for X, albeit rather cumbersome in form. Some of the representative analytical expressions are summarized in Table 2, and are plotted in Figure 7 for the creeping motion of Newtonian fluid spheres in power law fluids. An examination of the expressions given in Table 2 and the results shown in Figure 7 suggest that the drag force experienced by a fluid sphere is augmented as a result of the shear thinning behavior, albeit there is very little quantitative agreement among various theories listed in Table 2. One notable exception is the expression given by Fararoui and Kintner [31] which predicts a reduction in drag with increasing shear thinning. As mentioned earlier, although the power law model provides the simplest representation of shear rate dependent viscosity, its inability to predict a finite viscosity in the limit of vanishingly small shear rates has raised some doubts about its suitability in analyzing creeping flow situations. This deficiency has been convincingly demonstrated in the case of creeping flow around a rigid sphere [21, 26], and it is readily acknowledged that a fluid model containing zero shear viscosity is likely to yield more realistic results than the power law model. One such model which has found widespread use [21, 23–25] is the Carreau viscosity equation [19]. In steady shear, it is expressed as:

$$\frac{\eta - \eta_\infty}{\eta_0 - \eta_\infty} = [1 + (\lambda\dot\gamma)^2]^{(n-1)/2} \tag{10}$$

Usually [2, 15] η_∞ is much smaller than η_0, whence Equation 10 may be simplified as:

$$\eta = \eta_0 [1 + (\lambda\dot\gamma)^2]^{(n-1)/2} \tag{11}$$

Chhabra and Dhingra [23] have employed the variational principles referred to in the foregoing to obtain upper and lower bounds on a Newtonian fluid sphere (droplet or bubble) moving slowly in a continuous phase whose steady shear behavior could be represented by Equation 11. Once again, the results are expressed in the form of X, which now becomes a function of viscosity ratio (X_E), fluid flow index (n), and a new dimensionless parameter E, involving λ as ($2\lambda U_d/d_d$). Evidently, the increasing values of E, and the decreasing values of n, denote the increasing importance of non-

Table 2
Representative Empirical and Theoretical Expressions for Drag Coefficients of Bubbles and Drops in Non-Newtonian Fluids in Creeping Flow Regime

Investigator	Type of Work	Fluid Models Used	Equation	Range of Applicability and Remarks
Fararoui and Kintner [31]	Experimental	Power law	$X = 3^{n-1}$	Creeping flow for bubbles and drops
Kawase and Moo-Young [55]	Theoretical	Carreau fluid model	$X = \dfrac{2}{3}(3E^2)^{(n-1)/2}\dfrac{(13 + 4n - 8n^2)}{(2n + 1)(n + 2)}$	For Bubbles, and E > 10 and E1 > 10
		Ellis fluid model	$X = \dfrac{2}{3}\left(\dfrac{3}{E1^2}\right)^{(1-\alpha)/2}\left(\dfrac{-11 + 28\alpha - 8\alpha^2}{(4 - \alpha)(5 - 2\alpha)}\right)$	
Hirose and Moo-Young [49]	Theoretical	Power law	$X = (2^n)(3)^{(n-3)/2}\dfrac{(13 + 4n - 8n^2)}{(2n + 1)(n + 2)}$	For bubbles
Bhavaraju et al. [11]	Theoretical	Power law	$X = (2^n)(3)^{(n-3)/2}\{1 - 3.83(n - 1)\}$	For bubbles $1 \geq n \geq 0.7$
Kawase and Hirose [54]	Experimental	Power law	$X = [1 + \{1.1 - 17.6(n - .75)^2\}]$	For bubbles and drops $1 \geq n \geq 0.516$

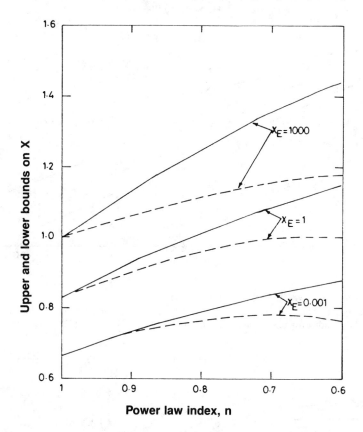

Figure 7. Upper and lower bounds on drag correction factor as functions of power law index n and viscosity ratio X_E. —— upper bound; ----- lower bound.

Newtonian effects. Figures 8-14 show the upper and lower bounds on X as functions of E and n for a range of values of the viscosity ratio (X_E). The two bounds are non-coincident and in absence of any definite information, the use of arithmetic average of the two bounds is recommended. Furthermore, the two bounds become independent of the viscosity ratios both for $X_E < 0.001$ and $X_E > 1,000$; thus these two values must be treated as corresponding to gas bubbles and solid spheres, respectively. Further examination of Figures 8-14 shows that, as expected, when n = 1(for all values of E), the two bounds approach the Newtonian behavior, i.e., X = 1. The upper bound starts to deviate from its Newtonian value at about E ~ 0.5. On the other hand, the lower bound approaches (n + 1)/2 times the Newtonian value in the limit of E → O for n ≠ 1. The reasons for this behavior are not at all clear at this stage; similar results have been reported by Mohan and Venkateswarlu [76] for the case of an Ellis model fluid. The effect of the viscosity ratio (X_E) on the drag correction factor X is shown in Figure 15 for a fixed value of E.

In a recent paper, Kawase and Moo-Young [55] have studied the creeping flow of gas bubbles rising through Carreau model fluids, and have derived the following analytical expression:

$$X = \frac{2}{3}(3E^2)^{(n-1)/2}\frac{(13 + 4n - 8n^2)}{(2n + 1)(n + 2)} \tag{12}$$

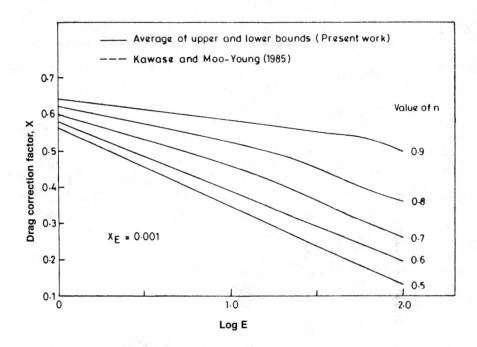

Figure 8. Average of upper and lower bounds on drag correction factor as a function of the fluid behavior index n and dimensionless parameter E for $X_E = 0.001$ [23].

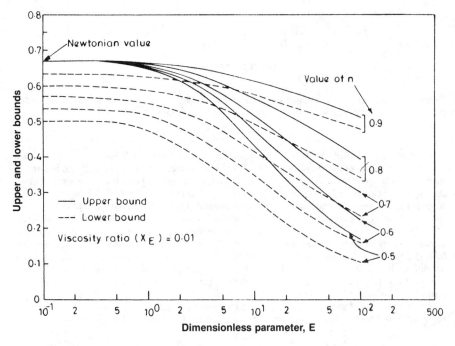

Figure 9. Upper and lower bounds on drag correction factor as functions of the fluid behavior index n and dimensionless parameter E for $X_E = 0.01$ [23].

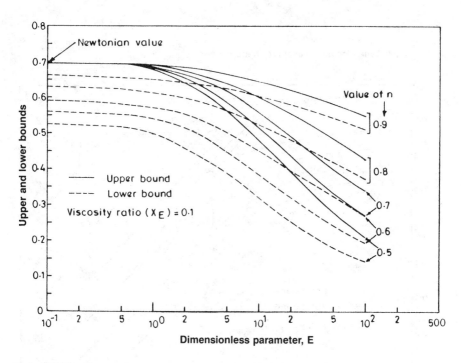

Figure 10. Upper and lower bounds on drag correction factor as functions of the fluid behavior index n and dimensionless parameter E for $X_E = 0.1$ [23].

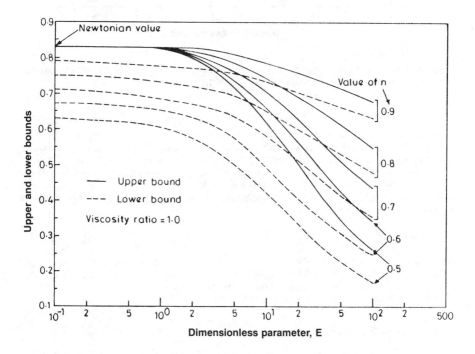

Figure 11. Upper and lower bounds on drag correction factor as functions of the fluid behavior index n and dimensionless parameter E for $X_E = 1$ [23].

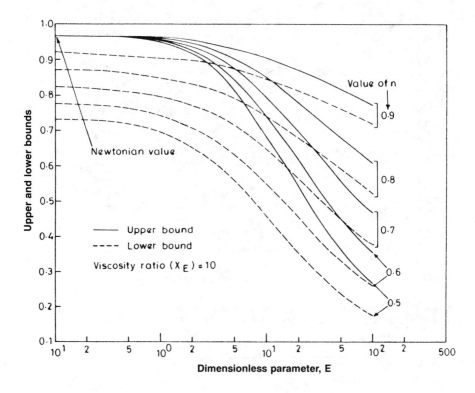

Figure 12. Upper and lower bounds on drag correction factor as functions of the fluid behavior index n and dimensionless parameter E for $X_E = 10$ [23].

Equation 12 was stated to be applicable for the conditions relating to $E > 10$, and the values of n not too different from unity; i.e., only for mildly shear thinning fluids. The predictions of Equation 12 and the theory of Chhabra and Dhingra [23] for $X_E = 0.001$ are compared in Figure 16, where a close correspondence is seen to exist between the two in the overlapping range of conditions. However, the divergence between the two increases for $n < 0.5$.

It is also evident that when $(\lambda\dot{\gamma})^2 \gg 1$, the Carreau Viscosity equation (Equation 11) reduces to the usual two parameter power law model as:

$$\eta = \eta_o(\lambda)^{n-1}(\dot{\gamma})^{n-1} \tag{13}$$

Thus, one would expect that the theory of Chhabra and Dhingra [23] should approach the results obtained using a power law model when sufficiently large values of the dimensionless parameter E are considered. Indeed, in this limiting case, the theory of Chhabra and Dhingra [23] reproduces the results of Mohan [72] and Mohan and Venkateswarlu [75] to within 0.5%.

Comparison with Experiments

Although a considerable amount of experimental work on the motion of drops or bubbles in non-Newtonian media has been reported, in most of these the two parameter power law model

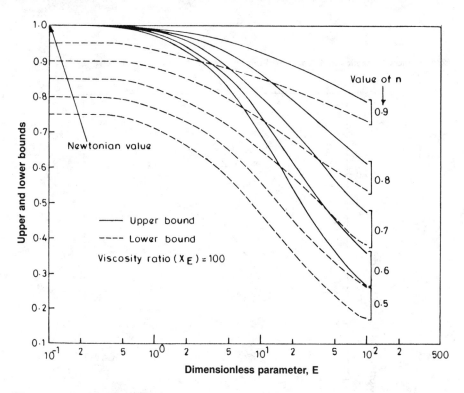

Figure 13. Upper and lower bounds on drag correction factor as functions of the fluid behavior index n and dimensionless parameter E for $X_E = 100$ [23].

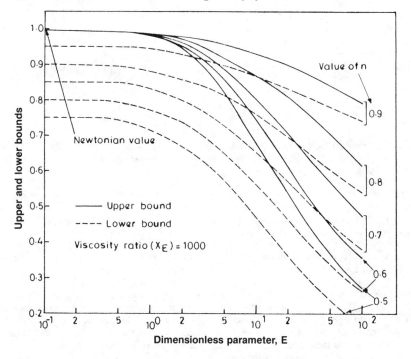

Figure 14. Upper and lower bounds on drag correction factor as functions of the fluid behavior index n and dimensionless parameter E for $X_E = 1,000$ [23].

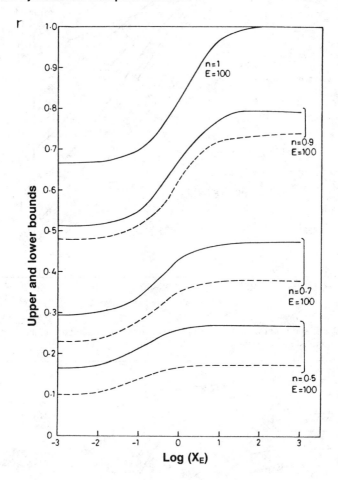

Figure 15. Upper and lower bounds on drag correction factor vs. viscosity ratio for a fixed value of E. (Replotted from [23].) ——— upper bound; −−−− lower bound.

has been used and the values of zero shear viscosities were not given; hence the quantitative comparisons with the theory of Chhabra and Dhingra are not yet possible. Furthermore, a detailed analysis of the experimental data reveals that the value of X_E was in the range of 10^{-4} to 10^{-3}. This is particularly so in the work of Kintner and co-workers [31, 69, 97], Mohan et al. [73], and Acharya et al. [4]. Hence these results really amount to gas bubbles rising through power law liquids. A comparison between the experiments and the theory of Chhabra and Dhingra [23] for large values of E and for $X_E = 0.001$ is presented in Figure 17. The agreement is reasonable.

Extensive data are available on the analogous situation of rigid spheres settling through Carreau model fluids [21], and it is worthwhile to validate the theory of Chhabra and Dhingra [23] in the limit of $X_E = 1,000$. Typical comparisons between experiments and theoretical predictions are depicted in Figure 18; the comparison, once again, is satisfactory. In fact, the theory predicts 150 individual sphere fall tests with an average error of 8%. Thus, the theory of Chhabra and Dhingra [23] performs well in the limiting cases of gaseous bubbles moving in power law fluids, and of the rigid spheres settling in Carreau model fluids.

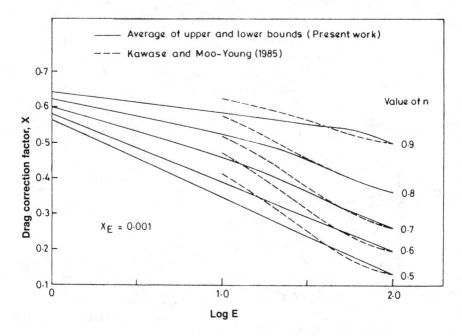

Figure 16. Comparison between the theories of Chhabra-Dhingra [23] and Kawase-Moo-Young [55].

High Reynolds Number Region

In contrast to the creeping flow, much less is known about the motion of bubbles or drops through shear thinning liquids at high values of Reynolds number. Nakano and Tien [82] have obtained approximate solutions to the relevant equations for the fluid sphere motions in power law liquids. They computed the drag coefficient in the range $5 \leq \mathrm{Re}_{PL} < 25$. Subsequently, Mohan and Raghuraman [74] have extended their approach to Ellis model fluids, and presented theoretical values of drag coefficients in the range $10 \leq \mathrm{Re} \leq 50$. Neither of these investigators have reported any comparison with the scant data available in the literature [3, 4, 9, 65]. Macedo and Yang [65] studied the bubble motion in aqueous solutions of Separaran AP-30, and observed that their measurements of drag were in agreement with the theory for solid spheres up to $\mathrm{Re} = 10$. Thus, there is virtually nothing available in terms of predictive methods for drag coefficients outside the creeping flow regime.

Viscoelastic Continuous Phase

Most viscoelastic fluids display shear thinning but in addition, in steady shear, also exhibit unequal normal stresses. During the last decade or so, few attempts have been made to elucidate the role of fluid viscoelasticity on the creeping motion of bubbles or drops in viscoelastic media. To date, most of the analyses [6, 92, 96] have employed perturbation methods. In this approach, the nonlinear term contributions are embodied in the framework of a small parameter perturbation expansion about the corresponding Newtonian kinematics. The analysis of Wagner and Slattery [96], based on the third order fluid of Coleman and Noll for both the phases, is a typical example of this type of approach. Other attempts include the works of Ajayi [6], Hirose and Moo-Young

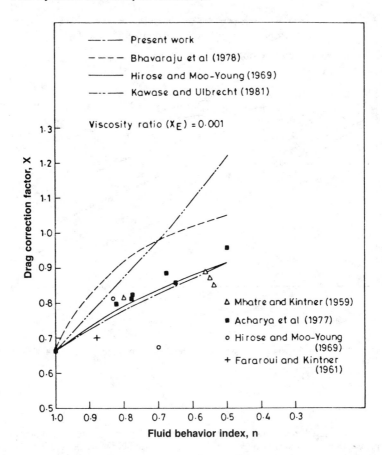

Figure 17. Comparison between the theory of Chhabra and Dhingra [23] and experimental data on moving gas bubbles.

[79], and Shirotsuka and Kawase [92]. All these analyses are valid only for Reynolds numbers and Weissenberg numbers much smaller than unity. The restriction on Reynolds number limits the applicability to creeping flow, while the more severe Weissenberg number limitation restricts the analysis to very low levels of fluid viscoelasticity. Within the range of validity of perturbation expansions, all the above-mentioned treatments predict very little difference between the kinematics for Newtonian and viscoelastic liquids.

Contrasted with these perturbation analyses are the results of Tiefenbruck and Leal [95] who have employed elegant numerical techniques to analyze the creeping motion of a spherical gas bubble through an Oldroyd model fluid. Detailed velocity and stress fields were reported, but the drag force was not noticeably different from that in a Newtonian fluid. In view of the near equivalence of all fluid models to the second order fluid, perhaps it is appropriate to say that the analyses cited above examine the influence of fluid elasticity in the absence of shear thinning behavior, whereas most real fluids exhibit both of these departures from Newtonian behavior.

On the other hand, Acharya et al. [3], Mitsuishi et al. [70], and Yamanaka and Mitsuishi [101] have resorted to experiments to establish the role of fluid viscoelasticity in determining the drag force on a fluid sphere. Acharya et al. [3] concluded that the drag force on a bubble was not influ-

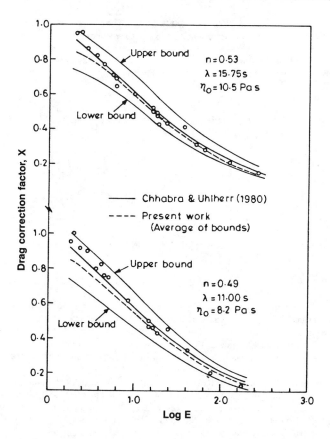

Figure 18. Comparison between the theory of Chhabra and Dhingra [23], and experiments with solid spheres. (Redrawn from [21].)

enced by the fluid elasticity in the region Re ≪ 1, whereas Yamanaka et al. [101] observed that the fluid viscoelasticity resulted in lower values of drag coefficient than the corresponding value in a purely viscous fluid. Similar conflicting results have also been reported by others [70]. Both Acharya et al. [3] and Yamanaka et al. [101] have presented empirical correlations for drag coefficients as a function of Reynolds number and Weissenberg number, but these are too tentative and restrictive to be included here.

This remains an area for future research activity.

Mass Transfer from Fluid Spheres to Continuous Phase

Mass transfer from bubbles or droplets to non-Newtonian liquids is encountered in a number of industrially important processes, including fermentation and food processing. In spite of its overwhelming pragmatic importance, the subject has received only scant attention. A few investigators [5, 11, 29, 43, 49, 51, 52, 58, 79, 98, 99] have theoretically studied the phenomenon of mass transfer from slowly moving fluid spheres (mainly gas bubbles) to power law liquids. It is now generally agreed that the value of the Sherwood number is increased above its Newtonian value as a consequence of shear thinning behavior of the continuous phase. Usually, the results

Table 3
Expression for X_m (Power Law Fluids)

Investigator	Equation
Bhavaraju et al. [11]	$X_m = \{1 - 1.62(n - 1)\}^{1/2}$
Hirose and Moo-Young [49]	$X_m = \left(\dfrac{-4n^2 + 6n + 1}{(2n + 1)}\right)^{1/2}$
Aiba et al. [5]	$X_m = \left(\dfrac{2(1 + 2n)}{3(1 + n)}\right)^{1/2}$ for small n
	$= \dfrac{2}{3}\left(\dfrac{1 + 2n}{1 + n}\right)$ for large n

have been expressed in the form of a correction factor, which signifies the extent of deviation from its Newtonian value, i.e.:

$$Sh = 0.65 \, Pe^{1/2} X_m \tag{14}$$

Alternately, the correction factor X_m can also be interpreted as the ratio of the mass transfer coefficient in a power law fluid to that in a Newtonian fluid. Like in the case of drag correction factor, the values of X_m reported by different investigators often do not agree. A typical selection of expression for X_m is given in Table 3; some of these are plotted in Figure 19. Included in this figure are the limited experimental data, where it is clearly above its Newtonian value on account of shear thinning.

Wellek and Gürkan [98] have used two different stream functions for examining the effect of non-Newtonian properties on mass transfer characteristics for the intermediate range of Reynolds number ($Re_{PL} < 25$), and have given graphical results for Sherwood number as a function of Pe, Re, and the fluid behavior index n. In general, the value of Sherwood number increases with decreasing values of n, everything else being the same. Dang et al. [29] have considered the case of mass transfer accompanied by a chemical reaction between gas bubbles a mildly shear thinning continuous phase.

Still less is known about the role of fluid elasticity. Preliminary investigations suggest that the fluid elasticity further enhances the mass transfer coefficients [102, 88].

BEHAVIOR OF MULTIPLE BUBBLES OR DROPS

Until now, discussion has been confined to the fluid mechanics of and mass transfer from single bubbles and drops. The influence of shear thinning and viscoelastic features was considered. However, in real life applications, e.g., dispersion of a gas into a liquid or dispersion of a liquid into another immiscible liquid, one comes across swarms of bubbles or drops. In contrast to the single particle studies, the analogous phenomenon involving multiple particles has received very little attention. In the case of high volume fractions of the dispersed phase, the relative proximity of particles alters the fluid streamlines, thereby influencing the rates of momentum, heat and mass transfer. Further complications arise when the continuous phase exhibits non-Newtonian behavior such as encountered in fermentation, food processing, etc. In all such applications, one is usually interested in estimating the terminal velocity of a swarm, which, in turn, permits the estimation of contact time; the latter being one of the key parameters in designing gas-liquid contactors such as bubble columns.

Gal-Or and Waslo [33] have employed the well known Happel's cell model [45] to incorporate the inter-particle interactions for the ensembles of bubbles or drops moving slowly through a New-

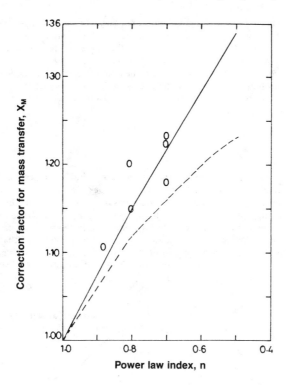

Figure 19. Correction factor for mass transfer as a function of the power law index. (———) Theory of Bhavraju et al. (11); (– – –) approximate analysis of Hirose and Moo-Young (49) and experimental points from Ref. (49).

tonian liquid. They were able to obtain the following analytical expression for the case of gas bubbles with clean interface:

$$X = \frac{2}{3(1 - \phi^{1/3})} \tag{15}$$

where ϕ is the volume fraction of gas, and X has the same meaning as in Equation 6. The equivalent expression for the case of liquid drops is a little bit more involved than Equation 15. At the other extreme of high Reynolds number, Marrucci [66] has presented an analysis based on the irrotational flow approximations. His analysis yielded:

$$X = 2\frac{1 - \phi^{5/3}}{(1 - \phi)^2} \tag{16}$$

Attention is drawn to the fact that there is a subtle difference between the two X's used in Equations 15 and 16. In arriving at Equation 15, it is implicitly assumed that the single bubble, as well as the swarm conditions, correspond to the creeping flow regime, and X is a measure of the deviation purely because of the hindrance phenomenon, whereas in Equation 16, X also includes the deviations due to inertial effects.

Chhabra and co-workers [22, 41, 42] and Jarzebski and Malinowski [51, 52] have extended the analysis of Gal-Or and Waslo [33] to the case where the continuous phase displays non-Newtonian shear thinning viscosity.

In view of the complex form of the governing equations, Chhabra and co-workers [22, 41, 42] and Jarzebski and Malinowski [51, 52] have employed variational principles to obtain upper and lower bounds on drag force (or terminal velocity). In the case of power law behavior of the continuous phase, the correction factor introduced in Equation 15 now becomes a function of the power law index, n. Since the quantity of interest is the terminal velocity rather than the drag force, it can be easily shown that for a swarm of bubbles rising through a pool of power law liquids, the ratio of the rise velocity of a swarm to that of a single bubble is related to the drag correction factor X via the following equation:

$$\frac{U_{sw}}{U_{si}} = \left(\frac{X_{si}}{X_{sw}}\right)^{1/n} \tag{17}$$

where the subscripts "sw" and "si" refer to a swarm and a single bubble, respectively. Typical results for a range of values of gas hold up and the power law index are shown in Figure 20. Note that the arithmetic average of the upper and lower bounds has been used in plotting this figure. Included in the same figure are the approximate results, in the range $1 \geq n \geq 0.71$, as reported by Bhavaraju et al. [11]; the agreement between the two theories is excellent. In a subsequent paper, Gummalam et al. [42] have reported similar results for a more realistic rheological model than the power law model, namely, the Carreau viscosity equation. Typical upper and lower bounds on the drag correction factor for a fixed value of n are shown in Figures 21 and 22. In this case, however, the

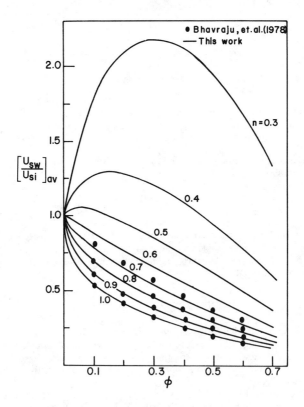

Figure 20. Swarm velocity for gas bubbles rising through power law liquids [41].

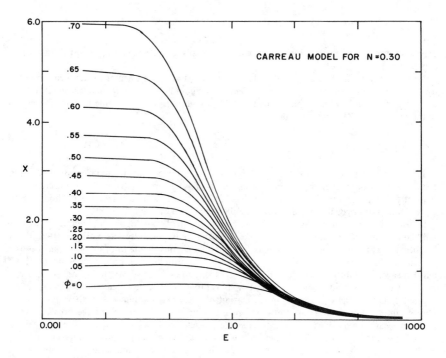

Figure 21. Upper bound on drag correction factor for a swarm of bubbles rising through Carreau model fluids [42].

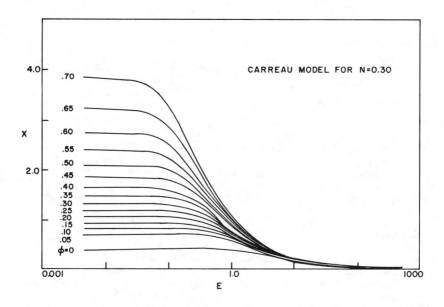

Figure 22. Lower bound on drag correction factor for a swarm of bubbles rising through Carreau model fluids [42].

dependence of the terminal velocity is much more involved than can be represented by a simple expression such as Equation 17.

Admittedly, a number of investigators [37, 56, 60, 61] have experimentally examined the hydrodynamics of bubble columns involving non-Newtonian liquid phase; unfortunately, sufficient details are not given in any of the publications to enable a comparison between the theories for swarms of bubbles and the experimental data.

CONCLUSION

This chapter has focused on the hydrodynamics of bubbles and drops in continuous media. Extensive literature is available when the continuous phase exhibits Newtonian flow behavior; consequently, a reasonably coherent picture has emerged, and reliable predictive methods for the calculation of drag coefficient, Sherwood number, etc., have evolved.

In contrast to this, not only is much less known about the analogous problem of Newtonian fluid spheres moving in non-Newtonian media, but more importantly, the work reported to date has been of scouring nature. It is thus neither possible nor justifiable to draw firm conclusions at this stage. For example, the different shapes and the "weird effects" reported by Wilkinson [100] and Hassager [48] for non-Newtonian media are likely to exert significant influence on the overall processes involving fluid particles. These as well as other aspects, e.g., predicting the magnitude of "velocity jump" in the case of gas bubbles, await physical explanation so that they can be incorporated into future models for transport processes. Variational principles have provided useful preliminary results on drag coefficients of single particles and swarms moving in purely viscous fluids. Unfortunately, the comparisons with experiments do not appear to be very encouraging. Probably some suitable revisions of theories and more careful experimentation will improve this situation in the near future. Virtually nothing is known about the role of fluid viscoelasticity in this non-viscometric flow field. Hence, considerable scope exists for experimentalists, as well as theoreticians, in this area of growing importance with particular reference to biotechnological applications.

NOTATION

C_D	drag coefficient	R_c	critical bubble radius (Equation 1)
d	particle diameter	Re	Reynolds number
E	dimensionless parameter $\left(= \dfrac{\lambda U}{d} \right)$	Re_{PL}	Reynolds number for a power law fluid (Equation 7)
E_0	Eötvös number	Sh	Sherwood number
g	acceleration due to gravity	U	terminal velocity
m	fluid consistency index (Equation 5)	X	drag correction factor (Equation 6)
M	Morton number	X_E	viscosity ratio (Equation 8)
n	fluid behavior index (Equation 5); also a parameter in Equations 10 and 11	X_m	correction factor for mass transfer (Equation 14)
Pe	Peclet number	Y	dimensionless factor (Equation 3)

Greek Symbols

α	surface tension gradient (Equation 2)	μ	Newtonian viscosity
γ	density ratio	η	apparent viscosity
$\dot{\gamma}$	shear rate	η_0	zero shear viscosity (Equation 10)
ρ	density	η_∞	infinite shear viscosity (Equation 10)
$\Delta\rho$	density difference	λ	Carreau model fluid parameter (Equation 10)
σ	surface tension or interfacial tension		
ϕ	volume fraction of dispersed phase	τ	shear stress

Subscripts

c	continuous phase	sw	swarm of bubbles or drops
d	dispersed phase	si	single bubble or drop

REFERENCES

1. Abdel-Alim, A. H., and Hamielec, A. E.: "A theoretical and experimental investigation of the effect of internal circulation on the drag of spherical droplets falling at terminal velocity in liquid media," *Ind. Eng. Chem. Fundam.*, *14* (1975) 308–312.
2. Abdel-Khalik, S. I., Hassager, O., and Bird, R. B.: "Prediction of melt elasticity from viscosity data," *Polym. Eng. Sci.*, *14* (1974) 859–867.
3. Acharya, A., Mashelkar, R. A., and Ulbrecht, J.: "Mechanics of bubble motion and deformation in non-Newtonian media," *Chem. Eng. Sci.*, *32* (1977) 863–872.
4. Acharya, A., Mashelkar, R. A., and Ulbrecht, J.: "Motion of liquid drops in rheologically complex fluids," *Can. J. Chem. Eng.*, 56 (1978) 19–25.
5. Aiba, S., and Okamoto, R.: *J. Fermentation Technology*, *43*, (1965) 609.
6. Ajayi, O. O.: "Slow motion of a bubble in a viscoelastic fluid," *J. Eng. Maths.*, *9* (1975) 273–280.
7. Astarita, G.: "Spherical gas bubble motion through Maxwell liquids," *Ind. Eng. Chem. Fundam.*, *5* (1966) 548–553.
8. Astarita, G., and Appuzzo, G.: "Motion of gas bubbles in non-Newtonian liquids," *AIChE J.*, 11 (1965) 815–820.
9. Barnett, S. M., Humphrey, A. E., and Litt, M.: "Bubble motion and mass transfer in Non-Newtonian fluids," *AIChEJ.*, 12 (1966) 253–259.
10. Bhaga, D., and Weber, M. E.: "Bubbles in viscous liquids: Shapes, wakes and velocities," *J. Fluid Mech.*, *105* (1981) 61–85.
11. Bhavaraju, S. M., Mashelkar, R. A., and H. W. Blanch, "Bubble motion and mass transfer in non-Newtonian fluids," *AIChEJ.*, 24 (1978) 1063–1076.
12. Bird, R. B., Armstrong, R. C., and Hassager, O.: *Dynamics of Polymeric Liquids, Vol 1: Fluid Mechanics*, Wiley & Sons (1977).
13. Bisgaard, C., and Hassager, O.: "An experimental investigation of velocity fields around spheres and bubbles moving in non-Newtonian liquids," *Rheo. Acta*, *21* (1982) 537–539.
14. Blanch, H. W., and Bhavaraju, S. M.: "Non-Newtonian fermentation broths: Rheology and mass transfer," *Biotech. Bioeng.*, *18* (1976) 745–761.
15. Boger, D. V.: "Demonstration of upper and lower Newtonian fluid behavior in a pseudoplastic fluid," *Nature*, *265* (1977) 126–127.
16. Boger, D. V.: "A highly elastic constant viscosity fluid," *J. Non-Newt. Fluid Mech.*, *3* (1977/78) 87–91.
17. Bond, W. N., and Newton, D. A.: "Bubbles, drops and Newton's law," *Phil. Mag.*, *5* (1928) 794–800.
18. Calderbank, P. H., Johnson, D. S. L., and Loudon, J.: "Mechanics and mass transfer of single bubbles in free rise through some Newtonian and non-Newtonian liquids," *Chem. Eng. Sci.*, 25 (1970) 235–256.
19. Carreau, P. J.: "Rheological equations from molecular network theories," *Trans. Soc. Rheo.*, 16 (1972) 99–127.
20. Carreau, P. J., et al.: "Dynamique des bulles en milieu viscoelastique," *Rheo. Acta 13* (1974) 477–489.
21. Chhabra, R. P.: "Steady non-Newtonian flow about a rigid sphere," *Encyclopedia of Fluid Mech.*, *1* (1986) 983–1032.
22. Chhabra, R. P.: "Some remarks on drag and mass transfer in multiple drop slow motion in a power law fluid," *Chem. Eng. Sci.*, in press.
23. Chhabra, R. P., and Dhingra, S. C.: "Creeping motion of a Carreau fluid past a Newtonian fluid sphere," *Can. J. Chem. Eng.*, *64* (1986) 897–905.
24. Chhabra, R. P., and Raman, J. R.: "Slow non-Newtonian flow past an assemblage of rigid spheres," *Chem. Eng. Commun.*, *27* (1984) 23–46.

25. Chhabra, R. P., Tiu, C., and Uhlherr, P. H. T.: "A study of wall effects on the motion of a sphere in viscoelastic fluids," *Can. J. Chem. Eng.*, 59 (1981) 771–775.
26. Chhabra, R. P., and Uhlherr, P. H. T.: "Shortcomings of the power law in describing creeping flow about a sphere," Proc. 2nd Nat. Conf. Rheo., Sydney, pp. 89–92 (1981).
27. Chhabra, R. P., Uhlherr, P. H. T., and Boger, D. V.: "The influence of fluid elasticity on the drag coefficient for creeping flow around a sphere," *J. Non-Newt. Fluid Mech.*, 6 (1979/80) 187–199.
28. Clift, R., Grace, J. R., and Weber, M. E.: "Bubbles, Drops and Particles," Academic Press, NY (1978).
29. Dang, V., Gill, W. N., and Ruckenstein, E.: "Unsteady mass transfer between bubbles and non-Newtonian liquids (Power law model) with chemical reactions," *Can. J. Chem. Eng.*, 50 (1972) 300.
30. Dekee, D., Carreau, P. J., and Mordarski, J.: "Bubble velocity and coalescence in viscoelastic liquids," *Chem. Eng. Sci.*, 41 (1986) 2273–2283.
31. Fararoui, A., and Kintner, R. C.: "Flow and shape of drops in non-Newtonian fluids," *Trans. Soc. Rheo.*, 5 (1961) 369–380.
32. Gal-Or, B., Klinzing, G. E., and Tavarides, L. L.: "Bubble and drop phenomena," *Ind. Eng. Chem.*, 61 (1969) 21–34.
33. Gal-Or, B., and Waslo, S.: "Hydrodynamics of an ensemble of drops and bubbles in the presence or absence of surfactants," *Chem. Eng. Sci.*, 23 (1968) 1431–1446.
34. Gill, W. N., et al.: "Fluid dynamics," *Ind. Eng. Chem.*, 59(12) (1967) 69–105.
35. Gill, W. N., et al.: "Fluid dynamics," *Ind. Eng. Chem.*, 61(1), (1969) 41–75.
36. Gill, W. N., et al.: "Fluid dynamics," *Ind. Eng. Chem.*, 62(12) (1970) 108–139.
37. Godbole, S. P., et al.: "Hydrodynamics and mass transfer in non-Newtonian solutions in a bubble column," *AIChEJ.*, 30 (1984) 213–220.
38. Grace, J. R.: "Hydrodynamics of liquid drops in immiscible liquids," *Handbook of Fluids in Motion* Ed: N. P. Cheremisinoff and R. Gupta, Ann Arbor, Mich. (1983) pp. 1003–1025.
39. Grace, J. R., and Wairegi, T.: "Properties and characteristics of drops and bubbles," *Encyclopedia of Fluid Mechanics*, 3 (1986) 43–56.
40. Grace, J. R., Wairegi, T., and Nguyen, T. H.: "Shapes and velocities of single drops and bubbles moving freely through immiscible liquids," *Trans. Inst. Chem. Engrs.*, 54 (1976) 167–173.
41. Gummalam, S., and Chhabra, R. P.: "Rising velocity of a swarm of spherical bubbles in a power law non-Newtonian liquid," *Can. J. Chem. Eng.*, in press.
42. Gummalam, S., Narayan, K. A., and Chhabra, R. P.: "Rise velocity of a swarm of spherical bubbles through a non-Newtonian fluid: Effect of zero shear viscosity," *Int. J. Multiphase Flow*, in press.
43. Gürkan, T., and Wellek, R. M.: "Mass transfer in dispersed and continuous phases for creeping flow of fluid spheres through power law liquids," *Ind. Eng. Chem. Fundam.*, 15 (1976) 45.
44. Hamielec, A. E., et al.: "Viscous flow around fluid spheres at intermediate Reynolds number," *Can. J. Chem. Eng.*, 40 (1962) 41–45. Also see 41 (1963) 246–251.
45. Happel, J.: "Viscous flow in multiparticle systems: Slow motion of fluids relative to beds of spherical particles," *AIChEJ.*, 4 (1958) 197–201.
46. Hara, S. K., and Schowalter, W. R.: "Dynamics of non-spherical bubbles surrounded by viscoelastic fluid," *J. Non-Newt. Fluid Mech.*, 14 (1984) 249–264.
47. Hassager, O.: Bubble motion in structurally complex fluids: Chem. Eng. with Per Soltoft, Teknisk for lagas, København (1977), pp. 105–117.
48. Hassager, O.: "Negative wake behind bubbles in non-Newtonian liquids," *Nature*, 279, No. 5712 (1979) pp. 402–403.
49. Hirose, T., and Moo-Young, M.: "Bubble drag and mass transfer in non-Newtonian fluids: Creeping flow with Power law fluids," *Can. J. Chem. Eng.*, 47 (1969) 265–267.
50. Ishikawa, H., Miki, T., Okamoto, M., and Hikita, H.: "Gas desorption from liquids: Mass transfer and drag coefficients, for single bubbles in free rise through Newtonian liquids," *Chem. Eng. Sci.*, 41 (1986) 2309–2319.
51. Jazebski, A. B., and Malinowski, J. J.: "Transient heat and mass transfer from drops or bubbles in slow non-Newtonian flows," *Chem. Eng. Sci.*, 41 (1986) 2575–2578, ibid. 2569–2573.

52. Jarzebski, A. B., and Malinowski, J. J.: "Drag and mass transfer in slow non-Newtonian flows over an ensemble of Newtonian spherical drops or bubbles," *Chem. Eng. Commun.*, 49 (1987) 235.

53. Johnson, R. E., and Sadhal, S. S.: "Fluid mechanics of compound multiphase drops and bubbles," *Ann. Rev. Fluid Mech.*, *17* (1985) 289–320.

54. Kawase, Y., and Hirose, T.: "Motion of drops in non-Newtonian fluid systems at low Reynolds number," *J. Chem. Eng. Japan*, 10 (1977) 68–70.

55. Kawase, Y., and Moo-Young, M.: "Approximate solutions for drag coefficient of bubbles moving in shearthinning elastic fluids," *Rheo. Acta*, 24 (1985) 202–206.

56. Kawase, Y., and Moo-Young, M.: "Influence of non-Newtonian flow behaviour on mass transfer in bubble columns with and without draft tubes," *Chem. Eng. Commun.*, 40 (1986) 67–83.

57. Kawase, Y., and Ulbrecht, J.: "On the abrupt change of velocity of bubbles rising in non-Newtonian liquids," *J. Non-Newt. Fluid Mech.*, 8 (1981) 203–212.

58. Kawase, Y., and Ulbrecht, J.: "Newtonian fluid sphere with rigid or mobile interface in a shearthinning liquid: Drag and mass transfer," *Chem. Eng. Commun.*, 8 (1981) 213–231.

59. Kawase, Y., and Ulbrecht, J.: "The effect of surfactant on terminal velocity of and mass transfer from a fluid sphere in a Non-Newtonian fluid," *Can. J. Chem. Eng.*, *60*, (1982) 87–92.

60. Kawase, Y., Ulbrecht, J., and Auyeung, K. F.: More on mixing of viscous liquids in bubble columns," *Chem. Eng. Commun.*, *35* (1985) 175–191.

61. Kelkar, B. G., and Shah, Y. T.: "Gas hold up and backmixing in bubble column with polymer solutions," *AIChEJ.*, *31* (1985) 700–702.

62. Kemblowski, Z., and Kritiansen, B.: "Rheometry of Fermentation liquids," *Biotech. Bioeng.*, *28* (1986) 1474–1483.

63. Leal, L. G., Skoog, J., and Acrivos, A.: "On the motion of gas bubbles in a viscoelastic liquid," *Can. J. Chem. Eng.*, *49* (1971) 569–575.

64. Levich, G.: *Physico-Chemical Hydrodynamics*, Prentice-Hall, New Jersey (1962).

65. Macedo, I. C., and Yang, W. J.: "The drag of air bubbles rising in non-Newtonian liquids," *Jap. J. Appl. Phys.*, 13 (1974) 529–533.

66. Marrucci, G.: "Rising velocity of a swarm of spherical bubbles," *Ind. Eng. Chem. Fundam.*, *4* (1965) 224–225.

67. Marrucci, G., Appuzzo, G., and Astarita, G.: "Motion of drops in non-Newtonian systems," *AIChEJ.*, 16 (1970) 538–541.

68. Mashelkar, R. A.: "Rheological problems in chemical engineering," *Rheology*, Vol. I, p. 219 (1980), Plenum Press, N.Y.

69. Mhatre, M. V., and Kintner, R. C.: "Fall of liquid drops through pseudoplastic liquids," *Ind. Eng. Chem.*, 51 (1959) 865–867.

70. Mitsuishi, N., Yamanaka, A., and Sueyasu, Y.: "Drag force on a moving bubble and droplet in viscoelastic fluids," *Proc. PACHEC-1972*, pp. 316–317.

71. Mohan, V.: "Fall of liquid drops in non-Newtonian media, Ph.D. Thesis, Indian Institute of Technology, Madras (1974).

72. Mohan, V.: "Creeping flow of a power law fluid over a Newtonian fluid sphere," *AIChEJ.*, 20 (1974), 180–182.

73. Mohan, V., Nagarajan, R., and Venkateswarlu, D.: "Fall of drops in non-Newtonian media," *Can. J. Chem. Eng.*, 50 (1972) 37–40.

74. Mohan, V., and Raghuraman, J.: "Viscous flow of an Ellis fluid past a Newtonian fluid sphere," *Can. J. Chem. Eng.*, 54 (1976) 228–234.

75. Mohan, V., and Venkateswarlu, D.: "Creeping flow of a power flow fluid past a fluid sphere," *Int. J. Multiphase Flow*, 2 (1976) 563–570.

76. Mohan, V., and Venkateswarlu, D.: "Creeping flow of an Ellis fluid past a Newtonian fluid •sphere," *Int. J. Multiphase Flow 2* (1976) 571–579.

77. Mohan, V., and Venkateswarlu, D.: "Lower bound on the drag offered to a Newtonian fluid sphere placed in a flowing Ellis Fluid," *J. Chem. Eng. Japan*, 7 (1974) 243–247.

78. Moo-Young, M., and Blanch, H. W.: "Design of Biochemical reactors. Mass transfer criteria for simple and complex systems," *Adv. Biochem. Eng.*, *19* (1981) 1–70.

79. Moo-Young, M., and Hirose, T.: "Bubble mass transfer in creeping flow of viscoelastic fluids," *Can. J. Chem. Eng.*, *50* (1972) 128–130.

80. Moo-Young, M., Hirose, T., and Ali, S.: "Rheological effects on liquid phase mass transfer in two phase dispersions: Results for creeping flow," Proc. 5th Int. Cong. Rheo., Kyoto (1970).
81. Nakano, Y., and Tien, C.: "Creeping flow of power law fluid over Newtonian fluid sphere," AIChEJ., 14 (1968) 145–151.
82. Nakano, Y., and Tien, C.: "Viscous incompressible non-Newtonian flow around fluid sphere at intermediate Reynolds number," AIChEJ., 16 (1970) 569–574.
83. Philippoff, W.: "The viscosity characteristics of rubber solutions," Rubber Chem. and Technology, 10 (1937) 76–104.
84. Rabiger, N., and Vogelpohl, A.: "Bubble formation and its movement in Newtonian and non-Newtonian liquids," Encyclopedia of Fluid Mech., 3 (1986) 58–88.
85. Rivkind, V. Y., and Ryskin, G. M.: "Flow structure in motion of a spherical drop in a fluid medium at intermediate Reynolds number," Fluid Dynamics 1 (1976) 5–12.
86. Rivkind, V. Y., Ryskin, G. M., and Fishbein, G. A.: "The motion of a spherical drop in the flow of a viscous fluid," Fluid Mech.-Sov. Res., 1 (1973) 142–151. Also see App. Math. Mech., 40 (1976) 687–691.
87. Sangani, A.: "Creeping flow around bubbles," Encyclopedia of Fluid Mech., 3 (1986) 89–109.
88. Schafermeyer, R. G., Gurkan, T., and Wellek, R. M.: "Liquid-liquid extraction by single droplets falling in non-Newtonian solutions," presented at the 25th Canadian Chemical Engineering Conf., Montreal (Nov., 1975).
89. Schechter, R. S., and Farley, R. W.: "Interfacial tension gradients and droplet behaviour," Can. J. Chem. Eng., 41 (1963) 103–107.
90. Shima, A., and Tsujino, T.: "The behaviour of gas bubbles in the Casson fluid," J. App. Mech., Trans. ASME, 45, (1978) 37–42.
91. Shirotsuka, T., and Kawase, Y.: "Motion and mass transfer of fluid spheres in non-Newtonian systems," J. Chem. Eng. Japan, 6 (1973) 432–437.
92. Shirotsuka, T., and Kawase, Y.: "Motion and mass transfer of fluid spheres in viscoelastic fluid systems," Chem. Eng. Japan 38 (1974) 797.
93. Skelland, A. H. P.: Non-Newtonian Flow and Heat transfer, Wiley & Sons (1967).
94. Slattery, J. C.: Momentum, Energy, and Mass Transfer in Continua, McGraw-Hill, NY (1972).
95. Tiefenbruck, G., and Leal, L. G.: "A numerical study of the motion of a viscoelastic fluid past rigid spheres and spherical bubbles," J. Non-Newt. Fluid Mech., 10 (1982) 115–155.
96. Wagner, M. G., and Slattery, J. C.: "Slow flow of a non-Newtonian fluid past a droplet," AIChEJ., 17 (1971) 1198–1207.
97. Warshay, M., Bogusz, E., Johnson, M., and Kintner, R. C.: "Ultimate velocity of drops in stationary liquid media," Can. J. Chem. Eng., 37 (1959) 29–36.
98. Wellek, R. M., and Gürkan, T.: "Mass transfer to drops moving through power law fluids in the intermediate Reynolds number region," AIChEJ., 22 (1976) 484–490.
99. Wellek, R. M., and Huang, C. C.: "Mass transfer from spherical gas bubbles and liquid droplets moving through power law fluids in the laminar flow regime," Ind. Eng. Chem. Fundam., 9 (1970) 480.
100. Wilkinson, W. L.: "Tailing of drops falling through viscoelastic liquids," Nature Phys. Sci., 240 (1972) 44.
101. Yamanaka, A., and Mitsuishi, N.: "Drag coefficient of a moving bubble and droplet in viscoelastic fluids," J. Chem. Eng. Japan, 10 (1977) 370–374.
102. Zana, E., and Leal, L. G.: "The dynamics and dissolution of gas bubbles in a viscoelastic fluid," Int. J. Multiphase Flow, 4 (1978) 237–262.
103. Zana, E., and Leal, L. G.: "The dynamics of bubbles and drops in a viscoelastic fluid," Proc. Int. Coll. on drops and bubbles (Eds. Collins, Plesset, and Saffren) 1974, Vol. II.

CHAPTER 10

NATURAL CONVECTION HEAT TRANSFER TO VISCOELASTIC FLUIDS

A. V. Shenoy*

Department of Materials Science and Engineering
University of Florida
Gainesville, Florida, USA

CONTENTS

INTRODUCTION

A number of fluid systems in the paint, polymer, food, and fermentation industries exhibit non-Newtonian flow behavior, and hence understanding the heat transport phenomena in such systems is certainly of great pragmatic importance. Inelastic non-Newtonian fluids have received considerable attention in the past and reliable theoretical analyses and experimental investigations are available, as has been shown in the comprehensive review of Shenoy [1]. However, there have been very limited efforts in the study of natural convection to viscoelastic fluids. The reason for this is twofold. Firstly, viscoelastic fluids exhibit a combination of properties of viscous fluids and elastic solids, including the complex phenomena of stress relaxation, strain recovery, die swell, finite normal stress difference, etc., which makes the theoretical analysis of the transport processes a rather difficult task. Secondly, viscoelastic fluids are often associated with high consistencies and hence, it is assumed that natural convection currents would be difficult to set up. However, it is not uncommon to find fluids which have viscosity but exhibit a significant level of elasticity, such as drag reducing fluids [2] and the Boger fluid [3]. Natural convection effects occur rather easily in such fluids. Further, a realization that most heat transport processes are basically a combination of forced and natural convection, emphasizes the importance of the study of the latter.

In the present chapter, we shall deal with the natural convection heat transfer to viscoelastic fluids. Choice of any specific constitutive equation to describe the flow behavior of the viscoelastic

---

* Current address: SMART, 64D Girgaum Road, Opera House, Bombay 400004, India.

fluid is always a difficult task. One type of constitutive equation would be dealt with in details though a number of others would be used in specific flow situations. Natural convection in both external and internal flow situations will be reviewed along with separate sections to discuss the effects of natural convection in forced convection heat transfer to viscoelastic fluids. The concluding remarks will highlight the various areas in the natural convection heat transfer to viscoelastic fluids that need attention and focus on the future research aspects that could be pursued.

GOVERNING EQUATIONS

The governing equations for natural convection heat transfer to viscoelastic fluids are not different from those which are conventionally used for analyzing momentum and energy transport, and can be written in the general form as follows:

$$\frac{\partial \rho}{\partial t} + \nabla \cdot (\rho v) = 0 \tag{1}$$

$$\rho \frac{Dv}{Dt} = \rho g - \nabla \bar{p} - \nabla \cdot \tau^{+} \tag{2}$$

$$\rho C_p \frac{DT}{Dt} = k \nabla^2 T - T \cdot \nabla v \tag{3}$$

Equations 1–3 acquire a valid form for viscoelastic fluids when the extra stress tensor τ^{+} is specified in terms of the relevant rheological equation of state. The choice of a specific constitutive equation for depicting the flow behavior of a viscoelastic fluid is never an easy task. The choice is very wide, as can be seen from Middleman [4] and Bird, et al. [5], and depends to a large extent on the anticipated flow field. In natural convection, as well as in forced and mixed convection involving boundary layer flows, a useful constitutive equation is the one that is able to realistically predict a quasiviscometric flow field in the vicinity of the solid surface. One such equation, as discussed in detail by Denn [6], is the following:

$$\tau = -\mu[\tilde{\Pi}]A_1 - \omega[\tilde{\Pi}]A_1^2 + \lambda[\tilde{\Pi}]A_2 \tag{4}$$

Here τ is the deviatoric stress tensor, while A_1 and A_2 are Rivlin-Ericksen tensors of the first and second order. The coefficients μ, ω, and λ are scalar functions of the second invariant of the rate of strain tensor. The functional form of $\mu[\tilde{\Pi}]$, $\omega[\tilde{\Pi}]$, and $\lambda[\tilde{\Pi}]$ are as follows:

$$\mu[\tilde{\Pi}] = k(\tfrac{1}{2}\tilde{\Pi})^{(n-1)/2} \tag{5}$$

$$\omega[\tilde{\Pi}] = l(\tfrac{1}{2}\tilde{\Pi})^{(\omega-2)/2} \tag{6}$$

$$\lambda[\tilde{\Pi}] = m(\tfrac{1}{2}\tilde{\Pi})^{(s-2)/2} \tag{7}$$

For $n = 1$ and $l = m = 0$, Equation (4) reduces to the Newtonian limit where $\tau = -\mu \cdot \Delta$. For values of $n \neq 1$ but with $l = m = 0$, it takes the form of a power-law model which is normally used for describing inelastic or purely viscous behavior. The material parameters I, ω, m, and s can be obtained by determining the primary and secondary normal stress differences in viscometric flows and relating these to shear rate. For example, the primary normal stress difference $(\tau_{xx} - \tau_{yy})$ is often determined by measuring the normal thrust during simple shear on a rheogoniometer and relating it to the shear rate as follows:

$$\tau_{xx} - \tau_{yy} = 2m(\dot{\gamma})^s \tag{8}$$

When $\omega = s = 2$ and $n = 1$, Equation (4) reduces to the so-called second-order fluid. This approximation is known to be valid for many dilute polymer solutions in the limit of vanishingly small rates of deformation.

The above constitutive equation is just one of the types that will be used in the analysis of natural convection heat transfer to viscoelastic fluids. A few others will be discussed in individual subsections when treating the various situations of flow.

NATURAL CONVECTION IN EXTERNAL FLOWS

Normally, when studying external flow situations, various surface geometries are often considered, such as the vertical flat plate, horizontal cylinder, vertical cone, or sphere. However, for viscoelastic fluids, the existing literature is limited to only the vertical flat plate and the horizontal cylinder, due to the obvious difficulties in the analysis of the problem.

Vertical Flat Plate

It is unfortunate that despite the fact that there exist at least five attempts to theoretically analyze the laminar natural convection flow past simplest flow geometry of the vertical flat plate as shown in Figure 1, none of them are truly useful, as they are either mathematically wrong or pragmatically unimportant.

Mishra [7] was the first to study the problem of laminar natural convection heat transfer to a second order fluid from a vertical flat plate and determine a similarity solution for the case of the excess wall temperature varying linearly with the distance along the wall. This solution led to a momentum and thermal boundary layer thickness which was invariant with reference to the distance along the plate. This is physically unsound, as it predicts a finite boundary layer thickness at the leading edge. In his second attempt to study another type of viscoelastic fluid, Mishra [8] considered the Walter's B fluid but came up with similar results as the boundary layer equations were the same. Consequently, the comments in the earlier case hold true again.

Amato and Tien [9] studied the same problem with respect to an Oldroyd fluid. But their derived boundary layer equations are incorrect because they contain the derivative of a single normal stress term instead of the derivative of the primary normal stress difference term. Moreover, in equating the buoyancy and viscous terms in the momentum boundary layer equation, as well as in equating the convection and conduction terms in the energy equation, they have equated the exponents

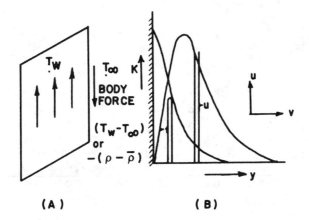

Figure 1. Convection with a body force (a) surface at T_w in a viscoelastic fluid at T_∞; (b) resulting temperature and velocity distributions flow past a flat vertical plate shown schematically.

over the respective nondimensional terms, which is mathematically unsound. Their final result indicates that the Nusselt number depends upon a viscoelasticity number, which is simply the ratio of the material parameters of the viscoelastic fluid under consideration. Normally, one would expect the characteristic time of the process to be equally important in such a problem and hence, should have appeared in the solution.

Soundalgekar studied the unsteady laminar natural convection heat transfer to viscoelastic fluid past an infinite plate with constant suction with [10] and without [11] viscous dissipation. The results are not very useful as both cases considered are pragmatically unimportant.

From the above, it is evident that the problem of laminar natural heat transfer from a vertical flat plate to a viscoelastic fluid still needs to be analyzed. Recourse to fully numerical method would have to be taken and it has been conclusively proved by Shenoy and Mashelkar [12] that no similarity solution exists for the simple vertical flat plate based on realistic enough constitutive equations. Certainly, the theoretical equations developed for inelastic non-Newtonian fluids do not apply for viscoelastic fluids as observed by Shenoy and Ulbrecht [13]. Figure 2 shows the experimental data points for dimensionless temperature θ versus η' where

$$\theta = \frac{T - T_\infty}{T_w - T_\infty} \tag{9}$$

$$\eta' = \frac{y}{x}\left(\frac{1}{3n + 1}\right)^{1/(3n + 1)} Gr_{xt}^{1/2(n + 1)} Pr_{xt}^{n/(3n + 1)} \tag{10}$$

$$Gr_{xt} = \rho^2 x^{n + 2}[g\beta_0(T_w - T_\infty)^{2 - n}]/K^2 \tag{11}$$

$$Pr_{xt} = (\rho C_p/k)\left(\frac{K}{\rho}\right)^{2/(n + 1)} x^{(n - 1)/[2(n + 1)]}[g\beta_0(T_w - T_\infty)] \tag{12}$$

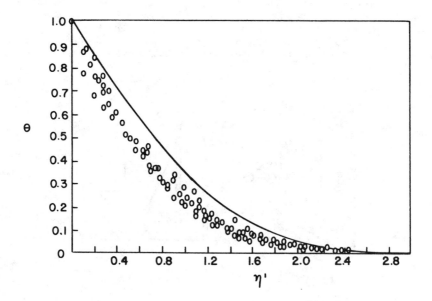

Figure 2. Variation of θ with η' for different concentrations of PEO showing how the theory for inelastic fluids does not match the experimental data for elastic fluids [13].

The PEO solutions at all four concentrations showed Newtonian viscosity behavior. However, the theoretical predictions did not match the experimental data. PEO solutions are known to be mildly elastic even at the low dilutions considered by Shenoy and Ulbrecht [13]; hence, their elasticity (though not measurable) could be the prime cause for the discrepancy between theory and experiment. It was shown by them that when inelastic solutions of CMC were used, the theoretical predictions matched experimental data for the shear thinning non-elastic solutions.

Horizontal Cylinder

Shenoy and Mashelkar [12] studied the laminar natural convection heat transfer to a viscoelastic fluid from a curved surface as shown in Figure 3. It was assumed that the flow was steady and that all physical properties of the fluid except the density in the buoyancy term were constant. Boundary layer approximations were shown to be valid in the flow circumstances and Equation 2 was reduced to the appropriate form as:

$$u\frac{du}{dx} + v\frac{du}{dy} = -\frac{1}{\rho}\frac{\partial \tau_{xy}}{\partial y} + \frac{1}{\rho}\frac{\partial}{\partial x}(\tau_{xx} - \tau_{yy}) + g(x)\beta_0(T - T_\infty) \tag{13}$$

It was assumed that the flow behavior was represented by the constitutive equation (Equation 4) and therefore the relevant stress components were:

$$\tau_{xy} = -k\left(\frac{\partial u}{\partial y}\right)^n + m\left(\frac{\partial u}{\partial y}\right)^{s-2}\left[u\frac{\partial^2 u}{\partial x\,\partial y} + v\frac{\partial^2 u}{\partial y^2} + 2\frac{\partial u}{\partial x}\frac{\partial u}{\partial y}\right] \tag{14}$$

$$\tau_{xx} - \tau_{yy} = 2m\left(\frac{\partial u}{\partial y}\right)^s \tag{15}$$

A further assumption was made regarding the gravity force field that:

$$g(x) = gx_1^p \tag{16}$$

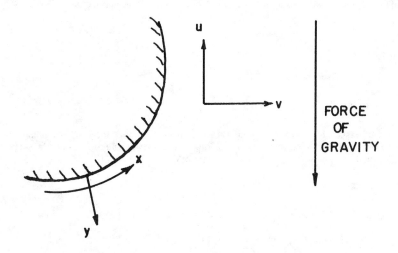

Figure 3. Schematic diagram of flow past a curved surface.

Finally, for the case of high Prandtl number, the inertial terms were neglected and the simplified non-dimensional integral forms of the boundary layer equations thus obtained were:

$$0 = x_1^p \int_0^1 \delta_{T_1} \theta \, d\eta_T - \frac{1}{\delta_1^n} \left(\frac{\partial u_1}{\partial \eta} \right)_{\eta=0}^n + Wi \frac{\partial}{\partial x_1} \int_0^1 \frac{1}{\delta_1^{s-1}} \left(\frac{\partial u_1}{\partial \eta} \right)^s d\eta \tag{17}$$

$$\frac{\partial}{\partial x_1} \int_0^1 \delta_{T_1} u_1 \theta \, d\eta_r = -\frac{Gr_{xt}^{(n-1)/[2(n+1)(n-2)]}}{\delta_{T_1} Pr_{xt}} \left(\frac{\partial \theta}{\partial \eta_T} \right)_{\eta_T=0} \tag{18}$$

where $x_1 = x/l_c$ $y_1 = y/l_c$ $u_1 = u/U_c$ $\hspace{2cm}$ (19)

$$\delta_1 = \delta/l_c \qquad \delta_{T_1} = \delta_T/l_c \qquad \theta = (T - T_\infty)/(T_w - T_\infty) \tag{20}$$

$$\eta = y_1/\delta_1 \qquad \eta_T = y_1/\delta_{T_1} \tag{21}$$

and $u_c = \{(k/\rho)[g\beta_0(T_w - T_\infty)]^n\}^{1/(n+2)}$ $\hspace{3cm}$ (22)

$$l_c = \{(k/\rho)^2[g\beta_0(T_w - T_\infty)]^{n-2}\}^{1/(n+2)} \tag{23}$$

$$Wi = (2m/\rho U_c^2)(U_c/l_c)^s \tag{24}$$

Gr_{xt} and Pr_{xt} are the same as defined by Equations 11 and 12. The Weissenberg number Wi mainly brings out the effects of elasticity and hence, when $Wi = 0$, Equations 17 and 18 are the same as those for the inelastic power-law fluids case as given in Shenoy and Ulbrecht [13].

The appropriate velocity and temperature profiles were chosen based on the correct boundary and compatibility conditions (the importance of which has been discussed in detail by Shenoy and Mashelkar [12]). Thus:

$$u_1(\eta) = C_1 \eta (1 - \eta)^5 \tag{25}$$

$$\theta(\eta_T) = (1 + \eta_T)(1 - \eta_T)^3 \tag{26}$$

A similarity solution was seen to exist when the following transformation could be made:

$$\delta_{T1} = B_1 x_1^{(n-p)/(3n+1)} \tag{27}$$

$$\delta_1 = B_2 x_1^{(n-p)/(3n+1)} \tag{28}$$

$$C_1 = B_3 x_1^{(3n+1+p)/(3n+1)} \tag{29}$$

$$s = (p + 1)(3n + 1)/(3p + 1) \tag{30}$$

Shenoy and Mashelkar [12] examined the realistic values of s, n, and p for which meaningful results could be obtained and found that the only validity of a similarity solution was for the stagnation region of the horizontal cylinder where the gravity field is:

$$g(x) = g \sin x_1 \simeq gx_1 \ (0 < x_1 < \pi/6) \tag{31}$$

The local and average Nusselt numbers derived for this case were:

$$Nu_x = 2\{[(297\bar{\alpha}_N - 50)f_1(\bar{\alpha}_N)]/980\bar{\alpha}_N^2\}^{1/4} Gr^{1/4} Pr^{1/4}(x/R)^{1/4} \tag{32}$$

$$\bar{Nu}_R = 2\{[(297\bar{\alpha}_N - 50)f_1(\bar{\alpha}_N)]/980\bar{\alpha}_N^2\}^{1/4} Gr_R^{1/4} Pr^{1/4} \tag{33}$$

where the relationship between $\bar{\alpha}_N$ and Wi is given as:

$$\left[\frac{245f_1(\bar{\alpha}_N)Pr}{(297\bar{\alpha}_N - 50)}\right]^{1/2}\left[\frac{495\bar{\alpha}_N(3\bar{\alpha}_N - 1)}{(297\bar{\alpha}_N - 50)}\right] = Wi \tag{34}$$

$$f_1(\bar{\alpha}_N) = \left[\frac{1}{15}\,\bar{\alpha}_N - \frac{5}{42}\,\bar{\alpha}_N^2 + \frac{3}{28}\,\bar{\alpha}_N^3 - \frac{1}{18}\,\bar{\alpha}_N^4 + \frac{1}{63}\,\bar{\alpha}_N^5 - \frac{3}{1540}\,\bar{\alpha}_N^6\right] \tag{35}$$

and Gr, Pr, Gr_R, and Wi for a second-order fluid are defined as:

$$Gr = \frac{\rho^2 x^3[g\beta_0(T_w - T_\infty)]}{\bar{\mu}^2} \tag{36}$$

$$Pr = \frac{\bar{\mu}C_p}{k} \tag{37}$$

$$Gr_R = \frac{\rho^2 R^3[g\beta_0(T_w - T_\infty)]}{\bar{\mu}^2} \tag{38}$$

$$Wi = \frac{2m}{\rho R^2} \tag{39}$$

Figure 4 shows the heat transfer predictions as given by Equation 33. Though there is a noticeable marginal enhancement in Nusselt number at very low values of Weissenberg number, the major effect of elasticity seems to be to reduce the heat transfer coefficient. This fact is supported by the experimental data of Lyons et al. [14] on natural convection from a horizontal cylinder to moderately elastic drag-reducing polyethylene oxide solutions. With increasing concentration of the

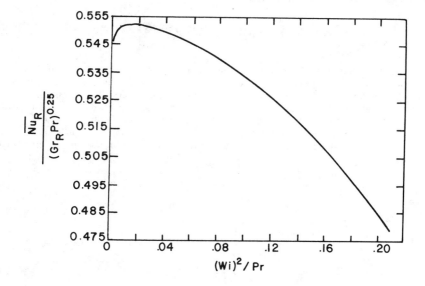

Figure 4. Variation of the average heat transfer rate with viscoelasticity for natural convection in the stagnation region of a heated horizontal cylinder [12].

polymer, the Nusselt number was found to decrease in comparison to the Newtonian value. A quantitative comparison between the experimental findings of Lyons et al. [14] and the theoretical predictions of Shenoy and Mashelkar [12] cannot be made because of lack of relevant information on material parameters such as relaxation times, etc. However, the theoretical analysis of Shenoy and Mashelkar [12] still stands as the only mathematically sound and systematically derived work on laminar pure natural convection heat transfer to viscoelastic fluids past an external surface.

NATURAL CONVECTION IN INTERNAL FLOWS

When dealing with internal flow situations one would normally give consideration to cases such as vertical pipes, horizontal pipes, enclosures created by two vertical parallel plates, enclosures created by two horizontal parallel plates, and so on. Unlike in the case of inelastic non-Newtonian fluids [1], there is very scanty information on internal flow situations in the literature with respect to viscoelastic fluids. The work would fall mainly under the following two categories—vertical parallel plates and horizontial parallel plates, and hence, the discussion would be limited to only those two cases.

Vertical Parallel Plates

The only effort to study laminar natural convection flow between vertical parallel plates was done by Ropke and Schummer [15]. They investigated the principal influence of a viscoelastic fluid on the transient cooling/heating process during laminar natural convection flow in a rectangular enclosure with adiabatic top and bottom. The whole system was at T_i at all time t less than zero. Then at t = 0, the temperature of the left and right was made to jump to T_H and T_c, respectively, such that $T_\mu > T_i > T_c$. This set up a laminar clockwise motion of the fluid free from physical instabilities. Ropke and Schummer [15] preferred to use the four-parameter Oldroyd constitute equation of the following form to describe the viscoelastic fluid:

$$\tau^+ + t_0\tau^\nabla + \bar{k}t_0(\tau^+ \cdot \Delta + \Delta \cdot \tau^+) = 2\eta_0\left[\Delta + t_0\frac{\eta_s}{\eta_0}(\Delta^\nabla + \overline{2k}\,\Delta^2)\right] \tag{40}$$

where t_0 represents the characteristic fluid time (a measure for the elastic response); the parameter K describes the shear rate dependency of viscosity and elasticity including the level of second normal stress difference; η_0 is the fluid viscosity at zero-stress rate; while η_s describes the influence of the solvent viscosity; the superscripts "∇" and the "$\cdot$" denote the upper convected and material derivative. Note that this model shows a second Newtonian region and overshooting for $\eta_s \neq 0$.

Based on the conventional Boussinesq approximation and the assumption of quasi-incompressibility, Ropke and Schummer [15] wrote the non-dimensional form of the relevant transient equations as:

$$\frac{\partial^2\psi}{\partial X^2} + \frac{\partial^2\psi}{\partial Y^2} = -\Omega \tag{41}$$

$$\frac{\partial\theta}{\partial t} + U\frac{\partial\theta}{\partial X} + V\frac{\partial\theta}{\partial Y} = Pr^{-1}\left[\frac{\partial^2\theta}{\partial X^2} + \frac{\partial^2\theta}{\partial Y^2}\right] \tag{42}$$

$$\frac{\partial\theta}{\partial t} + U\frac{\partial\Omega}{\partial X} + V\frac{\partial\Omega}{\partial Y} = \frac{\partial}{\partial X\,\partial Y}(\tau_{yy}^+ - \tau_{xx}^+) + \frac{\partial^2\tau_{yx}^+}{\partial X^2} - \frac{\partial^2\tau_{yx}^+}{\partial Y^2} - Gr\frac{\partial\theta}{\partial Y} \tag{43}$$

The above equations were solved numerically and the changes in the heat transfer characteristics

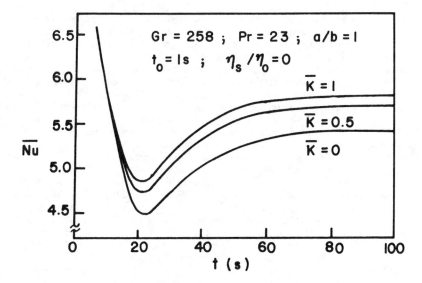

Figure 5. Effect of second normal stress difference on the natural convection flow of viscoelastic fluids [15].

with time were found using the following definition of Nusselt number:

$$\bar{N}u = \frac{b}{a} \int_0^{a/b} \left. \frac{\partial \theta}{\partial y} \right|_{wall} dx \tag{44}$$

where a is the length and b is the width of the enclosure.

Figure 5 shows the results of their numerical calculations. When $\bar{k} = 0$ the case is that of a shear-independent viscoelastic property with no second normal stress difference. Whereas when $0 < \bar{k} \leq 1$, then the viscoelastic properties would be shear dependent and the second normal stress difference would also exist. Thus it was seen that increasing elasticity increased the heat transfer. Care must be taken not to neglect the second normal stress difference term during analysis of natural convection in viscoelastic fluid, as that is seen to make a significant difference in the heat transfer characteristics.

Horizontal Parallel Plates

Natural convection flow that sets up between horizontal layers of fluid is the well-known Benard convection problem. When a fluid layer is placed between two infinite parallel plates separated by a distance d with the top plate at T_1 and bottom plate T_0, then conditions exist to set up cellular convection when $T_0 > T_1$. The initial heat transfer between the horizontal layers is known to take place by conduction and the Nusselt number (hd/k) is unity. But at the onset of convection, the value of Nasselt number increases many fold and this occurs at a critical value of $T_0 - T_1$, better expressed in terms of a dimensionless parameter (Rayleigh number) as:

$$Ra = g\beta_0(T_0 - T_1)\,d^3/\alpha_0 \tag{45}$$

This criterion is based on a linear stability analysis which basically exploits the linear behavior (for example, the linear temperature density relationship in case of convection) to seek approximate solutions to nonlinear partial differential equations. Such analyses are characterized by a study of the behaviour with time of a small disturbance of the form $\phi(x)e^{zt}$.

In Benard convection, the perturbations about the state of rest are small but the interest lies in finding out whether a steady secondary flow is set up leading to conditions of exchange of stability or whether overstability occurs leading to an oscillatory flow field which is periodic in time. The last aspect is of importance since recent investigations with rotation of the fluid layer [16], imposition of a magnetic field [17], etc. on the stability of thermally stratified fluids, have indicated that at least in certain ranges of the governing parameters, the fluid layers would become overstable and oscillatory convection may set in. Fluid rotation or a magnetic field is able to create conditions of overstability because of the extra dimension of elastic behaviour that is induced.

In the case of viscoelastic fluids, the investigations basically relate to finding the role of elasticity in shifting the critical Rayleigh number and on examining the role of elasticity of a Nusselt number in the supercritical region. While examining the hydrodynamic stability of viscoelastic fluids, the choice of the constitutive equation describing the viscoelastic behaviour is critically important. McIntire and Schowalter [18] have made a useful survey of the role of fluid model and the form of disturbance on the hydrodynamic stability of viscoelastic fluids. The study of overstability during free boundary convection flow was done by Green [19] for the two-parameter Oldroyd model, by Vest and Arpaci [20] as well as Van der Borght et al. [21] for Maxwell model, and by Sokolov and Tanner [22] for the so-called "simple fluid."

The results indicate that although oscillatory flow is theoretically possible during Benard convection in viscoelastic fluids, very high temperature gradients or high gravitational fields would be required to initiate the oscillations. Thus, in practical situations, one cannot expect to observe oscillatory motion during Benard convection in viscoelastic fluids. Van der Borght et al. [21] bring out the role of elasticity on the heat transfer in the supercritical region. A marginal increase in the Nusselt number is seen to occur at high enough Rayleigh numbers as can be seen from Table 1, which summarizes their numerical results. Rosenblat [23] has shed some new light on the onset of convection in a layer of viscoelastic fluid heated from below. It has been shown that there is a strong dependence on the choice of constitutive equation in order to arrive at various stages of the convection. For example, if a particular constitutive equation is used within certain parametric ranges, the theoretical analysis could result in a convection that is supercritical and stable. While if a different choice of constitutive equation is made, the convection would be subcritical and stable. Thus, Rosenblat [23] suggested that based on the convective behavior a test for constitutive equation to describe the nature of the fluid could be designed.

On the experimental side, the only investigation that exists to date on Benard convection in viscoelastic fluids is that of Liang and Acrivos [24]. They studied the buoyancy-driven convection in

Table 1
Influence of Viscoelasticity on Heat Transfer in the Supercritical Region

Ra	$\mathrm{Nu}(\theta_{re}\alpha_0/d^2 = 0)$ Newtonian Fluid	$\mathrm{Nu}(\theta_{re}\alpha_0/d^2 = 10^{-3})$ Viscoelastic Fluid
1×10^3	1.5995	1.6006
2×10^3	2.5830	1.5858
4×10^3	3.6410	3.6472
6×10^3	4.3372	4.3480
8×10^3	4.8800	4.8966
1×10^4	5.3335	5.3570
2×10^4	6.9547	7.0318
4×10^4	8.9690	9.2785
5×10^4	9.7180	10.2729

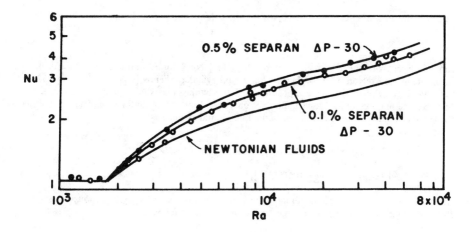

Figure 6. Variation of the Nusselt number with Rayleigh number in Separan AP-30 solutions by natural convection in horizontal layers heated from below [24].

horizontal layers of polyacrylamide solutions and found that the heat transfer characteristics as well as the associated convection patterns were quite similar to those of viscous non-Newtonian fluids. The Nusselt numbers were slightly but consistently higher than those of a Newtonian fluid of a comparable viscosity, as can be seen from Figure 6. Liang and Acrivos [24] found the critical Rayleigh numbers to be exactly the same in Newtonian and viscoelastic fluids studied by them, based on which they suggested that buoyancy-driven convection experiments could be used in practice to determine the zero-shear viscosity of viscoelastic fluids.

A few articles [25–28] have appeared, which consider the interaction of viscoelasticity and buoyancy in plane couette flow. This certainly has semblance to the Benard convection but for the fact that the hydrodynamic field has a finite shear influence on it. These studies were mainly undertaken to offer a mechanistic explanation of instabilities in polymer melt processing. However, Petrie and Denn [29] have shown that melt flow instabilities due to natural convection are unlikely to occur in polymer processing operations.

MIXED CONVECTION IN EXTERNAL FLOWS

In most heat transport processes, density differences are likely to arise leading to natural convection currents superimposing on a forced convection flow field. In circumstances where the forced convection process dominates, the natural convection effects can be neglected. However, there often exist cases where the forced and natural convection effects are of nearly comparable magnitude, in which case the heat transport is determined by the combined effect of both. When conditions for mixed convection exist, the theoretical analyses of the transport process becomes increasingly difficult. No rigorous mathematical solution can be easily done without taking recourse to sophisticated numerical techniques. In view of this, the only theoretical analysis that exists in the literature is that of Shenoy [30] who provides a correlating equation, which can give at least an estimate of the relative importance of the individual forced and free convection effects during laminar mixed convection.

Using the approximate interpolating procedure suggested by Churchill [31] and later established by Ruckenstein [32] for Newtonian fluids, Shenoy [30] showed that the same correlating equation held good for flow of viscoelastic fluids past the stagnation region of the horizontal cylinder. Thus:

$$Nu_{x,M}^3 = Nu_{x,N}^3 + Nu_{x,F}^3 \tag{46}$$

could be used with the new definitions of $Nu_{x,N}$ and $Nu_{x,F}$ for second-order viscoelastic fluid in the stagnation region of an isothermal horizontal cylinder. Shenoy [30] used Equation 32 for defining $Nu_{x,N}$, while deriving the expression for $Nu_{n,f}$ by the approximate integral technique. The final expression for combined forced and free convection heat transfer in the case of a second order fluid in the stagnation region of an isothermal horizontal cylinder is as follows:

$$\frac{Nu_{R,M}}{Re_R^{1/2}} = 2\{[(297\bar{\alpha}_N - 50)f_1(\bar{\alpha}_N)Pr/980\bar{\alpha}_N^2]^{3/4}[Gr_R/Re_R^2]^{3/4}$$
$$+ f_2(\alpha_F)Pr/\{(5/3)[1 - (104/35)Wi]\}^{1/2}\}^{1/3} \tag{47}$$

where $\bar{\alpha}_N$, $f_1(\bar{\alpha}_N)$, Pr, Gr_R, and Wi all have the same definitions as given by Equations 34–39. The Reynolds number Re_R is defined for the second-order fluid as follows:

$$Re_R = \frac{\rho U_\infty R}{\bar{\mu}} \tag{48}$$

The relationship between α_F and Wi is defined as

$$\frac{35}{104}\left[1 - \frac{3}{5\alpha_F^3 f_2(\alpha_F)Pr}\right] = Wi \tag{49}$$

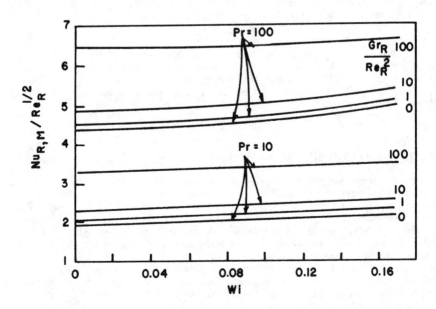

Figure 7. Variation of the average heat transfer rate with viscoelasticity for mixed convection in the stagnation region of a heated horizontal cylinder [30].

and $\quad f_2(\alpha_F) = \dfrac{2}{15} - \dfrac{3}{140}\,\alpha_F^2 + \dfrac{1}{180}\,\alpha_F^3$ $\hfill$ (50)

Figure 7 shows the results obtained by Shenoy [30]. The Nusselt number is seen to gradually rise with increasing viscoelasticity. The effect is a little more pronounced at higher Prandtl numbers. Natural convection currents assist in enhancing the heat transfer in the case of a second-order fluid in the stagnation region of an isothermal cylinder.

MIXED CONVECTION IN INTERNAL FLOWS

Mixed convection in internal flow situations, such as flows through heated or cooled (horizontal or vertical) tubes, has been recognized as a pragmatically important problem. Though there exist a number of theoretical and experimental investigations on laminar mixed convection in inelastic non-Newtonian fluids [1], no such studies exist in the case of viscoelastic fluids. The only study that deals with an internal flow situation for viscoelastic fluids is that of Shenoy [33]. He has provided a theoretical analysis to evaluate the effect of natural convection on heat transfer to drag-reducing fluids flowing under turbulent conditions in vertical pipes.

Shenoy [33] considered that the fluid with a fully-developed velocity profile and at a uniform temperature T_f was flowing upwards under turbulent conditions in a vertical circular tube of radius R and maintained at a constant temperature T_w. Due to the temperature difference $T_w - T_f$, the fluid in the boundary layer near the heated surface experiences a buoyancy force due to the reduced density. The buoyancy force acts in the direction of motion leading to a drop in the shear stress across the buoyant region resulting in reduced turbulence. As a consequence of the increased laminarization, the turbulence structure could be considered to be akin to a buoyancy flow at some reduced value of Reynolds number.

Based on this assumption, simple calculations of the governing momentum and energy equations were done in order to arrive at the following expression for the fractional reduction in shear stress due to buoyancy:

$$\frac{\Delta\tau}{\tau_w} = \left(\frac{2}{\alpha}\right)^{3/2} [e^{2.45 + 0.17\mathrm{De}}] \frac{\mathrm{Gr}}{\mathrm{Pr}^{1/2}\mathrm{Re}^{1.5(2-\beta)}} \left(\frac{\mu_w}{\mu_b}\right)\left(\frac{\rho_b}{\rho_w}\right)^{1/2}$$ $\hfill$ (51)

and the reduced Nusselt number expression as:

$$\frac{\mathrm{Nu}'}{\mathrm{Nu}} = \left\{1 - \left(\frac{2}{\alpha}\right)^{3/2} [e^{2.45 + 0.17\mathrm{De}}] \frac{\mathrm{Gr}}{\mathrm{Pr}^{1/2}\mathrm{Re}^{1.5(2-\beta)}} \left(\frac{\mu_w}{\mu_b}\right)\left(\frac{\rho_b}{\rho_w}\right)^{1/2}\right\}^{0.8/(2-\beta)}$$ $\hfill$ (52)

It was found that a 10% reduction in shear stress induced by buoyancy led to a 5% reduction in heat transfer coefficient. Using Equation 51, a criteria for a reduction of 5% or less in the heat transfer coefficient was set up as follows:

$$\frac{\mathrm{Gr}}{\mathrm{Pr}^{1/2}\mathrm{Re}^{1-5(2-\beta)}} \left(\frac{\mu_w}{\mu_b}\right)\left(\frac{\rho_b}{\rho_w}\right)^{1/2} < C$$ $\hfill$ (53)

where $\quad C = 0.1(\alpha/2)^{3/2}e^{-(2.45 + 0.17\mathrm{De})}$ $\hfill$ (54)

The value of C for increasing elasticity (i.e., increasing values of Deborah numbers) as shown in Table 2, indicates how increasingly difficult it becomes to maintain the reduction in heat transfer due to the effect of buoyancy to less than 5%.

The expression given by Equation 52 gives the Nusselt number for mixed convection when turbulent forced convection is slightly impaired by free convection in the case of upward flow of drag-reducing fluids in vertical pipes. However, it could be easily used for downward flow by introducing a positive sign in place of the negative sign because the buoyancy force in that circumstance would cause an increase in the stress across the buoyant layer.

Table 2 (Taken from [33])
C-Values for Increasing Elasticity

De	α	β	C
00 (Newtonian fluid)	0.0790	0.250	6.77×10^{-5}
1	0.0782	0.262	5.63×10^{-5}
2	0.0767	0.271	4.61×10^{-5}
3	0.0741	0.278	3.70×10^{-5}
4	0.0726	0.285	3.01×10^{-5}
5	0.0689	0.289	2.36×10^{-5}
6	0.0655	0.292	1.84×10^{-5}
7	0.0662	0.301	1.58×10^{-5}
8	0.0687	0.312	1.41×10^{-5}
9	0.0732	0.324	1.31×10^{-5}
10	0.0762	0.334	1.17×10^{-5}
$\gg 20$ (Max. drag reduction asymptote (34)).	0.42	0.55	—

CONCLUSION

In the foregoing, the developments which have taken place in the field of natural convection heat transfer to viscoelastic fluids have been summarized. It is evident that studies so far are limited and a great deal needs to be done in a number of cases.

Even for the simplest case of the vertical flat plate, there exists no correct and useful theoretical analysis. So also there is a need for theoretical study with various geometries such as the horizontal cylinder (other than stagnation region), vertical cone, and the sphere. The existing work has considered only the isothermal case, whereas constant heat flux and variable temperature case also need to be done. There exists no theoretical analysis for the external case during transient natural convection, and this should be an area lending mathematical challenge. Since it has been shown [12] that no similarity solution is possible in all the above cases, effective numerical techniques should be resorted to for obtaining a solution.

As regards mixed convection, the only available work gives a correlating equation for the very restricted case of the stagnation region of a horizontal cylinder. Since mixed convection would more commonly occur in practice than isolated natural or forced convection, work ought to be focused on this problem. Again, a numerical solution would be the only line to follow.

Turbulent natural convection in viscoelastic fluids past external surfaces would be rather uncommon in reality and can be given a low priority in the study. However, turbulent mixed convection in horizontal pipes should be considered extremely useful, especially because of the increasing importance of drag-reducing fluids [2, 34].

The problem of buoyancy-induced secondary flow in heated horizontal tubes is certainly a challenging and useful area to work in even when the forced flow is laminar. This is probably one of the most frequently occurring circumstances in actual practice.

Benard convection to viscoelastic fluids need not be pursued as the studies are quite comprehensive, and despite only one experimental work in the area [24], the results are conclusive enough to emphasize its importance. However, the problem of mixed convection in vertical tubes needs to be analyzed carefully and stability considerations could gain importance when studying elastic fluids.

The dearth of experimental data in all areas of natural convection to viscoelastic fluids is obvious from the above. With the introduction of Boger fluids [3], systematic experiments can be planned so that the isolated effect of elasticity on the heat transfer characteristic during natural convection external and internal flows can be brought out.

In summary, there is tremendous scope for the theoretician as well as the experimentalist to make a mark in the area of natural convection to viscoelastic fluids.

NOTATION

a	length of rectangular enclosure in (Equation (44) and Figure 5)	m	material parameter in Equation 7 for the specific constitutive Equation 4 chosen for a viscoelastic fluid
A_1, A_2	Rivlin-Erikson tensors of the first and second order (Equation 4)	n	power-law model parameter known as pseudoplasticity index
b	width of rectangular enclosure (Equation 44 and Figure 5)	Nu	average Nusselt number for rectangular enclosure as defined by Equation 44
B_1, B_2, B_3	coefficients (Equations 27 and 28)	Nu_R	local Nusselt number based on radius of the cylinder
C_1	coefficient in Equation 27 and defined by Equation 29	Nu_x	local Nusselt number based on on the local distance x on the heat transferring surface
C_p	specific heat per unit mass of fluid	$Nu_{xF}, Nu_{xM}, Nu_{xN}$	local Nusselt numbers based on the local distance x on the heat transferring surface for forced, mixed, and natural convection, respectively
d	distance between two plates (Equation 45 and Table 1)		
De	Deborah number (Table 2)		
$f_1(\bar{\alpha}_N)$	function of $\bar{\alpha}_N$ defined by Equation 35		
$f_2(\alpha_F)$	function of α_F defined by Equation 50	$Nu_{R,M}$	average Nusselt number based on the radius of the cylinder for mixed convection
g	acceleration due to gravity	p	exponent in the gravity field given by Equation 16
Gr	local distance-based Grashof number for a second order fluid defined by Equation 36	$\bar{p}$	pressure
		Pr	Prandtl number for a second order fluid defined by Equation 37
Gr_R	Grashof number for a second-order fluid based on the radius of the cylinder and defined by Equation 38	Pr_{xt}	power-law Prandtl number based on the local distance of a constant temperature heating surface and defined by Equation 12
Gr_{nt}	power-law Grashof number based on local distance of a constant temperature heating surface and defined by Equation 11		
		R	radius of the horizontal cylinder
		Ra	Rayleigh number defined by Equation 45
h	heat transfer coefficient appearing in the definition of Nusselt number	Re_R	Reynolds number for a second-order fluid based on the radius of the cylinder and defined by Equation 48
k	thermal conductivity of the fluid		
K	power-law model parameter known as consistency index		
$\bar{K}$	parameter describing the shear-rate dependency of viscosity and elasticity in Equation 40	s	normal stress power-law exponent (Equation 7)
l	material parameter in Equation 6 for the specific constitutive Equation 4 chosen for viscoelastic fluid	t	time
		t_0	characteristic fluid time (Equation 40)
l_c	characteristic length of the heat-transferring surface as defined by Equation (23)	T	temperature
		T_0	temperature of bottom plate in in Equation 45

T_1 temperature of top plate in Equation 45

T_c temperature of the right side of rectangular enclosure of time $t > 0$

T_H temperature of the left side of rectangular enclosure at time $t > 0$

T_i initial temperature of rectangular enclosure for all times $t < 0$

T_w uniform wall temperature .

T temperature of bulk of the fluid

u velocity component along x-coordinate

u_1 dimensionless velocity component along x-coordinate as defined in Equation 19

$u_1(\eta)$ velocity profile as defined by Equation 25

U dimensionless velocity component along x-coordinate (Equations 42 and 43)

U_c characteristic velocity for natural convection as defined by Equation 22

U characteristic velocity for forced convection; represents the velocity of fluid at infinity

$\mathbf{v}$ velocity vector

v velocity component along y-coordinate

V dimensionless velocity component along y-coordinate in Equations 42 and 43

w exponent in Equation 6 for the specific constitutive Equation 4 for a viscoelastic fluid

Wi Weissenberg number defined by Equation 39

x distance along a heated solid surface

x_1 dimensionless distance along a heated solid surface as defined in Equation 19

X dimensionless distance along the heated surface in Equation 42 and 43

y distance normal to the solid surface

y_1 dimensionless distance normal to the solid surface as defined in Equation 19

Y dimensionless distance normal to the heated surface in Equations 42 and 43

Greek Symbols

α thermal diffusivity of the fluid Equation 45

α_F ratio of the thermal to momentum boundary layer thickness for laminar forced convection to to a second-order fluid defined in Shenoy [30]

$\bar{\alpha}_N$ ratio of the thermal to momentum boundary layer thickness for laminar natural convection to a second-order fluid defined in Shenoy and Mashelkar [12]

β_0 volume expansion coefficient of the fluid evaluated at T_∞

$\dot{\gamma}$ shear rate

δ, δ_T momentum and thermal boundary layer thicknesses for laminar natural convection

δ_1, δ_{T_1} dimensionless momentum and thermal boundary layer thicknesses for laminar natural convection as defined in Equation 20.

∇ rate of deformation tensor

η, η_T variable defined in Equation 21

η' similarity variable defined by Equation 10

η_0 zero-shear viscosity in Equation 40

η_s solvent viscosity in Equation 40

λ scalar function of the second invariant of the rate of strain tensor defined by Equation 7

θ dimensionless temperature difference as defined by Equation 21

θ_{fl} fluid relaxation time for a viscoelastic fluid in Table 1.

μ scalar function of the second invariant of the rate of strain tensor defined by Equation 5

$\bar{\mu}$ viscosity of the second-order fluid

ρ density of the fluid

τ^+ deviatoric or extra stress tensor

τ_{xy}^+, τ_{yx}^+ shear stress components

$\tau_{xx} - \tau_{yy}$,	normal stress difference	ψ	stream function in Equation 41
$\tau_{yy}^{+} - \tau_{xx}^{+}$		Ω	velocity function in Equation 41
ω	scalar function of the second invariant of the rate of strain tensor defined by Equation 6	$\tilde{\Pi}$	second invariant of Rivlin-Eriksen tensor

Operational Symbols

$\dfrac{\partial}{\partial t}$	spatial derivative	∇	gradient operator
		∇'	divergence operator
$\dfrac{D}{Dt}$	material derivative	∇^2	Laplacian or Nabla operator

REFERENCES

1. Shenoy, A. V., "Natural Convection Heat Transfer to Power-Law Fluids," *Handbook of Heat and Mass Transfer*, ed. Cheremisinoff, N. P., Vol. 1, Section 1, Chapter 5, 1986, pp. 183–210.
2. Shenoy, A. V., "A Review on Drag Reduction with Special Reference to Micellar systems," *Colloid Polymer Science*, Vol. 262, 1984, pp. 319–337.
3. Binnington, R. J., and Boger, D. V., "Constant Viscosity Elastic Liquids," *J. Rheol.*, Vol. 29, 1985, pp. 887–904.
4. Middleman, S., *Fundamentals of Polymer Processing*, McGraw-Hill, New York, 1977.
5. Bird, R. B., Armstrong, R. C., and Hassager, O., *Dynamics of Polymeric Liquids: Volume I, Fluid Mechanics*, John Wiley and Sons, New York, 1977.
6. Denn, M. M., "Boundary Layer Flows for a Class of Elastic Fluids," *Chem. Eng. Sci.*, Vol. 22, 1967, pp. 395–405.
7. Mishra, S. P., "Free-convection Flow of a Second Order Fluid Past a Hot Vertical Plate," *Proc. Indian Acad. Sci.*, Vol. A64, 1966, pp. 291–303.
8. Mishra, S. P., "Free Convection Flow of an Elastico-Viscous Liquid Past a Hot Vertical Plate," *Indian Chemical Engineer*, Vol. 8, 1966, pp. 28–32.
9. Amato, W. S., and Tien, C., "National Convection Heat Transfer from a Vertical Plate to an Oldroyd Fluid," *Chem. Eng. Prog. Symp. Series*, Vol. 66, 1970, pp. 92–99.
10. Soundalgekar, V. M.,"Viscous Dissipation Effects on Unsteady Free Convective Flow Past an Infinite Vertical Porous Plate with Constant Suction," *Int. J. Heat Mass Transfer*, Vol. 15, 1972, pp. 1253–1261.
11. Soundalgekar, V. M., "Unsteady Free Convection Flow of an Elastoviscous Fluid Past an Infinite Plate with Constant Suction," *Chem. Eng. Sci.*, Vol. 26, 1971, pp. 2043–2050.
12. Shenoy, A. V., and Mashelkar, R. A., "Laminar Natural Convection Heat Transfer to a Viscoelastic Fluid," *Chem. Eng. Sci.*, Vol. 33, 1978, pp. 769–776.
13. Shenoy, A. V., and Ulbrecht, J. J., "Temperature Profiles for Laminar Natural Convection Flow of Dilute Polymer Solutions Past an Isothermal Vertical Flat Plate," *Chem. Eng. Communications*, Vol. 3, 1979, pp. 303–324.
14. Lyons, D. W., White, J. W., and Hatcher, J. D., "Laminar Natural Convection Heat Transfer in Dilute Aqueous Polymer Solutions," *Ind. Eng. Chem. Fund.*, Vol. 11, 1972, pp. 586–588.
15. Ropke, K. J., and Schummer, P., "Natural Convection of a Viscoelastic Fluid," *Rheol. Acta*, Vol. 21, 1982, pp. 540–542.
16. Chandrasekhar, S., "The Instability of a Layer of Fluid Heated Below and Subject to Coriolis Force," Proc. Royal Soc., London, Series A, Vol. 217, 1953, pp. 306–327.
17. Chandrasekhar, S., "On the Inhibition of Convection by a Magnetic Field," *Philos. Mag.*, Vol. 45, 1954, pp. 1177–1191.
18. McIntire, L. V., and Schowalter, W. R., "Hydrodynamic Stability of Viscoelastic Fluids: Importance of Fluid Model, Overstability and Form of Disturbance," *AIChEJ.*, Vol. 18, 1972, pp. 102–110.

19. Green III, T., "Oscillating Convection in an Elasticoviscous Liquid," *Phys. Fluids*, Vol. 11, 1972, pp. 1410–1412.
20. Vest, C. M., and Arpaci, V. S., "Overstability of a Viscoelastic Fluid Layer Heated from Below," *J. Fluid Mech.*, Vol. 36, 1969, pp. 613–623.
21. Van der Borght, R., Murphy, J. IO., and Steiner, J. M., "A Theoretical Investigation of Finite Amplitude Thermal Convection in Non-Newtonian Fluids," *Z. Aug. Math. Mech.*, Vol. 54, 1974, pp. 1–8.
22. Sokolov, M., and Tanner, R. I., "Convective Stability of a General Viscoelastic Fluid Heated from Below," *Phys. Fluids*, Vol. 15, 1972, pp. 534–539.
23. Rosenblat, S., "Thermal Convection in a Viscoelastic Fluid," *J. Non-Newtonian Fluid Mech.*, Vol. 21, 1986, pp. 201–223.
24. Liang, S. F., and Acrivos, A., "Experiments in Buoyancy Driven Convection in Non-Newtonian Fluid," *Rheol. Acta*, Vol. 9, 1970, pp. 447–455.
25. Herbert, D. M., "On the Stability of Viscoelastic Liquids in Heated Plane Couette Flow," *J. Fluid Mech.*, Vol. 17, 1963, pp. 353–359.
26. Bennett, W. S., and McIntire, L. V., "Dissipation Effects in Hydrodynamic Stability of Viscoelastic Fluids," *AIChEJ.*, Vol. 21, 1975, pp. 901–910.
27. McIntire, L. V., and Schowalter, W. R., "Stability of Viscoelastic Fluids in Plane Couette Flow with Superimposed Temperature Gradient," *Trans. Soc. Rheol.*, Vol. 14, 1970, pp. 585–603.
28. McIntire, L. V., "On the Initiation of Melt Fracture," *J. Appl. Polym. Sci.*, Vol. 16, 1972, pp. 2901–2908.
29. Petrie, C. J. S., and Denn, M. M., "Instabilities in Polymer Processing," *AIChEJ.*, Vol. 22, 1976, pp. 209–236.
30. Shenoy, A. V., "Combined Laminar Forced and Free Convection Heat Transfer to Viscoelastic Fluids," *AIChEJ.*, Vol. 26, 1980, pp. 683–686.
31. Churchill, S. W., "A Comprehensive Correlating Equation for Laminar Assisting Forced and Free Convection," *AIChEJ.*, Vol. 23, 1977, pp. 10–16.
32. Ruckenstein, E., "Interpolating Equations Between Two Limiting Cases for the Heat Transfer Coefficient," *AIChEJ.*, Vol. 24, 1978, pp. 940–941.
33. Shenoy, A. V., " Effects of Buoyancy on Heat Transfer During Turbulent Flow of Drag Reducing Fluids in Vertical Pipes," *Warmeund Stoffubertragung*, Vol. 21, 1987, pp. 15–19.
34. Virk, P. S., "Drag Reduction Fundamentals," *AIChEJ.*, Vol. 21, 1975, pp. 625–656.

CHAPTER 11

INTEGRAL METHODS FOR FORCED CONVECTION
HEAT TRANSFER IN POWER-LAW NON-NEWTONIAN FLUIDS

Akira Nakayama

Department of Energy and Mechanical Engineering
Shizuoka University
Hamamatsu, Japan.

CONTENTS

INTRODUCTION

A number of industrially important fluids such as molten plastics, polymers, pulps, foods, etc. exhibit non-Newtonian fluid behavior. Due to the growing use of these non-Newtonian substances in various manufacturing and processing industries, considerable efforts have been directed toward understanding their friction and heat transfer characteristics. Non-Newtonian fluids can be classified depending on the form of the constitutive equation describing the properties of real fluids quantitatively. Generally, they are subdivided into two categories: viscoelastic fluids where the stress depends on both the instantaneous strain rate and the past strain history; and viscoinelastic fluids where the stress depends on the current state of strain rate only. Such systems of rheological classification may be found elsewhere [1–3]. Many of the inelastic non-Newtonian fluids encountered in chemical engineering processes are known to follow the empirical Ostwald-de Waele model [4], or the so-called "power-law model" in which the shear stress varies according to a power function of the strain rate. We shall concentrate our discussion on such non-Newtonian power-law fluids.

While the power-law fluid flows within ducts have been covered rather well both theoretically and experimentally [2, 4], not many studies have been reported on the flows past external surfaces. An initiative work on forced convective heat transfer from external surfaces to power-law fluids was carried out by Acrivos, Shah, and Petersen [5] for the case of an isothermal flat plate, using a combined analytical-numerical approach. This innovative work was supplimented by Schowalter [6] considering the possibility of similarity transformations, and was later extended to the case of an isothermal right angle wedge by Lee and Ames [7].

Complexities of the problem lie in the high degree of non-linearity and coupling of the governing equations, as a direct consequence of the employment of the power-law model. Thus, similarity solutions are not possible even in the case of a flow over an isothermal flat plate. In order to deal with non-similar flows, the Blasius series approach was used by Wolf and Szewczyk [8] while Serth and Kiser [9] chose to work with the Goertler series method. A rapid computational procedure based on the Lighthill's formula [10] was suggested by Acrivos, Shah, and Petersen [5] and Shah, Petersen, and Acrivos [11]. Recently, Lin and Chern [12] and Kim, Jeng, and DeWitt [13] analyzed the power-law fluid flows using the Merk-Chao expansion method which leads to an improved version of the Lighthill's analysis [14–16].

Despite much effort, the extreme difficulty encountered in the boundary layer analysis on the power-law fluid flows still invites a more general and yet simpler method for analyzing the power-law fluids. Bizzele and Slattery [17] extended a simple integral method originally suggested for an isothermal flat plate by Acrivos, Shah, and Petersen [5] to examine the momentum equation for a pseudoplastic fluid flow past an axisymmetric body. However, no attempt was made to solve the corresponding energy equation.

The first three sections of this chapter are devoted to mathematical description of the power-law stress model, application of boundary layer approximations, and classical similarity transformation. In the remaining sections following these preliminary considerations, we shall proceed to discuss an approximate method based on the Kármán-Pohlhausen integral relations for obtaining solutions to both momentum and energy equations describing forced convection power-law fluid flows past wedges [18] and cones [19]. Subsequently, we shall extend this integral treatment to general cases of plane axisymmetric bodies of arbitrary geometrical configuration. The method may be viewed as an extended version of a highly accurate integral solution procedure developed for Newtonian fluid flows over a wedge of arbitrary included angle [20]. Following the procedure similar to the one employed for film condensation [21] and film boiling [22] problems, the momentum and energy equations are transformed into a pair of characteristic equations which can readily be solved once the geometry and wall temperature are specified as functions of the streamwise coordinate. No other methods for the power-law non-Newtonian fluids as general as the present one seem to have been reported elsewhere.

POWER-LAW STRESS MODEL

On the basis of the laws of tensor transformation, Oldroyd [23] argued that the effective viscosity can be expressed in terms of three invariants of the strain rates $(\partial u_i/\partial x_j + \partial u_j/\partial x_i)$, and suggested an expression for the stress tensor τ_{ij}, which runs for the case of incompressible flow as:

$$\tau_{ij} = K\left[\Phi^{(n-1)/2} + F\left(n, \left|\frac{\partial u_i}{\partial x_j}\right|\right)\right]\left(\frac{\partial u_i}{\partial x_j} + \frac{\partial u_j}{\partial x_i}\right) \tag{1a}$$

where
$$\Phi = \frac{\partial u_i}{\partial x_j}\left(\frac{\partial u_i}{\partial x_j} + \frac{\partial u_j}{\partial x_i}\right) \tag{1b}$$

and $|\partial u_i/\partial x_j|$ is the determinant of $\partial u_i/\partial x_j$. $F(n, |\partial u_i/\partial x_j|)$ is a function satisfying $F(1, |\partial u_i/\partial x_j|) = F(n, 0) = 0$ such that the expression reduces to the laminar deformation law:

$$\tau_{ij} = K\left(\frac{\partial u_i}{\partial x_j} + \frac{\partial u_j}{\partial x_i}\right) \tag{2}$$

for Newtonian flows, and to the empirical "power-law":

$$\tau_{ij} = K\Phi^{(n-1)/2}\left(\frac{\partial u_i}{\partial x_j} + \frac{\partial u_j}{\partial x_i}\right) \tag{3}$$

for rectilinear flows since $|\partial u_i/\partial x_j| = 0$ for two-dimensional flows. For the case of simple rectilinear flows in the x-y plane, Equation 3 further reduces to:

$$\tau_{xy} = K\left(\frac{\partial u}{\partial y}\right)^n \tag{4}$$

in which the coordinate x and velocity u are taken in parallel to the wall.

In this chapter, we shall concentrate our discussion exclusively on power-law fluids. Nevertheless, remember that the power-law model given by Equation 3 cannot represent accurately the behavior of very viscoelastic materials or materials exhibiting the Weissenberg effect; and that the power-law exponent n and consistency index K in general three-dimensional flows may vary directionally, since the fluid is not guaranteed to be isotropic.

APPLICATION OF BOUNDARY LAYER APPROXIMATIONS

For a steady, incompressible, two-dimensional flow, and in the absence of external force terms, the equation of continuity, the u and v momentum equations, and the energy equation may be given by:

$$\frac{\partial u}{\partial x} + \frac{\partial v}{\partial y} = 0 \tag{5a}$$

$$u\frac{\partial u}{\partial x} + v\frac{\partial u}{\partial y} = -\frac{1}{\rho}\frac{\partial p}{\partial x} + \frac{K}{\rho}\frac{\partial}{\partial x}\left(\Phi^{(n-1)/2}\,2\,\frac{\partial u}{\partial x}\right) + \frac{K}{\rho}\frac{\partial}{\partial y}\,\Phi^{(n-1)/2}\left(\frac{\partial u}{\partial y} + \frac{\partial v}{\partial x}\right) \tag{5b}$$

$$u\frac{\partial v}{\partial x} + v\frac{\partial v}{\partial y} = -\frac{1}{\rho}\frac{\partial p}{\partial y} + \frac{K}{\rho}\frac{\partial}{\partial y}\left(\Phi^{(n-1)/2}\,2\,\frac{\partial v}{\partial y}\right) + \frac{K}{\rho}\frac{\partial}{\partial x}\,\Phi^{(n-1)/2}\left(\frac{\partial u}{\partial y} + \frac{\partial v}{\partial x}\right) \tag{5c}$$

$$\rho C_p\left(u\frac{\partial T}{\partial x} + v\frac{\partial T}{\partial y}\right) = k\left(\frac{\partial^2 T}{\partial x^2} + \frac{\partial^2 T}{\partial y^2}\right) \tag{5d}$$

where $\quad \Phi = \left(\frac{\partial u}{\partial y} + \frac{\partial v}{\partial x}\right)^2 + 2\left[\left(\frac{\partial u}{\partial x}\right)^2 + \left(\frac{\partial v}{\partial y}\right)^2\right] \tag{5e}$

where $\quad \rho$ = density
$\quad\quad C_p$ = specific heat at constant pressure
$\quad\quad k$ = thermal conductivity.

The viscous dissipation term $\tau_{ij}(\partial u_i/\partial x_j)$ is neglected in the energy Equation 5d. Upon following Schlichting [24], we can inspect the relative magnitudes of the terms in Equations 5a–5d. Under the boundary layer approximation, namely, that the ratio of the boundary layer thickness δ to a characteristic length L is small ($\delta/L \ll 1$) as illustrated in Figure 1, the equation of continuity (Equation 5a) reveals:

$$u^*, x^* = O(1)$$

$$v^*, y^* = O(\delta^*)$$

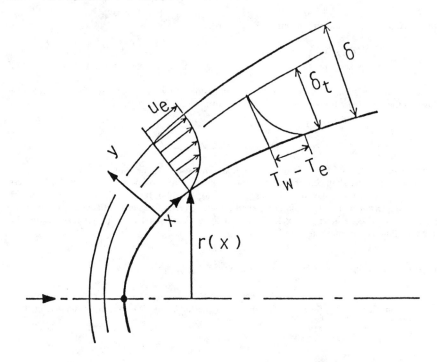

Figure 1. Physical model and its boundary layer coordinates.

and thus $\Phi^* \cong \left(\dfrac{\partial u^*}{\partial y^*}\right)^n = O(1/\delta^{*n})$

where the asterisk refers to the dimensionless quantities based on L and a characteristic velocity of external flow u_∞. Dropping some negligible terms in consideration of relative magnitudes, the u momentum equation (Equation 5b) may be rewritten in a dimensionless form as:

$$u^* \frac{\partial u^*}{\partial x^*} + v^* \frac{\partial u^*}{\partial y^*} = -\frac{\partial p^*}{\partial x^*} + \frac{1}{Re} \frac{\partial}{\partial y^*} \left(\frac{\partial u^*}{\partial y^*}\right)^n \qquad (6a)$$

where $Re = \dfrac{\rho u_\infty^{2-n} L^n}{K} \qquad (6b)$

is the Reynolds number representing the ratio of the inertia force to viscous force. Since the inertia terms are of order 1, the viscous term:

$$\frac{1}{Re} \frac{\partial}{\partial y^*} \left(\frac{\partial u^*}{\partial y^*}\right)^n = O(1/Re^*\delta^{n+1})$$

must also be of order 1 to give identical orders of magnitude to the inertia and viscous terms. This inspection suggests:

$$\delta^* \propto 1/Re^{1/(1+n)} \qquad (7)$$

The foregoing relation indicates that $Re = u_\infty^{2-n} L^n \rho / K$ must be sufficiently large for the boundary layer approximation $\delta^* \ll 1$ to be valid. We can make Re large by increasing the fluid velocity as long as n < 2. When n > 2, on the other hand, we must decrease the velocity to make Re large. However, such boundary layer flows do not seem to exist since all fluids approach Newtonian behavior if u_∞ is sufficiently small and in accordance with the well-known argument of Stokes, the inertia terms of the momentum equations may be neglected [5]. In fact, the power-law model, Equation 4, is valid only when the gradient $\partial u / \partial y$ is large. In our discussion, we shall assume that the material index n is in a possible range, $0 \leq n \leq 2$.

A similar inspection of the v momentum equation (Equation 5c) with aid of the proportional relation (Equation 7) leads to:

$$\frac{\partial p^*}{\partial y^*} = O(\delta^*)$$

indicating that the pressure is virtually constant in the normal direction, and is a function of x alone. Thus, under the boundary layer approximation, the momentum Equations 5b and 5c can be combined into the following simple expression:

$$\frac{\partial}{\partial x} u^2 + \frac{\partial}{\partial y} uv = u_e \frac{du_e}{dx} + \frac{\partial}{\partial y} K \left| \frac{\partial u}{\partial y} \right|^{n-1} \frac{\partial u}{\partial y} \tag{8}$$

where the pressure gradient term $-(1/\rho)(dp/dx)$ has been replaced by $u_e(du_e/dx)$ on the basis of the Bernoulli equation, implicit in Equation 6a. The external free stream velocity $u_e(x)$ can be determined from the potential flow theory. The energy Equation 5d can also be simplified following the same procedure. The resulting expression is:

$$\frac{\partial}{\partial x} uT + \frac{\partial}{\partial y} vT = \frac{k}{\varrho Cp} \frac{\partial^2 T}{\partial y^2} \tag{9}$$

Hence, for the boundary layer flow of a power-law fluid, we only have to consider the three equations, namely, the continuity equation (Equation 5a), the momentum equation (Equation 8) and the energy equation (Equation 9). These governing equations must satisfy the boundary conditions as follows:

$$y = 0: u = 0, v = 0, T = T_w(x) \tag{10a,b,c}$$

$$y \to \infty: u = u_e(x), T = T_e \tag{10d,e}$$

where the subscripts w and e refer to the wall and boundary layer edge, respectively.

SIMILARITY TRANSFORMATION AND SOLUTION PROCEDURE

Before discussing an approximate solution procedure based on Kármán-Pohlhausen integral relation, it is relevant here to follow the classical transformation procedure. Acrivos, et al. [5] introduced a solution procedure based on similarity transformation for the analysis of a power-law fluid over a flat plate. In what follows, we shall extend the similarity transformation procedure to general cases of non-similar power-law fluid flow and heat transfer from a non-isothermal wall.

The continuity Equation 5a may automatically be satisfied by introducing the stream function ψ such that:

$$u = \frac{\partial \psi}{\partial y} \quad \text{and} \quad v = -\frac{\partial \psi}{\partial x} \tag{11a,b}$$

Upon noting the proportional relationship (Equation 7), we introduce the following general transformations:

$$\psi = (u_e x / Re^{1/(n+1)}) f(x, \eta) \tag{12a}$$

$$T - T_e = \Delta T_w \theta(x, \eta) \tag{12b}$$

$$\text{and} \quad \eta = \frac{y}{x} Re_x^{1/(n+1)} \tag{12c}$$

$$\text{such that} \quad \frac{\partial}{\partial x} = \frac{\partial}{\partial x} - \frac{1 + (n-2)m}{n+1} \frac{\eta}{x} \frac{\partial}{\partial \eta} \tag{13a}$$

$$\text{and} \quad \frac{\partial}{\partial y} = \frac{Re_x^{1/(n+1)}}{x} \frac{\partial}{\partial \eta} \tag{13b}$$

$$\text{where} \quad \Delta T_w(x) = T_w(x) - T_e \tag{14a}$$

$$\text{and} \quad Re_x = \rho u_e^{2-n} x^n / K \tag{14b}$$

is the local Reynolds number while η is the proposed pseudo-similarity variable. The velocities are:

$$u = u_e f' \tag{15a}$$

$$\text{and} \quad v = -(u_e/Re_x^{1/(n+1)}) \left(\frac{1 + (2n-1)m}{1+n} f - \frac{1 + (n-2)m}{1+n} \eta f' + x \frac{\partial f}{\partial x} \right) \tag{15b}$$

$$\text{where} \quad m(x) = \frac{d \ln u_e}{d \ln x} \tag{15c}$$

and the primes in the above expressions denote differentiation with respect to η. We substitute Equations 12b–15b into Equations 8 and 9. After some manipulation, we obtain:

$$n(f'')^{n-1} f''' + \frac{1 + (2n-1)m}{n+1} ff'' + m(1 - f'^2) = x \left(f' \frac{\partial f'}{\partial x} - f'' \frac{\partial f}{\partial x} \right) \tag{16a}$$

$$\text{and} \quad \frac{1}{Pr_x} \theta'' + \frac{1 + (2n-1)m}{n+1} f'\theta' - m_t f'\theta = x \left(f' \frac{\partial \theta}{\partial x} - \theta' \frac{\partial f}{\partial x} \right) \tag{16b}$$

$$\text{where} \quad m_t(x) = \frac{d \ln \Delta T_w}{d \ln x} \tag{17a}$$

$$\text{and} \quad Pr_x(x) = \frac{\rho C_p}{k} \left(\frac{K}{\rho} \right)^{2/(1+n)} \left(\frac{x}{u_e^3} \right)^{(1-n)/(1+n)} \tag{17b}$$

is the local Prandtl number, which, unlike in Newtonian flows, varies locally.

The transformed boundary conditions corresponding to Equations 10 are given by:

$$\eta = 0: f = 0, f' = 0, \theta = 1 \tag{18a,b,c}$$

$$\eta \to \infty: f' = 1, \theta = 0 \tag{18d,e}$$

Equation 16a is not coupled with Equation 16b, and hence can be solved independently. Let us consider the momentum equation (Equation 16a) which is subjected to the boundary conditions of Equations 18a, b, and d. As the power-law exponent n and the external flow velocity distribution m(x) are given, we can integrate Equation 16a using available solution methods such as a local non-similarity method [25]. Even the local similarity method [25] in which the right hand side terms in Equations 16 are neglected may be found sufficiently accurate when the values of x or $\partial f/\partial x$ and $\partial f'/\partial x$ are small. Any standard numerical integration scheme such as Runge-Kutta scheme can be used to solve Equations 16. A straightforward procedure to find f satisfying the boundary conditions given by Equations 18a,b and 18d may be to iterate on $f''(x, 0)$ by carrying out the integration of Equation 16a with Equations 18a,b and a guessed value of $f''(x, 0)$, so that Equation 16d is eventually satisfied. (Our experience [26] shows that the upper bound of integration, namely, $\eta \to \infty$, may well be replaced by $\eta = 10$, while an increment of $\Delta\eta = 0.02$ is found usually small enough to resolve even steep velocity gradients at the wall.)

Knowing the f distribution in this way, the local friction coefficient can be obtained from:

$$C_{fx} = 2\tau_w/\rho u_e^2 = 2[f''(x, 0)]^n/Re_x^{1/(n+1)} \tag{19}$$

Similarity solutions to Equation 16a are possible when m remains constant so that:

$$n(f'')^{n-1}f''' + \frac{1 + (2n - 1)m}{n + 1} ff'' + m(1 - f'^2) = 0 \tag{20a}$$

where $\quad u_e(x) \propto x^m$ \hfill (20b)

The case corresponds to a flow over a wedge having an included angle $2\pi m/(1 + m)$. For n = 1, Equation 20a reduces to the well-known Falkner-Skan equation. Kim et al. [13] carried out a series of numerical integrations by changing the values of n and m. (Obviously, a flat plate flow treated by Acrivos et al. [5] can be derived by setting m = 0.) Approximate results based on the integral method (to be discussed shortly) will be compared against these exact solutions.

Now, let us turn our attention to the energy equation (Equation 16b) subjected to the boundary conditions given by Equations 18c and 18e. An iteration procedure similar to the one adopted for the momentum equation can be programmed to determine the correct boundary value of $\theta'(x, 0)$. Then, the local Nusselt number of our primary concern can be given by:

$$Nu_x = \frac{q_w x}{\Delta T_w k} = -\theta'(x, 0)Re_x^{1/(1+n)} \tag{21}$$

Especially when m, m_t, and Pr_x are all constants, similarity solutions to Equation 16b exist as:

$$\frac{1}{Pr_x} \theta'' + \frac{1 + (2n - 1)m}{n + 1} f\theta' - m_t f'\theta = 0 \tag{22a}$$

where $\quad \Delta T_w \propto x^{m_t}$ \hfill (22b)

Moreover, constancy of Pr_x (defined by Equation 17b) requires:

$$n = 1 \quad \text{or} \quad m = 1/3 \tag{22c}$$

Thus, in non-Newtonian power-law fluids, similarity solutions to the energy equation are possible only for a limited geometry, namely, a right angle wedge. (Note that a flat plate flow, m = 0, does not allow a similarity solution to the energy equation unless the fluid is Newtonian, i.e., n = 1.)

Especially for the case of isothermal wall, $m_t = 0$, we can easily integrate Equation 22a to the form:

$$\theta(\eta) = -\theta'(0) \int_\eta^\infty \exp\left[-\frac{1 + (2n - 1)m}{n + 1} \Pr_x \int_0^\eta f \, d\eta \right] d\eta \tag{23a}$$

$$\text{where} \quad \theta'(0) = -\left[\int_0^\infty \exp\left(-\frac{1 + (2n - 1)m}{n + 1} \Pr_x \int_0^\eta f \, d\eta \right) d\eta \right]^{-1} \tag{23b}$$

Since numerical values of f are already available, θ can also be determined numerically. Numerical heat transfer results for the case of a right angle wedge (i.e., $m = 1/3$) were furnished by Kim et al. [13].

INTEGRAL MOMENTUM AND ENERGY EQUATIONS

Although numerical integrations on the momentum and energy equations in a differential form are possible, as discussed in the preceding section, such a numerical integration procedure requires lengthy shooting processes to find the correct boundary values of f'' and θ' at the wall. For each guess, we must carry out integrations from the wall to far outside the boundary layer edge. Only a limited number of numerical integration results have been reported for different sets of parameters and geometrical configurations. While it is not always possible to extract meaningful asymptotic behaviors from a limited number of sets of numerical calculations, it is often more advantageous to appeal to an integral method than to a numerical integration scheme, in order to investigate effects of parameters involved in a particular problem on the friction and heat transfer characteristics. In what follows, we shall discuss such an integral treatment.

Upon integrating the momentum equation (Equation 8) along with the continuity equation (Equation 5a) across the viscous (velocity) boundary layer, we obtain a generalized Kärmän-Pohlhausen integral relation as:

$$\frac{d}{dx} \int_0^\delta (u_e u - u^2) \, dy + \frac{du_e}{dx} \int_0^\delta (u_e - u) \, dy = \frac{K}{\varrho} \left(\frac{\partial u}{\partial y} \right)^n \Bigg|_{y=0} \tag{24}$$

where δ is the velocity boundary layer thickness. An auxiliary relation can be reduced by rewriting Equation 8 at the wall where the inertia terms vanish as:

$$-\frac{K}{\varrho} \frac{\partial}{\partial y} \left(\frac{\partial u}{\partial y} \right)^n \Bigg|_{y=0} = u_e \frac{du_e}{dx}. \tag{25}$$

Let us assume a one-parameter velocity profile as:

$$u/u_e(x) = g\left(\frac{y}{\delta}, \Lambda(x) \right) \tag{26}$$

where $\Lambda(x)$ is some shape factor which may be chosen such that:

$$\Lambda \propto \frac{\partial^2 u}{\partial y^2} \Bigg|_{y=0}$$

The velocity profile function g must satisfy obvious boundary conditions as follows:

$$y/\delta = 0: g = 0 \tag{27a}$$

$$y/\delta = 1: g = 1 \quad \text{and} \quad \frac{\partial g}{\partial (y/\delta)} = 0 \tag{27b,c}$$

For a high order polynomial (a fourth order or higher), we may add the boundary conditions as:

$$y/\delta = 1: \frac{\partial^2 g}{\partial (y/\delta)^2} = \frac{\partial^3 g}{\partial (y/\delta)^3} = \text{------} = 0 \tag{27d}$$

As we specify a reasonable functional form for g, integrations and differentiations in terms of y can be carried out. Thus, Equations 24 and 25 yield two independent equations which can be solved for two unknowns, namely, the boundary layer thickness $\delta(x)$ and the shape factor $\Lambda(x)$. Knowing these quantities, the friction coefficient of our concern may readily be evaluated.

The energy equation (Equation 9) can be integrated in a similar fashion as:

$$\frac{d}{dx} \int_0^{\delta_t} u(T - T_e)\,dy = -\frac{k}{\varrho Cp} \frac{\partial T}{\partial y}\bigg|_{y=0} \tag{28}$$

where δ_t is the thermal boundary layer thickness. As we did for the momentum equation, we consider the energy equation (Equation 9) at the wall, and obtain the auxiliary relation:

$$\frac{\partial^2 T}{\partial y^2} = 0 \tag{29}$$

Equation 29 and the boundary conditions 10c and 10e may automatically be satisfied by assuming the temperature profile as:

$$(T - T_e)/\Delta T_w = \theta\left(\frac{y}{\delta_t}\right) = 1 - g\left(\frac{y}{\delta_t}, 0\right) \tag{30}$$

When the velocity and temperature profiles given by Equations 26 and 30 are substituted, the energy equation (Equation 28) yields an ordinary differential equation which can be solved for $\delta_t(x)$. As a result, we can determine the local heat flux q_w or Nusselt number Nu_x.

SELF-SIMILAR SOLUTION TO INTEGRAL MOMENTUM EQUATION

In this section, we shall seek possible similar solutions to the integral momentum equation.

Let us assume Falkner-Skan free stream velocity field characterized by Equation 20b such that:

$$\frac{dm}{dx} = 0 \tag{31}$$

A free stream velocity of this type may be realized for a flow passing over an infinite wedge or cone, but is found also in the vicinity of a sharp leading edge of any closed body, where the rate of heat transfer is most significant.

Upon substituting Equations 31 and 26 into the integral momentum equation (Equation 24), we can integrate it with respect to x, and obtain

$$(\delta/x)^{1+n} Re_x = \frac{(1+n)C^n}{G} I \tag{32a}$$

where

$$C = \frac{\partial g}{\partial \eta}\bigg|_{\eta=0} \tag{32b}$$

$$G = \int_0^1 (g - g^2)\,d\eta \tag{32c}$$

$$H = \int_0^1 (1 - g) \, d\eta/G \tag{32d}$$

$$I = 1/[1 + (3n + (1 + n)H)m] \tag{32e}$$

The transformed variable η defined by:

$$\eta = y/\delta \tag{32f}$$

varies across the boundary layer from 0 to 1. C, G, and H are the shape factors such that $G\delta$ and $GH\delta$ correspond to the momentum and displacement thicknesses, respectively. The factor I obviously becomes unity in the case of a flat plate flow. Using the above definitions, the auxiliary relation given by Equation 25 may be rewritten as:

$$(\delta/x)^{1+n}\text{Re}_x = 6nC^{n-1}\Lambda/m \tag{33a}$$

$$\text{where} \quad \Lambda = -\frac{1}{6}\frac{\partial^2 g}{\partial\eta^2}\bigg|_{\eta=0} \tag{33b}$$

For the velocity profile function g satisfying Equations 27a–27d, we choose Pohlhausen's polynomial of the fourth degree as:

$$g(\eta, \Lambda) = (2 + \Lambda)\eta - 3\Lambda\eta^2 - (2 - 3\Lambda)\eta^3 + (1 - \Lambda)\eta^4 \tag{34}$$

The above profile automatically satisfies Equation 33b.

Upon carrying out integrations as well as differentiations with respect to η using Equation 34, all shape factors such as C, G, and H can be expressed in terms of algebraic functions of Λ alone. Since, for a wedge flow, the velocity profile within the viscous boundary layer is found self-similar, Λ and all shape factors are constants. These algebraic expressions are substituted into the right hand side terms of Equations 32a and 33a. Upon equating Equations 32a and 33a, we obtain a characteristic equation involving m, n, and Λ:

$$m = \frac{\Lambda G}{\dfrac{1 + n}{6n} C - \Lambda\left(3nG + \dfrac{(1 + n)(6 - \Lambda)}{20}\right)} \tag{35a}$$

$$\text{where} \quad C = 2 + \Lambda \tag{35b}$$

$$\text{and} \quad G = (148 - 8\Lambda - 51\Lambda^2)/1{,}260 \tag{35c}$$

Equation 35a can readily be solved for the shape factor Λ as the power-law exponent n and the wedge flow parameter m are provided. Then, the local skin friction coefficient C_{fx} may be evaluated from:

$$C_{fx}\text{Re}_x^{1/(1+n)} = 2\left(\frac{mC^2}{6n\Lambda}\right)^{n/(1+n)}. \tag{36}$$

For the special case of a flat plate (i.e., $m = \Lambda = 0$), an explicit expression can be obtained from Equations 36 and 35a:

$$C_{fx}\text{Re}_x^{1/(1+n)} = 2\left(\frac{74}{315(1 + n)}\right)^{n/(1+n)} \tag{37}$$

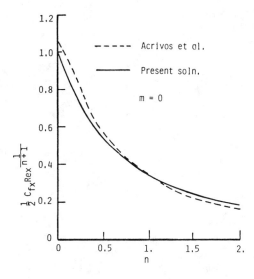

Figure 2. Friction coefficient for a flat plate.

The curve generated by Equation 37 is plotted in Figure 2, where reasonably good agreement is seen between the present solution and the exact solution [5]. The variation of the shape factor Λ is shown in Figure 3 where the abscissa variable is chosen to be the wedge flow parameter m. The effect of the wedge angle on Λ appears to be the same as for Newtonian fluids, namely, the increase in m (or ϕ) leads to a strong flow acceleration, which naturally increases the initial slope of the velocity profile. The figure also indicates a general trend that the velocity gradient at the wall becomes steeper as n decreases.

The corresponding local skin friction for wedges is plotted in Figure 4 in a similar fashion. The comparison of the present approximate solution and the available exact solutions [13, 27] reveals an excellent performance of the present integral method. The flow acceleration due to the increase in m suppresses the viscous diffusion process, resulting in a higher skin friction coefficient, while the increase in the power-law exponent n, as already seen for a flat plate, lowers the level of the skin friction grouping.

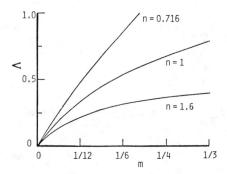

Figure 3. Velocity shape factor on a wedge.

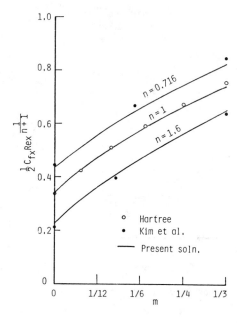

Figure 4. Friction coefficient for a wedge.

ASYMPTOTIC HEAT TRANSFER RESULTS FOR HIGH PRANDTL NUMBER

For most practical problems involving non-Newtonian fluids, the Prandtl number Pr_x is quite large. Before investigating more general cases, we shall obtain a useful asymptotic expression under the assumption of high Prandtl number. It will be shown that the resulting heat transfer expression is valid for arbitrary values of the Falkner-Skan parameter m, the power-law exponent n, and the exponent m_t describing the wall temperature distribution.

For large Prandtl number, the thermal boundary layer thickness δ_t is much less than the viscous boundary layer thickness δ, so that the velocity profile is almost linear across the thermal boundary layer. Thus, we can approximate the integral energy equation (Equation 28) as:

$$\frac{d}{dx} \int_0^{\delta_t} \frac{\partial u}{\partial y}\bigg|_{y=0} y(T - T_e)\,dy = -\frac{k}{\rho C_p}\frac{\partial T}{\partial y}\bigg|_{y=0} \tag{38}$$

Following Equation 30, we assume the temperature profile as:

$$\theta(\eta_t) = (T - T_e)/(T_w - T_e) = 1 - 2\eta_t + 2\eta_t^3 - \eta_t^4 \tag{39a}$$

where $\quad \eta_t = y/\delta_t \tag{39b}$

Now, let us assume the wall temperature distribution in the form of a power function as given by Equation 22b such that:

$$\frac{dm_t}{dx} = 0 \tag{40}$$

Equations 39 and 40 are substituted into Equation 38, which is then integrated. After some manipulation, we obtain:

$$(\delta_t/x)^2 = \frac{60k\zeta}{\rho C_p u_e x C} \frac{1}{1 + m + 2m_t - \dfrac{d \ln \zeta}{d \ln x}} \tag{41a}$$

where $\quad \zeta = \delta/\delta_t \tag{41b}$

is the boundary layer thickness ratio. Upon combining Equations 41a and 33a, we obtain:

$$\zeta \cong \left[\left(\frac{6nC^{n-1}\Lambda}{m} \right)^{2/(1+n)} \frac{2+\Lambda}{60} \left(1 + m + 2m_t - \frac{(1-n)(1-3m)}{3(1+n)} \right) \right]^{1/3} Pr_x^{1/3} \tag{42}$$

where Pr_x is the generalized Prandtl number defined by Equation 17b. Since ζ is readily calculable from Equation 41a by substituting Λ obtained from Equation 35a, the local Nusselt number $Nu_x = 2\zeta x/\delta$, of our primary concern, can easily be evaluated from:

$$Nu_x/Re_x^{1/(1+n)} \simeq \left[\left(\frac{m}{6nC^{n-1}\Lambda} \right)^{1/(1+n)} \frac{2(2+\Lambda)}{15} \left(1 + m + 2m_t - \frac{(1-n)(1-3m)}{3(1+n)} \right) \right]^{1/3} Pr_x^{1/3} \tag{43}$$

As in Newtonian flows, Nu_x increases with $Pr_x^{1/3}$. It is also interesting to note that, for the case of constant heat flux, the asymptotic formula (Equation 43) suggests that the surface wall temperature must vary in proportion to x^{m_t}, where:

$$m_t = \frac{2+n-3m}{3(1+n)} \tag{44}$$

The above equation suggests $m_t = 1/3$ for a right angle wedge (i.e., $m = 1/3$), irrespective of the value of n. In the case of an isothermal flat plate ($m = m_t = 0$), Equation 43 with the aid of Equation 42 reduces to:

$$Nu_x/Re_x^{1/(1+n)} Pr_x^{1/3} = \left[\frac{8}{45} \frac{1+2n}{1+n} \left(\frac{37}{630(1+n)2^{n-1}} \right)^{1/(1+n)} \right]^{1/3} \tag{45}$$

The foregoing equation, for example, predicts $Nu_x/Re_x^{1/(1+n)} Pr_x^{1/3} = 0.3253$ at $n = 0.5$, and 0.3808 at $n = 1.5$, which are very close to the values (namely, 0.3254 and 0.3566) obtained by Acrivos et al. using a combined analytical-numerical method based on Lighthill's formula [5].

It is also of great interest to investigate the local heat transfer around a two-dimensional stagnation point, where the free stream velocity increases in proportion to the distance x, measured along the wall surface from the stagnation point. Kim et al. [13] analyzed a stagnation flow over a horizontal isothermal circular cylinder employing the Merk-type of series expansion technique. The external velocity field was assumed to follow the empirical formula given by Shah et al. [11]:

$$u_e/u_\infty = 0.92(x/L) - 0.131(x/L)^3 \tag{46}$$

where u_∞ is the uniform approaching flow velocity and L is the radius of the cylinder. Upon approximating u_e/u_∞ by retaining only the first term on the right hand side of Equation 46, the local skin friction and heat transfer rate have been evaluated according to Equations 36 and 43. The results are presented in Figures 5 and 6, where Re, C_f, and Nu appearing in ordinate variables are defined as $Re = \rho u_\infty^{2-n} L^n/K$, $C_f = C_{fx}(u_e/u_\infty)^2$, and $Nu = Nu x(L/x)$, respectively. Reasonably good agreement may be observed between the present asymptotic results and those by Kim et al.

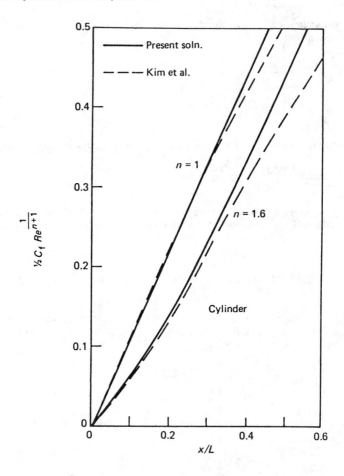

Figure 5. Wall shear stress around a stagnation point of a circular cylinder.

Heat transfer results obtained by the integration step-wise iterative procedure [18] (which will shortly be discussed) are also indicated in Figure 6. Comparison of the iterative solution and the asymptotic solution reveals the validity of the asymptotic expression derived in this section.

HEAT TRANSFER RESULTS IN PLANE FLOWS

In the preceding section, we assumed $Pr_x \gg 1$, or equivalently, $\delta_t \ll \delta$. However, the region where the assumption, $Pr_x \gg 1$, is violated does exist locally as the Prandtl number $Pr_x(x)$ varies in the streamwise direction. We shall reconsider the integral energy equation (Equation 28), and develop a more general solution procedure which is valid for any value of Pr_x.

Equation 28, when the velocity and temperature profiles given by Equations 34 and 39a are substituted, reduces to an ordinary differential equation which can be solved for δ_t^2 as:

$$(\delta_t/x)^2 = \frac{4}{\varrho C_p} \frac{k}{u_e x D} I_t \tag{47a}$$

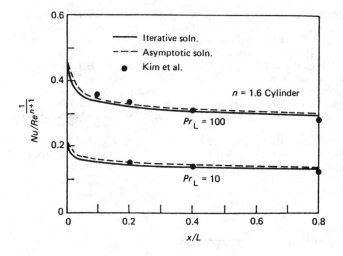

Figure 6. Heat transfer rate around a stagnation point of a circular cylinder.

where $I_t = \dfrac{\int_0^x D \, \Delta T_w^2 u_e \, dx}{D \, \Delta T_w^2 u_e x}$ (47b)

and $D = \int_0^{\delta_t} u(T - T_e) \, dy/u_e \, \Delta T_w \, \delta_t = \int_0^1 \theta(\eta_t) g(\min(\eta_t/\zeta, 1); \Lambda) \, d\eta_t$ (47c)

Therefore:

$$D = [756 - 126(6 - \Lambda)\zeta + 84(4 - \Lambda)\zeta^2 - 18(3 - \Lambda)\zeta^4 + (14 - 5\Lambda)\zeta^5]/2,520 \quad \text{for} \quad \zeta \leq 1 \quad (47d)$$

$$D = [168(2 + \Lambda)\zeta^3 - 180\Lambda\zeta^2 - 27(2 - 3\Lambda)\zeta + 14(1 - \Lambda)]/2,520\zeta^4 \quad \text{for} \quad \zeta \geq 1 \quad (47e)$$

Equations 33a and 47a are combined to give the following characteristic equation for ζ:

$$\zeta^2 = \frac{1}{4}\left(\frac{6nC^{n-1}\Lambda}{m}\right)^{2/(1+n)} \frac{D}{I_t} \, Prx \quad (48)$$

For the wedge with its wall temperature varying according to Equation 22b, the function I_t (defined by Equation 47b) appearing in Equation 47a becomes:

$$I_t = \int_0^x Dx^{m+2m_t} \, dx/Dx^{m+2m_t+1} \quad (49)$$

For Newtonian fluids over an isothermal flat plate ($m = m_t = 0$), the function I_t becomes unity while the Prandtl number defined by Equation 17b reduces to $Cp \, K/k$, namely, the conventional constant Prandtl number for Newtonian fluids. Hence, the characteristic equation (Equation 48) for this special case becomes the algebraic equation already reported [20]. For non-Newtonian fluids over a wedge, Equation 17b indicates:

$$Pr_x \propto x^{(1-3m)(1-n)/(1+n)} \quad (50)$$

Therefore, the Prandtl number Pr_x, which essentially determines $\zeta(x)$ through Equation 48, varies according to the power function of x. Whether Pr_x increases downstream or not, solely depends on the sign of the exponent $(1 - 3m)(1 - n)/(1 + n)$. Obviously, for the right angle wedge $(m = 1/3)$, Pr_x remains constant, and as in Newtonian fluids, Equation 48 reduces to an algebraic equation, which, then, yields similarity solutions for given n and m. In this way, one reaches the same conclusion on the right angle wedge as Schowalter [6], Lee and Ames [7], and Kim, Jeng, and DeWitt [13]. When the wedge angle is less than 90 degrees $(m < 1/3)$, Pr_x increases downstream for pseudoplastic fluids $(n < 1)$ and decreases for dilatant fluids $(n > 1)$. Thus, even for an isothermal plate or wedge where the similar velocity boundary layer prevails, the thermal boundary layer of non-Newtonian fluids, in general, is found to be non-similar, and hence, one must appeal to an iterative procedure at each integration step, using Equation 48, to find the streamwise variation of $\zeta(x)$.

In order to illustrate the generality acquired in the present integral method, an effort will be made to describe the solution procedure for a wedge of an arbitrary included angle with its surface wall temperature following the relation of Equation 22b. Upon noting the proportional relationship (Equation 50), the independent variable x may be replaced by Pr_x, so that the function I_t given by Equation 49 becomes:

$$I_t = \frac{\dfrac{1 + n}{(1 - n)(1 - 3m)} \displaystyle\int_{Pr_0}^{Pr_x} DPr_x^{(1+n)(1+m+2m_t)/(1-n)(1-3m)-1} \, dPr}{DPr_x^{(1+n)(1+m+2m_t)/(1-n)(1-3m)}} \tag{51a}$$

where
$$\begin{aligned} Pr_0 &= 0 && \text{for } (1 - n)(1 - 3m) > 0 \\ Pr_0 &= \infty && \text{for } (1 - n)(1 - 3m) < 0 \end{aligned} \tag{51b}$$

The integration near the singularity $(Pr_x \to Pr_0)$ should be carried out analytically using the corresponding asymptotic results. For $Pr_0 = \infty$, we can use the results for $Pr_x \gg 1$, presented in the foregoing section. For $Pr_0 = 0$, on the other hand, the results for the other asymptotic state, namely, $Pr_x \ll 1$ are needed. The asymptotic results for $Pr_x \ll 1$ are extracted from Equations 47d, 48, and 51a as:

$$\zeta \cong \left[\left(\frac{6nC^{n-1}\Lambda}{m} \right)^{2/(1+n)} \frac{3}{40} (1 + m + 2m_t) \right]^{1/2} Pr_x^{1/2} \tag{52a}$$

and
$$Nu_x/Re_x^{1/(1+n)} \cong \left[\frac{3(1 + m + 2m_t)}{10} \right]^{1/2} Pr_x^{1/2} \qquad \text{for } Pr_x \ll 1 \tag{52b}$$

Thus, the heat transfer grouping $Nu_x/Re_x^{1/(n+1)}$ monotonically increases with Pr_x. The exponent of Pr_x changes from $1/2$ to $1/3$ as in Newtonian fluids. The Prandtl number Pr_{xtr}, where two asymptotes given by Equations 52b and 43 intersect each other, may be given by:

$$Pr_{xtr} = \frac{\left(\dfrac{m}{6nC^{n-1}\Lambda} \right)^{2/(1+n)} \left[\dfrac{2(2 + \Lambda)}{15} \left(1 + m + 2m_t - \dfrac{(1 - n)(1 - 3m)}{3(1 + n)} \right) \right]^2}{\left[\dfrac{3}{10} (1 + m + 2m_t) \right]^3}. \tag{53}$$

In the case of an isothermal flat plate $(m = m_t = 0)$, the above equation reduces to:

$$Pr_{xtr} = 1.17 \left(\frac{0.118}{2^n(1 + n)} \right)^{2/(1+n)} \left(\frac{1 + 2n}{1 + n} \right)^2 \tag{54}$$

Thus, one may expect $Pr_{xtr} \ll 1$ for the range of interest, $0 < n < 2$, where the boundary layer theory holds.

These asymptotic results provide the boundary values needed for initiation of the step-wise iterative procedure. For given exponents n and m, the shape factor Λ can be determined using the characteristic Equation 35a, and the coefficients in $D(\zeta; \Lambda)$ may be evaluated. Once this is done, the characteristic Equation 48 can be used to find $\zeta(Pr_x)$. Since Equation 47b for I_t also involves the unknown ζ, the characteristic Equation 48 is implicit in ζ, and the determination of ζ requires an iterative procedure at each integration step. A simple way to find ζ may be to guess ζ at each end of the integration step, and evaluate I_t assuming a linear variation within each integration interval. Then, the results may be substituted into Equation 48 to check if the estimated ζ satisfies the characteristic equation. This sequence is repeated to determine ζ within a desired accuracy, before marching one step further. Once $\zeta(Pr_x)$ is calculated in this way, the local Nusselt number Nu_x may be evaluated from:

$$Nu_x/Re_x^{1/(1+n)} = 2\zeta\left(\frac{m}{6nC^{n-1}\Lambda}\right)^{1/(1+n)} \tag{55}$$

The integration-step-wise iterative calculations described above, have been carried out for an isothermal flat plate, and the results are presented in Figure 7 along with the finite difference calculation results obtained by Huang and Cheng [28]. Following their presentation, the abscissa variable is chosen to be x/L, where L is any reference length. The Prandtl number based on L, Pr_L, is related to Pr_x through:

$$Pr_x = Pr_L(x/L)^{(1-n)/(1+n)} \tag{56}$$

From the above equation, it is obvious that $Pr_x \to 0$ for pseudoplastic fluids and $Pr_x \to \infty$ for dilatant fluids, as $x/L \to 0$. Since the level of the heat transfer grouping $Nu_x/Re_x^{1/(1+n)}$ is virtually governed by the level of ζ (or Pr_x) as seen in Equation 55, the level of the heat transfer grouping becomes low for $n < 1$ and high for $n > 1$ near the leading edge. A reasonably good agreement has been achieved between the present approximate solutions and the numerical solutions.

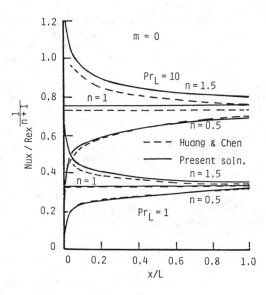

Figure 7. Heat transfer from an isothermal flat plate.

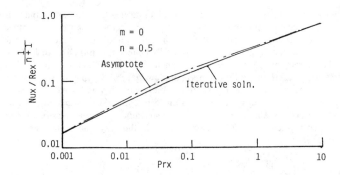

Figure 8. Asymptotes for heat transfer from an isothermal flat plate.

Since the independent variable in the characteristic Equation 48 has been changed from x to Pr_x, the results for wedges can most readily be presented in terms of Pr_x, without introducing an additional parameter such as Pr_L. The iterative calculation results for n = 0.5 are replotted in Figure 8 in such a manner. The asymptotes based on Equations 43 and 52b are also presented in the figure for the purpose of comparison. The iterative solution curve, in fact, follows closely along the two asymptotes. Even at $Pr_x = Pr_{xtr}$, the overestimation of the heat transfer level by the asymptotic curve is only about 13 percent. Except for the regions where the boundary layer theory itself fails, Pr_x for the actual non-Newtonian fluids is usually very large, whether the substances are pseudoplastic or dilatant. That is:

$$Pr_x \gg 1 \gg Pr_{xtr} \tag{57}$$

Hence, the asymptotic formula given by Equation 43 may be used for all practical evaluations of the heat transfer rates. The heat transfer rates, thus obtained, are guaranteed to agree closely with those obtained by the aforementioned step-wise iterative procedure.

Approximate curves for a flat plate generated by substituting Equation 44 into Equation 43 are plotted in Figure 9 with the finite difference calculation results [28] obtained under the constant heat flux condition. Although some discrepancy is appreciable for the pseudoplastic substances at $Pr_L = 10$, overall agreement between the two solutions appears to be generally good. The fact substantiates the validity of the asymptotic formula (Equation 43).

For the purpose of the speedy evaluation of the heat transfer from a flat plate, the heat transfer grouping $Nu_x/Re_x^{1/(1+n)}Pr_x^{1/3}$ is calculated for constant temperature and for constant heat flux using the asymptotic expression (Equation 43). These results are plotted in Figure 10 with the results on an isothermal plate obtained by Acrivos, Shah, and Petersen [5] using a combined analytical-numerical method based on the Lighthill's approximation.

As already indicated, a similarity solution is possible for a right angle wedge (m = 1/3). For constant heat flux, the surface wall temperature of a right angle wedge increases downstream in proportion to $x^{1/3}$, irrespective of the value of n. The results for a right angle wedge with the power-law exponent n = 1.6 are presented in Figure 11 for the cases of constant temperature and constant heat flux. The isothermal wedge results obtained numerically by Kim, Jeng, and DeWitt [13] are seen to overlap closely onto the present solution curve. Comparison will not be made here for the case of constant heat flux since no other calculation results are available.

For the wedge of an included angle other than 90 degrees, one, in principle, must solve the characteristic Equation 48 by the integration-step-wise iterative procedure. However, the comparison of such iterative calculation results and the asymptotic results has again confirmed that the asymptotic formula (Equation 43) is equally valid for the wedge flows with arbitrary values of n, m, and m_t. Thus, the heat transfer grouping $Nu_x/Re_x^{1/(1+n)}Pr_x^{1/3}$ has been evaluated using the

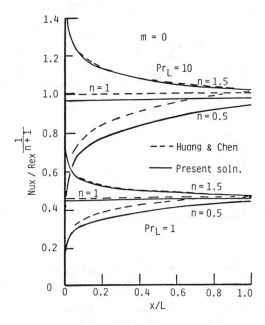

Figure 9. Heat transfer from a flat plate with a constant heat flux.

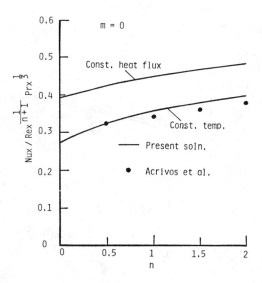

Figure 10. Asymptotic results for heat transfer from a flat plate.

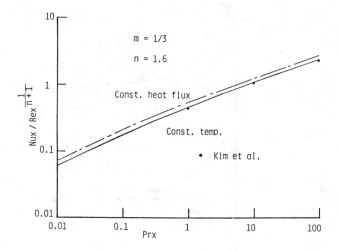

Figure 11. Heat transfer from a right angle wedge.

asymptotic formula (Equation 43) under the prescribed constant temperature or heat flux, and plotted in Figure 12 for n = 0.716, 1.0, and 1.6 with the abscissa variable m ranging from 0 to 1/3. As the wedge angle increases 90 degrees (i.e., m → 1/3), the level difference among different n values diminishes. In fact, the level of n = 0.716 slightly exceeds that of Newtonian fluids at m = 1/3. Such a trend can also be observed in the numerical calculation results on a right angle wedge reported by Kim, Jeng, and DeWitt [13].

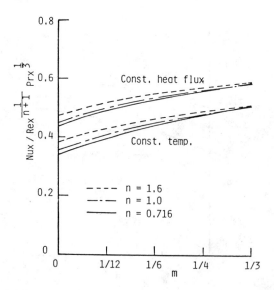

Figure 12. Asymptotic results for heat transfer from a wedge.

HEAT TRANSFER RESULTS IN AXISYMMETRIC FLOWS

While plane flows of non-Newtonian fluids have been investigated rather well, only a limited number of theoretical studies are available for axisymmetric non-Newtonian flows. Bizzel and Slattery [17] employed an integral method for axially symmetric, blunt bodies, while Chao's method [16] was adopted by Lin and Chern [12] for power-law fluid flows over a sphere. In these studies, however, no attempts were made to solve the energy equation. Later, Kim, Jeng, and Dewitt [13] followed an approach similar to Lin and Chern, to investigate temperature fields on plane and axisymmetric bodies. Yet, no heat transfer results were reported for the axisymmetric flow case. In this section, we shall extend our integral treatment to the problem of a power-law fluid flow and heat transfer over an axisymmetric body, following the recent work reported by Shenoy and Nakayama [19].

The boundary layer equations in the axisymmetric case are given by:

$$\frac{\partial}{\partial x} ru + \frac{\partial}{\partial y} rv = 0 \tag{58a}$$

$$\frac{\partial}{\partial x} ru^2 + \frac{\partial}{\partial y} ruv = ru_e \frac{du_e}{dx} + r \frac{\partial}{\partial y} \frac{K}{\rho} \left| \frac{\partial u}{\partial y} \right|^{n-1} \frac{\partial u}{\partial y} \tag{58b}$$

$$\frac{\partial}{\partial x} ruT + \frac{\partial}{\partial y} rvT = \frac{rk}{\rho C_p} \frac{\partial^2 T}{\partial y^2} \tag{58c}$$

For the case of a cone with an apex half angle ϕ, the function $r(x)$ representing wall geometry, and the external free stream velocity $u_e(x)$ may be specified as:

$$r = x \sin \phi \tag{59a}$$

$$\text{and} \quad u_e \propto x^m \tag{59b}$$

$$\text{where} \quad P'_{m+1}(-\cos \phi) = 0 \tag{59c}$$

In Equation 59c, the prime denotes differentiation and the function P_{m+1} is the Legendre function that remains finite when its argument equals unity for all values of its order $m + 1$. The function $m(\phi)$ evaluated by Hess and Faulkner [29] is plotted in Figure 13. For example, the cases of $\phi = 30°$ and $\phi = 90°$ (i.e., axial stagnation flow) correspond to $m = 0.11565$ and $m = 1$, respectively. These governing equations must be solved with the boundary conditions given by Equations 10.

The corresponding integral momentum equation can readily be obtained by integrating Equations 58a and 58b along with Equation 10.

$$\frac{d}{dx} \int_0^\delta (u_e u - u^2)\, dy + \left(H \frac{d}{dx} \ln u_e + \frac{d}{dx} \ln r \right) \int_0^\delta (u_e u - u^2)\, dy = \frac{K}{\rho} \left(\frac{\partial u}{\partial y} \right)^n \bigg|_{y=0} \tag{60}$$

where the shape factor H as defined by Equation 32d is the ratio of the displacement thickness to the momentum thickness. Moreover, integrating the energy Equation 58c with Equation 58a across the boundary layer, we obtain:

$$\frac{d}{dx} r \int_0^{\delta_t} u(T - T_e)\, dy = -\frac{rk}{\rho C_p} \frac{\partial T}{\partial y} \bigg|_{y=0} \tag{61}$$

Upon following a procedure similar to the one employed in plane flows, the two integral Equations 60 and 61 and the auxiliary Equations 25 and 29 can be combined to yield two distinct characteristic

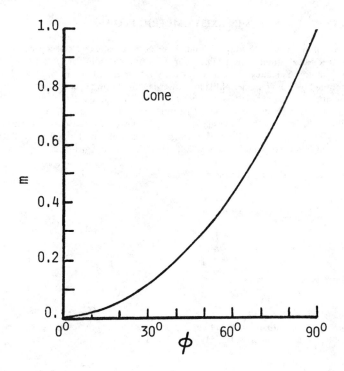

Figure 13. Free stream velocity exponent as a function of the apex half angle.

equations, which, for the case of a cone with its wall temperature varying according to Equation 22b, reduce to:

$$m = \frac{(2 + n)\Lambda G}{\dfrac{1 + n}{6n} C - \Lambda \left(3nG + \dfrac{(1 + n)(6 - \Lambda)}{20} \right)} \tag{62a}$$

and

$$\zeta^2 = \frac{1}{4}\left(\frac{6nC^{n-1}\Lambda}{m} \right)^{2/(1+n)} \frac{D}{I_t} Pr_x \tag{62b}$$

Equation 62a differs from the corresponding characteristic Equation 35a for a plane flow by the factor of $(2 + n)$. The other characteristic Equation 62b is identical to its two-dimensional version, namely Equation 48. But, the function I_t in Equation 48, for the case of axisymmetric flow, must be defined differently as:

$$I_t = \frac{\dfrac{1 + n}{(1 - n)(1 - 3m)} \displaystyle\int_{Pr_0}^{Pr_x} DPr_x^{(1 + n)(3 + m + 2m_t)/(1 - n)(1 - 3m) - 2} \, dPr_x}{DPr_x^{(1 + n)(3 + m + 2m_t)/(1 - n)(1 - 3m)}} \tag{63}$$

where Pr_x, Pr_0, and $D(\zeta; \Lambda)$ are the same as defined for plane flows. Upon determining the shape parameter Λ from the algebraic Equation 62a, we can work on the characteristic Equation 62b, and find the boundary layer thickness ratio ζ by the aforementioned iterative method. For the

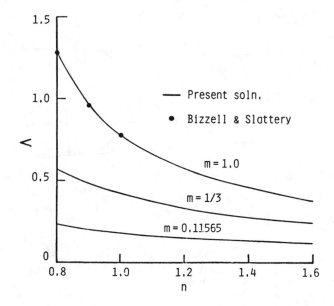

Figure 14. Velocity shape factor on a cone.

special case of m = 1/3 corresponding to a cone with $\phi = 53°$, Equation 62b reduces to an algebraic equation, and hence similarity solutions exist. (Note: $I_t = (3 + m + 2m_t)^{-1}$ for m = 1/3.) As we determine the values of Λ and ζ, the friction and heat transfer groupings $C_{fx}Re_x^{n/(1+n)}$ and $Nu_x/Re_x^{1/(n+1)}$ are readily calculable from Equations 36 and 55.

As in the case of a wedge flow [30], we can deduce the asymptotic expressions considering the asymptotic conditions, namely, $Pr_x \gg 1$ and $Pr_x \ll 1$. The results for axisymmetric flows are:

$$Nu_x/Re_x^{1/(1+n)} \simeq \left[\frac{3(3 + m + 2m_t)}{10}\right]^{1/2} Pr_x^{1/2} \quad \text{for } Pr_x \ll 1 \tag{64a}$$

and:

$$Nu_x/Re_x^{1/(1+n)} \simeq \left[\left(\frac{m}{6nC^{n-1}\Lambda}\right)^{1/(2+n)}\frac{2(2+\Lambda)}{15}\right.$$

$$\left.\times\left(3 + m + 2m_t - \frac{(1-n)(1-3m)}{3(1+n)}\right)\right]^{1/3} Pr_x^{1/3} \quad \text{for } Pr_x \gg 1 \tag{64b}$$

Figure 14 shows the variation of the velocity shape factor with n for various values of the free stream velocity exponent m. The value of m = 0.11565 corresponds to the cone apex angle $\phi = 30°$ while the value of m = 1 corresponds to $\phi = 90°$, namely, the axial stagnation flow. Each of the curves in Figure 14 has been generated by solving Equation 62a using Newton shooting technique. It can be seen that the present solution gives excellent agreement with the work of Brizzell and Slattery [17] for m = 1.

The curve generated by Equation 36 is plotted in Figure 15 and this gives the corresponding local skin friction. Unlike the velocity shape factor Λ, the skin friction grouping $C_{fx}Re_x^{1/(n+1)}$ is

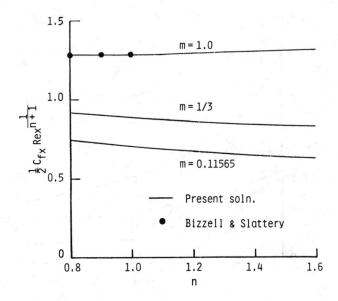

Figure 15. Friction coefficient for a cone.

fairly insensitive to n. Again, comparison of the predictions by the present integral method with the results of Brizzell and Slattery [17] for m = 1 shows excellent agreement.

Figure 16 depicts the effectiveness of the asymptotic results given by Equations 64. Calculations were carried out for the special case of m = 1/3, in which Pr_x is a constant. It can be seen that the asymptotic results based on high and low Prandtl numbers provide reasonable predictions. Especially, the asymptotic formula, Equation 64b, for high Pr_x is of great significance for evaluating heat transfer rates to non-Newtonian fluids having high consistencies.

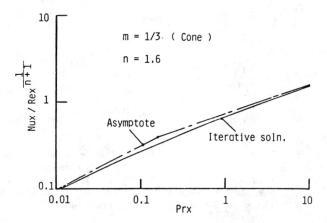

Figure 16. Heat transfer from a cone.

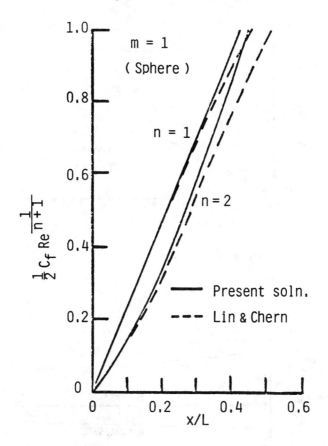

Figure 17. Wall shear stress around a stagnation point of a sphere.

The prediction of the present solution for axially symmetric stagnation flow for a sphere are shown in Figure 17, in which the shear stress is written as:

$$\frac{1}{2} C_f Re^{1/(1+n)} = \left(\frac{1}{2} C_{fx} Re_x^{1/(1+n)}\right)\left(\frac{3}{2}\right)^{3n/(1+n)}\left(\frac{x}{L}\right)^{2n/(1+n)} \tag{65}$$

where the characteristic length L is taken to be equal to the radius of a sphere, and the Reynolds number Re is based on L and the approaching velocity u_∞. The plots were generated reading the values of $\frac{1}{2}C_{fx}Re_x^{1/(n+1)}$ from Figure 15. It can be seen that the agreement with the present solution and numerical results of Lin and Chern [12] for n = 1 and n = 2 is fairly good. The present solution appears to be a good approximation for lower values of x/L, say those less than 0.3.

Figure 18 gives the heat transfer results based on the asymptotic expressions and compares them with the predictions of the step-wise iterative solution. Again, it is seen that, even for axisymmetric bodies, the asymptotic expressions would suffice to give accurate predictions of heat transfer at low and high Prandtl numbers.

The asymptotic formula given by Equation 64b for high Prandtl number is plotted in Figure 19 for various values of the free stream velocity exponent m. It is interesting to note that the ordinate is nearly independent of the power-law exponent n.

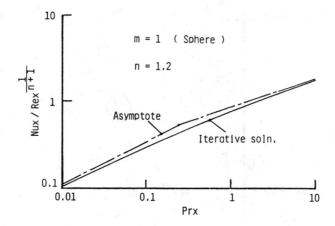

Figure 18. Heat transfer from a sphere.

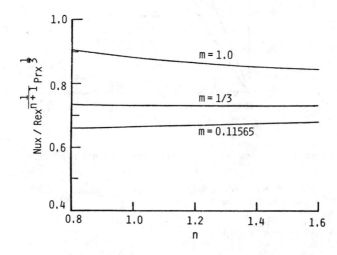

Figure 19. Asymptotic results for heat transfer from an isothermal sphere.

SOLUTION PROCEDURE FOR A FLOW OVER A BODY OF ARBITRARY SHAPE

So far, we have limited our discussion to cases in which the free stream velocity and wall temperature vary according to some power functions of x. In this section, we shall generalize our integral method such that the method can deal with all two-dimensional and axisymmetric bodies of arbitrary geometrical configuration. Both the free stream velocity and wall temperature are allowed to vary in an arbitrary fashion.

Upon following the same procedure as before, we can derive the following integral momentum equation common to both plane and axisymmetric flows:

$$\frac{d}{dx} \int_0^\delta (u_e u - u^2) \, dy + \left(H \frac{d}{dx} \ln u_e + \frac{d}{dx} l_n r^* \right) \int_0^\delta (uu_e - u^2) \, dy = \frac{K}{\rho} \left(\frac{\partial u}{\partial y} \right)^n \bigg|_{y=0} \tag{66a}$$

where
$$r^* = \begin{cases} 1: \text{plane flow} \\ r(x): \text{axisymmetric flow} \end{cases} \tag{66b}$$

This can be rewritten as:

$$\frac{d}{dx} \ln(\xi G^{n+1}) = \left[\frac{(1+n)C^n}{G\xi} - \frac{1}{I} \right] \frac{1}{x} \tag{67a}$$

where
$$\xi = (\delta/x)^{1+n} \text{Rex} \tag{67b}$$

and
$$I = 1 \bigg/ \left[1 + (3n + (1+n)H)m + (1+n) \frac{d \ln r^*}{d \ln x} \right] \tag{67c}$$

The classical potential theory may be employed for a particular geometry of concern, to determine $m(x)$ (defined by Equation 15c), which is no longer a constant but some function of x. The auxiliary Equation 25 may be rewritten in terms of the new variable ξ as:

$$\xi = 6nC^{n-1}\Lambda/m \tag{68}$$

where all the shape factors such as Λ, G, H, and C are the same as defined before. Equation 68 may be substituted into Equation 67a to eliminate ξ in favor of Λ. After some manipulation, we obtain:

$$\frac{d\Lambda}{dx} = \left[\frac{\dfrac{1+n}{6n} \dfrac{C}{G} \dfrac{m}{\Lambda} - \dfrac{1}{I} + \dfrac{d \ln m}{d \ln x}}{(n+1) \dfrac{\partial \ln G}{\partial \Lambda} + (n-1) \dfrac{\partial \ln C}{\partial \Lambda} + \dfrac{1}{\Lambda}} \right] \frac{1}{x} \tag{69}$$

Upon carrying out integrations and differentiations using the velocity profile given by Equation 34, all shape factors can be expressed in terms of algebraic functions of Λ alone. These algebraic expressions are substituted into the right hand side terms of Equation 69. Then, Equation 69 can be integrated downstream to find $\Lambda(x)$ as n, $m(x)$, and $r(x)$ are provided.

The boundary value $\Lambda|_{x=0}$, however, must be determined prior to the integration. Since a similar viscous layer covers around the front stagnation point (where the free stream velocity varies according to $u_e \propto x^{m|_{x=0}}$), the velocity shape factor Λ should remain constant there. Hence, the numerator in the right hand side term of Equation 69 must vanish. Thus, the differential Equation 69 reduces to the following algebraic equation:

$$m = \frac{\Lambda G(1 + (1+n)i)}{\dfrac{1+n}{6n} C - \Lambda \left(3nG + \dfrac{(1+n)(6-\Lambda)}{20} \right)} \tag{70a}$$

where
$$i = \begin{cases} 0: \text{plane flow} \\ 1: \text{axisymmetric flow} \end{cases} \tag{70b}$$

Naturally, Equation 70a reduces to Equation 35a for i = 0, and Equation 62a for i = 1. With $\Lambda|_{x=0}$ determined from Equation 70a, we can integrate Equation 69 downstream until the flow separates at C = 0 (i.e., $\Lambda = -2$). The local skin friction can then be evaluated from Equation 36 as before.

Now, the integral energy equation common to both plane and axisymmetric flows is given in a similar manner:

$$\frac{d}{dx} r^* \int_0^{\delta_t} u(T - T_e)\, dy = -\frac{r^* k}{\rho Cp} \frac{\partial T}{\partial y}\bigg|_{y=0} \tag{71}$$

The foregoing energy equation is solved for δ_t^2, and subsequently combined with Equation 68. This yields a characteristic equation which is identical to Equation 48, but with the function I_t defined in a more general fashion as:

$$I_t = \frac{\int_0^x D\, \Delta T_w^2\, u_e r^{*2}\, dx}{D\, \Delta T_w^2\, u_e r^{*2} x} \tag{72}$$

The function I_t cannot be simplified by using the proportional relationship (Equation 50), since both the external velocity $u_e(x)$ and wall-ambient temperature difference $\Delta T_w(x)$ are allowed to vary arbitrarily in the streamwise direction. After determining $\Lambda(x)$ from Equation 69 for given n, m(x),

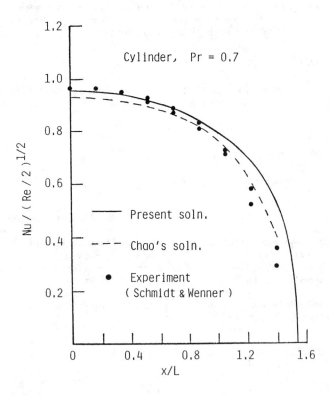

Figure 20. Heat transfer from an isothermal cylinder to a Newtonian fluid.

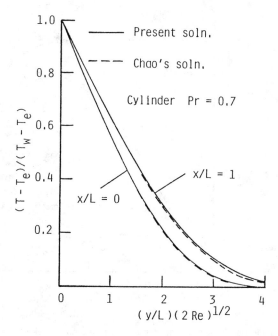

Figure 21. Temperature distribution across the boundary layer of a Newtonian fluid.

and r(x), we can work on the characteristic Equation 48 to find $\zeta(x)$ by a shooting procedure. Although a singularity appears at the front stagnation point ($x = 0$), we can carry out integration needed for I_t analytically in consideration of the asymptotic results, discussed previously. As $\Lambda(x)$ and $\zeta(x)$ are determined in this way, we can readily evaluate the heat transfer function from Equation 55.

In order to examine the accuracy acquired in the present approximate method, calculations were carried out for a Newtonian fluid flow over an isothermal circular cylinder, and the heat transfer results are compared against the experimental data of Schmidt and Wenner [31] and the series expansion results by Chao [15] in Figure 20. The Nusselt number $Nu = Nux(L/x)$ corresponds to the local heat transfer coefficient, while $Re = \rho u_\infty L/K$ is the Reynolds number based on the uniform approaching flow velocity and cylinder radius. The calculated local heat transfer rate shows good agreement with the experiment especially around the front stagnation point, where the Chao's analysis based on an improved Lighthill's formula somewhat underestimates the data. The predicted temperature profiles are plotted in Figure 21, along with the Chao's solution for $x/L = 0$ and 1. The abscissa variable in the figure is chosen as the similarity variable used by Chao, which may be translated into the present variable through $(y/L)(2Re)^{1/2} = \eta_t/\zeta(u_e/u_\infty/2\zeta x)^{1/2}$. The figure demonstrates that even the details of profiles agree closely with the series expansion solution. The external flow velocity u_e/u_∞ was set according to Hiemenz [32]:

$$u_e/u_\infty = 1.82(x/L) - 0.271(x/L)^3 - 0.0473(x/L)^5 \tag{73}$$

Kim, Jeng, and DeWitt [13] analyzed power-law fluid flows over an isothermal circular cylinder employing the Merk-Chao series expansion technique. The external velocity field was assumed to follow the empirical formula, Equation 46, which closely approximates the experimentally observed

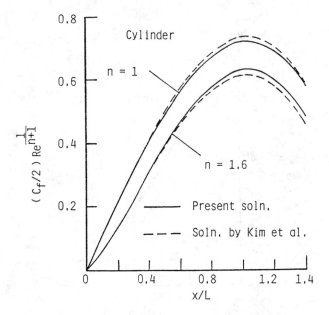

Figure 22. Wall shear stress around a circular cylinder.

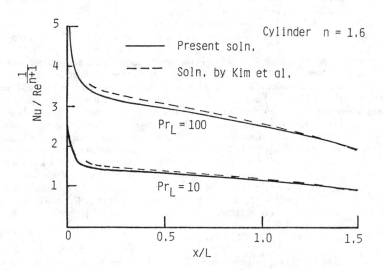

Figure 23. Heat transfer from an isothermal circular cylinder.

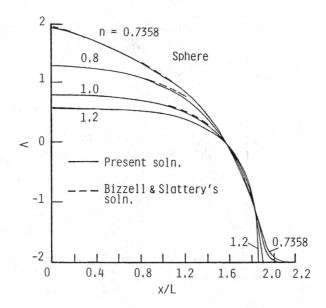

Figure 24. Velocity shape factor over a sphere.

external flow velocity for $0 \leq x/L < 1.05$. Using the same external flow field, calculations were carried out on the Newtonian and dilatant fluids. Calculated local skin friction and heat transfer coefficient are compared with their series expansion results in Figures 22 and 23, where Re and C_f appearing in ordinate variables are defined as $Re = \rho u_\infty^{2-n} L^n / K$ and $C_f = C_{fx}(u_e/u_\infty)^2$. Reasonably good agreement is observed in both the skin friction and heat transfer results. The local heat transfer coefficient decreases downstream as the boundary layer thickens. Naturally, the high Prandtl number case yields a high heat transfer rate.

As for the axisymmetric flow case, a flow past an isothermal sphere is treated. Bizzell and Slattery [15] attacked the Kármán-Pohlhausen integral momentum equation, and solved it for the case of a sphere. They, however, failed to obtain meaningful results for dilatant fluids (n > 1) because of the singularity at the front stagnation point. (No such difficulties have been encountered in the present method for either dilatant or pseudoplastic fluids.) Unfortunately, no attempt was made by them to solve the energy conservation equation. Calculations were performed assuming that the potential flow prevails outside the boundary layer, namely, $u_e/u_\infty = \frac{3}{2}\sin(x/L)$. The velocity shape factor Λ is presented in Figure 24 along with the Bizzell and Slattery's solutions for $n \leq 1$. The observed trend that the flow separation somewhat delays downstream for small n is consistent with the experimental evidence reported by Slattery and Bird [33]. Figure 25 shows the local wall shear distribution. Lin and Chern's solution [12] based on the Merk-Chao series expansion approach is also presented for the Newtonian fluid (i.e., n = 1) for the purpose of comparison. Upon assuming a high Prandtl number ($Pr_L = 100$), which is usually the case of non-Newtonian fluids, heat transfer calculations were carried out for n = 0.8, 1, and 1.2, and the results are presented in Figure 26. While the local heat transfer rates obtained for the Newtonian and dilatant fluids decrease monotonously, that for the pseudoplastic fluid increases sharply near the stagnation point, and attains a maximum value away from it. This thermal response reflected to the local heat transfer in the vicinity of the front stagnation point may be appreciated from the asymptotic expression, Equation 64b for high Prandtl numbers, which suggests $Nu \propto x^{(1-n)/3(1+n)}$ near x = 0.

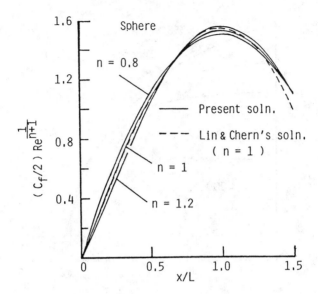

Figure 25. Wall shear stress over a sphere.

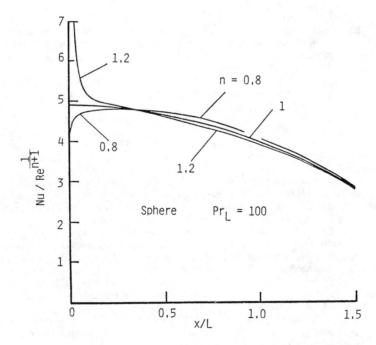

Figure 26. Heat transfer from an isothermal sphere.

CONCLUSION

In this chapter, we have discussed an integral treatment for obtaining solutions to the problem of forced convection heat transfer from heated external surfaces to power-law non-Newtonian fluids. Upon integrating the momentum and energy equations, a pair of characteristic equations were reduced, and solved for a velocity shape factor and a boundary layer thickness ratio. Comparison of heat transfer results thus obtained, and those from previous experimental and analytical studies revealed excellent performance of the integral solution scheme. Furthermore, it is found that a simple explicit asymptotic expression can provide a quite accurate estimation of heat transfer rates for all possible cases of power-law fluid boundary layer flows.

Although more elaborate finite difference solution schemes are now available, the author believes that an integral approach, such as the one presented in this chapter, still remains an effective means for quick and accurate estimations of heat transfer rates.

Acknowledgments

I would like to express my sincere thanks to Dr. A. V. Shenoy for bringing to my attention a possible extension of my integral method to non-Newtonian fluids. Thanks are also due to Mr. T. Endo for checking and running the computer program for the results presented in the last section. Finally, I must also thank Prof. Koyama for invaluable suggestions given on this work.

NOTATION

C, D, E, G, H	boundary layer shape factors	n	power-law exponent
C_{f_x}	local skin friction coefficient	Nu_x	local Nusselt number
C_p	specific heat	Pr_x	Prandtl number
g	velocity profile function	Re_x	Reynolds number
I, I_t	functions associated with the deviation from unity	$T, \Delta T_w$	temperature, and wall-ambient temperature difference
k	thermal conductivity	u, v	velocity components in the x and y directions
K	multiplicative constant in the power-law model	x, y	boundary layer coordinates
m	wedge flow parameter		
m_t	exponent for the wall temperature variation		

Greek Symbols

δ, δ_t	viscous and thermal boundary layer thicknesses	Λ	shape factor associated with the curvature of g at the wall
ζ	boundary layer thickness ratio	ϕ	wedge or cone half angle
η, η_t	dimensionless variable in the y direction		

Subscripts

e	boundary layer edge
t	thermal boundary layer
w	wall

REFERENCES

1. Schowalter, W., *Mechanics of Non-Newtonian Fluids*, Pergamon, Oxford, 1977.
2. Metzner, A. B., "Heat Transfer in Non-Newtonian Fluids," *Adv. Heat Transfer*, vol. 2, pp. 357–394, 1965.
3. Shenoy, A. V., and Mashelkar, R. A., "Thermal convection in non-Newtonian fluids," *Adv. Heat Transfer*, vol. 15, pp. 143–226, 1982.
4. Metzner, A. B., *Advances in Chemical Engineering*, ed. by T. B. Drew and J. W. Hoopes, Jr., vol. I, pp. 79–150, Academic Press, 1956.
5. Acrivos, A., Shah, M. J., and Petersen, E. E., "Momentum and Heat Transfer in Laminar Boundary Layer Flows of Non-Newtonian Fluids Past External Surfaces," *AIChE J.*, vol. 6, no. 2, pp. 312–317, 1960.
6. Schowalter, W. R., "The Application of Boundary Layer Theory to Power-Law Pseudoplastic Fluids: Similar solutions," *AIChE J.*, vol. 6, no. 24, pp. 24–28, 1960.
7. Lee, S. Y., and Ames, W. F., "Similarity Solutions for Non-Newtonian Fluids," *AIChE J.*, vol. 12, no. 4, pp. 700–708, 1966.
8. Wolf, C. J., and Szewczyk, A. A., "Laminar Heat Transfer to Power-Model Non-Newtonian Fluids from Arbitrary Cylinders," Proc. 3rd Int. Heat Transfer Conf., Chicago, Illinois, pp. 377–387, 1966.
9. Serth, R. W., and Kiser, K. M., "A solution of the Two Dimensional Boundary Layer Equations for an Ostwald-de Waele fluid," *Chem. Engrg. Sci.*, vol. 22, pp. 245–256, 1967.
10. Lighthill, M. J., "Contributions to the Theory of Heat Transfer through a Laminar Boundary Layer," *Proc. R. Soc. London*, vol. 202A, pp. 359–377, 1950.
11. Shah, M. J., Petersen, E. E., and Acrivos, A. M., "Heat Transfer from a Cylinder to a Power-Law Non-Newtonian Fluid," *AIChE J.*, vol. 8, no. 4, pp. 542–549, 1962.
12. Lin, F. N., and Chern, S. Y., "Laminar Boundary Layer Flow of Non-Newtonian Fluid," *Int. J. Heat Mass Transfer*, vol. 22, pp. 1323–1329, 1979.
13. Kim, H. W., Jeng, D. R., and DeWitt, K. J., "Momentum and Heat Transfer in Power-Law Fluid Flow over Two-Dimensional or Axisymmetric Bodies," *Int. J. Heat Mass Transfer*, vol. 26, no. 2, pp. 245–259, 1983.
14. Merk, H. J., "Rapid Calculation for Boundary-Layer Transfer Using Wedge Solutions and Asymptotic Expansions," *J. Fluid Mech.*, vol. 5, pp. 460–480, 1959.
15. Chao, B. T., "An Improved Lighthill's Analysis of Heat Transfer through Boundary Layers," *Int. J. Heat Mass Transfer*, vol. 15, pp. 907–920, 1972.
16. Chao, B. T., and Fagbenle, R. O., "On Merk's Method of Calculating Boundary Layer Transfer," *Int. J. Heat Mass Transfer*, vol. 17, pp. 223–240, 1974.
17. Brizzell, G. D., and Slattery, J. C., "Non-Newtonian Boundary Layer Flow," *Chem. Engrg. Sci.*, vol. 17, pp. 777–782, 1962.
18. Nakayama, A., Shenoy, A. V., and Koyama, H., "An Analysis for Forced Convection Heat Transfer from External Surfaces to Non-Newtonian Fluids," *Wärme-und Stoffübertragung*, vol. 20, pp. 219–227, 1986.
19. Shenoy, A. V., and Nakayama, A., "Forced Convection Heat Transfer from Axisymmetric Bodies to Non-Newtonian Fluids," *Canadian J. Chemical Engineering*, vol. 64, pp. 680–686, 1986.
20. Nakayama, A., Koyama, H., and Ohsawa, S., "An Approximate Solution Procedure for Laminar Free and Forced Convection Heat Transfer Problems," *Int. J. Heat Mass Transfer*, vol. 26, no. 11, pp. 1721–1726, 1983.
21. Nakayama, A., and Koyama, H., "An Integral Treatment of Laminar and Turbulent Film Condensation on Bodies of Arbitrary Geometrical Configuration," *J. Heat Transfer*, vol. 107, pp. 417–423, 1985.
22. Nakayama, A., and Koyama, H., "An Integral Method in Laminar Film Pool Boiling from Curved Surfaces," *J. Heat Transfer*, vol. 108, pp. 490–493, 1986.
23. Oldroyd, J. G., *Rheology*, Academic Press, New York, 1956.
24. Schlichting, H., *Boundary Layer Theory*, McGraw-Hill, New York, 1968.

25. Sparrow, E. M., and Yu, H. S., "Local Non-Similarity Thermal Boundary Layer Solutions," *J. Heat Transfer*, vol. 93, pp. 328–334, 1971.
26. Nakayama, A., and Koyama, H., "Free Convective Heat Transfer Over a Nonisothermal Body of Arbitrary Shape Embedded in a Fluid-Saturated Porous Medium," *J. Heat Transfer*, vol. 109, pp. 125–130, 1987.
27. Hartree, D. R., "On an Equation Occurring in Falkner and Skan's Approximate Treatment of the Equation of the Boundary Layer," *Proc. Camb. Phil. Soc.*, vol. 33, pp. 223–239, 1937.
28. Huang, M. J., and Chen, C. K., "Numerical Analysis for Forced Convection over a Flat Plate in Power-Law Fluids," *Int. Comm. Heat Mass Transfer*, vol. 11, pp. 361–368, 1984.
29. Hess, L. H., and Faulkner, S., "Accurate Values of the Exponent Governing Potential Flow about Semi-Infinite Cones," *AIAA J.*, vol. 3, p. 767, 1965.
30. Nakayama, A., and Koyama, H., "An Asymptotic Expression for Forced Convection in Non-Newtonian Power-Law Fluids," *Int. J. Heat Fluid Flow*, vol. 7, pp. 99–101, 1986.
31. Schmidt, E., and Wenner, K., "Wärmeabgabe über den Umfang eines angeblasenen Geheizten Zylinders," *Forsch. Geb. Ing.*, vol. 12, pp. 65–73, 1941.
32. Hiemenz, K., "Die Grenzschicht an einem in den gleichförmigen Flüssigkeitsstrom eingetauchten geraden Kreiszylinder," Thesis Göttingen 1911, *Dingl. Polytechn. J.*, vol. 326, 1911.
33. Slattery, J. C., and Bird, R. B., "Non-Newtonian Flow Past a Sphere," *Chem. Engrg. Sci.*, vol. 16, pp. 231–241, 1961.

CHAPTER 12

ANALOGIES BETWEEN MOMENTUM, HEAT AND MASS

TRANSFER IN DILUTE POLYMER SOLUTIONS

Aleksandar Duduković

Institute for Petrochemistry, Gas, Oil and Chemical Engineering
Faculty of Technology
University of Novi Sad, Yugoslavia

CONTENTS

INTRODUCTION

The analogies between momentum, heat and mass transfer played an important role in the development of heat and mass transfer theories for fluids in turbulent flow. Their use is not limited to prediction of heat and mass transfer coefficients from the pressure-drop data (which is much easier to measure than the heat or mass transfer rates), but also as the tools for the fundamental approach to the mechanism of heat and mass transfer and turbulence itself. Reynolds (in 1874) was the first scientist to recognize the existence of a relationship between heat transfer and skin friction [1]. After Prandtl, whose theoretical work refined Reynolds' approach, many investigations followed, mostly of an experimental nature. In the last fifty years there were a number a theoretical studies giving alternatives for the mathematical form of the analogies between momentum, heat, and mass transfer in both Newtonian and non-Newtonian fluids [1–5].

It is a goal of this text to present the possibilities of applying the analogies between momentum, heat, and mass transfer to drag-reducing dilute polymer solutions.

ANALOGIES BETWEEN MOMENTUM, HEAT AND MASS TRANSFER IN NEWTONIAN SOLUTIONS

The general approach to the problem of obtaining a relation between rates of momentum transport and heat or mass transfer is to obtain eddy viscosity as a function of the distance from the wall and other relevant variables from the correlations of velocity profiles. Next is to develop or assume the relationship between eddy viscosity and eddy diffusivity (usually taken to be equal or their ratio to be a constant). The obtained function for eddy diffusivity, combined with the equation for flux of mass or heat and integrated, leads to the analogies between momentum and heat or mass transfer.

All the analogies (except Reynolds') take into account the fact that in turbulent flow both mechanisms of transport, eddy and molecular, are present. The relative contribution of molecular transport increases approaching the wall, but at the same distance from the wall the contribution of molecular transport of the three processes is not the same as a consequence of different values of the kinematic viscosity, thermal diffusivity, and diffusion coefficient. This is the reason for the ratio of these properties, namely Prandtl and Schmidt number, to appear in all of the analogies proposed up to date. The Reynolds analogy is a special case for $Pr = Sc = 1$. So, the analogies have usual (though not necessarily explicit) form:

$$Nu = f(Re, Pr) \tag{1}$$

and equivalently:

$$Sh = f(Re, Sc) \tag{2}$$

Table 1
Dimensionless Groups for Heat and Mass Transfer

Heat transfer		Mass transfer	
Nusselt number	$Nu = \dfrac{hd}{k_T}$	Sherwood number	$Sh = \dfrac{kd}{D}$
Stanton number (for heat)	$St_H = \dfrac{h}{\rho C_p w}$	Stanton number (for mass)	$St_D = \dfrac{k}{w}$
j-factor for heat	$j_H = St_H Pr^{2/3}$	j-factor for mass	$j_D = St_D Sc^{2/3}$
Prandtl number	$Pr = \dfrac{v}{\alpha}$	Schmidt number	$Sc = \dfrac{v}{D}$

Table 2
Analogous Variables for Heat and Mass Transfer

	Heat Transfer		Mass Transfer
	Common form	Analogous form	
Transport variable	Temperature T	Energy per volume $\rho C_p T$	Concentration c
Fluid property	Thermal conductivity, K_T	Thermal diffusivity, $\alpha = k_T/\rho C_p$	Diffusion coefficient, D
Transport coefficient	Heat transfer coefficient, h	$h/\rho C_p$	Mass transfer coefficient, k

but they could be presented in several different ways using other dimensionless groups. The most frequently used dimensionless groups are presented in Table 1 for heat and mass transfer in the analogous mode.

To prevent possible confusion, one should keep in mind that the dimensionless groups are formed on the basis of the equations of heat transfer expressed in the form analogous to mass transfer [6], which is explained in Table 2.

POLYMER DRAG REDUCTION

It was a common belief that the frictional resistance to the relative motion of fluid and a solid surface is a unique function of the Reynolds number and relative roughness of the surface (For details see: *Encyclopedia of Fluid Mechanics*, vol. 1, pp. 433–439). It seemed that for a given geometry and fluid (i.e., fluid viscosity and density) there were no possibilities to reduce frictional losses. But, quite accidentally, it was discovered by Mysels and Toms (independently) that some fluids with small concentrations of additives exhibit much lower drag than would be expected [7–10]. Few discoveries in recent years in the area of fluid mechanics have created such intense interest as this phenomenon, commonly termed drag reduction or Toms phenomenon. It suggests practical benefits such as increased pipeline capacities and faster ships, but it is also interesting from the fundamental point of view, especially in the areas of wall turbulence and molecular rheology.

A wide variety of experimental and theoretical studies have been performed, both in order to understand the mechanism responsible for the effect and to provide information for engineering design. The largest part of the work has been devoted to dilute polymer solutions. Excellent reviews of most of these results have been provided by Hoyt [11, 12], Paterson et al. [13], Lumley [14], Kumor and Sylvester [15], Little et al. [16], and Virk [17] (For details see also: *Encyclopedia of Fluid Mechanics*, vol. 1., pp. 1060–1104).

Although a number of theoretical models have been proposed, the mechanism of drag reduction is still obscure; however, the following observations appear to be significant. The phenomenon results from some kind of interaction between the polymer molecules and the turbulent flow field. The polymer-turbulence interaction, however it occurs, markedly affects the region close to the wall, mostly the buffer zone [18, 19]. The phenomenon depends strongly on the concentration of the highest molecular weight species present in molecular weight distribution and appears to exist in the limit of infinite dilution [18].

It was experimentally shown [20, 21] that essentially all turbulence production occurs near the wall in the region $0 < y^+ < 100$. Visual studies revealed the presence of well organized spatially and temporally dependent motions within the laminar sublayer. These motions lead to the formation of "low-speed streaks" in the region very near the wall. Occasionally, "lift up" of these streaks occurs, resulting in oscillation, bursting, and ejection. It is believed that these processes play a dominant role in the production of turbulence [20]. It seems that polymer molecules interact and reduce a number of bursts, reducing in this way production of turbulence.

It is worthwhile to note that the result of the presence of high molecular weight polymer molecules is not only a reduction in turbulent intensity, but also in shifting the energy spectrum toward low frequency [22–25].

Maximum Drag Reduction

Drag reduction is best described by the observation of changes in the integral quantities (velocity profiles and friction losses) in turbulent flows in pipes. It has been found experimentally [26, 27] that the drag reduction for any given Reynolds number reaches a maximum for some condition and pipe size for each polymer type. Expressed another way, there is an asymptotic regime which ultimately limits the drag reduction possible. The maximum friction reduction achievable is about 80% of the friction reduction that would be attained if the flow were made completely laminar. On the basis of numerous data, Virk et al. [27, 28] have proposed the following equation for the maximum drag

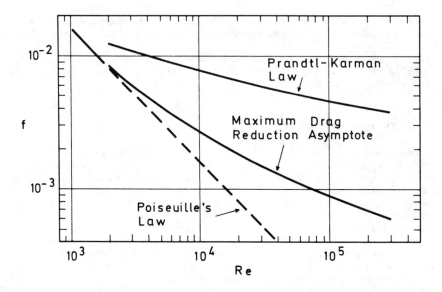

Figure 1. Friction factor plot illustrating polymer solutions behavior.

reduction asymptote:

$$\frac{1}{\sqrt{f}} = 19.0 \log(\text{Re } \sqrt{f}) - 32.4 \tag{3}$$

The equation is presented in a friction factor plot (Figure 1) and on Prandtl-Karman type coordinates (Figure 2), together with well known correlation of Prandtl-Kármán for Newtonian fluids:

$$\frac{1}{\sqrt{f}} = 4.00 \log(\text{Re } \sqrt{f}) - 0.4 \tag{4}$$

Equation 4 is in agreement with the explicit equation of Blasius in the region $4{,}000 < \text{Re} < 10^5$:

$$f = 0.0791 \text{ Re}^{-1/4} \tag{5}$$

The curvature of Equation 3 in the friction factor plot (Figure 1) is more pronounced than for Equation 4, but in the region $4{,}000 < \text{Re} < 40{,}000$ maximum drag reduction asymptote can be presented by a power-law expression, too:

$$f = 0.59 \text{ Re}^{-0.58} \tag{6}$$

In Figures 1 and 2 Poisseuille's law for laminar flow is also presented, for comparison.

Moderate Drag Reduction—Polymeric Regime

The region bounded in Figures 1 and 2 with curves representing Equations 3 and 4 represents polymer solutions which do exhibit drag reduction behavior, but to an extent lower than prescribed by Equation 3. Friction factor in such solutions depends not only on the Reynolds number, but also

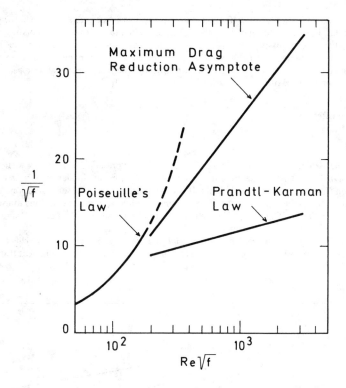

Figure 2. Correlations 3 and 4 on Prandtl-Karman coordinates.

upon the following variables: polymer, polymer-solvent combination, polymer molecular weight, molecular weight distribution, tube diameter, polymer structure etc. Extent of drag reduction is defined by [11, 14]:

$$DR = \left(\frac{\Delta P_o - \Delta P_s}{\Delta P_o} \right)_Q \tag{7}$$

where ΔP_o = pressure loss due to friction for solvent
    ΔP_s = pressure loss due to friction for polymer

The subscript Q indicates that the polymer solution is compared to the solvent at the same flowrate. Equal lengths, diameter, and roughness of the tube are assumed as well.

HEAT AND MASS TRANSFER IN DRAG-REDUCING POLYMER SOLUTIONS

Drag reduction in turbulent flow of dilute polymer solutions is accompanied by a reduction in heat and mass transfer. Though primary attention has been given to the effect of the polymers on the turbulent motion and momentum transfer, interest in heat and mass transfer in these flows has also been large, for both theoretical and practical reasons. The knowledge about heat and mass transfer under the conditions of drag reduction, which is still rather modest, will aid in understanding the fluid mechanics of the turbulent flow and the mechanism of drag reduction. On the other hand, the heat and mass transfer results will make it possible to obtain an overall picture of the gains that could be realized by the addition of polymers. This means that in the applications of drag reduction, which are attractive in many industrial situations involving momentum transfer, one must take into account the reduction in heat and mass transfer as well. These phenomena may even contribute to the positive economic effect of drag reduction (through the rate of corrosion or heat losses), or diminish it if intensive heat and mass transfer rates are desirable.

Experimental Results

Heat Transfer

Most of the available experimental heat transfer results are presented in Figure 3, with additional information in Table 3. All of the presented results were obtained in circular pipes with heat flux in the direction from the tube wall to the fluid. It should also be noted that some solutions were quite concentrated and revealed non-Newtonian phenomena, while very dilute solutions followed Newtonian behavior. Data of Corman [39] were not presented because the values of the Prandtl number were not available for these experiments.

The analysis of the data presented in Figure 3 and Table 3 leads to several conclusions. All the experimental facts prove that drag reduction is accompanied by the reduction in heat transfer. Fur-

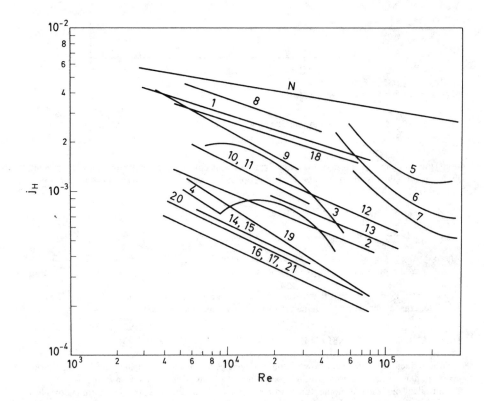

Figure 3. Heat transfer data for drag-reducing polymer solutions. Sources and additional data are given in Table 3. Pure solvent data (N) [38] are given for comparison [29].

Table 3
Summary of Heat Transfer Data

Entry	Source	Polymer	Conc. (wppm)	x/d
1	Pruitt, et al. [30]	Separan AP-30	10	—
2			100	
3	Marruci i Astarita [31]	ET-597	600	100
4			1000	
5	McNally [32]	Polyox WSR-301	2	52
6			10	
7			20	
8	Smith et al. [33]	Polyox N-3000	10	18
9			100	
10			1000	
11		Polyox WSR-301	10	
12	Debrule i Sabersky [34]	Polyox	10	40
13			50	
14	Ng, et al. [35]	Separan AP-273	1500, 2000	236
15		Polyox WSR-301	3500, 4500 5000	
16		Separan AP-273	1500, 2000	430
17		Polyox WSR-301	3500, 4500 5000	
18	Kwack et al. [36,37]	Separan AP-273	5, 10	430
19			50	
20			100	
21			300, 500 1000	

thermore, the reduction in heat transfer is greater than drag reduction. Great scatter among the data is obvious, which makes the analysis and testing of theories and correlations very difficult. This wide variation of heat transfer data reported in literature may be attributed to several causes, such as polymer degradation, the effect of the variable fluid properties due to large bulk-to-fluid temperature differences, and entrance effects [35, 40–42]. The role of the entrance effects seems to be of special interest, because it was shown by Yoo and Hartnett [43] and Ng et al. [35] that the temperature profile was not fully established, even after the tube length of 430 tube diameters. Later experiments [37] have shown that the thermal entrance length is a function of the polymer concentration and becomes larger than 400 equivalent diameters when the concentration is greater than 1,000 ppm. Theoretical work of Dimant and Poreh [40] explained longer thermal entrance lenghts in drag reducing solutions, but experimentally found values [37] are even greater.

On the basis of the experimental results of Ng et al. [35] and Kwack et al. [36] correlation for both thermaly developing and thermaly developed regions were evaluated [37]:

$$j_H = 0.13 \left(\frac{x}{d}\right)^{-0.24} Re_w^{-0.45} \qquad \text{for } x/d < 450 \tag{8}$$

$$\text{and} \quad j_H = 0.03\, Re_w^{-0.45} \qquad \text{for } x/d > 450 \tag{9}$$

Equation 9 is suggested to represent maximum heat transfer reduction asymptote. One should note that Equations 8 and 9 are based on data for relatively high concentrations of polymer. Equation 9 corresponds to the line representing entries 16, 17, and 21 in Figure 3.

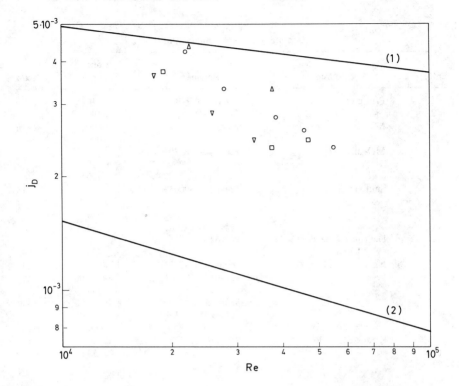

Figure 4. Mass transfer data for drag reducing polymer solutions. (1) Pure solvent, Notter and Sleicher [45], Equation 10. (2) Maximum mass transfer reduction, Virk and Suraiya [46], Equation 11. △ 50 ppm, ○ 150 ppm, □ 250 ppm, ▽ 325 ppm, McConaghy and Hanratty [44].

Mass Transfer

Some of the mass transfer data in drag-reducing dilute polymer solutions are presented in Figure 4. Data of McConaghy and Hanratty [44] correspond to moderate drag reduction (polymeric regime) and are lying between the results for pure solvent and for maximum mass transfer reduction. Mass transfer in pure Newtonian solvent is represented by the equation of Notter and Sleicher [45]:

$$j_D = 0.0149 \ Re^{-0.12} \tag{10}$$

The results for maximum mass transfer reduction asymptote were obtained experimentally by Virk and Suraiya [46] and correlated with the following equation:

$$j_D = 0.022 \ Re^{-0.29} \tag{11}$$

The data of McConaghy and Hanratty [44] were obtained by the electrochemical method, while Virk and Suraiya [46] used both the weight loss technique and the ultraviolet spectrophotometric technique.

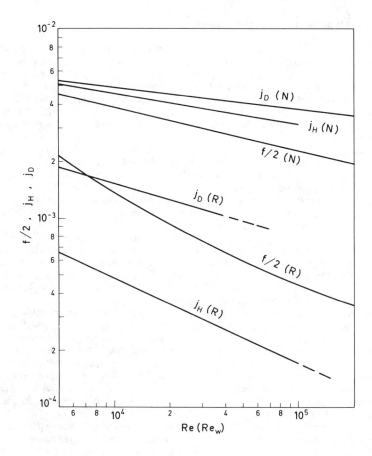

Figure 5. Comparison of momentum, heat and mass transfer data for no drag reduction (N) and maximum drag reduction (R) conditions.

Some of the available results were not presented in Figure 4 because they were affected by the polymer-solvent interaction or by entrance effects. The results of Sidahmed and Griskey [47] are restricted to conditions of entry region mass transfer. The same is true for the data of Teng et al. [48]. Few of these results that reach the fully developed mass transfer region are in agreement with the results of McConaghy and Hanratty [44]. Finally, Smith and Edwards [49] found a considerable effect of the electrolyte on drag reducing properties of the polymer solution. The drag reducing effect was greatly reduced. This presents a serious problem for the use of the electrochemical technique, when an excess of basic reagent is used. Such problems were avoided in the work of McConaghy and Hanratty because other materials were chosen.

In contrast with thermal entrance lengths, McConaghy [50] and Duković [51] found essentially equal entrance lengths for local mass transfer coefficients in both drag reducing solutions and pure solvent. Entrance lengths were about two equivalent diameters.

In Figure 5 the results for momentum and heat and mass transfer are compared at zero drag reduction and maximum drag reduction. Differences between the extents of drag reduction and reductions in heat and mass transfer are obvious.

Theoretical Models of Heat and Mass Transfer

A number of theoretical and semi-empirical models of heat and mass transfer in flows with drag reduction has been presented. In general, the proposed models resemble classical heat transfer models which had been used successfully for predicting heat or mass transfer in various turbulent flows of Newtonian fluid. All the models indicate that drag reduction is associated with a reduction in heat and mass transfer, but large differences exist between some of the models [40]. As shown by Smith et al. [33], models that correlate satisfactorily with some sets of data fail to agree with other sets. An excellent review on heat transfer in drag reducing fluids has been given by Dimant and Poreh [40].

Recently, three models for mass (or heat) transfer at maximum drag reduction [46, 52, 53] have been proposed. Reasonable agreement among those models indicates that heat or mass transfer at two asymptotes, i.e., the no drag reduction and the maximum drag reduction asymptotes, may be predicted with adequate accuracy [54].

In the field of moderate drag reduction, the proposed correlations do not agree with each other. Most of them contain adjustable parameters and, furthermore, the resulting expressions for the heat and mass transfer are complex and not readily usable [54].

Ghajar and Tiederman [55] used an eddy diffusivity distribution due to Cess [56], together with experimental data on frictional drag reduction, to determine their numerical evaluations of the Lyon equation for heat transfer. The results are in agreement with heat transfer data of several authors, for low Prandtl numbers. A similar approach was used by McConaghy and Hanratty [44], with both Cess' [56] and Leviton's [57] eddy viscosity function. Predicted values were lower than the measured ones, with Schmidt numbers from 700 to 1,300.

The analysis of Dimant and Poreh [40] is based on a phenomenological model for describing the velocity profiles in flows with drag reduction, which uses Van Driest's mixing lengths expression with a variable damping parameter. Hanna and Sandall [58] used a new modification of the drag reducing eddy diffusivity model developed by Dimant and Poreh. This modification was used together with the analytical relationships for heat and mass transfer, developed for drag reducing conditions in similar manner as for zero drag reduction [59]. The resulting equations contain an adjustible parameter and the semi-empirical form for mixing length. For several sets of data, the Dimant and Poreh model [40] gives better predictions, while for some other results the Hanna and Sandall [58] approach seems to have advantages.

Kawase [54] derived a model based on Levich's three zone concept, applicable to moderate drag reduction. As proposed by Seyer and Metzner [60] the extent of drag reduction is taken into account through the value of Deborah number. The model contains an empirical correlation for the laminar sublayer thickness and is in good agreement with some of the heat and mass transfer results.

Based on the previous work of Friend and Metzner [61] and Seyer and Metzner [60], starting from the analysis of Reichardt [62], Kale [63] derived a model for prediction of heat transfer results from the friction factor data. The model is in agreement with many of the heat transfer data in drag reducing solutions. However it overpredicts some of the recent heat transfer results [35, 36], but underestimates the mass transfer results for drag reducing solutions [44, 46]. Starting from similar equations Wells [64] derived another model for the prediction of heat transfer rates on the basis of pressure drop measurements. The model represents well the data of Pruitt et al. [30]. These two models [63, 64] take into account the extent of drag reduction through the value of Deborah number [63] or through the value of the velocity at the edge of the viscous sublayer [64]. Both could be determined from the friction factor data. However, these two models are inconsistent, especially at high Prandtl or Schmidt numbers.

Discussing the great variation among data and between proposed correlations for heat and mass transfer in drag reducing solutions, taking into account differences in extents of maximum drag reduction and maximum reductions in heat and mass transfer, as well as the differences in entrance lengths for these phenomena, Cho and Hartnett [42, 52] concluded that there is no simple and direct analogy between momentum and heat and mass transfer for drag reducing fluids in turbulent flow. In our opinion, it is not so important for an analogy to be simple, but to be fundamental with theoretical background.

THE ANALOGY BETWEEN MOMENTUM, HEAT AND MASS TRANSFER
IN DRAG-REDUCING SOLUTIONS

Mass Transfer

At the beginning of this chapter we explained the basis for the development of the analogies among momentum and heat and mass transfer in Newtonian fluids with no drag reduction. But fundamentals of the analogies are in the relation between turbulence characteristics and the mechanisms of momentum, heat and mass transfer. The rates of these phenomena are proportional to the intensity of turbulence, and this fact leads to the proportionality between dimensionless groups representing transport phenomena. These proportionalities contain the Prandtl or Schmidt number as well, due to the different contributions of molecular transport, as explained before. So, for mass transfer we have:

$$St_D = F(f, Sc) \tag{12}$$

Now, the question arises: is the contribution of turbulent transfer the same for all three phenomena? It was experimentally shown [65–67] that the high frequency turbulent pulsations have little effect on mass transfer rates. This brought us to the conclusion that the change in turbulence spectra should affect the relation between momentum and mass transfer, and should be taken into account through the value of turbulent Schmidt number. Duduković [68] has shown that such effect in Newtonian solutions exists due to the change in Reynolds number, but that the turbulent Schmidt number is only a weak function of Reynolds number, which is usually taken implicitly into account through the exponent on Reynolds number. As a consequence the analogy differs slightly from Equation 12 and can be represented by:

$$St_D = F(f, Re, Sc) = F(Re, Sc) \tag{13}$$

which is similar to Equation 2.

In drag reducing dilute polymer solutions this effect of turbulence spectra on the rate of mass transfer is much more pronounced. It was found [7, 22–25] that drag reducing polymers not only decrease the turbulent intensity but also move the turbulence spectra toward lower frequencies. The high frequency portion of turbulent spectra is much more suppressed. As a consequence, we expect the change in the value of turbulent Schmidt number. In dilute polymer solutions, both eddy viscosity and eddy mass diffusivity are reduced due to decrease in turbulence intensity. But eddy mass diffusivity is reduced less than eddy viscosity because mostly high frequency pulsations were suppressed, and they had a little contribution to mass transfer. As a result, turbulent Schmidt number should decrease with the extent of drag reduction.

In order to prove our predictions we derived the analogy in the form:

$$St_D = F(Re, Sc, Sc_t) \tag{14}$$

We started [69, 70] from the analysis of Reichardt, which applied to mass transfer may be represented in the form:

$$St_D = \frac{\dfrac{1}{Sc_t} \dfrac{f}{2} \dfrac{1}{\theta}}{\dfrac{1}{\phi} + (Sc^* - 1)b\left(\dfrac{f}{2}\right)^{1/2}} \tag{15}$$

where $b = \displaystyle\int_0^{U/w^*} \dfrac{d(u/w^*)}{1 + Sc^* E_M/\nu}$ \tag{16}

The assumptions involved are minor and not central to the present discussion. Several models are derived [4, 61, 63] or could be derived starting from the Reichardt approach, but the usual assumption was $Pr_t = 1$ or $Sc_t = 1$. Parameter $1/\phi$ was found to be 1.2 for Newtonian, non-Newtonian, and viscoelastic fluids [4, 61, 71]. For mass transfer it is appropriate to assume $\theta = 1$.

Integral b (Equation 16) is solved numerically. The radial variation of Sc_t number and its dependence on Reynolds number were neglected. It was shown [68] that Sc_t number is only a weak function of Reynolds number.

Deissler [72] has proposed the following semi-theoretical expression to represent conditions in the vicinity of the wall:

$$\frac{E_M}{\nu} = n^2 u^+ y^+ [1 - \exp(-n^2 u^+ y^+)] \qquad (17)$$

with the value $n = 0.124$ for Newtonian fluids. The corresponding velocity profile was used for the wall region:

$$u^+ = \int_0^{y^+} \frac{dy^+}{1 + n^2 u^+ y^+ (1 - e^{-n^2 u^+ y^+})} \qquad (18)$$

Further from the wall the logarithmic profile was assumed:

$$u^+ = A \ln y^+ + B \qquad (19)$$

Parameter A was kept at its Newtonian value of 2.5, as suggested earlier [60].

The transition point for every value of n was found from:

$$\left(\frac{du^+}{dy^+}\right)_{eq. (18)} = \left(\frac{du^+}{dy^+}\right)_{eq. (19)} \qquad (20)$$

To each value of n corresponds a value of B which was found from:

$$(u^+)_{eq. (18)} = (u^+)_{eq. (19)} \qquad (21)$$

at the transition point. Seyer and Metzner [60] correlated parameter B with viscoelastic properties of the fluid through a Deborah number.

The integral in Equation 16 was solved for different values of n and generalized Schmidt number Sc*. Taking into account the correspondence between n, B, and De number the computed results were approximated [70] with:

$$b = [9.2 + 1.2(De - 0.17De^2)]Sc^{*-0.255} \qquad (22)$$

Equations 15 and 22 together represent a new analogy between momentum and mass transfer. The extent of drag reduction is taken into account through the value of Deborah number, which can be determined directly from friction factor data, as shown by Seyer and Metzner [60]. Turbulent Schmidt number takes into account the shift in turbulence spectra. In order to check the prediction of the decrease of Sc_t number with the extent of drag reduction, Equations 15 and 22 are compared with the experimental results for mass transfer in drag reducing dilute polymer solutions [44, 46]. The obtained results are presented in Figure 6 as a plot of $Sc_t \cdot Sc^{0.3}$ vs. DR/DR_{max}, where DR_{max} corresponds to maximum drag reduction asymptote. Turbulent Schmidt number is multiplied by $Sc^{0.3}$ to take into account the dependence of Sc_t number on Sc number. The exponent of 0.3 is obtained [70] through the comparison of the theoretical equations with empirical equations. Some experimental evidence [67] indicate the exponent of 0.41.

Results in Figure 6 clearly confirm the decrease of Sc_t number with the relative extent of drag reduction, as predicted from the measurements of changes in characteristics of turbulence in drag

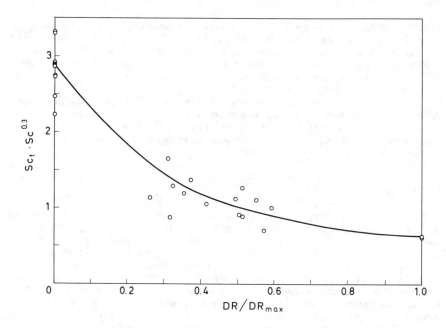

Figure 6. Turbulent Schmidt number as a function of the relative extent of drag reduction.

reducing systems. At the same time, the graph in Figure 6 makes possible the use of the analogy (Equations 15 and 22) for prediction of mass transfer rates on the basis of friction factor data. Equation 22 may be simplified for high Sc numbers:

$$St_D = \frac{\left(\dfrac{f}{2}\right)^{1/2}}{Sc\ b} \tag{23}$$

Equations 22 and 15, or 23, represent the general analogy between momentum, heat and mass transfer in both drag reducing solutions and fluids with no drag reduction. At the same time it offers new possibilities to obtain some insight into the detailed mechanism by which the polymer acts, from measurements of only macroscopic quantities such as mass transfer rates, pressure drops, and flow rates.

There are other ways to derive an analogy of the general type $Sc_t = F(Re, Sc, Sc_t)$. But the main point here was to show that a fundamental analogy between momentum and mass transfer exists and that it is based on the mechanisms of turbulence and drag and mass transfer reduction, i.e., on the changes in the world of turbulent eddies and their effect on the macroscopic quantities.

Heat Transfer

There are no fundamental reasons why the presented analogy of Equations 15 and 22 should not apply for heat transfer as well. When the plot in Figure 6 was used to predict turbulent Prandtl number, excellent agreement between the presented analogy and experimental results of McNally [32] and Smith et al. [33] was found.

On the other hand, the comparison of the analogy with the experimental results of Ng et al. [35] and Kwack et al. [36] gives no agreement. This comparison suggests the values of Pr_t number to be much higher than expected from Figure 6, even up to the value of eight. Such values of turbulent Prandtl number are not only unexpected and different from the results for mass transfer, but also could not be explained in terms of our knowledge of the mechanism of heat transfer.

Thus, inconsistency of heat transfer data makes it impossible to give a definite answer about this, and other existing theories. The theoretical analysis should help distinguish which of the available results are reliable.

Finally, a short note on the idea of the intruding phenomenon [73]. It was suggested, but not proved to date, that heat transfer rates in polymer solutions of higher concentrations could be affected by some intruding phenomenon, responsible for lower vaues of j_D and very long thermal entrance lengths. Soret effect was named as a possible phenomenon which could become important in such systems due to the very high molecular weight of polymer.

CONCLUSION

The existence of the analogy between momentum and heat and mass transfer in drag reducing dilute polymer solutions is shown. This analogy is of a general type and is applicable to other fluids which do not exhibit drag reduction. Such a general analogy should contain both Schmidt and turbulent Schmidt number (or equivalently Pr and Pr_t numbers). While the dependence on turbulence intensity is the basis for the relation between momentum and heat and mass transfer, the Schmidt (or Prandtl) number takes into account different relative contributions of molecular transport, while a turbulent Schmidt (or turbulent Prandtl) number represents the changes in turbulence spectra and their effect on the rates of the three processes. In Newtonian solutions the effect of the changes in turbulent spectra is not so pronounced, and can be taken into account through the exponent on Reynolds number, which leads us to Equation 1 or 2. Finally, for Prandtl or Schmidt number values close to one we come to the special case: the Reynolds analogy.

The presented analogy (containing turbulent Schmidt number) is of interest not only for classical reasons, i.e., for the prediction of heat and mass transfer rates on the basis of skin friction data, but because it offers the insight into the mechanism of drag reduction and turbulence itself on the basis of measurements of macroscopic quantities.

NOTATION

A, B	Parameters (Equation 19)	Pr_t	Turbulent Prandtl number ($=E_M/E_H$)
b	Integral defined in Equation 16	Re	Reynolds number ($=wd/v$)
C_p	Heat capacity at constant pressure	Re_w	Reynolds number based on the viscosity at the wall
D	Molecular diffusion coefficient		
De	Deborah number	Sc	Schmidt number, defined in Table 1
DR	Extent of drag reduction, defined in Equation 7	Sc*	Generalized Schmidt number ($=Sc/Sc_t$)
		Sc_t	Turbulent Schmidt number ($=E_M/E_D$)
d	Tube diameter	St_D	Stanton number for mass, defined in Table 1
E_D	Eddy mass diffusivity		
E_H	Eddy thermal diffusivity	St_H	Stanton number for heat, defined in Table 1
E_M	Eddy viscosity		
f	Fanning friction factor ($=2\tau_w/\rho w^2$)	T	Temperature
h	Heat transfer coefficient	U	Velocity at the pipe axis
j_D	Mass transfer j factor ($=St_D Sc^{2/3}$)	u	Velocity
j_H	Heat transfer j factor ($=St_H Pr^{2/3}$)	u^+	Dimensionless velocity ($=u/w*$)
k	Mass transfer coefficient	w	Average velocity
k_T	Thermal conductivity of fluid	w*	Friction velocity ($=(\tau_w/\rho)^{1/2}$)
Nu	Nusselt number, defined in Table 1	x	Axial distance
Pr	Prandtl number, defined in Table 1	y	Radial Distance from the wall
Pr*	Generalized Prandtl number ($=Pr/Pr_t$)	y^+	Dimensionless distance ($=yw*/v$)

Greek Symbols

α Thermal diffusivity, defined in Table 2

ϕ Ratio of maximum to average velocity $(= U/w)$

ν Kinematic viscosity

θ Ratio of mean to maximum temperature difference

ρ Density

τ_w Shear stress at the wall

REFERENCES

1. Knudsen, J. G., and Katz, D. L., *Fluid Dynamics and Heat Transfer*, McGraw-Hill, New York (1958), pp. 409–455.
2. Sherwook, T. K., Pigford, R. L ., and Wilke, C. R., *Mass Transfer*, McGraw-Hill, New York (1975), pp. 159–172.
3. Skelland, A. H. P., *Diffusional Mass Transfer*, J. Wiley & Sons, New York (1973), pp. 231–289.
4. Metzner, A. B., and Firend, P. S.," *Heat Transfer to Turbulent Non-Newtonian Fluids," Ind. Eng.*, *51*(7), 879 (1959).
5. Kawase, Y., and Ulbrecht, J. J., "Turbulent Heat and Mass Transfer in Non-Newtonian Fluids," ASME, 82-HT-57, (1982).
6. Cussler, E. L., *Diffusion-Mass Transfer in Fluid Systems*, Cambridge University Press, Cambridge (1984), pp. 439–448.
7. Toms, B. A., "Some Observations on the Flow of Linear Polymer Solutions through Straight Tubes at Large Reynolds Numbers," Proc. 1st Int. Rheology Congress, Part 2, 135 (1949).
8. Mysels, K. J., "Flow of Thickened Fluids," US Patent, 2,492,173 (Dec. 27, 1949).
9. Mysels, K. J., "Early Experiences with Viscous Drag Reduction," Chem. Eng. Progress Symp. Ser., *67*, (111), 45 (1971).
10. Agoston, G. A., Harte, W. H., Hottel, H. C., Klemm, W. A., Mysels, K. J., Pomeroy, H. H., and Thompson, J. H., "Flow of Gasoline Thickened by Napalm," *Ind. Eng. Chem.*, *46*, 1017 (1954)
11. Hoyt, J. W., "The Effect of Additives on Fluid Friction," *ASME J. Basic Eng.*, *94*, 258 (1972).
12. Hoyt, J. W., "Recent Progress in Polymer Drag Reduction," *Polymeres et Lubrification*, No 233 (1974).
13. Paterson, R. W., Zakin, J. L., and Rodrigues, J. M., "Drag Reduction-Polymer Solutions, Soap Solutions and Solid Particle Suspensions in Pipe Flow," *Ind. Eng. Chem.*, *61*, 22 (1969).
14. Lumley, J. L., "Drag Reduction by Additives"., *Ann. Rev. Fluid Mechanics*, *1*, 367 (1969).
15. Kumor, S. M., and Sylvester, N. D., "Effects of a Drag-Reducing Polymer on the Turbulent Boundary Layer," AIChE Symp. Ser., *69*, (130), 1 (1973).
16. Little, R. C., Hansen, R. J., Hunston, D. L., Kim, O. K., Patterson, R. L., and Ting, R. Y., "The Drag Reduction Phenomenon. Observed Characteristics, Improved Agents, and Proposed Mechanisms," *I&EC Fundamentals*, *14*, 283 (1975).
17. Virk, P. S., "Drag Reduction Fundamentals," *AIChE Journal*, *21*, 625 (1975).
18. Sylvester, N. D., and Kumor, S. M., "Degradation of Dilute Polymer Solutions in Turbulent Tube Flow," Chem. Eng. Progr. Symp. Ser., *69* (1973).
19. Paterson, R. W., and Abernathy, F. H., "Turbulent Flow Drag Reduction and Degradation with Dilute Polymer Solutions," *J. Fluid Mech.*, *43*, 689 (1970).
20. Kline, S. J., Reynolds, W. C., Schraub, F. A., and Runstadler, P. W., "The Structure of Turbulent Boundary Layers," *J. Fluid Mech.*, *30*, (4), 741 (1967).
21. Kim, H. T., Kline, S. J., and Reynolds, W. C., "The Production of Turbulence Near a Smooth Wall in a Turbulent Boundary Layer," *J. Fluid Mech.*, *50*, 133 (1970).
22. Taylor, A. R., and Middleman, S., "Turbulent Dispersion in Drag-Reducing Fluids," *AIChE Journal*, *20*, 454 (1974).
23. Fortuna, G., and Hanratty, T. J., "The Influence of Drag-Reducing Polymers on Turbulence in the Viscous Sublayer," *J. Fluid Mech.*, *53*, (3), 575 (1972).
24. Makarenkov, A. P., Vinogradniy, G. P., Skripachev, U. V., and Kanarskiy, M. V., "The Effect of Polymer Additives on the Pressure Drop Pulsations in the Boundary Layer," (Russ), Inzenerno-Fizicheskiy Zurnal, *25*, (6), 1006 (1973).

25. Berman, N. S., Griswold, S. T., Elihu, S., and Yuen, J., "An Observation of the Effect of Integral Scale on Drag Reduction, *AIChE Journal, 24*, 124 (1978).
26. Hoyt, J. W., and Fabula, A. G., "The Effect of Additives on Fluid Friction," Proc. 5th Symp. Naval Hydrodynamics, Bergen, Norway, Office of Naval Research, ACR-112, 947 (1964).
27. Virk, P. S., Mickley, H. S., and Smith, K. A., "The Ultimate Asymptote and Mean Flow Structure in Toms Phenomenon," *ASME J. Appl. Mech., 37*, 488 (1970).
28. Virk, P. S., "An Elastic Sublayer Model for Drag Reduction by Dilute Solutions of Linear Macromolecules," *J. Fluid Mech., 45*, (3), 417 (1971).
29. Duduković, A., and Sinadinović, S., "Heat Transfer in Dilute Polymer Solutions," 2nd Yugoslav Congress of Chemical Engng. Proceedings (in print), Dubrovnik (1987).
30. Pruitt, G. T., Whitsitt, N. F., and Crawford, M. R., Report contract No. NAS 7-369 Western Company Research Div., Dallas, Texas, For Natl. Aero-naut. Space Admin. Fluid Dynamics Branch Research Division, Office of Advanced Research and Technology (1966); cited and data represented by Wells, C. S., *AIChE Journal, 14*, 406 (1968).
31. Marrucci, G., and Astarita, G., "Turbulent Heat Transfer in Viscoelastic Fluids," *Ind. Eng. Chem. Fundamentals, 6*, 470 (1967).
32. McNally, W. A., "Heat and Momentum Transport in Dilute Polyethylene Oxide Solutions," Ph.D. Thesis, University of Rhode Island (1968).
33. Smith, K. A., Keuroghlian, G. H., Virk, P. S., and Merrill, E. W., "Heat Transfer to Drag-Reducing Polymer Solutions," *AIChE Journal, 15*, 294 (1969).
34. Debrule, P. M., and Sabersky, R. H., "Heat Transfer and Friction Coefficients in Smooth and Rough Tubes with Dilute Polymer Solutions," *Int. J. Heat Mass Transfer, 17*, 529 (1974).
35. Ng, K. S., Cho, Y. I., and Hartnett, J. P., "Heat Transfer Performance of Concentrated Polyethylene Oxide and Polyacrylamide Solutions," AIChE Symp. Ser., *76*(199), 250 (1980).
36. Kwack, E. Y., Cho, Y. I., and Hartnett, J. P., "Effect of Weissenberg Number on Turbulent Heat Transfer of Aqueous Polyacrylamide Solutions," Proc. 7th Int. Heat Transfer Conf., *3*(FC 11), 63 (1982).
37. Kwack, E. Y., Hartnett, J. P., and Cho, Y. I., "Turbulent Heat Transfer in Circular Tube Flows of Viscoelastic Fluids," Wärme-und Stoffübertragung, *16*, 35 (1982).
38. Allen, R. W., and Eckert, E. R. G., "Friction and Heat Transfer Measurements to Turbulent Pipe Flow of Water (Pr = 7 and 8) at Uniform Wall Heat Flux," *ASME Journal Heat Transfer, 86*, 301 (1964).
39. Corman, J. C., "Experimental Study of Heat Transfer to Viscoelastic Fluids," *Ind. Eng. Chem. Process Des. Develop., 9*, 254 (1970).
40. Dimant, Y., and Poreh, M., "Heat Transfer in Flows with Drag Reduction," *Advances in Heat Transfer*, Vol. 12, Academic Press, New York (1976).
41. Cho, Y. I., Ng. K. S., and Hartnett, J. P., "Viscoelastic Fluids in Turbulent Pipe Flow—a New Heat Transfer Correlation,"*Letts. Heat Mass Transfer, 7*, 347 (1980).
42. Cho, Y. I., and Hartnett, J. P., "Analogy for Viscoelastic Fluids—Momentum, Heat and Mass Transfer in Turbulent Pipe Flow," *Letts. Heat Mass Transfer, 7*, 339 (1980).
43. Yoo, S. S., and Hartnett, J. P., "Thermal Entrance Lengths for Non-Newtonian Fluids in Turbulent Pipe Flow," Letts. Heat Mass Transfer, *2*, 189 (1975).
44. McConaghy, G. A., and Hanratty, T. J., "Influence of Drag Reducing Polymers on Turbulent Mass Transfer to a Pipe Wall," *AIChE Journal, 23*, 493 (1977).
45. Notter, R. H., and Sleicher, C. A., "The Eddy Diffusivity in the Turbulent Boundary Layer Near a Wall," *Chem. Eng. Sci., 26*, 161 (1971).
46. Virk, P. S., and Suraiya, T., "Mass Transfer at Maximum Drag Reduction," Proc. 2nd Int. Conf. Drag Reduction, G3-41, BHRA Fluid Eng., Cranfield, England (1977).
47. Sedahmed, G. H., and Griskey, R. G., "Mass Transfer in Drag Reducing Fluid Systems," *AIChE Journal, 18*, 138 (1972).
48. Teng, J. T., Greif, R., Cornet, I., and Smith, R., "Study of Heat and Mass Transfer in Pipe Flows with Non-Newtonian Fluids," *Int. J. Heat Mass Transfer, 22*, 493 (1979).
49. Smith, R., and Edwards, M. F., "Pressure Drop and Mass Transfer in Dilute Polymer Solutions in Turbulent Drag-Reducing Pipe Flow," *Int. J. Heat Mass Transfer, 25*, 1869 (1982).

50. McConaghy, G. A., "The Effect of Drag Reducing Polymers on Turbulent Mass Transfer," Ph.D. Thesis, University of Illinois, Urbana (1974).
51. Duduković, A. P., "Mass Transfer Entrance Lengths in Dilute Polymer Solutions," *AIChE Journal*, *32*, (4) (1986).
52. Cho, Y. I., and Hartnett, J. P., "Mass Transfer in Turbulent Pipe Flow of Viscoelastic Fluids," *Int. J. Heat Mass Transfer*, *24*, 945 (1981).
53. Kawase, Y., and Ulbrecht, J. J., "Turbulent Heat and Mass Transfer in Dilute Polymer Solutions," *Chem. Eng. Sci.*, *37*, 1039 (1982).
54. Kawase, Y., "Turbulent Heat and Mass Transfer in Flows with Moderate Drag Reduction," *Physico-Chemical Hydrodynamics*, *4*, 29 (1983).
55. Ghajar, A. J., and Tiederman, W. G., "Prediction of Heat Transfer Coefficients in Drag Reducing Turbulent Pipe Flows," *AIChE Journal*, *23*, 128 (1977).
56. Cess, R. D., "A Survey of the Literature on Heat Transfer in Turbulent Tube Flows," Westinghouse Research Laboratories, Rept. 8-0529-R24 (1958).
57. Leviton, A. E., "A Correlation of Turbulent Temperature Profiles Using the Eddy Diffusivity Concept," M.S. thesis, University of Illinois, Urbana (1968).
58. Hanna, O. T., Sandall, O. C., and Mazet, P. R., "Heat and Mass Transfer in Turbulent Flow Under Conditions of Drag Reduction," *AIChE Journal*, *27*, 693 (1981).
59. Hanna, O. T., and Sandall, O. C., "Developed Turbulent Transport in Ducts for Large Prandtl or Schmidt Numbers," *AIChE Journal*, *18*, 527 (1972).
60. Seyer, F. A., and Metzner, A. B., "Turbulence Phenomena in Drag Reducing Systems," *AIChE Journal*, *15*, 426 (1969).
61. Friend, W. L., and Metzner, A. B., "Turbulent Heat Transfer Inside Tubes and the Analogy Among Heat, Mass, and Momentum Transfer," *AIChE Journal*, *4*, 393 (1958).
62. Reichardt, H., "The Principles of Turbulent Heat Transfer," *Trans. from Arch., Ges Warmtech.*, No. 6/7, 129 (1951), NACA TM-1408 (1957).
63. Kale, D. D., "An Analysis of Heat Transfer to Turbulent Flow of Drag Reducing Fluids," *Int. J. Heat Mass Transfer*, *20*, 1077 (1977).
64. Wells, C. S., "Turbulent Heat Transfer in Drag Reducing Fluids," AIChE Journal, *14*, 406 (1968).
65. Van-Shaw, P., and Hanratty, T. J., "Fluctuations in the Local Rate of Turbulent Mass Transfer to a Pipe Wall," *AIChE Journal*, *10*, 475 (1964).
66. Sirkar, K. K., and Hanratty, T. J., "Relation of Turbulent Mass Transfer to a Wall at High Schmidt Numbers to the Velocity Field," *J. Fluid Mech.*, *44*, (3), 589 (1970).
67. Shaw, D. A., and Hanratty, T. J., "Influence of Schmidt Number on the Fluctuations of Turbulent Mass Transfer to a Wall," *AIChE Journal*, *23*, 160 (1977).
68. Duduković, A. P., "Influence of the Turbulent Schmidt Number on Mass Transfer Rates Between Turbulent Fluid Stream and a Solid Surface," *AIChE Journal*, *30*, 1919 (1985).
69. Duduković, A., "Momentum, Heat and Mass Transfer in Drag Reducing Solutions," 2nd Yugoslav Congress of Chemical Engng. Proc. (in print), Dubrovnik (1987).
70. Duduković, A., and Herron, J., "Mass Transfer in Drag Reducing Dilute Polymer Solutions," (in preparation).
71. Gupta, M. K., Metzner, A. B., and Hartnett, J. P., "Turbulent Heat Transfer Characteristics of Viscoelastic Fluids," *Int. J. Heat Mass Transfer*, *10*, 1211 (1967).
72. Deissler, R. G., "Analysis of Heat Transfer, Mass Transfer and Friction in Smooth Tubes at High Prandtl and Schmidt Numbers, N.A.CA. TN-3145 (1954).
73. Duduković, A. P., "The Analogy Between Momentum, Heat and Mass Transfer in Drag-Reducing Fluids," 5th Yugoslavian-Austrian-Italian Chem. Eng. Conf., Portorož, Yugoslavia, Proc. 139 (1986).

SECTION II
SLIPPAGE AND DRAG PHENOMENA

CONTENTS

CHAPTER 13

STRESS MEASUREMENT OF VISCOELASTIC FLUIDS BY FLOW BIREFRINGENCE TECHNIQUE AND SLIP PHENOMENA OF POLYMER MELTS

K. Funatsu and T. Kajiwara

Department of Chemical Engineering
Kyushu University
Fukuoka, Japan

CONTENTS

INTRODUCTION

Since viscoelastic fluids are often dealt with in chemical engineering, it is important fundamentally and practically to determine their constitutive equations. Many constitutive equations have been proposed, but it has not been clear which is the most reasonable. Moreover, for the complicated properties of the constitutive equations of the viscoelastic fluids, it is usually difficult to analytically solve non-viscometric flows, which are technologically important. But it is hoped to be possible to obtain analytical or numerical solutions by using proper constitutive equations for many important flow fields. Therefore, the constitutive equations should be determined for each fluid. There have been many experimental attempts. The viscous terms of a fluid can be measured, but its elastic terms cannot be easily measured. For simple shearing flow, the elastic terms can be expressed with the material functions, which are three relations of each of shear stress, the primary and the secondary normal stress differences with shear rate. The material functions or the various flow fields of the viscoelastic fluids have been measured by various methods, and flow birefringence technique has been proved one of the most effective.

The flow birefringence technique has been used for both study of flow behaviour of polymers or particles in various solutions [1], and flow analysis similar to the stress analysis of solid materials by photoelasticity [2]. At an early stage of the study of the flow birefringence, Brewster's law for fluids was confirmed. The transmitted light technique has been applied to analysis of two-dimensional laminar flows. Various birefringent fluids, such as sesame oil, bentonite suspension, polymer solutions, and milling yellow aqueous solutions, were used as sample fluids [3–6].Prados et al.[7] and Durelli et al. [8] used a milling yellow aqueous solution, which has highly photoelastic sensitivity, and illustrated that the transmitted light flow birefringence technique is effective for analysis of two-dimensional flow field. Also, the technique has been applied to measurement of the normal stress differences and analysis of flow fields for polymer solutions and melts [9–11]. The scattered light flow birefringence technique has been developed for analysis of three-dimensional flows. McAfee et al. [12] applied it to analysis of tubular flow. Horsmann et al. [13] studied channel flow.

The slip on the wall of solid surfaces has been recognized as one of the flow characteristics of polymer melts, solutions, etc. The phenomenon of slip was found at the beginning of melt fracture for some kinds of polymer melts, such as polyethylene and polypropylene, where volume flow rates jump up discontinuously. Evaluation of slip is very important for determining flow characteristics of fluids. Neglecting the slip causes vital errors for velocity distribution, shear rate distribution, and other calculations. There are many polymer melts that have slip characteristics during steady laminar flows. For example, poly (vinyl chloride) melts slip on the wall of dies steadily over lower and higher shear rate range. From the viewpoint of the components, it contains stabilizers, lubricants, and other additives with pure resin. These low-molecular weight components form a thin layer near the wall and cause the bulk fluid to slip. By assuming that the slip velocity is a function of shear stress on the wall only, Mooney [14] developed the relation between shear stress, shear rate, and slip velocity on the wall of dies. This relation has been used to measure slip velocity for several polymer melts. But the assumption mentioned above is not confirmed for all fluids. In this case, since there are many factors concerned with the phenomena, further theoretical development has not been achieved. On the other hand, several attempts have been made to measure slip velocity. Chauffoureaux [15] measured the slip velocity by stopping the slip phenomena using a nozzle with a grooved wall.

This chapter will discuss the study of viscoelastic fluids by using flow birefringence technique. The principles of transmitted light and scattered light flow birefringence techniques will be described briefly and examples of measured normal stress difference and stresses of flow fields given. Next, we will discuss slip velocity and examples of measurement will be shown. Lastly, we will explain application of birefringence to evaluation of injection-molded objects.

FLUIDS USED FOR EXPERIMENTS

Polymer Melts and Solutions

Polymer melts and solutions used for experiments described in this chapter include: high density polyethylene (Hizex 5000H) melt, low density polyethylene (IUPAC A) melt, polystyrene (Styron 678, BASF 3) melt, polydimethylsiloxane (Siloprene RS) melt, and polyisobutylene oil (Oppanol B5) were used for normal stress differences measurement. Polyethylene melt, polypropylene melt, corn syrup, and polystyrene (Toporex 575) in toluene were used for measurement of stress distribution in two-dimensional flow fields. High density polyethylene (Marlex 6050, Staflen E 605) melts and PVC (Ryuron 700-D, SOLVIC 172RB, SOLVIC 264GA) melt with some additives were used for measurement of slip velocity.

Milling Yellow Aqueous Solution

Milling yellow [16] is one of the organic dyes. Its aqueous solution has shear-thinning viscosity and viscoelastic characteristics. Also, it has highly photoelastic sensitivity and has been used for investigation of flow fields by flow birefringence technique as one of the suitable sample fluids. The aqueous solution is prepared in the following manner. Milling yellow powder is added to distilled water that was about 1.5 times as much as the required amount of the solution. The mixture is concentrated to a necessary degree. Then, the solution is gradually cooled at room temperature. Suitable concentration is from 1 wt% to 2 wt%. The detail of preparation is explained in a previous paper [17].

PRINCIPLES OF FLOW BIREFRINGENCE TECHNIQUE AND BREWSTER'S LAW FOR VISCOELASTIC FLUIDS

Brewster's Law and Stress-Optical Coefficient

When a birefringent fluid is flowing, refractive index ellipsoid and stress ellipsoid are uniquely determined at an arbitrary point corresponding to state of flow. Both ellipsoids are shown in Figure 1. The principal values of the refractive index ellipsoid and stress ellipsoid are designated as n_1, n_2, and n_3, and σ_1, σ_2 and σ_3, respectively. The differences in principal values of refractive index ellipsoid and stress ellipsoid are called principal birefringence and principal stress difference, respectively. Stress analysis by the flow birefringence technique is based on Brewster's law, which assumes that the principal birefringence Δn is proportional to the principal stress difference $\Delta \sigma$ as shown in Equation 1, and the directions of the principal axes of both ellipsoids coincide with each other.

$$\Delta n = C\,\Delta\sigma \tag{1}$$

where   C = stress-optical coefficient.

Central sections cut by the plane perpendicular to the direction of light propagation in these ellipsoids are called secondary ellipses. If the ellipses contain the principal axes of ellipsoids, they are called primary ellipses, which are special cases of secondary ellipses. The principal values of a secondary refractive index ellipse are n_1' and n_2', and the difference between these values is called a double refractive index or birefringence. The principal values of the secondary stress ellipse, in other words, the secondary principal stresses, are σ_1' and σ_2'. The direction of the principal axes of these ellipses are χ and χ_m, respectively. χ is called an extinction angle.

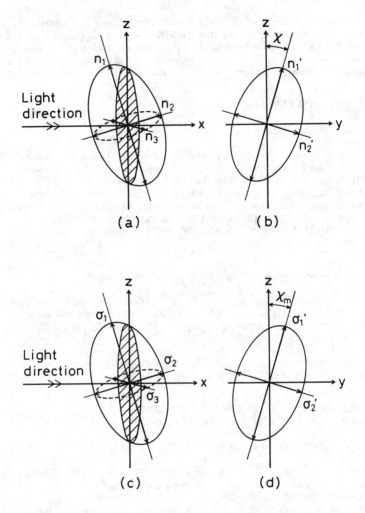

Figure 1. (a) Refractive index ellipsoid; (b) secondary refractive index ellipse; (c) stress ellipsoid; and (d) secondary stress ellipse.

An incident light wave is separated in the birefringent medium into the two plane-polarized light components that vibrate along the respective principal axes of the secondary refractive index ellipse. The light components propagate with different velocities corresponding to the respective refractive indices n'_1 and n'_2.

If Brewster's law is applied to the secondary ellipses, we obtain Equations 2 and 3:

$$n'_1 - n'_2 = C(\sigma'_1 - \sigma'_2) \tag{2}$$

$$\chi = \chi_m \tag{3}$$

These relations are valid in the low shear rate region.

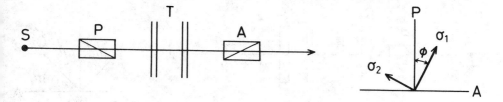

Figure 2. Arrangement of the optical elements in a plane polariscope (S: Light source, P: Polarizer, T: Test section, A: Analyzer).

Transmitted Light Flow Birefringence Technique

Transmitted light flow birefringence technique [18] is usually applied to analysis of the two-dimensional flow field.

The plane polariscope is shown in Figure 2. A polarizer P and an analyzer A are set up at both sides of the test section T, and the vibration directions of P and A are made to intersect each other perpendicularly. The plane-polarized light, after passing through the polarizer, is separated into two wave components in the test section and the phase difference between the two components is integrated along the light path. The two wave components are combined after passing through the analyzer and the intensity of composite wave is given by:

$$I = I_0 \sin^2 2\phi \sin^2 \frac{\delta}{2} \tag{4}$$

where I_0 = intensity of incident light
ϕ = angle of direction of the principal stress to the vibration direction of incident light
δ = total phase difference.

Then, for $\delta = 2\pi N$, I = zero when N = 0, 1, 2 . . . . These black lines are called isochromatic lines and N is called fringe order. If δ can be measured, the principal birefringence can be calculated from:

$$n_1 - n_2 = \frac{\lambda}{2\pi} \frac{\delta}{t} \tag{5}$$

Where t is width of test section and λ is wave length of light. Further, the principal stress difference can be obtained from Equation 1 if the stress-optical coefficient is known. Also, I = zero independently of δ when $\phi = 0$ or $\pi/2$. These black lines are called isoclinic lines. Since the direction of the principal stress and the vibration direction of incident light are assumed to coincide with each other on the isoclinic lines, the extinction angles can be obtained from them.

Next, the circular polariscope is shown in Figure 3. The quarter-wave plates Q_1 and Q_2 are set up as shown in the figure. The intensities of light after passing through analyzer A in cases of both the dark-field circular polariscope and the light-field circular polariscope are given by the following equations, respectively:

$$I = I_0 \sin^2 \frac{\delta}{2} \tag{6}$$

$$I = I_0 \cos^2 \frac{\delta}{2} \tag{7}$$

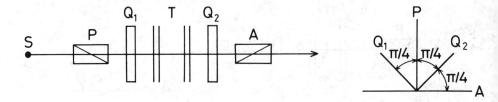

Figure 3. Arrangement of the optical elements in a (dark-field) circular polariscope (S: Light source, P: Polarizer, T: Test section, A: Analyzer, Q_1, Q_2: Quarter wave plates).

The isoclinic lines don't appear in the circular polariscope and this optical system is used for measurement of isochromatic lines. If the light propagates in the z direction, the following equations are established in the rectangular coordinates:

$$\tau_{xy} = \frac{1}{2}(\sigma_1 - \sigma_2)\sin 2\chi \tag{8}$$

$$\tau_{xx} - \tau_{yy} = (\sigma_1 - \sigma_2)\cos 2\chi \tag{9}$$

where $\sigma_1 > \sigma_2$ and χ is defined as the angle of direction of σ_1 to the x axis.

Scattered Light Flow Birefringence Technique

The scattered light flow birefringence technique [18] can be used for analysis of three-dimensional flow fields.

When the light propagates in three-dimensional birefringent fluid, the light is separated into two plane-polarized light components vibrating along the directions of the secondary principal stresses σ_1' and σ_2'. If the medium contains very tiny scattering particles, the scattered light by the particles is proved to have the same phase as the traveling light wave. The fringe pattern, which occurs with interference between the two scattered light components, can be seen from the direction of eyes' observation.

Now, the relation between the direction of the secondary principal stress and the direction of observation on the x-y plane at an arbitrary point is shown in Figure 4. It is assumed that the light propagates in the z direction. χ is defined as the angle of the direction of σ_1' to x axis. A_1 and A_2 are the amplitudes of the two components, respectively. α is arctangent of the amplitude ratio. When the scattered light is observed from the direction perpendicular to the direction of light propagation, the intensity of the scattered light is given by:

$$I = \mu^2 I_0\left[\sin^2(\Theta - \chi - \alpha) + \sin 2\alpha \sin 2(\Theta - \chi)\sin^2\frac{\delta}{2}\right] \tag{10}$$

where Θ is the direction of observation defined as the angle to x axis. μ is a coefficient of scattering and δ is total phase difference produced while the light travels from the incident point to an observation point. Since the variations of α and χ are usually smaller than that of δ and Θ can be set, the intensity may be governed by δ. The local value of the birefringence at an arbitrary point can be calculated by:

$$n_1' - n_2' = \frac{\lambda}{2\pi}\frac{d\delta}{dz} = \lambda\frac{dN}{dz} \tag{11}$$

Therefore, the secondary principal stress difference can be calculated from Equation 2, by using the values of $n_1' - n_2'$.

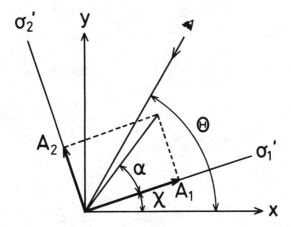

Figure 4. Definition of symbols for the scattered light flow birefringence technique.

If $\chi - \Theta = 0$ or $\pi/2$, the second term of the right side of Equation 10 is zero and the intensity of the scattered light is independent of δ. Therefore, the direction of the secondary principal stress is Θ or $\Theta + \pi/2$ at a point on the line where the interferometric fringe pattern does not appear and the intensity is uniform. This line is called an isoclinic line. It is found from Equation 10 that the light and dark fringes reverse across the isoclinic line. The reversing also occurs when $\alpha = 0$ or $\pi/2$. But, it is possible to distinguish between both cases, because only the positions of the isoclinic line vary with changes in the direction of observation. If the direction of the secondary principal stress varies little along the light propagation, the intensity of the scattered light for circularly polarized incident light is given by:

$$I = \frac{1}{2}\mu^2 I_0[1 - \sin 2(\Theta - \lambda) \sin \delta] \tag{12}$$

In Equation 12, the effect of α is found to be negligible.

Confirmation of Brewster's Law

In order to obtain stresses by the flow birefringence technique, the parameter for transformation from optical quantities to dynamical quantities, namely the stress-optical coefficient, is required. Brewster's law was verified by the following methods:

- The birefringence, the principal stress difference, and the inclinations of the refractive index ellipsoid and the stress ellipsoid should be independently obtained [19, 20].
- The birefringence, the inclination of the refractive index ellipsoid, and the shear stress should be measured and Equation 1 is verified by using the next equation:

$$\Delta n = \frac{2\tau}{\sin 2\chi} \tag{13}$$

where it is assumed that the inclinations of the refractive index ellipsoid and the stress ellipsoid coincide with each other [19, 20].

- Polyethylene melt is cross-linked into solid state by radiation, etc., and the relation between the stress-optical coefficient and the degree of cross-linking is obtained by the tension test. Then, the meet's value of it can be estimated by extrapolating the degree of cross-linking to zero [21].

Table 1
Stress-Optical Coefficients of Polymer Melts

Polymer	Molecular Weight	Temp. [°C]	C × 10^9 [Pa^-1]	Ref.
Polyethylene	4.09 × 10^4	170	1.3	22
	—	150	1.58	23
	4.2 × 10^4	190	1.72	24
Polystyrene	—	170	-4.4 ~ -4.9	25
Polypropylene	5.0 × 10^5	210	0.94	26
	—	200	0.741	24
Polyisobutylene	6.0 × 10^5	25	1.5	27

Table 2
Stress-Optical Coefficients of Polymer Solutions

Polymer	Molecular Weight	Solvent	Temp. [°C]	Conc. [g/100 cm^3]	C × 10^9 [Pa^-1]	Ref.
Polyethylene	4 × 10^4	Trans-decalin	160	2.3 ~ 5.4	1.5	28
	—	Tetralin	120	0.76 ~ 2.7	3.0	25
Polystyrene	9 × 10^6	Bromoform	25	0.98	-6.94	29
	4 × 10^5	Bromobenzene	25	0.5 ~ 3.8	-5.71	30
Polypropylene	5 × 10^5	Trans-decalin	150	0.78 ~ 1.95	0.8	31
Polyisobutylene	6 × 10^5	Decalin	25	0.1 ~ 9	1.5	27

Conc. [wt %]	Temp. [°C]	$C \times 10^5$ [Pa^{-1}]
1.46	20	3.60
1.60	17	4.84
1.73	18	5.09

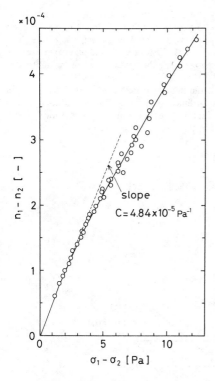

Figure 5. Confirmation of Brewster's law for 1.60 wt% milling yellow aqueous solution at 17°C.

The stress-optical coefficients of polymer melts, polymer solutions, and milling yellow aqueous solutions are listed in Tables 1, 2, and 3, respectively. It is known that milling yellow aqueous solutions have a large value of photoelastic sensitivity, and therefore, they can be used in investigation of flow fields as sample fluids. Confirmation of Brewster's law for 1.60 wt% milling yellow aqueous solution at 17°C is shown in Figure 5. The relation between the principal birefringence and the principal stress difference is linear in the low shear rate region, but it curves with increasing principal stress difference.

* * *

In this section, the principles of measurement by using both transmitted light and scattered light flow birefringence techniques are described. It is found that the transmitted light technique and the scattered light technique are available to stress analysis in the two-dimensional and three-dimensional laminar flow fields, respectively. The measured result of milling yellow aqueous solutions show to have highly photoelastic sensitivity. Brewster's law is confirmed for many fluids in the low shear rate region.

NORMAL STRESS MEASUREMENTS

Measurement for Polymer Melts by Using Flow between Two Parallel Plates [32, 33]

Principles of Measurement

Flow system, coordinates, and incident direction of lights are shown in Figure 6. Simple shear flow is used as a flow system. The 1 axis, 2 axis, and 3 axis mean the flow direction, the direction of velocity gradient, and the neutral direction, respectively. In this flow system, one of the three principal axes of the refractive index ellipsoid coincides with the 3 axis and the other two axes are in the 1–2 plane, and the extinction angle does not change along the light path when the light propagates in the 1–2 or 1–3 plane.

At first, we consider formulation in the case that the light propagates in the 1–2 plane. Light enters at the angle α from the 2 axis. Then, a new coordinate system $(1', 2', 3')$ is used as shown in Figure 6. The $1'$ axis coincides with the direction of light propagation and the $3'$ axis coincides with the 3 axis. The secondary principal stress difference in the $2'$–$3'$ plane is given as follows:

$$\Delta\sigma'_{2'3'} = (\tau_{11} - \tau_{22})\cos^2 \alpha + (\tau_{22} - \tau_{33}) + \tau_{12} \sin 2\alpha \tag{14}$$

Also, the total phase difference after transmission along the light path is obtained by:

$$\delta = \int_{-H/2}^{H/2} \frac{2\pi C \, \Delta\sigma'_{2'3'}}{\lambda} \, dz \tag{15}$$

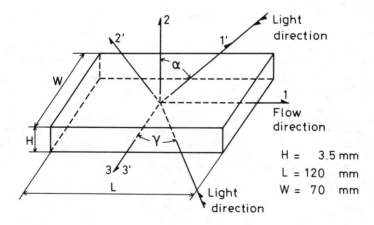

Figure 6. Structure of a slit nozzle and coordinates for measurement of normal stress difference by using the flow between two parallel plates [32, 33].

where z is the coordinate along the light path. After several tranformations of the equations an explicit form of the two normal stress differences is derived as:

$$(\tau_{11} - \tau_{22}) \cos^2 \alpha + (\tau_{22} - \tau_{33}) = \frac{\lambda \cos \alpha}{2\pi C} \frac{\partial}{\partial \tau_w} \left(\frac{\tau_w \delta}{H} \right)$$ (16)

It is known that the right side term of Equation 16 is linear against $\cos^2 \alpha$ for a given value of τ_w and the primary and secondary normal stress differences can be obtained from its slope and intercept, respectively. Particularly, when $\alpha = 0$ (that is, the direction of light path is perpendicular to shearing surfaces), Equation 16 becomes:

$$\tau_{11} - \tau_{33} = \frac{\lambda}{2\pi C} \frac{\partial}{\partial \tau_w} \left(\frac{\tau_w \delta}{H} \right)$$ (17)

Next, when the light enters at angle γ from the 3 axis in the 1–3 plane, similar transformation procedures give an equation corresponding to Equation 16.

$$(\tau_{22} - \tau_{33}) \tan^2 \gamma + (\tau_{11} - \tau_{22}) = \left[\left(\frac{\lambda \delta}{2\pi CW} \right)^2 - 4\tau_{12}^2 \right]^{1/2}$$ (18)

By a similar plot procedure of Equation 18, the secondary and primary normal stress differences can be obtained from its slope and intercept, respectively. Particularly, when $\gamma = 0$, Equation 18 becomes:

$$\tau_{11} - \tau_{22} = \left[\left(\frac{\lambda \delta}{2\pi CW} \right)^2 - 4\tau_{12}^2 \right]^{1/2}$$ (19)

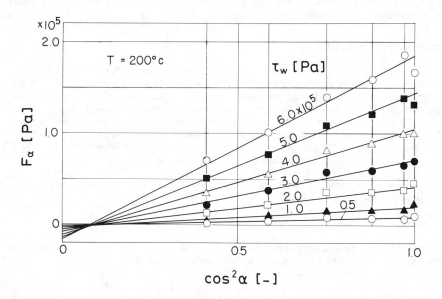

Figure 7. Relation between F_α and $\cos^2 \alpha$ for polyethylene (Hizex 5000H) melt at 200°C [32, 33].

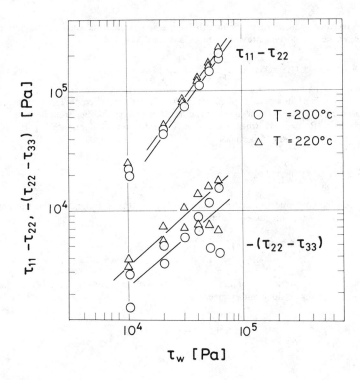

Figure 8. Dependence of the primary and secondary normal stress differences on shear rate for polyethylene (Hizex 5000H) melt [32, 33].

Examples of Experimental Results

An example of measurement by using Equation 16 is given below. High density polyethylene (Hizex 5000H) melt was used as a sample fluid. Dimensions of the nozzle used are shown in Figure 6. The relation between wall shear stress and phase difference was measured for various values of α. The right side of Equation 16 was denoted by F_α and the relation between F_α and $\cos^2 \alpha$ was plotted for a given value of τ_w. The result is shown in Figure 7. It is known that the relation is linear. The primary and secondary normal stress differences obtained from this figure are shown in Figure 8. The ratios of the secondary to the primary normal stress difference are from -0.1 to -0.2 and it is concluded that the measured values are reasonable.

Measurement of the Secondary Normal Stress Difference for Polymer Melts and Polymer Solutions by Using Capillary Flow

Principles of Measurement

Consider that the polymer melts flow in the capillary at steady states. If the light enters along the 1 axis, that is, the capillary axis, the secondary normal stress difference is given by:

$$\tau_{22} - \tau_{33} = \frac{\lambda\delta}{2\pi CL} \tag{20}$$

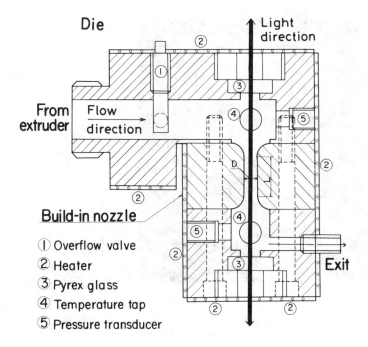

Figure 9. Structure of a die for measurement of the secondary normal stress difference by using the capillary flow [34].

where L is an effective length of the capillary. Actually, there are entrance and exit effects which cause difference from the fully developed flow. These effects should be eliminated. So the optical measurements were made carefully with some correction.

Examples of Experimental Results

Author et al. [34] measured the secondary normal stress difference of polyethylene (Hizex 5000H) melts by the above method. The experimental apparatus is shown in Figure 9. The capillaries were 5 and 10 mm in diameter, and 30, 60, and 100 mm in length. An example photograph of isochromatic pattern is shown in Figure 10. The measured values of phase difference vs. L/D were plotted for a given wall shear stress and the effects of entrance and exit were eliminated. The measurement result is shown in Figure 11. The ratio of the secondary to the primary normal stress difference was obtained and the result is shown in Figure 12. The ratios are between -0.1 and -0.2.

Also, Wales et al. [35] measured the birefringence $n_{22} - n_{33}$, corresponding to $\tau_{22} - \tau_{33}$, for various polymer fluids by using capillary flow. Using the data of $n_{11} - n_{22}$, corresponding to $\tau_{11} - \tau_{22}$, measured with the cone-and-plate, they obtained the ratio $(n_{22} - n_{33})/(n_{11} - n_{22})$, which is equivalent to the ratio of the secondary to the primary normal stress difference. The result is shown in Figure 13. The sample fluids are polystyrene (Styron 678, BASF 3) melt, low density polyethylene (IUPAC A) melt, polydimethylsiloxane (Siloprene RS) melt, polyisobutylene oil (Oppanol B5), and 23% polyisobutylene in oil. The ratios are between -0.05 and -0.14.

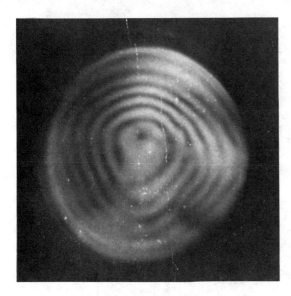

Figure 10. Example of isochromatic pattern for polyethylene (Hizex 5000H) melt ($\dot{\gamma}_w = 45.5 \text{ s}^{-1}$, $\tau_w = 8.0 \times 10^4$ Pa) [34].

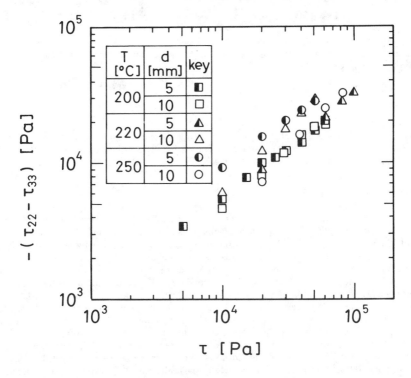

Figure 11. Dependence of the secondary normal stress difference on shear stress for polyethylene (Hizex 5000H) melt [34].

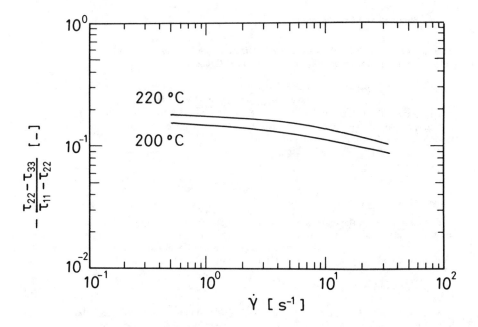

Figure 12. Ratio of the secondary to the primary normal stress difference as a function of shear rate for polyethylene (Hizex 5000H) melt [34].

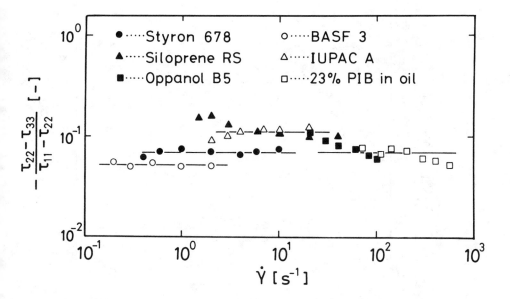

Figure 13. Ratio of the secondary to the primary normal stress difference as a function of shear rate for polystyrene (Styron 678, BASF 3) melts, low-density polyethylene (IUPAC A) melt, polydimethylsiloxane (Siloprene RS) melt, polyisobuthylene oil (Oppanol B5), and 23% polyisobutylene in oil [35].

Measurement of the Primary Normal Stress Difference for Milling Yellow Aqueous Solution by Using Tangential Flow between Coaxial Cylinders

Principles of Measurement

We consider the tangential flow between coaxial cylinders. The cylindrical coordinate system (r, θ, z) is employed as a coordinates system. The extinction angle χ is defined as an angle from the flow direction θ. Then, the following relations are established:

$$\tau_{12} = \tau_{r\theta} = \frac{1}{2}\Delta\sigma \sin 2\chi \tag{21}$$

$$\tau_{11} - \tau_{22} = \tau_{\theta\theta} - \tau_{rr} = \Delta\sigma \cos 2\chi \tag{22}$$

The relation between the extinction angle and the shear rate was measured. If the flow curve is known, the principal stress difference can be calculated from Equation 21, and moreover, the primary normal stress difference can be calculated from Equation 22. Also, if the relation between the birefringence and shear rate is measured, the stress-optical coefficient can be obtained.

Examples of Experimental Results

An example of measurement is shown. The 1.60 wt% milling yellow aqueous solution at 17°C was used as a sample fluid. Figure 14 shows the dependence of shear stress and the primary nor-

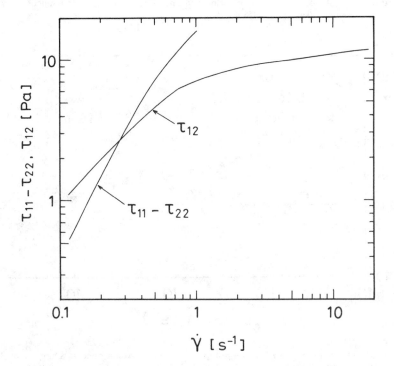

Figure 14. Dependence of shear stress and the primary normal stress difference on shear rate for 1.60 wt% milling yellow aqueous solution at 17°C.

mal stress difference on shear rate. The sample fluid has shear-thinning viscosity and viscoelastic characteristics.

* * *

In this section, the principles of measurement of the primary and secondary normal stress difference by using various flow systems were described. Especially, the method of using the flow between two parallel plates was found to be able to measure both the primary and secondary normal stress differences.

TWO-DIMENSIONAL STRESS DISTRIBUTION MEASUREMENT BY TRANSMITTED LIGHT FLOW BIREFRINGENCE TECHNIQUE

Stress Distribution in Slit Nozzle for Polymer Melts

Reservoir and Entrance Region

An example of isochromatic pattern in entrance region of a rectangular slit nozzle is shown in Figure 15. A sample fluid was polyethylene melt at 200°C and wall shear rate was 44.3 s^{-1}. The principal stress difference is very large at the edge of the entrance. If isochromatic and isoclinic patterns are measurable, the shear stress and the normal stress difference can be determined. Figure 16 shows both distributions in the entrance region at 200°C [36]. Flow rate is 16.6 cm^3/min.

Neyret et al. [37] studied steady flow of a Newtonian fluid in converging channels. They calculated the principal stress differences numerically by the finite element method and measured them experimentally by flow birefringence technique. Dies having different entry angles, 60°, 120°, and

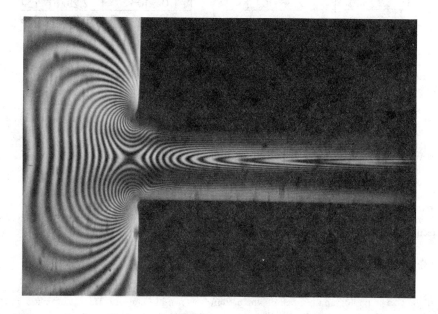

Figure 15. Example of isochromatic pattern in the entrance region of a slit nozzle for polyethylene melt at 200°C, ($\dot{\gamma}_w = 44.3$ s^{-1}).

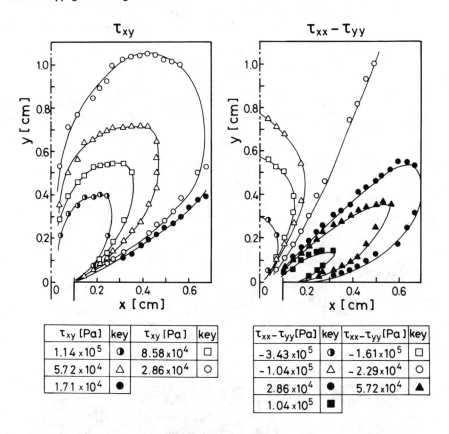

Figure 16. Distributions of shear stress and normal stress difference in the entrance region of a rectangular slit nozzle for high density polyethylene at 200°C [36].

180°, were used. A sample fluid was corn syrup (C = 3×10^{-11} Pa^{-1}, η = 150 Pa·s). The lines for constant principal stress differences measured by flow birefringence technique are compared with calculated one as shown in Figure 17. The two lines agree with each other very well.

Author et al. [33] measured stress distribution in a slit nozzle. The distributions of the primary normal stress difference and shear stress over various cross section are shown in Figure 18. A sample fluid was polyethylene melt at 150°C. Shear rate at the wall in fully developed flow was 1.80 s^{-1}. It is known that the flow is fully developed at least in section D. The primary normal stress difference in the center near the inlet is larger because the acceleration exists. The shear stress is larger away from the inlet because the shear stress is determined significantly by the velocity gradient in the direction perpendicular to the flow direction.

Exit and Die-Swell Region

Author et al. [33, 38] measured the stress distribution in the exit region for polypropylene melt at 200°C. The photograph of isochromatic pattern is shown in Figure 19. The isochromatic lines within the nozzle are parallel to the flow axis to the point near the exit and the fringe order decreases rapidly from the exit to the outside. Exit pressure, that is, pressure at the wall of the exit cross section which is larger than ambient pressure, is observed clearly. The exit pressure is characteristic

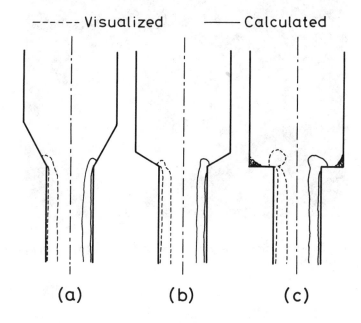

Figure 17. Comparison between visualized and calculated lines of constant principal stress difference in the converging channels having entry angle (a) 60°, (b) 120°, and (c) 180° [37].

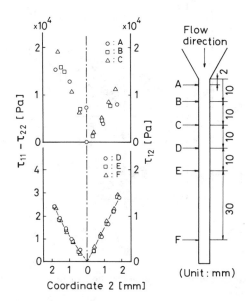

Figure 18. Distributions of the primary normal stress difference and shear stress in a slit nozzle for polyethylene melt at 150°C ($\dot{\gamma}_w = 1.80$ s^{-1}) [33].

Figure 19. Example of isochromatic pattern in the exit region of a slit nozzle for polypropylene at 200°C ($\dot{\gamma}_w = 5.0\ \mathrm{s}^{-1}$) [33, 38].

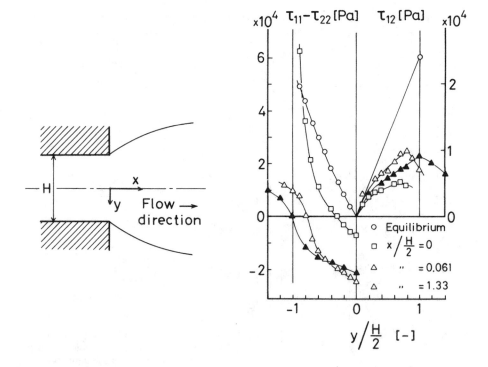

Figure 20. Distributions of normal stress difference and shear stress in the exit region for polypropylene at 200°C ($\dot{\gamma}_w = 10.1\ \mathrm{s}^{-1}$) [33, 38].

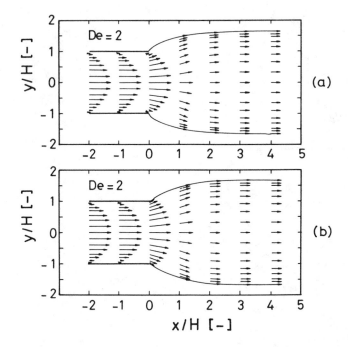

Figure 21. Numerical results of velocity fields in the exit region of a slit nozzle (a) for Boger fluid (viscosity and the primary normal stress coefficient are constant) and (b) for polystyrene melt [39].

of a viscoelastic fluid. The shear stress and the normal stress difference could be calculated from both the isochromatic and isoclinic patterns. The result for the wall shear rate 10.1 s^{-1} is shown in Figure 20. Outside the nozzle, the velocity gradient in the y direction is zero on the center axis and is nearly zero on the free surface. Therefore, it can be imagined that the velocity distribution has the point of inflection between the center axis and the free surface, and the shear stress is maximum near the point. The values of the normal stress difference are negative because of compressive deformation in the x direction and the elongational deformation in the y direction outside the nozzle.

Vlachopoulos et al. [39] studied numerically the exit flow and extrudate swell for a polymer melt by use of the finite element method. The calculated results of the velocity fields for a Boger fluid and a polystyrene melt when De = 2.0 are shown in Figure 21. In order to examine the calculated results, it is important to compare them with experimental results as much as possible.

Stress Distribution in an Agitated Vessel for a High Viscous Polymer Solution

A sample fluid employed was polystyrene (Toporex 575) in toluene. The upper and lower planes of agitated vessel used were made of transparent acrylic resin and its side wall was made of aluminum. The dimensions of the vessel were 120 mm in diameter and 90 mm in height. The impeller was a two-bladed paddle made of brass and was 60 mm in diameter, 88 mm in height, and 1 mm in thickness. The rotational speed of the impeller was 30 rpm and Reynolds number was 1.5×10^{-3}. It was assumed that the flow was approximately two-dimensional. The optical system was the same as that ordinarily used for two-dimensional photoelastic experiments.

$\tau_{r\theta} \times 10^{-3}$ [Pa]

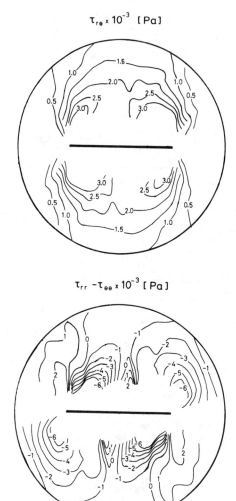

$\tau_{rr} - \tau_{\theta\theta} \times 10^{-3}$ [Pa]

Figure 22. Distributions of shear stress and normal stress difference in an agitated vessel for polystyrene (Toporex 575) in toluene (Rotational direction: counter-clockwise; Rotational speed: 30 rpm; Re = 1.50×10^{-3}).

The distributions of shear stress $\tau_{r\theta}$ and normal stress difference $\tau_{rr} - \tau_{\theta\theta}$ are shown in Figure 22. The coordinate system was set as follows: the center of the agitated vessel was chosen as origin, and θ was defined as the angle from impeller and was positive in the downstream direction. The impeller was rotated counter-clockwise.

$\tau_{r\theta}$ is larger near the impeller tip and smaller near the side wall. It is almost maximum along the locus of the impeller tip.

In the outer region, $\tau_{rr} - \tau_{\theta\theta}$ is negative in most regions except for upstream of the impeller, because compressive deformation in the r direction is very large by rotation of the impeller. It is positive upstream of the impeller. The elongational deformation in the r direction and the compressive deformation in the θ direction are larger there because the flow region widens. It was difficult to measure the stress distribution near the impeller.

* * *

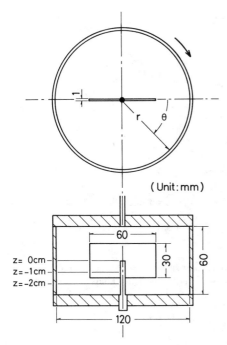

(Unit: mm)

Figure 23. Shape and dimensions of an agitated vessel, and coordinates system.

In this section, the examples of experimental results of two-dimensional stress distributions by transmitted light flow birefringence technique were shown. First, flows from entrance region to exit region in the slit nozzle for polymer melts were shown. Next, stress distribution in an agitated vessel for a high viscous polymer solution were described. Various information for these flow fields were obtained from experimental results.

THREE-DIMENSIONAL STRESS DISTRIBUTION MEASUREMENT BY SCATTERED LIGHT FLOW BIREFRINGENCE TECHNIQUE [40]

Stress Distribution in an Agitated Vessel for Milling Yellow Aqueous Solution

Experimental

Shape and dimensions of an agitated vessel used in this study are shown in Figure 23. The vessel was made of transparent acrylic resin and its geometry was 12 cm in diameter and 6 cm in height. A two-bladed impeller made of brass was 6 cm in diameter, 3 cm in height, and 1 mm in thickness. Since intensity of scattered light was very weak, and therefore a sufficiently long exposure time was required for photographing, the vessel was rotated with impeller fixed. To reduce optical distortion, the agitated vessel was surrounded by a rectangular solution bath which was filled with water.

A schematic diagram of experimental apparatus is shown in Figure 24. The light source was 60 mW He-Ne gas laser. Incident light was slit by passing through collimating and cylindrical lenses. Plane-polarized slit light, after passing through a polarizer, entered a test section and a scattered light pattern was shot from the direction perpendicular to the plane sliced by the slit light. Contrast of light and dark fringe pattern was varied with rotation of a polarizer. Therefore, its

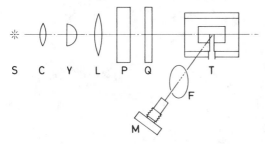

S: Laser   C: Condensing lens
P: Polarizer   Y: Cylindrical lens
T: Test section   L: Collimating lens
M: Camera   F: Field lens
Q: Quarter wave plate

Figure 24. Schematic diagram of optical system for the scattered light flow birefringence technique.

polarized plane was set up in order that most suitable contrast could be obtained. Slit lights entered in the axial (z), radial (r), and tangential (θ) directions, respectively. Three kinds of secondary principal stress differences could be analyzed from obtained interferometric patterns.

Measurement of direction of secondary principal stress was made in the only case that light entered in the axial direction. Though the values of χ can be obtained in principle by means of measurement of isoclinic lines observed from various angles, its measurement was difficult because

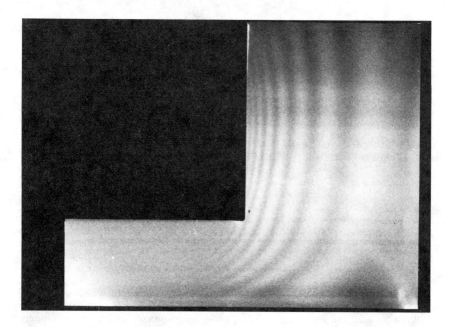

Figure 25. Example of scattered light pattern in an agitated vessel for 1.46 wt% milling yellow aqueous solution where light enters in the axial direction (light direction: from right to left).

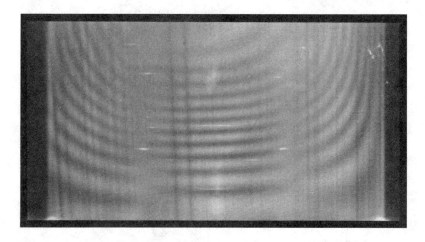

Figure 26. Example of scattered light pattern in an agitated vessel for 1.46 wt% milling yellow aqueous solution when light enters in the radial direction (light direction: upward).

of parallax. But, in the case that light enters in the axial direction, the patterns of isoclinic line obtained when angle of impeller is changed with the direction of observation fixed, is almost the same as those obtained when the direction of observation is changed with impeller fixed.

Examples of Scattered Light Pattern

Photographs of scattered light pattern are shown in Figures 25 and 26. In Figure 25, slit light enters in the radial direction (from right to left) parallel to the impeller. Stress is larger in the place where fringes appear more closely. In Figure 26, light enters in the axial (upward) direction. It is known that isoclinic line appears where light and dark fringes reverse across the lines, as mentioned before.

Distributions of Shear Stress $\tau_{r\theta}$ and Normal Stress Difference $\tau_{rr} - \tau_{\theta\theta}$

The coordinate system was set as shown in Figure 23. The center of an agitated vessel was chosen as origin. θ was defined as the angle from impeller and was positive in the downstream direction. z was positive in the upward vertical direction. The rotational speed was 30 rpm.

Distribution of $\tau_{r\theta}$ is shown in Figure 27. $\tau_{r\theta}$ is larger near the impeller tip and smaller near the side wall. It is almost maximum along locus of the impeller tip. $\tau_{r\theta}$ is negative in the outer region where θ is between 15° and 45°. This is because the directions of radial flow are opposite in both sides of $\theta = 0°$ and the fluid has larger angular velocity than that at the side wall. That was confirmed from measurement of velocities by using LDV.

Distribution of $\tau_{rr} - \tau_{\theta\theta}$ is shown in Figure 28. $\tau_{rr} - \tau_{\theta\theta}$ is negative where $\theta = 0°$, because elongational deformation in the θ direction is very large by accelerated flow occuring between the impeller tip and the side wall. Where θ is from 15° to 105°, it is negative in the inner region because fluid element flows into the back of the impeller after passing through the converged gap, and positive in the outer region because the elongational deformation in the r direction is larger for sudden relaxation. Where θ is over 120°, it is negative in the outer region because elongational deformation in the θ direction becomes larger with increasing velocity in the θ direction. Where θ is over 150°, it is positive in the inner region because fluid is intercepted by the impeller.

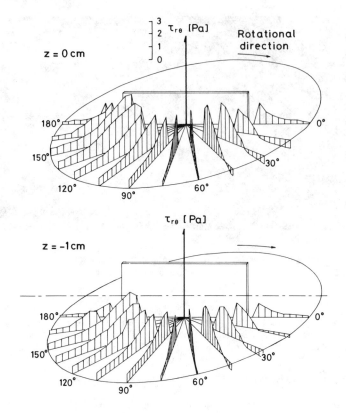

Figure 27. Distributions of the shear stress $\tau_{r\theta}$ in an agitated vessel for 1.46 wt% milling yellow aqueous solution [40].

Distributions of Secondary Principal Stress Difference $\Delta\sigma'_{z\theta}$ and $\Delta\sigma'_{rz}$

Radial distributions of $\Delta\sigma'_{z\theta}$ are shown in Figure 29. Since shear stress $\tau_{z\theta}$ is zero in the plane $z = 0$ cm, $\Delta\sigma'_{z\theta}$ indicates elongational or compressive deformation there. At $z = -1$ and -2 cm, it is effected by flow in the z direction for the impeller. $\Delta\sigma'_{z\theta}$ becomes larger in the inner region, especially at less than 90° of θ. Where θ is over 90°, $\Delta\sigma'_{z\theta}$ at $z = 0$ cm is smaller than the value at $z = -1$ or -2 cm because the fluid receiving deformation in the region near $\theta = 0°$ is relaxed and the velocity gradient in the θ direction becomes considerably small.

$\Delta\sigma'_{rz}$ is smaller in one order than that of $\Delta\sigma'_{r\theta}$ and $\Delta\sigma'_{z\theta}$ and its tendency is very difficult to find clearly.

Quantitative Evaluation of the Measured Stress

Analytical Method for Torque Calculation

The measured values of stress were evaluated quantitatively through comparison between values of torque measured by using a torque meter and those calculated from locally measured stresses. The torque acting on the side wall of vessel T_1 and the torque acting on the upper and

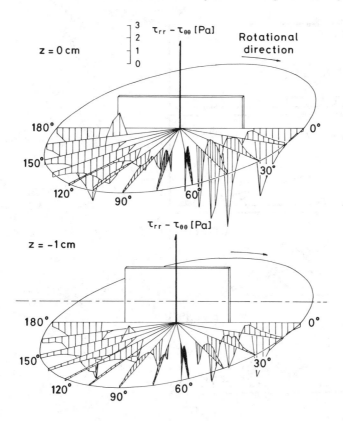

Figure 28. Distributions of the normal stress difference $\tau_{rr} - \tau_{\theta\theta}$ in an agitated vessel for 1.46 wt% milling yellow aqueous solution [40].

lower planes T_2 are given by the following equations, respectively:

$$T_1 = 2R^2 \int_0^\pi \int_{-Z}^Z \tau_{r\theta}\Big|_{r=R} dz \, d\theta \tag{23}$$

$$T_2 = 4 \int_0^\pi \int_0^R r^2 \tau_{z\theta}\Big|_{z=Z} dr \, d\theta \tag{24}$$

When light entered in the z direction, the angle of secondary principal stress χ varied little in the z direction near the side wall. If fringe order at incident point of light ($z = -Z$) is set as zero, then Equation 23 can be written by:

$$T_1 = \frac{\lambda}{C} R^2 \int_0^\pi (N \sin 2\chi)\Big|_{r=R, z=Z} d\theta \tag{25}$$

$\tau_{z\theta}$ could not be obtained because the corresponding angles of the principal stresses were difficult to measure. Therefore, it was assumed that the normal stress differences were negligible compared with shear stresses on the surface. In short, $\tau_{z\theta}$ was assumed by:

$$|\tau_{z\theta}| \doteq \frac{1}{2} \Delta\sigma'_{z\theta} = \frac{\lambda}{2C} \frac{dN}{dr} \tag{26}$$

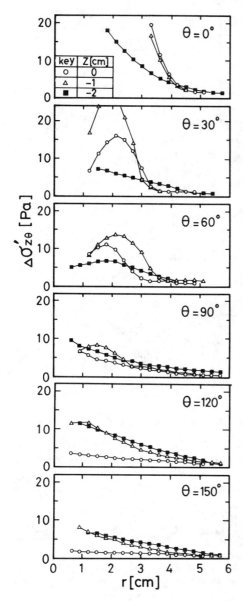

Figure 29. Distributions of the secondary principal stress difference $\Delta\sigma'_{z\theta}$ for 1.46 wt% milling yellow aqueous solution [40].

When slit light enters an agitated vessel parallel to upper and lower planes and scattered light pattern is observed from the vertical direction, the direction of secondary principal stress is vertical on isoclinic lines. Therefore, the line on which the angle of secondary principal stress in the $z - \theta$ plane is zero, can be obtained. Sign of $\tau_{z\theta}$ reverses across the line. Using this method, the region that the sign of $\tau_{z\theta}$ was minus could be obtained. If the fringe order at incident point of light ($r = R$)

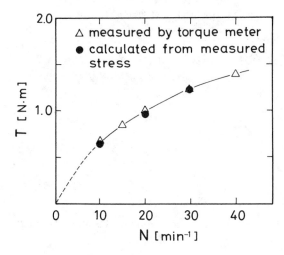

Figure 30. Comparison between the torque calculated from measured stress distributions and the torque measured by a torque meter [40].

is defined as zero, the following equation is established:

$$\int_0^R r^2 \left(\frac{1}{2} \Delta\sigma'_{z\theta} \right) dr = -\frac{\lambda}{C} \int_0^R rN \big|_{z=z} \, dr \tag{27}$$

T_2 was calculated from Equations 24, 26, and 27 by considering the sign of $\tau_{z\theta}$.

Comparison between Experimental and Predicted Values of Torque

The results of the calculated torque and the torque measured by a torque meter are shown in Figure 30. It indicates a good agreement between them. It can clearly be said that locally measured values of stresses were reasonable quantitatively and the assumption on stress-optical law was proper.

* * *

In this section, the experimental example of three-dimensional stress distribution by scattered light flow birefringence technique was obtained. Flow in an agitated vessel was selected as a flow system. Three kinds of secondary principal stress differences could be measured. Local values of shear stress and normal stress difference could be obtained and they were proved to be reasonable.

SLIP VELOCITY PREDICTION OF POLYMER MELTS

Measurement of Slip Velocity When It Can Be Assumed as a Function of Wall Shear Stress

Derivation of Mooney's Equation [14]

We consider steady laminar flow in a cylindrical tube of length L and radius R. We take cylindrical polar coordinates (r, θ, z) and assume that velocity components in the coordinate directions are

$(0, 0, u(r))$. We suppose that shear rate at any point is a function of shear stress only as follows:

$$-\frac{du}{dr} = f(r) \tag{28}$$

Shear stress at any radius is given by:

$$\tau = \frac{r}{2}\frac{\Delta P}{L} = \tau_w \frac{r}{R} \tag{29}$$

where ΔP is pressure drop over the tube section of length L and τ_w is shear stress at the tube wall. Also, volume rate of flow is given by:

$$Q = \int_0^R 2\pi r u \, dr \tag{30}$$

If there is slip velocity u_s at the wall, velocity u can be determined from Equations 28 and 29 and the following boundary condition:

$$u = u_s(\tau_w) \qquad \text{at } r = R \tag{31}$$

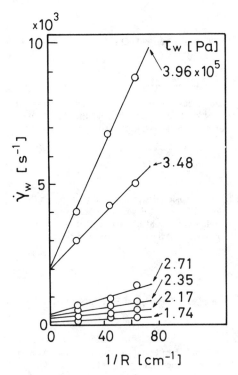

Figure 31. Dependence of wall shear rate on inverse radius of capillaries for polyethylene (Marlex 6050) melt with 30 wt% glass bead at 160°C [41].

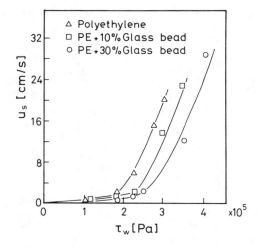

Figure 32. Dependence of slip velocity on wall shear stress for polyethylene (Marlex 6050) melt alone and with glass bead at 160°C [41].

where it is assumed that slip velocity is a function of the wall shear stress. Further, using Equation 30 and rearranging, we obtain the apparent wall shear rate as follows:

$$\dot{\gamma}_w = \frac{4Q}{\pi R^3} = \frac{4u_s}{R} + \frac{4}{\tau_w^3} \int_0^{\tau_w} \tau^2 f(\tau)\, d\tau \tag{32}$$

Examples of Measurement

Timothy [41] measured slip velocity in order to determine the interrelation between wall slippage and melt fracture. He used high density polyethylene (Marlex 6050) alone, and that with glass bead inclusion of 10% or 30% by weight as sample fluids. The relationship between the apparent wall shear rate $\dot{\gamma}_w$ and the wall shear stress τ_w was obtained from measured values of volume rate of flow Q and pressure drop ΔP for three sizes of tube radius, 0.1539 mm, 0.2298 mm and 0.4814 mm. All tubes were of 1 inch length. An example of plot of $\dot{\gamma}_w$ versus 1/R for a given τ_w is shown in Figure 31 as predicted in Equation 32. Linear relations are confirmed between them. From Equation 32, slip velocity can be calculated from slope of the linear relation for a given τ_w. Dependence of slip velocity on wall shear stress is shown in Figure 32. It appears that there is a critical value 2×10^5 Pa of wall shear stress which causes melt fracture and is characteristic of a fluid. Slip velocity is very small below the critical stress.

Ui et al. [42] found that increase of flow rate at onset of melt fracture depends on slip flow. They used high density polyethylene (Staflen E 605) as a sample fluid. An example of the measured relation between $\dot{\gamma}_w$ and τ_w is shown in Figure 33. The flow curve is independent of tube radius in the region where melt fracture does not occur and depends on tube radius after onset of melt fracture. Also, it can be known from Equation 32 that $\dot{\gamma}_w$ is a function of τ_w only if u_s is zero and $\dot{\gamma}_w$ depends on R if u_s is non-zero. From the characteristics of the equation, it is considered reasonable that increase of flow rate after onset of melt fracture region depends on the slip flow. Within a certain range of τ_w, the apparent wall shear rates were obtained in both regions where the melt fracture occurred and not for a given τ_w. The shear rate in the region where the melt fracture does not occur is equal to the second term of the right side of Equation 32 and the shear rate in the melt fracture region is the sum of the first and second term. Therefore, difference between them equals $4u_s/R$ and slip velocity can be calculated. The plot of the slip velocity vs. the wall shear stress is shown in Figure 34. It is known from Figure 34 that slip velocity is independent of R and is a function of τ_w only.

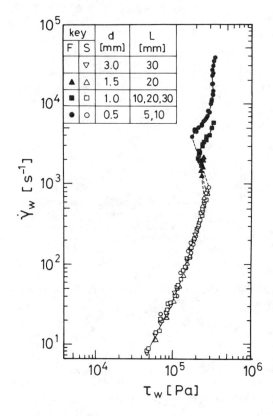

Figure 33. Dependence of wall shear rate on wall shear stress for high density polyethylene (Staflen E 605) melt at 210°C [42].

Measurement and Prediction of Slip Velocity When It Cannot Be Assumed Clearly as a Function of Wall Shear Stress

Properties of Poly (Vinyl Chloride) Melt

Since pure PVC resin is unstable for degradation, it is usually used blended with stabilizers, plasticizers, lubricants, etc. Content of additives not only gives wide variety in properties of products but also strongly influences processability. Many basic factors may relate to processability, such as flow characteristics, solid transport properties, thermal properties, etc. PVC melts have additional flow characteristics, such as slip at the wall of solid surface, because PVC melts contain stabilizers, lubricants, etc., which lead to a thin layer of low viscosity between the bulk polymer melt and the wall.

Principles of Measurement

Some kind of grooved nozzle was considered to stop slip on wall. The grooved nozzle means the one whose surfaces were cut vertically to the flow direction in long narrowly hollowed shape, as shown in Figure 35. Since the grooves are filled with PVC melt and the apparent wall surfaces are made of melt instead of metal, it seems that flow in smooth nozzle and grooved nozzle are different in velocity distribution shown in Figure 35.

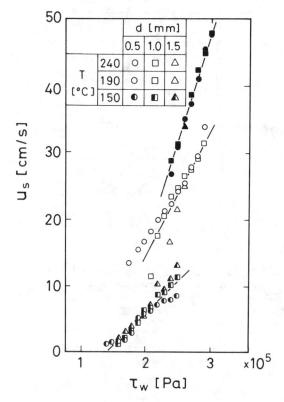

Figure 34. Dependence of slip velocity on wall shear stress for high density polyethylene (Staflen E 605) melt [42].

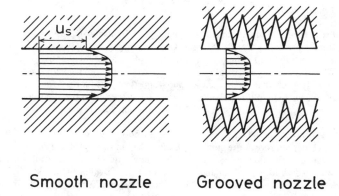

Smooth nozzle   Grooved nozzle

Figure 35. Flow patterns in smooth and grooved nozzles.

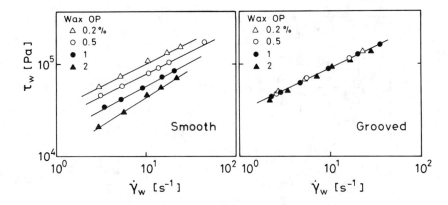

Figure 36. Dependence of wall shear stress on wall shear rate for PVC melt with lubricant (Wax OP) at 190°C [15].

Slip velocity u_s is calculated from the difference between measured flow rates at the same shear stress of the smooth nozzle and that of the grooved nozzle whose cross section covering tips of the grooved nozzle is the same as that of the smooth nozzle. Then, the slip velocities with capillary and rectangular slit dies are given by the following equations, respectively:

$$u_s = \frac{1}{\pi R^2}(Q_s - Q_g) \tag{33}$$

$$u_s = \frac{1}{WH}(Q_s - Q_g) \tag{34}$$

where Q_s is flow rate with slip and Q_g is that with no-slip.

Example of Experimental Results

Chauffoureaux et al. [15] investigated slip phenomena by using smooth and grooved slit dies. They added lubricant (Wax OP) to rigid PVC. Figure 36 shows the flow curves obtained for various quantities of the lubricant. Slipping is known to be dependent on quantity of lubricant added. On the other hand, the flow curves obtained with the grooved die coincide independently of quantity of lubricants. It seems that slip at the wall was stopped and the lubricant added does not appreciably change true viscosity of the polymer. Effect of the lubricant on the slip velocity is plotted in Figure 37 in the case that shear stress is 1×10^5 Pa. The slip velocity increases with increasing the lubricant.

Knappe et al. [43] also studied slip flow by using smooth and grooved slit dies. Thickness of slit (H) and pitch of the grooves are shown in Figure 38, and depth of the grooves was half of the pitch. They evaluated slip flow by plotting reduced flow rate Q/WH^2 vs. wall shear stress. The flow curves obtained with the smooth and grooved dies are shown in Figure 38. Shape of the rectangular die used in this measurement was 20 mm broad (W) and 90 mm long. Composition of the PVC-compound is given in Table 4. The flow curve with the smooth dies was dependent of H. The curve with the grooved dies coincides at shear stress below 5.2×10^5 Pa, which seems to be critical for onset of slip.

Author et al. [44] measured slip velocity by smooth and grooved nozzles. The resins used were PVC polymer (Ryuron 700-D) including stabilizer (TVS N-2000G) and plasticizer (DOP). Blend

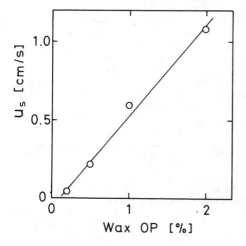

Figure 37. Dependence of slip velocity on quantity of lubricant (Wax OP) for PVC melt at 190°C ($\tau_w = 1 \times 10^5$ Pa) [15].

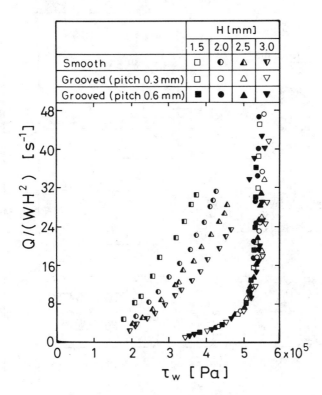

	H [mm]			
	1.5	2.0	2.5	3.0
Smooth	□	◐	◭	▽
Grooved (pitch 0.3 mm)	□	○	△	▽
Grooved (pitch 0.6 mm)	■	●	▲	▼

Figure 38. Dependence of reduced flow rate on wall shear stress for PVC melt at 190°C [43].

Table 4
Blend Ratio of PVC-Compounds [43]

Material	Trade Name	Blend Ratio*
E-PVC	SOLVIC 172RB	50
S-PVC	SOLVIC 264GA	50
Stabilizer	NAFTOVIN T90	3.0
Stabilizer	AUSTROSTAB 112	1.5
Stabilizer	AUSTROSTAB 310	0.5
Lubricant	STS stearic acid	0.3
Pigment	Sicopalbraun K2795	2.0
Chalk	Omyalite 95T	10.0

* Parts by weight.

Table 5
Blend Ratio of PVC-Compounds [44]

Material	Trade name	Blend Ratio*	
		Comp. 1	Comp. 3
PVC	Ryuron 700-D	100	100
Stabilizer	TVS N-2000G	4	4
Plasticizer	DOP	—	10

* Parts by weight.

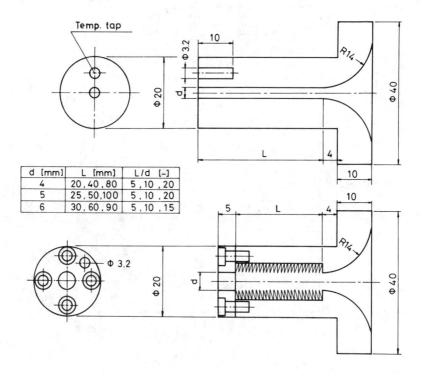

d [mm]	L [mm]	L / d [-]
4	20, 40, 80	5, 10, 20
5	25, 50, 100	5, 10, 20
6	30, 60, 90	5, 10, 15

Figure 39. Shape and dimensions of smooth and grooved capillary nozzles [44].

ratios are shown in Table 5. Shape and dimensions of the capillary nozzles are shown in Figure 39. Pitch of the groove was equal to depth and values were 0.5 mm and 1 mm.

Flow curves measured with grooved nozzles of various diameters are shown in Figure 40. They seem to be almost one curve at each temperature. The flow curves coincide independently of shapes of the nozzles, and it may be concluded that slip at the wall was stopped. Shear rate without effect of slip may be considered to show characteristics of only PVC melt and equal to that of PVC melt with no slip. Figure 41 shows an example of the flow curves of the smooth and grooved nozzles at three temperature levels for Compound 3. Slip velocities could be calculated by Equation 33 from these data. The slip velocities obtained are shown in Figure 42, which depends on geometrical difference. From these the slip velocities become larger with increasing shear stress. Moreover, they become larger with increasing temperature and with increasing nozzle diameter. This may be because the viscosities in the thin layer of stabilizers and plasticizers assumed to exist between bulk polymer and metal surface of the nozzle, got lower with increasing temperature.

Estimation of Slip Velocity [44]

A simple flow model was set up to interpret these results. It might be called a two-layer flow model, as flow is assumed to be stratified into two layers–namely, a very thin layer between nozzle metal surface and bulk polymer, and a much thicker layer of polymer melts in capillary core. The very thin layer was assumed to be formed by oozing of low-molecular-weight additives. A schematic diagram of the model for capillary flow is shown in Figure 43. Slip velocity u_s was set to be equal to the velocity at the most inner radial plane of the thin layer. It was assumed that the thin layer fluid and the core fluid are non-Newtonian, conforming to the power law model as indicated

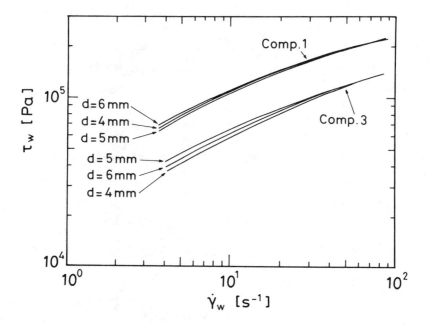

Figure 40. Dependence of wall shear stress on wall shear rate measured with grooved nozzles of different diameters for PVC melt at 190°C [44].

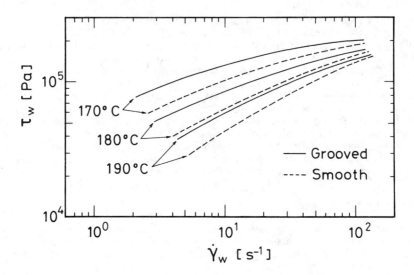

Figure 41. Dependence of wall shear stress on wall shear rate measured with smooth and grooved nozzles of 6 mm in diameter for PVC melt (Compound 3) [44].

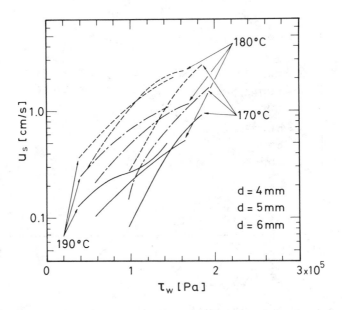

Figure 42. Dependence of slip velocity on wall shear stress for PVC melt (Compound 3) [44].

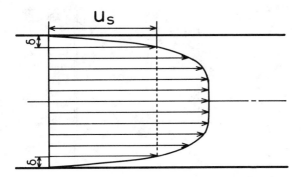

Figure 43. Schematic diagram of two-layer model [44].

in Equations 35 and 36:

$$\eta_1\left(-\frac{du_1}{dr}\right) = \left(\frac{\tau_w}{R}r\right)^1 \qquad \text{at } R - \delta \le r \le R \tag{35}$$

$$\eta_2\left(-\frac{du_2}{dr}\right) = \left(\frac{\tau_w}{R}r\right)^m \qquad \text{at } 0 \le r \le R - \delta \tag{36}$$

The suffixes 1 and 2 mean the thin layer and the bulk region, respectively. The boundary conditions were Equations 37 and 38:

$$u_1 = 0 \qquad \text{at } r = R \tag{37}$$

$$u_1 = u_2 \qquad \text{at } r = R - \delta \tag{38}$$

where δ is the thickness of thin layer. By solving Equations 35 through 38 the following equation is obtained:

$$\dot{\gamma}_w = \frac{4\delta}{\eta_1 R}\tau_w^1 + \frac{1}{\eta_2}\frac{4}{m+3}\left\{1 - (m+3)\frac{\delta}{R}\right\}\tau_w^m \tag{39}$$

Here, the next relations are assumed:

$$\frac{\delta}{R} = \beta\tau_w^{\alpha-1} \tag{40}$$

$$1 - (m+3)\frac{\delta}{R} = 1 \tag{41}$$

Equation 39 is rewritten by using the above two assumptions:

$$\frac{\dot{\gamma}_w}{\tau_w^\alpha} = \frac{4\beta}{\eta_1} + \frac{1}{\eta_2}\frac{4}{m+3}\tau_w^{m-\alpha} \tag{42}$$

The power m in power law model is selected as the gradient of the flow curves with no-slip. By substituting the measured values of τ_w and $\dot{\gamma}_w$ and the values of m obtained from the flow curve for

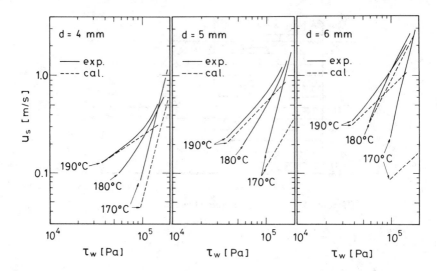

Figure 44. Comparison of slip velocities between experimental and predicted values for PVC melt (Compound 3).

Equation 39, α and $4\beta/\eta_1$ can be obtained numerically by a trial method. Since slip velocity u_s is velocity at $r = R - \delta$, u_s can be calculated from the following equation:

$$u_s = \frac{1}{4}\left(\frac{4\beta}{\eta_1}\right) R\tau_w^\alpha \qquad (43)$$

The result shown in Figure 44 indicates availability of the model. Consequently, slip velocity could be calculated through Equation 43. But the thickness of the thin layer calculated from the model was too thin to be reasonable. Therefore this model must be improved in the future for more accurate prediction.

* * *

In this section, slip velocity of polymer melt was discussed. First, Mooney's equation, which assumes that slip velocity is a function of wall shear stress only, was described. The experimental results of slip in melt fracture were introduced. It was found that melt fracture was dependent on the slip and slip velocity was obtained from Mooney's equation for some polymer melts.

Next, measurement by using a grooved nozzle for stopping slip was described. In this method, there is not assumption that slip velocity is a function of wall shear stress. The experimental results of slip velocity for PVC melt were shown. It was confirmed that slip stopped by the grooved nozzle, and the slip velocity could be calculated from flow rates with grooved and smooth nozzles. Further, prediction of slip velocity was discussed. A two-layer flow model was introduced and its availability was illustrated. The model must be improved for more accurate prediction.

APPLICATION OF BIREFRINGENCE TO EVALUATION OF INJECTION-MOLDED OBJECT

Preliminary Remarks

Recently there have been various kinds of plastics products developed for optical usage, such as, video disks, compact disks, and optical fibers. For this use, transparent plastic materials, such as polymethylmethacrylate, polycarbonate, and polystyrene, have been applied and reformed steadily in their properties. One of the most important properties is birefringence. It should be decreased as much as possible. For usual video disks and compact disks, the values of the birefringence should be lower than 10^{-5}.

Qualitative Relation among Molding Stress, Orientation, and Residual Stress

Disks that are being prepared for random access memory must have less than 10^{-7} birefringence. A lot of research and development has been done for synthesizing the most suitable materials and manufacturing them.

Injection molding is one of the most productive methods of processing these polymeric materials. During processing, polymers are melted within the screw part and injected into an attached die, where temperatures are set lower than those of the screw part. The stress occurring in the die causes orientations of molecules, which are freezed due to the die temperatures lower than the glass transition temperature or melting temperature.

The freezed molecular orientations in the solid polymers cause the birefringence and the residual stress. The residual stresses are as important as the birefringence for disk use, because the shape of the injection-molded objects will be deformed when the residual stresses are relieved by taking off from the die and annealing at some atmosphere with temperatures higher than those of the glass transition temperature or melting temperature. With annealing the molecules can move randomly at the intensity dependent upon the annealing temperature.

The sounds and/or images may be deformed by deformation of the materials, which must be made as small as possible.

Then, many studies on the birefringence and residual stress have been made in order to find the way for decreasing molecular orientations, residual stress, etc. The phenomena are very complicated: the flow in the die is non-Newtonian, nonisothermal, and structure-changing. So it has been approached experimentally rather than theoretically, since a theoretical formulation is very difficult to do.

Here notice that the flow in the molten state is vitally concerned with the optical property of end products, so flow-induced orientation and birefringence should be made clear for manufacturing good-quality end products.

Examples of Experimental Results

Takeshima et al. [45] measured the birefringence and shrinkage distributions along the distance from the gate of the die for an injection-molded disk of 30 cm in diameter and 1.5 mm in thickness, as shown in Figure 45. The measured average birefringence over thickness, $\langle n_{11} - n_{33} \rangle$, becomes smaller along the distance away from the gate and larger with increasing cylinder temperature. On the other hand, the molecular orientations were intensified more near the gate since the shear stress was higher there. The shrinkage was smaller with increasing cylinder temperature, larger with increasing annealing temperature, and anisotropic in the directions.

Hieber et al. [46] studied the injection molding process theoretically and experimentally. By applying a viscoelastic constitutive equation developed by Leonov to the non-Newtonian, nonisothermal flow of polymers, they predicted the birefringence, shear stress, shear rate, normal stress differences, etc. The measured principal birefringence was successfully compared with the predicted ones, but components of the birefringence didn't agree with each other.

Gapwise birefringence distributions at different locations away from the gate are shown in Figure 46. The maximum points in birefringence are near the gate and their values are different, but variation tendency in birefringence along the distance was almost the same. Ultimately the model constitutive equation could be found to be relatively good.

Wales et al. [47] studied the injection molding process of some amorphous polymers such as a toughed polystyrene and acrylonitrile-butadiene-styrene copolymer for a short molding and a flash molding. The measured birefringences were collected into one curve against shear stress, independent of temperatures, and moreover this relationship was almost the same between flow birefringence and shear stress in isothermal channel flow. The average birefringence over thickness was found to have developed higher away from the gate and have a maximum value at some location a little apart

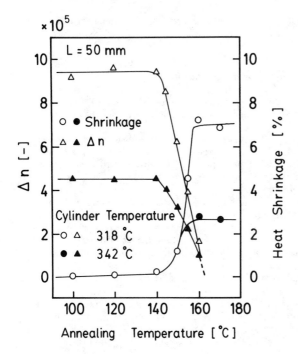

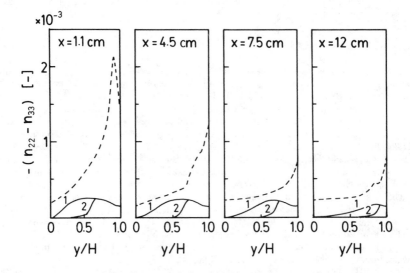

Figure 45. Change in heat shrinkage and birefringence after annealing at indicated temperature for 90 min [45].

Figure 46. Gapwise distributions of birefringence $-(n_{22} - n_{33})$ at different locations from gate (Solid lines: theoretical predictions (1) at end of flow and (2) at end of relaxation; dashed line: experimental results; x: distance from the gate in the flow direction; y: distance from the center plane in the gapwise direction) [46].

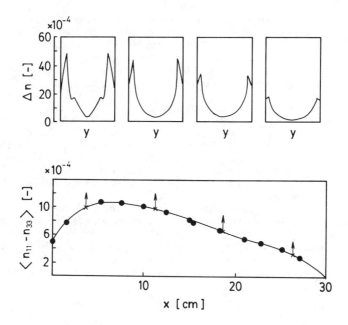

Figure 47. Distributions of absolute value of birefringence Δn in the direction of thickness at different locations from gate, and distribution of average birefringence $\langle n_{11} - n_{33} \rangle$ in the flow direction (x: distance from the gate in the flow direction; y: distance in the direction of thickness) [47].

from the gate. The birefringence distribution in the direction of thickness is shown in Figure 47. All four distributions have the same pattern, which has a minimum point near the central plane and extremum near both surfaces. During molding, the shear stress was at maximum value at the wall of the dies and at minimum at the center. However, while the molded object was taken and the birefringence was prepared for measurement, the stress was relaxed, which resulted in the two maximum points away from the surfaces. There was a difference between short and flash molding, which means overfilling molding: half-way from the gate, the birefringence of the flash molding was larger than that of the short molding. This is one of the important points to be solved for molding disks.

* * *

Since the birefringence occurring in flow is closely concerned with that in solid state, the birefringence in the injection-molded object is described as an example. Birefringence is one of the most important properties for optical usage and should be made lower to the extent possible.

CONCLUSION

It is very interesting to know bird's-eye views of stresses and velocities in order to establish more exact and detailed scale-up criteria. The transmitted and scattered light flow birefringence techniques were employed as one of the flow visualization and normal stress measurement techniques. The milling yellow aqueous solutions and the polymer melts were used for sample fluids.

Brewster's law was confirmed for both fluids over low Reynolds number. The isochromatic patterns and the isoclinic patterns were obtained for approximate two-dimensional flows in coaxial cylinders and two-dimensional agitated vessels by the transmitted light technique. The isochromatic scattered light patterns were obtained for a three-dimensional flow in an agitated vessel by the scattered light technique. Particularly, a method was developed for measuring the extinction angle. The stress distributions calculated as widely as possible in the whole apparatus were found to be reasonable qualitatively and quantitatively. The torques obtained from the scattered light technique were equal to the values directly measured by a torque meter.

Consequently, the flow birefringence technique may be one of the more effective methods for flow visualization and for analysis of low Reynolds number flow. In the future, bulk flow in various apparatuses should be investigated more in detail, and their whole stress patterns and velocities must be understood. Besides this, flows in boundary layers, which play an important role in transport phenomena concerning momentum, mass, and heat, will be most interesting to try to make clear. For this purpose, the scattered light flow birefringence technique seems effective, because it is applicable for measurement of local values.

In the last section of the paper the slip phenomena was studied. Slip velocities on the wall of various nozzles were measured for poly (vinyl chloride) melt and estimated by a simple flow model. The slip phenomena could be first discussed quantitatively. It was found that fluids having the property of slip on the wall have flow behavior very different from the usual fluids. In polymer processing, various materials have been developed and used having this kind of property. In the future, the slip should be taken into consideration for design and operation of polymer processing machines.

Acknowledgment

We would like to acknowledge the assistance of Yuji Tsuruta (Department of Chemical Engineering, Kyusyu University).

NOTATION

A_1, A_2	amplitude of plane polarized light	$\langle n_{11} - n_{33} \rangle$	average birefringence corresponding to $\tau_{11} - \tau_{33}$	
C	stress-optical coefficient, Pa^{-1}	Δn	birefringence	
De	Deborah number	ΔP	pressure drop, Pa	
d	diameter of a capillary nozzle, m	Q	volume flow rate, m^3/s	
F_α	right term of Equation 16, Pa	Q_g	volume flow rate with the grooved nozzle, m^3/s	
H	thickness of a slit nozzle, m	Q_s	volume flow rate with the smooth nozzle, m^3/s	
I	light intensity			
I_0	intensity of incident light	R	radius of an agitated vessel or a capillary nozzle, m	
L	length of a slit nozzle or a capillary nozzle, m	Re	Reynolds number	
l	parameter (Equation 35)	r	component of cylindrical coordinates, m	
m	parameter (Equation 36)	T	temperature, °C	
N	fringe order	T	torque, N·m	
N	rotational speed, s^{-1}	T_1	torque acting on the side wall of an agitated vessel, N·m	
n_1, n_2, n_3	principal refractive indices			
n'_1, n'_2	principal values of a secondary refractive index ellipse	T_2	torque acting on the upper and lower planes of an agitated vessel, N·m	
$n_{11} - n_{22}$	birefringence corresponding to $\tau_{11} - \tau_{22}$			
$n_{22} - n_{33}$	birefringence corresponding to $\tau_{22} - \tau_{33}$	t	length of light path in a test section, m	

u	velocity, m/s
u_s	slip velocity, m/s
u_1	velocity in the thin layer, m/s
u_2	velocity in the bulk region, m/s
W	width of a slit nozzle, m
x	component of rectangular coordinates, m

y	component of rectangular coordinates, m
Z	half of height of an agitated vessel, m
z	component of rectangular coordinates or cylindrical coordinates, m

Greek Symbols

α	arctangent of amplitude ratio of two polarized light waves, rad
α	angle of incident light from the 2 axis in the 1–2 plane, rad
α	parameter (Equation 40)
β	parameter (Equation 40)
γ	angle of incident light from the 3 axis in the 1–3 plane, rad
$\dot{\gamma}$	shear rate, s^{-1}
$\dot{\gamma}_w$	shear rate at the wall, s^{-1}
δ	phase difference, rad
δ	thickness of thin layer, m
η	viscosity, Pa·s
η_1	parameter (Equation 35)
η_2	parameter (Equation 36)
Θ	direction of observation, rad
θ	component of cylindrical coordinates, rad
λ	wave length of light, m
μ	coefficient of scattering

$\sigma_1, \sigma_2, \sigma_3$	principal stresses, Pa
σ'_1, σ'_2	secondary principal stresses, Pa
$\Delta\sigma$	principal stress difference, Pa
$\Delta\sigma'_{ij}$	secondary principal stress difference in i − j plane, Pa
τ_{ij}	ij component of stress tensor, Pa
τ_w	shear stress at the wall, Pa
τ, τ_{12}	shear stress, Pa
$\tau_{11} - \tau_{22}$	the primary normal stress difference, Pa
$\tau_{22} - \tau_{33}$	the secondary normal stress difference, Pa
ϕ	angle between the direction of principal stress and vibration direction of polarizer, rad
χ	extinction angle, rad
χ_m	direction of (secondary) principal stress, rad

REFERENCES

1. Cerf, R., and Scheraga, H. A., "Flow Birefringence in Solutions of Macromolecules," *Chem. Rev.*, *51*, 185 (1952).
2. Tsuji, J., Kawata, K., and Nishida, M., *Kodansei Jikkenho*, (Experimental Methods in Photo-elasticity), Nikkan Kogyo Sinbunsha, 1965.
3. Alcock, E. D., and Sadron, C. L., "An Optical Method for Measuring the Distribution of Velocity Gradients in a Two-Dimensional Flow," *Physics*, *6*, 92 (1935).
4. Hauser, E. A., and Dewey, D. R., II, "Visual Studies of Flow Patterns," *J. Phys. Chem.*, *46*, 212 (1942).
5. Weller, R., "The Optical Investigation of Fluid Flow," *J. Appl. Mech.*, *14*, 103 (1947).
6. Humphry, R. H., "Demonstration of the Double Refraction due to Motion of a Vanadium Pentoxide Sol, and Some Applications," *Proc. Phys. Soc.*, *35*, 217 (1923).
7. Prados, J. W., and Peebles, F. N., "Two-Dimensional Laminar-Flow Analysis, Utilizing a Doubly Refracting Liquid," *AIChE J.*, *5*, 225 (1959).
8. Durelli A. J., and Norgard, J. S., "Experimental Analysis of Slow Viscous Flow Using Photo-viscosity and Bubbles," *Exp. Mech.*, *12*, 169 (1972).
9. Fields, T. R., Jr., and Bogue, D. C., "Stress-Birefringent Patterns of a Viscoelastic Fluid at a Sharp-Edged Entrance," *Trans. Soc. Rheol.*, *12*, 39 (1968).
10. Wales, J. L. S., *The Application of Flow Birefringence to Rheological Studies of Polymer Melts*, Delft University Press, 1976.
11. Han, C. D., *Rheology in Polymer Processing*, Academic Press, New York, 1976.

12. McAfee, W. J., and Pih, H., "Scattered-Light Flow-Optic Relations Adaptable to Three-Dimensional Flow Birefringence," *Exp. Mech.*, *14*, 385 (1974).
13. Horsmann, M., and Merzkirch, W., "Scattered Light Streaming Birefringence in Colloidal Solutions," *Rheol. Acta*, *20*, 501 (1981).
14. Mooney, M., "Explicit Formulas for Slip and Fluidity," *J. Rheol.*, *2*, 210 (1931).
15. Chauffoureaux, J. C., Dehennau, C., and van Rijckevorsel, J., "Flow and Thermal Stability of Rigid PVC," *J. Rheol.*, *23*, 1 (1979).
16. Peebles, F. N., Prados, J. W., and Honeycutt, E. H., Jr., "Birefringent and Rheologic Properties of Milling Yellow Suspensions," *J. Polym. Sci.*, C *5*, 37 (1964).
17. Funatsu, K., "Normal Stress Measurement and Flow Visualization by Flow Birefringence Technique," *Polym. Eng. Rev.*, *4*, 1 (1984).
18. Flow Visualization Society of Japan, ed., *Shinban Nagare no Kashika Handbook*, (Handbook of Flow Visualization), Asakura Shoten, 1987, p. 349.
19. Philippoff, W., Gaskins, F. H., and Brodnyan, J. G., "Flow Birefringence and Stress. V. Correlation of Recoverable Shear Strains with Other Rheological Properties of Polymer Solutions," *J. Appl. Phys.*, *28*, 1118 (1957).
20. Philippoff, W., "Flow Birefringence and Stress," *J. Appl. Phys.*, *27*, 984 (1956).
21. Saunders, D. W., "The Photo-Elastic Properties of Cross-Linked Amorphous Polymers. Part 2—Polythene and Polymethylene," *Trans. Faraday Soc.*, *52*, 1425 (1956).
22. Murai, R., *Doctral Thesis*, University of Tokyo, 1965.
23. Nishida, K., et al., "Measurements of Stress Distribution of Molten Polyethylene in a Tapered Die by Flow Birefringence," *R.P.P.P. J.*, *17*, 201 (1974).
24. Funatsu, K., *Doctral Thesis*, University of Tokyo, 1972.
25. Janeschitz-Kriegl, H., "Flow Birefringence of Elastico-Viscous Polymer Systems," *Adv. Polym. Sci.*, *6*, 170 (1969).
26. Adamse, J. W. C., et al., "Some Rheological Properties of Molten Polypropylene," *J. Polym. Sci.*, A-II *6*, 871 (1968).
27. Brodnyan, J. G., Gaskins, F. H., and Philippoff, W., "On Normal Stresses, Flow Curves, Flow Birefringence, and Normal Stresses of Polyisobutylene Solutions. Part II. Experimental," *Trans. Soc. Rheol.*, *1*, 109 (1957).
28. Daum, U., "Flow Birefringence and Polydispersity," *J. Polym. Sci.*, A-II *6*, 141 (1968).
29. Philippoff, W., "Streaming Birefringence of Polymer Solutions," *J. Polym. Sci.*, C *5*, 1 (1964).
30. Janeschitz-Kriegl, H., "Zur Stromungsdoppelbrechung des Polystyrols," *Makromol. Chem.*, *33*, 55 (1959).
31. Janeschitz-Kriegl H., and Daum, U., "On the Flow Birefringence of Polypropylene in Solution," *Kolloid-Z.*, *210*, 112 (1966).
32. Funatsu, K., et al., "Measurement of Material Functions of Polymer Melts by Three-Dimensional Flow Birefringence," *Kagaku Kogaku Ronbunshu*, *2*, 485 (1976).
33. Funatsu, K., and Shinohara, H., "Studies on Flow Behavior of Polymer Melts by Flow Birefringence," *J. Soc. Rheol., Japan*, *4*, 111 (1976).
34. Funatsu, K., et al., "Measurement of the Second Normal Stress Difference of a Polyethylene Melt by Flow Birefringence," *Kagaku Kogaku Ronbunshu*, *4*, 602 (1978).
35. Wales, J. L. S., and Philippoff, W., "The Anisotropy of Simple Shearing Flow," *Rheol. Acta*, *12*, 25 (1973).
36. Han, C. D., *Rheology in Polymer Processing*, Academic Press, New York, 1976, p. 102.
37. Neyret, B., Agassant, J. F., and Chenot, J. L., "Finite Element Calculations and Experimental Investigations of Two-Dimensional Molten Polymer Flows," in *Industrial Forming Processes* (J. F. T. Pittman, R. D. Wood, J. M., Alexander, and O. C., Zienkiewicz, eds.), Pineridge Press, Swansea, U.K., 1982, p. 535.
38. Funatsu, K., Nishi, M., and Shinohara, H., "Measurement of Stress Distribution in Barus Effect of Polymer Melts by Flow Birefringence," *Kagaku Kogaku Ronbunshu*, *2*, 490 (1976).
39. Vlachopoulos, J., Mitsoulis, E., and Mirza, F. A., "Finite Element Analysis of Polymeric Liquid Flows," in *Advances in Rheology* (B. Mena, A. Garcia-Rejon, and C. Rangel-Nafaile, eds.), vol. 1, Universidad Nacional Autonoma de Mexico, 1984, p. 655.

40. Funatsu, K., Kajiwara, T., and Nakayama, T., "Normal Stress Measurement and Flow Visualization by Flow Birefringence Technique," *World Congr. III of Chem. Eng.*, Tokyo, vol. II, 204 (1986).

41. Timothy, T. S. L., "Capillary Extrusion of Composite Materials," *Polym. Eng. Sci., 11*, 240 (1971).

42. Ui, J., Ishimaru, Y., Saito, S., and Mori, Y., "A Rheometer Made from a Screw Extruder and Abnormal Flow Properties of High Density Polyethylene Melt," *Kobunshi Kagaku, 21*, 385 (1964).

43. Knappe, W., and Krumbock, E., "Evaluation of Slip Flow of PVC-Compounds by Capillary Rheometry," in *Advances in Rheology* (B. Mena, A. Garcia-Rejon, and C. Rangel-Nafaile, eds.), vol. 3, Universidad Nacional Autonoma de Mexico, 1984, p. 417.

44. Funatsu, K., and Sato, M., "Measurement of Slip Velocity and Normal Stress Difference of Poly (Vinyl Chloride)," in *Advances in Rheology* (B. Mena, A. Garcia-Rejon, and C. Rangel-Nafaile, eds.), vol. 4, Universidad Nacional Autonoma de Mexico, 1984, p. 465.

45. Takeshima, M., and Funakoshi, N., "Effect of Molding Conditions on the Birefringence of Injection-Molded Polycarbonate," *Kobunshi Ronbunshu, 41*, 125 (1984).

46. Isayev, A. I., and Hieber, C. A., "Toward a Viscoelastic Modelling of the Injection Molding of Polymers," *Rheol. Acta, 19*, 168 (1980).

47. Wales, J. L. S., van Leeuwen, Ir J., and van der Vijgh, R., "Some Aspects of Orientation in Injection Molded Objects," *Polym. Eng. Sci., 12*, 358 (1972).

CHAPTER 14

APPARENT SLIP FLOW OF POLYMER SOLUTIONS

Yoram Cohen

Department of Chemical Engineering
University of California, Los Angeles
Los Angeles, California USA

CONTENTS

INTRODUCTION

The choice of an appropriate boundary condition for the fluid velocity adjacent to a solid surface has been debated since the early days of fluid mechanics and rheology. Various investigators have documented apparent difficulties with the "no-slip" boundary condition for the flow of polymer solutions, polymer melts, dispersed systems (such as suspensions and emulsions), and polymer gels. Slip effects are often manifested by an abnormal flow enhancement, which may occur in wall-bounded laminar flows; unusually small film thickness for free surface films; either increase or decrease of mass and heat transfer fluxes at the fluid-wall interface; and the "slip-stick" phenomenon, which is linked to extrudate irregularities and melt fracture.

It is important to distinguish between two modes of slip flow. The first is true mechanical wall slip, which can occur with polymer melts and highly cross-linked polymer systems [1, 2]. Mechanical slip occurs when the shearing stresses are large enough to overcome the static friction between the wall and the flowing material. Mechanical slip can occur as either a steady-state phenomenon or as an "unsteady" phenomenon, which is known as "slip-stick" [1–3]. The second mode of slip

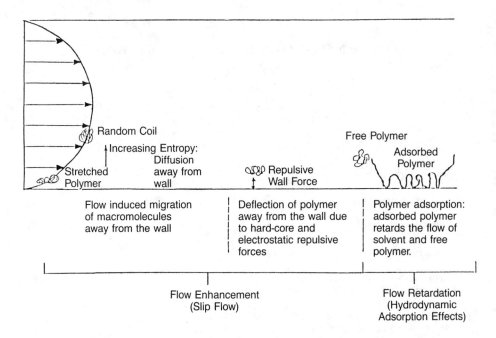

Figure 1. Wall-bounded laminar shear flow of polymer solutions. The viscosity of the wall region is lower than the viscosity in the core region.

is known as "apparent slip." Apparent slip is revealed through the observation of abnormally low apparent fluid viscosities exhibited by a fluid mixture in inhomogeneous stress fields [4]; or in the presence of direct fluid-wall interactions, such as steric interactions, hard-core repulsions, or electrostatic repulsions [5–9], when compared with the viscosities measured in uniform stress fields in the absence of direct wall effects (Figure 1). Apparent slip is primarily the result of depletion of the dispersed or polymeric component in the wall region, which leads to the formation of a fluid layer of lower viscosity near the wall (Figure 1). The remainder of the fluid continuum then may appear to "slip" through the flow channel even though the more dilute, less viscous solution near the wall does not violate the usual "no-slip" boundary condition. Direct measurements of the thickness of slip layers (estimated to be of the order of microns) and the dispersed or solute concentration in these layers are presently unavailable.

The detection of apparent slip is often complicated by the presence of other competing phenomena, such as adsorption, mechanical degradation of the dispersed or solute phase, viscous heating, viscoelastic effects, and end effects [10]. Although the apparent slip phenomenon is not new in the technical literature, it has often been neglected and set aside as an anomaly. Recent studies, however, have consistently demonstrated the regularity with which apparent slip effects occur for polymer solutions and their effect on the interpretation of rheological measurements [10–14] and heat and mass transfer at the solid-fluid interface [15–18].

This chapter reviews the apparent slip phenomenon in wall-bounded shear flows of polymer solutions. First, a brief historical account is provided of both apparent and mechanical slip phenomena in fluid systems. Subsequently, various methods of detecting and analyzing apparent wall slip in various geometries are reviewed. Finally, methods of predicting and correlating apparent slip effects are discussed.

BACKGROUND AND LITERATURE REVIEW

Apparent slip was first documented for the capillary flow of plastic-dispersed systems in the early work of Green [19], and later by Trilisky et al. [20] and Vinogradov et al. [21–23]. Slip effects for the flow of suspensions in capillary tubes were described in the pioneering work of Scott-Blair [24], Mooney [25], Vand [26, 27], and by later investigators [28–33]. Apparent slip effects are also documented for the gravity-driven flow of suspensions down an inclined plane [34]. Apparent slip is also known to occur for capillary flow of blood [35–39] and semi-solid foods [40]. Apparent slip in the flow of polymer solutions through capillary tubes has been documented in the early papers of Mooney [25], Reiner [41], Toms [42], and in later studies [4, 10, 21–23, 32, 43–48]. Apparent slip effects have also been detected in the gravity-driven flow down an inclined plane for polymer solutions [34, 49–51], and for free-surface coating of polymer solutions [12].

The porous media flow of polymer solutions and emulsions may also be accompanied by wall slip effects [11, 48, 52–55]. Wall slip effects have also been reported for the cylindrical Couette flow of suspensions [27, 56–58] and dispersed lubricant systems [22, 23]. Finally, mechanical slip effects have been described for the capillary flow of polymer melts [3, 59–64], thermosetts [65], and polymer gels [66–69], and in the channel flow of polymer gels [70].

Anomalous Effects in the Flow of Polymer Solutions

The early studies on apparent slip recognized that such slip effects are manifested by a decrease in the apparent viscosity, for a given value of the wall shear stress, with decreasing capillary diameter. Reiner [41] demonstrated, by comparing flow curves for different tube diameters, that significant slip effects occurred for the flow of 1.7% nitrocellulose solution in dibutyl phtalate. Later, the study of Toms [42] with the capillary tube flow of solutions of polymethylmethacrylate in monochlorobenzene revealed that, for large-diameter tubes, slip effects were only observable for sufficiently high polymer concentrations.

Anomalous effects for the flow of solutions of polyethyleneoxide through capillary tubes are illustrated in Figure 2 [46]. Although these data were not corrected for non-Newtonian excess pressure drop due to end effects, they clearly show that the relative viscosity (at the Newtonian plateau) decreases with decreasing capillary diameter. An unusual display of capillary diameter effect on the measured apparent viscosity of polyethyleneoxide solutions in glass capillary tubes is demonstrated in Figure 3 [71]. The apparent viscosity decreases (due to apparent slip effects) at a given shear rate, with decreasing tube diameter, until a critical diameter is reached. Below the critical diameter the apparent viscosity increases dramatically to values much greater than those attained with the large diameter tubes. The results of a number of recent studies suggest that adsorbed polymer layers may be responsible for the above increase in the apparent viscosity for small capillary tubes [72–75].

A more definitive illustration of slip effects in capillary tube flow was given by Metzner et al. [4], based on the data of Shertzer [76] for the tube flow of 0.6% polyacrylamide solution (Figure 4). These data were computed from pressure measurements with wall-mounted transducers. Therefore, the reported slip effects should be free of all entrance and exit effects which, if not accounted for, may obscure the interpretation of apparent slip measurements. In the above study, Metzner et al. [4] demonstrated that apparent slip effects for polymer solutions, in flow channels of dimensions much larger than the hydrodynamic macromolecular size, occur only in heterogeneous stress fields (i.e., where stress varies with position). These authors have shown that apparent slip effects were absent in a cone-and-plate viscometer in which the stress levels were everywhere constant. Figure 5 illustrates viscometric cone-and-plate measurements for a 0.7% aqueous polyacrylamide solution at various cone angles. In this homogeneous stress field, slip or scale of the apparatus effects are absent at this very high level of discrimination. This implies that the comparison of viscometric data for which slip effects are suspected with rheological data from a cone-and-plate viscometer should reveal any existing slip effects.

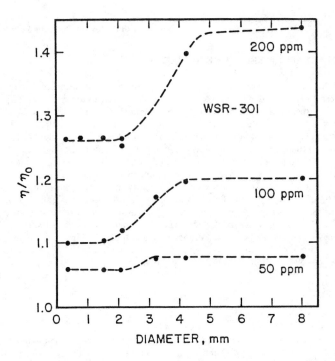

Figure 2. Diameter effects for the flow of aqueous polyethyleneoxide (WSR-301) solutions through capillary tubes. η_a is the apparent viscosity, and η_0 is the solvent viscosity. Data of Kalashnikov and Vlasov [46].

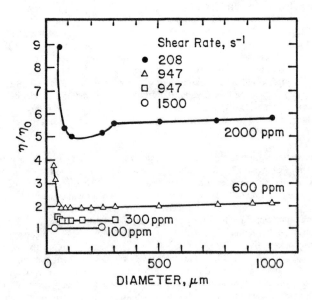

Figure 3. Diameter effects for the flow of aqueous polyethyleneoxide (WSR-301) solutions through glass tubes. Data of Quibrahim [71].

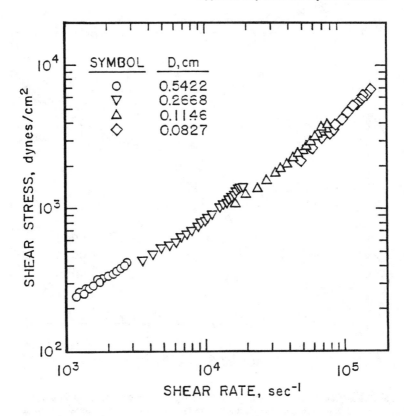

Figure 4. Flow curves in a capillary viscometer. Fluid: 0.6% polyacrylamide ET 597 in water. From Metzner et al. [4].

Cohen and Metzner [10, 72] reported definitive measurements of apparent slip effects free of adsorption and end-effects in capillary flow of solutions of polystyrene, partially hydrolyzed polyacrylamide, and carboxymethylcellulose. As an example, the capillary flow curves for two selected solutions for which apparent slip effects were detected [10] are given in Figures 6 and 7. Also included in these figures are the predictions (no-slip curves) calculated from viscometric cone-and-plate data. These data indicate that as the tube diameter decreases, the flow curves exhibit progressively higher shear rates (for a given τ_w) compared with the no-slip curves. This abnormal flow enhancement is an indication of apparent slip.

The detection of apparent slip is often complicated by polymer adsorption onto the capillary walls of the flow channels [10, 54]. The coupling of adsorption and apparent slip effects is demonstrated in Figure 8. The curves designated by NST, ST, and R refer to untreated capillary surface, surface-treated capillaries (silylated to prevent polymer adsorption), and viscometric (cone-and-plate) rheological predictions, respectively. These results demonstrate that for a given shear rate, the shear stress is higher for untreated tubes (curve NST) than for treated tubes (curve ST). In other words, a higher apparent viscosity is exhibited in the untreated tubes. At the same time, even in the presence of adsorption effects, the flow curves (both ST and NST) are below the viscometric predictions (curve R). This implies that both slip and adsorption can occur simultaneously, with slip effects dominating for this specific example (Figure 8).

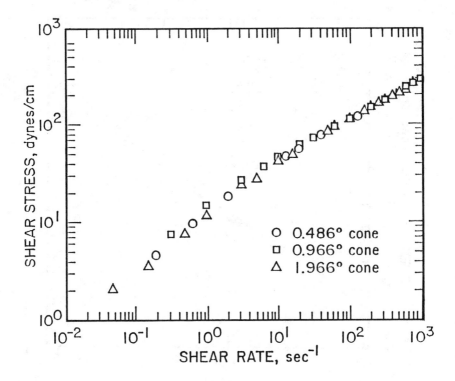

Figure 5. Rheological Measurements in a cone-and-plate viscometer, to illustrate the lack of any dependence of the results on cone angle. Fluid used: 0.7% polyacrylamide (Separan AP30) in water; Diameter of the cone-and-plate: 10 cm. Data of Cohen [4].

Apparent Slip Flow in Porous Media

Extensive reviews of the complex behavior of polymer solutions in porous media have been provided by numerous investigators [52, 77–80]. In particular, it has been demonstrated that in the flow of polymer solutions through a porous medium, "anomalous" behavior associated with the wall region in the pores may lead to either flow enhancement or retardation [52, 54, 81].

Polymer adsorption onto the pore walls is often accompanied by other complex phenomena such as hydrodynamic polymer retention [82–83] and viscoelastic effects [84], all of which contribute to permeability reduction [77, 78, 81]. In contrast, apparent slip effects, revealed through an abnormal flow enhancement, can lead to significant permeability enhancement. In enhanced oil recovery operations, such slip effects may lead to mobility enhancement and hence possible fingering that is undesirable. As shown by Cohen and Metzner [48], apparent slip is most significant in small pores. Consequently, apparent slip may counteract the reduction in mobility due to adsorption and elastic effects and thereby contribute to equalizing the frontal velocity of the injected polymer slug.

The flow behavior of non-Newtonian fluids through a porous medium can be described by coupling a pore geometry of a specific complexity with a purely viscous rheological model for the fluid behavior. Various studies [45, 52], have observed that predicted flow rates were either less than or greater than experimental flow rates by a significant amount. Typical plots of pressure drop vs. superficial velocity based on the capillary power law model [48, 72] are shown in Figures 9–11.

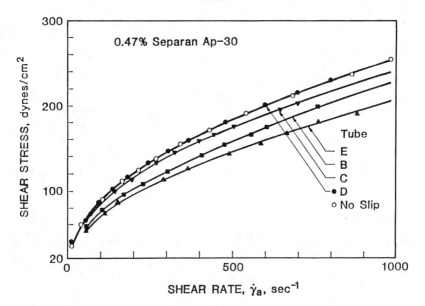

Figure 6. Capillary viscometer flow curves for the flow of 0.47% aqueous polyacrylamide (Separan AP30) solution. Demonstration of slip effects. Deviations from the uppermost curve (cone-and-plate data) are a measure of apparent slip effects. Data Cohen and Metzner [10]. Legend: E − D = 0.01906 cm, L/D = 1909; B − D = 0.02662 cm, L/D = 1996; C − D = 0.1097 cm, L/D = 997; (○)—cone-and-plate data.

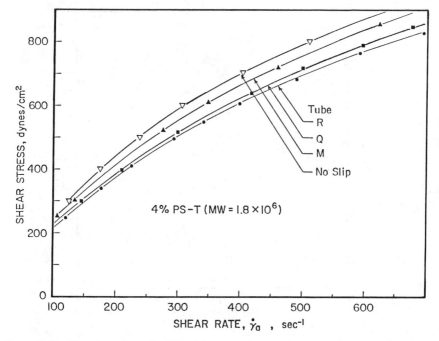

Figure 7. Capillary flow curves for 4% polystyrene-toluene solution (MW = 1.8 × 10⁶). Demonstration of slip effects. Deviations from the uppermost curve are a measure of apparent slip effects. Data of Cohen and Metzner [10]. Legend: R − D = 0.027 cm, L/D = 2013; Q − D = 0.052 cm, L/D = 1956; M − D = 0.084 cm, L/D = 1698.

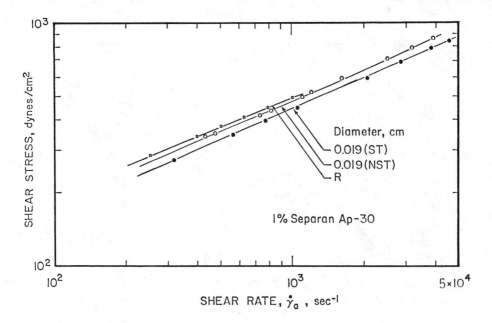

Figure 8. The coupled effect of adsorption and apparent slip on the capillary viscometer flow curves for an aqueous 1% polyacrylamide (Separan AP30) solution (Capillary diameter: 0.02662 cm). Data of Cohen and Metzner [72]. Legend: ST-surface treated tubes; NST-untreated tubes; R-cone-and-plate data.

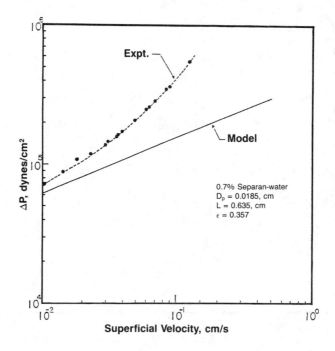

Figure 9. Viscoelastic effects for the flow of 0.7% aqueous polyacrylamide (Separan AP30) solution through a porous disk. The solid line represents the prediction of the capillary-power law model (Equation 48). Porosity: 0.357; Length of porous disk: 0.635 cm; Particle diameter: 0.0185 cm.

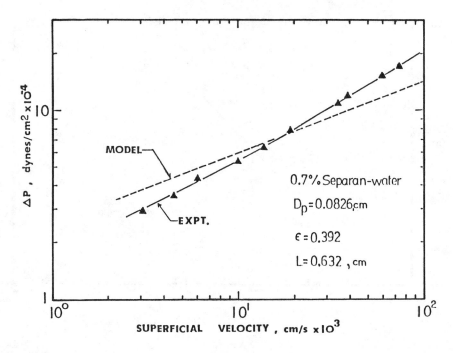

Figure 10. Apparent slip and viscoelastic effects for the flow of 0.7% aqueous polyacrylamide (Separan AP30) solution through a porous disk. The dotted line represents the capillary-power law model prediction: Porosity: 0.392; Thickness of porous disk: 0.632 cm; Particle diameter, 0.0862 cm. From Cohen and Metzner [48].

The overprediction of the superficial velocity as depicted in the upper right end of Figures 10 and 11 have usually been attributed to either permeability reduction due to pore blockage, adsorption, or to elongational flow [48, 77, 78, 84]. In contrast, underprediction of the superficial velocities as shown in the lower end of Figure 10 is unlikely to be caused by elongational flow, pore blockage, or inertial effects. It also appears [48, 72] that this deviation increases with decreasing flow rates. Such a behavior has significant implications in enhanced oil recovery where flow rates are much lower than can be achieved in most laboratory experiments. Finally, note that the interpretation of apparent slip effects from experiments with packed beds of large particle to column-diameter ratio may be complicated by column wall effects as described in "Apparent Slip Effects in Porous Media" later in this chapter.

DETECTION OF APPARENT SLIP EFFECTS

Overview

The detection of apparent slip effects can in principle be accomplished by comparing measurement of the exact velocity profile with the velocity profile predicted based on the shear viscosity of the fluid measured in a slip-free viscometer (e.g., cone-and-plate viscometer). Since slip layers are estimated to be of the order of a few microns in thickness [10], precise velocity measurements are required in the immediate vicinity of the wall. In polymer solutions, velocity measurement techniques such as laser

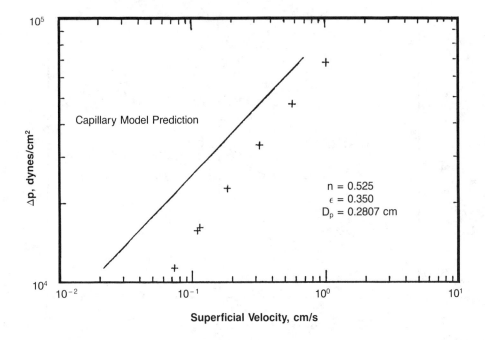

Figure 11. Apparent slip effects in the flow of 0.5% aqueoushydroxy ethylcellulose (Natrosol, 250H) solution through a packed bed (Data of Sadowski [112]). Solid line represents the capillary-power law mode prediction (Equation 48).

differential microanemometry (LMA) [85, 86] and total reflection microscopy (TRM) allow a resolution of about 0.5 μm–1 μm near the wall with an average scatter of $\pm 25\%$ in the measured velocity. Both TRM and LMA rely on tracking gold particles ($\approx 0.15\ \mu$m in diameter) that are about the hydrodynamic size of the polymer molecules in systems for which apparent slip effects have been detected [10, 48, 72]. In polymeric systems, particle-polymer interactions (e.g., adsorption) and particle-wall interactions [6, 87] can complicate the interpretation of velocity measurements with LMA and TRM. Nonetheless, future studies with LMA and TRM should provide useful information on apparent slip effects for systems in which the slip layer is sufficiently thick.

Recently, Ausserre et al. [88, 89] have adapted the technique of total internal reflection in the visible range to determine the concentration profiles of fluorescence-labeled polystyrene and Dextran macromolecules near confining walls in a channel. These authors have clearly demonstrated the existence of a depletion layer under stagnant conditions. Their technique is particularly promising for the determination of the consistency of apparent slip layers under flow conditions.

Another recent method of detecting slip effects that relies on an electrochemical technique was developed by Wein et al. [58, 90, 91]. In this technique, measurements of mass transfer at the wall, using a flush-mounted wall electrode, are made under conditions of diffusion-controlled reaction rate of a redox system. The electrochemical reaction involves the reduction of ferricyanide ion from a solution of potassium ferri-ferrocyanide and a buffer such as sodium carbonate-bicarbonate. Since the mass transfer rate at the wall is related to the velocity field near the wall (assumed to be linear in the slip layer), it is possible to determine the velocity profile near the wall. This technique is applicable to suspensions of particles, but is more difficult to apply to polymer solutions, since the rheological behavior of the polymer is usually strongly affected by the electrolytes in solution.

An convenient alternative approach to detecting and quantifying apparent slip effects follows the analysis first proposed by Mooney [25] for detecting apparent slip flow in capillary tubes and cylindrical Couette viscometers. This analysis is based on the concept of an effective wall slip velocity, and it is appropriate only for thin slip layers [10, 92]. To illustrate this approach, only the tube flow analysis is reviewed here in detail. Subsequently, the parallel methods of detecting slip effects in channels, inclined planes, cylindrical Couettes, and in porous medium geometries are discussed.

Apparent Slip Flow in a Tube

The flow rate Q for laminar flow through a tube can be written as:

$$Q = 2\pi \int_0^R ur \, dr \tag{1}$$

where u = local velocity
r = radial position
R = tube radius

After integrating by parts and assuming a non-zero velocity, V_s, at the tube wall, Equation 1 is expressed by:

$$\frac{Q}{2\pi} = \frac{ur^2}{2} \Big|_{r=0}^{r=R} - \int_{V_s}^{u(r=R)} \frac{r^2}{2} \, du \tag{2}$$

which reduces to:

$$\frac{4Q}{\pi R^3} = \frac{4V_s}{R} - \frac{4}{R^3} \int_{V_s}^{u(r=R)} r^2 \, du \tag{3}$$

By letting $-du/dr = f(\tau)$, in which τ and τ_w are the local and wall shear stresses, respectively, and $f(\tau)$ is the shear-rate function, Equation 3 is rewritten, after a change of variables, to yield:

$$\dot{\gamma}_a = \frac{32Q}{\pi D^3} = \frac{4V_s}{R} + \frac{4}{\tau_w^3} \int_0^{\tau_w} \tau^2 f(\tau) \, d\tau \tag{4}$$

where $\dot{\gamma}_a$ is recognized as the apparent Newtonian shear rate at the tube wall. Differentiating Equation 4 with respect to $1/D$, at a constant value of the wall shear stress, τ_w, gives:

$$\frac{\partial(32Q/\pi D^3)}{\partial(1/D)} \bigg|_{\tau_w} = 8V_s \tag{5}$$

Therefore, plots of $32Q/\pi D^3$ vs. $1/D$ should yield straight lines with a slope equal to $8V_s$.

The preceding analysis assumes a linear stress distribution (as in a fully developed laminar tube flow) and a slip layer thickness δ, such that $\delta/R \ll 1$. This latter condition implies that V_s should be independent of the tube diameter. The analysis also assumes that the effective wall slip velocity does not vary with tube length. The application of this analysis requires accurate measurements that overlap at constant values of τ_w, thus enabling the derivatives of Equation 5 to be accurately determined. The values of V_s can subsequently be used to obtain the contribution of slip flow, Q_s, to the total flow rate Q:

$$Q_s = \frac{\pi D^2 V_s}{4} \tag{6}$$

and to determine the slip-free apparent Newtonian shear rate, $\dot{\gamma}_{ns}$:

$$\dot{\gamma}_{ns} = \frac{32(Q - Q_s)}{\pi D^3} \tag{7}$$

Following the Mooney-Rabinowitsch analysis [93] the following expression is obtained for evaluating the shear-rate function $f(\tau)$:

$$f(\tau) = \frac{32Q}{\pi D^3} \left[\frac{3n' + 1}{4n'} \right] \tag{8a}$$

$$\text{where} \quad n' = \frac{d \ln(\tau_w)}{d \ln(32Q/\pi D^3)} \tag{8b}$$

Example 1

The flow curves for a 0.5% by weight, partially hydrolyzed polyacrylamide (Separan AP-30, Dow Chemical Co.) are given in Figure 7 along with the corresponding cone-and-plate viscometric data. These flow curves were obtained from flow rate-pressure drop measurements, ΔP_m, in which the wall shear stress was calculated from:

$$\tau_w = \frac{(\Delta P_m - \Delta P_e)}{4(L/D)} \tag{9}$$

where ΔP_e is the excess pressure drop (due to end-effects), which was determined from the following correlation [10]:

$$\frac{\Delta P_e}{\rho V^2} = \frac{2146}{N_{Re}^{1.19}} \tag{10}$$

$$\text{where} \quad N_{Re} = \frac{\rho D^{n'} V^{2-n'}}{8^{n'-1} K'} \tag{11a}$$

$$K' = K \left(\frac{3n + 1}{4n} \right) \tag{11b}$$

and n' is defined by Equation 8b, and K and n are the power law parameters for the fluid (i.e., $\tau = K\dot{\gamma}^n$). The above correlation is based on data for aqueous solutions of polyacrylamide (Separan AP-30) and carboxymethylcellulose (Na-CMC-7F, Hercules Inc.) at a concentration range of 0.1% to 2% (by weight). Reviews of various methods of correlating and predicting end-effects are described in several excellent references [94–98].

The apparent slip phenomenon can be quantified in terms of the effective slip velocity V_s, according to Equation 5. This is accomplished by curve fitting the flow curves (Figure 7) and then plotting the Newtonian shear rate $(\dot{\gamma}_a)$ vs. 1/D for given values of the wall shear stress. The resulting plot of $\dot{\gamma}_a$ vs. 1/D is shown in Figure 12. The linearity of this plot indicates, at this level of discrimination, that the slip velocity (Equation 5) is independent of the tube diameter. This supports the thin slip layer hypothesis which formed the basis of the analysis leading to Equation 5. Also note that the slip velocities can be checked according to Equation 4 using the cone-and-plate rheological data for the function $f(\tau)$.

The resulting slip velocities as a function of the wall shear stress are plotted in Figure 13. The effective wall slip velocity increases with the wall shear stress, and this dependency appears to follow

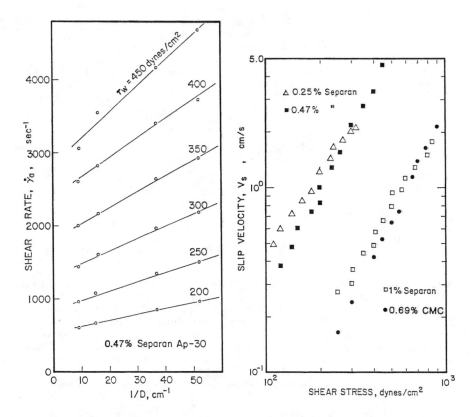

Figure 12. Dependence of apparent shear rate on capillary diameter for aqueous 0.47% polyacrylamide solution (Separan AP30). Determination of effective wall slip velocity. Data of Cohen and Metzner [10].

Figure 13. Variation of slip velocity with wall shear stress for aqueous 0.47% polyacrylamide solution (Separan AP30). Based on data of Figure 12.

the following empirical relation [10]:

$$V_s = a\tau_w^m \tag{12}$$

The values of the parameters a and m for various polymeric systems are given in Table 1.

The fractional contribution of slip flow to the total flow rate (Q_s/Q) can be expressed by combining Equation 4 with Equation 12. In addition, the shear rate-shear stress behavior (Figure 7) can be described by a power-law model $(\tau_w = K\dot{\gamma}^n)$ which is well suited for the range of application of Equation 12. The resulting relation for Q_s/Q (also equivalent to the ratio V_s/V) is:

$$\frac{V_s}{V} = \frac{Q_s}{Q} = \left[\left(\frac{4n}{3n+1}\right)\frac{\tau_w^{(1/n)-m}}{aK^{1/n}}D + 1\right]^{-1} \tag{13}$$

Equation 13 shows that Q_s/Q increases with decreasing tube diameter as verified by the experimental data (Figure 14). Therefore, the apparent slip phenomenon becomes more important in small channels. In this particular example, the contribution of slip flow to the total flow rate

Table 1
Slip Velocities for Polymer Solutions

Polymer Solution	a cm/s(dynes/cm²)ᵐ	m	τ_w dynes/cm²	Flow Field
0.25% Separan AP-30	6.73×10^{-4}	1.39	110–320	Tube flow [10]
0.47% Separan AP-30	3.53×10^{-5}	1.92	100–450	
1% Separan AP-30	6.5×10^{-5}	1.50	250–450	
0.69% CMC-7F	2.62×10^{-6}	2.00	250–90	
1% PS-toluene (MW = 2×10^7)	1.35×10^{-3}	1.08	100–450	
4% PS-toluene (MW = 1.8×10^6)	7.7×10^{-6}	1.64	300–800	
3.15% PS-decalin (MW = 1.8×10^6)	5.31×10^{-6}	1.70	450–750	
2% CMC	8.95×10^{-1}	0.6		Inclined plane [34]

amounts to as much as 45% at a shear stress of 200 dynes/cm² for the smallest capillary tube of 0.0192 cm. Data with high molecular weight, semi-dilute polymer solutions [10] reveal that for most cases the exponent $(1/n - m) > 0$ (see Equation 13). Thus, when $1/n > m$, the viscosity of the fluid decreases more rapidly (due to shear thinning) than the corresponding increase in the effective slip velocity. Consequently, the contribution of slip to the total flow rate becomes increasingly more important at low stress levels. It is expected, however, that below some "critical" wall shear stress level, Q_s/Q will decrease toward zero, since V_s must vanish as $\tau_w \to 0$.

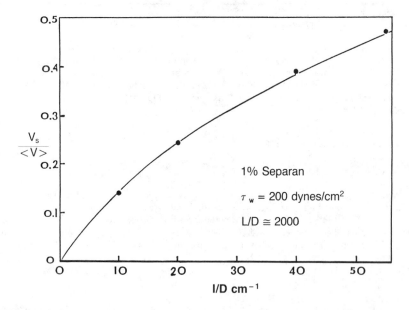

Figure 14. The contribution of apparent slip to the total flow rate as a function of tube diameter for aqueous 0.47% polyacrylamide solution (τ_w = 200 dynes/cm²). Based on data of Figure 12.

In the preceding example, and other cited studies of apparent slip flow of polymer solutions, the effective slip velocity is found to be independent of tube length. A slip velocity that varies with tube length should be detectable in the Bagley pressure drop vs. 1/D plots [99, 100], as shown schematically in Figure 15. The measured pressure drop, ΔP_m (determined between the capillary exit and entry planes), includes an excess pressure drop, ΔP_e. Thus the pressure drop, ΔP_a, across the fully developed flow section is evaluated from:

$$\Delta P_a = \Delta P_m - \Delta P_e \tag{14}$$

The determination of ΔP_e follows the Bagley procedure [99, 100], where Equations 10 and 14 are combined to give:

$$\Delta P_m = 4(L/D)\tau_w + \Delta P_e \tag{15}$$

Therefore, a plot of ΔP_m vs. L/D, at a given Newtonian shear rate ($\dot{\gamma} = 32Q/\pi D^3$), should yield a straight line with a slope equal to $4\tau_w$ and an intercept of ΔP_e (Figure 15). It is also common to express ΔP_e in terms of an equivalent tube length, L_{eq}, in which case Equation 15 becomes:

$$\Delta P_m = 4\tau_w(L/D + L_{eq}/D) \tag{16}$$

Deviations from a linear dependence of ΔP_m on L/D, for a given shear rate, may occur in the case of apparent slip flows. In the first case, slip effects (i.e., the contribution of slip to the total flow rate) are independent of tube length. In the second case, the effective wall slip velocity may depend on tube length. The effects of these two cases are best illustrated by considering two capillary tubes A and B of lengths L_A and L_B, respectively, but of identical diameters. The corrected apparent shear rate, $\dot{\gamma}_A$, $\dot{\gamma}_B$ for tubes A and B, may be expressed by:

$$\dot{\gamma}_A = 32(Q_A - Q_{SA})/\pi D^3 \tag{17}$$

$$\dot{\gamma}_B = 32(Q_B - Q_{SB})/\pi D^3 \tag{18}$$

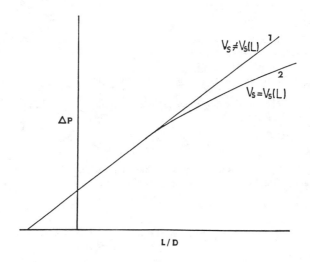

Figure 15. Determination of excess pressure drop (Bagley plot) with slip effects.

where Q_A, Q_B and Q_{SA}, Q_{SB} are the total flow rates and the contributions of apparent slip to the total flow rate for tubes A and B, respectively. Q_{SA} and Q_{SB} are functions of the wall shear stress and may in principle vary with tube length. In constructing the Bagley plot (Figure 15) one should compare tubes at the apparent shear rate as defined in Equations 17–18. Unfortunately, Q_{SA} and Q_{SB} are not known a priori and hence the determination of end-effects becomes an iterative process, linked to the evaluation of Q_{SA} and Q_{SB}.

The determination of end-effects is generally done by comparing tubes of different L/D at the same shear rate, based on the total measured flow rate (Equation 15). Such a comparison is made assuming that $Q_A = Q_B = Q_0$; thus, the combination of Equations 17–18 leads to the following relation:

$$\frac{\dot{\gamma}_A}{\dot{\gamma}_B} = \frac{1 - Q_{SA}/Q_0}{1 - Q_{SB}/Q_0} \tag{19}$$

If Q_{SA} and Q_{SB} are independent of the tube length such that $Q_{SA} = Q_{SB}$, for a given apparent Newtonian shear rate given by $\dot{\gamma}_0 = 32Q_0/\pi D^3$, then it follows that $\dot{\gamma}_A = \dot{\gamma}_B$. Therefore, the Bagley plot (Figure 14) is in fact made at the same corrected Newtonian shear rate. This is described by curve 1 in Figure 14. The situation is different when Q_{SA} and Q_{SB} vary with tube length. For example, if Q_{SA} and Q_{SB} increase with tube length [4] and $L_A > L_B$, then $Q_{SB}/Q_{SA} > 1$. Thus from Equation 19 it is evident that $\dot{\gamma}_A > \dot{\gamma}_B$. Therefore, as one plots ΔP_m for increasing values of L/D for a given flow rate, $\dot{\gamma}_0$ (the corrected shear rate, see Equations 17–18) decreases with increasing tube length. It is then expected that part of the increase in ΔP_m which is due to the increase in tube length will be offset by the increasing contribution of slip to the total flow rate. The qualitative description of this behavior is depicted by curve 2 in Figure 15. Consequently, if end-effects are determined for tubes with large L/D ratios and when $V_s = V_s(L)$, then one would expect the excess pressure drop to be overestimated.

Channel Flow

The analysis of slip effects for a fully developed flow in a channel results in the following equation:

$$\frac{Q}{2WB^2} = \frac{V_s}{B} + \frac{1}{\tau_w^2} \int_0^{\tau_w} \tau f(\tau) \, d\tau \tag{20}$$

where   Q = flow rate
W = width of the channel
2B = thickness of the channel
τ_w = wall shear stress at the fully developed flow region

Differentiation of Equation 20 with respect to 1/B at a constant value of τ_w gives:

$$\left. \frac{\partial(Q/2WB^2)}{\partial(1/B)} \right|_{\tau_w} = V_s \tag{21}$$

Thus, plots of $Q/2WB^2$ vs. 1/B should yield straight lines with slopes equal to V_s. Once V_s is determined, the slip-free flow rate, Q', can be determined:

$$Q' = Q - 2WBV_s \tag{22}$$

Subsequently, the shear rate-shear stress behavior can be obtained (as in the analysis leading to Equation 8) from:

$$f(\tau_w) = \frac{Q'}{2WB^2} \left[\frac{2n' + 1}{n'} \right] \tag{23}$$

where $\quad n' = \dfrac{\partial \ln(\tau_w)}{\partial (Q'/2WB^2)}$ $\hspace{4cm}$ (24)

V_s can also be obtained directly from experimental data using Equation 20, given the function $f(\tau)$. Such an approach, which can be carried out for a single channel thickness, is less definitive in discriminating between cone-and-plate viscometric measurement errors (in obtaining $f(\tau)$) and errors in flow rate-shear stress measurements.

Example 2

The recent study of Choplin and Carreau [94] for the flow of polymer solutions through a channel, using wall-mounted pressure transducers to measure τ_w, provided shear stress-flow rate data from which the effective wall slip velocity can be obtained using the reported cone-and-plate data for the shear stress-shear rate behavior. The calculated slip velocities (from Equation 22) for Separan AP30 solutions in water and in corn syrup are given in Figure 16. Although there is some scatter in the data, the slip velocities are of similar magnitude to the values reported elsewhere [10] for slip flow in capillary tubes. Moreover, based on this limited data set, it appears that polyacrylamide solutions in corn syrup (viscoelastic fluids of constant shear viscosity) display a slip behavior that is independent of shear stress. Further experimental work with channels of different thicknesses is required in order to clearly quantify apparent slip effects for non-shear thinning elastic fluids.

Gravity-Driven Flow Down an Inclined Plane

The analysis of the slip phenomenon for gravity-driven flows down an inclined plane (Figure 17) can be analyzed similarly to the case of slip in a tube flow. At full development, in the absence

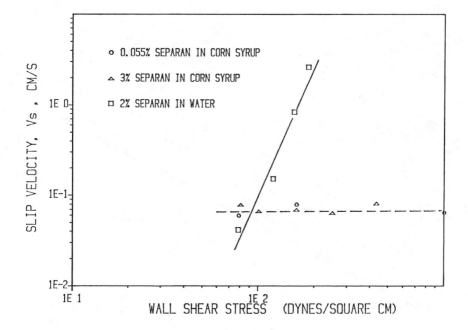

Figure 16. Apparent slip velocities for the flow of polyacrylamide solutions through a slit. Slit thickness: 0.3175 cm; Slit length: 63.5 cm; Slit width: 6.35 cm. Data of Choplin and Carreau [44].

of surface waves, at a given value of the wall shear stress τ_w, the following integral equation for apparent slip flow is obtained:

$$\frac{q}{h^2} = \frac{V_s}{h} + \frac{1}{\tau_w^3} \int_0^{\tau_w} \tau f(\tau) \, d\tau \qquad (25)$$

where q = volumetric flow rate per unit width
       h = film thickness
       w = width of the flow field
       V_s = effective wall slip velocity

The wall shear stress τ_w is given by:

$$\tau_w = \rho g h \cos \beta$$

where ρ = fluid density
       β = inclination angle (see Figure 17)
       g = acceleration due to gravity

Differentiation of Equation 25 with respect to 1/h at a given value of the shearing stress τ_w gives:

$$\left.\frac{\partial(q/h^2)}{\partial(1/h)}\right|_{\tau_w} = V_s \qquad (26)$$

Thus the apparent slip velocity, V_s, can be determined from the slope of the straight line plots of q/h^2 vs. 1/h. The slip-free flow rate q' is determined from:

$$q' = q - V_s h \qquad (27)$$

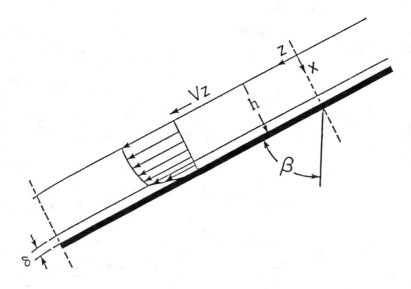

Figure 17. Schematic of slip flow down an inclined plane.

Subsequently, an analysis following that which led to Equation 8 yields:

$$f(\tau_w) = \frac{3q'}{h^2}\left[\frac{2n' + 1}{3n'}\right] \tag{28}$$

where $n' = \dfrac{d \ln(\tau_w)}{d \ln(q'/h^2)}$ (29)

Example 3

The flow curves for the gravity-driven inclined plane flow of an aqueous solution of 2% carboxymethylcellulose (CMC) are given in Figure 18 in terms of the flow rate vs. the film thickness for different inclination angles. The effective slip velocity is determined by plotting q/h^2 vs. $1/h$ as shown in Figure 19, at different levels of the wall shear stress, and subsequently calculating the slopes as specified by Equation 26. The linearity of these plots (see Figure 19) indicates that indeed $\delta/h \ll 1$, which supports the thin slip layer assumption. Finally, the dependence of V_s on τ_w is shown in Figure 20 [4] and is seen to obey a powerlaw dependence as suggested by Equation 12.

Example 4

The effective Wall slip velocity, V_s, for gravity flow down an inclined plane, can also be determined directly from Equation 25 given the function $f(\tau)$ from independent slip-free cone-and-plate viscometric data, as suggested by Carreau et al. [50]. An example of the results of such an approach is presented in Figures 21 and 22 which display the cone-and-plate viscometric data and

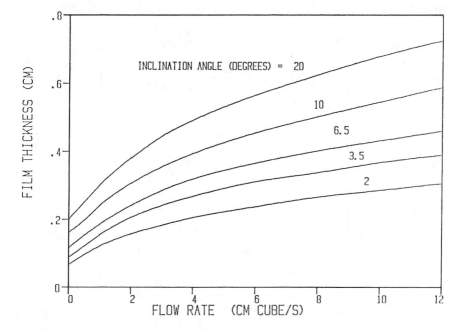

Figure 18. Flow curves for the flow of 2% CMC solution down an inclined plane. Data of Astarita et al. [34]; Width of inclined plane = 5.8 cm.

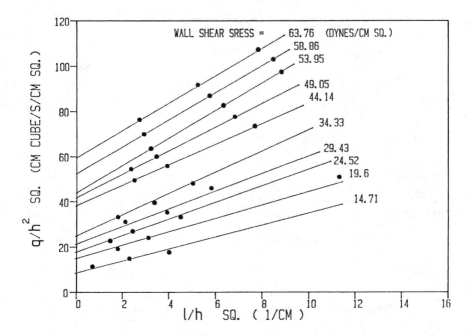

Figure 19. Determination of apparent slip for the gravity driven flow of a 2% CMC solution down an inclined plane (see Figure 16).

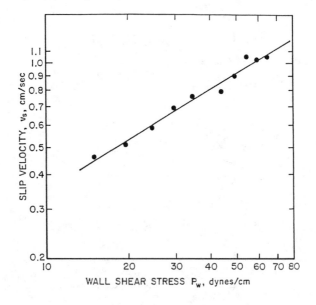

Figure 20. Effective wall slip velocity for the flow of 2% CMC solution flowing by gravity down an inclined plane (based on Figure 18).

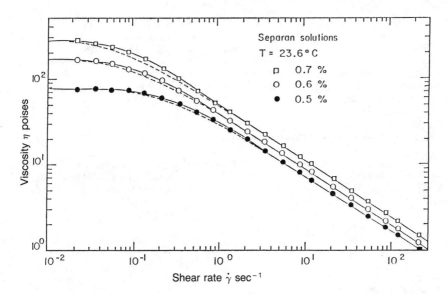

Figure 21. Rheological properties of aqueous polyacrylamide (Separan AP30) solutions determined in a cone-and-plate viscometer. Data of Carreau et al. [50].

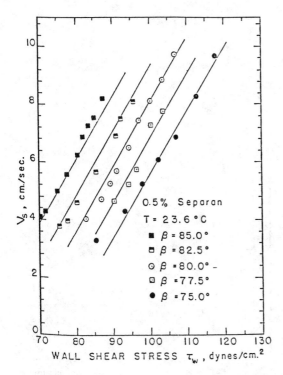

Figure 22. Dependence of slip velocity on shear stress and film thickness in the gravity-driven flow down an inclined plane for Separan solutions. Data of Carreau et al. [50].

the calculated effective wall slip velocities for the gravity-driven flow down an inclined plane for Separan solutions [50]. This method is less precise, as has been pointed out. As in other cases reviewed previously, V_s varies with the wall shear stress according to Equation 12, although the values of V_s are much higher than in capillary tubes at the same stress levels for reasons that are yet unclear. Finally, the dependence of the slip velocity on the film thickness (Figure 22) suggests that the slip layers are thick; hence, the analysis based on Equation 25, which requires $\delta/h \ll 1$, may be improper.

Apparent Slip in a Cylindrical Couette Viscometer

The analysis of apparent slip in a cylindrical Couette viscometer (Figure 23) can be carried out by assuming an effective slip velocity at the walls of the bob (inner cylinder) and cup (outer cylinders). For a narrow gap viscometer, the following equation, which incorporates slip effects, can be derived [25]:

$$\Omega_{io} = \frac{V_s(\tau_i)_i}{R_i} + \frac{V_s(\tau_o)_o}{R_o} + \frac{1}{2} \int_{\tau_o}^{\tau_i} \frac{f(\tau)\, d\tau}{\tau} \tag{30}$$

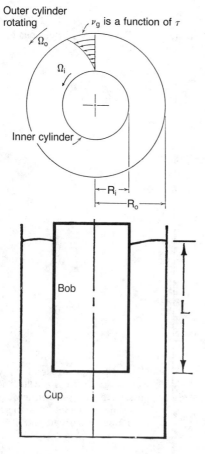

Figure 23. Cylindrical Couette viscometer.

where   subscripts i and o = outside surface of the bob and inside surface of the cup

R_i and R_o = radii of the bob and the cup

$\Omega_{io} = \Omega_i - \Omega_o$

Ω_{io} = net angular velocity

Ω_i, Ω_o = angular velocities of the bob and cup

$V_s(\tau)_i$ and $V_s(\tau)_o$ = slip velocities at the bob and cup surfaces in contact with the fluid

The local shear stress τ is given by:

$$\tau = \Gamma/2\pi r^2$$

where Γ is the torque per unit length of the cylindrical Couette viscometer. Once the slip velocities are determined, the shear rate function, $f(\tau)$, can be determined by standard methods [26, 93, 98].

In order to evaluate V_s, measurements of the torque (Γ) as a function of the relative angular velocity Ω_{io} are carried out for at least three different combinations of R_i and R_o. Accordingly, the following equations are obtained, based on Equation 30, for each of the three combinations:

$$\Omega_{12} = \frac{V_s(\tau_1)_i}{R_1} + \frac{V_s(\tau_2)_o}{R_2} + \frac{1}{2}\int_{(\tau_2)_o}^{(\tau_1)_i} \frac{f(\tau)\,d\tau}{\tau} \tag{31}$$

$$\Omega_{13} = \frac{V_s(\tau_1)_i}{R_1} + \frac{V_s(\tau_3)_o}{R_3} + \frac{1}{2}\int_{(\tau_3)_o}^{(\tau_1)_i} \frac{f(\tau)\,d\tau}{\tau} \tag{32}$$

$$\Omega_{23} = \frac{V_s(\tau_2)_i}{R_2} + \frac{V_s(\tau_3)_o}{R_3} + \frac{1}{2}\int_{(\tau_3)_o}^{(\tau_2)_i} \frac{f(\tau)\,d\tau}{\tau} \tag{33}$$

If R_i and R_o are selected such that $R_3 > R_2 > R_1$, then at a given value of the torque, $\tau_1 > \tau_2 > \tau_3$; thus, Equations 31–33 can be combined such that the integral terms cancel each other. For example, one can derive the following equation:

$$(\Omega_{12} + \Omega_{23}) - \Omega_{13} = \left[\frac{V_s(\tau_2)_i}{R_2} + \frac{V_s(\tau_2)_o}{R_2}\right] \tag{34}$$

from which V_s can be determined assuming that the effective wall slip velocity is only a function of the wall shear stress, and it is also independent of the ratio R_i/R_o.

The preceding analysis assumes that the slip velocities are identical at both the bob and cup surfaces at equal stress levels. Such an analysis may be an oversimplification if apparent slip effects occur due to net-particle or disperse-phase migration across curvilinear streamlines toward the inner cylinder. The phenomenon of particle migration toward the inner cylinder has been documented in the literature, for both particles and rigid macromolecules [87, 101–106]. In order to evaluate the difference in the apparent slip velocity between the inner and outer cylinders, one may first carry out viscometric measurements with two bobs of different diameter (R_1 and R_2) in infinite fluids (i.e., $R_i \ll R_o$). Accordingly, the following equations arise:

$$\Omega_1 = \frac{V_s(\tau_1)}{R_1} + \frac{1}{2}\int_0^{\tau_1} \frac{f(\tau)\,d\tau}{\tau} \tag{35}$$

$$\Omega_2 = \frac{V_s(\tau_2)}{R_2} + \frac{1}{2}\int_0^{\tau_2} \frac{f(\tau)\,d\tau}{\tau} \tag{36}$$

By equating Equations 35 and 36 at a given value of the stress at the bob surface (i.e., $\tau_1 = \tau_2$), V_s can be determined from the following relation:

$$V_s(\tau) = \frac{R_1 R_2(\Omega_1 - \Omega_2)}{R_2 - R_1} \tag{37}$$

The values of $V_s(\tau)$ obtained from Equation 37 can be compared with the values of V_s obtained from Equation 34 in order to assess the validity of the assumption made in deriving Equation 34. Alternatively, one could determine the shear stress vs. angular velocity (at the bob surface) for different bob diameters and then plot Ω_{io} vs. $1/R$ at a given value of the shear stress—the slope of the resulting straight lines being equal to the apparent wall slip velocity.

Another approach of determining apparent slip effects in the cylindrical Couette viscometer is to compare the viscometric measurements for various combinations of smooth and rough bobs and cups. The underlying assumption is that slip effects will occur for smooth walls but will be eliminated at rough walls. Three different methods of determining slip effects with roughened walls are described here. Additional details regarding the analyses can be found elsewhere [22, 23, 56, 57]. The first of the rough wall methods is based on the use of one smooth bob and one rough bob of the same diameter, in the same rough cup. Since slip is assumed to occur only at the smooth bob surface, it follows that:

$$\Omega_{so} = \Omega_s - \Omega_o = \frac{V_s(\tau_s)}{R_s} + \frac{1}{2}\int_{\tau_o}^{\tau_s} \frac{f(\tau)\,d\tau}{\tau} \tag{38}$$

where the subscripts, s and o refer to the surface of the smooth bob and rough cup, respectively, and R_s is the diameter of the smooth bob. With the rough bob and cup combination there is no slip at either surface. Thus:

$$\Omega_r - \Omega_o = \frac{1}{2}\int_{\tau_o}^{\tau_r} \frac{f(\tau)\,d\tau}{\tau} \tag{39}$$

where the subscript r refers to the surface of the rough bob. If both the smooth and rough bobs are of the same diameter, then at the condition when the stress at the cup surface is identical for both experiments (identical to comparing the two experiments at a given value of the torque), $V_s(\tau_s)$ is evaluated from:

$$V_s(\tau_s) = R_s(\Omega_s - \Omega_r) \tag{40}$$

In the second method one utilizes a smooth bob in a smooth cup, and the same bob in a rough cup of the same diameter as the smooth one. The resulting equation for the slip velocity is:

$$V_s(\tau_s) = R_o(\Omega_s - \Omega_o) \tag{41}$$

where the subscripts s and o refer to the smooth bob and the cup (either smooth or rough), respectively.

The third method is based on the use of one smooth and one rough bob, of the same diameter, in an infinite fluid. In this case the slip velocity at the bob surface, at a given value of the stress level, is given by:

$$V_s(\tau_s) = R_s(\Omega_s - \Omega_r) \tag{42}$$

where the subscripts s and r refer to the smooth and rough bobs, respectively.

Example 5

Figure 24 [57] illustrates the approach of using roughened walls with tomato ketchup. Although the various methods of determining effective wall slip velocity yield similar values, it is clear that there are consistent differences. These differences may be due to the fact that wall slip is not entirely eliminated by use of a rough surface. For example, a study of Jiang et al. [67] teaches that slip effects for polymer gels do occur at rough surfaces, although to a lesser extent than with smooth surfaces. Thus, in order to accurately determine the apparent slip for a given wall roughness, it is recommended

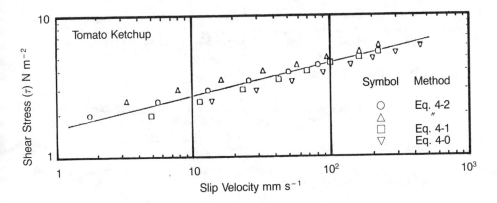

Figure 24. Slip velocity for tomato ketchup determined from cylindrical couette viscometer measurements. Data of Cheng and Parker [57]. Legend: ($\bigcirc$), ($\triangle$)—Equation 42; ($\square$)—Equation 41; ($\triangledown$)—Equation 40.

that the method of Equation 34 be used in conjunction with apparent slip measurements using two bobs of different diameter in an infinite fluid (Equation 39).

Apparent slip in cylindrical Couette viscometry has been detected for dispersed systems, particularly when the dispersed phase is of large size, is flocculent or fibrous, or exhibits syneresis. Materials that have exhibited apparent slip in cylindrical Couette viscometers include suspensions [56, 58], plastic dispersed systems (i.e., grease) [21, 22], lead slurries, fermentation broth, meal mixture, ketchup, and blood [57]. To date, however, apparent slip effects in the cylindrical Couette flow of polymer solutions have not been reported.

Apparent Slip Effects in Porous Media

The quantification of slip effects in the flow of polymer solutions through porous media requires the adaptation of a specific pore geometry. Although many models have been proposed to describe the complex geometry of porous media [107, and references therein] they seem to offer no measurable improvement in prediction of pressure drop-flow rate relationship for inelastic fluids. Thus, in the present analysis, the most simplistic capillary model is adopted. Detailed discussions on the use of the capillary model can be found elsewhere [52, 108–110].

There are two alternate methods of analyzing for apparent slip flow in the flow of polymer solutions through porous media. In the first method, Equation 4 is simply adapted to a porous medium with the capillary model for the pore geometry. The changes that are made are through the definition of the effective channel diameter, which is defined as:

$$D_{eff} = 4R_H = 4\epsilon D_p / 6(1 - \epsilon) \tag{43}$$

where ϵ = porosity
         D_p = particle diameter
         R_H = hydraulic radius [111].

In addition, the average interstitial velocity, V (equivalent to $Q/\pi D^2$), is related to the superficial velocity, V_o, by [107]:

$$V = V_o L_e / \epsilon L \tag{44}$$

where L_e is the effective channel length. The tortuosity factor, L_e/L, will vary depending on the geometry of the particles and the degree of randomness of the packing. An analysis of apparent slip, which parallels the analysis for capillary tube flow, results in the following expression [52–54]:

$$\dot{\gamma}_{ap} = \frac{8V}{4R_H} = \frac{8V_{sp}}{4R_H} + \frac{4}{\tau_{wp}^3} \int_0^{\tau_{wp}} \tau^2 f(\tau)\, d\tau \tag{45}$$

where $\dot{\gamma}_{ap}$ is the apparent Newtonian shear rate at the pore wall and V_{sp} is the effective wall slip velocity in the pore. The wall stress, τ_{wp}, at the pore wall in the porous medium is given by:

$$\tau_{wp} = \Delta P/[(L_e/L)(L/R_H)] \tag{46}$$

where ΔP is the pressure drop across a bed of length L. The differentiation of Equation 45 with respect to $1/R_H$ at a constant τ_{wp} leads to:

$$\left.\frac{\partial(2V_o/\epsilon R_H)}{\partial(1/R_H)}\right|_{\tau_{wp}} = \frac{V_{sp}}{(L_e/L)} \tag{47}$$

from which V_{sp} can be determined, using data for several different particle diameters. Such a procedure was applied by Kozicki et al. [53] to the data of Sadowski [112]. The use of Equation 47 requires extremely accurate data to facilitate the differentiation step. This is difficult to do in packed beds due to complications such as end-effects, adsorption, pore-blockage, non-uniform particle size, and wall-effects [77, 107].

The second method consists of comparing experimental pressure drop-flow rate results to model predictions. Various models are possible based on the combination of the rheological model in steady shear with the capillary model for the pore geometry. For example, based on the power law model for the shear rate-shear stress behavior ($\tau = K\dot{\gamma}^n$), the pressure drop-flow rate prediction becomes:

$$V_o = \left[\frac{4n}{3n+1}\right]\left[\frac{\Delta P}{2KL}\right]^{1/n}\left[\frac{D_p\epsilon}{3(1-\epsilon)}\right]^{(n+1)/n}\frac{\epsilon}{2B} \tag{48a}$$

where $B = K_o(L_e/L)^{(n+1)/n}$ \hfill (48b)

where K_o is a geometric factor that accounts for the inadequacy in the choice of a proper effective diameter. The capillary-power law (CPL) model is strictly valid for purely viscous power law fluids, as demonstrated by Cohen and Cheng-Nian [55].

Example 6

The applicability of the CPL model is demonstrated in Figure 25 for the flow of purely viscous but shear-thinning water-in-oil microemulsions in porous media. Following the discussion of Cohen and Metzner [107] the numerical values of K_o and L_e/L, consistent with the capillary model for a randomly packed bed of spheres, are taken to be 2 and $\sqrt{2.5}$, respectively [10]. The shear stress-shear rate behavior for both porous media and capillary viscometer data superimposes with an average scatter of less than 6 percent.

The predicted superficial velocity V_o, based on Equation 48, can now be compared to the experimental superficial velocity V_{ex} for a given pressure drop. A plausible correlating parameter for viscoelastic effects in porous media flow is the Deborah number, N_{DE}, defined here as [84]:

$$N_{DE} = \theta V/D_p \tag{49}$$

where V is defined by Equation 44 and θ is defined as the Maxwell relaxation time for the fluid

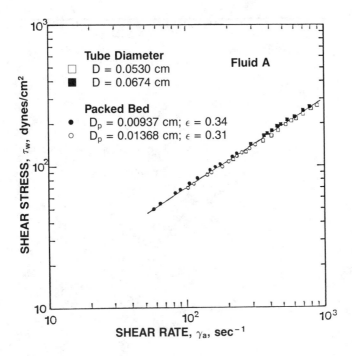

Figure 25. Flow curve of water in oil microemulsion in porous media. Demonstration of the applicability of the capillary-power law model for purely viscous shear-thinning fluids. Data of Cohen and Cheng-Nian [55].

($\theta = N_1/2\tau$, where N_1 is the primary normal stress difference measured in steady shear). The use of the Deborah number as a correlating parameter implies that both slip and viscoelastic effects are connected with the degree of stretching of the polymer molecules. Therefore, the procedure of separating apparent slip and viscoelastic effects consists of plotting V_{ex}/V_o vs. N_{de}. A ratio of $V_{ex}/V_o < 1$ indicates apparent slip, while a ratio of $V_{ex}/V_o > 1$ implies viscoelastic effects (provided that adsorption effects have been eliminated). This procedure is applicable as long as the fluid's rheological behavior at steady shear can be described by a power law model. The extension of the approach to other rheological models is straightforward.

Example 7

The preceding approach is illustrated in Figure 26 for the flow of an aqueous 0.7% polyacrylamide (Separan AP30) solution in a porous medium. These data are free of pore blockage effects due to the relatively large pore size, and free of adsorption effects owing to a surface silylation treatment [54]. The results depicted in Figure 26 suggest that at a Deborah number greater than about 0.08, the experimental flow rates are lower than predicted by Equation 48. This "critical" Deborah number marks the onset of viscoelastic effects. This is in agreement with the results of Marshall and Metzner [84] after the inclusion of the factor L_c/L in their definition of the Deborah number. Below a Deborah number of about 0.08, the experimental flow rates are higher than the CPL model prediction. This flow enhancement is the consequence of apparent slip effects that become significant at low Deborah numbers, while viscoelastic effects diminish.

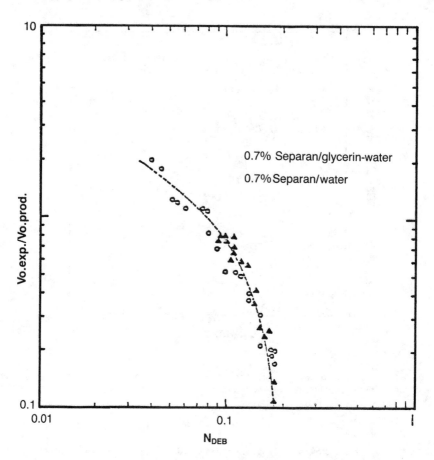

Figure 26. Correlation of measured/predicted superficial velocities for Separan solutions in porous media. Data of Cohen [54].

Column Wall Effects in Packed Beds

Laboratory experiments of flow through porous media are usually conducted in packed columns of finite size. In using Equations 43–48, however, it is assumed that column wall effects are negligible. Column wall effects may obscure the proper interpretation of viscoelastic and apparent slip effects in packed beds of small bed-to-particle diameter ratio. Column wall effects are linked to non-random porosity variations near the wall of beds randomly packed with particles of uniform size. A typical porosity profile, based on the data of Roblee et al. [113] and Ridgway and Tarbuck [114] for cylindrical columns packed with uniform size spheres is shown in Figure 27. Such a porosity profile coupled with the capillary model for the pore geometry can be used to assess column wall effects as described by the triregional capillary-power law model of Cohen and Metzner [107]. In the triregional model, the bed is divided into three distinct regions (Figure 28). The region extending from the wall to x_t is considered the wall region. The second region, which extends from x_t to x_b, is defined as the transition region. This region exhibits damped porosity oscillations that persist

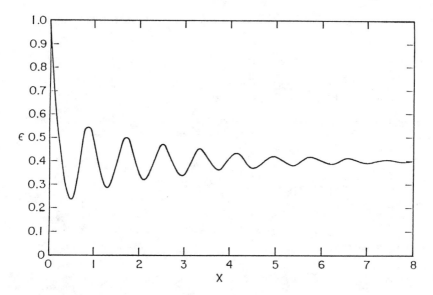

Figure 27. Voidage variations near the wall of a cylindrical column, randomly packed with spheres of uniform size. From Cohen and Metzner [107]. Legend: X-distance from the wall, non-dimensionalized with respect to the particle diameter, D_p.

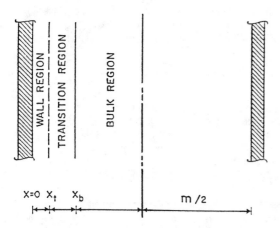

Figure 28. Schematic representation of the triregional model [107].

to a distance x_b, beyond which the local porosity is constant and is equal to the bulk porosity. Since the particle diameter is an inner-length scale in the bed, it is reasonable to take the wall region as one particle diameter in thickness [115–118]. The transition region is assumed to extend to 5 particle diameters away from the wall (Figure 27), beyond which voidage variations are less than 5 percent. Thus, for beds with a particle to column-diameter ratio of less than about 10, only the wall and transition regions exist.

The mass flux G in each of the three regions of the triregional model are described as follows [107]:

Bulk Region

$$G_b = \rho \left[\frac{4n}{3n+1}\right]\left[\frac{\Delta P}{2KL}\right]^{1/n}\left[\frac{D_p\epsilon_b}{3(1-\epsilon_b)}\right]^{(n+1)/n}\frac{\epsilon_b}{2B_b(n)} \qquad x > x_b \qquad (50)$$

where the subscript b designates the bulk region, ρ is the fluid density, and ϵ_b and $B_b(n)$ are the values of the porosity and the parameter $B(n)$ (Equation 48b) in the bulk region.

Transition Region

$$G_t = \rho \left[\frac{4n}{3n+1}\right]\left[\frac{\Delta P}{2KL}\right]^{1/n}\left[\frac{D_p}{3}\right]^{(n+1)/n}\left[\frac{1}{A_t}\right]\oint_{A_t}\left[\left(\frac{\epsilon}{(1-\epsilon)}\right)\frac{\epsilon}{2B_t(n)}\right]dA, \qquad x_t < x < x_b \qquad (51)$$

where A_t is the cross-sectional area of the transition region and $B_t(n)$ is the value of the parameter $B(n)$ in the transition region.

Wall Region

$$G_w = \rho \left[\frac{4n}{3n+1}\right]\left[\frac{\Delta P}{2KL}\right]^{1/n}\left[\frac{2R_H}{2B_w(n)}\right]^{(n+1)/n}, \qquad x < x_t \qquad (52)$$

where $\qquad R_H = \dfrac{D_p(m-x_t)x_t\epsilon_{w_{av}}}{m+6x_t(m-x_t)(1-\epsilon_{w_{av}})} \qquad (53)$

in which $m = D_c/D_p$ (D_c is the column diameter), and $\epsilon_{w_{av}}$ and $B_w(n)$ are the average values of the porosity and the $B(n)$ parameter in the wall region.

Finally, the mass flux through the packed column, G_T, can be determined from:

$$G_T = \frac{G_bA_b + G_tA_t + G_wA_w}{A_c} \qquad (54)$$

where A_b, A_t, and A_w are the cross-sectional areas of the bulk, transition, and wall regions, respectively, and A_c is the cross-sectional area of the entire column. The average mass flux based on the single region model, G_{as}, is determined based on the average bed porosity (ϵ_{av}):

$$G_{as} = \rho \left[\frac{4n}{3n+1}\right]\left[\frac{\Delta P}{2KL}\right]^{1/n}\left[\frac{D_p\epsilon_{av}}{3(1-\epsilon_{av})}\right]^{(n+1)/n}\frac{\epsilon_{av}}{2B_{av}(n)} \qquad (55)$$

where the subscript av refers to the area average parameter for the entire column.

A comparison is made of the mass flux G_T, predicted by the triregional model, with the mass flux G_{as}, predicted by the single region model (based on the average bed porosity). The comparison is made at the same pressure drop for different power law indices. For Newtonian fluids (n = 1), the flow rate predicted by the triregional model is lower than that predicted by the single region model. For example, at a D_c/D_p ratio of 12, the error in using the single region model is about 10%, and it increases dramatically as the bed to particle-diameter ratio decreases further. Similar behavior is illustrated for n < 1. Thus, if the single region model is used for small D_c/D_p ratios, the predicted flow rate will be overestimated. Therefore, the overprediction of the single region model is not due to viscoelastic effects or other causes of permeability reduction. Shear thinning fluids exhibit a greater tendency to channel through the most permeable parts of the packed bed

[77]. For sufficiently low values of the power law index, n, the average mass flux may be under-estimated by the single region model. This underprediction of the overall mass flux, based on the single region model, may lead to the erroneous conclusion that slip effects are present. It is merely due to an improper description of the porosity variations in the packed bed.

The most important conclusion from the triregional model is that only data for beds with D_c/D_p ratios of about 30 or higher should be utilized in separating elastic and apparent slip effects.

THEORIES OF APPARENT SLIP FLOW

Overview

In practically all systems involving flowing polymer solutions, the polymer molecules are in "contact" with a solid surface. The dynamics of polymer molecules near the solid surface may be affected by either steric, repulsive, or attractive surface-polymer interactions [5, 6–9]. Attractive surface-molecule forces may result in polymer adsorption, which influences the flow behavior of both the solvent and free molecules in solution in the proximity of the wall. It is now well known that polymer adsorption leads to flow retardation [72, 81]. In contrast, steric effects, and repulsive forces such as those due to hard-core or electrostatic repulsion, may lead to the formation of a thin boundary wall layer which is depleted of polymer molecules [7, 9, 88, 89, 119]. Therefore, in small channels, the effective viscosity is a strong function of the channel dimensions.

Steric effects, or electrostatic or hard-core repulsion of macromolecules from the wall region may be partially responsible for the apparent slip phenomenon in small flow channels, as has been demonstrated by various analyses, based on the elastic dumbbell model [5–7]. The polymer concentration is predicted to decrease as the wall is approached and thus the fluid viscosity also decreases. The effective viscosity for dilute polymer solutions is predicted to decrease with decreasing channel dimensions (i.e., channel gap, or radius for tube flow).

Steric exclusion and hard-core repulsion may lead, at most, to a solvent slip layer of a thickness that is probably no larger than the hydrodynamic diameter of the polymer molecules in solutions [8, 13, 119, 120]. Brunn [7] and Brunn and Grisafi [8] have conclusively shown, based on the linear elastic-dumbbell model, that such wall effects, in large channels, may lead to a boundary layer region that is about $1.663R_o$, in which R_o is the equilibrium extension of the macromolecule. Conservative estimates of the slip-layer thickness, in large flow channels (parallel walls), gravity-driven thick film flows, and large tubes ($d/R_o > 100$, in which d is the channel dimension, tube radius, or film thickness) for various non-dilute polymer solutions (Table 2) reveal slip layer thicknesses that are as much as two orders of magnitude larger than the macromolecular size. Thus, wall exclusion effects cannot account for the abundant data of large slip effects observed for non-dilute polymer solutions flowing in wide flow channels (i.e., $d/R_o \gg 1$).

The presence of a wall also reduces the number of possible configurations that a molecule may assume in the vicinity of the wall (i.e., steric effects). Molecules near the wall align themselves more strongly with the flow than molecules away from the wall, and thus transport less flow-wise momentum across the flow than would otherwise be the case [9]. Also, since molecules are of finite size, their concentration (located at their center of gravity) drops to zero at the wall.

An alternative explanation for apparent slip is linked to the existence of deformation gradients in wall-bounded shear flows. These deformation gradients may result in the migration of polymer molecules away from the wall, where the stresses are generally higher than in the bulk of the flow. Several investigators [4, 77, 121, 122] have argued that macromolecules will migrate away from the region where they are highly extended (high stress regions) and therefore are at a lower entropy level than those molecules located in an adjacent lower shearing stress region at a higher entropy level. Several investigators have demonstrated that the theory of deformation-induced diffusion explains the existence of thick slip layers [119, 120]. Unfortunately, the phenomenological approach does not provide a mechanistic description of macromolecular migration.

Available experimental data and theoretical analyses both suggest that there are two regimes of apparent slip for the flow of polymer solutions. The first, which is due to direct polymer-wall interactions, is observable only in small flow channels ($d/R_o < 100$). This regime has been demonstrated

Table 2
Lower Limit Estimate of the Thickness of Apparent Slip Layers for
Non-Dilute Polymer Solutions (d/R$_o$ ≥ 400)

Polymer Solution	$\delta/\langle r^2 \rangle^{1/2}$	τ_w, dynes/cm^2	Reference
0.25% Separan AP-30	3.5–5.4	110–320	Cohen and Metzner [10]
0.47% Separan AP-30	2.1–8.2	100–450	
1% Separan AP-30	0.85–1.14	250–450	
0.69% CMC-7F	0.69–2.48	250–900	
3.15% PS-decalin (MW = 1.8 × 10^6)	0.56–0.80	450–750	
4% PS-toluene (MW = 1.8 × 10^6)	0.41–0.8	300–800	
1% PS-toluene (MW = 2 × 10^7)	2.01–2.25	100–450	
0.7% Separan-MG 700	9.9–17.8	130–168	Carreau et al. [50]
0.6% Separan-MG 700	24–41	87–140	
0.5% Separan-MG 700	59–73	75–110	
1% CMC-7H	4.1–8.2	70–145	
0.75% CMC-7H	80–82	50–115	
0.5% CMc-7H	122–144	36–90	
2% CMC	14–17	17–65	Astarita et al. [34]

* Separan—polyacrylamide made b Dow Chemicals
CMC—carboxymethylcellulose made by Hercules

experimentally with dilute polymer solutions flowing through nucleopore filters and through packed beds [5, 11, 123] as well as in channel flow [88, 89]. Although available theories are strickly valid for dilute polymer solutions, Aubert and Tirrell [5], through scaling arguments, have extended the range of applicability of their predictions to the semi-dilute regime. The second regime of apparent slip is linked to the generation of thick slip layers due to deformation-induced migration of macromolecules. To date, however, these apparent slip layers have not been directly observed, and hence a mystery still surrounds their nature.

In this section different theoretical approaches of portraying apparent slip are discussed. First we consider the limiting case of diffusion from a planar layer. Secondly, an analysis based on thermodynamic "equilibrium" between the bulk and the slip layer is discussed. Thirdly, a theory of apparent slip flow based on a flow-induced migration model is presented. Finally, the theoretical predictions of apparent slip effects, based on elastic-dumbbell models, in narrow flow channels are reviewed.

Variation of the Slip Velocity with Shear Stress

A simple estimate of the likely magnitude of apparent slip effects can be obtained by assuming macromolecules to diffuse through a very thin but planar layer near the wall of the flow channel [4]. The time that is required for the molecules to diffuse out of the thin wall layer can be approximated by:

$$t = \delta^2/D_o \qquad (56)$$

in which D_o is the polymer diffusion coefficient, and δ is the slip layer thickness. Since the residence time for molecules in the slip layer can be approximated by $t = L/V_s$, in which L is the length of the flow channel, this gives:

$$\delta = D_o L/V_s \tag{57}$$

Assuming that the viscosity of the slip layer, μ_s, is much lower than in the bulk viscosity, μ_b, and that the slip layer is very thin ($\delta \ll d$), then the shear stress at the wall can be approximated by [10]:

$$\tau_w = \mu_s V_s/\delta \tag{58}$$

The effective wall slip velocity and the slip layer thickness can then be determined by combining Equations 56–58:

$$V_s = (\tau_w/\mu_s)^{2/3}(D_o L)^{1/3} \tag{59a}$$

$$\delta = [D_o L \mu_s/\tau_w]^{1/3} \tag{59b}$$

If the viscosity of the slip layer and the diffusivity are assumed to be constant (this is consistent with the assumption of a solvent slip layer) then Equation 59a indicates that the slip velocity increases with the shear stress to the 2/3 power, and it also increases with increasing length of the flow path. Indeed, a 2/3 power dependence of V_s on τ_w is revealed by the data of Astarita et al. [34] as indicated in Figure 20. The recent data of Cohen and Metzner [10], however, indicate that the exponent of τ_w varies from about one to two.

A different dependence of the slip velocity on wall shear stress, for tube flow, is obtained from the thermodynamic approach of Vinogradov et al. [22]. In this approach one assumes that molecules (or dispersed-phase particles) in the slip layer are in "local equilibrium" with the macromolecules in the bulk of the flow. Additionally, this approach allows for a discontinuity in the velocity gradient at the edge of the slip layer. While this may be objectionable on physical and mathematical grounds, it does allow a rough estimation of the dependence of the apparent slip velocity and the thickness of the slip layer on shear stress and tube diameter. In this two region model, one assumes that the viscosity can be described by the Eyring model [124, 125], which relates the viscosity of the fluid to the free activation energy for viscous flow. Accordingly:

$$\eta_b = A_b \exp(\Delta G_b/RT) \tag{60a}$$

$$\eta_s = A_s \exp(\Delta G_s/RT) \tag{60b}$$

where   subscripts s and b = slip layer and bulk regions, respectively
ΔG = free activation energy for viscous flow
η = fluid viscosity
R = the gas constant
T = absolute temperature

If the two regions are considered to be in "equilibrium", then the following equality must hold:

$$\frac{\Delta G_b}{\rho_b v_b} + \frac{\tau_w \dot{\gamma}_s}{\rho_b m_s} = \frac{\Delta G_s}{\rho_s v_s} + \frac{\tau_w \dot{\gamma}_w}{\rho_s m_s} \tag{61}$$

where the first and second terms on the right- and left-hand sides of the equation represent the rate of chemical potential transport and rate of viscous energy dissipation per unit mass within the wall slip layer. The molar volume and density are designated by v and q, respectively, and $\dot{\gamma}_w$, $\dot{\gamma}_s$ are the shear rates at the wall and at the edge of the slip layer, respectively. Finally, m_s is the mass flow rate in the slip layer. This parameter can also be viewed as the inverse of the residence time during which a unit weight of the wall layer will be in equilibrium with the bulk, at the interface between the two regions. By approximating the velocity profile within the slip layer to be linear, and using the following approximate relationship [10]:

$$V_s \approx \tau_w \delta \left[\frac{1}{\eta_s} - \frac{1}{\eta_b} \right] \tag{62}$$

and subsequently substituting and rearranging Equation 61, the following expression for V_s is obtained:

$$V_s = \frac{a(\tau_w)\tau_w^{3/2}}{R^{1/2}} \tag{63}$$

where $a(\tau_w) = \dfrac{[v_b/\pi\rho_s]^{1/2}[1 - \eta_s/\eta_b]}{\eta_s(\Delta G_b - v_b \, \Delta G_s/v_s)^{1/2}}$

in which η_s and η_b refer to the viscosities of the slip and bulk regions, respectively. Equation 63 predicts that the slip velocity varies with the 3/2 power of the wall shear stress, provided that η_s is independent of the wall shear stress. The recent study of Jiang et al. [67] with polymer gels demonstrates that, in capillary tubes, $V_s \propto \tau_w^{3/2}$, consistent with the above prediction. The study of Cohen and Metzner [10] with polymer solutions indicates a power law exponent in the range of one to two. The dependence of the slip velocity on $R^{1/2}$ (Equation 63) has only been observed for the flow of greases [22–23]. Most experimental data with polymer solutions indicate that V_s is independent of the tube diameter. Experimental data for non-dilute solutions in small channels are lacking, thus it is not possible to conclude whether Equation 63 has a range of applicability for polymer solutions.

Deformation-Induced Migration Theory of Apparent Slip

The postulate that apparent slip flow in heterogeneous stress fields is a consequence of flow-induced migration of macromolecules has emerged out of the conviction that the diffusion of macromolecules is governed by a generalized chemical potential gradient [4, 119]. Accordingly, in heterogeneous stress fields, spatial entropy variations induce concentration changes as the system tends toward equilibration of the free energy gradients implied by deformation-induced entropy gradients [4, 122, 126]. In capillary tube flow, for example, macromolecules will migrate away from the wall region, where chains are highly extended and hence are at a lower entropy level than those located away from the wall, where shearing stresses are lower. This diffusion phenomenon leads to depletion of macromolecules in the wall region and consequently to the formation of a low viscosity fluid layer near the tube wall [4, 7, 48, 72, 119, 121, 127]. Theoretical studies of flow-induced migration [119, 120] have shown that apparent slip effects are due to the development of a thin concentration boundary layer near the tube wall. The predicted concentration changes are yet to be detected experimentally.

A theoretical justification for the thermodynamic theory of deformation-induced migration of macromolecules was provided by Cohen and Metzner [128]. These authors have shown that the existence of a diffusion flux due to deformation gradients can be deduced from a thermomechanical theory of mixtures. A similar conclusion based on an internal variable thermodynamic theory was reached by Drouot [129] and Drouot and Maugin [130].

Sekhon et al. [104], Jhon [131], Brunn [87, 132], and Brunn and Chi [133] provided theoretical analyses of the migration of flexible bead-spring molecules in heterogeneous flows. It was shown conclusively, from the elastic dumbbell model, that in heterogeneous flows, the inclusion of a finite bead volume and hydrodynamic interactions result in the prediction of macromolecular migration across stream lines even in Poiseuille flow. While the conclusion of the above studies is in agreement with the thermodynamic approach, they fell short of providing a quantitative evaluation of apparent slip. Brunn [87] concluded that the time scale for cross-streamline migration is very long, and hence direct observations of concentration changes in either tube or channel flow may not be feasible.

Apparent Slip Due to Flow-Induced Diffusion of Macromolecules

The prediction of apparent slip based on the theory of flow-induced diffusion consists of coupling the equation for polymer migration with the equation of motion. The flow-induced migration of macromolecules can be described using the constitutive diffusion theory as described by Cohen and Metzner [128]. Subject to the slow flow approximation, and in the absence of acceleration effects and external forces, the diffusion flux for a polymer solute $J^{(2)}$ in an isothermal polymer-solvent system is given by [128]:

$$J^{(2)} = -D_{12}[\Phi \, \nabla C + C \, \nabla f] \tag{64}$$

where C is the polymer concentration and D_{12} is a phenomenological diffusion coefficient. The parameter Φ is a thermodynamic parameter defined as:

$$\Phi = \frac{\partial}{\partial \ln C}\left(\frac{\Delta \mu_2^F}{R_c T}\right) \tag{65a}$$

where   T = temperature
R_c = gas constant
f = the entropic function, given by:

$$f = \Delta \mu_2^D / R_c T \tag{65b}$$

where $\Delta \mu_2^F$ is part of the chemical potential change of the polymer in solution, which is a unique function of concentration. This quantity can, for example, be approximated by the Flory-Huggins expression [134]. The term $\Delta \mu_2^D$ represents the entropic contribution of deformation and orientation to the chemical potential change. The entropic function f in laminar shear flow can be approximated based on a dumbbell model for the polymer molecules with a linear spring constant [134, 135]:

$$f = (\theta \dot{\gamma})^2 - \frac{1}{2}\ln[1 + 2(\theta \dot{\gamma})^2] \tag{66}$$

where θ is the molecular relaxation time of the polymer solution and $\dot{\gamma}$ is the local shear rate. An alternative expression, which is also based on a dumbbell model is [136]:

$$f = \text{tr}(\sigma)/CR_c T \tag{67}$$

where $\text{tr}(\sigma)$ is the trace of the stress tensor.

The diffusion equation for steady laminar shear flow can be obtained by substituting the diffusive flux expression (Equation 64) into the standard component continuity equation [111]:

$$\frac{\partial C}{\partial t} + \frac{V_i \, \partial C}{\partial x_i} = -\frac{\partial J_i^{(2)}}{\partial x_i} \tag{68}$$

where   V = fluid velocity
$J_i^{(2)}$ = polymer diffusive flux
t = time variable
x = spatial coordinate

The solution of the diffusion equation requires that the velocity profile be specified as is indicated explicitly in Equation 68 and implicitly by Equation 66. Such an approach, however, requires knowledge of the concentration dependence of the viscosity, normal stresses (or relaxation time), and the diffusion coefficient. Even if such data is available, the complex flow field in the channel

entry makes the computations extremely difficult. Alternatively, two simplified approaches of estimating the magnitude of apparent slip effects are possible. The first level of approximation is to
solve the concentration profile using an assumed velocity profile and subsequently estimate the
apparent slip velocity assuming that the slip layer develops very slowly. The second approach is
to determine the upper bound on the apparent wall slip velocity by solving the equations at full
development. As an illustration, the analysis that follows is for apparent slip in cylindrical tube
flow.

An approximate apparent slip model. An approximate analysis of apparent slip flow in a tube
based on the previously-mentioned flow-induced diffusion model consists of solving the diffusion
equation, assuming (as a first order approximation) that the velocity field can be (Equation 68)
approximated by a parabolic velocity profile (see Figure 1):

$$\frac{V_z}{\langle V \rangle_z} = 2\left[1 - \left(\frac{r}{R}\right)^2\right] \tag{69}$$

where V_z and $\langle V_z \rangle$ are the local and average velocities in the tube. Subject to the assumption of
a constant diffusion coefficient and negligible radial component of the velocity field, the first order
solution of the concentration profile is obtained in the form [119]:

$$\frac{C}{C_o} = C\left[\frac{r}{R}, N_{ws}, Z^* = \frac{z}{DN_{pec}}\right] \tag{70}$$

where N_{ws} is the Weissenberg number, defined based on the "no-slip" condition:

$$N_{ws} = \theta_{ns}\dot{\gamma}_{ns} \tag{71}$$

where $\dot{\gamma}_{ns}$ = wall shear rate
θ_{ns} = relaxation time corrected for slip effects
(i.e., in the absence of macromolecular migration)
C_o = initial concentration at the tube entry
N_{pec} = the Peclet number defined as:

$$N_{pec} = R\langle V_z \rangle / D_o \tag{72}$$

where D_o is the diffusion coefficient defined at the initial concentration, C_o. In view of the expected
slow development of the concentration profiles, the momentum equation can be simplified to:

$$-\frac{dV_z}{dr} = \frac{\tau_w}{\eta}\left(\frac{r}{R}\right) \tag{73}$$

Equation 73 is assumed to hold at any given axial position (excluding the entry region) with the
viscosity η given by:

$$\eta = \eta(\dot{\gamma}, C) \tag{74}$$

where C is the local concentration as determined from the solution of the diffusion equation. The
contribution of slip to the total flow rate can then be approximated from:

$$\frac{V_s}{\langle V_z \rangle} = 1 - \frac{8\langle V_z \rangle_{ns}/D}{8\langle V_z \rangle/D} = 1 - \frac{\dot{\gamma}_{ns}}{\dot{\gamma}_a} \tag{75}$$

where $\dot{\gamma}_{ns}$, and $\dot{\gamma}_a$ (actual apparent Newtonian shear rate) are determined from the following integral equation (see Equation 4):

$$\dot{\gamma} = \frac{4}{\tau_w^3} \int_0^{\tau_w} \tau^2 f(\tau)\, d\tau \tag{76}$$

where the function $f(\tau)$ is a function of concentration and must be determined from separate visco-metric measurements under slip-free conditions, coupled with the solution for the concentration profile (Equation 70); and $\dot{\gamma}_{ns}$ is determined from Equation 76 with a uniform concentration equal to the inlet concentration.

Typical results for the radial concentration profiles, based on the previous analysis, are shown in Figure 29 [119]. The concentration near the wall decreases downstream from the tube entry, while the concentration in the core region remains virtually unchanged for a considerable distance. Eventually, the rise in the core concentration, above the inlet concentration into the tube, becomes observable. Note that a maximum in the concentration profiles occurs prior to the establishment of a fully developed profile. The important feature of the migration phenomenon, as depicted in Figure 30, is the rapid depletion of polymer molecules from the wall region. The rapid decrease in the wall concentration even for short distances suggests that the apparent slip phenomenon can be detected, as observed experimentally, long before the concentration profiles become fully developed. Figure 31 illustrates the slip velocity predictions of the above approach for a 1% polyacrylamide solution. The predictions are compared with the experimental data of Cohen and Metzner [10] for tubes of $L/D = 2,000$, and estimated diffusion coefficient values of $D_o = 4 \times 10^{-8}$ cm²/s and $D_o = 1 \times 10^{-8}$ cm²/s (Curves 1 and 2, respectively). Curve 2 also corresponds to a tube of

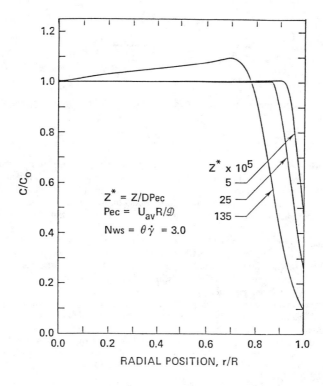

Figure 29. Radial polymer concentration profiles for $N_{ws} = 3$ [119].

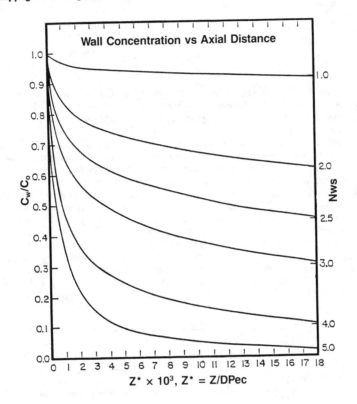

Figure 30. Axial variations of the wall concentration at different values of the Weissenberg number [119].

$L/D = 500$ with a diffusion coefficient of $D_o = 4 \times 10^{-8}$ cm^2/s. The predictions indicate that apparent slip is more pronounced for longer tubes and for higher diffusion coefficients. The results also suggest that the flow-induced migration mechanism for apparent slip flow does portray the main quantitative features of apparent slip. Future model improvements and accurate viscometric and diffusivity data will be necessary before precise quantitative predictions are possible.

Upper-bound analysis of apparent slip. This type of analysis can be carried out by calculating the slip velocity at full development. Although the theoretical calculations of the previous section demonstrate that full development is unlikely to be achieved, but for extremely long tubes, the upper-bound analysis can provide useful insight regarding the likely magnitude and variations of the slip velocity with various parameters.

The concentration and velocity profiles at full development can be obtained by solving the momentum and diffusion equations simultaneously. The velocity profile at full development is represented by Equation 73, in which the viscosity is given by Equation 74 where $\dot{\gamma} = |dV_z/dr|$ and $C = C(r)$. The diffusion equation (Equation 68) is simplified by requiring that at full development $J^{(2)} = 0$. Thus, by combining Equations 74 and 68, the following differential equation is obtained:

$$\frac{dC}{dr} = \frac{C(\partial f/\partial c)(d\dot{\gamma}/dr)}{\Phi + C(\partial f/\partial C)} \qquad (77)$$

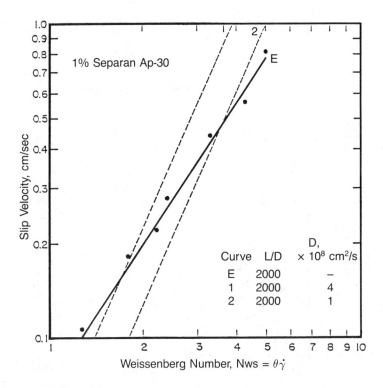

Figure 31. Comparison of predicted and experimental effective slip velocities for a 1% poly-acrylamide solution. Curve E is a best fit through the experimental data points [119].

where it is understood that $f = f(\dot{\gamma}, C)$. The boundary condition is obtained by requiring mass conservation;

$$\int_0^1 \bar{V}_z \bar{C} \bar{r} \, d\bar{r} = \frac{1}{2}$$ (78)

where $\quad \bar{C} = C/C_o$
$\quad\quad\quad \bar{r} = r/R$
$\quad\quad\quad \bar{V}_z = V_z/\langle V_z \rangle$
$\quad\quad\quad C_o = $ the initial concentration at the tube entry

The solution of Equations 73 and 77 requires specification of a rheological model for the shear viscosity, in which the concentration dependence of the model parameters is known. Additionally, the thermodynamic factor Φ, which reflects the dependence of the diffusion coefficient on concentration, is required. An example of the results of the above approach is given in Figure 32 [120] for the flow of polyacrylamide solution through capillary tubes with the diffusion coefficient approximated by $D/D_o = 1 + 2.5C$ (C being the polymer concentration in weight percent [120]). As expected, the analysis provides an upper-bound estimate of the maximum likely magnitude of the contribution of slip flow to the total flow rate. The precise theoretical value of the effective wall slip velocity lies somewhere between the predictions for the fully developed apparent slip conditions and the predictions for the developing slip region.

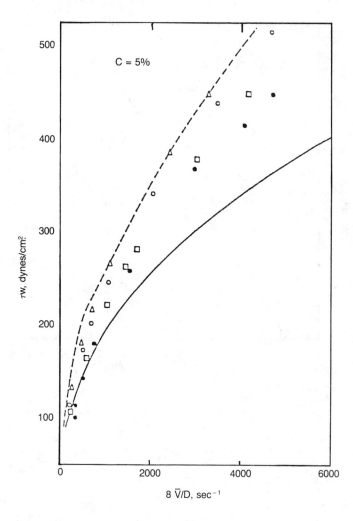

Figure 32. Comparison between experimental and predicted flow curves for 1% polyacrylamide (Separan AP30) solution. Prediction of Equations 73–74, 77. From Dutta and Mashelkar [15] (Data of Cohen and Metzner [10]). Legend: ($\triangle$) D = 0.1097 cm, L/D = 997.4; ($\bigcirc$) D = 0.0626 cm, L/D = 1909; (∇) — D = 0.0358 cm, L/D = 1916; ($\square$) D = 0.026 cm, L/D = 1996; ($\bullet$) D = 0.0191 cm, L/D = 1963.

Slip Effects Due to Wall-Macromolecular Interactions

Apparent slip is known to occur for polymer solutions flowing through narrow channels (generally with channel dimension/molecular size < 100 [11]). The presence of confining walls restricts the number of configurations available to macromolecules, thereby reducing the contributions that they make to the fluid stress. A zone of concentration depletion and dynamic restriction exists near the wall. This zone ranges to about one hydrodynamic diameter for the macromolecules so that it becomes increasingly important for narrow channels [5, 7].

Several models that describe the flow of polymer solutions through narrow channels have been advanced in recent years [5–7, 9]. These models are based on the idealization of the macromolecule as an elastic dumbbell. Approximate analytical and numerical solutions have been obtained for simple shear flow of dilute suspension of dumbbell molecules flowing between infinite parallel plates. A brief review of these models is given in the following sections.

Theory of Apparent Slip Effects in Narrow Channels

The modeling approach for slip flow of dilute polymer solution in narrow channels follows the description of a macromolecule by the elastic dumbbell model [137], with two identical beads as illustrated schematically in Figure 33. The macromolecule is idealized as an "elastic dumbbell" consisting of two spherical "beads," joined by a non-bendable "spring." The location of the centers of the two beads are given by position vectors r_1 and r_2 with respect to the origin of a fixed coordinate system. The configuration vector $R = r_2 - r_1$ specifies the instantaneous distance between the bead centers and the angular orientation of the dumbbell in space. The center of mass is located at $R_c = (r_1 + r_2)/2$. For steady flows, subject to the neglect of acceleration terms, a force balance on each bead of the dumbbell yields [8]:

$$0 = F_i^{(h)} + F_i^{(B)} + F_i^{(c)} + F_i^{(w)} \tag{79}$$

where $F_i^{(h)}$ is the hydrodynamic (drag) force given by:

$$F_i^{(h)} = -\zeta_i(\dot{r}_i - v_i) \tag{80}$$

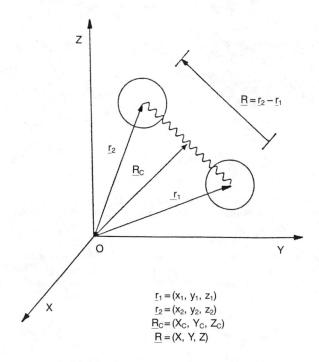

$$
\begin{aligned}
r_1 &= (x_1,\ y_1,\ z_1) \\
r_2 &= (x_2,\ y_2,\ z_2) \\
R_c &= (X_C,\ Y_C,\ Z_C) \\
R &= (X,\ Y,\ Z)
\end{aligned}
$$

Figure 33. The linear elastic dumbbell model.

where v_i is the fluid velocity at the location of the ith bead and ξ_i is the stokes friction coefficient for bead i. The Brownian motion force $F_i^{(B)}$ is expressed by:

$$F_i^{(B)} = -kT \frac{\partial \ln \Psi}{\partial r_i} \qquad (81)$$

where $\Psi(r_1, r_2)$ is the probability density of the dumbbell configurations such that $\Psi(r_1, r_2) \, dr_1 \, dr_2$ is the number of dumbbells that will be found with bead 1 at r_1 to $r_1 + dr_1$ and bead 2 at r_2 to $r_2 + dr_2$. The assumption of identical beads imposes the following symmetry condition:

$$\Psi(r_1, r_2) = \Psi(r_2, r_1) \qquad (82)$$

The intramolecular force $F_i^{(c)}$ is the force on bead i due to tension in the connector. This force can be expressed by:

$$F_i^{(c)} = -\frac{\partial \varphi_i^{(c)}}{\partial r_i} \qquad (83)$$

where $\varphi_i^{(c)}$ is the connector potential which is a function of the configuration vector R. For example, for a linear dumbbell $\varphi_i^{(c)} = \frac{1}{2}HR^2$, in which H is the spring constant. Various non-linear spring models have been proposed [137], e.g., the Warner model in which $\varphi_i^{(c)} = \frac{1}{2}HR_o^2 \ln[1 - (R/R_o)^2]$, where R_o is the maximum possible spring extension. Finally, due to wall interactions, there is a wall force on the beads, $F_i^{(w)}$, given by:

$$F_i^{(w)} = -\frac{\partial E}{\partial r_i} \qquad (84)$$

where E is the wall potential. All of the current models assume that the wall potential is purely repulsive (i.e., hard-core potential), such that:

$$E_i = \begin{cases} 0 & \text{(away from the wall)} \\ \infty & \text{(otherwise)} \end{cases} \qquad (85)$$

The steady-state continuity equation (or conservation equation) for the polymer molecules must be satisfied:

$$0 = \sum_{i=1}^{2} \frac{\partial J_i}{\partial r_i} \qquad (86)$$

where J_i is the "bead flux" defined by $J_i = \dot{r}_i \Psi$, in which $\dot{r}_i$ is the velocity of bead i.

At equilibrium (no-flow condition), the following boundary condition for Ψ can be employed [5, 6]:

$$\Psi \to 0 \quad \text{as} \quad R^2 \to \infty \qquad (87)$$

The more general wall boundary condition, however, is the impenetrability condition for a purely repulsive wall, which states that the bead flux has no normal component at the wall. For example, for steady flow between infinite parallel plates (Figure 34), the zero flux boundary condition at the wall becomes:

$$\frac{\partial \Psi}{\partial z_i} + \Psi \frac{\partial \varphi}{\partial z_i} = 0 \qquad \text{at } z_i = \pm d \qquad (88)$$

where 2d is the separation distance between the plates, and z_i is the vertical coordinate at the location of the center of bead i. Once the distribution function is obtained (by solving Equations

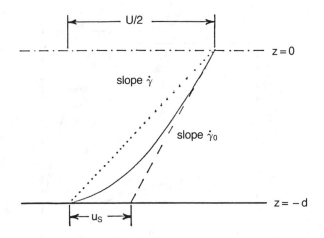

Figure 34. Velocity profile in simple shear (solid line) and the slip velocity u_s. Legend: U-velocity of top plate.

79–88), the polymer concentration n (for identical beads) is determined from [137]:

$$n(r) = \int d^3r_2 \Psi(r_1, r_2) \tag{89}$$

The set of Equations 79–85 can be solved once the velocity profile is known. This requires a numerical solution of the simultaneous solution of the flow field and the distribution function [138, 139]. Approximate solutions can be obtained if one assumes, in solving for Ψ, that the velocity field can be approximated by the Newtonian velocity profile [5, 7].

The concentration profile. Under equilibrium conditions (no-flow) the configurational distribution can be shown to be:

$$\Psi = n_b \frac{H}{2\pi kT} e^{(-\varphi + E)/kT} \tag{90}$$

where n_b denotes the equilibrium polymer concentration that would prevail for an unbounded fluid (i.e., $d/R_o \to \infty$). For a linear elastic dumbbell, at the equilibrium condition, the polymer concentration in the channel becomes [5, 8]:

$$\frac{n}{n_b} = \frac{1}{2}\left\{ \text{erf}\left(\sqrt{\frac{3}{2}}\frac{d+z}{R_o}\right) + \text{erf}\left(\sqrt{\frac{3}{2}}\frac{d-z}{R_o}\right) \right\} \tag{91}$$

where R_o is the root-mean-square equilibrium extension of the dumbbell, $R_o = 3kT/H$. Figure 35 depicts the concentration profiles, which clearly demonstrate that the polymer concentration is non-uniform and that as $d/R_o \gg 1$, $n \to n_b$. For the case of $d/R_o > 50$, one finds that $n/n_b > 0.995$, i.e., the polymer concentration everywhere in the channel approaches the bulk concentration for the unbounded system.

In general, the concentration profile depends on the type of flow, e.g., simple linear shear flow, pressure-driven flow in a channel, etc. For these cases, the distribution function Ψ can be approximated by assuming that the shear field is unperturbed by the change in the concentration profile.

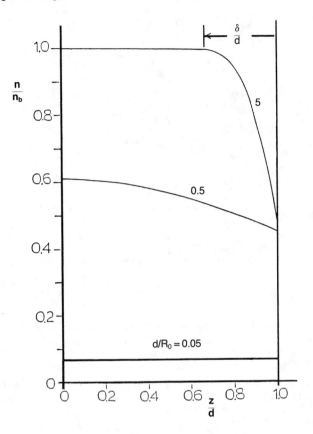

Figure 35. Concentration profiles between parallel plates at equilibrium. From Brunn and Grisafi [8].

Accordingly, the concentration profile can be represented by [7]:

$$n/n_b = (n/n_b)_{eq}/J_c \qquad (92)$$

where J_c is the normalization constant which depends on the type of flow, while $(n/n_b)_{eq}$ is the concentration profile at equilibrium. For simple shear flow (top plate moving with a constant velocity), $J_c = 1$. The constant J_c for pressure driven flow in a channel is given in Figure 36. As Figure 36 indicates, for $d/R_o > 10$, $J_c \to 0.99$, which suggests that for sufficiently large channels the concentration is uniform except very near the wall. For large channels, for which $d/R_o > 100$, the finiteness of the system can be neglected, at least insofar as the viscosity is concerned, since the effect of the wall is restricted to a boundary layer region of the order $\delta/R_o \approx 1.663$ [7].

The slip velocity. The shear stress, τ_{xz}, in the channel is the sum of the contributions of the solvent and the polymer to the total shear stress:

$$\tau_{xz} = \eta_s \frac{du}{dz} + \tau_{xz}^{(p)} \qquad (93)$$

where η_s is the solvent viscosity, and $\tau_{xz}^{(p)}$ is the polymer contribution to the total stress. For simple linear shear flow in a channel with an upper plate moving at a constant velocity U, the stress field

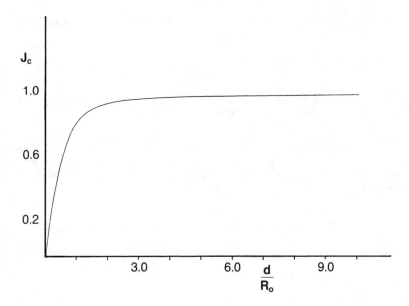

Figure 36. The constant of normalization J_c for plane channel flow. From Brunn [7].

is uniform (see Figure 35). Thus, the shear stress evaluated at the center of the channel can be expressed by:

$$\tau_{xz} = \eta_s \dot{\gamma}(0) + \tau_{xz}^{(p)}(0) = \eta_{eff} \dot{\gamma}_\infty \tag{94}$$

where $\dot{\gamma}(0)$ and $\tau_{xz}^{(p)}(0)$ are the shear rate and polymer contribution to the shear stress at the center of the channel, $\dot{c}_\infty = (U/2d)$ is the shear rate for the case of $d/R_o \to \infty$, and η_{eff} is the effective viscosity in the channel, defined by:

$$\eta_{eff} = \eta_s + \eta^{(p)}(0) \tag{95}$$

where $\eta^{(p)}(0)$ is the contribution of the polymer to the effective viscosity. The shear stress $\tau_{xz}^{(p)}(o)$ can be expressed, using Equations 94–95, as:

$$\tau_{xz}^{(p)}(0) = \eta^{(p)}(0)\dot{\gamma}(0) \tag{96}$$

Thus $$\frac{\eta_{eff}}{\eta(0)} = \frac{\dot{\gamma}(0)}{\dot{\gamma}(\infty)} \tag{97}$$

The ratio $\dot{\gamma}(0)/\dot{\gamma}(\infty)$ can be related to the effective slip velocity at the wall (see Figure 34), which is defined as:

$$u_s = d[\dot{\gamma}(\infty) - \dot{\gamma}(0)] \tag{98}$$

Consequently, the expression for u_s becomes, with the use of Equation 98:

$$\frac{u_s}{U} = \frac{1}{2}\left(1 - \frac{\eta_{eff}}{\eta(0)}\right) \tag{99}$$

For sufficiently large d/R_o ratios, $\eta(0)$ can be replaced by the effective viscosity $\eta(\infty)$ for an unbounded system. The effective viscosity η_{eff} can be obtained from [7]:

$$\frac{\eta_{\mathrm{eff}}}{\eta_s} = 1 + \frac{1}{\eta_s U} \int_{-d}^{d} \tau_{xz}^{(p)} \, dz \tag{100}$$

where $\tau_{xz}^{(p)}$ is obtained once the density distribution function for the dumbbell center of mass is known, given the contribution of the spring tension in the x direction crossing any z plane [5, 9, 137].

Figure 37 illustrates the dependence of the effective viscosity on the molecular size relative to the channel size, based on the perturbation solution of Aubert and Tirrell [5] about the equilibrium distribution function for the dumbbell configuration. As expected, the effective viscosity decreases with decreasing channel dimensions. At sufficiently large d/R_o values, the effective vis-

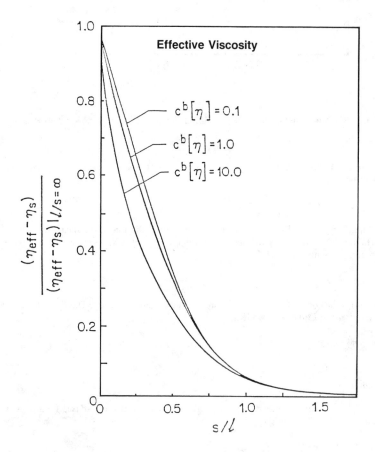

Figure 37. The effective viscosity in Couette flow between infinite parallel plates as a function of molecular to channel size ratio and concentration. $[\eta]$ and c^b are the intrinsic viscosity and the bulk concentration, respectively. From Aubert and Tirrell [5]. ℓ-half separation of the plates; s-radius of gyration.

cosity can be approximated by [6, 9]:

$$\frac{\eta_{\text{eff}}}{\eta(0)} = 1 - \frac{n\xi R_o}{\beta\eta_s}\left(\frac{R_o}{d}\right) \tag{101}$$

where the constant β equals 48 according to the analysis of Brunn [6] who used boundary conditions 88 and a purely repulsive wall. The analysis of Goh et al. [9] who also used the zero "bead flux" boundary condition at the wall, but neglected the wall potential force, results in the numerical constant of $12\sqrt{6\pi}$ for β. The effective slip velocity, according to Equation 99, can then be represented by:

$$\frac{u_s}{u} = \frac{n\xi R_o^2}{\beta\eta_s}\left(\frac{R_o}{2d}\right) \tag{102}$$

Equation 102 demonstrates that the slip velocity is inversely proportional to the channel thickness, 2d. For a linear dumbbell, u_s increases linearly with the shear rate, $\dot{\gamma}(\infty)$, while for the non-linear Warner dumbbell [137], u_s increases with less than a linear dependence on the shear rate [9]. A similar conclusion was recently reached by the more detailed numerical simulation of Petruccione and Biller [138] and Biller and Petruccione [139].

Direct comparison of the above theories with experimental observations can not be made at present, since slip measurements for simple linear shear flow of polymer solutions are not yet available. Nonetheless, Aubert and Tirrell [5] have compared their model for flow in a channel (in simple linear shear flow) with the experimental results of Chauveteau [11] for the flow of dilute Xanthan solutions through a series of Nucleopore filter membranes. This was accomplished by neglecting the wall curvature, in the solution for Ψ. Figure 38 illustrates the excellent agreement

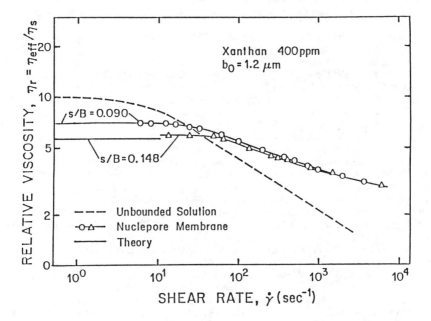

Figure 38. Viscosity data and model prediction for Xantham (400 ppm) in flow through a series of Nucleopore filter membranes. From Aubert and Tirrell [5]. s-radius of gyration; b_0-rms end-to-end distance of the dumbbell at equilibrium, B-pore radius.

between the model calculations of Aubert and Tirrell [5] for a purely repulsive wall, and the experimental results at the low shear rate region to which the model is restricted.

CONCLUSION

In closure, apparent slip effects are present in the flow of both dilute and non-dilute polymer solutions. In the case of dilute polymer solutions, apparent slip effects (in the absence of polymer adsorption effects) are observable when the ratio of the flow-channel-dimension/polymer-molecule-size decreases below about 100 (d/R_o ≪ 100). In the case of non-dilute solutions, apparent slip effects have been observed even for large channels for which d/R_o > 100. Apparent slip effects for the flow of polymer solutions can be detected and quantified using relatively simple flow measurement techniques. Future studies with various optical and spectroscopic techniques may provide a new way to detect and probe apparent slip layers. The theory of polymer solution flow in confined channels describes the occurrence of apparent slip for dilute polymer solutions in the limit of d/R_o ≪ 100. This theoretical approach cannot account for the large apparent slip effects observed for the flow of non-dilute polymer solutions in large channels for which d/R_o > 100. For this latter case the theory of flow-induced diffusion of macromolecules appears to provide a reasonable prediction of the apparent slip phenomenon. Unfortunately, the flow-induced diffusion theory is phenomenological theory and thus it falls short of providing a mechanistic description of apparent slip.

REFERENCES

1. Lau, H. C., and Schowalter, W. R., *J. Rheology*, 30(1):193 (1986).
2. Leonov, A. I., *Rheol. Acta*, 23:591 (1984).
3. Ramamurthy, A. V., *J. Rheology*, 30(2):337 (1986).
4. Metzner, A. B., Yoram Cohen, and Rangel-Nafaile, C., *J. Non-Newtonian Fluid Mech.*, 5:449 (1979).
5. Aubert, J. H., and Tirrell, M., *J. Chem. Phys.*, 77:553 (1982).
6. Brunn, P., *Rheol. Acta.* 15:23 (1976a).
7. Brunn, P. O., *J. Rheology*, 29(6):859 (1985a).
8. Brunn, P. O., and Grisafi, S., *Chem. Eng. Commun.*, 36:367–383 (1985b).
9. Goh, C. J., Atkinson, J. D., and Phan-Thien, N., *J. Chem. Phys.* 82(2):15 (1985).
10. Cohen, Y., and Metzner, A. B., *J. Rheology*, 29:67–102 (1985).
11. Chauveteau, G., *J. Rheology*, 26:111 (1982).
12. Dutta, A., and Mashelkar, R. A., *Rheol. Acta*, 21:52 (1982).
13. Dutta, A., and Mashelkar, R. A., *Rheol. Acta*, 22:455 (1983a).
14. Dutta, A., and Mashelkar, R. A., *AIChEJ.*, 29:519 (1983b).
15. Peev, G., and Nikolova, A., *J. Non-Newt. Fluid Mech.*, 8:319–326 (1981).
16. Mashelkar, R. A., and Dutta, A., *Chem. Eng. Sci.*, Vol. 37, No. 7, 969 (1982).
17. Ju, Y-H, and Chou, Y-S, *J. Chinese Inst. Chem. Engrs.*, 15:103–109 (1984).
18. Yih, Siu-Ming, and Hsu, Tien-Yu, *Chem. Eng. Commun.*, 34:65 (1985).
19. Green, H., Proc. Am. Soc. Testing Materials II, 20:451 (1920).
20. Trilisskii, K. K., Froishteter, G. B., Smorodinsky, E. L., and Grishchuk, V. I., *Kolloidnyi Zhurnal*, 35:1109 (1973).
21. Vinogradov, G. V., Froishteter, G. B., K. K. Trilisky, and E. L. Smorodinsky, *Rheol. Acta*, 14:209 (1975).
22. Vinogradov, G. V., Froishteter, G. B., Trilisky, K. K., and Smorodinsky, E. L., *Rheol. Acta.* 14:765 (1975).
23. Vinogradov, G. V., Froishteter, G. B., and Trilisky, K. K., *Rheol. Acta*, 17:156 (1978).
24. Scott-Blair, G. W., *J. Rheology*, 1:127 (1930); see also Schofield, R. K., and Scott-Blair, G. W., *J. Phys. Chem.*, 34:248 (1930).
25. Mooney, M., *J. Rheology* 2:210 (1931).
26. Vand, V., *J. Phys. Colloid Chem.*, 52:277 (1948).
27. Vand, V., *J. Phys. Colloid Chem.*, 52:300 (1948).

28. Jastrzebski, Z. B., *Ind. Eng. Chem. Fundam.*, 6:445 (1967).
30. Cox, R. G., and Mason, S. G., *Ann. Rev. Fluid Mech.*, 3:291 (1971).
31. Gorislavets, V. M., and Dunets, A. A., *Inzhenerno-Fizicheskii Zhurnal*, 29:273 (1975).
32. Eklund, Dan, *Tappi*, Vol. 62, No. 5:43 (1979).
33. Quemada, D., *Proc. VIIIth Int. Congress on Rheology*, G. Astarita, L. Nicolais, and G. Marrucci (Eds.), Naples, Italy, Plenum Press (1980).
34. Astarita, G., Marrucci, G., and Palumbo, G., *Ind. Eng. Chem. Fundamentals*, 3, 3 33 (1964).
35. Fahraeus, R., and Lindquist, T., *Am. J. Physiol.*, 12:287 (1931).
36. Bugliarello, G., Kapur, C., and Hsiao, G., Proc. Int. Cong. Rheol., 4:351 (1964).
38. Blackshear, P. L., Forstram, R. J., Dorman, F. D., and Voss, G. O., Fed. Proc., 30:1600 (1971).
39. Charm, S. E., and Krland, G. S., *Blood Flow and Microcirculation*, John Wiley and Sons, New York (1974).
40. Kokini, J. L., and Chou, T. K., "The Phenomenon of Slip in the Steady Shear Capillary Flow of Four Semi-Solid Foods," paper presented in the Winter Meeting of the Society of Rheology, January 18–21, 1987, Santa Monica, California.
41. Reiner, M. J., *J. Rheology*, 2:337 (1931).
42. Toms, B. A., *J. Colloid Sci.*, 4:511 (149).
43. Mineshita, Takeshi, Watanabe, Takehiko, and Ono, Sozaburo, *J. of Polymer Science*: Part C, 23:533 (1968).
44. Watanabe, Takehiko, Mineshita, Takeshi, and Ono, Sozaburo, *Bulletin of the Chemical Society of Japan*, 42:583 (1969).
45. Kozicki, W. C., Pasari, S. M., Rao, A. R. K., and Tiu, C., *Chem. Eng. Sci.*, 25:41 (1970).
46. Kalashnikov, V. N., and Vlasov, S. A., *Rheol. Acta*, 17:296 (1978).
47. Vlasov, S. A., and Kalashnikov, V. N., *Fluid Mech. Soviet Res.*, 12:104 (1973).
48. Cohen, Y., and Metzner, A. B., AIChE Symp. Series, No. 212, 78, 77 (1982a).
49. Therien; Coupal, B., and Corneille, J. L., *Can. J. Chem. Eng.*, 48:17 (1970).
50. Carreau, P. J., Bui, Q. H., and Leroux, P., *Rheol. Acta*, 18:606 (1979).
51. Cheng, D. C. H., *Ind. Eng. Chem. Fundam.*, 13:394 (1974).
52. Savins, J. G., *Ind. Eng. Chem.*, 61:18 (1969).
53. Kozicki, W. C., Hsu, C. J., and Tiu, C., *Chem. Eng. Sci.*, 22:487 (1967).
54. Cohen, Y., *Advances in Rheology*, Volume 2, p. 299, Mena, B., A. Garcia-Rejon, and C. Rangel-Nafaile (Eds.), Universidad National Autonoma De Mexico (1984).
55. Cohen, Y., and Cheng-Nian, C., *Chem. Eng. Comm.*, 28:73–84 (1984).
56. Morrison, S. R., and Harper, J. C., *Ind. and. Eng. Chem. Fund.*, 4:176 (1965).
57. Cheng, D. C., and Parker, B. R., *Proc. 7th Int. Congress Rheol.*, Klason, C., and J. Kubat (Eds.), pp. 518–519 (1976). Publisher: Swed. Soc. Rheol.
58. Wein, O., Mitschka, P., Tovchigrechko, V. V., Kovalevskaya, N. D., Yushkina, T. V., and Pokryvaylo, N. M., *Chem. Eng. Commun.*, 32:153–170 (1985).
59. Wales, J. L. S., *J. Polym. Sci. Symp.*, No. 50:469 (1975).
60. Angerer, G., and Wolff, D., *Rheol. Acta*, 15:57 (1976).
61. Menning, G., *Rheol. Acta*, 15:199 (1976).
62. Uhland, E., *Rheol. Acta*, 15:30 (1976).
63. Lin, Y. H., *J. Rheology*, 29(6):605 (1985).
64. Knappe, W., and Krumbock, E., *Rheol. Acta*, 25:296 (1986).
65. Williams, R. J. J., Civit, E. M., Cuadrado, T. R., Gutierrez, D. G., and Rojas, A. J., *Chem. Eng. Sci.* 33:1552 (1978).
66. Kraynik, A. M., and Schowalter, W. R., *J. Rheology*, 25:97 (1981).
67. Jiang, T. Q., Young, A. C., and Metzner, A. B., *Rheol. Acta*, 25:397 (1986).
68. Clark, P. E., "Stimulation Fluid Rheology-A New Approach," SPE paper 8300 (1979).
69. Cloud, J. E., and Clark, P. E., "Stimulation Fluid Rheology III," SPE paper 9332 (1980).
70. Pilehvari, Ali, and Clark, P. E., SPE, *J. of Pet. Technol.*, 1840 (1985).
71. Quibrahim, A., *Phys. Fluids*, 21:4 (1978).
72. Cohen, Y., and Metzner, A. B., *Macromolecules*, 15:1425 (1982b).
73. Barham, P. J., Hikmet, R. A. M., Narh, K. A., and Keller, A., *Colloid Polymer Sci.*, 264:515 (1986).

74. Hikmet, R. A. M., Narh, K. A., Barham, P. J., and Keller, A., *Prog. Colloid Polymer Sci.*, 71:32 (1985).
75. Narh, K. A., Barham, P. J., Hikmet, R. A. M., and Keller, A., *Colloid Polymer Sci.*, 264:507 (1986).
76. Shertzer, C. R., Ph.D. thesis, University of Delaware, Newark (1965).
77. Metzner, A. B., *Improved Oil Recovery by Surfactant and Polymer Flooding*, D. O. Shah and Schechter, R. S., (Eds.), Academic Press (1977).
78. Whillhite, G. P., and Dominguez, J. G., *Improved Oil Recovery by Surfactants and Polymer Flooding*, Shah, D. O., and Schechter, R. S., (Eds.), Academic Press (1977).
79. Wang, H. L., Duda, J. L., and Klaus, E. E., SPE Paper 8418, 54th Annual SPE Meeting, Las Vegas, 1977.
80. Dreher, K. D., and Gogarty, W. B., *J. Rheology*, 23:209 (1979).
81. Cohen, Y., and Christ, R. F., *SPE Reservoir Eng.*, p. 113, March 1986.
82. Maerker, J. M., *J. Petr. Techn.*, 25:1307 (1973).
83. Cheaveteau, G., and Kholer, N., SPE paper 9295, 55th Annual Technical Conference, Dallas, September (1980).
84. Marshall, R. J., and Metzner, A. B., *Ind. Eng. Chem. Fundam.*, 6:393 (1967).
85. Reuter, B., and Kratzer, M., "Microanalysis of the Velocity Profile in Blood Vessel Models," in Laser 79 Opto-Electronics, W. Waidelich, Ed., IPC Science and Technology Press, Munich, 209 (1979); see also Reuter, B., and Talukder, N., SPIE 236: (1980).
86. Müller-Mohnssen, H., Löbl, H.P., and Schauerte, W., *J. Rheology*, 31(4): 323–336 (1987).
87. Brunn, P. O., *Int. J. Multiphase Flow*, 9:187–202 (1983).
88. Ausserre, D., H. Hervet, and Rondelez, F., *Physical Rev. Letters*, 54: 1948 (1985).
89. Ausserre, D., Hervet, H., and Rondelez, F., *Macromolecules*, 19:85 (1986).
90. Wein, Q., and Kovalevskaya, N. D., *Collection Czechoslovak. Chem. Commun.*, 49:1289 (1984).
91. Wein, Ondrej, Pavel Mitschka, Tovchigrechko, Valentin V., Kovalevskaya, Nella D., Yushkina, Tatyana V., and Pokryvaylo, Naum A., *Chem. Eng. Commun.*, 32:153 (1985).
92. Oldroyd, J. G., *J. Colloid Sci.*, 4:333 (1949).
93. Bird, R. B., Armstrong, R. C., and Hassager, O., *Dynamics of Polymeric Liquids: Fluid Mechanics*, Vol. 1, John Wiley and Sons, Inc., New York (1977).
94. Choplin, L., and Carreau, P. J., *J. Non-Newtonian Fluid Mech.*, 9:119 (1981).
95. Boger, D. V., and Denn, M. M., *J. Non-Newtonian Fluid Mech.*, 6:163 (1980).
96. Vrentas, J. S., Duda, J. L., and Hong, Seong-Ahn, *J. Rheology*, 26:347 (1982).
97. Boger, D. V., "Circular Entry Flows of Inelastic and Viscoelastic Fluids," *Advances in Transport Phenomena*, Vol. II, Mujunidar, A. S., and Machelkar, R. M., (Eds.), Wiley Eastern, New Delhi (1982).
98. Walters, K., *Rheometry*, Wiley (1975).
99. Bagley, E. B., *J. Appl. Phys.*, 28:624 (1957).
100. Bagley, E. B., *Trans. Soc. Rheol.*, 5:355–368 (1961).
101. Aubert, H. J., and Tirrell, M., *J. Chem. Phys.*, 72:1694 (1980).
102. Aubert, J. H., Prager, S., and Tirrell, M., *J. Chem. Phys.*, 73:4103 (1980).
103. Brunn, P. O., *J. Polym. Phys.: Polym. Phys. Ed.*, 23:89–103 (1985b).
103a. Brunn, P. O., *J. Chem. Phys.*, 80:3420 (1984a).
104. Sekhon, G., Armstrong, R. C., and John, M. S., *J. Polym. Sci.: Polym. Phys. Ed.*, 20:947–952 (1982).
105. Shafer, Richard H., Nora Laiken, and Zimm, Bruno H., *Biophysical Chemistry*, 2:180 (1974).
106. Shafer, Richard H., *Biophysical Chemistry*, 2:185 (1974).
107. Cohen, Y., and Metzner, A. B., *AIChE. J.*, 27, 705 (1981).
108. Scheidegger, A. E., "The Physics of Flow through Porous Media," University of Toronto Press, Toronto (1974).
109. Dullien, F. A. L., *Chem. Eng. J.*, 10:1 (1975).
110. MacDonald, S. F., El-Sayed, M. E., Mow, K., and Dullien, F. A. L., *Ind. and Eng. Chem. Fund.*, 12:99 (1979).
111. Bird, R. B., Stewart, W. E., and Lightfoot, E. N., "Transport Phenomena," John Wiley and Sons, Inc., New York (1960).

112. Sadowski, T. J., Ph.D. Thesis, University of Wisconsin, Madison, Wisconsin (1963).
113. Roblee, L. H. S., Baird, R. M., and Tierney, J. W., *AIChE J.*, 4, 460 (1958).
114. Ridgway, K., and Tarbuck, K. J., *Chem. Eng. Sci.*, 23:1147 (1968).
115. Saunders, O. A., and Ford, N., *J. Iron and Steel Inst.*, 141:291 (1940).
116. Rose, H. E., *Proc. Inst. Mech. Engr.*, 153:141 (1945).
117. Schwartz, C. E., and Smith, J. M., *Ind. Eng. Chem.*, 45:1211 (1953).
118. Marivoet, J., Teodovair, P., and Wajc, S. J., *Chem. Eng. Sci.*, 29:1836 (1974).
119. Cohen, Y., and Metzner, A. B., *Rheol. Acta*, 25:28 (1986).
120. Dutta, A., and Mashelkar, R. A., *J. Non-Newtonian Fluid Mech.*, 16:279 (1984).
121. Tirrell, M., and Malone, M. F., *J. Polym. Sci., Polym. Phys. Ed.*, 15:1569 (1977).
122. Schreiber, H. P., Storey, S. H., and Bagley, E. B., *Trans. Soc. Rheol.*, 10:275 (1966).
123. Chauveteau, G., Tirrell, M., and Omari, A., *J. Colloid Interface Sci.*, 100:41 (1984).
124. Eyring, H. J., *Chem. Phys.*, 4, 283 (1936).
125. Glasstone, S. K., Laidler, K. J., and Eyring, H., "The Theory of Rate Processes," McGraw-Hill, New York (1941).
126. Busse, W. F., *J. Polym. Sci.*, A-2, 5:1261 (1967).
127. Garner, F. H., and Nissan, A. H., *Nature*, 158:634 (1946).
128. Cohen, Y., and Metzner, A. B., *Chem. Eng. Comm.* 41:73–99 (1986).
129. Drouot, R., *Rheol. Acta*, 21:639 (1982).
130. Drouot, R., and Maugin, G. A., *Rheol. Acta* 22:336 (1983).
131. Jhon, M. S., *J. Polym. Sci.*: Polym. Phys. Ed., 23:955–971 (1985).
132. Brunn, P. O., *J. Chem. Phys.*, 80:5821 (1984b).
133. Brunn, P. O., and Chi, S., *Rheol. Acta*, 23:163–171 (1984).
134. Flory, P. J., *Principles of Polymer Chemistry*, Cornell University Press, Ithaca (1953).
135. Peterlin, A., *Pure Appl. Chem.*, 12:563 (1966).
136. Marrucci, G., *Trans. Soc. Rheology*, 16:321–330 (1972).
137. Bird, R. B., Hassager, O., Armstrong, R. C., and Curtiss, C. F., *Dynamic of Polymeric Liquids*, Vol. 2, *Kinetic Theory*, John Wiley and Sons, New York (1977).
138. Petruccione, F., and Biller, P., *J. Rheology*, 32(1): 1–21 (1988).
139. Biller, P., and Petruccione, F., *J. Non-Newtonian Fluid Mech.*, 25: 347–364 (1987).

CHAPTER 15

RHEOLOGICAL STUDY OF LAMINAR-TURBULENT TRANSITION IN DRAG-REDUCING POLYMERIC SOLUTIONS

P. N. Tandon, A. K. Kulshreshtha and
Rekha Agarwal

Department of Mathematics
Harcourt Butler Technological Institute
Kanpur, India

CONTENTS

INTRODUCTION

When a body moves in a fluid or fluid moves over a body, some forces act to minimize the motion. These forces are called drag forces. Our main concern in all such engineering processes is to reduce these forces either by suitable design or by addition of some foreign materials known as drag-reducing agents. It is convenient to separate the total drag forces into the components:

1. Skin friction drag
2. Pressure drag

Skin friction drag is due to viscous shear stresses. Pressure drag is due to normal stresses and can be further classified into three components:

1. Form drag
2. Lift-induced drag
3. Wave drag

The lift-induced drag and the wave drag can be reduced by careful designs, whereas the form drag may be reduced by preventing boundary layer separation or by some other means of boundary layer suction, by downstream blowing, or by the use of moving surfaces. The remarkable reduction in frictional resistance of the flow of liquids in pipes and in boundary layers of moving bodies by addition of small amounts of certain substances has engendered many scientific and engineering questions and problems. Credit for the first drag reduction experiment with an additive should probably be given to H. S. Hele-Shaw [15]. He was interested in the skin friction on marine animals and tried to simulate their soluble slime by the addition of fresh bile to water. Flow visualization showed that this somewhat bizarre additive appeared to reduce flow resistance. Although Hele-Shaw carried out his experiments around the end of the previous century, it is only in relatively recent years that this phenomenon has been studied in detail, and only now that engineering applications are being investigated.

The earliest work published in the open literature on drag reduction by means of very dilute polymer solutions appears to have been that of Toms [54]. In 1946, Toms was investigating the mechanical degradation of high polymer solutions in pipe flow. It was found that a solution of polymethyl methacrylate in monochlorobenzene required a lower pressure gradient then the solvent alone to produce the same flow rate.

From this time onward numerous investigators began to study the phenomenon from both the theoretical and practical points of view. For the purpose of drag reduction, different drag-reducing agents are used for industrial purposes such as Guar, Poly-ethylene-oxide (PEo), Polyacrylamide (PAM), Modified Polyacrylamide, Polyacrylic Acid (PAA), Association colloids, polyphosphates, Sodium Carboxymethyl Cellulose (CMC).

OTHER EFFECTS DISPLAYED BY FLOWING POLYMER SOLUTIONS

The study of drag reduction has brought forth a number of other effects displayed by flowing polymer solutions, as briefly mentioned below. Each of these effects is itself an area for extensive investigation and further detailed elucidation of the fluid dynamics principle involved.

Diameter Effect

One of the interesting effects of polymer solution drag reduction is the *diameter effect*. As the pipe diameter increases for a given polymer type and concentration, the point at which drag reduction commences shifts toward larger and larger Reynolds numbers. Savins [41] was perhaps the first to point out that this could be interpreted as being due to the influence of polymer molecules on the boundary next to the wall of the pipe.

The theory of Tomita [53] indicates a diameter effect at constant Reynolds number, but evaluation of the theory required rheological constants and comparison with experimental data which were not available. At high Reynolds numbers the diameter effect becomes less important.

Degradation Effect

If a dilute drag-reducing polymer solution is subjected to extensive shearing the drag reducing property is partly lost, rapidly at the first instant and then more gradually due to progressive degradation of the polymer. Presumably, it starts with the highest molecular weight fraction, which appears to be the most effective in reducing drag; thereafter, the effectiveness decreases in decreasing order of molecular weights of the polymer. The ability of the solution to reduce drag does not appear to be regained upon allowing the solution to stand.

The degradation study was performed in a capillary flow system at three different Reynolds numbers. The solution of the linear PAM and PEo shows a very rapid decline in percent drag reduction with an increasing number of passes in a capillary. The rate of decrease in percent drag reduction is much slower for the branched PAM. These specially designed polymers now offer great potential for application in pumping systems and other processes involving chemical engineering and marine technology where closed circuit flow systems are commonly used.

Maximum Drag Reduction Effect

Any given drag-reducing polymer can produce a maximum value of friction reduction for a given pipe size and velocity, if the concentration is adjusted. This maximum was first shown by Hoyt and Fabula [17] in a plot of friction reduction as a function of Reynolds number based on solvent properties. Experiments of Pruitt and Crawford [33, 34] have shown that the maximum Drag reduction is independent of the Reynolds number. Virk [55] has shown that besides being independent of the Reynolds number, the maximum drag reduction is strikingly insensitive to polymer species, molecular weight, and concentration.

Wall Roughness Effects

Hoyt and Fabula [17] first demonstrated that the polymer additives were more effective on rough walls. Many others [24, 44, 57] have used commercial pipes of normal roughness in their experiments. According to Barenblatt et al. [1], polyethylene oxide is more effective in rough pipes than polyacrylamide. In smooth pipes, both these polymers depict identical drag-reducing properties, whereas, in rough pipes, polyacrylamide showed much less friction reduction. Pillipenko [32] has shown that the flow over rough surfaces corresponds to the flow over smooth surfaces but with a low Reynolds number.

Effect on Velocity Profiles

Bogue and Metzner [2] found that drag-reducing polymer additives produce more complicated velocity profiles. The data of Nicodemo et al. (1969) show that the profiles are much flatter than those of water.

Transition Delay

If the shear stress required for the onset of friction reduction occurs in the laminar flow regime, than the friction factor-Reynolds number plot will form a smooth curve extending from the laminar line. The effect can be considered as transition delay, with transition defined as the point where departure from the laminar line occurs. White and McElogot [57] made extensive studies of the transition delay in the tubes for mixtures of polyethylene oxide and polyacrylamide polymers with different molecular weights. They found extensive transition delay, with the transition influenced most strongly by the highest molecular weight component of the dissolved solution.

THEORIES OF DRAG REDUCTION

We now briefly summarize various theories which have been put forward to explain the phenomenon of drag reduction. There is no single theory of drag reduction that fits all the experimental evidence with different additives in different situations. Several hypotheses have been proposed to explain this interesting phenomenon.

The Effective Wall Layer Theory

Oldroyd (1949) postulated that the tube walls might induce a preferred orientation of the polymer molecules close to the wall in such a way that an abnormally mobile laminar sublayer could arise. The existence of such mobile layers is known in the case of non-Newtonian suspensions. As a mathematical convenience, the existence of a layer near the wall with properties different from those of the bulk solution can be explained by means of effective velocities of slip of the fluid at the wall. Kozicki et al. [21] have shown that the effective slip approach is capable of explaining the observed drag reduction effects.

Anisotropic Viscosity Theory

Shin [42] postulated the possibility of anisotropic viscosity effects in flowing polymer solutions. Lumley's review [25] centers on the turbulence aspects of polymer flow and how the expansion of random coils of the polymer molecules can reduce the drag. The trend in this explanation of drag reduction centers on the observations that the elongational viscosity of polymer solutions is very high [9, 37, 52].

Viscoelastic Theory

If the additive molecules are assumed to be viscoelastic, they will be able to store kinetic energy given up by the main flow as potential energy of elongation or deformation [28]. Other theoretical approaches include those of Kohn [19, 20], who computed the energy storage capability of polymer molecules and used this with reasonable success to predict the onset of drag reduction in turbulent flow.

Adsorption Theory

It can be imagined that the additive adsorbed on the wall will provide a resilient wall layer or appreciably thickened laminar sublayer, which will also have the effect of reducing frictional drag. Elperin et al. [5] have suggested that the adsorption may lead to hydrophobization and an effective slip phenomenon. Little (1967) reported the same fact.

Microcontinuum Theory

The most general theory formulated to describe the rheological behavior of microfluent media was presented by Eringen [7] in which he introduced the motion of simple micropolar fluids to describe the behavior of some fluids that can support the stress moments and body moments, and possess local spin inertia. Physically micropolar fluids may represent adequately the fluid consisting of barlike elements [7]. There is evidence that some of the molecules in polymeric solutions combine into rod-like elements [22]. These elongated molecules in a shear flow behave like micropolar fluids. Therefore, the micropolar fluid theory may also explain the drag reduction phenomenon for the dilute polymeric solutions.

Energy Production and Dissipation Theory for Particle-Fluid Mixtures

The production and dissipation of energy in a two-phase model for particle-fluid turbulent flow has been considered by Drew [4]. For plane parallel mean flow, use of several scaling arguments yields a balance between production and drag dissipation. Energy balance considerations are made for situations where drag reduction by the addition of particles is observed. Significant drag reduction is found to occur at sufficiently large Reynolds numbers. Discussions of the extra effectiveness of polymers for reduction is given within the framework of energy balance. The turbulent flow of a particle-fluid mixture occurs in many physical situations. An example with currently-recognized importance is combustion. Many combustion situations involve the burning of small droplets of solid particles of fuel in an airflow [6]. Often it is desirable for mixing purposes that the flow be turbulent. A further example, also with energy generation implications, is electrogasdynamic power generation [16]. Here a suspension of charged particles flows against an electric field, causing power generation. The flow must be turbulent to prevent precipitation, as well as for efficiency. Such suspended particles therefore have a potential effect on drag reduction; and the particles, being immiscible, can be filtered out after the transport of fluid system and used again and again. Thus the energy required to transport can be minimized.

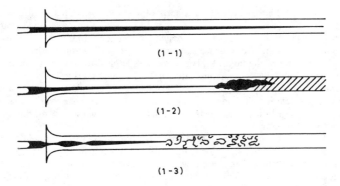

Figure 1. Laminar-turbulent transition in steps.

DELAYED LAMINAR-TURBULENT TRANSITION THEORY

Osborne Reynolds was the first to demonstrate the transition to turbulent flow in a classical experiment in which he examined an outlet from a large water tank through a small tube (Figure 1a). At the end of the tube there was a stopcock used to vary the speed of water through the tube. The junction of the tube with the tank was nicely rounded, and a filament of colored fluid was introduced at the mouth. When the speed of water was slow, the filament remained distinct through the entire length of the tube. When the speed was increased, the filament broke up at a given point and diffused throughout the cross section. Reynolds identified the governing parameter:

$u_m d / v$ (the Reynold number)

where u_m is the mean velocity, d is the diameter, and v is the kinematic viscosity. The point at which the color diffuses throughout the tube is the transition point from laminar to turbulent flow in the tube. Rothfus and Prengle [35] reported that some disturbances of the flow first occurred on the axis of the pipe at a Reynolds number as low as 932, and as the Reynolds number increased, the disturbances spread toward the wall of the pipe, and finally most of the flow changed to turbulent flow at Reynolds number 2,300. On the other hand, Lindergren (1968) concluded from similar experiments that the critical position was in the vicinity of the wall. From the basic concept of the transition, it is pictured that the process of laminar-turbulent transition takes place in few steps: formation of two-dimensional waves (Figure 1b); three-dimensional waves; turbulent spot and its propagation to the entire flow field (Figure 1c). Concerning Newtonian fluids flowing in a circular pipe, the critical position where the first disturbance occurs and the process of laminar-turbulent transition has been studied with electro-chemical technique. The critical position predicted from theoretical considerations is at a distance of $0.577R_w$ the axis of the tube where R_w is the radius of the tube. This has also been confirmed by experiments where the transitional process has been described by the probability density distribution of the velocity fluctuations, intermittency factor, peak numbers, and maximum range of velocity fluctuations. The relations of these factors to each other has been brought out and discussed [30]. Reynolds found that transition occurred at the Reynolds number between 2,000 and 13,000, depending on smoothness of the entry conditions. When extreme care is taken, the transition can be delayed at a Reynolds number as high as 40,000. On the other hand, a value of 2,000 appears to be the lowest value obtained on a rough entrance.

Thus, in pipe line design for which one needs a means of ascertaining whether the flow will be laminar or turbulent, the Reynolds number is the enterian for Newtonian fluids. Savins [40] suggested that the drag reduction in polymer solutions might be a result of delayed laminar turbulent transition employing temporary suspension of turbulence.

Ryan and Johnson [39] have extended the concept of Reynolds criterion and introduced a more general criterian to characterize the flow regime and to test this form in application to various non-Newtonian fluids representing drag-reducing polymeric solutions. Intuitive physical arguments suggested the use of a stability factor which is a function of the ratio of input energy to the energy dissipated for an element of the fluid. If this parameter is applied to Newtonian fluid in laminar pipe flow, one finds that it has a maximum value of 0.385 times the critical Reynolds number, or 808. As the criterion is a general one, the value of 808 defines the boundary between stable laminar and stable turbulent flow for all fluids. The results have been varified for various pseudoplastic fluids. Rotta [36] measured the velocity distribution of the transitional state of air flow in a circular pipe with a hot wire anemometer.

Shirto et al. [43] investigated the process of laminar-turbulent transition in fluid flows in a circular pipe in detail, and measured the velocity fluctuations and compared with experimental values of the critical positions. Ryan and Johnson's treatment has later on extended to include the heated flow of pseudoplastic liquids in smooth pipes by Hanks and Christensen (1962) for Bingham plastic fluids. The problem of laminar-turbulent transition in a drag-reducing polymeric solution becomes more important as White and McElogot [57] have reported that drag-reducing polymeric solutions delay the turbulence and drag in laminar regime is roughly eighty percent less than that in turbulent medium. Therefore, the delayed laminar turbulent transition and identification of suitable polymers which, when added to transporting fluid for delaying the transition, constitute potential study.

Tandon and his associates have studied various aspects of the phenomenon of drag reduction. A systematic experimental design [45] for identification of the parametric values of various polymeric solutions depending on their concentration has also been presented in reference to the experimental results of Mc Comb [26]. Tandon and Kulshrestha [49] have also studied laminar-turbulent transition in certain drag-reducing polymeric solutions. The theory has also been applied to study the microstructural effects on drag reduction phenomena based on laminar-turbulent transition. The theoretical results presented below have also been compared with the experimental data obtained for a large number of pseudoplastic fluids having widely variant rheological properties. The following two sections briefly describe the analysis of laminar-turbulent transition in various drag-reducing polymeric solutions represented by power law non-Newtonian fluids and simple micropolar fluids so as to include the possibility of the applicability of the microstructures in delaying the turbulence.

Laminar-Turbulent Transition in Drag-Reducing Polymer Solutions

Apart from the experimental and theoretical investigations, relatively little attention has been paid to laminar-turbulent transitional flow of very dilute solutions of drag-reducing agents. Virtually no theoretical attempt has been made because of the formidable mathematical complexity involved. The purpose of this work is to undertake detailed study of laminar-turbulent transition in power law fluids which form a representative class of drag-reducing polymer solutions of various concentrations. Three typical geometries, i.e., Circular pipes, parallel plates, and concentric annuli have been considered. The results of this work may be valuable in accounting for drag reduction phenomena which still need a satisfactory explanation.

Formulation of the Problem

Let $\tilde{u}$ be the velocity vector, $\tilde{F}$ the external applied force, $\bar{\rho}$ the density, p the pressure, and t the time.

The corresponding Navier-Stokes equation for an incompressible fluid is expressed as follows:

$$\bar{\rho}\frac{D\tilde{u}}{Dt} = \bar{\rho}\tilde{F}ge - \nabla pge + \nabla T \tag{1}$$

Where T is the stress tensor and ge is the gravitational conversion factor.

The scalar product of ũ with Equation 1 gives the equation of kinetic energy:

$$\tilde{u}\left(\bar{\rho}\frac{D\tilde{u}}{Dt}\right) = \bar{\rho}(\tilde{u} \cdot \tilde{F})ge - (\tilde{u} \cdot \nabla p)ge + \tilde{u} \cdot (\nabla T) \tag{2}$$

For power law fluids, the stress tensor T is given by:

$$T = \eta\Delta \quad \text{where } \eta = m\{\sqrt{(\tfrac{1}{2})\Delta{:}\Delta}\}^{n-1} \tag{3}$$

Where Δ is the rate of deformation tensor and η is the apparent viscosity.

Throughout the following analysis, the external force F has been neglected and analysis has been made separately for each geometry.

Case 1: Circular Pipes

The motion of the fluid is analyzed into mean motion with velocity components u_r, u_θ, u_z, and superposed turbulent fluctuations with velocity components u_r', u_θ', u_z'. The velocity component of the total motion may be expressed as:

$$u_i = \bar{u}_{i1} + u_i' \quad i = \gamma, \theta, z \tag{4}$$

Likewise, the pressure is also composed of mean pressure and fluctuating pressure, i.e.:

$$p = \bar{p} + P' \tag{5}$$

For the steady motions in circular pipes, introducing the velocity components as:

$$U_r = U_r' \quad U_\theta = U_\theta' \quad U_z = \bar{U}_z + U_z' \tag{6}$$

the equation of the kinetic energy (Equation 2) may be written for axisymmetric flow of power law fluids in circular pipes as:

$$\frac{\bar{\rho}}{2}\frac{D}{Dt}\{U_r'^2 + U_\theta'^2 + U_z'^2\} + \bar{\rho}\frac{D}{Dt}(U_z'\bar{U}_z)$$

$$= -ge\left\{U_r'\frac{\partial p'}{\partial r} + U_z'\frac{\partial}{\partial z}(\bar{p} + p') + \bar{U}_z\frac{\partial p'}{\partial z} + \phi - \Psi\right\} \tag{7}$$

where
$$\Psi = \bar{\rho}U'\bar{U}_z\frac{\partial \bar{U}_z}{\partial r} \tag{8}$$

and
$$\phi = U_r'\left\{\frac{1}{r}\frac{\partial}{\partial r}\left(r\eta\frac{\partial U_r'}{\partial r}\right) - \eta\frac{U_r'}{r^2} + \frac{\partial}{\partial z}\left(\eta\frac{\partial}{\partial r}U_z'\right)\right\} + \bar{U}_z\left\{\frac{1}{r}\frac{\partial}{\partial r}\left(\eta r\frac{\partial U_z'}{\partial r}\right)\right.$$

$$+ \frac{\partial}{\partial z}\left(\eta\frac{\partial U_z'}{\partial z}\right)\right\} + U_z'\left\{\frac{1}{r}\frac{\partial}{\partial r}\left(\eta r\frac{\partial}{\partial r}\right)(\bar{U}_z + U_z') + \frac{\partial}{\partial z}\left(\eta\frac{\partial U_z'}{\partial z}\right)\right\} \tag{9}$$

where
$$\eta = m\left[2\left(\frac{\partial U_r'}{\partial r}\right)^2 + \left(\frac{U_r'}{r}\right)^2 + \left(\frac{\partial U_z'}{\partial z}\right)^2 + \left\{r\frac{\partial}{\partial r}\left(\frac{u_\theta'}{r}\right)^2 + \left(-\frac{u_\theta'}{z}\right)^2\right\}\right.$$

$$\left. - \left\{\frac{\partial u_r'}{\partial z} + \frac{\partial}{\partial r}(\bar{u}_z + u_z')\right\}^2\right]^{(n-1)/2} \tag{10}$$

Thus terms on the left hand side of Equation 7 represent the rate of increase in the surplus kinetic energy per unit volume by the velocity fluctuations, Ψ represents the rate of additional energy supplied from the base flow, and ϕ represents the rate of dissipation of velocity fluctuation energy.

If $\phi > \Psi$, the disturbances may be damped out and the flow remains laminar.

If $\phi < \Psi$, the disturbances will grow up and the laminar flow will be unstable.

Now, we define the stability index:

$$I_s = \frac{\Psi}{\phi} \tag{11}$$

As the disturbance is introduced at only one position, the corresponding differential terms of the velocity fluctuations with respect to the position in the stability index need not be considered; and further, as the fluctuations are very small, the square of the velocity fluctuations are neglected. Therefore:

$$\phi = u_z' \left\{ \frac{\partial}{\partial r} \left(\eta \frac{\partial \bar{u}_z}{\partial r} \right) + \frac{\eta}{r} \frac{\partial \bar{u}_z}{\partial r} \right\} \tag{12}$$

where $\quad \eta = m \left| \dfrac{\partial \bar{u}_z}{\partial r} \right|^{n-1} \tag{13}$

Hence:

$$I_s = \frac{\Psi}{\phi} = \frac{\rho u_r' \bar{u}_z \dfrac{\partial \bar{u}_z}{\partial r}}{m u_z' \left[\dfrac{\partial}{\partial r} \left\{ \left| \dfrac{\partial \bar{u}_z}{\partial r} \right|^{n-1} \dfrac{\partial \bar{u}_z}{\partial r} \right\} + \dfrac{1}{r} \left| \dfrac{\partial \bar{u}_z}{\partial r} \right|^{n-1} \dfrac{\partial \bar{u}_z}{\partial r} \right]} \tag{14}$$

Since fluctuating velocities in the directions of r and z are of the same order:

$$I_s = \bar{\rho} \bar{u}_z \frac{\partial \bar{u}_z}{\partial r} \Big/ m \left\{ \frac{\partial}{\partial r} \left(\left| \frac{\partial \bar{u}_z}{\partial r} \right|^{n-1} \frac{\partial u_z}{\partial r} \right) + \frac{1}{r} \left| \frac{\partial \bar{u}_z}{\partial r} \right|^{n-1} \frac{\partial \bar{u}_z}{\partial r} \right\} \tag{15}$$

For power law fluid introducing:

$$\bar{U}_z = \langle u_z \rangle \frac{3n+1}{n+1} \left\{ 1 - \left(\frac{r}{R} \right)^{(n+1)/n} \right\} \tag{16}$$

We get:

$$I_s = \left[\frac{\bar{\rho}}{2m} \left\{ \langle u_z \rangle \frac{3n+1}{n+1} \right\}^{2-n} \left\{ \left(\frac{n+1}{n} \right)^{1-n} \right\} R^n \right] \left[\left(\frac{r}{R} \right)^{1/n} \left\{ 1 - \left(\frac{r}{R} \right)^{(n-1)/n} \right\} \right] \tag{17}$$

The maximum value of I_s exists where $dI_s/d(r/R) = 0$

i.e., at $\quad \dfrac{r}{R} = \left(\dfrac{1}{n+2} \right)^{n/n+1} \tag{18}$

When $\quad n = 1, \dfrac{r}{R} = 1/\sqrt{3} = 0.577$

Therefore, for Newtonian fluid the disturbance first grows at r = 0.577R, which is same as obtained by Shirto et al. [43].

Case II: Concentric Annulus

In the case of the concentric annulus, the mean velocity $\bar{u}_z$ for power law fluid is:

$$\bar{u}_z = \langle u_z \rangle \left[\frac{1+m}{1+n} \right] \left[\frac{(3n+1)(2n+1)}{(2n+1)(1+m)+2n\lambda} \right] [1 - \xi^{n+1/n}] \tag{19}$$

Where $\lambda = \bar{r}/r_2$

$\bar{r}$ = radius of the zero shear stress layer

r_1, r_2 = inner and outer radius of the annulus

ξ = the non-dimensional distance from the zero shear stress layer

As such:

$$\xi = \frac{\bar{r}-r}{\bar{r}-r_1} \qquad \text{for } r_1 \leqq r < \bar{r}$$

$$= \frac{r-\bar{r}}{r_2-\bar{r}} \qquad \text{for } \bar{r} \leqq r < r_2 \tag{20}$$

Following a similar procedure as in Case I we observe that the stability index is maximum at:

$$\xi = \left(\frac{1}{n+2} \right)^{n/n+1} \tag{21}$$

where ξ is the distance measured from the zero shear stress layer in the annulus.

Here, we observe that as n decreases this position moves toward the walls of the annulus, and as n increases, this position moves toward the zero shear stress layer in exactly the same manner as observed above in Case I.

Case III: For Parallel Plates

In Cartesian coordinates, the equation of the kinetic energy of the fluctuating components of velocity reduces to the following form:

$$\frac{\bar{\rho}}{2} - \frac{D}{Dt}[u_x'^2 + u_y'^2 + u_z'^2] + \bar{\rho}\frac{D}{Dt}(u_z'\bar{u}_z)$$

$$= -ge\left\{ u_x' -\frac{\partial p}{\partial x} + u_z'\frac{\partial}{\partial z}(\bar{p}+P') + \bar{u}_z -\frac{\partial p'}{\partial z} \right\} + \phi - \Psi \tag{22}$$

where $\phi = \left[u_x'\frac{\partial}{\partial z}\left\{ \eta\frac{\partial}{\partial x}(u_z'+\bar{u}_z) \right\} + u_z'\frac{\partial}{\partial x}\left\{ \eta\frac{\partial}{\partial x}(u_z'+\bar{u}_z) \right\} \right.$

$$\left. + \bar{u}_z\left\{ \frac{\partial}{\partial x}\left(\eta -\frac{\partial u_z'}{\partial x} \right) + \frac{\partial}{\partial z}\left(\eta\frac{\partial u_z'}{\partial z} \right) \right\} \right] \tag{23}$$

and $\Psi = \bar{\rho}u_x'\bar{u}_z\frac{\partial\bar{u}_z}{\partial x} \tag{24}$

Now, following a similar process as in case I and introducing the mean velocity $\bar{U}_z$ as given below:

$$\bar{u}_z = \frac{n}{n+1}\left(\frac{1}{m}\frac{\partial p}{\partial z}\right)^{1/n}(h^{(n+1)/n} - x^{(n+1)/n}) \tag{25}$$

We observe that the stability index is maximum at:

$$\frac{|x|}{h} = \left(\frac{1}{n+2}\right)^{n/n+1} \tag{26}$$

Where 2h is the distance between the plates and x is the distance from the zero shear stress layer, i.e., central layer.

Calculation of the Critical Velocity

It is assumed that the maximum value of the stability index remains constant [29] for all fluids. Therefore the critical velocity of the power law fluids ($\langle u_{z2} \rangle$) where the stability index is maximum is

$$\langle u_{z2} \rangle = \frac{1}{3n+1}\left[\frac{4}{3^3}\frac{\rho_1}{\rho_2}\frac{m}{\mu}n^{1-n}(n+2)^{(n+2)/(n+1)}\right]^{1/2-n} R^{(1-n)/(2-n)}\langle u_{z1}\rangle^{1/2-n} \tag{27}$$

Where $\langle u_{z1} \rangle$ is the critical velocity for the Newtonian fluid, and ρ_1, ρ_2 are the densities of the water and solution, respectively.

On Laminar-Turbulent Transition in Micropolar Fluid

In the recent past, much attention has been paid to the study of laminar-turbulent transition in certain non-Newtonian fluids, so as to observe the effect of non-Newtonian fluid parameters. These non-Newtonian fluids both, viscous and viscoelastic, have been introduced to represent the polymer suspensions. In almost all the work to date in reference to the polymer suspensions, the classical Navier-Stokes equations have been used. Classical continuum mechanics is based on the idea that the material bodies possess continuous mass densities and the laws of motion and axioms of constitution are valid for every part of the body regardless of its size. Thus, continuous media are dense collections of point masses devoid of internal structures. The inadequacy of the classical continuum approach to describe the complex fluids such as liquid crystals, polymeric suspensions, animal blood, etc., has led to the development of microcontinua. The microcontinuous media are now regarded as sets of structured particles which possess not only velocity and mass, but also a structure with which is associated a moment of inertia and microdeformation tensor. One such theory on fluid microcontinua is that of micropolar fluids [8]. This theory has found wide application in physiological and engineering problems. Physically, this theory may serve as a satisfactory model for the description of the flow behavior of polymer fluid, real fluid suspension, animal blood, etc. Therefore, in this section, we present a study on the laminar turbulent transition phenomenon for such an important suspension as drag reducing agent and compare with the earlier representations.

The equation of motion governing the flow of micropolar fluid in the vector form is:

$$\bar{\rho}\frac{d\bar{v}}{dt} = (\lambda_\alpha + 2\mu_\alpha + K_\alpha)\,\bar{\nabla}(\bar{\nabla}\cdot\bar{v}) - (\mu_\alpha + K_\alpha)\,\bar{\nabla}\chi\,\bar{\nabla}\chi\bar{V} + K_\alpha(\bar{\nabla}\chi\bar{W}) - g_c\,\bar{\nabla}p + \bar{\rho}F \tag{28}$$

where $$\bar{\rho}J\frac{d\bar{W}}{dt} = (\alpha_\alpha + \beta_\alpha + \gamma_\alpha)\,\bar{\nabla}(\bar{\nabla}\bar{W}) - \gamma_\alpha(\bar{\nabla}\chi\,\bar{\nabla}\chi\bar{W}) + K_\alpha(\bar{\nabla}\chi\bar{V}) - 2K_\alpha\bar{W} + \bar{\rho}\bar{I} \tag{29}$$

The scalar product of $\bar{V}$ with Equation 28 gives the equation of kinetic energy:

$$\bar{\rho}\bar{V}\frac{d\bar{V}}{dt} = (\lambda_\alpha + 2\mu_\alpha + K_\alpha)\bar{V}\cdot\bar{\nabla}(\bar{\nabla}\cdot\bar{V}) - (\mu_\alpha + K_\alpha)\bar{V}\cdot(\bar{\nabla}\chi\,\bar{\nabla}\chi\bar{V})$$

$$+ K_\alpha\bar{V}\cdot(\bar{\nabla}\chi\bar{W}) - g_c\bar{V}\cdot\bar{\nabla}_p + \bar{\rho}\bar{V}\cdot\bar{F} \tag{30}$$

Throughout the analysis given here, the external body force F and external body couple vector I have been neglected.

The equation of kinetic energy, in the cylindrical polar coordinates, can be written as:

$$\frac{\bar{\rho}}{2}\left\{\frac{\partial v^2}{\partial t} + U_r\frac{\partial v^2}{\partial r} + \frac{1}{r}U_\theta\frac{\partial v^2}{\partial \theta} + U_z\frac{\partial v^2}{\partial z}\right\}$$

$$= (\lambda_\alpha + 2\mu_\alpha + K_\alpha)\left[U_r\left\{\frac{\partial}{\partial r}\left(\frac{\partial}{\partial r}U_r\right) + \frac{\partial}{\partial r}\left(\frac{1}{r}\frac{\partial}{\partial \theta}U_\theta\right)\right.\right.$$

$$+ \frac{\partial}{\partial r}\left(\frac{U_r}{r}\right) + \frac{\partial}{\partial r}\left(\frac{\partial}{\partial z}U_z\right)\right\} + \left\{\frac{1}{r}U_\theta\frac{\partial}{\partial \theta}\left(\frac{\partial}{\partial r}U_r\right) + \frac{\partial}{\partial \theta}\left(\frac{1}{r}\frac{\partial}{\partial \theta}U_\theta\right) + \frac{\partial}{\partial \theta}\left(\frac{U_r}{r}\right)$$

$$+ \frac{\partial}{\partial \theta}\left(\frac{\partial}{\partial z}U_z\right)\right\} + U_z\left\{\frac{\partial}{\partial z}\left(\frac{\partial}{\partial r}U_r\right) + \frac{\partial}{\partial z}\left(\frac{1}{r}\frac{\partial}{\partial \theta}U_\theta\right) + \frac{\partial}{\partial z}\left(\frac{U_r}{r}\right) + \frac{\partial}{\partial z}\left(\frac{\partial}{\partial z}U_z\right)\right\}\right]$$

$$- (\mu_\alpha + K_\alpha)\left[U_r\left\{\frac{1}{r}\frac{\partial}{\partial \theta}\left(\frac{\partial}{\partial r}U_\theta - \frac{1}{r}\frac{\partial}{\partial \theta}U_r + \frac{1}{r}U_\theta\right) - \frac{\partial}{\partial z}\left(\frac{\partial}{\partial z}U_r - \frac{\partial}{\partial r}U_z\right)\right\} + U_\theta\right.$$

$$\times\left\{\frac{\partial}{\partial z}\left(\frac{1}{r}\frac{\partial}{\partial \theta}U_z - \frac{\partial}{\partial z}U_\theta\right) - \frac{\partial}{\partial r}\left(\frac{\partial}{\partial r}U_\theta - \frac{1}{r}\frac{\partial}{\partial \theta}U_r + \frac{1}{r}U_\theta\right)\right\}$$

$$+ U_z\left\{\frac{\partial}{\partial r}\left(\frac{\partial}{\partial z}U_r - \frac{\partial}{\partial r}U_z\right) - \frac{1}{r}\frac{\partial}{\partial \theta}\right.$$

$$\left.\left.\times\left(\frac{1}{r}\frac{\partial}{\partial \theta}U_z - \frac{\partial}{\partial z}U_\theta\right) + \frac{1}{r}\left(\frac{\partial}{\partial z}U_r - \frac{\partial}{\partial r}U_z\right)\right\}\right]$$

$$+ K_\alpha\left[U_r\left\{\frac{1}{r}\frac{\partial}{\partial \theta}W_z - \frac{\partial}{\partial z}W_\theta\right\} + U_\theta\right.$$

$$\left.\times\frac{\partial}{\partial z}\left\{W_r - \frac{\partial}{\partial r}W_z\right\} + U_z\left\{\frac{\partial}{\partial r}W_\theta - \frac{1}{r}\frac{\partial}{\partial \theta}W_r + \frac{1}{r}W_\theta\right\}\right]$$

$$- \left[U_r\frac{\partial p}{\partial r} + \frac{1}{r}U_\theta\frac{\partial p}{\partial \theta} + U_z - \frac{\partial p}{\partial z}\right]g_c \tag{31}$$

where $\quad V^2 = U_r^2 + U_\theta^2 + U_z^2 \tag{32}$

The motion of the fluid is analyzed into mean motion and superposed turbulent fluctuations:

$$U_i = \bar{U}_i + U_i' \qquad i \equiv r, \theta, z \tag{33}$$

$$W_i = \bar{W}_i + W_i' \tag{34}$$

Likewise, the pressure is also composed of mean pressure and fluctuating pressure, i.e.:

$$p = \bar{p} + p' \tag{35}$$

For steady motion in a circular pipe:

$$U_r = U'_r, \qquad U_\theta = U'_\theta, \qquad U_z = \bar{U}_z + U'_z \tag{36}$$

$$\text{and} \qquad W_r = W'_r, \qquad W_\theta = \bar{W}_\theta + W'_\theta, \qquad W_z = W'_z \tag{37}$$

Also, since the disturbance is introduced at only one position, the corresponding differential terms of the fluctuating components with respect to the position need not be considered. Further, as the fluctuations are very small, the square of the fluctuating components are also neglected. Considering these facts and introducing Equations 35, 36, and 37 into Equation 31, the equation of kinetic energy may be written for axisymmetric flow of micropolar fluid in circular pipes as:

$$\frac{\bar{\rho}}{2}\frac{D}{Dt}\{U'^2_r + U'^2_\theta + U'^2_z\} + \bar{\rho}\frac{D}{Dt}(U'_z\bar{U}_z)$$

$$= -g_c\left\{U'_r\frac{\partial p'}{\partial r} + U'_z\frac{\partial}{\partial z}(\bar{p} + p') + \bar{U}_z\frac{\partial p'}{\partial z}\right\} + \Psi \tag{38}$$

where $\quad \Psi = \bar{\rho}U'\bar{U}_z\dfrac{\partial}{\partial r}\bar{U}_z$

and $\quad \phi = (\mu_\alpha + K_\alpha)U'_z\left\{\dfrac{\partial^2}{\partial r^2}\bar{U}_z + \dfrac{1}{r}\dfrac{\partial}{\partial r}\bar{U}_z\right\} + K_\alpha\left[U'_z\left\{\dfrac{\partial}{\partial r}(\bar{W}_\theta) + \dfrac{1}{r}\bar{W}_\theta\right\}\right] \tag{40}$

The terms on the left hand side of Equation 38 represent the rate of increase in the surplus kinetic energy per unit volume by the velocity and rotation fluctuations. Ψ represents the rate of additional energy supplied from the base flow and ϕ represents rate of dissipation of the velocity and fluctuation energy.

If $\phi \geq \Psi$, the disturbances may be damped out and the flow remains laminar.

If $\phi \leq \Psi$, the disturbances will grow up and the laminar flow will be unstable.

Now, the stability index:

$$I_s = \frac{\Psi}{\phi} \tag{41}$$

may be written as:

$$I_s = \frac{\bar{\rho}\bar{U}_z\dfrac{\partial}{\partial r}\bar{U}_z}{(\mu_\alpha + K_\alpha)}\left[\left\{\dfrac{\partial}{\partial \rho^2}\bar{U}_z + \dfrac{1}{\rho}\dfrac{\partial}{\partial \rho}\bar{U}_z\right\} - NR\left\{\dfrac{\partial}{\partial \rho}(\bar{W}_\theta) + \dfrac{1}{\rho}(\bar{W}_\theta)\right\}\right]^{-1} \tag{42}$$

For micropolar fluid [8]:

$$U_z = \langle U_z\rangle\left[(1 - \rho^2) + \frac{N}{\lambda}\frac{I_0(\lambda)}{I_1(\lambda)}\left\{\frac{I_0(\lambda)}{I_1(\lambda)} - 1\right\}\right] \tag{43}$$

$$W_\theta = \langle U_z\rangle\left[\frac{1}{R}\left\{\rho - \frac{I_0(\lambda)}{I_1(\lambda)}\right\}\right] \tag{44}$$

where $\quad \rho = \dfrac{r}{R}, \qquad N = \dfrac{K_\alpha}{\mu_\alpha + K_\alpha}$

$$\lambda = \left(\frac{2\mu_\alpha + K_\alpha}{\mu_\alpha + K_\alpha} \frac{K_\alpha}{\gamma_\alpha}\right)^{1/2} R \tag{45}$$

and $$\langle U_z \rangle = \frac{1}{2} R^2 (2\mu_\alpha + K_\alpha)^{-1}\left(-\frac{\partial p}{\partial z}\right) \tag{46}$$

Also, for small values of $\lambda(\lambda < 3.75)$ we have:

$$I_0(\lambda) = 1 + \frac{\lambda^2}{4} \tag{47}$$

$$I_1(\lambda) = \frac{\lambda}{2}\left(1 + \frac{\lambda^2}{8}\right) \tag{48}$$

Therefore, the average velocity in a circular pipe for micropolar fluid takes the following form:

$$\langle U_z \rangle = \frac{R^2}{4(\mu_\alpha + K_\alpha)}\left(-\frac{\partial p}{\partial z}\right)\left(1 - \frac{4N}{8 + \lambda^2}\right) \tag{49}$$

Thus:

$$U_z = 2\langle U_z \rangle (1 - \rho^2) \tag{50}$$

$$W_\theta = 2\langle U_z \rangle \frac{\lambda^2}{8 + \lambda^2}\left(1 - \frac{4N}{8 + \lambda^2}\right)\frac{1}{R}\rho(1 - \rho^2) \tag{51}$$

Hence, Equation 42 reduces to:

$$I_s = \frac{R\bar{\rho}\langle U_z \rangle}{(\mu_\alpha + K_\alpha)} \frac{\rho(1 - \rho^2)}{1 + \frac{N}{2}\frac{\lambda^2}{8 + \lambda^2}\left(1 - \frac{4N}{8 + \lambda^2}\right)^{-1}(1 - 2\rho^2)} \tag{52}$$

The value of I_s is maximum at:

$$\rho^2 = \frac{1}{4}\left[(3N_1 + 1) - \sqrt{(3N_1 + 1)^2 - 8(N_1 + 1)}\right] \tag{53}$$

where $$N_1 = \frac{2}{N}\left(\frac{8 + \lambda^2}{\lambda^2}\right)\left(1 - \frac{4N}{8 + \lambda^2}\right) \tag{54}$$

Thus, we obtain the geometric position of first transition point from Equation 53.

Calculation of the Critical Velocity

The maximum stability index is the same for all fluids [29]. Hence, the critical velocity U_{z2} for micropolar in a circular pipe at which the first transition point appears is given by

$$\langle U_{z2} \rangle = U_{z1}\frac{\rho_1}{\rho_2}\frac{\mu_\alpha + K_\alpha}{3\sqrt{3}\mu}\frac{X}{\rho(1 - \rho^2)} \tag{55}$$

Where $X = 1 + \dfrac{N}{2} \dfrac{\lambda^2}{8 + \lambda^2} \left(1 - \dfrac{4N}{8 + \lambda^2} \right)^{-1} (1 - 2\rho^2)$ (56)

and ρ is given by Equation 53.

Possible Applications of Laminar-Turbulent Transition to Blood Flows

The Hagen Poiseuille problem relating to Newtonian flows can be modified to account for blood [10]. It has been demonstrated that non-linear blood rheology on the resistance of blood flow in arteries is relatively minor. It has also been observed experimentally that the blood flows continue laminar regime at a pretty high Reynolds number. This might be due to the elasticity and or viscoelasticity of the walls.

The elasticity of the walls modifies the radius of the tube given by:

$$a(x) = a_0 \left[1 - \frac{a_0}{E \cdot h} p(x) \right]^{-1}$$ (57)

where p(x) is the transmural pressure difference [11]. A simpler relation between pressure-radius can be assumed as:

$$a = a_0 + \frac{\alpha p}{2}$$ (58)

where α is the compliance constant. This equation is a good representation of the pulmonary blood vessels. One can illustrate that the elasticity and compliance are analogous to drag reduction phenomenon, as in the case of power law fluids such as polymer suspensions which follow drag reduction phenomenon in rigid pipes (see [51]). As mentioned above, turbulence develops gradually in laminar flows. It takes time for some unstable modes of motion in a flow to grow into turbulence. This concept may be applied to blood flow in arteries. In a period of rising velocity, the Reynolds number increases slowly until it reaches a value of 2,300 at which the flow could be expected to become turbulent under steady flow conditions. In the case of unsteady flows, the velocity as well as Reynolds number are much higher than 2,300. Thus, the critical Reynolds number in the case of blood flow depends on the rate of change of velocity, as well as on the eddies upstream and roughness of the pipe, as mentioned in the beginning. Nerem [31] and Nerem and Seed [30] have observed turbulence during deceleration of systolic flow.

Qualitative study of laminar-turbulent transition reveals that the critical Reynolds number is a function of frequency parameter of the pulsatile flows with wide variations of velocity and heart rate.

Turbulence in blood flows implies fluctuating pressure acting on the arterial wall and fluctuating, increased shear rates. These stresses are indicated in murmurs, post stenotic dilatation, and atherogenesis. Therefore, the study of laminar turbulent transition depending on wall compliance, Womersley number, and rheology of the blood [46, 47, 51] both in normal and diseased subjects forms an important, valuable diagnostic tool. The subject needs thorough understanding and mathematical modeling before suitable experiments are designed. The effect of peripheral layer viscosity [48] and or micro-structural effects of the blood in capillaries [50] may play a dominant role in laminar-turbulent transitions. It may be remarked that the higher peripheral layer viscosity in diabetic patients initiates early turbulence. Infusion of dextron 40 solution in case of acute myocardial infection results in reduction of blood viscosity. Thus, Dextron 40 solution dilutes the blood and the process is known as hemodilution.

Early turbulence experiments indicate that the degree of destabilization of the flow, as measured by the decrease of onset Reynolds number from the critical Reynolds number, increases with increasing solvent viscosity while it first increases and then decreases with increasing polymer concentration [12]. The subject laminar-turbulent transition is, therefore, a very important area for both theoretical and experimental studies and its possible applications toward physiological diagnostic purposes are remarkable.

CONCLUSION

Geometric Position of the First Critical Point

The formulation of the turbulent spot is a local phenomenon, and it has been observed that its formation coincides with the point at which the stability index is maximum. Though the development of instability depends upon the local conditions, the critical radius does not remain unaffected by velocity profiles and rheological properties of the fluid.

Figure 2 depicts the variation of the geometric position of the first transition point with N (a nondimensional parameter of micropolar fluid). We observe that, as the value of N increases, the first transition point moves toward the walls of the pipe, and this fact is similar to that observed for the power law fluid for decreasing value of n (a parameter of power law fluid), shown in Figure 3 for pseudoplastic fluids. Therefore, we can say that as the value of N increases in the micropolar fluid, the drag-reducing property of the fluid increases. Also, as the parameter λ increases, the rate of shifting of the first transition point toward the walls increases. This fact also shows that the increasing values of parameter λ are favorable for drag-reduction phenomena similar to the pseudoplasticity of the polymer suspension, as obtained by Tandon and Kulshreshtha [45] for the power law fluid from the data obtained for the experimental results of McComb [26].

Early Transition

Figure 4 describes the variation of critical velocity at which the transition occurs, with the pseudoplasticity of the power law fluid taking $\rho_1 = \rho_2$, $\mu = 0.01$, and m = 0.012. We conclude that, as

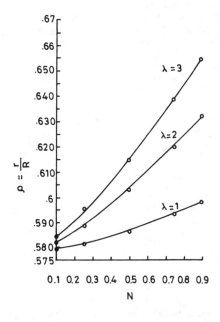

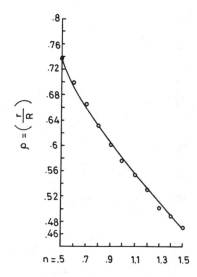

Figure 2. Variation of critical point (r/R = ρ) with N for different values of λ.

Figure 3. Variation of critical point (r/R) with flow behavior index (n), in a circular pipe.

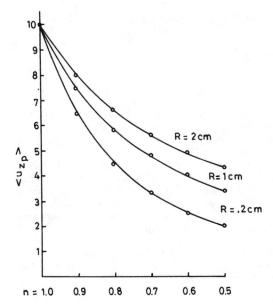

Figure 4. Variation of critical velocity with pseudoplasticity where $(U_{zw}) = 10$ cm/sec.

the pseudoplasticity of the fluid increases, the first disturbance appears earlier. Similar results have been reported by Hansen and Little [13] and Jones et al. (1976). Mishra and Tripathi [29] have observed that the pseudoplasticity delays the laminar-turbulent transition, which might be the effect of higher viscosity due to the addition of a greater amount of polymer to the solvent.

Figure 5 describes the variation of critical velocity at which the first transition occurs, with the parameter N of the micropolar fluid taking $\rho_1 = \rho_2$ and $K_\alpha = 5 \times 10^{-3}$, $\mu = 1 \times 10^{-2}$. From this

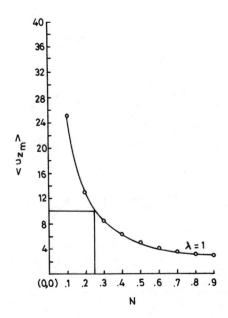

Figure 5. Variation of the critical velocity (U_{22}) with N for different values of N where $K = 5 \times 10^{-3}$, $(u_z) = 10$, and $\lambda = 1$.

figure, we observe that as the parameter N increases, the critical velocity decreases, i.e., the transition occurs earlier. This result is quantitatively similar to that of Harro Kuemmever [14] between two parallel walls.

From these results, we conclude that the onset of early turbulence phenomena occurs in dilute solutions of the drag-reducing agents.

Acknowledgment

The authors gratefully acknowledge the Department of Science and Technology, Government of India, New Delhi for financial support in the preparation of this manuscript.

REFERENCES

1. Barenblatt, G. I., Ger. Stev., V. A., and Kala Shinkvr, V. N. (1969) "Turbulence of Anomolous Fluids," *Heat Transfer Soviet Research* Vol. 1, p. 102.
2. Bogue, D. C., and Metzner, A. B. (1963) "Velocity Profiles in Turbulent Pipe Flow, Newtonian and Non-Newtonian Fluids," *Ind. and Engg. Chem. Funda.* Vol. 2, p. 143.
3. Christensen, E. B., and Richard, W. H. (1962), "The Laminar-Turbulent Transition in Nonisothermal Flow of Pseudo Plastic Fluids in Tubes," *AIChE. Journal*, Vol. 8 No. 4 page 467–471.
4. Drew, D. A. (1975) "Turbulent Transport over a Flat Bottom Using Momentum Balance," Transactions of the ASME, *J. of Applied Mechanics*, p. 38.
5. Elperin, I. T., Galershtein, D. M., and Levental, L. T. (1964) "The Influence of Surface Effects and Transient Phenomenon on Transfer Processes in Heterogeneous Systems," *Inzhenerno Fizicheskii Zhurnal*, Vol. 7 No. 8, p. 16.
6. Emmons, H. W. (1971) "Fluid Mechanics and Combustion" Thirteenth Symposium (International) on Combustion, Salt Lake City, Utah.
7. Eringen, A. C. (1964). "Simple Microfluids," *Int. J. Engng. Sci.*, Vol. 2, p. 205.
8. Eringen, A. C. (1966) "Theory of Microfluids," *J. Math. Mech.* Vol. 16, p. 1.
9. Everage, A. E. (Jr.), and Gordon, R. J. (1971) "On the Stretching of Dilute Polymer Solutions," *AIChE Journal* Vol. 17, p. 1257.
10. Fung, Y. C. (1981) *Biomechanics Mechanical Properties of Living Tissues*, Springer Verlag, New York.
11. Fung, Y. C. (1984) *Biodynamics: Circulation*, Springer Verlag, New York.
12. Hansen, R. J. (1972), "Stability of Laminar Pipe Flows of Drag Reducing Polymer Solutions" *AIChE Journal*, Vol. 10, p. 213.
13. Hansen, R. J., and Little, R. C. (1974a) "Stability and Laminar to Turbulent Transition Pipe Flows in Drag Reducing Polymer Solutions," Int. Conf. on Drag reduction, Cambridge, Paper B. 8, p. 12.
14. Harro Kuemmever (1978) "Stability of Laminar Flows of Micropolar Fluids between Parallel Walls," *Physics of Fluids*, Vol. 21(10), p. 1688.
15. Hele-Shaw, H. S. (1897) "Experiments on the Nature of Surface Resistance in Pipe and on Ships," *Trans. Inst. Naval Arch.* 39, p. 145.
16. Ho, K. F., and Coffee, R. A. (1974) "Electrogasdynamic Generation Using Solid-Gas Suspension in Turbulent Pipe Flow," *Journal of Applied Physics*, Vol. 45, pp. 1135–1143.
17. Hoyt, J. W., and Fabula, A. C. (1964) "The Effect of Additive on Fluid Friction," Proceedings fifth symposium on Naval Hydrodynamics, Bergen Norway, Office of Naval Research ACR-112, p. 947.
18. James, D. F. (1972) "Constitutive Equations for Dilute Polymer Solutions," *Trans. Soc. Rheology*, Vol. 16, p. 175.
19. Kohn, M. C. (1974) "Criteria for the Onset of Drag Reduction," *AIChEJ.*, Vol. 20, p. 185.
20. Kohn, M. C. (1973) "Energy Storage in Drag Reducing Polymer Solutions," *J. of Polymer Science* (Polymer Physics ed.) Vol. 11, p. 2339.
21. Kozicki, W., and Tie, C. (1968) "Anomolous Wall Effects and Associated Drag Reduction," *Chem. Engg.* Vol. 23, p. 231.

22. Kudin (1973) "On the Size of Molecular Clusturs Reducing Hydrodynamic Drag in Polymeric Solutions," *Fluid Mechanics Soviet Research*, Vol. 2, No. 5, p. 112.
23. Kulshreshtha, A. K. (1983) "A Study of Drag Reduction Phenomenon," A Thesis submitted to Kanpur University, Kanpur, India.
24. Lindgren, E. R., and Hoot, T. G. (1968) "Effects of Dilute High Mol. Wt. Polymers on Turbulent Flows of Water in Very Rough Pipes," *J. of Applied Mech.*, Vol. 35, Trans ASME, Vol. 90 series E No. 2 p. 417.
25. Lumley, J. T. (1973) "Drag Reduction in Turbulent Flow of Polymer Additives," *J. of Polymer Science*, Macromolecular Reviews Vol. 7. p. 263.
26. Mc Comb, W. D. (1974) "Drag Reduction Polymer and Liquid Column Oscillations," *Nature*, Vol. 251, p. 598.
27. Metzner, A. B., and Reed, J. C. (1955) "Flow of Non-Newtonian Fluids—Correlation of the Laminar Transition and Turbulent Regions," *AIChE Journal* Vol. 1 (No. 4), p. 434.
28. Metzner, A. B., and Park, M. G. (1964) "Turbulent Flow Characteristics of Viscoelastic Fluids," *J. of Fluid Mech.*, Vol. 20, p. 291.
29. Mishra, P., and Tripathi, G. (1971) "Transition from Laminar to Turbulent Flow of Purely Viscous Non-Newtonian Fluids in Tubes," *Chem Engg. Sci*, Vol. 26, No. 6., p. 915.
30. Nerem, R. M., Seed, W. A., and Wood, N. B. (1972). "An Experimental Study of Turbulence in the Aorta," *J. Fluid Mechanics*, Vol. 52, p. 137–160.
31. Nerem, R. M. (ed.) (1981) "Hemodynamics in the Arterial Wall," *J. Biomech. Eng. 103*: introduction p. 171. Technical papers, pp. 172–212.
32. Pillipenko, V. N. (1978) "Simulation of Turbulent Flows in Dilute Polymer Solutions" *Fluid Mechanics, Soviet Research*, Vol. 7, No. 2, p. 31.
33. Pruitt, G. T., and Crawford, H. R. (1963) "Drag Reduction Rheology and Capillary End Effects of Some Dilute Polymer Solutions," Westco Research Final Report on Contract No. 60530, 8250 to Naval, Ordnance test Station.
34. Pruitt, G. T., and Crawford, H. R. (1965) The Western Company Research Division, Lellas, U.S.A., Report No. DTMB-1.
35. Rothfus, R. R., and Prengle, R. S. (1952) *Ind. Eng. Chem.*, Vol. 44, p. 1683.
36. Rotta, J. (1966) "An Experimental Contribution to the Transition from Laminar to Turbulent Flow in a Pipe," Proc. IXth Intern. Cong. of Applied Mech. Vol. 3., p. 350.
37. Ruckenstein, E. (1971a) "On the Flow Mechanism of Drag Reduction in Turbulent Pipe Flow of Viscoelastic Liquids," *Chemical Engg. Science*, Vol. 26, p. 1075.
38. Ruckenstein, E. (1973) "A Note on the Mechanism of Drag Reduction," *J. of App. Polymer Science*, Vol. 17, p. 3229.
39. Ryan, N. W., and Johnson, M. M. (1959) "Transition from Laminar to Turbulent Flow in Pipes," *AIChE Journal*, Vol. 5, p. 433.
40. Savins, J. G. (1963) "On Non-Newtonian Fluid Mechanics," 56th Annual AIChE Meeting, Houston, Texas.
41. Savins, J. G. (1964) "Drag Reduction Characteristics of Solutions of Macromolecules in Turbulent Pipe Flow," *Society of Petroleum Engg. J.* Vol. 4, p. 203.
42. Shin, H. (1965) "Drag Reduction in Turbulence by Dilute Polymer Solutions," Sc. D. Thesis, Massachusetts Inst. of Tech.
43. Shirto, I. T. O., Ogawa, K., and Urushiyama, S. T. (1971) "Transition from Laminar to Turbulent Flow of Liquids in a Circular Pipe," *J. of Chem. Engg. of Japan*, Vol. 4., p. 128.
44. Spangler, J. G. (1969) "Studies of Viscous Drag Reduction with Polymers Including Turbulence Measurements and Roughness Effects," *Viscous Drag Reduction* pp. 131–155, C. S. Wells (Ed.) Plenum Press, New York.
45. Tandon, P. N., and Kulshreshtha, A. K. (1978). "Behavior of Drag-Reducing Polymer Solutions in a U-Tube," Natl. Acad. Sci. Lett., Vol. 1(6), p. 219.
46. Tandon, P. N., Misra, J. K., and Srivastava, K. K. (1982). "Microstructural and Peripheral Layer Viscosity Effects on Peristaltic Transport of Seminal Fluid," *Biorheology*, Vol. 9, p. 707–715.
47. Tandon, P. N., Misra, T. K., and Verma, R. L. (1982) "Peripheral Layer Viscosity and Microstructural Effects on the Capillary-Tissue Fluid Exchange," Vol. 7, p. 7–22.

48. Tandon, P. N., and Misra, J. K. (1982) "Microstructural and Peripheral Layer Viscosity Effects on Flow of Blood through an Artery with Mild Stenosis," Trans. New York Acad. of Sci. 404, 59–62.
49. Tandon, P. N., and Kulshrestha (1985) "A Rheological Study of Laminar-Turbulent Transition in Drag Reducing Polymeric Solutions," *Journal of Applied Polymer Science*, Vol. 30, p. 4235–4242.
50. Tandon, P. N., and Agarwal, Rekha (1986) "Micro Structural Effects in Blood Flow through a Mild Developing Stenosis," *J. Inst. of Engns.*, Vol. 67 (IDPI), p. 13–16.
51. Tandon, P. N., and Agarwal, Rekha (1987) "Flow through Expanding or Contracting Pipes: A Model for Human Bronchial Tube," To appear in *GANITA*, Vol. 37.
52. Ting, R. Y. (1972) "Water Soluble Polymers," Ed. N. M. Bikarlers, Plenum Press, New York, p. 51.
53. Tomita, Y. (1966) "A Study on Flows of Dilute Polymer Solutions," *Bulletin of the JSME*, Vol. 16, No. 92, p. 291.
54. Toms, B. A. (1949) "Some Observations on the Flow of Linear Polymeric Solutions through Straight Tubes at Large Reynolds Number," Proc. 1st Inst. Cong. Rheol., Amsterdam.
55. Virk, P. S. (1975) "Drag Reduction Fundamentals," *American J. of Chem. Engg.*, Vol. 21(4), p. 625.
56. White, A. (1968) "Studies of Flow Characteristics of Dilute High Polymer Solutions," Hendon College of Tech. Research Bulletin No. 5, p. 113.
57. White, W. D., and Mc Elogot, D. M. (1970) "Transition of Mixtures of Polymers in a Dilute Solution," *J. of Basic Engg.*, Trans. ASME, Vol. 92, p. 411.

CHAPTER 16

TURBULENT FLOW VELOCITY PROFILES IN DRAG-REDUCING FLUIDS

A. V. SHENOY*

Department of Materials Science and Engineering
University of Florida
Gainesville, Florida USA

CONTENTS

INTRODUCTION

The phenomenon of drag reduction in turbulent flow resulting from the addition of minute quantities of certain additives has been the subject of extensive study over the past several years. A summary of the work done in this area can be obtained from a number of comprehensive reviews already available in the literature [1–13]. Drag-reducing fluids are normally associated with a Newtonian-type viscosity accompanied by a mild degree of elasticity. During steady shear flow, the molecules undergo extensions in the conventional manner but, due to the elastic nature of drag-reducing fluids, they show a tendency to relax. The time required for molecular relaxation, represented as θ_{fl}, is taken as a measure of the degree of fluid elasticity. In dimensionless terms, the extent of elasticity of such fluids is described by the Deborah number (De) which is the ratio of the fluid relaxation time θ_{fl} and the characteristic process time v/u^{*2}, where v is the kinematic viscosity and u^* is the friction velocity. The propriety of the choice of the characteristic time scales like the above for describing De has been discussed in detail by a number of investigators [10, 14, 15]. Reported experimental data on fluid relaxation times published by Seyer and Metzner [15] show that θ_{fl} varies as $\dot{\gamma}^{-m}$ where m lies between 0.5 and 1.0. The general practice is to assume m as equal to 1 so that the Deborah number can be taken as a constant independent of shear rate $\dot{\gamma}$ knowing that u^{*2}/v is proportional to wall shear rate. The added rheological complexities due to elasticity of the drag-reducing fluids along with chaotic random motion of the fluid elements during turbulent flow makes the fluid mechanics rather difficult to handle theoretically. Thus, very often an empirical approach is taken based on the results of experimental data on the time-averaged velocity profile and the pressure gradient.

---

* Current address: SMART, 64D Girgaum Road, Opera House, Bombay 400004, India.

This chapter deals exclusively with the velocity profiles of drag-reducing fluids flowing under turbulent conditions in various flow situations such as in straight circular pipes, through annular ducts, and in curved tubes.

VELOCITY PROFILES

Expressions for turbulent velocity profiles during flow of drag-reducing fluids have been developed along similar lines to those for Newtonian fluids and power-law fluids. The overall cross section of the pipe is assumed to be divisible in two regions: a turbulent core wherein inertial effects are dominant and a wall region wherein the constitutive properties of the fluid assume importance. The laminar sublayer in the wall region is assumed to extend from the wall ($y = 0$) to $y = y_{SL}$ and the turbulent core from $y = y_{SL}$ to $y = R$.

Smooth Straight Circular Pipes

The time-averaged velocity at a point during turbulent flow of a drag-reducing fluid would depend on six independent variables, namely, R, ρ, τ_w, μ, θ_{fl}, y. These are no different from those appearing for Newtonian fluids except for the additional parameter θ_{fl} to include the elasticity of drag-reducing fluid. Based on the two-region model as mentioned above, it is obvious that in the wall region:

$$u = \phi_1(\rho, \tau_w, \mu, \theta_{fl}, y) \tag{1}$$

and in the turbulent core:

$$u_m - u = \phi_2(R, \rho, \tau_w, y) \tag{2}$$

Following the conventional dimensional analysis as given by Langhaar (16) and used by Seyer and Metzner [17] for drag-reducing fluids, it can be shown that over the entire cross section:

$$\frac{u}{u^*} = \phi(R^*, \xi, De) \tag{3}$$

where u^* is the friction or shear velocity defined as $\sqrt{\tau_w/\rho}$, R^* is the Reynolds number based on friction velocity and defined as $Ru^*\rho/\mu$, and ξ is the dimensionless location parameter defined as y/R.

Expressions for the velocity profiles during turbulent flow have been developed by a number of investigators [10, 17–19], and though each has proposed a different expression for the turbulent core region, there is an agreement regarding the expression in the wall region given as:

$$u^+ = y^+ \quad \text{for } y \le y_{SL} \tag{4}$$

where u^+ is a dimensionless velocity defined as u/u^* and y is the distance-based Reynolds number defined as $yu^*\delta/\mu$.

For the turbulent core, Meyer [18] observed that the velocity profiles in turbulent pipe flow of very dilute drag-reducing fluids could be correlated by a modified form of the universal law of the wall as follows:

$$u^+ = 2.5 \ln y^+ + 5.5 + \alpha^* \ln\left(\frac{u^*}{u^*_{crit}}\right) \tag{5}$$

The parameters α^* and u^*_{crit} are, respectively, measures of the drag-reducing effectiveness and onset of wall shear stress above which drag reduction occurs, and these are constant for a given fluid system. The effect of these parameters on the velocity profile is to create a shift in the logarithmic portion without a change in slope from the Newtonian law of the wall—thus indicating an effective thickening of the viscous sublayer with no apparent change in the mixing-length distribution.

Elata et al. [19] also modified the conventional Newtonian law-of-the-wall expression but gave a different type of correction term involving the Deborah number as follows:

$$u^+ = 2.5 \ln y^+ + 5.5 + \alpha' \ln De \tag{6}$$

Seyer and Metzner [17] proposed a more general equation by replacing the last term in Equation 6 by a general function B(De) which was evaluated by them empirically. The expression they proposed is:

$$u^+ = A \ln y^+ + B \tag{7}$$

where $A = 2.46$ \hfill (8)

$$B = 5.6 + 1.55De \quad \text{(for } 0 \le De \le 10) \tag{9}$$

Virk [10] developed an expression for the velocity profile based on the elastic sublayer model he proposed. The essential physical notion is that the stimulation of polymer molecules by a turbulent shear flow creates a zone, called the elastic sublayer, which is characteristic of the drag reduction phenomenon. The elastic sublayer originates at the onset of drag reduction and grows with increasing drag reduction until it finally occupies the entire pipe cross section at maximum drag reduction. The mean velocity profiles during drag reduction would thus show two extremes: at low drag reduction the entire outer flow, $y^+ > 50$, say, is shifted upward from parallel to the Newtonian wall law by an amount S^+, defined as the effective slip; whereas at maximum drag reduction the ultimate velocity profile has a semilogarithmic form similar to the Newtonian law of wall except for the mixing-length constant, which equals 0.085 instead of 0.4 as in the Newtonian case. Thus, the following expressions were proposed by Virk [10].

In the elastic sublayer region, where the profile can be approximated by a segment of the ultimate profile as:

$$u^+ = 11.7 \ln y^+ - 17.0 \qquad y_{SL}^+ < y^+ < y_E^+ \tag{10}$$

In the Newtonian plug region, the profile is parallel-shifted upward by S^+, relative to the Newtonian law of wall as:

$$u^+ = 2.5 \ln y^+ + 5.5 + 9.2 \ln y_E^+/y_{SL}^+ \qquad y_E^+ \le y^+ \le R \tag{11}$$

A schematic diagram of the velocity distribution as described above is shown in Figure 1 taken from Sellin et al. [11].

The logarithmic expressions for the velocity profile in the turbulent core as given by Equations 6, 7, 10, and 11 are able to predict the velocity distributions even beyond the range of experimentation due to their asymptotic nature. However, these expressions have an incongruity in that they fail to predict a zero velocity gradient at the center of the pipe. Shenoy and Talathi [20], thus, proposed a new velocity profile model that is devoid of this limitation and would, therefore, be the correct theoretical velocity profile expression for the turbulent core during flow of drag reducing fluids. The form of expression assumed by them was similar to that of Seyer and Metzner [17], except for an added correction term $C(\xi, De)$, as:

$$u^+ = A(\ln y^+ + C(\xi, De)) + B(De) \tag{12}$$

where $C(\xi, De) = \sigma_1(De) \exp\left\{-\frac{1}{2}\left[\frac{y^* - 0.8}{\sigma_2(De)}\right]^2\right\}$ \hfill (13)

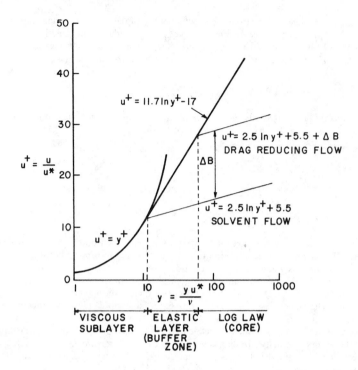

Figure 1. Velocity distribution based on typical velocity profile models for turbulent flow of drag reducing fluids (from Sellin et al. [11]).

The expressions for $\sigma_1(\mathrm{De})$ and $\sigma_2(\mathrm{De})$ were determined with the precondition that the velocity gradient is zero at the centerline:

$$\sigma_1(\mathrm{De}) = 0.4398 + 0.123\mathrm{De} + 0.0135\mathrm{De}^2 \tag{14}$$

$$\sigma_2(\mathrm{De}) = 0.254(1 + 0.2\mathrm{De}) \tag{15}$$

From Equation 12, an implicit expression for friction factor was derived and compared with that of Seyer and Metzner [17] so that A and B(De) could be determined. The final form of the expression of Shenoy and Talathi [20] for velocity profile in the turbulent core during flow of drag reducing fluids is as follows:

$$
u^+ = 2.46\left\{\ln y^+ + (0.4398 + 0.123\mathrm{De} + 0.0135\mathrm{De}^2)\right.
$$
$$
\left. \times \exp\left[-\frac{(\xi - 0.8)^2}{0.129(1 + 0.2\mathrm{De})^2}\right] + 1.3676(1 - 0.09\mathrm{De} - 0.01\mathrm{De}^2)\right\}
$$
$$
+ 5.6 + 1.55\mathrm{De} - G \tag{16}
$$

A choice of $G = 4.0$ gives excellent agreement within less than 1% error for all values of $\mathrm{De}(1 - 10)$ over a range of Reynolds number from 10^4 to 10^6 when compared with the predictions of Equation 7.

The value of ξ in Equation 16 can be obtained by rearrangement of the terms in the definition of y^+ as:

$$\xi = \left(\frac{y^+ 2\sqrt{2}}{\text{Re}\,\sqrt{f}} \right) \tag{17}$$

The value of f is often estimated from the expression given by Seyer and Metzner [17] for drag reducing fluids over a wide range of Reynolds numbers from 4×10^3 to 10^6 as follows:

$$\sqrt{\frac{2}{f}} = A'(1 - \xi_1)^2 \frac{\ln \text{Re}\,\sqrt{f}}{2\sqrt{2}} + (1 - \xi_1)^2 - G \tag{18}$$

where ξ_1 is the dimensionless sublayer thickness defined by Equation 17 with y^+ replaced by y_{SL}^+. Due to the implicit nature of Equation 18 in terms of f, an iterative procedure becomes necessary in order to get estimates of f. However, the following explicit expression was found to give values of f within an error boundary of $\pm 5\%$ for the range of De between 0 and 10 over the Reynolds number region covering 10^4 to 10^6:

$$\frac{1}{\sqrt{f}} = 3.57 \log \frac{\text{Re}^{1 + 0.175\text{De}^{(1 - 0.04 \log \text{Re})}}}{(6.5)^{1 + 0.725\text{De}^{0.7}}} \tag{19}$$

Equation 16 certainly gives the correct description of the velocity profile during turbulent flow of drag reducing fluids, but there is always an inclination to look for simpler expressions that are good approximations of the exact one at least in a limited region. The one-seventh power-law expression for the velocity profile in the case of Newtonian fluids was developed with this view in mind. In the case of drag-reducing fluids, such a correlation has also been developed [21, 22].

The Blasius-type correlation developed by Shenoy and Mashelkar [21] for drag-reducing fluids gives the following form for friction factor:

$$f = \frac{\alpha}{\text{Re}^\beta} \qquad 5 \times 10^3 \le \text{Re} \le 10^5 \tag{20}$$
$$0 \le \text{De} \le 10$$

α and β values are both functions of Deborah number and their values for varying De were given by Shenoy and Shintre [22]. Virk et al. [23] suggested that the maximum drag reduction that can be achieved in practice can be described by a unique asymptote given by $\alpha = 0.42$ and $\beta = 0.55$ in the above equation. Detailed explanation of the maximum drag reduction asymptote and its uniqueness are available in the exhaustive article of Virk [10].

Now, noting that the wall shear stress $\tau_w = (f/2)\rho V^2$ by definition, the following expression can be written by algebraic adjustment of Equation 20:

$$\tau_w = \frac{\alpha}{2^{1+\beta}} \rho V^{2-\beta} v^\beta R^{-\beta} \tag{21}$$

Using the definition of $u^* = (\tau_w/\rho)^{1/2}$ and the fact that $V = \psi u_m$, Equation 21 can be written as:

$$\frac{u_m}{u^*} = \left[\frac{2^{1+\beta}}{\alpha \psi^{2-\beta}} \right]^{1/(2-\beta)} \left[\frac{Ru^*\rho}{\mu} \right]^{\beta/(2-\beta)} \tag{22}$$

The expression for ψ is desirable along the lines of Skelland [24] for power-law fluids using the value of $n = 1$ in the suggested expression. Thus:

$$\psi = (2 - \beta)^2/(4 - \beta) \tag{23}$$

The validity of the above expression is on the simple basis that Skelland's equations for power-law fluids are valid for Newtonian fluids as well and hence, if β is a function of De, then Equation 23 should hold for drag-reducing fluids which are Newtonian in viscosity with a mild level of elasticity as exemplified by De.

The key assumption for getting the simplified form of the velocity profile lies in an approximation that Equation 23 is valid at any wall distance y rather than at R specifically. Thus:

$$u^+ = A_1 y^{+B_1} \tag{24}$$

$$\text{where} \quad A_1 = \frac{2^{(1+\beta)/(2-\beta)}[4-\beta]}{\alpha^{1/(2-\beta)}[2-\beta]^2} \tag{25}$$

$$B_1 = \frac{\beta}{2-\beta} \tag{26}$$

Due to the simplifying assumptions made during the derivation of Equation 24, it does not truly give an accurate description of the velocity profile. It does not predict a zero velocity gradient at the centerline and also has a limited range of validity to Reynolds numbers between 5×10^3 and 10^5. Despite all its limitations, it has extensive use in engineering design especially for estimating the turbulent entrance length, as will be shown later.

A number of attempts have been made to experimentally measure the velocity profiles during turbulent flow of drag-reducing solutions [19, 25–31]. Initial velocity profile measurements were made using an impact tube, but erroneous evaluations resulted due to the normal stress contribution of the viscoelasticity of drag-reducing fluids leading to lower bulk mean velocities when integrated

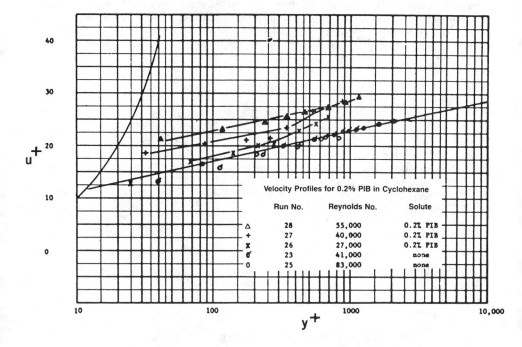

Figure 2. Velocity profiles for 0.2% polyisobutylene in cyclohexane (from Patterson and Florez [31]).

over the pipe area. The extent of the error involved depended upon the magnitude of the normal stress effect and hence, on the type, concentration, and effective molecular weight of the drag-reducing additive. Ernst [26] and Wells [27] found errors of less than 7 percent as against those of Pruitt and Crawford [28] which were so large that the apparent velocity head was negative near the wall. Errors as large as 29% were obtained during velocity measurements of flowing drag-reducing fluids by Astarita and Nicodemo [29] through the use of the pitot tube. No calibration procedure for the velocity profile measurements by impact tubes could be used because the normal stress effects of the drag-reducing fluid varied with wall shear rate and also over the radial profile. In order to overcome these limitations of the impact tubes, other techniques were tried [30–33] for velocity profile measurements such as hot-film anemometry and the gas bubble tracer technique.

In hot-film anemometry, the heat transfer rate from the hot-film to the fluid primarily depends on the fluid velocity and hence, a calibration procedure for velocity vs. heat transfer rate correlation could be specified. Smith et al. [30] observed a radial variation in cylindrical hot-film sensitivity during measurements which seemed to disappear with degradation of the polymer. However, since their conclusions were based on comparisons with data from the impact tube, their results cannot be taken at face value. Patterson and Florez [31] measured velocity profiles during drag reduction flow of viscoelastic polymer and soap solutions using hot-film anemometry. The $u^+ - y^+$ plot obtained by them for 0.2 percent polyisobutylene in cyclohexane is shown in Figure 2. There is an obvious strong tendency towards viscous boundary layer thickening as observed by Ernst [26] and Wells [27] and predicted by Elata et al. [19]. In more concentrated solutions, such a tendency was found to be stronger. However, soap-solution velocity profiles showed [31] a different kind of behavior as compared to polymer solutions. Figure 3 shows a plot of u^+ vs. y^+ for 1% Aluminum Dioleate in toluene, clearly indicating no tendency for viscous boundary layer thickening. The reason for this mainly lies in the fact that the mechanism of drag reduction is different in micellar systems [13] than in polymeric systems.

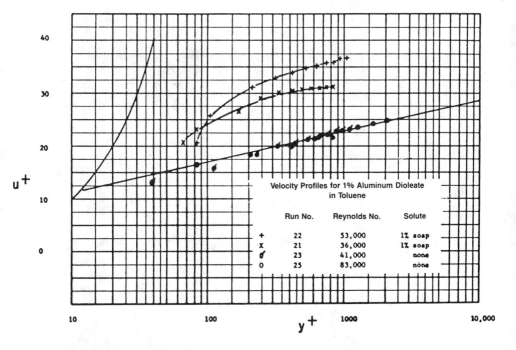

Figure 3. Velocity profiles for 1% aluminum dioleate in toluene (from Patterson and Florez [31]).

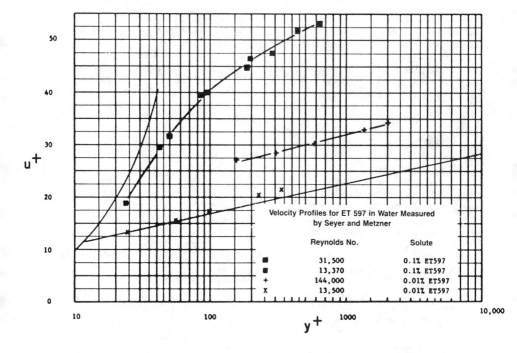

Figure 4. Velocity profiles for ET597 in water (from Seyer and Metzner [32]).

Seyer and Metzner [32] also reported velocity profile measurements during turbulent flow of drag reducing solutions using a tracer technique. Small gas bubbles were photographed intermittently and their streak lengths on the film were used as a measure of the velocity. Since the movement of bubbles relative to the fluid was slow, the average velocity measured by averaging many streak lengths at a given point was quite accurate to an extent of less than 3% error. Figure 4 shows the results of their velocity profile measurements, indicating the increasing viscous sublayer thickening with increasing polymer concentration as in Figure 2.

In general, velocity profile measurements are relatively difficult experimentally. Though hot-film anemometers are an improvement over the pitot tubes, Friehe and Schwartz [33] have shown that cylindrical hot-film anemometer probes cannot be used to measure velocity under certain conditions, as was also shown by Fabula [34] and James [35]. The anomalous effects seem to be associated with stagnation points, as was indicated by results with conical probes which showed that there was no great difference between drag-reducing solutions and water [33].

Annular Pipes

The only work that exists in the literature on turbulent velocity profiles for flow of drag-reducing fluids in an annular duct is that of Shenoy and Shintre [22]. Due to the presence of two wall boundaries in an annulus, the flow model was divided into two regions, namely the outer region and the inner region, each having a separate velocity profile. Furthermore, an assumption was made that the effect of the inner cylinder on the velocity profile in the outer region is small enough to be neglected. Thus, the expression for the velocity profile given by Equation 24 for smooth straight circular pipes would be valid for the outer region of the annulus in the following form:

$$u_o^+ = A_1 y_o^{+B_1} \tag{27}$$

where the subscript o represents the outer region of the annulus, and A_1 and B_1 have the same form as given by Equations 25 and 26, respectively.

An expression of a similar form is assumed to hold for the inner region, and it is further assumed that the slopes of u_o^+ vs. y_o^+ and u_i^+ vs. y_i^+ are nearly identical so that the exponent on y_o^+ and y_i^+ is the same, thus giving:

$$u_i^+ = \bar{A}_1 y_i^{+B_1} \tag{28}$$

where the subscript i represents the inner region of the annulus.

The momentum balance for the inner and outer flow regions of the annuli gives the following expressions for shear stress τ_{wi} and τ_{wo}:

$$\tau_{wi} = \frac{r_i}{2} \left[\frac{\lambda^2}{k^2} - 1 \right] \frac{\Delta P}{L} \tag{29}$$

$$\tau_{wo} = \frac{r_o}{2} [1 - \lambda^2] \frac{\Delta P}{L} \tag{30}$$

where
$$\lambda = \frac{r_m}{r_o}$$

$$\tag{31}$$

$$k = \frac{r_i}{r_o}$$

In Equations 29–31, r_i, r_o, and r_m represent the radius of the inner cylinder, radius of the outer pipe, and radius of maximum velocity, respectively.

Using the definition of $u^* = \sqrt{\tau_w/\rho}$ for the inner and outer regions, the following expression can be easily obtained:

$$\frac{u_o^*}{u_i^*} = \left[\frac{k(1 - \lambda^2)}{(\lambda^2 - k^2)} \right]^{1/2} \tag{32}$$

The expression for $\bar{A}_1$ in Equation 28 can be derived, using the fact that $u_i = u_o$ at $r = r_m$, and equating Equations 27 and 28 as:

$$\bar{A}_1 = A_1 \left[\frac{k(1 - \lambda^2)}{(\lambda^2 - k^2)} \right]^{(B_1 + 1)/2} \left[\frac{1 - \lambda}{\lambda - k} \right]^{B_1} \tag{33}$$

The velocity profile for the inner region of the annulus can thus be written as:

$$u_i^+ = A_1 \left[\frac{k(1 - \lambda^2)}{(\lambda^2 - k^2)} \right]^{(B_1 + 1)/2} \left[\frac{1 - \lambda}{\lambda - k} \right]^{B_1} y_i^{+B_1} \tag{34}$$

Equations 27 and 34 thus define the complete velocity profile for drag-reducing fluids in an annulus. Due to lack of experimental data in the literature, no comparison between theory and experiments can be done to support the above-predicted trends.

Curved Pipes

Flow through a curved pipe represents a very interesting situation wherein a secondary flow, set up by virtue of the centrifugal force due to curvature, gets superimposed on the axial velocity flow field. The fluid at the center is actually driven toward the outer wall and then pushed back along the wall toward the inner side, setting up a double motion as shown schematically in Figure 5.

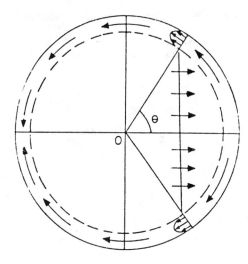

Figure 5. Schematic representation of the flow model for curved pipes showing the boundary layer, the inviscous core, and the continuity of secondary flow (from Shenoy et al. [36]).

Shenoy et al. [36] studied this turbulent flow problem of drag-reducing fluids in curved pipes. The flow was considered to be representable by a two-region model consisting of a central inviscid core and a thin boundary layer near the wall as in Figure 5. The angular and axial velocity distributions in the boundary layer were assumed to have the following form based on boundary conditions and continuity of flow.

$$v = D_1 \left(\frac{\xi}{\delta}\right)^{\beta/(2-\beta)} \left(1 - \frac{\xi}{\delta}\right) \tag{35}$$

$$w = w_1 \left(\frac{\xi}{\delta}\right)^{\beta/(2-\beta)} \tag{36}$$

where $\xi = \bar{a} - r$ with $\bar{a}$ as the radius of the pipe and r as the radial position. δ is the boundary layer thickness.

In order to numerically solve the relevant equations, the following expressions were used for non-dimensionalizing:

$$\delta = \delta_c \bar{a} \{Re(\bar{a}/\bar{R})^{1/2\beta}\}^{-\beta/(\beta+1)} \tag{37}$$

$$D_1 = D_c(v_m \sqrt{\bar{a}/\bar{R}}) \tag{38}$$

$$w_1 = w_c(v_m) \tag{39}$$

and the values of δ_c, D_c, and w_c were obtained by expanding in the neighborhood of $\theta = o$ using:

$$\delta_c = \delta_1(1 + \delta_2\theta^2 + \cdots) \tag{40}$$

$$D_c = D_2\theta(1 + D_3\theta^3 + \cdots) \tag{41}$$

$$w_c = 1 + \frac{\bar{B}\bar{a}}{v_m}\left(1 - \frac{\theta^2}{2!} + \frac{\theta^4}{4!} - \cdots\right) \tag{42}$$

In the above equations, $\bar{R}$ is the radius of curvature of the pipe, V_m is the mean axial velocity, and θ is the angular position in cylindrical coordinates.

The non-dimensionalized differential equation, when integrated using the Runge-Kutta-Merson technique, gives the variation of the non-dimensional turbulent boundary layer thickness, δ_c; the non-dimensional axial velocity w_c at the outer edge of the boundary layer; and the non-dimensional characteristic angular velocity D_c with θ. Figures 6–8 show the functions $\delta_c(\theta)$, $w_c(\theta)$, and $D_c(\theta)$ for drag-reducing fluids with different Deborah numbers. It is evident from Figures 7 and 8 that the

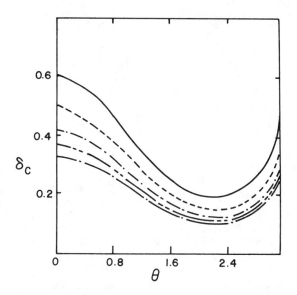

Figure 6. Variation of the dimensionless turbulent boundary layer thickness δ_c with θ for varying Deborah numbers in the case of curved pipes (from Shenoy et al. [36]).

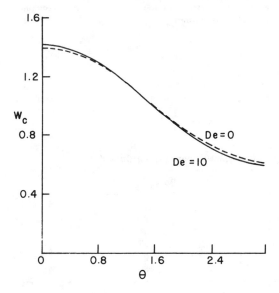

Figure 7. Variation of the dimensionless axial velocity at the outer edge of the boundary layer w_c with θ for varying Deborah numbers in the case of curved pipes (from Shenoy et al. [36]).

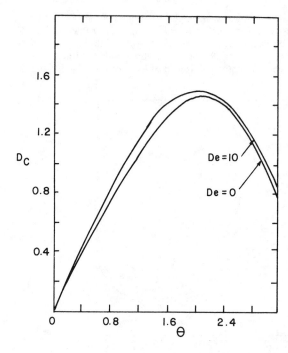

Figure 8. Variation of the dimensionless characteristic angular velocity D_c with θ for varying Deborah numbers in the case of curved pipes (from Shenoy et al. [36]).

dimensionless axial velocity component w_c and the dimensionless characteristic angular velocity component D_c do not change significantly with increasing De. However, Figure 6 shows that there is a marked decreasing trend in the dimensionless boundary layer thickness δ_c with increasing De. Figures 6–8 in conjunction with Equations 35–39 describe the complete velocity distribution for turbulent flow of mildly elastic drag-reducing fluids through a curved tube.

The velocity distribution in the central core is described by the following equation obtained through straightforward derivation from the equation of motion:

$$w = V_m\left[1 + \left(\frac{\bar{B}\bar{a}}{V_m}\right)\frac{r}{\bar{a}}\cos\theta\right] \qquad (43)$$

The values of $\bar{B}\bar{a}/V_m$ for varying De are given in Table 1. Presently, there exist no experimental data on the velocity distribution in curved pipes, and hence, a verification of the above theoretical predictions cannot be made.

Table 1
Values of Ba/V_m for Varying Deborah Numbers (36) for Curved Pipes

De	$\bar{B}\bar{a}/V_m$
0	0.37929
2	0.37548
4	0.37524
6	0.37988
8	0.38820
10	0.39904

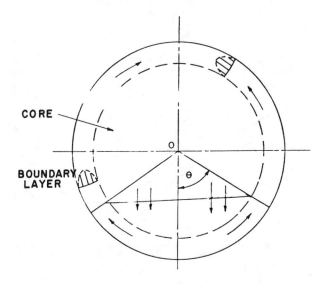

Figure 9. Schematic diagram of the flow model for rotating straight circular pipes showing the boundary layer, the inviscid core, and the continuity of secondary flow (from Shenoy [37]).

Rotating Straight Circular Pipes

A theoretical study of the turbulent flow of mildly elastic drag-reducing fluids in a tube rotating around an axis perpendicular to its own, at high Reynolds numbers and in the range of high rotational parameters, has been done by Shenoy [37]. In this flow situation, the Coriolis force arising from the rotation sets up a secondary flow which gets superimposed on the axial velocity field. The effects are similar to those of the centrifugal force on the flow in curved pipes as can be seen from the schematic diagram shown in Figure 9. An assumption of high Reynolds numbers and a range of high rotational parameters is made so that boundary layer analysis can be applied. Thus, in the thin boundary layer the velocity is affected by the viscosity of the fluid, while in the core region the velocity field is affected mainly by the secondary flow and the effect of viscosity is disregarded. The resulting similarity of the above-mentioned model to the curved pipe case shows that a like approach could be adapted to the present flow situation, too.

The angular and axial velocity distributions in the boundary layer would, therefore, have the same forms as Equations 35 and 36. However, the forms of the expressions used for non-dimensionalizing are as follows:

$$\delta = \delta_o \bar{a} \{ Re(2\bar{a}\Omega/V_m)^{1/2\beta} \}^{-\beta/(\beta+1)} \tag{44}$$

$$D_1 = D_c (V_m 2a\Omega)^{1/2} \tag{45}$$

$$w_1 = w_o V_m \tag{46}$$

The values of δ_o, D_c, and w_o were obtained by expanding in the neighborhood of $\theta = 0$ using expressions similar to Equations 40–42, and the Runge-Kutta-Merson technique was used for the numerical integration.

The numerical results of δ_o, w_o, and D_c are plotted as functions of θ in Figures 10–12 for fluids with different Deborah numbers. Figure 10 shows that there is a marked decreasing trend in the

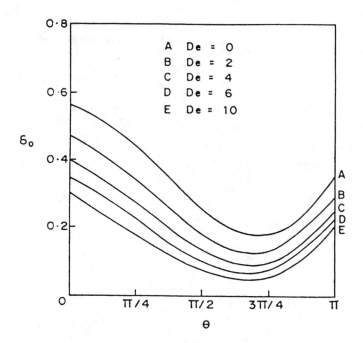

Figure 10. Variation of the dimensionless boundary layer thickness δ_0 with θ for varying Deborah numbers in the case of rotating straight circular pipes (from Shenoy [37]).

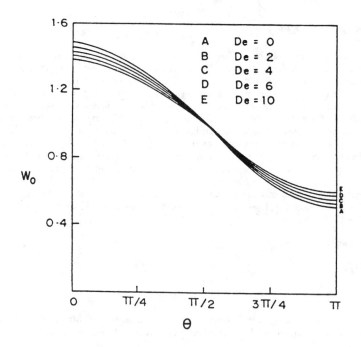

Figure 11. Variation of the dimensionless axial velocity at the outer edge of the boundary layer w_0 with θ for varying Deborah numbers in the case of rotating straight circular pipes (from Shenoy [37]).

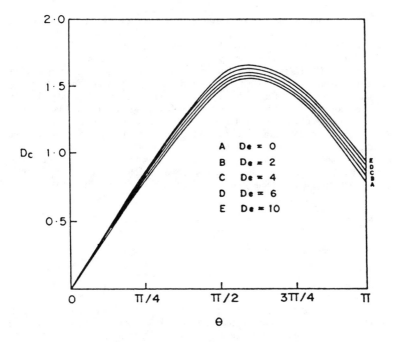

Figure 12. Variation of the dimensionless characteristic angular velocity D_c with θ for varying Deborah numbers in the case of rotating straight circular pipes (from Shenoy [37]).

dimensionless boundary layer thickness δ_o with increasing elasticity. However, w_o and D_c are affected to a much lesser extent. Figures 10–12, along with Equations 44–46, above, provide the complete velocity distribution for turbulent flow of dilute drag-reducing fluids through a pipe rotating around an axis perpendicular to its own.

The velocity distribution in the central core is described by Equation 43, but the values of $\overline{B}\overline{a}/V_m$ for varying Deborah numbers are different from the curved pipe case and are given in Table 2.

Rough Pipes

All the velocity profiles developed in the foregoing sections had an underlying assumption that the pipe considered was free from defects on the inside and hence could be considered to be smooth.

Table 2
Values of Ba/V_m for Varying Deborah Numbers (37) for Rotating Straight Pipe

De	$\overline{B}\overline{a}/V_m$
0	0.42712
2	0.44860
4	0.46931
6	0.49003
10	0.53167

However, in reality, all pipes have a certain level of surface defects marked by protrusions or indentations. The actual dimensions of this roughness do not have as great an effect as the relative roughness due to the size of the protrusions or indentations in comparison with the dimensions of the pipe. If the average height of the roughness projections is expressed as ε, then the relative roughness factor is written as ε/D. This could mean that the relative roughness factor is zero for smooth pipes.

A rough surface does not always act rough, but depends on the relative magnitude of the size of the surface elements and the thickness of the viscous sublayer when the fluid is flowing under turbulent conditions. As the Reynolds number is increased, the relative thickness of the viscous sublayer decreases and eventually the roughness elements protrude through the sublayer. When this occurs, the predominant source of pressure drop becomes form drag caused by the roughness elements, and the flow is then termed "fully rough."

The velocity profile in rough pipes is normally obtained by simply adding terms to the Newtonian law of the wall as has been done by Fenter [38] and Spangler[39]. The latter provided the expression for drag-reducing fluids by modifying the profile in Equation 5 suggested by Meyer [18]. Thus:

$$u^+ = 2.5 \ln y^+ + 5.5 + \alpha^* \ln \frac{u^*}{u^*_{crit}} - F \tag{47}$$

where the roughness function F is defined as:

$$F = \sqrt{2} \left\{ \left(1.77 + \frac{\alpha^*}{\sqrt{2}} \right) \ln Re_w \sqrt{f} - \frac{1}{\sqrt{f}} - 0.394 - \frac{\alpha^*}{\sqrt{2}} \ln \frac{\sqrt{2} \, Du^*_{crit}\rho}{\mu} \right\} \tag{48}$$

Equation 48 allows the determination of the value of the roughness function for a drag-reducing fluid from friction factor—Reynolds number data taken in a rough pipe when α^* and u^*_{crit} for the fluid are known. The roughness functions as experimentally obtained by Spangler [39] for water and polymer drag-reducing fluid (31 wppm P-295 in water) are shown in Figures 13 and 14. It can be seen that the roughness function F for drag-reducing fluids becomes larger than the roughness function F_N for Newtonian fluids after a critical shear stress is exceeded. Moreover, for drag-reducing fluids F is found to depend on the value of D/ε, whereas for Newtonian fluids it does not. Another

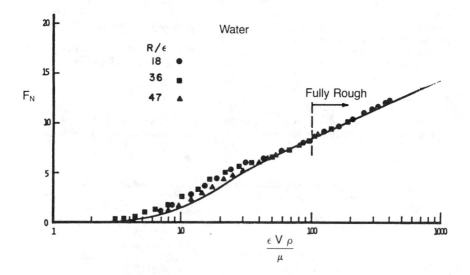

Figure 13. Roughness function for water (from Spangler [39]).

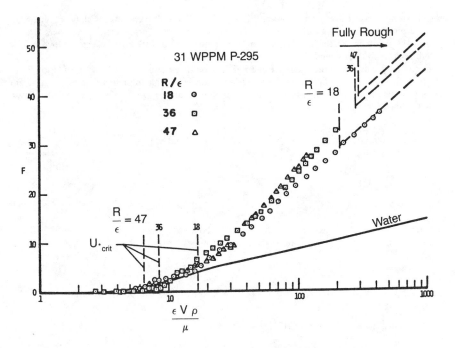

Figure 14. Roughness function for drag reducing fluid (from Spangler [39]).

approach for obtaining F based on the experimental findings is to assume the following form of Equation 39:

$$F = F_N + \alpha^* \ln \frac{u^*}{u^*_{crit}} \qquad \text{for } u^* > u^*_{crit} \tag{49}$$

From Fenter [38], for Newtonian fluids it is clear that the expression for F_N in the fully rough regime can be given exactly by:

$$F_N = 2.5 \ln \frac{\rho u^* \varepsilon}{\mu} - 3.0 \tag{50}$$

Combining Equations 49 and 50 gives:

$$F = (2.5 + \alpha^*) \ln \frac{\rho u^* \varepsilon}{\mu} - \alpha^* \ln \frac{\rho u^*_{crit} \varepsilon}{\mu} - 3.0 \tag{51}$$

Combining Equations 47 and 51 gives the conventional Newtonian form for the velocity profile in the rough pipes as:

$$u^+ = 2.5 \ln \frac{y}{\varepsilon} + 8.5 \tag{52}$$

This is because in the fully rough regime all the drag reduction effectiveness of the additive is annulled by the pipe roughness, and hence, the velocity profile can be expected to be no different from the Newtonian case. In very rough pipes, White [40] did find that there was insignificant change in the frictional characteristics with drag reducing agents even at very large Reynolds numbers. Brandt et al. [41] also came to the conclusion that drag reducers had little or no effect on flow in fully rough regimes, but they tended to delay the onset of this regime.

In the fully rough regime, though Equation 52 would represent the velocity profile for drag-reducing fluids, it again suffers from the limitation of not being able to predict the velocity gradient as zero at the centerline. A new expression similar to Equation 16 can be easily derived as follows.

A modified form of Equation 16 can be written as:

$$
\begin{aligned}
u^+ = 2.46 \left\{ \ln(y/\varepsilon) + \ln \frac{\rho u^* \varepsilon}{\mu} + (0.4398 + 0.123\mathrm{De} + 0.0135\mathrm{De}^2) \right. \\
\left. + \exp\left[\frac{-(\xi - 0.8)^2}{0.129(1 + 0.2\mathrm{De})^2} \right] + 1.3676(1 - 0.09\mathrm{De} - 0.01\mathrm{De}^2) \right\} \\
+ 5.6 + 1.55\mathrm{De} - \mathrm{G}
\end{aligned}
\tag{53}
$$

The term $2.46 \ln (\rho u^* \varepsilon / \mu)$ assumes a value of 3.0, as obtained by comparing Equation 52 with the following expression for Newtonian fluids in smooth pipes:

$$
u^+ = 2.5 \ln y^+ + 5.5
\tag{54}
$$

Thus, the velocity profile for drag-reducing fluids in rough pipes can be written as:

$$
\begin{aligned}
u^+ = 2.46 \left\{ \ln(y/\varepsilon) + (0.4398 + 0.123\mathrm{De} + 0.0135\mathrm{De}^2) \right. \\
\left. \times \exp\left[\frac{-(\xi - 0.8)^2}{0.129(1 + 0.2\mathrm{De})^2} \right] + 1.3676(1 - 0.09\mathrm{De} - 0.01\mathrm{De}^2) \right\} \\
+ 8.6 + 1.55\mathrm{De} - \mathrm{G}
\end{aligned}
\tag{55}
$$

As the flow approaches the fully rough regime, the drag reduction effectiveness decreases and De → 0. Thus, the expression in the fully rough regime would be as follows:

$$
u^+ = 2.46 \ln(y/\varepsilon) + 1.082 \exp\left[\frac{-(\xi - 0.8)^2}{0.129} \right] + 7.964
\tag{56}
$$

ENTRANCE LENGTH ESTIMATION

Smooth Straight Circular Pipes

The velocity profiles discussed in the foregoing section all refer to the fully developed turbulent flow region. However, there is always a region upstream of the flow where the fluid is in the developing region and becomes fully developed only after a certain entrance length. Since the velocity distributions in the entrance region are significantly different from those in the fully developed region, one would need to have an estimate of the entrance region. For drag-reducing fluids, a theoretical prediction along with an experimental verification of the hydrodynamic entrance length during turbulent flow has been done by Shintre et al. [42]. A numerical integration technique was used to obtain the variation of entrance with Reynolds number for different Deborah numbers. A simple and elegant approach was used by Shenoy and Masbelkar [21] to obtain reasonable estimates of the hydrodynamic entrance lengths for turbulent flow of drag-reducing fluids. They found close agreement with the results of Shintre et al. [42] and hence, the straightforward method based on an ordering technique of Shenoy and Mashelkar [21] is discussed in the following.

The simple-form of the velocity profile as given by Equation 24 is assumed to be applicable to the edge of the boundary layer (i.e., $y = \delta$ where $u = u_o$) thus giving:

$$\frac{u_o}{u^*} = \frac{2^{(1+\beta)/(2-\beta)}[4-\beta]}{\alpha^{1/(2-\beta)}[2-\beta]^2}\left[\frac{\delta u^*\rho}{\mu}\right]^{\beta/(2-\beta)} \tag{57}$$

Rearranging Equation 57 and using $\tau_w = \rho u^{*2}$ gives:

$$\tau_w = \frac{\alpha}{2^{1+\beta}}\left[\frac{(2-\beta)^2}{(4-\beta)}\right]^{2-\beta}\rho u_0^{2-\beta}\left[\frac{\mu}{\rho\delta}\right]^{\beta} \tag{58}$$

An alternative form of τ_w in the turbulent boundary layer for drag-reducing fluids can be written as:

$$\tau_w = \psi_1 \rho u^2 \frac{d\delta}{dx} \tag{59}$$

where $\psi_1 = \frac{(2-\beta)(1+\beta)}{2(2+\beta)}$ \tag{60}

Comparing Equations 58 and 60 and solving for δ gives:

$$\delta = \left\{\frac{(1+\beta)\alpha\psi^{2-\beta}}{\psi_1 2^{1+\beta}}\right\}^{1/(1+\beta)}\left[\frac{\mu}{\rho u_o}\right]^{\beta/(1+\beta)}\left[\frac{1}{1+\beta}\right]x \tag{61}$$

In order to get an estimate of the turbulent entry length, x is set equal to x_e (the entrance length). δ is set equal to $D/2$ (the pipe centerline), and u_o is set equal to u_m (the maximum velocity at pipe center-line $= V/\psi$). Then, by simplification, the following expression for the turbulent entrance length for drag-reducing fluids in smooth circular pipes is derived:

$$\frac{x_e}{D} = \left[\frac{\psi_1}{(1+\beta)\alpha\psi^2}\right]Re^{\beta} \tag{62}$$

Figure 15 shows a plot of the dimensionless turbulent entrance lengths for flow of drag-reducing fluids through smooth straight circular pipes. Seyer and Catania [43] and Shintre et al. [42] have provided experimental data on turbulent entrance lengths. A comparison of the theoretical predictions and the experimental data with approximately estimated De shows satisfactory agreement. At maximum drag reduction asymptote, it can be seen that the entrance lengths are significantly larger, and hence, care must be exercised when measuring velocity profiles of effective drag-reducing solutions to make sure that it is in the fully developed regime.

Annular Pipes

Shenoy and Shintre [22] have provided expressions for the entrance length estimates in the case of annular pipes. As noted earlier, the shear stresses at the inner and outer wall are different, and hence, the velocity profiles in the two regions develop differently. Two boundary layer thicknesses develop simultaneously, one starting at the inner wall, namely δ_1, and the other at the outer wall, namely δ_o. It is now assumed that the velocity profiles given by Equations 27 and 28 are valid at the edge of the corresponding boundary layers. This assumption, though not strictly valid, provides a useful step in the estimation of the entrance lengths. Now following the same line of argument as for the straight smooth circular pipe described earlier, the expressions for the entrance lengths

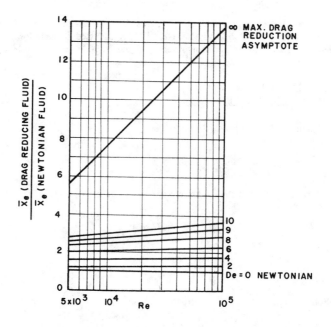

Figure 15. Estimated normalized turbulent entrance length ratios as a function of Reynolds number and Deborah number, along with a comparison of the available experimental data for smooth straight circular pipes.

can be written as:

$$\frac{x_{eo}}{F_o D_o} = \left[\frac{\psi_1}{(1 + \beta)\alpha\psi^2}\right] Re_o^\beta \tag{63}$$

$$\frac{x_{ei}}{F_i D_i} = \left[\frac{\psi_1}{(1 + \beta)\alpha\psi^2}\right] Re_i^\beta \tag{64}$$

where x_{eo} and x_{ei} = entrance lengths for the outer and inner region
        D_o and D_i = outer and inner pipe diameters
        Re_o and Re_i = Reynolds numbers based on outer and inner equivalent diameters
                as defined below
        F_o and F_i = geometric factors as shown in the following:

$$Re_o = \frac{\rho D_{eo} U}{\mu} \qquad Re_i = \frac{\rho D_{ei} U}{\mu} \tag{65}$$

$$D_{eo} = 2r_o(1 - \lambda^2) \qquad D_{ei} = 2r_i\left(\frac{\lambda^2}{k^2} - 1\right) \tag{66}$$

$$F_o = \frac{(1 - \lambda)}{(1 + \lambda)^\beta} \qquad F_i = \frac{(1 - \lambda^2)}{(\lambda + k)}\left[\frac{k(1 - \lambda)}{(\lambda^2 - k^2)}\right]^\beta \tag{67}$$

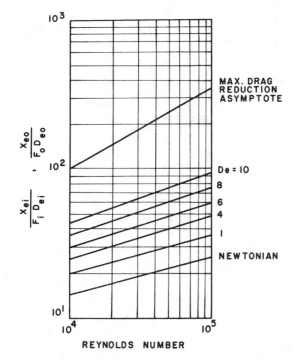

Figure 16. Entrance lengths as a function of Reynolds number and Deborah number for the inner and outer region of the annulus.

The radius of maximum velocity is determined as discussed by Singh et al. [44] from the following:

$$\frac{\lambda - k}{1 - \lambda} = k^{0.343} \tag{68}$$

The above equation is quite general, as can be seen by its application to the two limiting cases of the annulus geometry: namely, a circular pipe and a parallel plate channel. Thus, in the case of a circular pipe, $k = 0$ and $\lambda = 0$, irrespective of the type of fluid. Equation 68 does indeed predict $\lambda = 0$, and in the case of a parallel plate, $\lambda = 1$ irrespective of the type of the fluid. Equation 68 can therefore reliably hold, even for drag-reducing fluids. Figure 16 shows a plot of x_{ei}/F_iD_{ei}, x_{eo}/F_oD_{eo} as functions of Reynolds numbers in the range of $10^4 < \text{Re} < 10^6$ for varying Deborah numbers from 1 to 10 and at the maximum drag reduction asymptote. It can be seen that for conditions of maximum drag reduction, the entrance lengths are an order of magnitude higher than that for the Newtonian case. The maximum drag reduction corresponds to a Deborah number > 20. Thus, from Figure 16, it can be clearly seen that elasticity alone can create such large differences in the levels of entrance lengths.

CONCLUSION

This chapter has dealt with the nature of the time-averaged velocity profiles of drag-reducing fluids during turbulent flow. Theoretical expressions for velocity profiles have been provided for a number of different geometric flow situations—the straight circular pipe, annulus, and curved pipe as well as a tube rotating around the axis. The limited experimental data available in the literature have been discussed. It is evident that there are a number of aspects relating to velocity profiles in turbulent flow of drag reducing fluids that need to be investigated.

Future work could focus on developing better experimental techniques to measure velocity profiles so that reliable data could be generated for interesting flow situations, such as in the curved tube and the tube rotating around its own axis wherein an interesting secondary flow exists. Experimental determination of the velocity profiles in an annulus could also be done to verify the proposed theoretical velocity profiles in the inner and outer regions. On the theoretical side, velocity profiles in pipes of arbitrary cross-sectional shapes, i.e., non-circular pipes could be attempted. Entrance length expressions could be derived for the curved pipe, non-circular pipe, or pipe rotating on its axis. Thus, the area is still open to investigation and it is hoped that this chapter will provide the necessary background and incentive to pursue this area of research.

NOTATION

$\bar{a}$ radius of curved pipe

A   coefficient appearing in Equations 7 and 12 and given by Equation 8

A_1 coefficient appearing in Equations 24 and 27 and defined by Equation 25

$\bar{A}_1$ coefficient appearing in Equation 29 and defined by Equation 33

B   coefficient appearing in Equations 7 and 12 and defined by Equation 9

$\bar{B}$ coefficient appearing in Equations 42 and 43

B_1 exponent appearing in Equations 24 and 27 and defined by Equation 26

C   correction factor appearing in Equation 12 and defined by Equation 13

D   pipe diameter

D_1 coefficient appearing in Equation 35 and defined by Equations 38 and 45 for the case of curved pipe and rotating pipe, respectively

D_c characteristic angular velocity in Equations 38 and 45

D_i diameter of the inner pipe of an annulus

D_o diameter of the outer pipe of an annulus

D_{ei}, D_{eo} equivalent diameter defined by Equation 66

De   Deborah number

f   friction factor

F   roughness function defined by Equations 48 and 49

F_N roughness function for Newtonian fluids defined by Equation 50

F_i, F_o geometric factors defined by Equation 66 for an annulus

G   constant in Equation 16

k   geometric factor defined by Equation 31 for an annulus

L   length of pipe

ΔP pressure drop across the length of the pipe

r   radial position

r_i radius of inner cylinder of an annulus

r_m radius of maximum velocity inside an annulus

r_o radius of outer pipe of an annulus

R   pipe radius

$\bar{R}$ radius of curvature of a curved pipe as Equations 37 and 38

R^* Reynolds number based on pipe radius and friction velocity

Re   Reynolds number

Re_i, Re_o Reynolds number for drag-reducing fluids as given in Equation 65 based on equivalent inner and outer diameter of an annulus

Re_w Reynolds number for water

S^+ effective slip as defined by Virk [10]

u   time-averaged velocity at a point

u_o velocity at the edge of the boundary layer

u^* friction velocity

u^+ dimensionless velocity defined as u/u^*

u_i^* friction velocity for inner region of the annulus

u_o^* friction velocity for outer region of the annulus

u_i^+ dimensionless velocity for inner region of the annulus

u_o^+ dimensionless velocity for outer region of the annulus

u_m maximum velocity as given in Equations 22 and 57

u_{crit}^* friction velocity for onset of drag reduction

v   angular velocity for a curved pipe as defined by Equation 35

v_m average axial velocity for the curved

	pipe appearing in Equations 38 and 39 and for the rotating straight pipe in Equations 44–46	x_{ei}	entrance length for the inner region of an annulus defined by Equation 64
V	mean velocity of a drag-reducing fluid in a smooth circular pipe appearing in Equation 21	x_{eo}	entrance length for the outer region of an annulus defined by Equation 63
w	axial velocity for a curved pipe as defined by Equation 36	y	distance from pipe wall
w_1	coefficient appearing in Equation 36	y_{SL}	laminar sublayer thickness
w_c	dimensionless axial velocity for a curved pipe as defined by Equations 39 and 42	y^*	dimensionless location parameter defined by y/R
		y^+	distance-based Reynolds number
w_o	dimensionless axial velocity for a rotating straight pipe as defined by Equation 46	y_i^+	distance-based Reynolds number for the inner region of an annulus
		y_o^+	distance-based Reynolds number for the outer region of an annulus
x_e	entrance length for smooth circular pipe defined by Equation 62	y_E^+	elastic sublayer thickness as defined by Virk [10]

Greek Symbols

α	coefficient appearing in Equation 20	ν	kinematic viscosity of the fluid
α'	coefficient appearing in Equation 6	ξ	dimensionless distance from the wall
α^*	coefficient appearing in Equation 5	ξ_1	dimensionless viscous sublayer thickness
β	exponent appearing in Equation 20		
$\dot{\gamma}$	shear rate	ρ	density of the fluid
δ	boundary layer thickness	μ	fluid viscosity
δ_c	dimensionless boundary layer thickness as defined by Equation 37 for a curved pipe	σ_1	function of De defined by Equation 14
δ_o	dimensionless boundary layer thickness as defined by Equation 44 for a rotating straight circular pipe	σ_2	function of De defined by Equation 15
		τ_w	shear stress at the wall
ε	average height of the roughness projections	τ_{wi}, τ_{wo}	shear stress at the wall for the inner and outer wall, respectively, of the annulus
λ	dimensionless parameter for an annulus as defined by Equation 31	ψ	function of β defined by Equation 23
θ	angular coordinate for a curved pipe as shown in Figure 5	ψ_1	function of β defined by Equation 60
		ζ	distance from the wall for the curved pipe
θ_{fl}	fluid relaxation time	Ω	angular velocity of the rotating pipe

REFERENCES

1. Lumley, J. L., "Drag Reduction by Additives," in Sears, W. R., ed., *Annual Review of Fluid Mechanics*, Annual Review, Inc., Palo Alto, CA, Vol. 1, 1969, pp. 367–384.
2. Patterson, G. K., Zakin, J. L., and Rodriquez, J. M., "Drag Reduction in Polymer Solutions, Soap Solutions and Solid Particle Suspensions in Pipe Flow," *Ind. Eng. Chem.*, Vol. 61, 1969, pp. 22–30.
3. Gadd, G. F., "Friction Reduction," *Encyclopedia of Polymer Science and Technology*, New York, Vol. 15, 1971, pp. 224–253.
4. Darby, R., "A Review and Evaluation of Drag Reduction Theories," Naval Research Lab., NRL Memo Rept. 2446, 1972.
5. Hoyt, J. W., "The Effect of Additives on Fluid Friction," Trans. ASME, *J. Basic Eng.*, Vol. 94, 1972, pp. 258–285.

6. Landahl, M. T., "Drag Reduction by Polymer Addition." Proc. 18th Intern. Theor. and Appl. Mechanics, Moscow, Becker, E., and Mikhailov, G. K., eds., 1973, p. 177.

7. Lumley, J. L., "Drag Reduction in Turbulent Flow by Polymer Additives," *J. Polym. Sci., Macromolecular Reviews*, Vol. 7, 1973, pp. 263–290.

8. Fisher, M. C., and Ash, R. L., "A General Review of the Concepts for Reducing Skin Friction including Recommendations for Future Studies," NASA TMX-2894, 1974.

9. Palyvos, J. A., "Drag Reduction and Associated Phenomena in Internal and External Liquid Flows," Thermodynamics and Transport Phenomena Lab., Natl. Tech. Univ., Athens, Greece, Report No. 741, 1974.

10. Virk, P. S., "Drag Reduction Fundamentals, Journal Review," *AIChE J.*, Vol. 21, 1975, pp. 625–656.

11. Sellin, R. H. J., Hoyt, J. W., and Scrivener, O., "The Effect of Drag-Reducing Additives on Fluid Flows and Their Industrial Applications, Part 1: Basic Aspects," *J. Hydraulic Res.*, Vol. 20, 1982, pp. 29–68.

12. Sellin, R. H. J., Hoyt, J. W., Pollert, J., and Scrivener, O., "The Effect of Drag-Reducing Additives on Fluid Flows and their Industrial Applications, Part 2: Present Applications and Future Proposals," *J. Hydraulic Res.*, Vol. 20, 1982, pp. 235–292.

13. Shenoy, A. V., "A Review of Drag Reduction with Special Reference to Micellar Systems," *Colloid Polymer Science*, Vol. 262, 1984, pp. 319–337.

14. Astarita, G., "Possible Interpretation of the Mechanism of Drag Reduction in Viscoelastic Liquids," *Ind. Eng. Chem. Fundamentals*, Vol. 4, 1965, pp. 354–356.

15. Seyer, F. A., and Metzner, A. B., "Drag Reduction in Large Tubes and the Behavior of Annular Films of Drag-Reducing Fluids," *Can. J. Chem. Eng.*, Vol. 47, 1969, pp. 525–529.

16. Langhaar, H. L., *Dimensional Analysis and Theory of Models*, John Wiley and Sons, New York, 1951.

17. Seyer, F. A., and Metzner, A. B., "Turbulence Phenomena in Drag-Reducing Systems." *AIChEJ.*, Vol. 15, 1969, pp. 426–434.

18. Meyer, W. A., "A Correlation of the Frictional Characteristics for Turbulent Flow of Dilute Non-Newtonian Fluids in Pipes," *AIChEJ.*, Vol. 12 1966, pp. 522–525.

19. Elata, C., Lehrer, J., and Kahanovitz, A., "Turbulent Shear Flow of Polymer Solutions," *Israel J. Tech.*, Vol. 4, 1966, pp. 87–95.

20. Shenoy, A. V., and Talathi, M. M., "Turbulent Pipe Flow Velocity Profile Model for Drag Reducing Fluids," *AIChEJ.*, Vol. 31, 1985, pp. 520–522.

21. Shenoy, A. V., and Mashelkar, R. A., "Engineering Estimate of Hydrodynamic Entrance Lengths in Non-Newtonian Turbulent Flow," *Ind. Eng. Chem. Process Des. Dev.*, Vol. 22, 1983, pp. 165–168.

22. Shenoy, A. V., and Shintre, S. N., "Developing and Fully Developed Turbulent Flow of Drag Reducing Fluids in an Annular Duct," *Can. J. Chem. Eng.*, Vol. 64, 1986, pp. 190–195.

23. Virk, P. S., Merrill, E. W., Mickley, H. S., Smith, K. A., and Mollo-Christiansen, E. L., "The Toms Phenomenon: Turbulent Pipe Flow of Dilute Polymer Solutions," *J. Fluid Mech.*, Vol. 30., 1967, pp. 305–328.

24. Skelland, A. H. P., *Non-Newtonian Flow and Heat Transfer*, John Wiley and Sons, New York, 1967, pp. 288–291.

25. Shaver, R. G., and Merrill, E. W., "Turbulent Flow of Pseudoplastic Polymer Solutions in Straight Cylindrical Tubes," *AIChEJ*, Vol. 5, 1959, pp. 181–188.

26. Ernst, W. D., "Investigation of the Turbulent Shear Flow of Dilute Aqueous CMC Solutions," *AIChEJ.*, Vol. 12, 1966, pp. 581–586.

27. Wells, C. S., "Anomalous Turbulent Flow of Non-Newtonian Fluids," *A.I.A.A. J.*, Vol. 3, 1965, pp. 1800–1805.

28. Pruitt, G. T., and Crawford, M. R., "Investigation for the Use of Additives for the Reduction of Pressure Losses," Final Report of Western Company, Contract No. DA-23-072-AMC-209(T), 1965.

29. Astarita, G., and Nicodemo, L., "Velocity Distributions and Normal Stresses in Viscoelastic Turbulent Pipe Flow," *AIChEJ.*, Vol. 12, 1966, pp. 478–484.

30. Smith, K. A., Merrill. E. W., Mickley, H. S., and Virk, P. S., "Anomalous Pitot Tube and Hot Film Measurements in Dilute Polymer Solutions," *Chem. Eng. Sci.*, Vol. 22, 1967, pp. 619–626.
31. Patterson, G. K., and Florez, G. L., "Velocity Profiles during Drag Reduction," *Viscous Drag Reduction*, Wells, C. S. (ed.), Plenum Press, New York, 1969, pp. 233–250.
32. Seyer, F. A., and Metzner, A. B., "Turbulence Phenomena in Drag Reducing Systems," presented at the 60th Annual AIChE Meeting, New York, Nov. 1967.
33. Friehe, C. A., and Schwarz, W. H., "The Use of Pitot-Static Tubes and Hot-Film Anemometers in Dilute Polymer Solutions," *Viscous Drag Reduction*, Wells, C. S. (ed.), Plenum Press, New York, 1969, pp. 281–296.
34. Fabula, A. G., "An Experimental Study of Grid Turbulence in Dilute High-Polymer Solutions," Ph.D. Thesis, Pennsylvania State University, 1966.
35. James, D. F., "Laminar Flow of Dilute Polymer Solutions Around Circular Cylinders," Ph.D. Thesis, California Institute of Technology, 1967.
36. Shenoy, A. V., Ranade, V. R., and Ulbrecht, J. J., "Turbulent Flow of Mildly Viscoelastic Liquids in Curved Tubes," *Chem. Eng. Commun.*, Vol. 5, 1980, pp. 268–286.
37. Shenoy, A. V., "Turbulent Flow of Mildly Elastic Fluids Through Rotating Straight Circular Tubes," *Appl. Sci. Research*, Vol. 43, 1986, pp. 39–54.
38. Fenter, F. W., "The Turbulent Boundary Layer on Uniformly Rough Surfaces at Supersonic Speeds," Report No. RE-E9R-2. Vought Research Center, Chance Vought Aircraft, Inc., December 1959.
39. Spangler, J. G., "Studies of Viscous Drag Reduction with Polymers including Turbulence Measurements and Roughness Effects," *Viscous Drag Reduction*, Wells, C. S. (ed.), Plenum Press, New York, 1969, pp. 131–157.
40. White, A., "Turbulence and Drag Reduction with Polymer Additives," Research Bulletin No. 4, Hendon College of Technology, January 1967.
41. Brandt, H., McDonald, A. T., and Boyle, F. W., "Turbulent Skin Friction of Dilute Polymer Solutions in Rough Pipes," *Viscous Drag Reduction*, Wells, C. S. (ed.), Plenum Press, New York, pp. 159–171.
42. Shintre, S. N., Mashelkar, R. A., and Ulbrecht, J., "An Approximate Theoretical Analysis and Experimental Verification of Turbulent Entrance Region Flow of Drag Reducing Fluids," *Rheol. Acta*, Vol. 16. 1977, pp. 490–496.
43. Seyer, F. A., and Catania, P. J., "Laminar and Turbulent Entry Flow of Polymer Solutions," *Can. J. Chem. Eng.*, Vol. 50, 1972, pp. 31–36.
44. Singh, R. P., Nigam, K. K., and Mishra, P., "Developing and Fully Developed Turbulent Flow in an Annular Duct," *J. Chem. Eng. Japan*, Vol. 13, 1980, pp. 349–352.

CHAPTER 17

MECHANISMS OF DRAG REDUCTION IN
TURBULENT NON-NEWTONIAN PIPELINE FLOW

K. C. Wilson

Department of Civil Engineering
Queen's University at Kingston
Ontario, Canada

CONTENTS

INTRODUCTION

Slurries with a significant fraction of fine particles often exhibit non-Newtonian rheological behavior, affecting the frictional resistance of pipeline flow. The laminar-flow case is well understood, but the effect of non-Newtonian rheology on turbulent flow has not been easy to analyze, and comparison with the turbulent flow of other materials may be instructive. As is well known, the addition of small amounts of long-chain polymers can have a profound effect on aqueous turbulent flows, reducing the friction factor to values well below those obtained for equivalent flows of water alone [1]. The mechanism responsible for this type of drag reduction appears to be the viscoelastic behavior associated with stretching the randomly-coiled macromolecules [2, 3]. However, drag reduction is also obtained for slurries having rigid particles in the size range of tens or even hundreds of microns, and in this case the operative mechanism must be different from that for polymeric solutions, as noted by Lee et al. [4]. A good example is provided by the slurries of nylon fibers tested by Bobkowicz [5, 6]. The largest effect was found for fibers with length near 1 mm and diameter approximately 20 microns. The results of Bobkowicz's tests with the largest concentrations of these fibers (2 percent and 4 percent by weight) are displayed on Figure 1, which shows the ratio of the observed friction factor to that for Newtonian flow of water alone (for the same shear velocity) plotted against the shear velocity. It should be noted that the friction-factor ratio depends on fiber concentration as well as on shear velocity. As shown, the reduction of the friction factor can amount

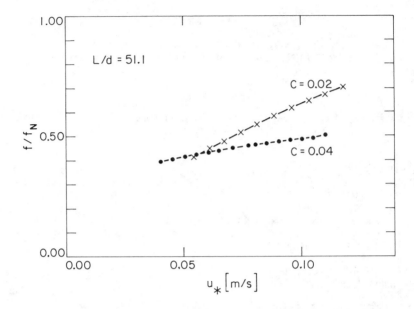

Figure 1. Friction-factor ratio for Bobkowicz's nylon-fiber slurries.

to more than 50 percent in favorable circumstances, implying equivalent reductions in the pressure drop and the power required for pumping.

Before considering the mechanisms associated with such drag reduction, it is appropriate to mention some of the major features of turbulence. Although consideration of generalized cases of turbulent flow has given rise to mathematical treatments of great complexity, these are not necessary for engineering analysis of the simple case of axisymmetric incompressible flow in a pipe. For this flow, the pressure diminishes uniformly in an axial direction and the variation of other quantities depends only on the distance from the pipe wall, y. For a wall that is hydraulically smooth, there is a viscous sub-layer at very small values of y, and within this sub-layer the flow approximates laminar behavior. Farther from the wall, the effect of viscosity can be ignored; and the velocity gradient is determined by momentum transfer (inertial mixing) which is governed by the size of the larger turbulent eddies, i.e., the mixing length or turbulent macro-scale. This length depends only on the distance from the pipe wall, and is usually expressed as κy where κ (which has a value very near 0.4) is the von Karman coefficient. This formulation gives rise directly to the well-authenticated logarithmic velocity profile. As κ is a "universal" constant which is not influenced by the viscosity of Newtonian fluids, it should also be unaffected by equivalent rheological properties of non-Newtonians.

Although the turbulent macro-eddies determine the velocity profile, as noted above, they are only the upper extreme of a whole series of eddies of progressively smaller size. This series can also be visualized in terms of an energy spectrum in which there is a cascade of energy from the largest energy-extracting scales of motion to successively smaller scales. Eddies within this cascade simply receive their energy from those of larger size and pass it on to those of lesser size, but as the eddies become smaller the shearing stresses increase, setting a lower limit to eddy size by means of viscous dissipation of energy. This limit is known as the dissipative (Kolmogorov) micro-scale of turbulence. For a Newtonian fluid of density ρ and viscosity μ, this micro-scale is proportional to $\rho u_*/\mu$, where u_* is shear velocity.

SUB-LAYER THICKENING AND DRAG REDUCTION

Drag reduction in turbulent flow of non-Newtonian slurries has recently been the subject of a new analysis [7]. As noted earlier, the viscoelastic mechanism associated with the expansion of coiled macromolecules cannot apply here. Of the two other potential mechanisms of drag reduction, one—velocity-profile changes accompanying density gradients—is also not applicable to non-settling slurries. The remaining mechanism, which is believed to be the principal cause of drag reduction in non-Newtonian turbulent flow, is associated with thickening of the viscous sub-layer. This sub-layer thickening phenomenon has been described by Lumley [1, 8], and is illustrated in Figure 2, which graphs distance from the wall in the vertical direction and representative eddy size in the horizontal direction. As noted previously, the size of the largest eddies (the macro-scale of turbulence) is directly proportional to the distance from the wall. This is shown in the figure, together with the size of the smallest eddies (the dissipative, or Kolmogorov, micro-scale) which changes only slightly with distance from the wall. At large values of y the inertial macro-eddies are much larger than the dissipative micro-eddies, and between them is the range of turbulent eddy sizes associated with the energy cascade, shown by hatching on the figure.

As the pipe wall is approached, the range of possible eddy sizes shrinks until the size of the largest and smallest eddies are equal. At this point y equals δ_v, the thickness (in a statistical sense) of the viscous sub-layer. The dashed line in Figure 2 shows that increasing the size of the dissipative micro-eddies leads to an increase in the viscous sub-layer thickness. If other quantities are unaffected, this increase will produce a higher mean velocity for the same wall shear stress, i.e., a reduced friction factor. It may be remarked that the picture presented here is based on the usual "engineering" velocity profile in which the logarithmic portion of the velocity distribution is joined directly to the viscous sub-layer. It is believed that the extra complexity of considering an intermediate "buffer layer" [9] is not warranted, and that the "elastic sub-layer" [9] is not warranted, and that the "elastic sublayer" proposed by Virk [3] for flows with randomly-coiled macromolecules is not applicable to non-Newtonian slurry flow.

As mentioned previously, the unsteady nature of turbulent flow involves a series rapid dissipative events as eddies drop from the inertial to the dissipative size range. There is an analogy between this process and the dynamic loading of a structure, for which strain energy is determined from

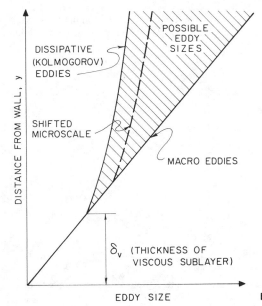

Figure 2. Eddy scales in turbulent flow.

the integral of the stress-strain curve. As proposed by Wilson and Thomas [7], the typical rate of energy dissipation of a turbulent eddy is determined by the integral of the curve of shear stress vs. strain rate, i.e., the area beneath the rheogram.

Rheograms are based on viscometric measurements under laminar conditions, plotted as shear stress τ vs. transverse strain rate dU/dy. (Of course it is equally valid to consider the shear stress as the independent variable, which determines the shear rate.) Figure 3 illustrates the rheogram shape displayed by many non-Newtonian materials, with no permanent deformation taking place until the applied shear stress exceeds a certain yield value, τ_y. At shear stresses greater than τ_y there is, in the general case, a non-linear relation between stress and strain rate, although this often approaches a linear asymptote at high strain rates. As for a Newtonian fluid, the viscosity, μ, is defined as the ratio of τ to dU/dy. This ratio represents the slope of a secant line joining the origin to any point of interest on the curve, as shown on Figure 3. Another quantity associated with viscosity is the slope of a tangent to the curve of τ vs. dU/dy, denoted by η_t and sometimes referred to as "tangent viscosity" or "incremental viscosity".

The ratio of the integrals under the non-Newtonian and Newtonian rheograms (for the same values of τ and dU/dy at the upper limit) is denoted by α. For the typical conditions illustrated in Figure 3, the area under the non-Newtonian rheogram is significantly larger than that of the triangle which defines Newtonian behavior, and it can be seen that for this type of behavior α will lie between 1.0 and 2.0. The increased area under the non-Newtonian rheogram does not imply a greater rate of energy dissipation, since the energy cascade dictates the energy dissipation rate which will be imposed on the smallest eddies. Instead, the increased area indicates that, as far as the dissipative turbulent eddies are concerned, the non-Newtonian fluid acts as if it were a Newtonian fluid with viscosity $\alpha\mu$. Since the dissipation process imposes a constant-Reynolds-number relation on the smallest eddies, it follows that the product of eddy size and typical velocity for these eddies will be proportional to $\alpha\mu/\rho$.

At the interface between the inertial (logarithmic) layer and the viscous sub-layer, the length scales of the largest and smallest eddies effectively coincide, as shown in Figure 2. The same applies to the velocity scales of these eddies, which are proportional to the shear velocity u_*. As the product of velocity and eddy size varies with α, it follows that the minimum eddy size for a non-Newtonian fluid is larger than that for a Newtonian fluid (of the same μ) by the factor α. Based on the geometric relationship shown in Figure 2, it can be seen directly that the same factor applies to the thickness of the viscous sub-layer, δ_v.

For a smooth-walled pipe, conditions can be taken as essentially steady-state within the viscous sub-layer, so that the viscosity μ (evaluated at the wall shear stress τ_w) is appropriate for any fluid,

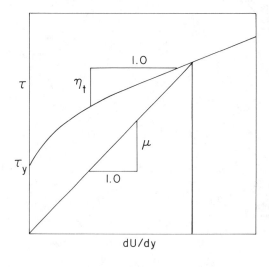

Figure 3. Representative non-Newtonian rheogram

and the velocity distribution, both Newtonian and non-Newtonian, is given by:

$$U/u_* = \rho u_* y/\mu \tag{1}$$

For the Newtonian case, the intercept with the logarithmic profile occurs at distance $\delta_v = 11.6\mu/\rho u_*$ and velocity $U_v = 11.6 u_*$. For the non-Newtonian case, with its thickened viscous sublayer, 11.6 must be replaced by 11.6α. In the logarithmic zone, the general form of the velocity profile is given by:

$$U/u_* = 2.5 \ln(y/\delta_v) + U_v/u_* \tag{2}$$

where 2.5 is the inverse of the von Karman coefficient. Substitution of $U_v/u_* = 11.6$ and $\delta_v = 11.6\mu/\rho u_*$ yields the classic expression for the Newtonian case of smooth-wall flow:

$$U/u_* = 2.5 \ln(\rho u_* y/\mu) + 5.5 \tag{3}$$

The equivalent non-Newtonian expression becomes [7]

$$U/u_* = 2.5 \ln(\rho u_* y/\mu) + 5.5 + 11.6(\alpha - 1) - 2.5 \ln(\alpha) \tag{4}$$

Since the area ratio α (like the viscosity μ) is evaluated for $\tau = \tau_w$, the last two terms of Equation 4 will be constant throughout a pipe of internal diameter D, and thus their contribution to the velocity ratio U/u_* will apply equally to the ratio of the throughput velocity V to u_*.

It will be convenient to denote by V_N the throughput velocity for an equivalent Newtonian flow, i.e., flow with the same τ_w for a Newtonian fluid with μ corresponding to the non-Newtonian value at $\tau = \tau_w$. For smooth-walled pipes, V_N can be evaluated from the expression:

$$V_N/u_* = 2.5 \ln(\rho D u_*/\mu) \tag{5}$$

A final term, Ω, has been included in the throughput velocity equation to represent any effect of a possible blunting of the velocity profile in the logarithmic or core regions of the flow. The expression for throughput velocity then becomes:

$$V/u_* = V_N/u_* + 11.6(\alpha - 1) - 2.5 \ln \alpha - \Omega \tag{6}$$

As the flow in the logarithmic and core regions is governed by inertia, not viscosity, non-Newtonian viscosity *per se* should have virtually no effect in these regions, implying a zero value for Ω. However, non-Newtonians with a yield stress must have a flat velocity profile in the area near the pipe axis where τ is less than τ_y. As a result, in this case Ω should depend on τ_y/τ_w (for convenience this ratio will be denoted by ξ). One way of approximating this effect [7] can be expressed by the equation:

$$\Omega = -2.5 \ln(1 - \xi) - 2.5\xi(1 + 0.5\xi) \tag{7}$$

More detailed study of this feature would be required to obtain complete understanding, but for most turbulent flows of practical interest ξ is much less than unity, and only a small portion of the flow is affected. In such cases the influence on throughput velocity is less than would be caused by uncertainties in other flow-related parameters, and Ω can be ignored without loss of accuracy.

Up to this point, attention has been directed to flow in pipes with hydraulically-smooth walls, as this is the condition most likely to be encountered in turbulent flow of non-Newtonians. However, the analysis can readily be extended to account for pipe-wall roughness. For a very rough wall, the viscosity of a Newtonian fluid does not come into play, and neither will the rheologic properties of a non-Newtonian. In this case the Nikuradse formula can be applied, with the Ω term included for completeness, i.e.:

$$\frac{V}{u_*} = 2.5 \ln\left[\frac{3.7}{\varepsilon/D}\right] - \Omega \tag{8}$$

where ε/D is relative roughness. For smaller relative roughnesses a generalization of the Colebrook-White equation is required. On multiplying that equation through by $\sqrt{8}$, including the Ω term and introducing some function of α to take account of sub-layer thickening, one obtains:

$$\frac{V}{u_*} = -2.5 \ln\left[\frac{\varepsilon/D}{3.7} + \frac{\text{fcn}(\alpha)}{\rho D u_*/\mu}\right] - \Omega \tag{9}$$

If $\rho u_* D/\mu$ is sufficiently large, the second term within the brackets can be neglected, giving Equation 8. Similarly, if ε/D is negligible, the result should be the smooth-wall solution, i.e.:

$$\frac{V}{u_*} = 2.5 \ln[\rho D u_*/\mu] + 11.6(\alpha - 1) - 2.5 \ln(\alpha) - \Omega \tag{10}$$

This gives the basis for evaluating fcn(α), which is found to equal $\alpha e^{-4.64(\alpha-1)}$, giving:

$$\frac{V}{u_*} = -2.5 \ln\left[\frac{\varepsilon/D}{3.7} + \frac{\alpha e^{-4.64(\alpha-1)}}{\rho D u_*/\mu}\right] - \Omega \tag{11}$$

For the Newtonian fluid, with $\alpha = 1$ and $\Omega = 0$, the second term within the brackets differs from that in the Colebrook-White equation by about 12 percent, which is negligible after the logarithm is taken, and occurs only because of the slight difference from the smooth-wall Newtonian expression used here and the form used by Colebrook in the 1930s.

The relationships discussed above are of a general nature, and can readily be applied to those problems for which the wall shear stress τ_w is known in advance, permitting the area ratio α to be determined from the rheogram. Conversely, if the observed friction factor is available, together with the Newtonian one, the associated value of α can be calculated. These calculations were made for the nylon-fiber data of Bobkowicz [5, 6], mentioned previously in connection with Figure 1, and it was verified that the values of α for these data all fall between 1.0 and 2.0, as expected.

ANALYSIS OF FLOW MODELS

Bingham Model

Rheograms are often approximated by simple algebraic formulas, and these can be used to give equations for evaluating the area ratio α. The simplest model, that of Bingham, was discussed by Wilson and Thomas [7]. This model is defined by the two-parameter linear relation:

$$\tau = \tau_y + \eta\, dU/dy \tag{12}$$

where τ_y is the yield stress and η is called the "tangent" or "plastic" viscosity. For a material obeying this relation, it can easily be shown that ξ, i.e., τ_y/τ_w, is equal to $(\alpha - 1)$ where α is the area ratio of the rheogram. By substituting into Equation 6, a solution can be obtained without difficulty in cases were τ_w is known in advance. For other cases it may be preferable to recast the equation in terms of two dimensionless parameters, the "plastic" shear Reynolds number, $\text{Re}'_* = \rho D u_*/\eta$, and the Hedstrom number, $\text{He} = \rho D^2 \tau_y/\eta^2$. With these parameters, the ratio ξ is expressed as He/Re'^2_*. Using Equation 5, the Newtonian velocity ratio V_N/u_* is then written as:

$$V_N/u_* = 2.5 \ln(\text{Re}'_*\, \eta/\mu) \tag{13}$$

From Equation 12, it can be shown that $\eta/\mu = 1 - \xi$, giving:

$$V_N/u_* = 2.5 \ln \text{Re}'_* + 2.5 \ln(1 - \xi) \tag{14}$$

Combining the equations for the Bingham-plastic formulation (for which $\alpha = 1 + \xi$) gives:

$$V/u_* = 2.5 \ln \text{Re}'_* + 2.5 \ln[(1 - \xi)^2/(1 + \xi)] + \xi(14.1 + 1.25\xi) \tag{15}$$

In this equation, the term in Re'_* can be thought of as representing a "Newtonian" value of V/u_* based on the "plastic" (tangent) viscosity. When the sum of the remaining terms was plotted against ξ, a maximum value of approximately 3.2 was found at ξ of about 0.65. It follows that, for a particular value of Re'_*, the largest V/u_* is given by:

$$(V/u_*)_{max} = 2.5 \ln(Re'_*) + 3.2 \tag{16}$$

This value will be reached only if $\xi = 0.65$ is included in the portion of the constant-Hedstrom curve to the right of the laminar-turbulent intercept, which is the case for all $He > 4.5 \times 10^5$ (corresponding to $Re'_* > 830$ and $\rho DV/\eta > 1.7 \times 10^4$). The right limb of the envelope on the diagram of friction factor vs. plastic Reynolds number has been plotted on this basis in Figure 4. For smaller values of He the envelope has been based on the intercept of the turbulent expression given above and the laminar expression:

$$V/u_* = [3 - \xi(4 - \xi^3)]\, Re'_*/24 \tag{17}$$

For the Bingham model, the predictions have been given in Figure 4 as friction factor vs. Reynolds number based on the plastic viscosity, and with the Hedstrom number, He, as parameter. The first thing to note is that the theory predicts a maximum deviation below the "Newtonian" line of between 15% and 25%, occurring at or shortly after laminar-turbulent transition. Thereafter the predicted curve approaches the "Newtonian" line, effectively reaching it at a Reynolds number some five times the transition value. A similarly rapid convergence is shown by the data of Bain and Bonnington [10] for chalk slurries, also plotted in Figure 4. The same trend has also been found [7] for a sizeable body of data which had been analyzed, not as a Bingham plastic, but as a power-law fluid. This behavior is exemplified by the data of Metzner and Reed [11] for a variety of materials and by the findings of Kemblowski and Kolodziejski [12] for a kaolin slurry.

A different pattern, with the experimental results lying below the Newtonian line and nearly parallel to it, is shown by other experimental data, including those of Caldwell and Babbitt [13], Wilhelm et al. [14], D. G. Thomas [15, 16], and A. D. Thomas [17]. The existence of two populations differing in behavior indicated the need for further analysis using more sophisticated rheologic models, and this analysis will be presented in subsequent sections.

The most important point to note is that the data follow the laminar curve until it has dropped below the Newtonian line, and then may either run parallel to the latter line, or approach it from below. For both types of behavior it is clear that drag reduction is taking place. In fact, the drag reduction is more pronounced than would appear from Figure 4, since this figure is based on the "tangent" viscosity, which is considerably less than the true (secant) viscosity. It should also be noted that the drag-reduction behavior displayed in Figure 4 is quite different from the "extended transition" predicted by the theory of Hanks [18] for Hedstrom numbers in excess of about 5×10^5. Curves exemplifying that prediction, which are also shown on the figure, typically lie above both the laminar line and the Newtonian turbulent line, implying little or no drag reduction. For further commentary see Wilson and Thomas [7].

Analysis for Yield-Power-Law Model

As noted above, the two-parameter Bingham model is unable to simulate all the experimental data, and better simulation requires a more sophisticated rheologic model. Thus the analysis was extended to the three-parameter yield-power-law model [19], also known as the Herschel-Bulkley model.

The equation that defines yield-power-law rheological behavior is:

$$\tau = \tau_y + k\left(\frac{dU}{dy}\right)^n \tag{18}$$

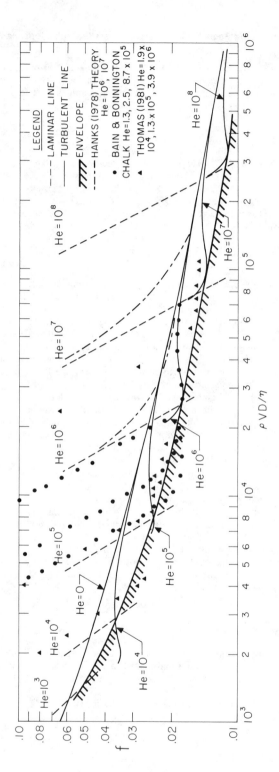

Figure 4. Comparison of experimental data with analysis for Bingham model.

where τ = shear stress
τ_y = yield shear stress
dU/dy = velocity gradient

For this model it is found that the area ratio α is given by:

$$\alpha = 2(1 + \xi n)/(1 + n) \tag{19}$$

where $\xi = \tau_y/\tau_w$, as before. It can be seen that when $n = 1$, Equation 19 reduces to $\alpha = 1 + \xi$, which is the relation already found for the Bingham model. On the other hand, for $\tau_y = 0$, it reduces to $\alpha = 2/(n + 1)$, which is the relation for a power-law fluid [7]. In the general case the area ratio α can be calculated by Equation 19, and substituted into Equation 6 to predict the effect of the thickening of the viscous sub-layer.

Figure 5 shows laminar-flow rheograms for kaolin clay slurries [17], based on data from a 7.2 mm diameter tube viscometer. As noted by A. D. Thomas [20], other tests in this tube viscometer using clays from the same source showed excellent agreement with laminar flow data from recirculating pipe systems with internal diameter 18.9 mm and 105 mm. In the previous section the slurry with 7.5% clay was analyzed as a Bingham plastic ($n = 1.0$), but it can be seen that a yield-power-law model with $n = 0.875$ fits the data better. (Correlation coefficient 0.9983 vs. 0.9971 for the Bingham model.)

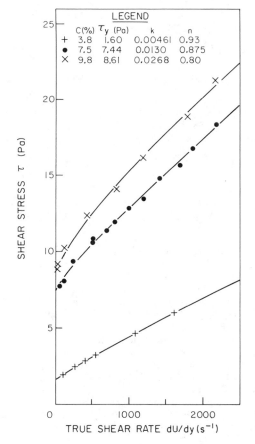

Figure 5. Rheograms for kaolin slurries at various concentrations.

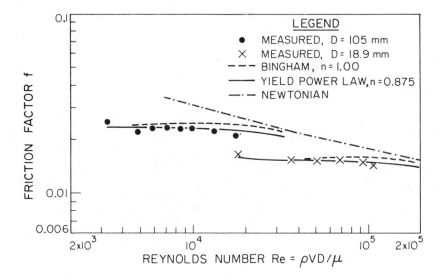

Figure 6. Turbulent-flow friction factor for slurry of 7.5 percent kaolin.

Figure 6 shows turbulent-flow behavior predicted by Equation 6 for the 7.5% kaolin slurry in two pipe sizes, 18.9 mm and 105 mm. The experimental data obtained by A. D. Thomas [17] for these pipe sizes have also been plotted on the figure. The Reynolds number used for this figure is based on the viscosity μ, evaluated at $\tau = \tau_w$. The turbulent-flow data are in better agreement with the yield-power-law prediction, n = 0.875, than with the prediction of the Bingham model. Note that for such a value of n the yield-power-law prediction shows less rapid convergence towards the Newtonian line than does the Bingham (n = 1) prediction.

It was noted above that for the kaolin clay slurry at 7.5% concentration by volume, a yield-power-law model with n = 0.875 is appropriate. Figure 5 also shows plots based on the tube viscometer data for concentrations 9.8%, and 3.8%. The yield-power-law curves for these slurries that are shown in the figure represent the best fit as determined by linear regression (with the value of n selected at intervals of 0.01). It can be seen that the solids concentration affects the parameters of the yield-power-law, with the best-fit value of n decreasing with increasing concentration; and it is suggested that this behavior is typical of many slurries.

Slurries of the same kaolin clay were tested at a number of different concentrations in the 105 mm pipe with turbulent flow conditions. Figure 7 shows predictions for two concentrations—3.56% and 8.95% by volume. The appropriate yield-power-law parameters were found by interpolation from the three values already discussed in connection with Figure 5. Also shown, as dashed lines, are predictions based on the Bingham model. For the lower-concentration slurry the predictions using the yield-power-law and the Bingham model are similar, both showing a maximum error of about 6%. In the case of the higher-concentration slurry the difference between the two predictions is more pronounced, with the yield-power-law prediction following the data more closely, having a maximum error around 10%. It can be seen that the lower-concentration data tend to converge to the Newtonian line with increasing Reynolds number, whereas for the higher-concentration slurries the trend of the data remains significantly below the Newtonian line, approximately paralleling it. If the friction factor is plotted against the plastic Reynolds number (based on the tangent viscosity η_t), the difference in trends between the two concentrations becomes even more evident.

The nature of the trends can best be shown by numerical example. Suppose for this purpose that the rheogram for some non-Newtonian material has been obtained for a limited range of strain rate, say near $dU/dy = 1,000 \text{ s}^{-1}$, for which $\tau = 10$ Pa and the tangent viscosity $\eta_t = 0.0040$ Pa.s.

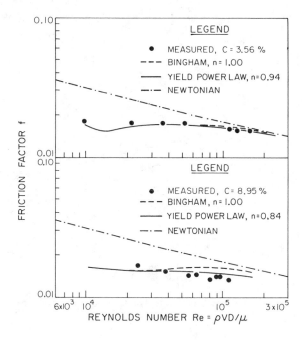

Figure 7. Turbulent-flow friction factors for slurries of 3.56 and 8.95 percent kaolin in 105 mm pipe.

A series of yield-power-law rheologic relations can be fitted to these data, corresponding to various values of n in Equation 18. For this type of problem, once n has been selected, the corresponding values of k and τ_y can be calculated. The meaningful range of n in this case is from unity (Bingham plastic with $\tau_y = 6.0$ Pa) to n = 0.4 (power-law fluid with $\tau_y =$ zero).

With the limited data postulated above, a material of this type would probably be treated as a Bingham plastic, using the plastic Reynolds number $\rho VD/\eta_t$ based on the value of η_t near dU/dy = 1,000 s^{-1}. For $\rho = 1,100$ kg/m³, and using D = 0.100 m, the results are shown on Figure 8, which is a plot of turbulent-flow friction factor vs. plastic Reynolds number. As expected, the Bingham-plastic line (calculated according to the present theory and marked n = 1.0 on the figure) lies below the line of Newtonian behavior, but rises rapidly to converge with that line. If, however, the assumed Bingham relation is not the true one, and the actual value of n is significantly less than 1.0, the predicted behavior is different, as shown in Figure 8. Note that the lines for the various values of n pass through a common point on the figure, and diverge to the right of this point. The prediction for n = 0.8 lies approximately parallel to the Newtonian line, while that for n = 0.6 and for n = 0.4 (corresponding to the power law for the present example) diverge downward with increasing plastic Reynolds number (as before, the plastic Reynolds number is based on the "observed" tangent viscosity of 0.0040 Pa·s).

It may be noted in particular that for n = 0.8, the curvature of the rheogram is modest, and the yield stress τ_y of 5.0 Pa is not greatly different from the Bingham value of 6.0 Pa. In such a case, the approximation using the Bingham model would normally appear quite appropriate, but the present analysis shows that the behavior of the turbulent-flow friction factor could be strongly affected. As noted previously, the exponent n of the yield-power-law rheogram has a tendency to increase with increasing solids concentration. The analysis indicates that this would result in a change of behavior with increasing concentration—from converging toward the Newtonian line

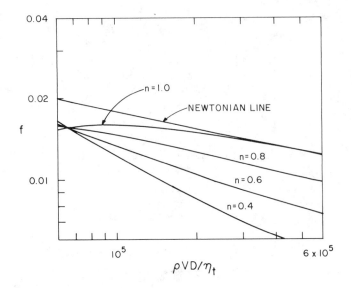

Figure 8. Predicted turbulent-flow friction factors for numerical example.

to paralleling it, or even diverging. This prediction is in full accord with the behavior mentioned above in connection with Figure 7. Agreement is also found in the work of D. G. Thomas [21], who noted a similar change in behavior with increasing concentration for slurries of kaolin and thorium oxide, including downward divergence from the Newtonian line in some cases.

The foregoing analysis has provided an answer to the question raised previously as to why data for some slurries with a yield point tend to converge towards the Newtonian line while other data more nearly parallel it. It is now seen that at low concentrations, the Bingham model is reasonably appropriate (with consequent convergence towards the Newtonian line), but as the concentration is increased, the rheogram diverges from the Bingham model and the three-parameter yield-power-law model can give better results.

Asymptotic Model

Before the computer came into common use, it was desirable to use very simple functions for rheologic models. This simplicity is no longer necessary, and more complex modeling functions can now be considered. The yield-power-law model is a step in this direction, but it often fails to simulate actual behavior near the ends of the range of rheological measurement. For example, at sufficiently high shear stress, rheograms very often approach a straight line, which can be defined by the relation:

$$\tau = \tau_i + \eta \, dU/dy \tag{20}$$

Here η is the limiting tangent viscosity, i.e., the slope of the high-shear asymptote on the rheogram, and τ_i is the intercept of this asymptote when projected back to the shear axis. The rheogram itself will also intercept the shear axis; this occurs at the yield shear stress τ_y, which in general will be different from τ_i.

To complete the mid-range of such a rheogram, a function is required which passes through τ_y and approaches Equation 20 at high shear stress. As noted in an earlier paper [22], this requirement can be achieved by incorporating a term that has an exponential decrease in magnitude with dU/dy, i.e.:

$$\tau = \tau_i + \eta \, dU/dy - (\tau_i - \tau_y) \exp[-\lambda \, dU/dy] \tag{21}$$

As the Bingham model is a particular case of Equation 21, it is clear that this equation has the potential to surpass the Bingham formulation in fitting rheologic data. In addition to the Bingham parameters τ_i and η, use of Equation 21 requires evaluation of the true yield stress τ_y and the shape parameter λ.

In comparing the asymptotic model of Equation 21 to the yield-power-law function, it should be recalled that the latter tends to give a reasonable simulation in the mid-range of the variables, but shows weaknesses toward both ends of the range. In particular, it has a vertical tangent as dU/dy approaches zero (actual materials, with or without a yield stress, typically have a non-vertical tangent at this location). Also, at high shear stress, the yield-power-law formulation predicts a constantly-diminishing viscosity μ. As noted by Fredrickson [23] and shown graphically by A. D. Thomas [24], this progressive diminution of viscosity usually does not reflect reality.

The proposed asymptotic model is not subject to these difficulties at the ends of the range, and for representative values of the parameters in Equation 21 gives a good approximation to the yield-power-law model throughout the middle of the range. Moreover, with other values of the parameters, less usual behavior can also be duplicated; for example, the concave-upward rheogram for a Bentonite slurry obtained by Engelund and Wan [25] can be represented by Equation 21 with τ_y set greater than τ_i.

Up to this point, the asymptotic model for non-Newtonian flow has been presented only in the form suitable for a constant stress field. In a pipe, however, the shear stress varies, and integration is required to obtain the velocity distribution and the discharge (and hence the throughput velocity V). The results for laminar pipe flow are usually presented as a function (or graph) linking the wall shear stress τ_w with the flow number 8V/D. For the proposed model, the relation is not given in closed form but can readily be evaluated by numerical integration.

Figure 9 shows data obtained by the GIW Hydraulic Laboratory for phosphate slimes of a strongly non-Newtonian character. These data could not be represented in a satisfactory way by

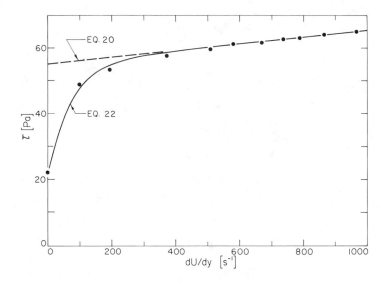

Figure 9. Rheogram for phosphate slimes tested at GIW.

either Bingham or yield-power-law models, but are matched closely by the asymptotic model, expressed by the equation:

$$\tau = 55.0 + 0.0105 \, dU/dy - 33.0 \exp[-0.0135 \, dU/dy] \tag{22}$$

The evaluation of α was made earlier for the Bingham and yield-power-law models. For the proposed new model, α is given by:

$$\alpha = \frac{1}{\tau}\left[2\tau_i + \eta \frac{dU}{dy} - \frac{2(\tau_i - \tau_y)}{(\lambda \, dU/dy)}\left[1 - \exp\left(-\lambda \frac{dU}{dy}\right)\right]\right] \tag{23}$$

where τ is to be evaluated by Equation 21.

Figure 10 is a plot of wall shear stress vs. 8V/D, showing the fit line and the data points for laminar flow previously plotted in Figure 9, together with associated data points obtained by the GIW Hydraulic Laboratory for turbulent flow of this slurry. Also shown in the figure are various calculated curves in the turbulent-flow range. The curve furthest to the left, marked "N," is based on the viscosity μ (i.e., $\tau/[dU/dy]$), evaluated using Equation 22. It represents the first or Newtonian term of Equation 6, and predicts the velocity that would occur (for given τ_w) in the absence of drag reduction from sub-layer thickening. It can be seen that the observed velocities are about 20 percent in excess of this prediction, showing that significant drag reduction has occurred. Although it is widely held that the throughput velocity can be calculated by using the tangent viscosity η_t in place of μ in a Newtonian formulation (e.g., Equation 5), there is no physical rationale for this method. The line representing this postulate has been plotted in Figure 10, marked "TV." As shown, it has a steeper slope than the other curves, and significantly under-predicts the throughput velocity of the highest experimental points.

The curve furthest to the right in Figure 10, marked "WT," includes the terms in α and Ω of Equation 6, with α evaluated using Equations 22 and 23, and Ω using Equation 7. It can be seen that, at least for conditions just above the laminar-turbulent transition, this curve predicts velocities significantly greater than those observed. The reason for this over-prediction may be found in the thickness of the portion of the flow dominated by viscosity, which is normally such a small

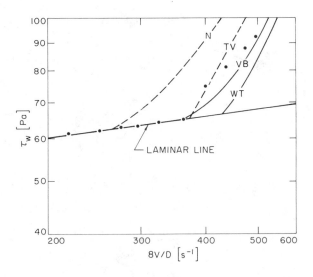

Figure 10. Flow curves for phosphate slimes tested at GIW.

fraction of the pipe radius that it can be ignored in the calculation of throughput velocity (as in Equation 6). The case considered here is unusual in this respect. For wall shear stress less than 75 Pa, the viscous sub-layer thickness δ_v exceeds 5% of the pipe radius. In these circumstances both the viscous sub-layer and the buffer layer between it and the logarithmic portion of the profile should be taken into account in predicting throughput velocity. Such calculations are not entirely straightforward, even for Newtonian flows. However, indicative computations have been carried out, based on the simple buffer-layer formulation of von Karman [9]. The results are shown by the line marked "VB" on Figure 10. This line intersects the laminar line at the last experimental point for this type of flow, and is also in good accord with the two turbulent-flow observations at the largest values of τ_w.

EFFECTS OF TIME-DEPENDENT RHEOLOGY

In addition to slurries that display non-Newtonian behavior of the type described above, there are slurries that have rheograms that depend on the duration of testing. Such time-dependent behavior can sometimes be expressed mathematically by a quasi-Newtonian relation in which the viscosity μ depends on the duration of the test, t, in accord with an exponential-decay law of the type:

$$\mu = \mu_\infty + (\mu_o - \mu_\infty)e^{-k_1 t} \tag{24}$$

where μ_o is the value of viscosity at t = 0 and μ_∞ is the value approached at extremely large test durations.

In other cases, the behavior of the time-dependent material resembles that of a Bingham plastic for which the yield stress varies between τ_{io} at t = 0 and $\tau_{i\infty}$ at very large test times, as given by the equation:

$$\tau = \tau_{i\infty} + \eta \, dU/dy + (\tau_{io} - \tau_{i\infty})e^{-k_2 t} \tag{25}$$

The form of Equation 25 is somewhat similar to that of Equation 21. However, the evaluation of α is now made more complicated by the necessity of integrating over time as well as over strain rate. The appropriate time span for the eddies at the edge of the viscous sublayer is proportional to the time scale for micro-eddies, which is given by $\mu/(\rho u_*^2)$ for Newtonian flow and by $\alpha\mu/(\rho u_*^2)$ for the non-Newtonian case considered here.

There are great practical difficulties in the evaluation of time-dependent relationships such as Equations 24 and 25, not only because of the involvement of the unknown α in the time scale, but also because viscometers are generally not well suited for obtaining accurate measurements at the small durations that are of interest in these cases. Fortunately, the required time scale (and the associated value of α) depends only on the properties of the material and on the shear velocity u_*. This fact has led to the development of a scaling technique, which will be described in the following section.

Time dependence has also been found in the recovery of rheologic parameters after the cause of deformation has ceased to act. This matter was investigated by Chu and Wang [26], who observed the fall of spheres through a non-Newtonian material that had previously been agitated. Particles with insufficient submerged weight to overcome the force produced by the yield stress of the material will not settle, as noted earlier by Ansley and Smith [27]. Chu and Wang found that the maximum size of non-settling particles increased with the time elapsed since agitation, with an asymptotic approach to a constant value at large elapsed times. This behavior clearly indicates a corresponding increase of yield stress with time. As with the other aspects of time-dependent flow mentioned above, the variation of yield stress with time will have an indirect effect on the quasi-steady-state turbulent flow in a pipe. Once again, the flow within the viscous sub-layer approximates the long-term or steady-state situation, while the adjacent turbulent eddies follow the dissipative, or Kolmogorov, scale.

Tests of the fall of particles in a material having a yield stress were also made by Highgate and Whorlow [28] and by A. D. Thomas [24]. In their experiments, the material was contained in the annulus between two coaxial cylinders with vertical axes, arranged so that one of the cylinders could be rotated to set up stress and deformation. It was observed that particles in the annulus fell more rapidly as the transverse shear between the cylinders was increased. When this finding is applied to pipeline flow of similar mixtures, it is seen that below a certain wall shear stress (with its associated shear velocity u_*) the coarse particles will be completely supported by the non-Newtonian carrier fluid; but at higher wall shear stress the particles may begin to settle. Flows with settled or contact-load solids require high pumping power, and thus settling of solids should be avoided.

As the boundary between settling and non-settling behavior is determined by u_* (for specified coarse particles and carrier fluid), maintaining u_* constant will give similar results in this regard. The shear velocity also fixes the quantities μ and α for the non-Newtonian and time-dependent slurries discussed above, and thus it appears that scaling relations for turbulent flow should be based on constant u_*.

SCALING TURBULENT FLOW

For important pipelines involving turbulent flow of slurries, it is highly desirable to carry out pilot-plant tests under turbulent conditions. Usually the diameter of the test pipe is less than that of the prototype line, and scaling relations are employed to obtain prototype values. These relations are generally based on power-law approximations, an approach which follows the early work of Blasius [29].

For non-Newtonian flows, it is better to lay aside the power-law scaling formulation and re-consider the question of hydraulic similitude. On the basis of the analysis put forward above it is found that, for all non-settling mixtures, similitude can be achieved by maintaining the shear velocity at a constant value. Constant wall shear stress, and hence constant u_*, implies a constant value of both the viscosity μ and the rheogram-area ratio α, leading to similitude in the behavior of the viscous sub-layer. Likewise, for a material with a yield shear stress, the value of u_* fixes ξ (i.e., τ_y/τ_w) and hence produces a constant term Ω for the yield-effect correction in the core of the velocity profile. Thus, for a given u_*, all the terms on the right-hand side of Equation 6 will be constant except the first, which can be written $2.5 \ln(\rho D u_*/\mu)$. This result is used in obtaining ex-pressions for the throughput velocities V_1 and V_2 in pipes of diameters D_1 and D_2, respectively. On comparing the two expressions, based on the condition that u_* is the same in both pipes, it is found that:

$$V_2 = V_1 + 2.5 u_* \ln(D_2/D_1) \tag{26}$$

The only condition for the use of this equation—that the area occupied by the viscous sub-layer (and any buffer layer) is a small fraction of the pipe area—is almost always met in practice. The associated pressure gradients $(\Delta p/\Delta x)_1$ and $(\Delta p/\Delta x)_2$ must also be scaled, using a second relation based on the constant value of wall shear stress, i.e.:

$$(\Delta p/\Delta x)_2 = (\Delta p/\Delta x)_1 (D_1/D_2) \tag{27}$$

The combined use of Equations 26 and 27 allows the scale-up of individual data points for tur-bulent non-Newtonian flow from one pipe size to another. Such separate scaling of velocity and pressure gradient on a point-by-point basis may at first appear unusual, but it is no different in practice from the scaling of, say, head-discharge curves for centrifugal water pumps.

The technique is illustrated in Figure 11, using A. D. Thomas's data for a 7.5% kaolin slurry. This material has a non-Newtonian rheogram similar in form to Figure 3, and displays significant drag reduction [7, 17]. Figure 11 plots pressure gradient vs. throughput velocity for two pipe sizes ($D_1 =$ 18.9 mm, $D_2 = 105$ mm). The points from the smaller pipe have been scaled up individually using Equations 26 and 27, and, as shown on the figure, these scaled points are in excellent accord with the observations from the larger pipe.

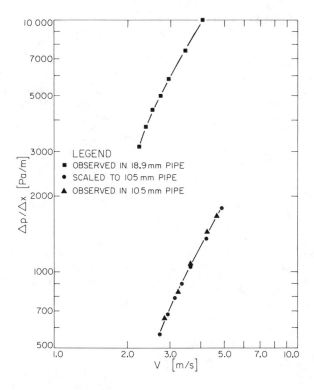

Figure 11. Scale-up for Thomas's 7.5% kaolin slurry.

It should be noted that the experimental points do not plot as straight lines on the logarithmic co-ordinates of Figure 11, and this is to be expected for non-Newtonian flow. The strength of the proposed scaling technique is shown by the fact that this non-linear behavior is correctly scaled to the larger pipe size.

CONCLUSION

Fine-particle slurries often show non-Newtonian behavior in tests under laminar conditions. The friction factor for turbulent flow of such slurries is also affected, primarily through an increase in the size of the small dissipative eddies, which in turn increases the thickness of the viscous sub-layer. In favorable circumstances, the drag reduction caused by this mechanism can reduce the friction factor to less than half the value for an equivalent Newtonian flow.

The analysis of this behavior links the sub-layer thickening, and hence the drag reduction, to rheogram shape. Specific comparisons have been made for Bingham-plastic and yield-power-law rheological models, and also for an asymptotic model (Equation 21). All predictions agree with the experimental data in showing drag reduction, but the Bingham model is limited in applicability, while the more sophisticated models give quantitive agreement for a broader range of material characteristics.

Time-dependent rheological behavior also occurs for some slurries, greatly increasing the difficulty of predicting the turbulent-flow friction factor from viscometric data. For these cases it is best to use pilot plant testing in the turbulent range, which can be scaled to prototype values by means of the constant-shear-velocity relations. These are given by Equations 26 and 27 and are generally applicable to non-settling slurries—Newtonian, non-Newtonian, and time-dependent.

NOTATION

C	concentration of solids in slurry	δ_v	thickness of viscous sub-layer
D	internal diameter of pipe	ε	Nikuradse sand-grain roughness for pipe wall
d	diameter of particle or fiber		
f	friction factor	η	slope of Bingham line or high-stress asymptote
f_N	value of f for equivalent Newtonian flow		
He	Hedstrom number $[\mathrm{He} = \rho D^2 \tau_y / \eta^2]$	η_t	slope of the curve of τ vs. dU/dy
k	coefficient in yield-power law (Equation 18)	κ	von Karman coefficient for turbulent mixing length
k_1, k_2	parameters in Equations 24 and 25	λ	shape parameter in Equation 21
L	length of fiber	μ	viscosity $[\mu = \tau/(dU/dy)]$
n	exponent in yield-power law (Equation 18)	ξ	yield stress ratio $[\xi = \tau_y/\tau_w]$
p	pressure	ρ	density of pseudo-fluid
Re'_*	"plastic" shear Reynolds number $[Re'_* = \rho Du_*/\eta]$	τ	shear stress
		τ_i	intercept of high-stress rheogram asymptote
t	time		
U	velocity (time-mean) in x direction	τ_w	shear stress at pipe wall
U_v	value of U at edge of viscous sub-layer	τ_y	yield value of shear stress
u_*	shear velocity $[u_* = \sqrt{(\tau_w/\rho)}]$	Ω	velocity correction term, see Equation 7
V	throughput velocity [discharge/pipe area]		
V_N	value of V for equivalent Newtonian flow		
x	distance along pipe		
y	distance from pipe wall		

Subscripts

1, 2	model and prototype conditions, used in scale-up
o	value at t = 0
∞	value approached at very large t

Greek Symbols

α	ratio of integral under non-Newtonian and Newtonian rheograms

REFERENCES

1. Lumley, J. L.: "Drag Reduction in Turbulent Flow by Polymer Additives," *Jnl. Poly. Sci. Macromol. Rev.*, 7., 263–290, A. Peterlin (Ed.), Interscience, New York, 1973.
2. Virk, P. S., Mickley, H. S., and Smith, K. A.: "The Ultimate Asymptote and Mean Flow Structure in Toms' Phenomenon," Trans A.S.M.E., *Jnl. App. Mech.*, 37, 488, 1970.
3. Virk, P. S.: "An Elastic Sublayer Model for Drag Reduction by Dilute Solutions of Linear Macromolecules," *Jnl. Fluid Mech.*, 45, 417, 1971.
4. Lee, W. K., Vaseleski, R. C., and Metzner, A. B.: "Turbulent Drag Reduction in Polymeric Solutions Containing Suspended Fibres," *AIChE Jnl.*, 20, 128, 1974.
5. Bobkowicz, A. J.: *The Effect of Turbulence on the Flow Characteristics of Model Fiber Suspensions*, Ph.D. Thesis, McGill Univ., 1963.
6. Bobkowicz, A. J., and Gauvin, W. H.: "The Turbulent Flow Characteristics of Model Fibre Suspensions," *Canad. Jnl. Chem. Engng.*, 43, 87, 1965.
7. Wilson, K. C., and Thomas, A. D.: "A New Analysis of the Turbulent Flow of Non-Newtonian Fluids," *Canad. Jnl. Chem. Engng.*, 63, 539, 1985.

8. Lumley, J. L.: "Two-Phase and Non-Newtonian Flow," Chap. 7 of *Turbulence*, P. Bradshaw (Ed.), Topics in Applied Physics, Vol. 12, Springer-Verlag, Berlin, 1978.

9. Reynolds, A. J.: *Turbulent Flows in Engineering*, 186–190, Wiley, London, 1974.

10. Bain, A. G., and Bonnington, S. T.: *The Hydraulic Transport of Solids by Pipeline*, Pergamon Press, Oxford, 1970.

11. Metzner, A. B., and Reed, J. C.: "Flow of Non-Newtonian Fluids—Correlation of the Laminar, Transition and Turbulent Flow Regimes," *AIChE Jnl.*, *1*, 434, 1955.

12. Kemblowski, A., and Kolodziejski, J. "Flow Resistances of Non-Newtonian Fluids in Transitional and Turbulent Flow," *Int. Chem. Engng.*, *13*, 265, 1973.

13. Caldwell, D. H., and Babbitt, H. E., "Flow of Muds, Sludges and Suspensions in Circular Pipe," *Ind. and Eng. Chem.*, *33*, 249, 1941.

14. Wilhelm, R. H., Wroughton, D. M., and Loeffel, W. F.: "Flow of Suspensions through Pipes," *Ind. and Eng. Chem.*, *31*, 622, 1939.

15. Thomas, D. G.: "Heat and Momentum Transport Characteristics of Non-Newtonian Aqueous Thorium Oxide Suspensions," *AIChE Jnl.*, *6*, 631, 1960.

16. Thomas, D. G.: "Transport Characteristics of Suspensions: Part IV, Friction Loss of Concentrated Flocculated Suspensions in Turbulent Flow," *AIChE Jnl*, *8*, 266, 1962.

17. Thomas, A. D.: "Slurry Pipeline Rheology," *Proc. 2nd Natl. Conf. on Rheology*, Sydney, Aust., 1981.

18. Hanks, R. W.: "Low Reynolds Number Turbulent Pipeline Flow of Pseudo Homogeneous Slurries," *Proc. Hydrotransport 5*, BHRA Fluid Engineering, Cranfield, UK, 1978.

19. Thomas, A. D., and Wilson, K. C.: "New Analysis of Non-Newtonian Turbulent Flow—Yield-Power-Law Fluids," *Canad. Jnl. Chem. Engng.*, *65*, April, 1987.

20. Thomas, A. D., "Coarse Particles in a Heavy Medium—Turbulent Pressure Drop Reduction and Deposition under Laminar Flow," *Proc. Hydrotransport 5*, BHRA Fluid Engineering, Cranfield, UK, 1978.

21. Thomas, D. G., "Non-Newtonian Suspensions Part II. Turbulent Transport Characteristics," *Ind. Eng. Chem.*, *55*, 1963.

22. Wilson, K. C.: "Modeling the Effects of Non-Newtonian and Time-dependent Slurry Behavior," *Proc. Hydrotransport 10*, BHRA Fluid Engineering, Cranfield, UK, 1986.

23. Fredrickson, A. G.: *Principles and Applications of Rheology*, pp. 22–23, p. 87, Prentice-Hall, Englewood Cliffs, N.J., 1964.

24. Thomas, A. D.: "Settling of Particles in a Horizontally Sheared Bingham Plastic," Proc. *1st Natl. Conf. on Rheology*, Melbourne, Aust., 1979.

25. Engelund, F., and Wan, Z.: "Instability of Hyperconcentrated Flow," *Jnl. of Hydr. Engng*, ASCE, *110*, 219, 1984.

26. Chu, J., and Wang, Z.: "Settling Velocity of a Sphere in Homogeneous Bingham Fluid," Paper I-1, *Proc. Internatl. Workshop on Flow at Hyperconcentrations of Sediment*, IRTCES, Beijing, China, Sept. 1985.

27. Ansley, R. W., and Smith, T. N.: "Motion of Spherical Particles in a Bingham Plastic," *AIChE Jnl.*, *13*, 1193, 1967.

28. Highgate, D. J., and Whorlow, R. W.: "The Viscous Resistance to Motion of a Sphere Falling through a Sheared Non-Newtonian Liquid," *Brit. Jnl. Appl. Phys.*, *18*, 1019, 1967.

29. Blasius, H.: "Das Aehnlichkeitsgesetz bei Reibungsvorgaengen in Fluessigkeiten," *V.D.I. Forschungsheft No. 131*, Verein Deutsche Ingenieure, 1913.

SECTION III

POLYMER RHEOLOGY AND PROCESSING

CONTENTS

CHAPTER 18

DETERMINATION OF MORPHOLOGY AND MECHANICAL MICROPROCESSES IN POLYMERS

Goerg H. Michler

Scientific and Coordination Centre in the VEB CHEMISCHE WERKE BUNA and Institute of Solid State Physics and Electron Microscopy of the Academy of Sciences of GDR German Democratic Republic

CONTENTS

INTRODUCTION

The mechanical properties of polymers play a decisive role in many applications. The mechanical behavior is determined by different micromechanical processes, e.g., chain scission, micro-void formation, crack initiation and propagation, or yield and flow processes. The processes of yielding or plasticity occur not only on a macroscopic scale, but often also on a microscopic one. In brittle glassy polymers, for instance, craze initiation and growth represent the characteristic deformation process associated with highly localized yielding. Inside the crazes the material is plastically deformed, usually to some hundred percent.

A better understanding of the mechanical behavior requires detailed knowledge of the micromechanical processes, which usually are strongly influenced by the morphology or supermolecular structure of the polymers. Thus, the exact knowledge of the morphology and micromechanical processes favors the determination of structure-property relations, which is often realized by various methods and techniques of electron microscopy. This chapter summarizes successful electron microscope techniques to study micromechanical processes. Yield processes in glassy and rubber-modified polymers are discussed in more detail on a microscopic scale, considering also aspects of molecular flow processes.

ELECTRON MICROSCOPIC DETERMINATION OF THE
MORPHOLOGY OF POLYMERS

In general, direct investigations of polymers by electron microscopy involve three general problems:

1. Preparing ultra-thin specimens from bulk polymers (as conventional 100 kV transmission electron microscopy (TEM) usually requires) is often difficult.
2. Polymers (as organic substances) are particularly sensitive to electron beam irradiation.
3. The contrast between structural details is very low, since polymers usually consist of the same light elements.

From the morphological point of view, polymers can be classified in different groups: amorphous and semi-crystalline polymers, chemically homogeneous and heterogeneous polymers, monophase and multiphase polymers, and combinations with inorganic substances (fibers, filler particles). Some of the preparation techniques for electron microscopic investigations are applicable to several polymers, and others only to special polymers.

For investigating the morphology of polymers, two methods are generally available:

• Preparation of special surfaces (brittle fracture surfaces, smooth and selectively etched surfaces), yielding information on the internal structure of the material. These surfaces are investigated by means of replicas in the TEM or directly in the SEM.
• Preparation of thin sections by ultramicrotomy, generally following special fixation and staining procedures. Investigations are carried out by conventional TEM or HVEM.

These investigation techniques are summarized in the following section. Some recent and unconventional techniques are then described.

Standard Techniques

Investigation of Surfaces by TEM and SEM

The external surfaces of polymeric solids do not yield any information on the internal morphology, because they are strongly modified by the processing conditions (with the sole exception of fibers or freely crystallized foils). Therefore, special surfaces from the interior have to be prepared.

The traditional method is to produce brittle fracture surfaces, which is usually done at low temperatures to avoid plastic deformation, which would hide the morphology. The fracture path occasionally follows structural details so that they become visible.

The second possibility of producing internal surfaces consists in polishing [1] or sectioning them in a microtome. Selective etching of these surfaces may lead to a "development" of a structure. Etching can be performed chemically by solvents [2], and physically by ion-etching or by the more effective method of etching in activated oxygen [3]. If the etching rate of several components (crystalline and amorphous parts, several polymer phases, inorganic particles) is different, these components appear on the surface. But the etching-figures represent the morphology only at the initial stages of etching; at advanced stages, special figures often occur, which are more influenced by the etching conditions.

The surfaces can be investigated by TEM (transmission electron microscopy) by the replica technique. Since it is difficult to remove a replica from a polymer surface, two-stage techniques are usually necessary (e.g., by using a silver matrix, reinforced by an electrolytically produced copper layer, or by a polymeric matrix).

The contrast between structural details can be enhanced by coating the replicas with heavy metal atoms at small angles. Previously, SEM (scanning electron microscopy) has been used increasingly, since here only a coating of the surfaces with a conductive layer (C or C/Au) is necessary. This easy preparation of surfaces is very effective, but the disadvantage lies in the resolution not being better than about 10 nm for polymeric materials. The application of SEM using the material contrast enables the investigation of structural parts containing heavy elements, such as inorganic filler particles or rubber particles selectively stained by heavy atoms in a polymer matrix [4].

The methods described above are applicable only to polymers with clearly distinct structural elements, which influence the fracture path or which can be etched at different rates.

Investigation of Ultra-Thin Sections by TEM

The second principal method of determining the morphology of bulk polymers is the TEM investigation of ultra-thin sections. Several improvements in the instrumentation and sample preparation during the past 15 years made ultramicrotomy a method which is applicable almost universally. It enables the production of thin specimens from bulk polymeric material and direct observation by TEM [5]. Ultramicrotomy is a mechanical technique of cutting, the success of which depends essentially on the compressibility and plastic deformability of polymeric material in terms of cutting parameters (e.g., knife angle, cutting velocity). The possibility of artefacts being produced by local plastic deformation (smearing, chatter, folds, scratches) should always be taken into consideration.

Hard or brittle polymers (e.g. PS, PMMA, PVC) can be cut immediately after production and trimming without any special preparation. Mechanically unstable samples, such as fibers and foils, are embedded (mostly into epoxy resin) prior to cutting. Here, a good adhesion is especially important; this can be improved by an increased roughness of polymer surfaces (by physical or chemical etching). However, directly produced ultra-thin sections often do not give good results, because the contrast between structural details is too low in TEM. This difficulty can be overcome by chemical staining, i.e., by the selective deposition of heavy metal atoms. Staining can be performed on the bulk material or on the thin section after cutting. An example is shown in Figure 1. Here in PVC, primary particles (approximately 1 μm in diameter) and domains (approximately 0.1 μm in diameter) are detected by selectively staining the particle boundaries [6].

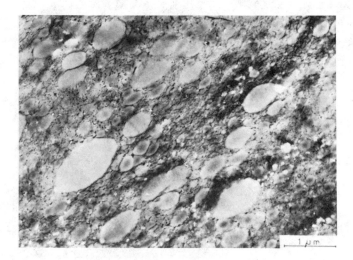

Figure 1. Structure of PVC (emulsion type), composed of primary particles and domains; the boundaries between them are selectively stained by chlorosulphonic acid and osmium tetroxide (ultra-thin section, TEM micrograph).

Elastic or weak polymers or polymers of weak constituents would be smeared or pressed during ultramicrotomy. Therefore, they have to be fixed or hardened before being cut. In general, there are two methods:

- Chemical fixation or hardening. Bulk polymeric samples are treated with chemical agents; several reactions (e.g., cross-linking, material deposition) cause a fixation or a hardening of the material. For the most part, these reactions are highly selective. Accordingly, a selective staining of structural details takes place as a positive secondary effect. This effect can be enhanced by special staining procedures. It is frequently applied to investigate phase-distributions in rubber modified, high-impact polymers (staining with OsO_4 after Kato [7]—see Figure 2) and to determine lamellae in semi-crystalline polymers (staining with chlorsulphonic acid after Kanig [8]—see Figure 3).
- Physical fixation. Polymers with a distinct tendency toward cross-linking by irradiation can be fixed by γ- or electron-irradiation using doses up to a few 10 MGy, thus ensuring a good preparation of ultra-thin sections [9, 10]. Cryo-ultramicrotomy has been widely used. Polymeric samples are cooled below their glass-transition temperature T_g and cut at these temperatures [11]. The temperature of the samples should be about 10°C below T_g, since there may be a local rise in temperature. A selective chemical staining to enhance the contrast is occasionally helpful.

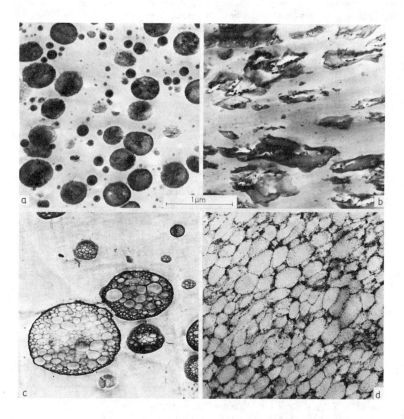

Figure 2. Two-phase structures of different rubber-modified (high-impact) polymers: (a) ABS graft polymer, (b) ABS blend, (c) HIPS graft polymer, and (d) PVC/EVA graft polymer (ultra-thin sections, rubber-phase fixed and stained by osmium tetroxide, TEM).

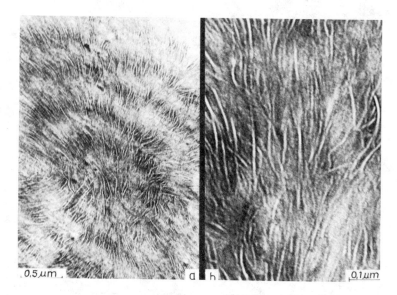

Figure 3. Lamellae in LDPE. (a) radially arranged lamellae inside a spherulite, (b) structure of the lamellae (fixation and selective staining by means of chlorosulphonic acid and osmium tetroxide, ultra-thin section, TEM).

Non-Standard Techniques

Effects of Irradiation-Induced Contrast Enhancement

To investigate semi-crystalline polymers the usual techniques (surface etching, cryo-ultramicrotomy, chemical fixation and staining) can be complemented by an alternative method, based on an irradiation technique.

As mentioned above, during γ- or electron-irradiation polyethylene (PE) is known to show a stronger tendency to cross-linking than to chain scission, yielding a fixation effect [9, 10]. Here, irradiation doses up to 10 MGy are sufficient. It is important that after irradiation doses of 20 MGy and more it is possible to attain a resolution higher than 10 nm and to identify individual lamellae. The lamellae appear as bright lines in a darker amorphous surrounding. The thickness of the lamellae is about 10 nm, which corresponds with the values of the lamellae measured on the chemically stained sections.

The contrast visible is not owing to natural differences in density between crystalline and amorphous parts (on the contrary, the crystalline lamellae have a higher density than the amorphous parts, yielding an effect in the opposite direction). The interpretation is as follows [12] (see Figure 4): the irradiation-induced cross-linking predominantly occurs in the amorphous interlamellar regions, yielding a reduction in the thickness of the amorphous layers between the lamellae and a dilatation in the length of the amorphous parts as a consequence of constant volume or density. In places where the boundary layers of the lamellae are oriented parallel to the normal direction of ultra-thin section and to the electron beam direction, the transmitted thickness increases in the amorphous layers, yielding darker amorphous zones and brighter lamellae. This effect is an "irradiation-induced contrast enhancement." The above interpretation of the predominant cross-linking in the amorphous parts is supported by the appearance of clear diffraction contrast in the electron microscope even after irradiation doses up to 10 MGy [10].

The cross-linking of the amorphous zones brings on a second contrast effect: the appearance of the concentric rings inside the spherulites (comparable with Figure 3a.). In rings with the lamellae

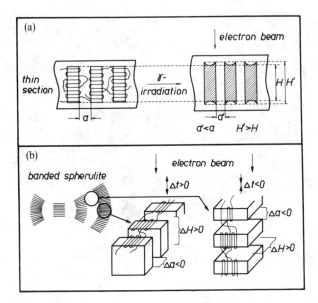

Figure 4. Scheme of the development of contrast between (a) crystalline zones (lamellae) and amorphous zones and (b) concentric rings inside the spherulites, as a consequence of irradiation.

in parallel orientation to the electron beam ("edge-on" position), the enlarged amorphous zones cause a darker contrast of the rings. Owing to the reduced thickness of the amorphous zones, the circumference of the rings decreases, whereas the circumference of the intermediate rings (of lamellae in "flat-on" position) is constant. Thus, a ripple surface of the thin section is likely to form in places of the rings. This "ripple" effect was first discussed by Grubb and Keller [13] for the direct influence of electron beam, but on the wrong assumption that the preferential cross-linking appears in the interior of the lamellae.

The effect of irradiation-induced contrast enhancement also occurs in other polymers. Figure 5 shows a cryo-thin section of a segmented polyurethane [12, 14]. At the very beginning of electron beam irradiation the spherulites can be seen only in a weak contrast (micrograph a). After electron irradiation for some seconds the spherulites appear rich in contrast, with the radial elements inside the spherulites definitely sharper. The interior structure of the spherulites has been visualized in more detail by a special chemical fixation and staining treatment [15]: the radial fibrils, as can be seen in Figure 5, consist of parallel lamellae, similar to those in PE.

By the conventional chemical staining treatment in the interior of the lamellae in PE, stained layers can be identified, which are accumulations of non-crystallizable material as in the boundary layers. But only the thickest of these impurity layers are visible by this technique. The visibility can be improved, however, by combining chemical staining with irradiation [16]: Figure 6 shows lamellae with many of these impurity layers, with individual crystalline blocks in between. These blocks correspond to the micro-paracrystals of Hosemann [17]. There are two possibilities for contrast enhancement of the impurity layers:

1. Conventional chemical staining and thereafter defined *in situ* irradiation of the thin section in the TEM. It is assumed that during irradiation, the mobility of the staining material (residual atoms, small clusters, particles) is enhanced and reactions occur with radicals, formed by irradiation in the amorphous zones and in the impurity layers.
2. Irradiation with γ-rays or with electrons, and simultaneous or subsequent chemical staining of the material. Irradiation activates the material to better react with the staining agent.

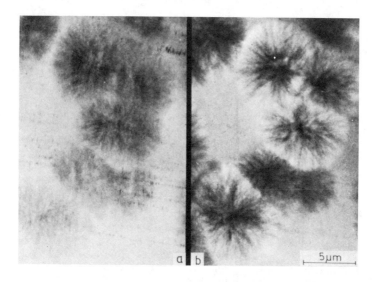

Figure 5. Improvement of the visibility of spherulites in segmented polyurethane by an "irradiation-induced contrast enhancement" inside the HVEM [12] (a) at the beginning of electron irradiation (b) after intense electron irradiation.

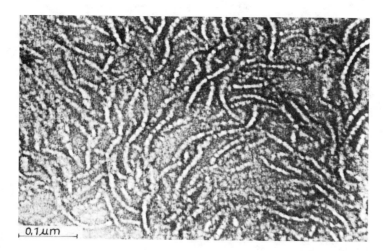

Figure 6. Crystalline blocks inside the lamellae of branched PE ("micro paracrystals"); contrast enhancement by combined influence of chemical staining and irradiation.

In summary, the irradiation-induced effects can improve the visibility of structural elements of different sizes:

- Impurity layers with thicknesses up to some nm inside the lamellae—Figure 6 (contrast improvement by a better chemical staining reaction as a result of an irradiation-induced activation of the material).

- Lamellae with thicknesses of about 10 nm inside spherulites (visibility without any chemical staining, only by cross-linking and contraction and dilatation mainly in the amorphous zones).
- Interior structure of spherulites (concentric rings in PE or fibrils in PU) of sizes of some tenths of μm—Figure 5 (secondary effects as a result of local cross-linking and contraction).

Effect of Straining-Induced Contrast Enhancement

A new possibility of structure determination arose from HVEM studies of deformation processes of several polymers [19]. The experimental technique of preparing the samples is relatively simple: From the polymer material, sections of thicknesses usually between 0.5 and 5 microns are produced using an ultra-microtome. These sections are reinforced at the edges with a polyester film and mounted inside a tensile device. During deformation, structural elements, which differ in Young's modulus or the extensibility from the surrounding—even for only small differences—appear with a better contrast. This effect is called "straining-induced contrast enhancement" [12]. The principle of this is described in the following:

Figure 7 is the schematic drawing of some structures represented by particles dispersed in a matrix. Figure 7a is a rather simple example of large particles with the diameter only slightly smaller than the thickness of the film. The differences in density between particles and matrix are very small. Hence, the differences in the intensity of the electron beam are too small for a visible contrast (on the left-hand side). The Young's modulus of the particles is assumed to be slightly smaller than the modulus of the matrix (or the extensibility of the particles is assumed to be somewhat higher);

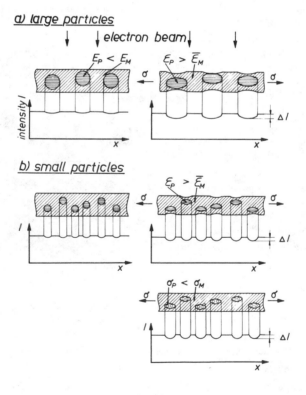

Figure 7. Scheme of the effect of "straining-induced contrast enhancement" [12].

accordingly, during elongation of the film, the particles are deformed preferentially. In the direction of the electron beam, the thickness of the film decreases in places of the particles, thus causing a difference in the intensity of the electron beam and a detectable contrast between particles and matrix (on the right-hand side).

Figure 7b, showing smaller particles, is more interesting. The particles are also deformed to a higher degree than in the matrix on an average. Experience has shown that this effect clearly occurs even with particles smaller in diameter than a tenth of the film thickness. A modified case is when the particles do not have a smaller Young's modulus, but a lower strength. During loading the particles can rupture, yielding a smaller density and therefore an enhanced contrast.

The applicability of this effect is demonstrated in the next micrographs. Figure 8a shows a rubber-modified high-impact polymer (ACS-acrylonitrile-chlorinated polyethylene-styrene) with clearly distinguishable polymer phases after slight elongation. The section is 1 μm thick. Due to the lower density and to the stretching of the particles of chlorinated polyethylene, the latter appear brighter than the SAN matrix. An opposite morphology is shown in Figure 8b: a network of a rubber phase contains small particles of a hard polymer. Owing to the lower density and the predominant deformation of the rubber phase, the particles appear dark and the rubber phase bright. This morphology was confirmed by investigating selectively stained ultra-thin sections, which is the traditional technique applied to these polymers. Investigations of several two-phase polymer systems showed that in semi-thin sections there is a contrast between polymer phases, if the densities differ by more than 10 to 15%.

These examples prove the applicability of this technique to the investigation of the morphology. In the following it is applied to amorphous glassy polymers. In general, amorphous polymers such as polystyrene (PS), polymethylmethacrylate (PMMA), and polycarbonate (PC) are supposed to have a super-molecular structure. Only small differences in density and molecular packing of the structural elements are expected. Therefore, their determination is associated with considerable difficulties. Yeh, Geil, and others investigated replicas of fracture surfaces or etched ones using dark field electron microscopy. They reported on structures in the form of domains or grains of sizes

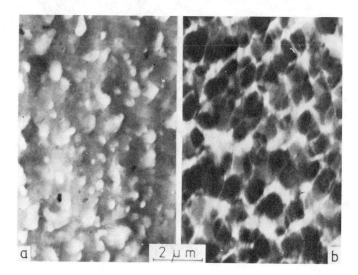

Figure 8. Effect of "straining-induced contrast enhancement" in high-impact polymers: the rubber phase (particles of CPE in (a) and network of EVA in (b)) appears brighter due to its lower density and preferred deformation (1-μm thick section after little deformation, HVEM). (a) SAN/CPE. (b) PVC/EVA.

between 3 and 7 nm (these results are reviewed in [20, 21]). Recent investigations, however, show that the interpretation of dark field images is very difficult [22]. In the presence of these difficulties in investigating any structure of amorphous polymers the technique, discussed above, is of special interest.

Figure 9 shows a strained section of a SAN-copolymer with a deformed zone ahead of a crack tip. Outside the deformation zone no structure is detectable, but inside the deformation zone bright domains of diameters between about 50 and 100 nm are clearly visible. Further investigations showed that the acrylonitrile content is slightly higher for the domains than for the surrounding, and that the domains are easier to extend. A typical amorphous glassy polymer is PS. The typical deformation structure of PS is the craze, which is discussed later in this chapter. Ahead of the craze tip, the earliest deformation step is visible (Figure 16b). In a completely structureless surrounding, small bright domains are visible of diameters between 10 and 30 nm. The domains are arranged in a very small band; the bright lines on either side of the band are furrows on either surface of the section. Based on the results of SAN and the high-impact polymers (Figures 8, 9) it seems reasonable to consider the domains as a consequence of real structural elements. Possible explanations of the nature of these domains are given in [12, 23].

Use of HVEM

To demonstrate the advantage of HVEM (high voltage electron microscopy) for investigating polymeric materials, different polymers have been used. The samples were investigated in a 1,000 kV JEOL HVEM.

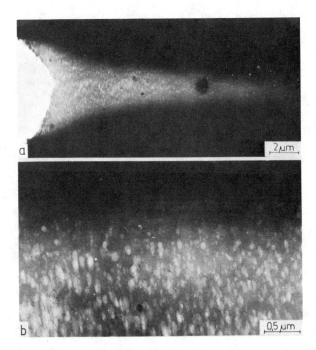

Figure 9. Domain structure of a SAN copolymer: small domains are visible in the plastic zone ahead of a crack tip (stretched 0.5-μm thick section, HVEM, stretching direction vertical). (a) plastic zone ahead of a crack tip. (b) detail of plastic zone at higher magnification.

The use of the enlarged penetration depth. The main advantage of HVEM lies in its enlarged penetration depth. Because of the low density of polymeric materials, specimens of up to several micrometers thickness can be investigated. Relatively thick specimens are advantageous in several respects.

Specimen preparation. It is much easier to prepare semi-thin specimens than ultra-thin specimens needed for conventional 100 kV TEM. A very useful preparation technique generally applied is ultramicrotomy. Before cutting ultra-thin sections, the polymeric materials usually have to be fixed or hardened, since polymers are relatively weak materials. Semi-thin sections have a noticeably increased mechanical stability and can therefore be cut in an ultramicrotome, often without the necessity of fixing or hardening the samples. These sections can have essentially enlarged areas, too. Therefore, structural heterogeneities are better and easier to determine.

Spatial analysis of structural details. Larger structural details are better visible when semi-thin specimens are used [12, 24]. By way of example, in high-impact polymers the shape and real size of the dispersed rubber particles can be determined more easily (see Figure 10). For a commercial sample of a high-impact polystyrene (HIPS), sections of 0.1 to 4.5 μm thickness were investigated in the HVEM. The rubber particles were selectively stained with osmium tetroxide, leading to their dark appearance. The particles with small inclusions of polystyrene in their interior are dispersed in the matrix of polystyrene. Far better than Figure 10a, Figure 10c of the thick section shows the "blackberry-like" shape and proves the existence of large rubber particles. The diagram compares the frequency distributions of the particle diameters on the 0.1 μm ultra-thin sections, and the 1 μm and 4.5 μm thick sections. The largest particles of about 2.5 μm in diameter appear only in the thick sections (4.5 μm thick) with a practically measurable probability.

This technique has a great practical advantage over the frequently used mathematical corrections of the frequency distribution, determined on ultra-thin sections. Mathematical solutions exist for spheres and some other regularly shaped particles [25, 26]. Practical disadvantages of these mathematical corrections are that the largest particle must be known which, in general, is not given because the ultra-thin sections contain the true diameters of the largest particles with only extremely low probability. Therefore, the mathematical corrections merely shift the maximum frequency distribution toward slightly larger diameters, but do not yield any information on the largest particles actually present. See curve a$^+$ in Figure 10d, which is the mathematically corrected distribution of curve a. Information on these largest particles is important, since the particles contain a relatively high phase volume content and usually have a very negative influence on mechanical properties (on strength, elongation, and fracture toughness).

Determination of inorganic filler particles. Composite materials of a polymeric matrix and dispersed inorganic filler particles form an important group of polymers. Hard particles often have diameters of up to some micrometers; thus, they cannot be determined by using ultra-thin specimens. On the other hand, semi-thin sections of composite polymers most clearly show the shape, size, and distribution of inorganic particles.

Observations in a state of reduced specimen damage. Polymers are particularly sensitive to electron beam. The sensitivity to irradiation increases with decreasing carbon content in the polymeric samples, in the sequence PS, PE, PC, PMMA, PVC, PTFE [27]. The "critical dose" for damaging the molecular structure is about 0.01 C/cm^2 for PE [18]. The irradiation doses of the sample, necessary for exposing usual photographic material at some 1000-fold magnification, are nearly the same, i.e., the specimens are damaged solely during exposure. Polymers in a state of strongly damaged molecules are frequently well suited for detecting the super-molecular structure or morphology, because the morphology is often not altered by molecular processes.

There are, however, several problems making the investigation of polymeric material in an undamaged state necessary. Using an HVEM reduces the damaging rate to a third, compared with

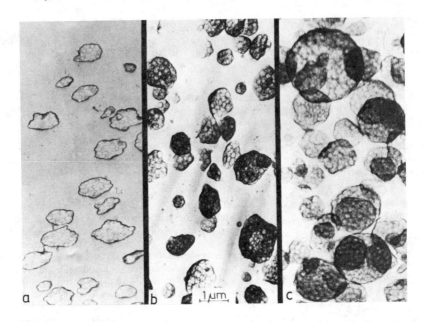

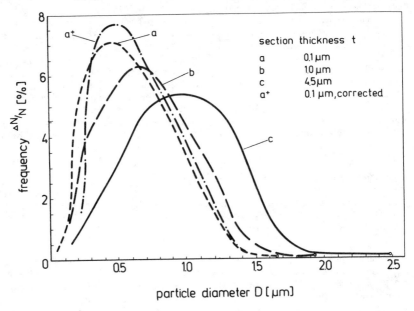

Figure 10. Visibility of particle structure of HIPS depending on the thickness of the sections (sections stained with OsO_4) [24]. Section thickness t: (a) 0.1 μm (b) 1 μm (c) 4.5 μm; (d) frequency distribution of particle diameters.

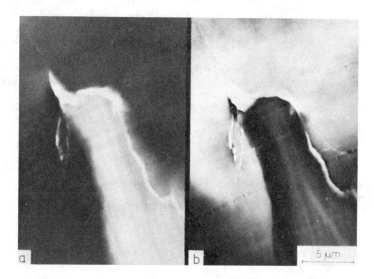

Figure 11. Different mass-loss of the two polymer phases, PVC and SAN in a polymer blend, by electron irradiation in the HVEM [24] (a) at the beginning (b) after intense irradiation.

the 100 kV TEM [28]. An appreciably-reduced damaging rate was achieved by using highly sensitive X-ray films [29]. Their high sensitivity arises from double coating with thicker emulsion layers or higher silver-halide content. They can therefore be used in the HVEM due to the greater penetration power.

Determination of irradiation-induced changes. The reduced radiation damage enables the resulting changes in morphology to be investigated over a longer time. Figure 11 shows the same area of a two-phase polymer blend immediately after the beginning of irradiation (a) and after stronger irradiation (b). The dominant process of radiation damage is mass-loss. Mass-loss is much stronger for the surrounding phase and lower for the particle phase. The blend consists of the two components PVC (polyvinylchloride) and SAN (styrene-acrylonitrile copolymer). Mass-loss is known to be stronger for PVC than for SAN, indicating that the surrounding phase is PVC and the particle is SAN. Therefore, the determination of mass-loss is useful to distinguish between several polymer phases.

Determination of molecular order. The reduced radiation damage yields a longer life-time of the molecular arrangement and of the crystalline structure of semi-crystalline polymers. Thus, images in bright-field and dark-field contrast and diffraction patterns can be taken from one and the same area of the specimen [29].

Deformation experiments. Thick specimens to be used in HVEM have a noticeably increased mechanical stability, which facilitates deformation experiments. The investigation of deformed specimens is effective in two ways:

• The morphology of polymers can be determined using a special effect of straining-induced contrast enhancement.
• Deformation structures and mechanical microprocesses can be investigated. Results of deformation tests of several polymers are described in the following section.

ELECTRON MICROSCOPIC DETERMINATION OF YIELD PROCESSES

Experimental

The investigated samples are commercial types of polystyrene (PS) and high-impact polystyrene (HIPS). The experimental technique for preparing the specimens is relatively easy: From the bulk polymer material, sections 0.5 to 5 microns thick are produced in an ultramicrotome. These sections are reinforced at the edges with a polyester film and transferred into a micro-tensile device. A uniaxial deformation of the specimens was carried out in several ways:

- Deformation outside the electron microscope in air under light-microscopical control (for prevention of any kind of radiation damage), followed by observation in the HVEM.
- Deformation inside the HVEM at very low magnifications (50- to 400-fold).
- Deformation in-situ at magnifications up to some thousand times.

The deformed specimens were investigated in the HVEM at an accelerating voltage of 1 MV and at magnifications up to 80,000-fold.

Crazes in Amorphous Polymers (PS)

General characterization of the structure of crazes

To illustrate the deformation technique used, Figure 12 shows three successive stages of deformation of a thin PS film inside the HVEM [30]. Micrograph 12a shows the undeformed specimen with two artificial cracks, to define the area of the later craze and crack path. Micrograph 12b shows in the stress field between the cracks (after deformation) many bright, long, narrow bands— the crazes. Their length of up to 100 μm is partly limited only by the sample boundaries. After somewhat stronger deformation, cracks propagate quickly through the crazes (Figure 12c).

The interior structure of crazes is shown in Figure 13 at higher magnification: The polymeric material inside the craze is strongly plastically deformed into fibrils. The fibrils are arranged nearly parallel to each other and perpendicular to the craze boundaries, and show diameters mostly between 5 and 10 nm. This regularly fibrillated structure is often accredited for the typical feature of crazing. But various other structures can appear [19, 31]. Some examples are shown in Figure 14.

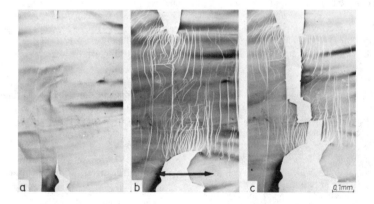

Figure 12. Deformation of a 0.5-μm thick specimen of PS in the HVEM (a) before deformation with artificial cracks (b) after deformation (about 10%) with crazes (c) after crack propagation (deformation direction horizontal—see arrow).

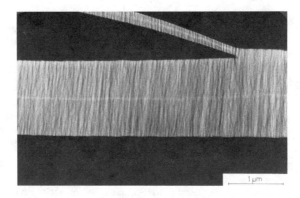

Figure 13. Interior structure of a craze with clearly pronounced fibrillation (1-μm thick section of PS; deformation direction perpendicular).

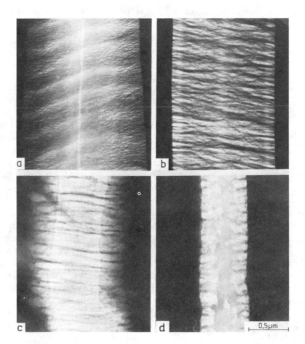

Figure 14. Crazes in PS with different interior structure (direction of deformation horizontal) [30]: (a) mesh network, finely fibrillated (b) fibrillated with brighter zones in the middle (mid rib) and at the boundaries (c) coarsely fibrillated (d) larger voids along the boundaries.

The craze of micrograph 14a consists of a finely fibrillated network with mesh (or void) diameters of about 10 to 20 nm. The area in the middle appears more homogeneous as a consequence of the larger transmitted thickness of crazes (superposition of lots of meshes). The fibrillated crazes in Figures 13, 14a, and 14b show bright lines in the middle (mid-rib) and the craze of Figure 14b also at the boundaries. An essentially coarser structure is to be seen in the craze of Figure 14c, consisting of coarse fibrils with thicknesses up to 25 nm and elongated large voids with sizes of about 0.1 μm. Between the coarse fibrils and across the voids fine fibrils are spanned only a few nm thick. The visible broad-boundary layer is a consequence of a tilt of the craze in the specimen.

The different structures of crazes appear partly in the same material. Therefore, they show the range of variation of deformation structures in PS. But partly they are a consequence of different deformation conditions (specimen nature, loading state and velocity, surroundings) or they represent different stages of growth.

The crazes mentioned before were generated in stress-fields ahead of crack tips. But also, interior defects can yield stress concentrations high enough to initiate crazes [32].

At higher mechanical loading the crazes rupture. Starting points of cracks can be the same points of stress concentration which formerly have caused the formation of crazes (crack tips, heterogeneities) or defects inside the crazes. After the fracture or after unloading the stress inside the crazes is reduced. Mainly the elastic component of stretching relaxes and the order of fibrils worsens, but the craze continues to exist. The ruptured crazes are occasionally to be seen on fracture surfaces of bulk samples. Such fracture surfaces show small hillocks with diameters of about 100 to 200 nm, which are the remains of ruptured, relaxed, and fused fibrils [32].

The crack propagation through the crazes occurs without any essential plastic deformation. Particularly in long crazes (as in Figure 12) the crack propagates very quickly without hindrance. In this respect, the crazes can be seen as the main reason of the brittle behavior of PS. On the other hand, the small plastic deformation of PS is based on the formation of crazes; in this sense crazes appear as a positive phenomenon, which can be a source of increasing fracture toughness.

Interior structure of crazes

Fibrils. The first section of this chapter and Figures 13 and 14 show that the crazes vary in their interior structure, but the regular arrangement of parallel fibrils should be regarded as the characteristic structure of crazes in PS (see Figure 13). The diameters of fibrils, measured directly in the electron micrographs, vary between 2.5 and 10 nm with a mean value of nearly 5 nm. The center-to-center distances ("long period l") are between 9 and 40 nm. The method of laser diffraction of the electron micrographs easily enables the determination of the long period [30]. The laser diffraction diagram is uniaxial and elongated, corresponding to the parallel-arranged fibrils with different distances. The usual evaluation of the diffraction pattern yields long periods of between 10 and 50 nm.

However, this direct measuring is valid only with reservations. The dark lines in the micrographs are not identical to the single fibrils, because many fibrils are packed one upon the other (in the direction of electron beam) and single fibrils cannot be resolved. Under the assumption of a mean fibril diameter of d = 5 nm and a mean distance between them of 5 nm (i.e., a long period l = 10 nm) the result is that in a 1 μm thick craze dozens of fibrils are superimposed in the electron-beam direction. Figure 15 shows in a high magnification that the apparent fibrils are in reality superposition structures: only short, isolated, dark strips are to be seen. A model calculation of contrast-changes with increasing sample thickness (increasing number of superposed fibrils) shows that the result of the superposition is not a compensation, but a distribution of contrast, similar to that of the isolated fibrils [12]. But the values of "fibril thickness" and "long period" are somewhat enlarged. Therefore, the smallest measured values are reasonable data of the true ones.

Deformation inside the crazes. The deformation of the polymeric material inside the crazes was measured by several methods, described in detail in [30]. The results of these various methods show that the craze deformation is at least 150%, mostly between 150% and 200%.

100 nm

Figure 15. Craze at high magnification. The apparently visible "fibrils" inside the craze are in fact superposition structures of a lot of true fibrils [30].

In this connection a discussion of the influence of the specimen thickness on the crazing is necessary. This influence was studied in detail [33] by a) HVEM-deformation tests of specimens 0.5 to 5 μm thick; b) SEM-deformation tests of specimens up to 10 μm thick; c) investigation of the craze structure in bulk material after staining the crazes with osmium tetroxide; and d) by deformation tests (σ-ε-behavior) of specimens 0.5 to 20 μm thick, using a micro-tensile device.

The results of all of these various investigations are [33]:

- In general, the microstructure of crazes is not changed by the specimen thickness above 0.5 μm.
- The elongation to fracture increases with decreasing specimen thickness. Specimens with thicknesses of a few μm show fracture elongations larger by a factor 2 . . . 3 than the bulk material.

These results show that investigations of thin specimens (thickness larger than about 0.5 μm) yield valid information on the craze structure of the bulk material, too. The increased extensibility of the thin specimens can be connected with a greater number of crazes.

Various values of craze deformation appear in the literature. In the classical papers of Kambour [34], by measuring the refraction index of crazed material a craze elongation of $\varepsilon_{cr} \approx 65\%$ was determined. Doyle [35], also by optical methods, measured a craze deformation of $\varepsilon_{cr} = 220 \ldots 300\%$. In bulk material he found smaller values [36]. Grosskurth [37] (using a surface etching of stretched bulk PS) estimated elongations of 50 to 100%. Recently, methods of quantitative electron microscopy have been used: Brown [38] measured an elongation of $\varepsilon_{cr} \approx 230\%$ without any variation over length and cross section of crazes. Kramer et al. [39, 40] calculated values of $\varepsilon_{cr} \approx 270\%$ up to $\varepsilon_{cr} \approx 400\%$. But these high values of $\varepsilon_{cr} \approx 400\%$ should be considered with reserve, both from experimental [30] and theoretical points of view [23].

Initiation of crazes

It is well-known that initiation points of crazes are heterogeneities at the surfaces of the samples (scratches, notches) or in the interior (structural defects, voids, impurities). Their common characteristic is the ability to produce a local stress concentration in an outer stress field. In these zones of locally increased stress the amorphous material is transformed into the strongly plastically stretched structure of the crazes.

Examples of the first visible structures in the transformation area at the head of the craze tips are shown in the next micrograph. In Figure 16 a craze is shown in full view and at a higher magnification of the zone ahead of the craze tip ("pre-craze"). The place of the pre-craze correlates with the area on the left-hand side of Figure 16a. The pre-craze consists of bright spot-like "domains"

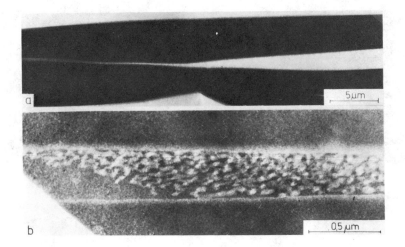

Figure 16. Craze in full view (a) and at a higher magnification of the pre-craze (b). In this case the pre-craze is a narrow deformation band inside the sample (deformation direction vertical) [41].

with diameters of between 20 and 50 nm. These "domains" are brighter than the surrounding material; therefore, they are slightly deformed plastically. All domains are arranged in a narrow band, which has nearly the same thickness as the diameters of the domains. The band is at an oblique angle in the specimen, and both the bright lines limiting the band are furrows at both surfaces of the sample. This result has been proven by tilting the specimen in the HVEM [19, 41].

The initiation of the crazes shown in Figure 16 occurred by interaction with the sample surfaces (surface furrows). Analogous craze-tip regions have also been found at crazes, which are initiated inside the samples. This can successfully be proven by using rubber-modified, high-impact polystyrene (HIPS) with the rubber particles acting as initiation places of the crazes [42].

The smallest values of the thicknesses of craze tips and pre-crazes measured at many crazes are 15 and 10 nm, respectively, [30, 41]. These measurements correlate with the diameters of the smallest visible domains inside the pre-crazes.

Craze-tip advance

Length-growth of crazes or craze-tip advance is a propagation of the craze tip perpendicular to the loading direction with a continuous formation of the described structure of the craze tip (cf. Figure 16). There is no difference in the structure of the tips of crazes in their different stages of growth, i.e., for crazes immediately after formation and for longer crazes. Therefore, both the processes of craze initiation and craze-tip advance are characterized by a principally equal mechanism of "heterogeneity of deformation."

Craze growth is associated with the transformation of the polymeric material into highly plastically deformed fibrils. The weak domain-like areas or microvoids inside the pre-craze act as stress-concentrators and yield a plastic deformation of the neighboring polymeric material. The irregularly shaped, plastically deformed zones between the voids rupture at their smallest places and split up into small strips, yielding the fibrils. This splitting is similar to the well-known splitting of semi-crystalline polymers. Another analogy is the fibrillation of rubber layers, stretched between hard boundaries. Figure 17 demonstrates this behavior, showing a two-phase polymer system with a network structure, consisting of weak rubber layers between hard polymer particles (rubber-modified PVC) [43]. In the first stages of loading, microvoids appear in the thin rubber layers

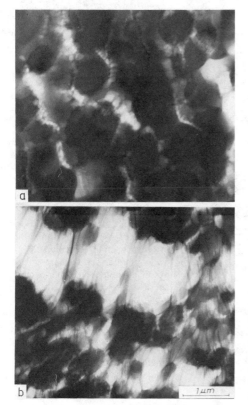

Figure 17. Analogy to craze initiation: Weak rubber layers between hard polymer boundaries (polymer particles—dark) are stressed (polymer system-rubber modified polyvinylchloride). (a) appearance of microvoids (bright domains). (b) transformation into a structure of elongated and connected voids and strongly stretched fibrils (deformation direction vertical).

(see Figure 17a). At local places molecular links are ruptured, and by interaction with deformation and the rupture of neighboring molecular segments, molecularly-weakened domains or microvoids appear ("heterogeneity of deformation" as in the pre-craze). During continuous loading, the domains or microvoids are transformed into elongated voids. Between these voids the rubber material is plastically deformed into strongly-stretched fibrils with a relatively constant thickness (see Figure 17b).

The mechanism of the transformation of the closed cell structure of microvoids into the open cell structure of fibrils is shown schematically in Figure 18 in three consecutive stages. A growing craze is shown on the left in the same direction as it is to be seen in the electron microscope (direction "A") and on the right in cross section (direction "B").

Whereas craze initiation is a transformation of polymer material due to stress concentration at a static place (defect), craze-tip advance is a transformation of material due to stress concentration at a moving craze tip. Therefore, craze tip advance is a continuous process of microvoid nucleation in the stress field ahead of the craze tip with succeeding plastic deformation and fibrillation of the neighboring polymer material, as shown in the scheme in Figure 18. Therefore, there is no need to assume any other mechanism, as for example the meniscus instability. The so-called "meniscus instability" is usually discussed in connection with the deformation of a liquid layer between two rigid plates, if the plates are forced apart; or during the pulling off of a strip of adhesive tape from a substrate [44, 45]. It has been applied by Argon [46] instead of the idea of the repeated nucleation of voids.

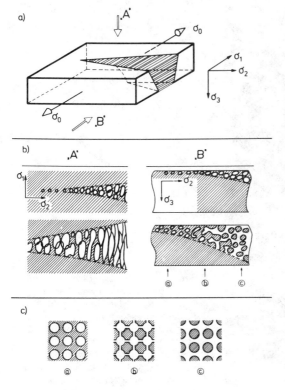

Figure 18. Scheme of the transformation of the craze nuclei in the pre-craze zone into the fibrillar structure of the developed craze [41]. (a) Total view of a craze in a sample stressed by σ_0. (b) A growing craze is shown on the left in the same direction as it is to be seen in the electron microscope (direction "A") and on the right in cross section (direction "B"); transformation of the pre-craze nuclei into microvoids; microvoids act as stress concentrators yielding a plastic deformation of the neighboring polymeric material. (c) View in direction "B": plastically deformed zones between the microvoids, which rupture at their smallest places and split up into small strips, yielding the fibrils.

Yield Processes in High-Impact Polymers

High-impact polymers with dispersed rubber particles

Most of the high-impact polymers consist of a matrix of a brittle polymer with dispersed rubber particles, after the model of the well-known high-impact polystyrenes (HIPS) and ABS-polymers (acrylonitrile-butadiene-styrene). The effect of the incorporated rubber particles is the initiation of energy-absorbing deformation processes in the matrix polymer, i.e., of crazing or shearing. This mechanism was first deduced by Bucknall as "multiple crazing" [47, 48]. The various structural parameters (size, size distribution, and shape of rubber particles; volume content and Young's modulus of the rubber phase; connection between the phases, etc.) influence the formation of crazes and other micromechanical processes and the fracture energy. Therefore, these polymers are appropriate to show the possibilities of improving mechanical properties by modification of their morphology. The direct study of the deformation processes by HVEM yields results, which are described as a three-stage mechanism [42, 49, 50]:

Stage 1: Craze-initiation (Figure 19). Each rubber particle concentrates the stress. In the surroundings of the particles material of the matrix will be transformed into crazes. The micrograph shows such crazes around rubber particles in a sample of high-impact polystyrene. The rubber particles appear somewhat brighter than does the polystyrene matrix; they are elongated in the direction of tension (see arrow). The highest concentration of stress is along the equatorial zones of the rubber particles; these are the zones vertical to the tension direction. The crazes start from the equatorial zones of the particles and propagate perpendicularly to the tension direction. The separate initiation of crazes around particles is the basic mechanism.

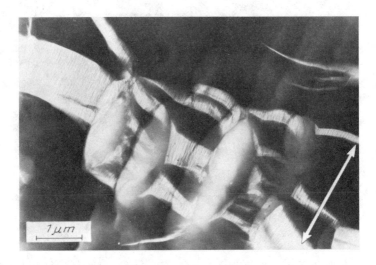

Figure 19. Initiation of crazes at rubber particles in HIPS (1-μm thick section, deformation direction-see arrow, HVEM) [50].

Stage 2: Superposition effect (Figure 20). For a rubber content of more than 15 vol.-% the stress-fields of neighboring particles and of particles and craze-tips superimpose, favoring the formation of broad crazes, and broad, long craze bands. These long craze bands propagate in large polymer areas, in which the orignal stress concentration was too low for craze initiation. Here the energy absorption essentially increases.

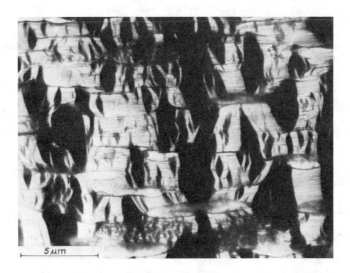

Figure 20. Formation of long and broad craze-bands in HIPS due to the superposition of the individual stress fields around each rubber particle (deformation direction horizontal).

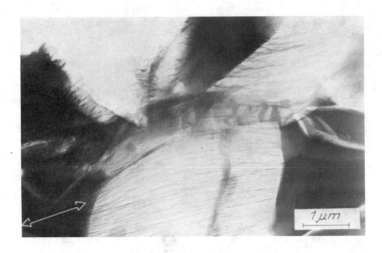

Figure 21. Crack propagation inside the crazes in HIPS (deformation direction-see arrow).

Stage 3: Crack propagation (Figure 21). High-impact polymers fracture by rupture of the crazes, as happens with glassy polymers. But the modified structure modifies the crack propagation. Figure 21 shows a crack inside a craze. The main crack is from above. In the stress field ahead of the crack the craze is ruptured. The length of the cracks is limited by length of the crazes. These mechanisms of crack, by stopping and restricting the crack lengths, delay the propagation of cracks and the ultimate fracture.

Detailed knowledge of the microprocesses of deformation and fracture enables quantitative correlations between morphology and fracture toughness to be obtained. An example is the influence of the volume content of the rubber particles on the energy absorption. The influence of the rubber content on the mechanical properties (impact toughness, fracture elongation, etc.) has been described in many previous papers (cf. [48]). On the other hand, only a few investigations exist on the corresponding changes of the mechanical microprocesses [50–52].

Figure 22 compares the craze formation of three ABS polymers of different rubber content. The upper micrographs show stress-whitened areas at small magnifications, whereas the micrographs at the bottom show particles and crazes at higher magnifications. In 22a the rubber content is low (0.6 vol.-%), yielding large spacings between the rubber particles. Only a few long crazes are formed. In 22b the rubber content is somewhat higher (2.4 vol.-%) so that some more crazes are formed. In 22c with a rubber content of about 21 vol.-% the superposition effect is operative, yielding a large number of crazes and craze-bands over a large area.

The changes in size and shape of crazes in dependence on the volume content of rubber particles were measured directly from the micrographs of deformed specimens. From this the volume of a single craze around a rubber particle was calculated, and in addition knowledge of the number of rubber particles (and of the number of crazes) enabled the total volume of all crazes to be calculated. With increasing rubber content, an appreciable increase of the total craze volume is observed. The formation of the crazes needs energy and recently [42] the amounts of energy of the main energy-absorbing processes of deformation and fracture have been evaluated. It was shown that in intensively-crazed materials, the amount of energy required to form crazes is more than 90% of the total fracture work. Therefore, the change of total craze volume reveals rather well the change of the total fracture work with increasing rubber volume content.

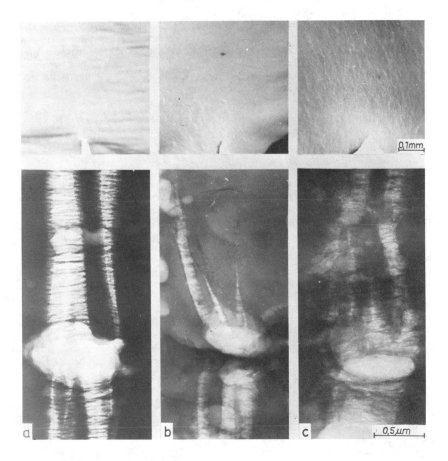

Figure 22. Influence of the rubber volume content on the size of the crazed area ("stress-whitened" area ahead of the crack tip) in the micrographs at the top, and the size and shapes of crazes in the micrographs at the bottom [50]. Rubber volume content: (a) 0.6% (b) 2.4% (c) 21%.

High-impact polymers with network rubber phase

A group of high-impact polymers—mostly based on polyvinylchloride (PVC)—has an opposite structure: a network of rubber around particles of the hard polymer. Examples are PVC/EVA or PVC/CPE systems with about 1 μm large primary particles of PVC surrounded by a very thin-walled rubber network (cf. Figure 8b). As a consequence of the opposite morphology, a fundamentally different mechanism of plastic deformation exists. This was proposed several years ago [32, 43] and corroborated and explained theoretically later [53, 54]. The main stages of this mechanism are:

- At the beginning of the deformation, the weaker rubber phase is stretched elastically or a little plastically, and a three-dimensional stress state is built up everywhere in the network (cf. Figure 17a).

- The three-dimensional stress state enables the rubber phase to transfer stresses from one PVC particle to the next, high enough to reach the yield stress of the PVC particles. The particles will be deformed plastically. This plastic deformation of the individual PVC particles absorbs the main part of the total fracture energy.
- By rupture of parts of the rubber network, microvoids between fibrillated rubber material appear, initiating formation of the main crack (cf. Figure 17b).

Initiation of Crazes in Terms of Multiplicity of Glass Transition

Multiplicity of glass transition

One of the most important questions is why the polymer material can flow at low temperatures far below the normal pressure glass temperature T_g. A high molecular mobility is a prerequisite to any flow; it is not possible at normal pressure below T_g. Many different theories and models have been suggested [55, 56] to explain this pheonomenon.

Designating the complex non-uniaxial stress pattern, which plays an important role in craze formation, as "negative pressure" implies the question: How is the molecular motion promoted by negative pressure at $T < T_g$? This was previously discussed in [23].

The transition from the glassy state to a molecularly mobile state is a rather universal phenomenon [57] revealing quite similar features in different materials under different conditions (effective time, pressure, solvent). The question therefore arises as to how the glass transition appears at low temperatures and negative pressures.

Several dispersion zones can be distinguished in the glass transition in polymers. The molecular mobility increases in these several stages (multiplicity of the glass transition [57]). The main transition α is splitted up into a fine structure of three components, GTZ, FZ*, HZ [58]; and the flow transition, too, probably has to be splitted. The zones important for crazing [23] are briefly characterized as follows:

GZ = glassy zone: Probably contains secondary relaxations γ which are not connected with local modes or the main transition (e.g., motion of side groups).

GTZ = proper glass
transition zone: Cooperative motion of about 50 or more monomeric units; length scale of correlations is about 2 nm.

FZ* = confined flow zone: Flow-like motion of chain segments within the network of topologically defined entanglement points; mode length lies between about 2 and 10 nm.

HZ = hindering zone: Increasing hindering of the FZ*-type motion by an additional friction due to the entanglement points if the increasing mode lengths reach the order of entanglement spacing; length scales about 7...12 nm.

PZ = rubbery plateau: Still unknown modes that are responsible for the relatively constant level of modulus (diffusion of entanglements; used to estimate the molecular weight M_e between entanglement points).

EZ = flow transition
zone: Loosing and interlinking of entanglements by cooperative motion of several longer parts of chains or whole chains with emphasis of longitudinal motion (reptation model); details are not known yet; mode lengths are up to the order of the radius of macromolecules R.

FZ = flow zone: Individual motion (diffusion of the mass center) of single macromolecules.

The following trends are observed in the given order:

1. Increasing relaxation times (for a given state).
2. Increasing characteristic lengths of molecular modes ("mode lengths").
3. Increasing dependence of mobility on the existent long polymer chains.

Point 1., increasing relaxation times, can be discussed in connection with the increasing mode lengths: In the confined flow zone FZ*, the flow units are chain segments which are confined to regions between entanglements (which can neither be tied nor loosed in the time scales of this zone). In the flow transition zone EZ, the flow units are longer parts of chains, the viscosity of which is increased by reptation-like mechanisms. The confined flow zone FZ* of the main transition and the "high frequency" part of the flow transition zone EZ seem to be the most important dispersion zones for the crazes. They are connected with mode lengths in the range of 2 to 10 nm in FZ* and up to R in EZ where R = molecule radius, approximately $0.7 \, nm \cdot P^{1/2}$; P = degree of polymerization, number of monomeric units (the value of 0.7 nm holds for vinylpolymers).

Description of craze formation and growth

The starting point is a continuity argument. During craze formation, the material is transformed from the frozen state into a flow state. Due to the universality of the glass transition, it can be assumed that the two zones FZ* and EZ are also distinguishable at low temperatures and negative pressures, and that these two zones are reached one after another by a growing external stress [23]. This is a new aspect compared with previous trials (e.g., [59, 60]) to join the onset of molecular mobility at $T < T_g$ with the glass transition. To maintain both the flow processes (in FZ* and EZ) a negative pressure in the order of 100 MPa is necessary.

The experimental observations (cf. Figure 16) permit a decomposition of the total craze into a separate "pre-craze," characterized by a domain-like structure; and the proper craze, generally characterized by a more or less fibrillation of the material [19, 30, 41]. The existence of a separate pre-craze is an important refinement of the craze features generally known. Both craze and pre-craze propagate very quickly (jump-like), where "quickly" is used for the visual observation in the high voltage electron microscope (HVEM) when they propagate in jumps. It is still an open question if the jumps of craze and pre-craze are coupled in some way and if the velocity of propagation is equal in both cases. Unlike that, the crack propagates relatively slowly in the craze materials, and its propagation can be regulated from outside [30].

Craze formation (processes in the pre-craze). First, the processes near the craze tip are considered, disregarding the velocities of craze propagation. Due to the applied loading, the negative pressure near the craze tip increases continuously till the confined flow zone FZ* is reached. The confined flow in FZ* starts in the neighborhood of freezed defects, which are caused by the molecular mobility of the proper glass transition zone GTZ (for a discussion see "Defects" later in this chapter). If the distance between the active defects is sufficiently great, flow regions of lower densities are created having dimensions up to about 10 nm, according to the typical lengths of FZ*. By joining neighboring flow regions they can reach slightly larger dimensions, too. This correlates with the structures observed in the pre-craze having domain diameters of at least 10 nm to a few 10 nm, cf. Figure 16.

The pre-craze material is therefore characterized by deformations in the confined flow zone FZ*, i.e. by segment motions between entanglements. The confined flow is stopped by processes in the broad hindering zone HZ, still unknown in detail.

These findings explain the following experimental observations:

- Typical dimensions of pre-craze structures (the minimal diameters of the craze nuclei amount to 10 . . . 15 nm; the distance between the domains is a few 10 nm).
- Invariability in the shape of the craze tip.

Developed craze (formation of fibrillated craze). Further increasing the local stress yields a transformation of the low-density domains into microvoids (starting in the neighborhood of defects and other weak points of structure). The polymer material between the microvoids is additionally stressed by stress concentration and will be transformed into craze fibrils. The number of fibrils per unit area (fibril density) is therefore connected with the density of activated GTZ defects. The transformation described is schematically shown in Figure 18 [41].

The pre-craze/craze transition takes place in the pre-craze material after the possibilities of deformation in the confined flow zone FZ* are exhausted. At this stage, the pre-craze material is considered to be frozen due to the unloading immediately after the jump of the pre-craze tip. Afterwards, the negative pressure generated by the applied load increases till the flow transition zone EZ with its other parameters is reached.

The molecular mobility in the EZ is characterized by a loosening and interlinking of entanglements, thus enabling greater parts of individual chain molecules to move ("reptation"). The stretching of the craze material is limited at extension ratios smaller than the extension ratio theoretically possible (the maximum extension of chains between the deformed entanglement points is $\lambda_e \approx 4 \ldots 7$ for PS [39]). The existence of a sufficient number of chain connections seems to be necessary for maintaining the negative pressure [23]. This correlates with extension ratios experimentally found (by investigating crazes in PS using HVEM) of about $\lambda_c = 2.5 \ldots 3.5$ [30].

Defects. The so-called "defect diffusion model" of the glass transition explains the defect formation in glassy (amorphous) materials. This model is presented in Jäckle's review [61] (besides many others, since at present there is no generally accepted microscopic theory of glass transition). Here a defect is defined as a small spatial region (some 0.1 nm), in which the cooperative motion of the GTZ is thought to be concentrated.

The universal glass transition, termed as GTZ (proper glass transition zone), is a dispersion zone between GZ and FZ*. It is characterized by a typical mode length in the range of 2 nm for polymers [57, 62]. This means that the average separation between the primary "GTZ-defects" is about 2 nm.

An analysis of the T_g-effect on the low-temperature (T < 1 K) anomalies of the specific heat and other variables points to the fact that energy parameters of the defects are distributed rather homogeneously in the interval between 0 and kT_g (k Boltzmann constant). If the defects, which can be activated during the craze formation, are only such defects with energy parameters near T_g, then, of course, the separation between the effective defects is greater than 2 nm. An optimum density of such defects (separation between them is in the order of magnitude of 10 nm) is necessary to create fibrillated crazes. Correlations between the defect density, the interior structure of crazes, and the influence of physical aging (annealing below T_g) are discussed in detail in [23].

Acknowledgments

I am indebted to Mrs I. Naumann and Mrs. H. Steinbach for preparation of some of the polymer samples investigated.

ABBREVIATIONS

TEM	transmission electron microscopy	ABS	acrylonitrile-butadiene-styrene terpolymer
SEM	scanning electron microscopy		
HVEM	high voltage electron microscopy	ACS	acrylonitrile-chlorinated polyethylene-styrene terpolymer
PS	polystyrene		
PMMA	polymethylmethacrylate	EVA	ethylene-vinylacetate copolymer
SAN	styrene-acrylonitrile copolymer	PE	polyethylene
PVC	polyvinylchloride	LDPE	low-density PE
PC	polycarbonate	HDPE	high-density PE
HIPS	high-impact polystyrene	PU	polyurethane

REFERENCES

1. Linke, U., and Kopp, W. U., *Prakt. Metallogr.*, *17*:479 (1980).
2. Olley, R. H., Hodge, A. M., and Bassett, D. C., *J. Polym. Sci., Polym. Phys. Ed.*, *17*: 627 (1979).
3. Jakopic, E., *Proc. 2nd Europ. Reg. Conf. El. Micr.* Delft, 1960, Vol. 1, p. 559.
4. Hobbs, S. Y., and Watkins, V. H., *J. Polym. Sci., Polym. Phys. Ed.*, *20*:651 (1982).
5. Michler, G. H., in *Elektronenmikroskopie in der Festkörperphysik*, (H. Bethge, J. Heydenreich eds.), VEB Deutscher Verlag der Wissenschaften, Berlin, 1982, p. 359.
6. Michler, G. H., *Plaste und Kautschuk*, *27*:301 (1980).
7. Kato, K., *J. Electron Microsc.*, *14*:220 (1965).
8. Kanig, G., *Kolloid-Z. Z. Polym.*, *251*:782 (1973).
9. Hendus, H., *Angew. Makromol. Chem.*, *12*:1 (1970).
10. Michler, G. H., Gruber, K., and Steinbach, H., *Acta Polymerica*, *33*:550 (1982).
11. Andrews, E. H., Bennett, M. W., and Markham, A., *J. Polym. Sci.*, *A-2 5*:1235 (1967).
12. Michler, G. H., *Ultramicroscopy*, *15*:81 (1984).
13. Grubb, D. T., and Keller, A., *J. Mater. Sci.*, *7*:822 (1972).
14. Foks, J., and Michler, G. H., *J. Appl. Polym. Sci.*, *31*:1281 (1986).
15. Michler, G. H., Naumann, I., and Foks, J., *Proc. 11.* Tagung Elektronenmikroskopie, Dresden, GDR, 1984; and *Polymer*, *28*:2195 (1987).
16. Michler, G. H., and Gruber, K., *Acta Polymerica*, *31*:771 (1980).
17. Hosemann, R., *J. Polymer Sci. Polymer Symp.*, *20*:1 (1967).
18. Grubb, D. T., *J. Mater. Sci.*, *9*:1715 (1974).
19. Michler, G. H., *Kristall Technik*, *14*:1357 (1979).
20. Geil, P. H., *Ind. Eng. Chem. Products Res. Develop.*, *14*:59 (1975).
21. Kämpf, G., *Progr. Colloid Polymer Sci.*, *57*:249 (1975).
22. Roche, E. J., and Thomas, E. L., *Polymer.*, *22*:333 (1981).
23. Donth, E., and Michler, G. H. Proc. 31, IUPAC "MACRO '87," Merseburg, 1987, p. IV, 140; and *Colloid & Polymer Sci.*, in press.
24. Michler, G. H., in *Morphology of Polymers*, (B. Sedláček ed.), Walter de Gruyter & Co., Berlin, New York, 1986, p. 749.
25. Lenz, F., *Z. wiss. Mikroskopie*, *63*:50 (1956).
26. Voss, K., *Biometrical J.*, *20*:425 (1978).
27. Vesely, D., Low, A., and Bevis, M., in *Developments in Electron Microscopy and Analysis*, (J. A., Venables ed.) Academic Press, London, New York, San Francisco, 1976, p. 333.
28. Richardson, M. J., and Thomas, K., *Proc. 5th Europ. Congr. El. Micr.*, Manchester 1972 p. 562.
29. Michler, G. H., and Dietzsch, Ch., *Crystal Res. & Technol.*, *17*:1241 (1982).
30. Michler, G. H., *Colloid & Polymer Sci.*, *263*:462 (1985).
31. Michler, G., Gruber, K., Pohl, G., and Kästner, G., *Plaste und Kautschuk*, *20*:756 (1973).
32. Michler, G. H., and Gruber, K., in *Strukturabhängiges mechanisches Verhalten von Festkörpern* (U. Hofmann, O. Henkel, D. Schulze, eds.) Akademie-Verlag, Berlin, 1979, p. 329.
33. Michler, G., and Schmidt, V., *Plaste und Kautschuk*, *34*:1 (1987).
34. Kambour, R. P., *Macromolec. Rev.*, *7*:1 (1973).
35. Doyle, M. J., *J Mater. Sci.*, *8*:1165 (1973).
36. Doyle, M. J., and Wagner, J. G., in *ACS* No 154 Washington 1976, p. 63.
37. Großkurth, K. P., *Kautschuk u. Gummi, Kunststoffe*, *26*:43 (1973).
38. Brown, H. R., *J. Mater. Sci.*, *14*:237 (1979).
39. Kramer, E. J., in *Crazing in Polymers*, (H. H. Kausch ed.), Springer-Verlag Berlin, Heidelberg 1983 (Adv. Polym. Sci. *52/53*) p. 1.
40. Chan, T., Donald, A. M., and Kramer, E. J., *J. Mater. Sci.*, *16*:676 (1981).
41. Michler, G. H., *Colloid & Polymer Sci.*, *264*:522 (1986).
42. Michler, G. H., *Plaste und Kautschuk*, *26*:497, 680 (1979).
43. Michler, G., and Gruber, K., *Plaste und Kautschuk*, *23*:496 (1976).
44. Taylor, G. I., *Proc. Roy. Soc.*, A *201*:192 (1950).
45. Saffmann, P. G., and Taylor, G. I., *Proc. Roy. Soc.*, A *245*:312 (1958).
46. Argon, A. S., and Salama, M. M., *Philos. Mag.*, *36*:1217 (1977).

47. Bucknall, C. B., and Smith, R. R., *Polymer, 6*:437 (1965).
48. Bucknall, C. B., *Toughened Plastics*, Applied Science Publishers Ltd., London 1977.
49. Michler, G. H., *Acta Polymerica, 36*:285 (1985).
50. Michler, G. H., *Polymer, 27*:323 (1986).
51. Dillon, M., and Bevis, M., *J. Mater. Sci., 17*:1895 (1982).
52. Michler, G. H., *Acta Polymerica, 36*:325 (1985).
53. Michler, G. H., *Plaste und Kautschuk, 28*:191 (1981).
54. Michler, G. H., in *1. Dresdne Polymerdiskussion, Polymer Blends* Dresden, AdW der DDR 1986 vol. 1, p. 177; vol. 2, p. 94.
55. Kausch, H. H., (ed.), *Crazing in Polymers*, Springer-Verlag, Berlin, Heidelberg, 1983.
56. Narisawa, I., *Strength and Fracture of Polymeric Materials* (Japan.), Omsha, Tokyo 1982.
57. Donth, E., *Glasübergang*, Akademie-Verlag, Berlin 1981.
58. Donth, E., and Schneider, K., *Acta Polymerica, 36*:213, 273 (1985).
59. Newman, S., and Strella, S., *J. appl. Polym. Sci., 9*:2297 (1965).
60. Strella, S., *J. Polym. Sci.* A-2, *4*:527 (1966); *Appl. Polym. Symp, 7*:165 (1968).
61. Jäckle, J., *Rep, Progr. Phys., 49*:171 (1986).
62. Donth, E., *J. Non-Cryst. Solids, 53*:325 (1982).

CHAPTER 19

CONSTITUTIVE ANALYSIS OF THE NONLINEAR VISCOELASTIC PROPERTIES IN SIMPLE EXTENSION OF POLYMERIC FLUIDS AND NETWORKS: A COMPARISON

Paul J. R. Leblans and Boudewijn J. R. Scholtens

DSM Research
Geleen, The Netherlands

CONTENTS

INTRODUCTION

The remarkable dynamic and mechanical properties of molten polymers result from the tremendous number of different configurations which these flexible molecules may pass through [1–3]. The difference between a polymer melt and a polymer network is that in the latter type of material the chains are permanently interconnected to form a three-dimensional network, whereas in the former they are not. As a consequence, polymer melts are basically fluids, which only behave as networks under special conditions; whereas polymer networks must be considered as solids with an equilibrium modulus.

Until some time ago no experimental results were available to compare the nonlinear viscoelastic behaviors of these two types of material because of both experimental and theoretical complications. Polymer melts can be subjected to large shear strains, but networks cannot because of slippage at the shearing surfaces at relatively low strains. Because of their high elasticity, crosslinked networks can be stretched uniaxially more easily than polymer melts. In the field of rubber elasticity both experimentalists and theoreticians have mainly concentrated on the equilibrium stress-strain relationship of rubber networks [1, 3]. This approach is obviously impossible for polymer melts.

In the last decade, much progress has been achieved toward solving these complications. Apparatuses have been built to measure the simple extensional properties of polymer melts [4, 5]. Also, the general factorable single integral constitutive equation has been shown to describe well the viscoelastic properties of a large class of crosslinked rubbers [6, 7] and the elasticoviscous properties of many polymer melts [8–10] under various types of deformation. Thus, an appropriate way to compare the stress-strain relations of polymer melts and networks is to calculate the strain-dependent function contained in this constitutive equation from experimental results and to compare the strain measures so obtained. Finally, molecular theories have been developed for the nonlinear behavior of polymer melts [11, 12] and polymer networks [13–17].

This chapter compares the strain measures in extension of a number of polymeric materials, including both polymer melts and networks. In addition, these will be examined in the light of recent molecular theories.

THE FACTORABLE SINGLE INTEGRAL CONSTITUTIVE EQUATION AND THE SIGNIFICANCE OF THE STRAIN MEASURE $S_E(\epsilon)$

General

A single integral constitutive equation with an integrand factorable into a memory function only dependent on time and a tensorial functional of the strain history has proven successful in describing transient and steady-state rheological properties in unidirectional shear flow of a class of polymer melts [10, 18]. As the factorability of strain and time effects was actually discovered and developed in the field of crosslinked rubbers [19, 20], it is not surprising that the factorable single integral constitutive equation is also appropriate to describe the stress-strain relation for crosslinked rubbers [6, 7].

One way to arrive at the single integral constitutive equation is to apply the Boltzmann superposition principle to a non-specified tensor functional $S(C^{-1})$ of the macroscopic strain, represented by the Finger strain tensor C^{-1}. The present state is chosen as the reference state in describing the macroscopic strain history, i.e., the strain at the present time t is measured with respect to all previous states at previous times t' by the relative Finger strain tensor $C_t^{-1}(t')$. The total stress tensor at present time t, $P(t)$, is then related to the strain history by:

$$P(t) = -P_0 1 - \int_{-\infty}^{t} G(t - t') \frac{dS(C^{-1})}{dt'} dt'$$
$$= -P_0 1 + G_e S[C_t^{-1}(0)] + \int_{-\infty}^{t} \frac{dG(t - t')}{dt'} S(C^{-1}) dt' \tag{1}$$

The isotropic pressure field is denoted by $P_0 1$, $G(t)$ is the stress relaxation shear modulus, and G_e is the equilibrium shear modulus, which equals zero for polymer melts but has a finite value for crosslinked rubbers. C^{-1} under the integral stands for the relative Finger strain tensor $C_t^{-1}(t')$. The slope of the modulus function $dG(t - t')/dt'$ is often identified with a memory function $m(t-t')$ [8]. It is our experience that in order to give a quantitative description of the linear viscoelastic behavior of a polymer melt or network, the memory function has to be represented by a continuous spectrum of exponentially decaying terms over a broad range of relaxation times [21, 22]. Thus Equation 1 transforms into:

$$P(t) = -P_0 1 + G_e S[C_t^{-1}(0)] + \int_{-\infty}^{t} m(t - t') S(C^{-1}) dt'$$

with $\quad m(t - t') = \int_{-\infty}^{+\infty} \frac{H(\tau)}{\tau} e^{-(t-t')/\tau} d \ln \tau \tag{2}$

As will be shown in a subsequent paragraph, the equilibrium modulus and the memory function can be obtained from measurements in the linear viscoelastic region.

The Strain Tensor in Simple Extensional Deformation

In the case of simple extensional deformation the appearance of the strain tensor is quite simple. In this type of deformation only the 11-, 22-, and 33-components of the stress tensor differ from zero. Therefore, all components of the strain tensor other than the diagonal components are equal to zero. On the strength of symmetry considerations the 22- and 33-components of the strain tensor must be equal if the 1-direction is chosen as the elongational direction. Consequently the strain tensor has the shape:

$$S_t(t') = \begin{pmatrix} S_t(t')_{11} & 0 & 0 \\ 0 & S_t(t')_{22} & 0 \\ 0 & 0 & S_t(t')_{33} \end{pmatrix} \tag{3}$$

where $\quad S_t(t')_{22} = S_t(t')_{33}$

The dependence of S on the time difference $(t - t')$ is due to the dependence on the relative Finger strain tensor $C_t^{-1}(t')$. From the principles of continuum mechanics [23, 24] it is known that any isotropic function $S(C^{-1})$ of the Finger strain tensor may be employed to measure strain. Therefore S must be determined by the first and second invariants, $I_t(t')$ and $II_t(t')$, of the relative Finger strain tensor. In the case of uniaxial extension these invariants can always be expressed in the difference between the Hencky strain at time t, $\epsilon(t)$, and the Hencky strain at time t', $\epsilon(t')$, or equivalently in the ratio of the stretch ratios at times t, $\lambda(t)$, and t', $\lambda(t')$. The strain functional in this type of deformation is therefore:

$$S_t(t') = S[\epsilon(t) - \epsilon(t')] = S\left[\frac{\lambda(t)}{\lambda(t')}\right] \tag{4}$$

Introduction of Equation 4 into Equation 2 yields the following expression for the components of the stress tensor for an extensional strain with an arbitrary strain history $\epsilon(t')$ at $t' \leq t$:

$$P_{ij}(t) = -P_0\delta_{ij} + G_e S_{ij}[\epsilon(t)] + \int_{-\infty}^{t} m(t - t') S_{ij}[\epsilon(t) - \epsilon(t')]\, dt' \tag{5}$$

where δ represents the Kronecker delta.

The Strain Measure $S_E(\epsilon)$

In simple extension, the difference between the stress in the elongational (1-direction) and that in the direction perpendicular to the elongational direction (2-direction) is measured. For conciseness, this stress difference will be denoted by σ_E. According to Equation 5 σ_E is determined by the difference between the 11- and 22-components of S, which will be denoted by S_E. Thus, the expression for σ_E is:

$$\sigma_E(\epsilon, t) = G_e S_E[\epsilon(t)] + \int_{-\infty}^{t} m(t - t') S_E[\epsilon(t) - \epsilon(t')]\, dt' \tag{6}$$

The relative strain history for an instantaneous extension of a sample to a Hencky strain ϵ at zero time is given by:

$$\epsilon(t) - \epsilon(t') = 0 \qquad \text{for } t' > 0$$

$$\epsilon(t) - \epsilon(t') = \epsilon \qquad \text{for } t' < 0 \tag{7}$$

Inserting this strain history into Equation 6 yields:

$$\sigma_E(\epsilon, t) = G_e S_E(\epsilon) + S_E(\epsilon) \int_{-\infty}^{0} m(t - t') \, dt' = S_E(\epsilon)[G_e + G_r(t)] \tag{8}$$

where $G_r(t)$ is the relaxing part of the shear modulus. At equilibrium conditions, at infinite time after the imposition of the strain, $G_r(t)$ has completely decayed and the familiar equation of rubber elasticity results:

$$\sigma_E(\epsilon) = G_e S_E(\epsilon) \tag{9}$$

Different Ways to Introduce Nonlinearity

The definition of a nonlinear strain tensor and strain measure may seem superfluous and confusing at first glance. In the theories on the nonlinear elastic behavior of crosslinked rubbers, like the theory of Flory and Erman, the modulus is made dependent on the strain [14–17]. This approach to nonlinearity is also the most obvious one when analyzing the experimental data: as for small values of the strain, so for larger values the modulus is calculated by dividing the tensile stress by the macroscopic strain, which yields a strain-dependent quantity.

Yet, a theoretical argument is in favor of defining a nonlinear strain tensor instead of a nonlinear modulus. The modulus of a network is determined only by the concentration of elastically-active chain segments between crosslinks. As long as no chemical bonds are broken, this number remains constant in a permanent network. So there is no reason to adapt the value of the modulus, even if the network is subjected to large strains. On the other hand, the microscopic deformation of the chain segments is probably nonaffine in the large, macroscopic strain—an assumption also made in Flory's theory—which means that the microscopic strain is different from the macroscopic strain. In this light the definition of a strain measure relating the microscopic strain to the macroscopic deformation (in an average way) is certainly justified and conceptually more sound than the introduction of a nonlinear modulus. In temporary networks, like polymer melts, network segments may disappear because of the imposition of strain. If the origin of nonlinearity appears to be the same for crosslinked rubbers and polymer melts, on the other hand, the use of a nonlinear strain tensor is appropriate for the whole class of polymeric materials.

EXPERIMENTAL METHODS AND MATERIALS

Linear Viscoelastic Measurements

In the linear viscoelastic range, the viscosity and modulus are independent of the magnitude of the deformation. Our experiments were performed on a 7200 Rheometrics Mechanical Spectrometer (RMS-7200) equipped with the parallel-plate or cone-and-plate geometry which was located in a thermostatted oven containing a nitrogen atmosphere. Figure 1 depicts the essential parts of the spectrometer and explains how measurements are performed and analyzed with this apparatus in parallel plate geometry. More details can be found in [21, 25]. A block diagram of this experimental system is given in Figure 2.

From linear viscoelastic data over a wide frequency (ω) range such as the storage modulus G' and the loss modulus G'' (or the dynamic modulus G_d and viscosity η_d and the phase angle δ), the relaxation time spectrum, $H(\tau)$, can be determined by various approximate methods [2]. For amorphous polymers these data are usually obtained from time-temperature $(t - T)$ superposition of isothermal oscillation measurements at various temperatures well above the glass transition temperature T_g [2]. With oscillation measurements it is possible to apply a particularly sensitive method of $t - T$ superposition [10, 25, 26]. Firstly, the horizontal shift function, a_T, is obtained from the superposition of the phase-angle isotherms, a prime experimental characteristic which can be determined very accurately by merely horizontal shifting. Next, the vertical shift function, b_T, is determined from the vertical shifting of both the G'- and G''-curves after application of the shift

OSCILLATION MEASUREMENTS with the MECHANICAL SPECTROMETER

input: periodic deformation
$$\theta = \theta_0 \sin \omega t \quad (\omega \text{ in rad/s})$$

strain: $\gamma = \gamma_0 \sin \omega t$, $\gamma_0 = R\theta_0/h$

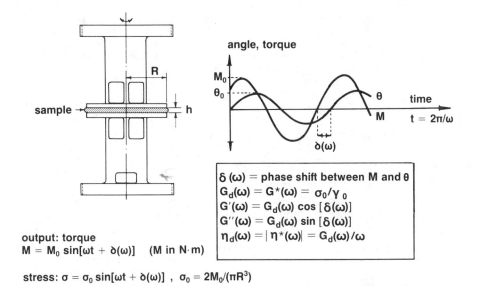

angle, torque

M_0

θ_0

θ

time

sample

M

h

$t = 2\pi/\omega$

$\delta(\omega)$

output: torque
$$M = M_0 \sin[\omega t + \delta(\omega)] \quad (M \text{ in N·m})$$

$\delta(\omega) = $ phase shift between M and θ
$G_d(\omega) = G^*(\omega) = \sigma_0/\gamma_0$
$G'(\omega) = G_d(\omega) \cos[\delta(\omega)]$
$G''(\omega) = G_d(\omega) \sin[\delta(\omega)]$
$\eta_d(\omega) = |\eta^*(\omega)| = G_d(\omega)/\omega$

stress: $\sigma = \sigma_0 \sin[\omega t + \delta(\omega)]$, $\sigma_0 = 2M_0/(\pi R^3)$

Figure 1. Parallel-plate geometry in the Rheometrics Mechanical Spectrometer and interpretation of the measuring results.

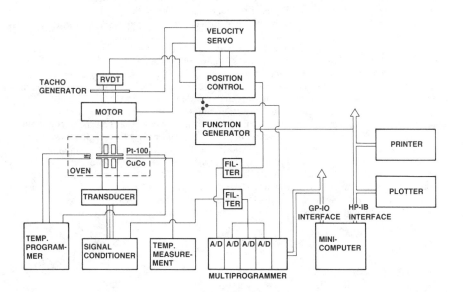

Figure 2. Block diagram of a simple shear measuring system, the Mechanical Spectrometer.

function a_T just mentioned. The superimposability of the $\delta(\omega, T)$ curves ensures the subsequent superimposability, with the same function a_T, of all other viscoelastic characteristics, as explained in [25]. This procedure is, in our opinion, the most accurate today and it is very sensitive to deviations from thermoviscoelastically-simple behavior [25, 26].

Although there are several approximate methods [2] to determine the relaxation spectrum $H(\tau)$, one can be recommended in particular [22]. It is an iterative method that can be applied after having obtained a provisional spectrum with one of these approximate methods. This provisional spectrum, which only describes well the original G''-master curve in the middle of its frequency range, is first extrapolated at both ends. Next it is optimized by trial-and-error corrections of $H(\tau)$ in such a way that, over the entire reduced frequency interval, G'' calculated with:

$$G''(\omega) = \int_{\ln \omega_{max}}^{\ln \omega_{min}} H(\tau) \frac{\omega\tau}{1 + \omega^2\tau^2} \, d \ln \tau \tag{10}$$

approximates G'' measured; and G' measured minus G' calculated with:

$$G'(\omega) = \int_{-\infty}^{+\infty} H(\tau) \frac{\omega^2\tau^2}{1 + \omega^2\tau^2} \, d \ln \tau \tag{11}$$

is zero over the entire frequency range. The value of the adjustable parameter $G'(0)$ so obtained equals the best estimate for the equilibrium modulus:

$$G'(0) = G_e \tag{12}$$

for a permanent network and is zero for polymer melts [22].

Measurement of the Nonlinear Viscoelasticity in Simple Extension

Polymer Melts

Some of the results shown shortly have been obtained on the basis of measurements performed on a uniaxial stretching apparatus for polymer melts of the conventional-clamp type [27], the Göttfert-Rheostrain. This tensile rheometer is a modified version of the one designed by Münstedt [28]. Figure 3 shows the configuration of the system. The sample is contained in a cylindrical glass measuring chamber filled with silicon oil. The oil has almost the same density as the polymer melt and therefore counterbalances for the greater part the effect of gravity in the vertically disposed chamber. Two more glass cylinders surround the measuring chamber. A heat transfer silicon oil, circulating through the inner jacket of the glass dewar, provides close temperature control of the inner, non-circulating fluid. Constancy of the temperature was monitored using three Pt-100 thermometers, one at the bottom, one at the top, and one that could be moved from the bottom to the top of the chamber. The temperature deviations are within 0.25°C. To make sure that the sample is at the same temperature as the surrounding oil at the beginning of the experiment, it has to be placed in the chamber for 5 to 10 minutes before the experiment is started, depending on the difference between the measuring temperature and the melting temperature of the sample.

The cylindrical sample is glued onto a T-clip at both sides. The lower sample clip is held in a spring-and-peg assembly, attached directly to the load cell, and the upper sample clip is attached to a thin metal tape. The sample is stretched when a disk rolls up the metal tape. The force needed to stretch the sample is measured by the load cell. The difference between the stress in the direction of elongation and the stress in the direction perpendicular thereto is related to this force f by:

$$\sigma_E = P_{11} - P_{22} = \frac{f}{A} \tag{13}$$

where A is the cross-sectional area of the sample.

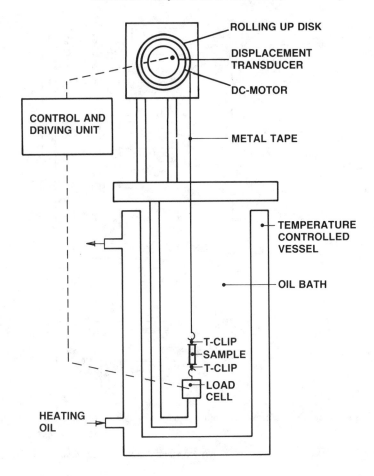

Figure 3. Configuration of a simple elongation apparatus, the Göttfert Rheostrain.

Different types of experiment may be performed with the help of a "closed loop" device. Figure 4 is a block diagram of the experimental system.

In the constant-elongation rate experiment the sample length is regulated by the position control servo loop according to:

$$l(t) = l_0 + \dot\epsilon_0 \int_0^t l(t') \, dt' \tag{14}$$

where $\dot\epsilon_0$ is the constant Hencky strain rate and l_0 is the initial sample length.

In the so-called constant-stretching rate experiments, the sample is stretched by the upper clip moving with a constant speed v_0. By means of the position control servo loop the length of the sample is adjusted according to:

$$l(t) = l_0 + v_0 t \tag{15}$$

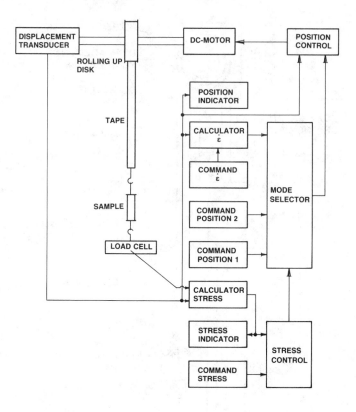

Figure 4. Block diagram of the experimental system for simple elongational measurements.

In the case of a creep experiment under constant stress σ_E the sample is elongated according to:

$$l(t) = \frac{\sigma_E A_0 l_0}{f(t)} \tag{16}$$

where A_0 is the initial sample cross section and $f(t)$ is the force as a function of time. In this case the stress control compares the real stress value from the calculator with the command stress and provides the position control via the mode selector with the necessary signals for stretching the sample according to Equation 16.

In stress relaxation experiments the sample is first stretched at a constant rate until the desired length is reached and subsequently the length is kept constant.

A description of the sample preparation for this kind of apparatus and of the possible sources of error is contained in [21].

Uncured Elastomers and Polymer Networks

Dynamic, true stress-strain curves were measured with an Instron 1195 tensile tester equipped with a TNO nitrogen thermostat (± 0.1 K) and automated with an HP 85 calculator and an HP 6940 B multiprogrammer (both Hewlett Packard). Seven cross-head speeds were chosen between 5 and 500 mm/min, at temperatures T = 300, 345, and 390 K.

Table 1
Some Properties of the LDPE Material

Grade	$[\eta]^1$ (dg/l)	Density[2] (kg/m^3)	Melt Index[3] (dg/min)	$\bar{M}_n^4$	$\bar{M}_m^4$ (kg/mol)	$\bar{M}_z^4$
Stam 2800	1.32	920	0.3	24	150	440

[1] In decalin at 408 K.
[2] At 296 K.
[3] At 463 K.
[4] With gel permeation chromatography.

Rectangular elastomeric samples, about 4 mm wide and 2 mm thick, were used for these experiments. Special precautions, described in [7], guaranteed homogeneous elongation and no slippage of both the uncured and the cross-linked EPDM (ethylene propylene diene monomer) elastomers. The initial sample length was about 50 mm, and the maximum sample length possible in the thermostat was about 370 mm. More experimental details were published recently [7].

Materials

For the simple extensional experiments some polymer melts were selected which display a different nonlinear behavior in simple shear flow [21]. They are all polyolefines and commercial grades of DSM: two high-density polyethylenes (HDPE) and a low-density polyethylene (LDPE). As only the properties of the LDPE melt could be fitted using the factorable single integral constitutive equation, only the measuring results on this material have been taken into consideration in this study. Characteristics of the LDPE melt are collected in Table 1.

The characteristics of the non-crosslinked elastomers are collected in Table 2. These elastomers are terpolymers of ethylene, propylene, and a diene monomer (EPDM). Permanent networks were obtained by mixing these with various amounts of dicumyl peroxide and curing these mixtures for 10 min in a mold at 450 K and 20 MPa. The cured elastomers are designated by the sample code followed by a number indicating the weight percentage of peroxide used for crosslinking (0.2–1.6 wt%). The uncured elastomers are designated by 0.0. More details on the materials and the preparation of these networks are given in [25].

Calculation of the Nonlinear Strain Measure $S_E(\epsilon)$ from Measuring Results

Once the memory function has been obtained from linear viscoelastic measurements, various types of transient measurements offer the possibility to determine the components of the tensor functional $S_t(t')$ for different types of deformation. In [21] shear flow and simple elongational flow tests are discussed. Here, the procedures to determine $S_E(\epsilon)$ from experiments involving step-strain

Table 2
Characteristics of the Noncrosslinked EPDM Elastomers

Sample code	Composition (mol %)		GPC results (kg/mol)		Mooney index at 398 K
	ethylene	diene	$\bar{M}_n$	$\bar{M}_m$	$ML_w(1+4)$
K	64.6	2.7	45	180	48
N	64.8	1.1	40	90	21
D	58.2	0.8	50	125	28

stress relaxation, constant strain rate, creep under constant tensile stress, and constant stretching rate will be discussed.

Step-strain stress relaxation measurements have frequently been used to determine $S_E(\epsilon)$ for polymer melts [12, 29, 30]. If a sample is instantaneously extended to a Hencky strain ϵ at zero time, the relative strain history is given by Equation 7 and the tensile stress by Equation 8, where the relaxing part of the shear modulus can be calculated from the relaxation time spectrum:

$$G_r(t) = \int_{-\infty}^{+\infty} H(\tau)e^{-t/\tau} d \ln \tau \tag{17}$$

Equation 8 shows that if separation of time and strain effects is possible for a polymer network, the stress after a step elongational strain can be factored into a time-dependent function, $G_r(t)$ for polymer melts and $G_r(t) + G_e$ for polymer networks, and a strain-dependent function, the nonlinear strain measure $S_E(\epsilon)$. Therefore the stress relaxation moduli, defined as $\sigma_E(\epsilon)/(e^{2\epsilon} - e^{-\epsilon})$, obtained after several steps in Hencky strain, are all similar in form to the linear relaxation modulus when plotted in a double-logarithmic scale. The vertical shift factor required for superposition thus yields the value of $S_E(\epsilon)/(e^{2\epsilon} - e^{-\epsilon})$ at any value of ϵ.

The most common way to obtain the strain measure for permanent networks is to measure the equilibrium stress as a function of strain. Thus at equilibrium conditions, at infinite time after the imposition of the strain, $G_r(t)$ has completely decayed, and Equation 9 results.

The relative strain history function for a constant-Hencky strain rate experiment started at time $t' = 0$ is:

$$\epsilon(t) - \epsilon(t') = \dot{\epsilon}t \qquad \text{for } t' < 0$$
$$\epsilon(t) - \epsilon(t') = \dot{\epsilon}(t - t') \qquad \text{for } t' \geq 0 \tag{18}$$

Therefore build-up of the tensile stress σ_E^+ is described by:

$$\sigma_E^+(t, \dot{\epsilon}) = S_E(\epsilon)[G_r(t) + G_e] + \int_0^t m(s)S_E(\dot{\epsilon}s)\, ds \tag{19}$$

where $\epsilon = \dot{\epsilon}t$ and $s = t - t'$. Equation 19 can be transformed into an equation in which the strain measure $S_E(\epsilon)$ appears explicitly [8, 21]:

$$S_E(\epsilon) = \frac{\sigma_E^+(t, \dot{\epsilon})}{G_r(t) + G_e} - \int_0^\epsilon m\left(\frac{\epsilon'}{\epsilon}\right) G_r^{-2}\left(\frac{\epsilon'}{\epsilon}\right) \sigma_E(\epsilon')\, d\epsilon' \tag{20}$$

This method has been applied to obtain the strain measure $S_E(\epsilon)$ for polymer melts [8, 21].

Creep experiments differ from the two previously-presented types of experiment in that the sample is subjected to a definite stress program and in that the measured quantity is the strain as a function of time: a constant tensile stress σ_E is applied instantaneously and the build-up of the Hencky strain is measured. If the start of the experiment is taken to be at zero time, the relative deformation $\epsilon(t) - \epsilon(t')$ being equal to $\epsilon(t)$ for $t' \leq 0$, Equation 6 can be simplified to:

$$\sigma_E = S_E[\epsilon(t)][G_r(t) + G_e] + \int_0^t m(t - t') S_E[\epsilon(t) - \epsilon(t')]\, dt' \tag{21}$$

This is a nonlinear Volterra integral equation of the second kind. To obtain the strain measure from it, it has to be solved by numerical methods. An application of this method to obtain $S_E(\epsilon)$ is given in [21] and [31].

Constant-stretching rate experiments have been used to characterize crosslinked rubbers in uniaxial extension in the nonlinear viscoelastic region [32–35] and also to investigate the rheological properties of polymer melts [7, 21, 31]. The elongation is brought about by moving the upper end of the sample with a constant speed. The Hencky strain at present time t relative to that at previous time t' is related to the initial sample length l_0 and the draw speed v_0 by the equation:

$$\epsilon(t) - \epsilon(t') = \ln \frac{l_0 + v_0 t}{l_0 + v_0 t'} = \ln \frac{1 + \dot{\lambda}t}{1 + \dot{\lambda}t'} \tag{22}$$

where $\dot{\lambda} = v_0/l_0$ is the stretching rate [7]. The general formula for the stress, Equation 6, can be simplified to an equation similar to that for the creep experiments. Only, for this type of experiment the stress difference is the measured function, and the Hencky strain as a function of time the imposed one, whereas for the creep experiment it is the opposite:

$$\sigma_E(t, \lambda) = S_E[\epsilon(t)][G_r(t) + G_e] + \int_0^t m(t - t') S_E[\epsilon(t) - \epsilon(t')] \, dt' \tag{23}$$

where $\epsilon(t) - \epsilon(t')$ is given by Equation 22. It is not surprising, therefore, that the same computational method as applied to creep curves can be used to compute the strain measure from the measuring results [21, 31, 35].

An analytical approach to Equation 23 shows that a simple, albeit somewhat less accurate, way to analyze the measuring results is possible for slowly relaxing crosslinked rubbers [35]. It also indicates the connection between the quantity Smith [32, 33] obtained and the strain measure $S_E(\epsilon)$ as it is used here. A lower limit of the tensile stress is obtained by setting the integral in Equation 23 equal to zero [35]. This simple formula immediately yields a value of $S_E(\epsilon)$ which is an upper limit:

$$S_E[\epsilon(t)] \le \frac{\sigma_E(t, \epsilon)}{G_r(t) + G_e} \tag{24}$$

An upper limit of the stress results if the strain measure $S_E[\epsilon(t) - \epsilon(t')]$ in the integral is replaced by the strain measure corresponding to the Finger tensor, i.e., by $e^{2[\epsilon(t) - \epsilon(t')]} - e^{-[\epsilon(t) - \epsilon(t')]}$. It is known that the statistical theories of rubber elasticity that lead to this strain measure overpredict the stress at large strain when the modulus is adjusted to the linear viscoelastic data. A few minor approximations and substitution of the relaxation modulus $G_r(t)$ in the time scale of interest by:

$$G_r(s) = G(1)s^m, \qquad \text{with } m \le 0 \tag{25}$$

where m is not necessarily constant but is allowed to vary with s, leads to [35]:

$$\sigma_E(t, \epsilon) \le [G_r(t) + G_e] \left[S_E(\epsilon) - m(e^\epsilon + \epsilon - e^{-\epsilon}) + \frac{3m^2(e^\epsilon - 1)}{1 + m} \right] \tag{26}$$

or:

$$S_E(\epsilon) \ge \frac{\sigma_E(t, \epsilon)}{G_r(t) + G_e} + m(e^\epsilon + \epsilon - e^{-\epsilon}) + \frac{3m^2(e^\epsilon - 1)}{1 + m} \tag{27}$$

Introduction of the linear approximation for the strain measure, i.e.:

$$S_E(\epsilon) = 3\epsilon \tag{28}$$

into the integral of Equation 26 yields:

$$S_E(\epsilon) = \frac{\sigma_E(t, \epsilon)}{G_r(t) + G_e} + \frac{3m(1 - e^{-\epsilon})}{1 + m} \tag{29}$$

The magnitude of the terms additional to $S_E(\epsilon)$ of Equation 24 in Equations 27 and 29 has been calculated for a typical set of $S_E(\epsilon)$ values with $m = -0.1$ [35]. It was shown that the use of the

Finger strain tensor, which is known to give rise to too large stresses, leads to values of $S_E(\epsilon)$ of at most 11% lower than the values obtained using Equation 24. The linear approximation, known to lead to stresses that are too low, yields only extra contributions between -10 and -2% depending on the value of ϵ. This means that the use of the very simple relation of Equation 24 overestimates $S_E(\epsilon)$ by at most 11% for slowly relaxing networks. However, in practice this overestimation will be less serious since Equation 27 was obtained for the so-called finite linear viscoelastic limit with $S_E(\epsilon) = e^{2\epsilon} - e^{-\epsilon}$ in the integral of Equation 23.

In crosslinked rubbers, in the temperature region of practical interest where m usually ranges between 0 and -0.1 [7, 32–34], Equation 26 may be further simplified. For that purpose we introduce the constant stretch rate modulus F(t), which is related with G(t) by [33]:

$$(1 + m)F(t) = 3[G_r(t) + G_e] \qquad \text{where } m = \frac{d \log F(t)}{d \log t} \qquad (30)$$

As $S_E(\epsilon)$ calculated by Equation 24 with $m = -0.1$ is about 10% smaller than $S_E(\epsilon)$ calculated by Equation 27, Equation 27 can be closely approximated by:

$$S_E(\epsilon) \geq \frac{1}{1 + m} \frac{\sigma_E(t, \epsilon)}{G_r(t) + G_e} \qquad (31)$$

$$\text{or} \quad \sigma_E(t, \epsilon) \leq \frac{F(t)S_E(\epsilon)}{3} \qquad (32)$$

The empirical equation by Smith [32] reads in our notation:

$$\sigma_E(t, \epsilon) = \frac{F(t)(e^{2\epsilon} - e^{-\epsilon})}{g[\epsilon(t)]} \qquad (33)$$

which is very similar to our approximate Equation 32. This leads to the following interrelationship:

$$S_E(\epsilon) = \frac{3(e^{2\epsilon} - e^{-\epsilon})}{g(\epsilon)} \qquad (34)$$

The analytical approach to Equation 23 shows that the only restrictions necessary to derive Smith's empirical Equation 33 from the factorable single integral constitutive equation are that $|m|$ should be smaller than 0.1 over the whole time range of interest and that the nonlinearity not be too strong. These restrictions frequently hold for elastomeric networks.

THEORY

Polymer Networks

Constitutive equations relating the elastic strain to the stress in polymeric networks were developed before the constitutive analysis of the rheological properties of polymer fluids was undertaken. As a matter of fact, many ideas from the molecular models for crosslinked rubbers were later applied to derive constitutive equations for polymer melts and concentrated polymer solutions. Therefore, this discussion deals with the molecular theories for permanent networks first.

The molecular or statistical theories of rubber elasticity predict the relationship between the equilibrium stress and strain for an isothermally deformed polymer network [1, 3].

In the early version of the theory of rubber elasticity an affine displacement of the average positions of the network junctions with the macroscopic strain was assumed. This is equivalent to the assertion that the crosslinks are completely encapsulated in the network of which they are part. The elastic constitutive equation derived on this basis leads to an equation of the form of Equation 9 for simple extension at constant volume. The strain measure obtained is:

$$S_E(\epsilon) = C_E^{-1}(\epsilon) = e^{2\epsilon} - e^{-\epsilon} \tag{35}$$

and the equilibrium modulus:

$$G_e = \nu kT \tag{36}$$

where ν represents the concentration of elastically active network chains, k is the Boltzmann constant and T the absolute temperature.

James and Guth [36] took the view that only the junctions located on the boundary surfaces should be considered as fixed, while all other junctions should be allowed complete statistical freedom, subject only to the restrictions imposed by their interconnectedness. As Flory pointed out later [14] this is tantamount to the assumption that the chains' only action is to exert forces on the junctions to which they are attached, but the chain segments can pass freely through each other. The chains thus being devoid of material characteristics, the theory by James and Guth was later called the phantom network model [14]. Notwithstanding the different starting point of this theory, it also yields a stress-strain relation of the form of Equation 9 with $S_E(\epsilon)$ given by Equation 35. Only, the equilibrium modulus G_e takes a different value:

$$G_e = \xi kT \tag{37}$$

where ξ is the cycle rank per unit volume of the network. The number of active chains ν and the cycle rank ξ of a perfect network free of defects are related by the following equations [14, 17]:

$$\xi = \nu - \mu \tag{38}$$

and

$$\nu = \frac{\mu\phi}{2} \tag{39}$$

μ is the concentration of junctions with functionality ϕ.

For a perfect network with $\phi = 4$, for instance, the equilibrium modulus calculated using Equation 37 is half that calculated using Equation 36. James and Guth pointed out that in their theory the mean positions of the junctions are affine in the macroscopic strain, but the fluctuations from these mean positions are Gaussian and independent of strain. As a result, the instantaneous positions, being a combination of the mean positions and fluctuations, change nonaffinely.

It turns out that even for noncrystalline elastomeric networks in (quasi) equilibrium, considerable deviations exist between the experimental stress-strain curves and the theoretical curves derived from Equations 35 and 36 or 37. The tensile stress, σ_E, increases less rapidly with ϵ than is predicted by Equation 35.

For decades, this behavior has been described with the phenomenological Mooney-Rivlin equation [2, 3, 37–39]. This equation is, however, not factorable into a strain and a time function. The nonlinear strain measure corresponding to it depends on the ratio of two parameters, namely C_2/C_1, according to the equation:

$$\begin{aligned} S_E(\epsilon) &= \frac{1 + e^{-\epsilon}C_2/C_1}{1 + C_2/C_1} C_E^{-1}(\epsilon) \\ &= \frac{1 + e^{-\epsilon}C_2/C_1}{1 + C_2/C_1} (e^{2\epsilon} - e^{-\epsilon}) \end{aligned} \tag{40}$$

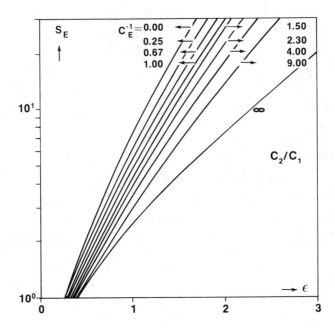

Figure 5. Variation of $S_E(\epsilon)$ with the ratio of the Mooney-Rivlin constants C_2/C_1, as determined with Equation 40.

In general, C_2/C_1 is time-dependent [2, 38]. Therefore $S_E(\epsilon)$ according to Equation 40 is a function of time as well. Only at equilibrium conditions where the stress and therefore also C_1 and C_2 become time-independent, can the quantity given by Equation 40 be considered as a strain measure in the sense it is defined in the previous section. Figure 5 shows how $S_E(\epsilon)$ varies with C_2/C_1.

The Mooney-Rivlin equation being phenomenological, the parameters C_1 and C_2 lack a clear molecular interpretation [2, 3, 37–39]. Besides, it turns out to be nonconstitutive in the sense that a different pair of parameters is needed to describe the stress-strain relation in simple extension and in biaxial extension or uniaxial compression. A constitutive equation based on a molecular picture is less likely to suffer from these imperfections.

The recent theory by Flory and Erman [15–17] blends the ideas of the affine deformation theory and the phantom theory to account for the effect of chain entanglements. It was suggested by Ronca and Allegra [13] and by Flory [14] that real rubber networks show departures from the theoretical Equations 35 and 36 or 37 as a result of a transition from an affinely deformable network to a network in which the motions of the junctions are less restricted with increasing strain (phantom network). This hypothesis was the basis of the theory developed in subsequent papers [15–17]. Extensive interpenetration of neighboring but topologically remote chains restricts the fluctuations of the network crosslinks at small strains. The parameter κ in the theory of Flory and Erman [16] indicates the severity of the constraints imposed by the network chains on the junctions relative to those imposed by the phantom network ($\kappa = 0$ means no constraints, corresponding to a phantom network; $\kappa = \infty$ means completely constrained, corresponding to an affinely deformable network). As the strain increases, the freedom of motion of the network junctions becomes less restricted in the direction of principal extension. In other words, the domain of constraints is deformed in such a way that its dimension in the direction of the principal extension becomes larger. The parameter ζ describes the departures from affine transformation of the shape of the domains of constraints. The resulting equilibrium stress-strain relation takes the form of Equation

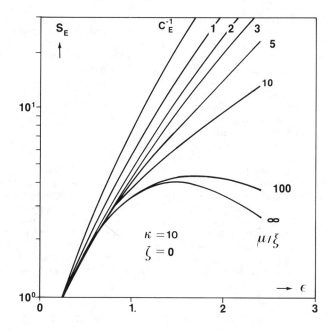

Figure 6. The nonlinear strain measure $S_E(\epsilon)$ calculated with Equation 41 and Flory's theory [16] for various values of μ/ξ, with $\kappa = 10$ and $\zeta = 0$.

9 with:

$$S_E(\epsilon) = \left[\frac{1 + (f_c/f_{ph})_\epsilon}{1 + (f_c/f_{ph})_{\epsilon=0}}\right](e^{2\epsilon} - e^{-\epsilon}) \tag{41}$$

and $$G_e = \xi[1 + (f_c/f_{ph})_{\epsilon=0}]kT \tag{42}$$

where f_c/f_{ph} is a complicated function of ϵ containing the network characteristic μ/ξ, and the parameters κ and ζ [16]. For $\kappa = 0$, $f_c/f_{ph} = 0$ and Equations 41 and 42 degenerate to Equations 35 and 37, respectively. For $\kappa \to \infty$, Equation 41 still degenerates to Equation 35, but $\lim_{\kappa\to\infty} f_c/f_{ph} = \mu/\xi$; so in that case Equation 42 becomes equal to Equation 36. Figure 6 shows the strain measures predicted by the Flory-Erman theory for different values of μ/ξ, for $\kappa = 10$ and $\zeta = 0$.

Polymer Melts

The theory of temporary networks for polymer melts is based on some of the ideas of the molecular theories of rubber elasticity. It is due largely to Green and Tobolsky [40], Lodge [41], and Yamamoto [42]. The starting point of this theory is the observation that polymeric fluids have much in common with crosslinked elastomers. Both types of material consist of long-chain molecules, interconnected to form a three-dimensional network. In polymeric fluids all these connections are of a temporary nature and are called entanglements, whereas a crosslinked rubber contains permanent connections, the crosslinks, in addition to entanglements.

The rubberlike-liquid or temporary-network theory [41, 43] also contains the assumption of affine deformation, i.e., a deformation of all subchains between entanglements identical with the macroscopic strain. Since the connections between the chains in a polymer fluid are entanglements and are therefore temporary, a continuous "creation and destruction" of chain segments is assumed.

The theory leads to a constitutive equation that predicts a relaxing stress after instantaneous extension of the material. The stress equation is of the form of Equation 8, with $G_e = 0$ and $S_E(\epsilon) = e^{2\epsilon} - e^{-\epsilon}$. The stress in the sample relaxes because after the step deformation, strained chain segments continuously disappear and are substituted by segments having the equilibrium end-to-end distance. The constitutive equation also predicts the transients and has the factorable single-integral form of Equation 2 with G_e equal to zero and S equal to C^{-1}.

As for crosslinked rubbers, so for polymer melts considerable deviations exist between the experimental observations and the predictions of the affine deformation theories. The rubberlike-liquid theory leads to a steady-state shear viscosity that is independent of the shear rate, and to stress-relaxation moduli which are independent of the step strain, both in simple shear and in simple extension. Therefore, constitutive equations with more realistic predictions have been derived.

One of the recent theories based on molecular-kinetic grounds is that of Doi and Edwards [11]. In the model of Doi and Edwards, the effect of the surrounding macromolecules on a chain is considered to be that of a deformable tube with a diameter that is constant over the tube length. The tube is subdivided into tube segments, each containing a subchain which is the part of the polymer chain between so-called localized entanglements. An instantaneous strain results in an affine deformation of the subchains, as in the classical theory of rubber elasticity for fixed chains. In the case of simple elongational strain, imposed at t = 0, the stress is therefore given by Equation 8, with $G_e = 0$; $S_E(\epsilon) = e^{2\epsilon} - e^{-\epsilon}$; and in analogy with Equation 36, the relaxation modulus at $t = 0^+$ equals:

$$G_r(0^+) = cNkT \tag{43}$$

where cN = the number of subchains per unit volume. Neighboring subchains have in general a different orientation before the step strain is imposed. Subchains are therefore deformed in different ways by the macroscopic strain and the tensile forces acting on neighboring subchains are in general unequal.

The connections between subchains are not chemical crosslinks as in permanent networks. So the tensile forces on the subchain ends can be balanced by a sliding motion of a part of the chain over the temporary link—the entanglement—that separates the subchains. During this relaxation process the chain retracts to its equilibrium length inside the affinely-deformed tube. During this process the tube segments' lengths do not change, but their diameters return to the equilibrium value. As a consequence, after completion of this relaxation step with relaxation time τ_A, the number of tube segments and subchains, i.e., parts of the chain contained in one tube segment, has decreased and the subchains are no longer strained. The stress in the sample is now entirely due to the orientation of the chains; it is still given by an equation of the form of Equation 8 with $G_r(t \gg \tau_A)$ equal to cNkT, but the strain measure now equals [11]:

$$S_E(\epsilon) = Q_E(\epsilon) = \frac{15}{4} \frac{e^{3\epsilon} + 0.5}{e^{3\epsilon} - 1} \left[\frac{1 - \dfrac{4e^{3\epsilon} - 1}{2e^{3\epsilon} + 1} \dfrac{\sinh^{-1}\sqrt{e^{3\epsilon} - 1}}{\sqrt{e^{3\epsilon}}\sqrt{e^{3\epsilon} - 1}}}{1 + \dfrac{\sinh^{-1}\sqrt{e^{3\epsilon} - 1}}{\sqrt{e^{3\epsilon}}\sqrt{e^{3\epsilon} - 1}}} \right] \tag{44}$$

The second relaxation process is a diffusion process whereby the chain leaves the tube gradually. The stress decays further during this relaxation step because the newly created subchains have random orientations. The characteristic time of this second relaxation process, τ_B, is considerably higher than τ_A for long, linear chains, so that the two processes are well separated in time. Since the degree of stress decay during process A only depends on the magnitude of the strain, whereas process B is independent of the macroscopic strain, the stress is given by a factorable constitutive

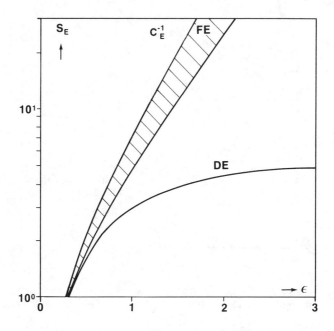

Figure 7. The nonlinear strain measure $S_E(\epsilon)$ predicted by the Doi-Edwards theory (DE) [11], by the affine deformation model, and by the Flory-Erman theory [16] for $\mu/\xi = 2$, $\zeta = 0$, and $\kappa = 0$ to ∞ (shaded area).

equation (Equation 2) for times longer than τ_A and strain rates smaller than τ_A^{-1}. The equilibrium modulus G_e equals zero and $m(t - t')$ has a definite shape, which is of no concern to us here. $S_E(\epsilon)$ is given by Equation 44; a graphical representation is given in Figure 7.

RESULTS AND DISCUSSION

Results

As discussed earlier, the nonlinear strain measure $S_E(\epsilon)$ for polymer melts can be obtained via many different types of experiment. Some authors [44, 45] obtained a so-called damping function, $h(\epsilon)$, from their measuring results. The function $h(\epsilon)$ is related to the strain measure $S_E(\epsilon)$ by:

$$S_E(\epsilon) = h(\epsilon)(e^{2\epsilon} - e^{-\epsilon}) \tag{45}$$

Figure 8 shows the strain measures obtained in a number of studies on the nonlinear viscoelastic properties of polymer melts. Information on the materials and on the way $S_E(\epsilon)$ has been obtained is contained in Table 3.

The strain measure for permanent networks is usually determined by measuring the equilibrium stress as a function of strain. We have shown that $S_E(\epsilon)$ may also be obtained from stress measurements at constant stretching rates in a fairly easy way for crosslinked materials with a slowly relaxing modulus and nonlinearity that is not too severe. If the factorable single integral equation is

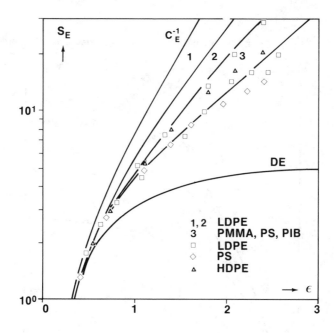

Figure 8. The nonlinear strain measures $S_E(\epsilon)$ for a number of polymer melts identified in Table 3, together with the theoretical strain measure derived in the Doi-Edwards theory [11].

Table 3
Identification of the Polymer Melts of Figure 8

Sample Characteristics	Type of Measurement	Reference	Curve Number or Symbol
LDPE $\bar{M}_w = 4.8 \cdot 10^5$ $\bar{M}_w/\bar{M}_n = 2.8$	constant rate of strain creep at constant stress	[8, 44]	1
LDPE $\bar{M}_w = 1.5 \cdot 10^5$ $\bar{M}_w/\bar{M}_n = 6.2$ See also Table 1	constant rate of strain constant stretching rate creep at constant stress step strain	[21, 31] [21, 31]	2
PMMA	step strain	[29]	3
PS	step strain	[29]	3
PIB $\bar{M}_n = 8 \cdot 10^4$; $\bar{M}_\eta = 3.8 \cdot 10^5$ $\eta_{0,20°C} = 1.5 \cdot 10^8$ Pa.s $\eta_{0,20°C} = 8 \cdot 10^5$ Pa.s	step strain	[29]	3
PS	constant rate of strain	[45]	◇
HDPE	constant rate of strain	[45]	Δ
LDPE	constant rate of strain	[45]	□

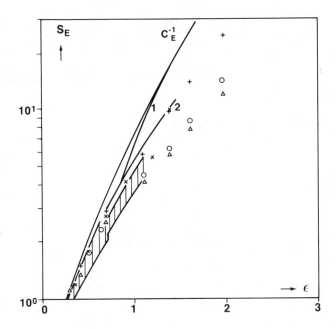

Figure 9. The nonlinear strain measures for a number of cross-linked rubbers obtained from transient measurements (symbols) and from equilibrium measurements (shaded area). The materials are identified in Table 4.

appropriate to describe the stress-strain relationship for a material, the same strain measure is obtained when applying Equation 31 to the measuring data obtained at different stretching rates. Therefore, the constant stretching rate experiment also yields information on the possibility of separation of time and strain effects [7, 32, 35]. The strain functions in Figure 9 for the EPDM vulcanisates identified in Table 4 have been obtained from constant-stretching rate experiments. Also shown in Figure 9 is the strain measure arrived at by Smith for a crosslinked styrene-butadiene rubber. Equation 34 has been used to obtain $S_E(\epsilon)$ from his function $g(\epsilon)$. Hong et al. [34] used the same analytical method to analyze constant-stretching rate data to obtain a function $\Gamma(\epsilon)$. The strain measure $S_E(\epsilon)$ is equal to their $\Gamma(\epsilon)/3$ and is also shown in Figure 9.

In these three studies the strain measures obtained are independent of the stretching rate. This indicates that time and strain effects are separable for the investigated materials. This implies that the same $S_E(\epsilon)$ is appropriate for the relaxational part of the modulus and for the equilibrium part.

The strain functions $S_E(\epsilon)$ for dry (unswollen) networks of a large number of natural rubbers, butadiene-styrene and butadiene-acrylonitrile copolymers, polydimethylsiloxanes, polymethylmethacrylates, polyethylacrylates, and polybutadienes with different degrees of crosslinking and measured at various temperatures [46–50] are confined within the shaded area in Figure 9. In all cases $S_E(\epsilon)$ was determined from quasi-equilibrium measurements. The strain dependence of the tensile stress was given in terms of the Mooney-Rivlin equation. Therefore the strain measures were calculated applying Equation 40.

The variation of $S_E(\epsilon)$ with the degree of crosslinking has also been investigated. For the D samples $S_E(\epsilon)$ increases slightly with crosslink density, as exemplified in Figure 10. It is interesting to note that even the uncrosslinked D 0.0, which is a polymer melt [25], has a nonlinear strain function not much different from that of the permanent networks D 0.4 and D 0.8. The dependence on the crosslink density for the K samples (Table 2) is even almost nonexistent, as shown in Figure 11.

Table 4
Identification of the Rubber Networks of Figure 9

Sample Characteristics	Type of Measurement	Reference	Curve Number or Symbol
SBR vulcanizate, vulcanized with 0.57 wt% dicumylperoxide at 162°C for 60 min	constant stretching rate	[34]	1
SBR vulcanizate	constant stretching rate	[33]	2
K 0.2 (cf. Table 2 and section on "The Strain Measure S_E")	constant stretching rate	[7]	+
N 0.4 (cf. Table 2 and section on "The Strain Measure S_E")	constant stretching rate	[7]	Δ
D 0.4 (cf. Table 2 and section on "The Strain Measure S_E")	constant stretching rate	[7]	○
PDMS elastomer	equilibrium stress-strain measurements	[50]	x

The value of $S_E(\epsilon)$ generally increases with rising temperature, in particular for $\epsilon > 1$, as shown in Figure 12 for a typical sample. A similar phenomenon has been observed by Chang et al. [51]. Finally, the type of prepolymer has a considerable effect on $S_E(\epsilon)$ as demonstrated in Figure 13 for three networks prepared with different prepolymers but of comparable crosslink density.

Discussion

Comparison of Figures 8 and 9 shows that crosslinked rubbers and polymer melts differ very little in their deviation from linear viscoelastic behavior. The strain measures for polymer melts and for crosslinked networks lie in exactly the same range. Figures 10 and 11 indicate that if the chains of a network and a melt have the same composition, the strain measures $S_E(\epsilon)$ for network and melt are almost identical. In addition, the degree of nonlinearity does not seem to depend strongly on the crosslink density for vulcanized EPDM rubbers.

Figure 9 reveals that nonlinear strain measures obtained from equilibrium measurements on a large number of crosslinked rubbers lie in the same range as those obtained from transient measurements on the same types of material. Moreover, time and strain effects are separable over a large time scale for various crosslinked rubbers. This is revealed by the stretching rate independence of the strain measures calculated for these networks.

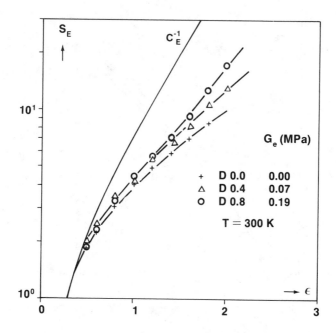

Figure 10. Dependence of the nonlinear strain measure $S_E(\epsilon)$ on the cross link density for the D elastomer (cf. Table 2).

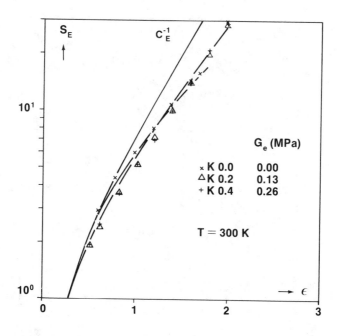

Figure 11. Dependence of the nonlinear strain measure $S_E(\epsilon)$ on the cross link density for the K elastomer (cf. Table 2).

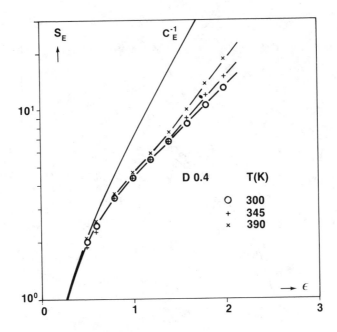

Figure 12. Dependence of the nonlinear strain measure $S_E(\epsilon)$ on the temperature for the D0.4 elastomer (cf. Table 2).

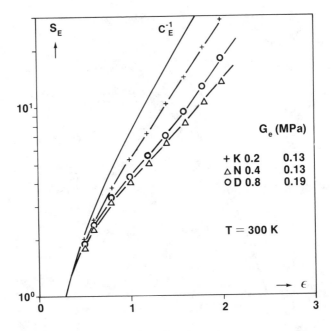

Figure 13. Dependence of the nonlinear strain measure $S_E(\epsilon)$ on the prepolymer type at comparable values of the modulus.

It must be concluded, therefore, that the nonlinearity is of a similar origin for crosslinked rubbers and polymer melts, and that the nonlinear relation between stress and strain is similar for permanent and temporary structures in a network. This conclusion cannot be reconciled with the molecular models discussed shortly.

The strain measure derived in the Doi-Edwards theory differs largely from those obtained for polymer melts and crosslinked rubbers. Moreover, the fact that the nonlinearity is comparable for rubbers and melts cannot be explained by the Doi-Edwards model. According to this theory the chain retraction is the basis for the nonlinearity displayed by melts. This can obviously not take place in crosslinked rubbers, where most chains are connected to the network at both ends.

One of the basic elements in the Flory theory is the presence of permanent junctions between the polymer chains. These are absent in polymer fluids. As a consequence, the observation that the strain measures for polymer melts and crosslinked rubbers lie in the same range cannot be explained by this theory either. It is all the more remarkable, therefore, that the experimentally obtained $S_E(\epsilon)$-curves for the EPDM materials of Table 2 (including the noncrosslinked D 0.0 and K 0.0) can be fitted very well with Equation 41 derived by Flory, using μ/ξ and κ as adjustable parameters. Some examples are given in Figure 14. A possible explanation for this finding in terms of the constrained-junction theory is that many two-functional junctions, or chain segments, are also restricted in their mobility [7]. This idea has also been put forward by Staverman [52] and is compatible with the fact that the values of μ/ξ are in general much higher than two, which is the value of this quantity for a perfect network with tetrafunctional junctions. In other words, the restriction of possible chain configurations must play a very important role as well. This hypothesis explains why $S_E(\epsilon)$-curves for polymeric solids and fluids have the same position and shape.

It is interesting to note that with Flory's theory, a reasonable explanation can be given for the more linear behavior of the K networks (cf. Figures 10 and 11). In an earlier study it was concluded

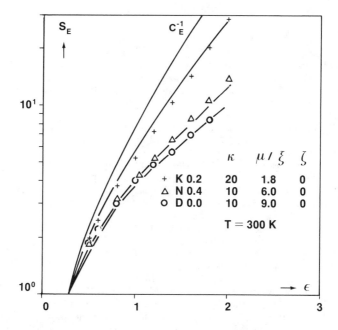

Figure 14. Fit of the experimentally determined strain measures $S_E(\epsilon)$ with Equation 41 and Flory's theory [16] using κ and μ/ξ as adjustable parameters.

that due to the high diene content of this sample, functionalities higher than four are probably obtained [25]. This results in a lower value of μ/ξ and, with Flory's theory, in a more linear behavior as demonstrated in Figure 6.

Another experimental observation that can be explained at least qualitatively with this theory is the increase in linearity with increasing degree of crosslinking (cf. Figure 12). According to Dusek [53] this causes an increase in the average functionality, so that μ/ξ decreases and $S_E(\epsilon)$ becomes more linear (cf. Figure 6). The general increase in linearity with rising temperature might be ascribed to the presence of fewer constraints on the chain configurations at higher temperatures in the small strain range due to the higher Brownian motions of the chains. As a result, $(f_c/f_{ph})_{\epsilon=0}$ would decrease with rising temperature, so that $S_E(\epsilon)$ approaches $C_E^{-1}(\epsilon)$ more closely. Thus, several observations can be explained qualitatively with this theory.

CONCLUSION

The results on the cured elastomers indicate that the nonlinearity is essentially independent of time. It is identical for the relaxational and equilibrium parts of the modulus. Its dependence on temperature, surprising at first glance, might be explained qualitatively with Flory's molecular theory. This theory also makes it possible to explain the differences in nonlinearity between various EPDM networks with roughly equal equilibrium modulus. Our data suggest that the crosslink density is not an important factor for the nonlinearity. Comparison with Flory's theory indicates that the crosslinks are not the only loci restricted, but there seems to be an additional important contribution from restricted chains as well.

Comparison of the results for polymer melts and networks shows that the origin of the nonlinearity is very similar for these two classes of materials. Existing molecular models are inconsistent with this finding. These are all of a nature to explain the nonlinear viscoelasticity of one of the two types of material only. This situation calls for the development of a unified model that deals with the nonlinearity of both types of materials.

REFERENCES

1. Flory, P. J., *Principles of Polymer Chemistry*, Cornell University Press, Ithaca, NY, 1953.
2. Ferry, J. D., *Viscoelastic Properties of Polymers*, 3rd ed., Wiley, New York, 1980.
3. Treloar, L. R. G., *The Physics of Rubber Elasticity*, 3rd ed., Clarendon, Oxford, 1975.
4. Meissner, J., *Rheol. Acta 8*, 78 (1969).
5. Münstedt, H., *Rheol. Acta 14*, 1077 (1975).
6. Chang, W. V., Bloch, R., and Tschoegl, N. W., *Rheol. Acta 15*, 367 (1976).
7. Scholtens, B. J. R., and Leblans, P. J. R., *J. Rheol. 30*, 313 (1986).
8. Wagner, M. H., *Rheol. Acta 18*, 681 (1979).
9. Petrie, C. J. S., *J. Non-Newtonian Fluid Mech. 5*, 147 (1979).
10. Booij, H. C., and Palmen, J. H. M., *Rheol. Acta 21*, 376 (1982).
11. Doi, M. S., and Edwards, S. F., *J. Chem. Soc. Faraday Trans. II, 14*, 1789, 1802, 1818 (1978).
12. Marrucci, G., and de Cindio, B., *Rheol. Acta 19*, 68 (1980).
13. Ronca, G., and Allegra, G., *J. Chem. Phys. 63*, 4990 (1975).
14. Flory, P. J., *Proc. Roy. Soc. London A351*, 351 (1976).
15. Flory, P. J., *J. Chem. Phys. 66*, 5720 (1977).
16. Flory, P. J., and Erman, B., *Macromolecules 15*, 800 (1982).
17. Flory, P. J., *British Polym. J. 17*, 96 (1985).
18. Larson, R. G., and Monroe, K., *Rheol. Acta 23*, 10 (1984).
19. Tobolsky, A. V., and Andrews, R. D., *J. Chem. Phys. 13*, 3 (1945).
20. Guth, E., Wack, P. E., and Anthony, R. L., *J. Appl. Phys. 17*, 347 (1946).
21. Leblans, P. J. R., Ph.D. Thesis, Universitaire Instelling Antwerpen, Antwerpen, 1986.
22. Scholtens, B. J. R., and Booij, H. C., in *Elastomers and Rubber Elasticity*, ACS Symp. Ser. 193, Mark, J. E., and J. Lal, eds., American Chemical Society, Washington DC, 1982, chap. 28, p. 517.

23. Truesdell, C., and Noll, W., in "The Non-Linear Field Theories of Mechanics," *Encyclopedia of Physics* III/3, Flügge, S., ed., Springer-Verlag, Berlin, 1965.
24. Phillips, M. C., *J. Non-Newtonian Fluid Mech. 2*, 109 (1977).
25. Scholtens, B. J. R., *J. Polym. Sci. Polym. Phys. Ed. 22*, 317 (1984).
26. Scholtens, B. J. R., *J. Polym. Sci. Polym. Phys. Ed. 23*, 1325 (1985).
27. Petrie, C. J. S., *Elongational Flows*, Pitman Publishers Ltd., London, 1979.
28. Münstedt, *J. Rheol. 23*, 421 (1979).
29. de Cindio, B., *Polymer 25*, 1049 (1984).
30. Titomanlio, G., Spadaro, G., and La Mantia, F. P., *Rheol. Acta 19*, 477 (1980).
31. Leblans, P. J. R., Sampers, J., and Booij, H. C., *J. Non-Newtonian Fluid Mech. 19*, 185 (1985).
32. Smith, T. L., and Dickie, R. A., *J. Polym. Sci.*, A-2, *7*, 635 (1969).
33. Smith, T. L., *Trans. Soc. Rheol. 6*, 61 (1962).
34. Hong, S. D., Fedors, R. F., Schwarzl, F., Moacanin, J., and Landel, R. F., *Polym. Eng. Sci. 21*, 688 (1981).
35. Scholtens, B. J. R., Leblans, P. J. R., and Booij, H. C., *J. Rheol. 30*, 301 (1986).
36. James, H. J., and Guth, E., *J. Chem. Phys. 11*, 455 (1943); ibid. *15*, 669 (1947); *J. Polym. Sci. 4*, 1531 (1949).
37. Schwarz, J., *Kolloid-Z.u.Z. Polymere 251*, 215 (1973).
38. Mark, J. E., *Rubber Chem. Technol. 48*, 495 (1975).
39. Boyer, R. F., and Miller, R. L., *Rubber Chem. Technol. 50*, 798 (1977); ibid. *51*, 718 (1978).
40. Green, M. S., and Tobolsky, A. V., *J. Chem. Phys. 14*, 80 (1946).
41. Lodge, A. S., *Trans Faraday Soc. 52*, 120 (1956).
42. Yamamoto, M., *J. Phys. Soc. Japan 11*, 413 (1956).
43. Lodge, A. S., *Rheol. Acta 7*, 379 (1968).
44. Wagner, M. H., Raible, T., and Meissner, J., *Rheol. Acta 18*, 427 (1979).
45. Laun, H. M., *Colloid Polymer Sci. 259*, 97 (1981).
46. Gumbrell, S. M., Mullins, L., and Rivlin, R. S., *Trans. Faraday Soc. 49*, 1495 (1953).
47. Ciferri, A., and Flory, P. J., *J. Appl. Phys. 30*, 1498 (1959).
48. Mullins, L., *J. Appl. Polym. Sci. 2*, 1 (1959).
49. Kraus, G., and Moczvgemba, G. A., *J. Polym. Sci. A2*, 277 (1964).
50. Erman, B., and Flory, P. J., *Macromolecules 15*, 806 (1982).
51. Chang, W. V., Bloch, R., and Tschoegl, N. W., in *Chemistry and Properties of Crosslinked Polymers*, Labana, S. S., ed., AP, New York, 1977, p. 431.
52. Staverman, A. J., *Adv. Polym. Sci. 44*, 73 (1982).
53. Dusek, K., *Faraday Disc. Chem. Soc. 57*, 101 (1974).

CHAPTER 20

MODELING COMPLEX VISCOSITY AS A RESPONSE FUNCTION

J. Stastna, D. De Kee, and M. B. Powley

Department of Chemical Engineering
University of Windsor
Windsor, Ontario, Canada

CONTENTS

INTRODUCTION

A common method for studying physical systems is to use an external force which disturbs the system only slightly from equilibrium and then measure the linear time-dependent response to this force. Many experimental methods fall into this category, e.g., infrared and Raman spectra, dielectric or spin relaxation experiments, and studies of transport behavior. In all of these experiments the dynamic behavior of spontaneous fluctuations about the known equilibrium is studied. To explain these fluctuations, the required information is less specific than the information contained in the microscopic state. According to the linear response theory, these fluctuations may be described in terms of time-dependent correlation functions. These are products of pairs of dynamic variables at different times, which are averaged over a thermal ensemble. These functions are powerful theoretical probes for the investigation of nonequilibrium behavior of systems.

The linear response theory is applied here to viscoelastic fluids. These fluids exhibit generally nonlinear mechanical behavior manifested by the nonlinear viscosity function and the non-zero normal stress differences at steady state. Also, the stress growth and the stress relaxation functions are generally nonlinear functions of the shear rate. Knowing the linear dynamic response of these fluids, i.e., knowing the complex viscosity function, it is possible, at least theoretically, to find the relaxation modulus and obtain a complete constitutive equation in the linear viscoelastic region. Such information, even if limited only to the (small deformation) linear region, is important for the understanding of the microstructure of the viscoelastic liquid. Moreover, this information can be used for the extension of linear viscoelastic models into the quasilinear and nonlinear domains of larger deformations. Using the fundamental properties of the linear dynamic response (complex viscosity η^*) one can propose compatible models for η^*, with the help of these models then compute various material functions such as, for example, the steady-state shear viscosity, the primary normal stress coefficient, and the stress growth and relaxation functions.

In the next section, we define the commonly used material functions starting with steady simple shear flow and including transient and oscillatory shear flows. The "Theory" section covers the basics of the linear dynamic response theory and the relation of this theory to the complex viscosity. "Relation to Molecular Structure" deals briefly with the relation between molecular structure and η^*. Phenomenological models for η^* are discussed in "Phenomenological Models," and the use of complex viscosity models for the construction of quasilinear constitutive equations is demonstrated in "General Material Functions."

MATERIAL FUNCTIONS

Simple Shear Flow

Simple shear flow is defined as follows: A fluid is contained between two infinite flat parallel plates as illustrated in Figure 1. Momentum is transported in the positive y-direction. Eventually, provided the gap between the plates is small enough and a laminar flow regime prevails, a linear velocity profile will be established for which we can write:

$$V_x = \dot{\gamma}_{yx}y \qquad V_y = V_z = 0 \tag{1}$$

where the shear rate $\quad \dot{\gamma}_{yx} = [dV_x/dy]$ (2)

The force per area required to keep the lower plate moving defines a shear stress τ_{yx} which is proportional to the plate velocity and which is inversely proportional to the distance between the plates. That is to say:

$$\tau_{xy} \sim [dV_x/dy] = \dot{\gamma}_{yx} \tag{3}$$

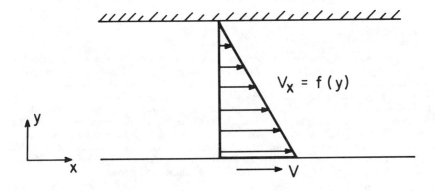

Figure 1. Sketch defining unidirectional shear flow.

Steady-State Simple Shear Flow

For steady shear flow, where the shear rate $\dot{\gamma}_{yx}$ is constant, we define the following material functions:

The Non-Newtonian Viscosity

$$\eta(\dot{\gamma}_{yx}) = -\tau_{yx}/\dot{\gamma}_{yx} \tag{4}$$

The Primary Normal Stress Coefficient

$$\psi_1(\dot{\gamma}_{yx}) = -(\tau_{xx} - \tau_{yy})/(\dot{\gamma}_{yx})^2 \tag{5}$$

The Secondary Normal Stress Coefficient

$$\psi_2(\dot{\gamma}_{yx}) = -(\tau_{yy} - \tau_{zz})/(\dot{\gamma}_{yx})^2 \tag{6}$$

The quantities $(\tau_{xx} - \tau_{yy})$ and $(\tau_{yy} - \tau_{zz})$ represent the primary normal stress difference and the secondary normal stress difference, respectively. The relation between ψ_1 and ψ_2 is normally taken as $\psi_2 = -0.1\psi_1$. Therefore, in the majority of the flow situations, the secondary normal stress coefficient ψ_2 is not all that important. Figures 2 and 3 show typical viscosity-shear rate and primary normal stress-shear rate behavior, respectively, for a variety of viscoelastic solutions. Figures 4 and 5 also show the dependence of the non-Newtonian viscosity η and of the primary normal stress difference $-(\tau_{11} - \tau_{22})$ on the shear rate $\dot{\gamma}$, for a 2.0% solution (by weight) of polyacrylamide (Separan AP 30) in a 50% mixture (by weight) of water and glycerine and for a 6.0% solution (by weight) of polyisobutylene (PIB) in Primol 355, respectively. Note the tremendous drop in viscosity over the shear rate range shown. This behavior is typical for viscoelastic solutions. The solutions appearing in Figures 4 and 5 are also compared with other fluids in Figures 2 and 3.

Sinusoidal Shear Flow

For small-amplitude oscillatory shear flow, for which the lower plate in Figure 6 would be required to oscillate back and forth in the x-directions, with small amplitude, under a variety of frequencies ω, we define a complex viscosity:

$$\eta^* = \eta' - i\eta'' = -\tau_{yx}^0/\dot{\gamma}^0 \tag{7}$$

with $\dot{\gamma}(t) = \text{Re}[\dot{\gamma}^0 e^{i\omega t}]$ $\qquad\qquad$ (8)

and $\tau_{yx}(t) = \text{Re}[\tau_{yx}^0 e^{i\omega t}]$ $\qquad\qquad$ (9)

Here, $\dot{\gamma}^0$ and τ_{yx}^0 represent the complex amplitudes of $\dot{\gamma}$ and τ_{yx}, respectively. η' is referred to as the dynamic viscosity and is associated with energy dissipation, while the coefficient of i, η'' represents an elastic contribution which is associated with energy storage.

It is also possible to work in terms of a quantity G*, defined as:

$$G^* = G' + iG'' \tag{10}$$

where the storage modulus $G' = \omega\eta''$ and the loss modulus $G'' = \omega\eta'$ (see Figures 4 and 5) illustrate the dependence of the dynamic viscosity η' and of the storage modulus G' on the frequency ω, for the 2.0% polyacrylamide solution and for the 6.0% polyisobutylene solution mentioned earlier.

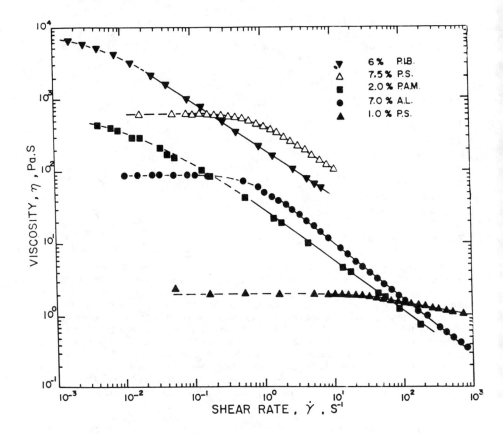

Figure 2. Viscosity-shear rate plots for typical viscoelastic solutions. The 1.0 and 7.5 P.S. are, respectively, 1.0% and 7.5% solutions of narrow molecular weight polystyrene (M_w = 860,000) in Aroclor 1248 (Data from Ashare [2]). The 7.0% A.L. is a 7.0% solution of aluminum laurate in decalin and m-cresol [Data from Huppler, 1965]. The 2.0% P.A.M. is a 2.0% solution of polyacrylamide (A.P. 30 of Dow Chemical) in a 50%/50% mixture of water and glycerine. The 6% P.I.B. is a 6.0% solution of polyisobutylene ($M_w \sim 1.5 \times 10^7$) in Primol 355 (Data from De Kee [3]).

Notice that as a rough estimation, the data for $\eta'(\omega)$ almost superpose the data for $\eta(\dot{\gamma})$, and that the data for $2\eta''(\omega)/\omega$ almost superpose those for $\psi_1(\dot{\gamma})$. The η, η' superposition becomes exact in the limit of low $\dot{\gamma}$ or ω.

Transient Shear Flow

For stress growth, after onset of steady simple shear (the lower plate in Figure 1 starts moving in the positive x-direction) we have:

$$\dot{\gamma}_{yx}(t) = \dot{\gamma}_0 h(t) \qquad (11)$$

where $\dot{\gamma}_0$ is the constant velocity gradient for $t > 0$. $h(t)$ is the unit step function: $h(t) = 0$ for $t < 0$ and $h(t) = 1$ for $t > 0$. We define the time-dependent shear stress and normal stress coefficients as

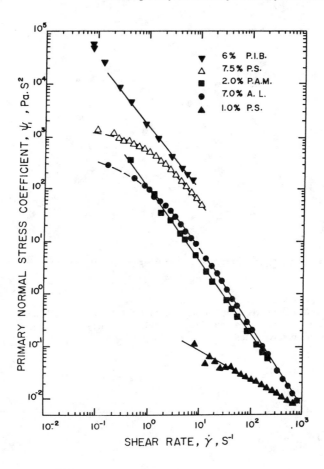

Figure 3. Primary normal stress coefficient-shear rate plots of the solutions shown in Figure 2.

follows:

$$\eta^+(t, \dot{\gamma}_0) = -\tau_{yx}(t)/\dot{\gamma}_0 \tag{12}$$

$$\psi_1^+(t, \dot{\gamma}_0) = -[\tau_{xx}(t) - \tau_{yy}(t)]/\dot{\gamma}_0^2 \tag{13}$$

$$\psi_2^+(t, \dot{\gamma}_0) = -[\tau_{yy}(t) - \tau_{zz}(t)]/\dot{\gamma}_0^2 \tag{14}$$

Figures 7 and 8 illustrate the shear stress and normal stress growth coefficients, respectively, for the 6.0% PIB solution referred to earlier. Note that the normal stress growth process evolves over a longer time period than the shear stress growth process. This behavior is typical for viscoelastic solutions.

Similarly, for stress relaxation after cessation of steady simple shear (the lower plate in Figure 1 stops):

$$\dot{\gamma}_{yx}(t) = \dot{\gamma}_0[1 - h(t)] \tag{15}$$

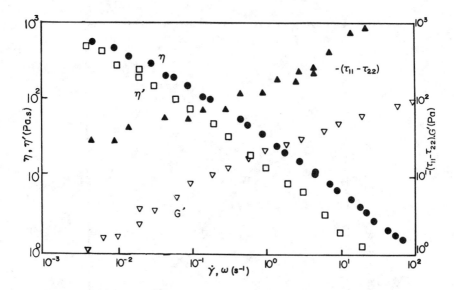

Figure 4. Non-Newtonian viscosity, primary normal stress difference, dynamic viscosity, and storage modulus. for a 2.0% solution (by weight) of polyacrylamide in a 50% mixture (by weight) of water and glycerine.

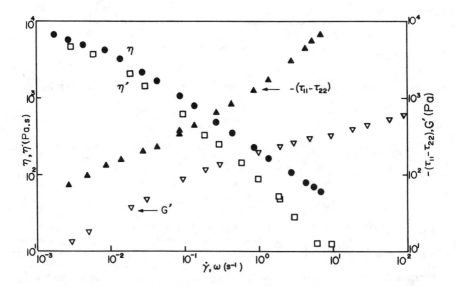

Figure 5. Non-Newtonian viscosity, primary normal stress difference, dynamic viscosity, and storage modulus for a 6.0% polyisobutylene solution (by weight) in Primol 355.

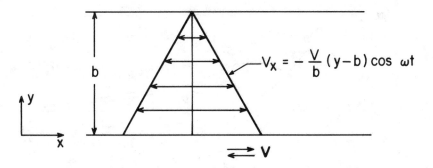

Figure 6. Sketch defining sinusoidal shear flow.

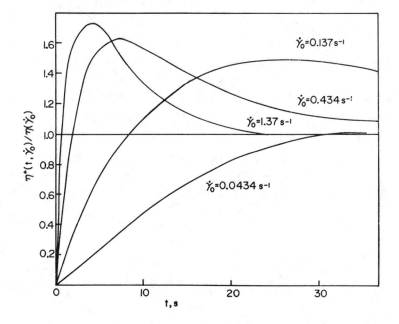

Figure 7. Shear stress growth for a 6.0% PIB solution (by weight) in Primol 355.

Here, $\dot{\gamma}_0$ is the initial constant shear rate, and the transient shear stress and normal stress coefficients are defined as:

$$\eta^-(t, \dot{\gamma}_0) = -\tau_{yx}(t)/\dot{\gamma}_0 \tag{16}$$

$$\psi_1^-(t, \dot{\gamma}_0) = -[\tau_{xx}(t) - \tau_{yy}(t)]/\dot{\gamma}_0^2 \tag{17}$$

$$\psi_2^-(t, \dot{\gamma}_0) = -[\tau_{yy}(t) - \tau_{zz}(t)]/\dot{\gamma}_0^2 \tag{18}$$

Figures 9 and 10 show stress and normal stress relaxation data, respectively, for the 2.0% polyacrylamide solution referred to earlier.

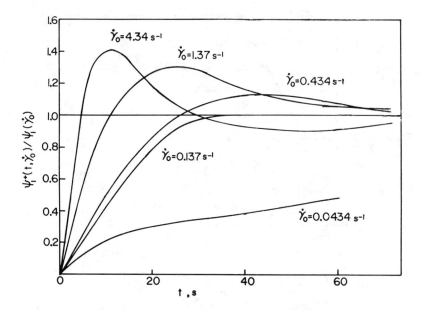

Figure 8. Normal stress growth for a 6.0% PIB solution (by weight) in Primol 355.

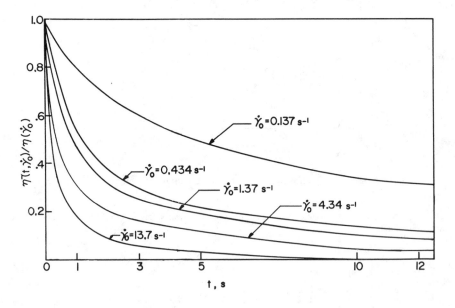

Figure 9. Shear stress relaxation for a 2.0% solution (by weight) of polyacrylamide in a 50% mixture (by weight) of water and glycerine.

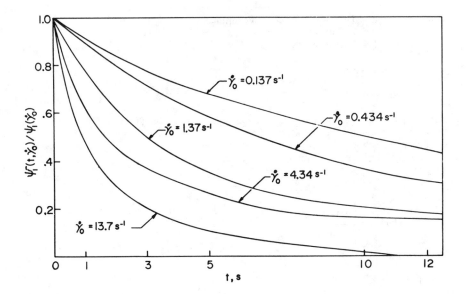

Figure 10. Normal stress relaxation for a 2.0% solution (by weight) of polyacrylamide in a 50% mixture (by weight) of water and glycerine.

THEORY

Linear Dynamic Response

In this section, the analysis of the response of a system to external disturbances is discussed and the basics of the linear dynamic response method are outlined.

In the study of dynamic processes, one usually tests the system with the help of an external force which disturbs the system from equilibrium, and one then measures the time-dependent response to this force. Many experimental methods belong to this category, e.g., inelastic scattering of light, neutrons or electrons on a sample, infrared and Raman spectra, acoustic attenuation, transport behavior, and many others. In all of these experiments, the subject of the study is the dynamic behavior of spontaneous fluctuations about the known equilibrium state.

According to the linear response theory, these fluctuations may be described in terms of time-dependent correlation functions. These functions proved to be a powerful tool for the investigation of non-equilibrium behavior of various physical systems [4–6]. Only the basic ideas of the theory of linear response will be outlined here.

Let us consider a macroscopic system in a state of statistical equilibrium. The properties of the system are described by the distribution function f_0 (e.g., by the canonical distribution [4]). We shall study the response of the system to the sudden action of an external perturbation, which can be represented by the Hamiltonian $H'(t)$. The perturbed Hamiltonian is written in the form:

$$H = H_0 + H'(t), \qquad H'(t) \ll H_0 \tag{19}$$

Assume that our classical system can be described by the canonical distribution function f_0:

$$f_0 = Z^{-1} e^{-\beta H}, \qquad Z = \int e^{-\beta H} \, dp \, dq \tag{20}$$

$$\beta = 1/kT$$

where   p and q = the sets of momenta and coordinates
        k = the Boltzmann constant
        T = absolute temperature

To simplify the calculations, assume that:

$$H' = -B(p, q)\delta(t) \tag{21}$$

(here $\delta(t)$ represents the delta function). This assumption means that at time = 0 the system is perturbed by a certain impulse and we are interested in the changes of the system caused by a small dynamic perturbation.

The distribution function f satisfies Liouville's equation, e.g., [7, 8]:

$$\frac{\partial f}{\partial t} = \{H, f\} \tag{22}$$

where $\{H, f\} = \sum \left(\dfrac{\partial H}{\partial q} \dfrac{\partial f}{\partial p} - \dfrac{\partial H}{\partial p} \dfrac{\partial f}{\partial q} \right)$

is the classical Poisson bracket [8]. Writing:

$$f = f_0 + f' \tag{23}$$

where f' is due to the perturbation, one can solve Equation 22 and write:

$$f' = -\{B(0), f_0\} \tag{24}$$

Here, $B(0) \equiv B(p(0), q(0))$ and $f'|_{t=-\infty} = 0$. Since for any mechanical quantity we can write:

$$\dot{A} = \frac{dA}{dt} = \sum \left(\frac{\partial A}{\partial q} \frac{dq}{dt} + \frac{\partial A}{\partial p} \frac{dp}{dt} \right) = \sum \left(\frac{\partial A}{\partial q} \frac{\partial H_0}{\partial p} - \frac{\partial A}{\partial p} \frac{\partial H_0}{\partial q} \right)$$

the solution in Equation 24 can be written as:

$$f' = \beta \dot{B}(0) f_0 \tag{25}$$

Now, we can calculate the average value of any dynamic variable A and find the change of this average caused by the perturbation:

$$\langle \Delta A(t) \rangle = \int [A(t)(f_0 + f') - A(t)f_0] \, dp \, dq$$

$$= \beta \int \dot{B}(0) A(t) f_0 \, dp \, dq = \beta \langle \dot{B}(0) A(t) \rangle_0 \tag{26}$$

where the index o refers to an equilibrium average.

This formula describes the change in the average value of an arbitrary quantity A under the action of an impulse. We can denote this change by Φ_{AB} and write:

$$\Phi_{AB}(t) = \beta \langle \dot{B}(0) A(t) \rangle_0 \tag{27}$$

and also:

$$\langle \Delta A \rangle = \int \Phi_{AB}(t - t') \delta(t') \, dt' \tag{28}$$

where Φ_{AB} is the response of the system. In the more general case, we can assume a perturbation to the system to be of the form:

$$H' = -B(p, q)F(t) \tag{29}$$

where $F(t)$ is a given function of time. In the linear approximation (small perturbations) the change of the average values under the action of perturbations as given by Equation 29 can be considered as a superposition of impulse perturbations. Equation 28 can then be replaced by:

$$\langle \Delta A \rangle = \int_{-\infty}^{t} \Phi_{AB}(t - t')F(t') \, dt' = \beta \int_{-\infty}^{t} \langle \dot{B}(0)A(t - t') \rangle_0 F(t') \, dt' \tag{30}$$

Since we assume that the system was originally in equilibrium, the function F must satisfy the conditions $F|_{t \to \infty} = 0$.

An important case of perturbation is a sudden adiabatic start of a periodic perturbation, i.e.:

$$F(t) = \text{Re}\left(\lim_{\epsilon \to 0} e^{\epsilon t + i\omega t} \right) \tag{31}$$

where ϵ is a positive number and Re represents the real part. Then, Equation 30 yields:

$$\langle \Delta A \rangle = \text{Re}(a_{AB} e^{i\omega t}) \tag{32}$$

where

$$a_{AB} = \lim \int_{0}^{\infty} e^{-i\omega t' + \epsilon t'} \Phi_{AB} \, dt' \tag{33}$$

This complex quantity (representing the Fourier component of the response Φ_{AB}) is called the generalized complex response function and has been studied by Kirkwood [9], Callen and Welton [10], and most generally by Kubo [11]. Let us note that in calculating the generalized complex response function, one has to perform two limiting processes: a statistical mechanics limit for $V \to \infty$ ($V/N =$ const.) in statistical averages, and a limit for $\epsilon \to 0$. The correct order is: $V \to \infty$ first, and then $\epsilon \to 0$ [7]. With the help of the condition:

$$\frac{d}{dt} \langle B(0)A(t) \rangle_0 = 0$$

Equation 30 can be written as:

$$\langle \Delta A \rangle = -\beta \int_{-\infty}^{t} \langle B(0)\dot{A}(t - t') \rangle_0 F(t') \, dt' \tag{34}$$

Using the Fourier transform ($\hat{F}[\ ]$), Equation 34 can be written as follows:

$$J(\omega) = a(\omega)F(\omega) \tag{35}$$

where

$$J(\omega) = \int_{0}^{\infty} \langle \Delta A \rangle e^{-i\omega t} \, dt, \qquad F(\omega) = \hat{F}[F(t)] \tag{36}$$

and

$$a(\omega) = -\beta \int_{0}^{\infty} e^{-i\omega\sigma} \langle B(0)\dot{A}(\sigma) \rangle_0 \, d\sigma$$

The quantity $J(\omega)$ can be called the mean "flux" which is connected with the "force" $F(\omega)$ through the relation in Equation 35. The integral representation of this basic relation can be applied to many physical phenomena [4]. We can say that the response of the system (the output signal $= J(t)$) is given by the following formula:

$$J(t) = \int_{0}^{\infty} \Phi(s)F(t - s) \, ds \tag{37}$$

where $\Phi(s) = 0$ for $s < 0$, and is bounded for $s > 0$.

The generalized complex response function a(ω) is given by:

$$a(\omega) = \int_0^\infty \Phi(s)e^{-i\omega s}\, ds \tag{38}$$

The input signal (or the driving force) is described by the function F(t) and the behavior of the system under the influence of the input F(t) is described completely by the function a(ω). For instance, the imaginary part of a(ω) describes the dissipation of energy in the system [12] (the source of this energy is the driving force F(t)). Since any real process is accompanied by some energy dissipation (positive), then $-a''(\omega) > 0$ (a(ω) = a'(ω) $-$ ia''(ω)). From the definition of a(ω) (Equation 38), one can see that in the lower-half plane of ω ($\omega = \omega' + i\omega''$), the generalized complex response function is a one-to-one function with no singularities there. On the real axis ($\omega'' = 0$), the function a(ω) has no poles except possibly for the origin. It also follows from Equation 38 that $\bar{a}(\omega) = a(-\bar{\omega})$ (here, $^-$ denotes the complex conjugate); hence, a(ω) is a real function on the imaginary axis ($\omega = i\omega''$). Using the theory of complex functions [13] one can show that a(ω) has no real values in the lower-half plane, except for the points on the imaginary axis where a(ω) is monotonously decreasing from a(io) to a(i∞). Also, one can see that a(ω) has no zeros in the lower-half plane [12, 14]. With the help of Cauchy's theorem [13] one can find the following integral expression for a(ω) [14]:

$$a(\omega) = \frac{i}{\pi}\, P \int_{-\infty}^\infty \frac{a(x)}{x - \omega}\, dx \tag{39}$$

where P represents the principal value of the intergral. From this expression one can immediately write the known Kramers-Kronig relations [4, 15]:

$$a'(\omega) = \frac{1}{\pi}\int_{-\infty}^\infty \frac{a''(x)\, dx}{x - \omega}$$

$$a''(\omega) = -\frac{1}{\pi}\int_{-\infty}^\infty \frac{a'(x)}{x - \omega}\, dx \tag{40}$$

These formulas are among the most general relations between quantities which characterize dispersion processes and absorption processes in physics [15].

Complex Viscosity

One can apply the results of the previous paragraph to viscoelastic fluids. These fluids exhibit much more complicated behavior than the one described by Hooke's and Newton's laws. Even in the case of small deformations, they may exhibit a combination of liquid-like and solid-like behavior [16]. Mathematically, the properties of a viscoelastic system are described by a constitutive equation which relates the stress tensor $\underset{\sim}{\tau}$ and an appropriate deformation measure [17–20].

Assume that a fluid particle that at time t is at the point $\underset{\sim}{x}$ was, at time $t' < t$, at the position $\underset{\sim}{x}'(\underset{\sim}{x}, t')$. Then the relative deformation gradient $\underset{\sim}{F}_t$ is given as [17]:

$$\underset{\sim}{F}_t = \nabla_x \underset{\sim}{x}' \tag{41}$$

and the relative Cauchy-Green tensor is defined as follows:

$$\underset{\sim}{C}_t = \underset{\sim}{F}_t^+ \underset{\sim}{F}_t \tag{42}$$

(+ denotes the transposition, i.e., $(A_{ij})^+ = A_{ji}$).

It is known that the most general form for a phenomenological constitutive equation of an incompressible fluid can be written as [17–20]:

$$\underset{\sim}{\pi} = P\underset{\sim}{I} + \overset{\infty}{\underset{s=0}{\Lambda}} \{\underset{\sim}{G}(t-s)\} \equiv -P\underset{\sim}{I} + \underset{\sim}{\tau} \tag{43}$$

where P is the hydrostatic pressure; $\underset{\sim}{G}(t-s) = \underset{\sim}{F}_t^+(t-s)\underset{\sim}{F}_t(t-s) - \underset{\sim}{I}$; $\underset{\sim}{I}$ represents the unit tensor; and $\Lambda\{\quad\}$ is an isotropic functional such that $\Lambda\{\underset{\sim}{0}\} = \underset{\sim}{0}$.

In the linear approximation one can write constitutive Equation 43 in the simple integral form:

$$\underset{\sim}{\tau}(t) = \int_0^\infty \Phi(s)\underset{\sim}{\dot{\gamma}}(t-s)\, ds \tag{44}$$

Here, $\underset{\sim}{\tau}$ is the extra stress tensor (see Equation 43), Φ is the relaxation modulus (or relaxation function), and the rate of deformation tensor $\underset{\sim}{\dot{\gamma}}$ is twice the symmetric part of the velocity gradient. With the help of the Fourier transform one can write the linear constitutive equation in the form [14]:

$$\hat{F}[\underset{\sim}{\tau}] = \eta^*(\omega)\hat{F}[\underset{\sim}{\dot{\gamma}}] \tag{45}$$

where

$$\eta^*(\omega) = \int_0^\infty \Phi(s)e^{-i\omega s}\, ds \tag{46}$$

This complex function represents the generalized complex response function of our viscoelastic system (incompressible viscoelastic fluid). In the linear approximation the behavior of the viscoelastic fluid, i.e., the response to the deformation, is described by the function $\eta^*(\omega)$, which is called the complex viscosity. The name complex viscosity can be justified by the following simple analysis of a dynamic experiment. In the case of a periodic simple shear experiment (as shown in Figure 6), the deformation tensor is given by the matrix:

$$[\gamma]_{ij} = \begin{pmatrix} 0 & \gamma_{12} & 0 \\ \gamma_{21} & 0 & 0 \\ 0 & 0 & 0 \end{pmatrix} \tag{47}$$

with

$$\gamma_{21} = \gamma_{21}^0 \sin \omega t \tag{48}$$

where ω is the frequency ($[\omega] = \text{rad s}^{-1}$) and γ_{21}^0 is the amplitude of the deformation (we assume that γ_{21}^0 is small).

Then, $\dot{\gamma}_{21} = \omega\gamma_{21}^0 \cos \omega t$ and the linear constitutive Equation 44 yields:

$$\tau_{21}(t) = \left(\gamma_{21}^0 \omega \int_0^\infty \Phi(s)\cos \omega s\, ds\right)\cos \omega t + \left(\gamma_{21}^0 \omega \int_0^\infty \Phi(s)\sin \omega s\, ds\right)\sin \omega t \tag{49}$$

This equation is usually written as:

$$\tau_{21}(t) = \gamma_{21}^0 G' \sin \omega t + \gamma_{21}^0 G'' \cos \omega t \tag{50}$$

where

$$G'(\omega) = \omega \int_0^\infty \Phi(s)\sin \omega s\, ds$$

and

$$G''(\omega) = \omega \int_0^\infty \Phi(s)\cos \omega s\, ds \tag{51}$$

The two frequency-dependent functions G' and G'' are called the shear storage modulus and the loss modulus, respectively [16]. It is possible to introduce complex quantities for the description of periodic flow [47–48]. To do this, it is convenient to change the phase of all quantities by $\pi/2$

and write:

$$\gamma_{21} = \text{Re}(\gamma_{21}^0 e^{i\omega t}) \tag{52}$$

$$\tau_{21} = \text{Re}(\tau_{21}^* e^{i\omega t}) \tag{53}$$

where again Re represents the real part of an appropriate complex quantity. One can then also write:

$$\tau_{21}^* = \gamma_{21}^0 G^* \tag{54}$$

In a periodic simple shear the complex deformation is $\gamma_{21}^*(t) = \gamma_{21}^0 e^{i\omega t}$ and the rate of deformation is $\dot{\gamma}_{21}^*(t) = i\omega\gamma_{21}^*(t)$. Hence, defining $\eta^* = G^*/i\omega$ we can write:

$$\tau_{21} = \text{Re}(\eta^* \dot{\gamma}_{21}^*(t)) \tag{55}$$

It is now clear why the function η^* is referred to as the complex viscosity. Using the definition of η^* (Equation 46) we can establish the relation between η^* and G^*, i.e., for:

$$\eta^*(\omega) = \eta'(\omega) - i\eta''(\omega) \tag{56}$$

where $\quad \eta'(\omega) = \int_0^\infty \Phi(s) \cos \omega s \, ds \quad$ and $\quad \eta''(\omega) = \int_0^\infty \Phi(s) \sin \omega s \, ds$

we have:

$$\eta' = \frac{G''}{\omega} \quad \text{and} \quad \eta'' = \frac{G'}{\omega} \tag{57}$$

The form of the time-dependence of $\Phi(t)$ (relaxation modulus) can be found with the help of the Fourier transform of Equations 50 and 51, i.e.:

$$\Phi(t) = \frac{2}{\pi} \int_0^\infty \frac{G'(\omega)}{\omega} \sin \omega t \, d\omega \tag{58}$$

or $\quad \Phi(t) = \frac{2}{\pi} \int_0^\infty \frac{G''(\omega)}{\omega} \cos \omega t \, d\omega$

During the early era of rheology two models have been very popular for the description of visco-elastic materials. These are the Maxwell and the Kelvin (Voigt) model, shown in Figure 11. To model the behavior of a viscoelastic system, one has to combine a sufficient number of elastic elements (springs) and viscous elements (dashpots) [16]. For one Maxwell element (k), one can introduce the spring constant G_k and the friction constant of the dashpot η_k. Then the relaxation time of the element is $\lambda_k = \eta_k/G_k$ and the relaxation modulus Φ becomes:

$$\Phi(t) = G_k e^{-t/\lambda_k} \tag{59}$$

For a periodic deformation one obtains:

$$G' = G_k \frac{\lambda_k^2 \omega^2}{1 + \lambda_k^2 \omega^2} \quad \text{and} \quad G'' = G_k \frac{\lambda_k \omega}{1 + \lambda_k^2 \omega^2} \tag{60}$$

Similarly, in the case of a Kelvin-Voigt element, the complex compliance $J^* = (G^*)^{-1}$ has the following components [16]:

$$J' = J_k \frac{1}{1 + \lambda_k^2 \omega^2} \quad \text{and} \quad J'' = J_k \frac{\lambda_k \omega}{1 + \lambda_k^2 \omega^2} \tag{61}$$

MAXWELL MODEL

KELVIN – VOIGT MODEL

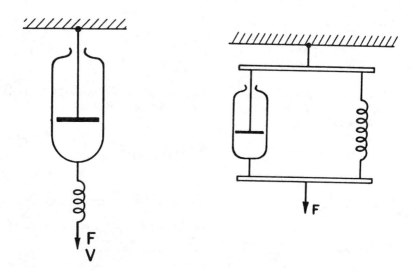

Figure 11. The Maxwell and Kelvin-Voigt elements.

where $J_k = (G_k)^{-1}$ and λ_k is the retardation time of the Kelvin-Voigt element. To model a real viscoelastic system, one has to form composite models, i.e., use the principle of superposition [16, 21, 22]. For the generalized Maxwell model one then obtains a spectrum of discrete relaxation times (similarly for the generalized Kelvin-Voigt model a spectrum of discrete retardation times can be obtained) [16]. Recent molecular theories are compatible with the discrete relaxation spectra [18–19], but it is customary to use continuous spectra in the classical theory of linear viscoelasticity. Since in practice a logarithmic time scale is much more useful, we can define the function $H(\lambda)$ as:

$$H(\lambda) d \ln \lambda = \Phi(\lambda) \, dn \tag{62}$$

where dn is the number of discrete relaxation times in the interval $(\lambda, \lambda + d\lambda)$. Then Equations 60 and 61 can be written as follows:

$$\Phi(t) = \int_{-\infty}^{\infty} H(\lambda) e^{-t/\lambda} d \ln \lambda \tag{63}$$

$$G'(\omega) = \int_{-\infty}^{\infty} H(\lambda) \frac{\omega^2 \lambda^2}{1 + \omega^2 \lambda^2} \, d \ln \lambda \tag{64}$$

$$G''(\omega) = \int_{-\infty}^{\infty} H(\lambda) \frac{\omega \lambda}{1 + \omega^2 \lambda^2} \tag{65}$$

Strictly speaking these relations hold for viscoelastic fluids. In the case of a solid one relaxation time must be infinite, i.e., an equilibrium term must be added to the right sides of Equations 64 and 65. The use of relaxation time spectra for calculating various material functions has been initiated by Ninomiya and Ferry [23] and the approximate theory developed by F. R. Schwarzl and collaborators [24–29]. For instance, for the so called stress growth experiment in which at t = 0 a sudden jump ($\dot{\gamma} = \dot{\gamma}_0$) in the shear rate is introduced, one has:

$$\tau_{21}^+(t) = \dot{\gamma}_0 t \int_{-\infty}^{\infty} H(\lambda) \frac{1 - e^{-t/\lambda}}{t/\lambda} \, d \ln \lambda \tag{66}$$

and $$(\tau_{11}(t) - \tau_{22}(t))^+ = 2\dot{\gamma}_0^2 t^2 \int_{-\infty}^{\infty} H(\lambda) \frac{1 - (1 + t/\lambda)e^{-t/\lambda}}{(t/\lambda^2)} \, d \ln \lambda \tag{67}$$

for the transient shear stress and the transient primary normal stress difference [21, 30]. From these equations, the following relations between the steady-state stress components and the dynamic moduli can be derived:

$$\lim_{\omega \to 0} \frac{G'}{\omega^2} = \lim_{t \to \infty} \frac{(\tau_{11} - \tau_{22})^+}{2\dot{\gamma}_0^2} \tag{68}$$

$$\lim_{\omega \to 0} \frac{G''}{\omega} = \lim_{t \to \infty} \frac{\tau_{21}^+}{\dot{\gamma}_0} \tag{69}$$

These are known relations obtained by Coleman and Markovitz [31] for a simple fluid [17]. In the approximation theory of Schwarzl and Struik [28] it is assumed that the functions τ_{21}^+, $(\tau_{11} - \tau_{22})^+$, $G'(\omega)$ and $G''(\omega)$ can be written in terms of the relaxation spectrum $H(\lambda)$, as is mentioned above. Each of these functions is an integral transform of $H(\lambda)$ with different kernels. From the behavior of these kernels it can be found that for short times the behavior of τ_{21}^+ and $(\tau_{11} - \tau_{22})^+$ is described by $G'(\omega)$. For longer times the behavior of τ_{21}^+ is described by $G''(\omega)$, and the behavior of $(\tau_{11} - \tau_{22})^+$ is given by $G'(\omega)$ [21, 28, 30]. For instance, Gortemaker et al. [30] calculated the following approximative equations:

$$\tau_{21}^+ = \dot{\gamma}_0 t[G'(\omega) - 0.322G''(0.5\omega) + 0.58G''(2\omega)]_{\omega = 1/t} \tag{70}$$

with maximum relative error 0.055 and:

$$(\tau_{11} - \tau_{22})^+ = \dot{\gamma}_0^2 t^2[1.683G'(0.6\omega) - 5.405G'(\omega) + 4.74G'(1.2\omega)]_{\omega = 1/t} \tag{71}$$

with maximum relative error 0.048.

Several other empirical relations relating material functions and involving components of η^* have appeared in the literature. One of those is the well known Cox-Merz rule [32] given by:

$$\eta(\dot{\gamma}) = |\eta^*(\omega)|_{\omega = \dot{\gamma}} \tag{72}$$

It has been found that the Cox-Merz rule is satisfied for some high-density polyethylenes [21] but the approximation is more problematic for other polymeric systems (e.g., polystyrene). Another empirical relation between the nonlinear steady-state shear stresses, first normal stress differences, and the transient linear quantities has been proposed by Gleissle [33]. It is interesting that in some cases the measurement of dynamic quantities as functions of frequency enables one to obtain a fairly realistic picture about the behavior of steady-state material functions. Hence, we have an interesting situation where nonlinear properties of polymeric systems are to some extent predicted from purely linear dynamic quantities [34, 35].

RELATION TO MOLECULAR STRUCTURE

Birefringence

Here, we briefly describe the basics of this optical method. A detailed discussion of this technique can be found in a monograph by Janeschitz-Kriegl [21]. It is known that some substances split light into two polarized waves which propagate at different speeds. These substances are called birefringent. Many substances which are not birefringent under normal conditions become birefringent under the actions of external forces such as deformations and/or electric and/or magnetic fields. Only the first type of induced birefringence will be discussed here. The fact that some fluids which in the rest state exhibit no birefringence but are birefringent when flowing was discovered in the nineteenth century [36, 37].

For the description of both polarized waves in a birefringent substance one can use the Fresnel ellipsoid [38] or the Fresnel tensor $\underset{\sim}{K}$ (the ellipsoid is just a usual geometrical quadric which can be associated with any second-order tensor). In the principal axes of the Fresnel tensor we can write:

$$v_1^2 x'^2 + v_2 y'^2 + v_3^1 z'^2 = 1 \tag{73}$$

Here, v_i are the principal wave speeds (related of course to the eigenvalues of $\underset{\sim}{K}$) and $\{x', y', z'\}$ are Cartesian coordinates with origin at a point $\underset{\sim}{x}$ of the substance. The tensor $\underset{\sim}{K}$ (and its quadric) generally depends on the material properties of the studied body. If the body is a slab of material between the planes $z = \pm \ell/2$ and $\underset{\sim}{K}$ has its proper vector $\underset{\sim}{k}_3$ parallel to the z-axis, the Fresnel analysis is particularly simple. When a light wave propagates along the z-axis it will split into two polarized waves with mutually perpendicular dielectric vectors. These two waves propagate along the z-axis with different speeds v_1 and v_2. Their electric vectors are parallel to the eigenvectors $\underset{\sim}{k}_1$ and $\underset{\sim}{k}_2$. Introducing the principal indices of refraction $n_i = \bar{c}/v_i$ $(i = 1, 2)$, where $\bar{c}$ is the speed of light in vacuum, we can find the relative retardation time (t_R) of both waves as:

$$t_R = \ell(n_1 - n_2) \quad \text{or} \quad \Delta n = t_R/\ell \tag{74}$$

where Δn is the birefringence of the body (horizontal slab).

The relative retardation time and the directions of two of the principal axes $\underset{\sim}{k}_1$ and $\underset{\sim}{k}_2$ are determined by a plane polariscope. The analyzer of the polariscope transmits two waves, which will interfere if $t_R = N\lambda$, where λ is the wave length of the light in vacuum and $N = 0, \pm 1, \pm 2, \ldots$. For each value of N, the set of points (x, y) with $t_R = N\lambda$ forms the N-th isochromatic line (isochromatic fringe). The whole family of isochromatic lines is then called the isochromatic fringe pattern. From this isochromatic pattern, the birefringence Δn can be found at every point (x, y). For the intensity (I) of the light transmitted by the analyzer one can find the following relation [38]:

$$I \sim \sin^2(2\psi) \sin^2\left(\frac{\pi\ell}{\lambda} \Delta n\right) \tag{75}$$

where ψ is the angle between $\underset{\sim}{k}_1$ and the axis of the polarizer. More details about the practice of flow birefringence and related problems can be found elsewhere [21]. The basic idea of flow birefringence and its relation to rheology has been studied by Coleman et al. [39]. These authors used the phenomenological theory of simple fluids [17] and showed that for an incompressible simple fluid with fading memory only in the limit of slow flow, each eigenvector (g_i) of the rate of deformation tensor $\underset{\sim}{\dot{\gamma}}$ is also a principal axis of refraction $\underset{\sim}{k}_i$. Principal indices of refraction, in this theory, are related to the eigenvalues (g_i) of $\underset{\sim}{\dot{\gamma}}$ by a linear relation. Hence, the birefringence Δn is given as [39]:

$$\Delta n = 2\eta_N(g_1 - g_2), \quad |g_i| = g_i \tag{76}$$

for the wave propagating in the direction $\underset{\sim}{k}_3$. Since in the limit of slow motion, the simple fluid model coincides with the Navier-Stokes fluid (in which the directions of the principal axes of the stress coincide with the eigenvectors of $\dot{\gamma}$, and the principal stresses (τ_I, τ_{II}, τ_{III}) are related again by a linear relation to the eigenvalues of $\dot{\gamma}$) one can assume that the linear stress-optical relation holds:

$$\Delta n \sim (\tau_I - \tau_{II}) \tag{77}$$

These classical ideas are used in many different arrangements of flow birefringence experiments. For instance, in simple shear one can write:

$$\frac{\tau_{11} - \tau_{22}}{2\tau_{21}} = \cot 2\chi \tag{78}$$

where χ is the time-dependent orientation angle of the stress ellipsoid. This extinction angle can be evaluated on the basis of the linear stress-optical relation [21, 30].

Of course, there is no general reason to assume that the linear stress-optical relation holds for all fluids at arbitrary shear rates. On the other hand, there is a vast amount of experimental material on various flow situations and polymeric systems which confirms the linear stress-optical relation [21]. Unfortunately, even the most advanced molecular theories of Doi and Edwards [40–43] and Bird and Curtiss [44] provide no conclusive answer for this peculiar problem.

Molecular Theories

Early molecular theories of the complex viscosity have been developed by Rouse [45] and Zimm [46]. The dependence of η^* on the thermodynamic properties of solvents has been studied by Tschoegl [47]. The complex viscosity function given by the Rouse-Zimm theory can be written as:

$$\eta^* - \eta_s = \sum_{n=1}^{N} \frac{a_n}{1 + i\omega\lambda_n}, \quad a_n = \frac{6(\eta_0 - \eta_s)}{\pi n^2}$$

$$\lambda_n = \frac{6M(\eta_0 - \eta_s)}{\pi^2 cRTn^2} \tag{79}$$

Here, η_s is the solvent viscosity, η_0 is the zero-shear rate viscosity, M is the molecular weight, T is the temperature, c is the concentration, and R is the universal gas constant.

Doi and Edwards [42], in their theory of concentrated polymer systems, derived the following form for $\eta^*(\omega)$:

$$\eta^*(\omega) = \frac{3ckTL}{5a} \sum_{n \text{ odd}} \frac{8}{n^4\pi^2} \frac{\lambda_d}{1 + i\omega(\lambda_d/n^2)} \tag{80}$$

where La, the mean square end-to-end distance of the primitive chain, is assumed to be equal to the mean square end-to-end distance $N_0 b^2$ of the real chain (N_0 is the degree of polymerization and b is the effective bond length of the real chain); k is the Boltzmann constant; and λ_d is the longest relaxation time (disengagement time of de Gennes [48]).

Doi and Edwards have found that the empirical Cox-Merz rule [32] comparing the steady-state viscosity function $\eta(\dot{\gamma})$ to $|\eta^*(\omega)|$ is not sufficiently accurate for their constitutive equation. They have noted, however, that with an appropriate choice of the memory function the correlation of $\eta(\dot{\gamma})$ and $|\eta^*(\omega)|$ may be fairly good.

Curtiss and Bird [49], in their reptation treatment, have obtained the following expression for $\eta^*(\omega)$:

$$\eta^*(\omega) = NnkT \left\{ \frac{8\bar{\lambda}}{5\pi^2} \left[\sum_{n \text{ odd}} \frac{1}{n^2(\pi^2 n^2 + i\bar{\lambda}\omega)} \right] + \frac{1}{90} \epsilon\bar{\lambda} \right\} \tag{81}$$

where nN is the number density of beads (the macromolecule is modeled as a Kramers freely-jointed bead-rod chain); $\bar{\lambda}$ is a time constant ($\bar{\lambda} \sim \eta_0 \sim M^{3+\beta}$, β is suggested to be about 0.4 or 0.5); and ϵ is a "link tension coefficient" which lies between 0 and 1.

In the Curtiss-Bird theory the Cox-Merz rule holds only for small values of $\bar{\lambda}\omega$, which probably suggests some inadequacy of the Kramers chain model for the description of small-scale oscillations.

The role of the molecular weight distribution on the viscoelastic properties of polymeric systems has been studied by many authors. For example, Middleman [22] modified Bueche's theory [50] to account for the effect of polydispersity on the viscosity and concluded that the polydispersity index (M_w/M_n) is insufficient to express completely the effect of polydispersity on the viscosity function. Montfort et al. [51] studied the influence of the molecular weight distribution on the linear viscoelastic properties of molten polymers. They developed a double retardation model for monodisperse samples and an empirical blending law for binary systems. This blending law has been generalized [52] by these authors and the properties for the system have been predicted from its molecular weight distribution. Onogi and coworkers [53] have studied rheological properties of polystyrene melts. They observed abnormal behavior of the viscosity and rigidity curves in the case of bimodal molecular weight distribution curves and they emphasized the role of micro-Brownian motion on the flow properties of polymer melts at higher frequencies (or shear rates). The effect of temperature on melt viscosity and the relation of complex and steady-state viscosities have also been studied by Ballman and Simon [54]. Their verification of the Cox-Merz rule was unsuccessful.

PHENOMENOLOGICAL MODELS

Some of the earlier phenomenological models describe the complex viscosity quite well. More complete information is presented in the work of Bird et al. [18–19].

In particular, the models by Lodge [55], Walters [56], Spriggs [57], and Carreau [58] describe the behavior of η^* very well. Roscoe's model [59], although designed to fit $\eta^*(\omega)$ data, lacks some flexibility. Stastna et al. [60] proposed what we believe to be a more flexible group of models. Even for a relatively small number of parameters, one is capable of correctly portraying the complex viscosity function for typical viscoelastic liquids.

Our proposed complex viscosity model [60] can be written as follows (the solvent viscosity is neglected):

$$\eta^*(\omega) = \eta_0 \left[\frac{\prod_{k=1}^{r} (1 + i\omega\mu_k)^{n_k}}{\prod_{k=1}^{s} (1 + i\omega\lambda_k)^{m_k}} \right]^{\beta}$$

$$\sum_{k=1}^{r} n_k < \sum_{k=1}^{s} m_k \tag{82}$$

where η_0 = zero-shear rate viscosity,
          β, μ_k, and λ_k are real
          n_k, m_k, r and s are integers

Since it has been shown [60] that $\eta^*(\omega)$ has no zeros, no poles, and no real values in the lower-half of the complex plane except on the imaginary axis, where $\eta^*(\omega)$ is real, then $\mu_k > 0$ and $\lambda_k > 0$. These are time constants for the model. The function $\eta^*(\omega)$, which is a complex function, can be studied as two real functions: an amplitude $|\eta^*(\omega)|$ and a phase angle Φ; that is:

$$\ln|\eta^*| = \ln \eta_0 + \frac{\beta}{2} \sum_{k=1}^{r} n_k \ln(1 + \omega^2\mu_k^2) - \frac{\beta}{2} \sum_{k=1}^{s} m_k \ln(1 + \omega^2\lambda_k^2) \tag{83}$$

and $$\Phi = \beta \sum_{k=1}^{r} n_k \arctan \omega\mu_k - \beta \sum_{k=1}^{s} m_k \arctan \omega\lambda_k \tag{84}$$

In order to keep the number of model parameters realistic, the following two special cases have been investigated and applied to polymer solutions.

A three parameter model of the form:

$$\eta^*(\omega) = \frac{\eta_0}{(1 + i\omega\lambda)^\beta} \tag{85}$$

and a four parameter model given by:

$$\eta^*(\omega) = \eta_0 \left[\frac{1 + i\omega\mu}{(1 + i\omega\lambda)^2} \right]^\beta \tag{86}$$

For data fitting one can rewrite both models (Equations 85 and 86) in polar form, and use the nonlinear regression program discussed by Powley and De Kee [61].

A comparison of these models with experimental data for several polymer solutions follows. The tested solutions are:

1. 5 (wt%) solutions of polystyrene of varying molecular weights ($M_w = 4.11 \times 10^5$ with $M_w/M_n = 1.06$; $M_w = 8.6 \times 10^5$ with $M_w/M_n = 1.15$; and $M_w = 1.8 \times 10^6$ with $M_w/M_n = 1.2$) in a chlorinated diphenyl (Aroclor) solvent with chlorine content of 48%. The viscosity of this Aroclor solvent is 0.3 Pa·s., at 298 K.
2. 1, 2, and 3 (wt%) solutions of polyacrylamide (separan AP-30) in a 50% mixture (by weight) of water and glycerine. The molecular weight and the distribution of the polymer are unknown.
3. A 6 (wt%) solution of polyisobutylene (P.I.B.) in Primol 355 (a pharmaceutical grade white oil with a viscosity of about 0.15 Pa·s. at 298 K.

The data on the polystyrene solutions are taken from Ashare [2] and the other data were obtained by De Kee [3]. All data (n' and η'') were obtained on a Weissenberg rheogoniometer, allowing $|\eta^*(\omega)|$ and $\Phi(\omega)$ to be computed.

The parameters of both models (Equations 85 and 86) are listed in Table 1. For polystyrene solutions the first number refers to concentration, the second gives the molecular weight, and the third represents the percentage of chlorine in the Aroclor solvent.

Figures 12 and 13 compare the predictions of the three-parameter model (Equation 85) with the experimental data for the separan and P.I.B. solutions. Figure 14 compares the prediction of the four-parameter model (Equation 86) with experimental data for polystyrene solutions. Both the three- and four-parameter models are able to portray quite accurately the $|\eta^*| - \omega$ portion of the presented Bode-type plots over a wide frequency range. However, the convex character of the $\Phi - \omega$ part of the Bode-type representation necessitates a fourth parameter.

Figures 12 and 13 clearly show that $d\Phi/d\omega$ approaches zero as ω tends to infinity, for the three-parameter model. The nature of the data in Figure 14 requires the use of a four-parameter model

Table 1
Model Parameters for Equations 85 and 86

Fluid	η_0 [Pa·s.]	β [-]	μ [s]	λ [s]
1%—separan	117.06	0.643	—	61.58
2%—separan	309.46	0.669	—	45.58
3%—separan	975.01	0.704	—	67.99
6%—P.I.B.	9830.5	0.704	—	295.9
P.S. 5–411–48	25.17	0.437	0.070	0.071
P.S. 5–860–48	109.42	0.321	0.011	0.429
P.S. 5–1800–48	687.56	0.334	0.010	5.152

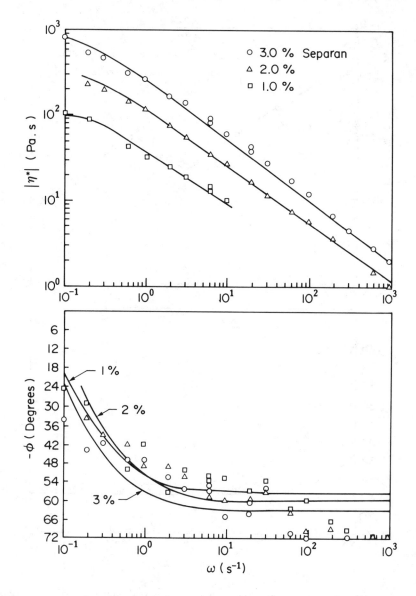

Figure 12. Complex viscosity components for separan (AP-30) solutions in a 50 (wt%) mixture of water and glycerine. The solid lines are predictions of Equation 85.

to adequately describe the $\Phi - \omega$ portion. De Kee et al. [62] present figures illustrating the effect of molecular weight, concentration, and type of solvent, respectively, on the complex viscosity.

Figures 12 and 13 show the dependence of the separan and P.I.B. solutions on the concentrations. Unfortunately, the molecular weights are not known for these polymer solutions. The agreement with $|\eta^*|$ data is good. The scatter of the $\Phi(\omega)$ data might be caused by the high polydispersity of these

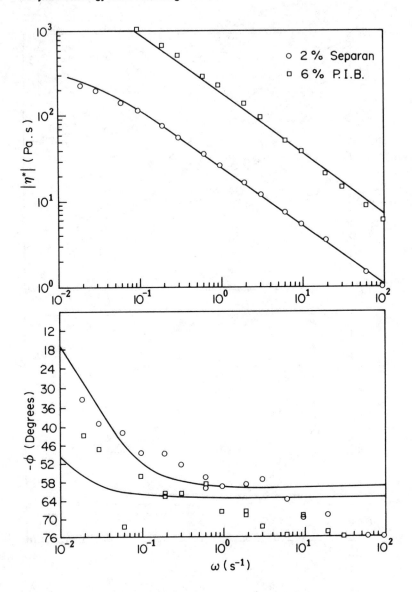

Figure 13. Complex viscosity components for a 2(wt%) separan solution in a 50(wt%) mixture of water and glycerine and a 6 (wt%) solution of polyisobutylene in Primol 355. The solid lines are predictions of Equation 85.

samples. It can be seen from Figure 14 that $|\eta^*(\omega)|$ depends strongly on the molecular weight at lower frequencies, while it becomes less sensitive to molecular weight variations at higher frequencies. This is in agreement with the observations of Onogi et al. [53]. They reported that η' curves for polystyrene melts with molecular weight higher than a certain critical value unite into one curve

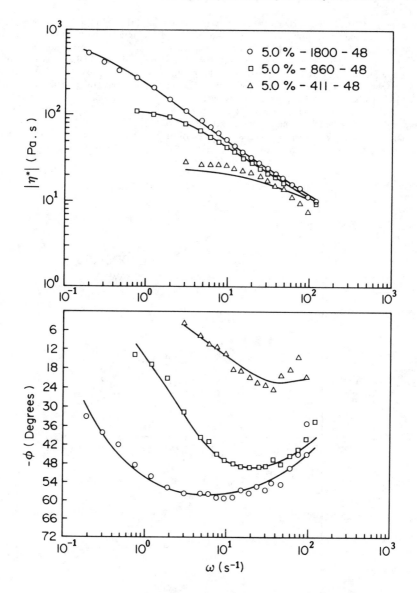

Figure 14. Complex viscosity components for 5 (wt%) polystyrene solutions in Aroclor 1248. $\bigcirc$: $M_w = 1.8 \times 10^6$, $\square$: $M_w = 8.6 \times 10^5$, $\triangle$: $M_w = 4.11 \times 10^5$. Data of Ashare [2]. The solid lines are predictions of Equation 86.

at an angular frequency of about 10^3 s^{-1}. We observe a similar trend at the higher frequencies, but one has to bear in mind that we are dealing with solutions and that we are plotting $|\eta^*|$ values vs. ω for different polymer molecular weight averages. Again, a similar trend can be noticed for the $\Phi - \omega$ relation.

It is clear that the low molecular weight polystyrene solution ($M_w = 4.11 \times 10^5$) deviates from the trend discussed above; however, the model properties seem to agree with Onogi's observations.

The empirical Cox-Merz rule [32] cannot be applied to all of the investigated solutions. The empiricism seems to be satisfactory for the 5-1800-48, polystyrene solution. PIB and separan solutions do not follow the Cox-Merz rule. To unite the $|\eta^*|$ and η curves for these solutions, one would have to apply some shifting, but there is no unique shifting factor. Hence, the practical use of the Cox-Merz rule as a general approximation is questionable and more detailed studies are needed. There is also some preliminary evidence of a linear relation between $\log \eta_0/\lambda^\zeta$ and $\log c$, where ζ is β or 2β for the three or four parameter model, respectively.

Finally, one example for melts is presented. We described the complex viscosity of melts of linear low-density polyethylene (LLDPE) by:

$$\eta^*(\omega) = \frac{\eta_0}{[(1 + i\omega\lambda_1)(1 + i\omega\lambda_2)]^\beta} \tag{87}$$

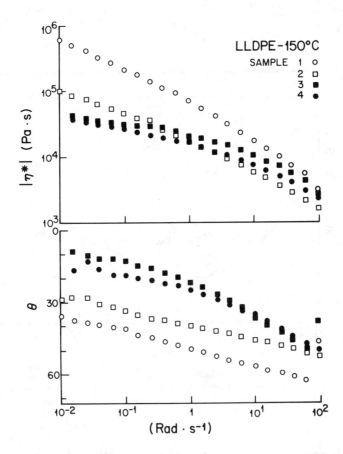

Figure 15. Complex viscosity components for commercial LLDPE resins at 150°C; (1) $\bar{M}_w = 4.84 \times 10^5$, $\bar{M}_n = 4.13 \times 10^4$, (2) $\bar{M}_w = 2.13 \times 10^5$, $\bar{M}_n = 2.94 \times 10^4$, (3) $\bar{M}_w = 2.65 \times 10^5$, $\bar{M}_n = 6.68 \times 10^4$, (4) $\bar{M}_w = 2.27 \times 10^5$, $\bar{M}_n = 6.26 \times 10^4$.

The tested melts are commercial LLDPE resins studied in the Industrial Materials Research Institute of the NRCC. The data on LLDPE melts have been provided by Utracki (63).

Figure 15 shows the experimental data for four LLDPE melts taken at 150°C. The data for $|\eta^*|$ can be portrayed by the four-parameter model (Equation 87) for $\omega \in (0.01, 100)$. The fit is very good in the whole region. Sample no. 1 is a melt with a very broad molecular weight distribution (MWD). Calculations indicate that the function $\Phi(\omega)$ is portrayed well by Equation 87 only in the region $\omega \in (0.2, 3)$. Sample no. 2 represents a melt with a broad MWD. In this case, Equation 87 can describe the function $\Phi(\omega)$ rather well in the region $\omega \in (0.02, 10)$. Samples 3 and 4 are melts with a narrow MWD. Here the function $\Phi(\omega)$ is very well described by Equation 87 in the same ω-region as sample no. 2. It becomes apparent that, in order to cover very broad regions of frequency, one has to consider models with more than two characteristic times. It is also obvious, as indicated for the polymer solutions, that the complex viscosity function is sensitive to the molecular weight distribution.

GENERATED MATERIAL FUNCTIONS

To illustrate the use of complex viscosity models in the construction of constitutive equations, we can consider the following specification of the model presented by Equation 82:

$$\eta^*(\omega) = \eta_0 \frac{(1 + i\omega\mu)^\beta}{(1 + i\omega\lambda)^{2\beta}} \tag{88}$$

The relaxation modulus $\Phi(s)$ is given as the inverse Fourier transform $\Phi(s) = F^{-1}[\eta^*(\omega)]$, i.e.:

$$\Phi(s) = \frac{1}{2\pi} \int_{-\infty}^{\infty} \eta_0 \frac{(1 + i\omega\mu)^\beta}{(1 + i\omega\lambda)^{2\beta}} e^{i\omega s}\, d\omega \tag{89}$$

This integral can be evaluated with the help of the degenerate hypergeometric function $_1F_1$ [64]:

$$\Phi(s) = \eta_0 \left(\frac{\mu}{\lambda^2}\right)^\beta \frac{e^{-s/\lambda} s^{\beta-1}}{\Gamma(\beta)}\, _1F_1\left(-\beta, \beta; \left(\frac{1}{\lambda} - \frac{1}{\mu}\right) s\right) \qquad s > 0 \tag{90}$$

where Γ is the gamma function.

Knowing the relaxation modulus $\Phi(s)$ one can write constitutive Equation 44 in the form:

$$\underset{\sim}{\tau}(t) = \frac{\eta_0}{\Gamma(\beta)} \left(\frac{\mu}{\lambda^2}\right)^\beta \int_{-\infty}^{\infty} e^{-s/\lambda} s^{\beta-1}\, _1F_1\left(-\beta, \beta; \left(\frac{1}{\lambda} - \frac{1}{\mu}\right) s\right) \underset{\sim}{\dot{\gamma}}(t - s)\, ds \tag{91}$$

where η_0, β, λ, and μ are parameters of the complex viscosity model (88).

It is possible to rewrite the linear viscoelastic model (91) in a corotating reference frame. Models obtained by this method are referred to as quasilinear corotational. They are nonlinear relations between $\underset{\sim}{\tau}$ and $\underset{\sim}{\dot{\gamma}}$, but they are linear when written in terms of the analogous quantities defined in a corotating frame of reference.

In a corotating frame of reference, Equation 44 takes the form [18]:

$$\underset{\sim}{\tau}(t) = \int_0^\infty \Phi(s) \underset{\sim}{\dot{G}}\, ds \tag{92}$$

where for steady shear flow:

$$\underset{\sim}{\dot{G}} = \begin{pmatrix} \sin \dot{\gamma}s & \cos \dot{\gamma}s & 0 \\ \cos \dot{\gamma}s & -\sin \dot{\gamma}s & 0 \\ 0 & 0 & 0 \end{pmatrix} \dot{\gamma} \tag{93}$$

and where $\dot{\gamma}$ represents a constant shear rate.

Combining Equations 90, 92, and 93, one can write the steady shear rate viscosity $\eta(\dot\gamma)$ as:

$$\eta(\dot\gamma) = \frac{\eta_0}{\Gamma(\beta)}\left(\frac{\mu}{\lambda^2}\right)^\beta \int_0^\infty e^{-s/\lambda}s^{\beta-1}\,_1F_1(-\beta,\beta)\left(\frac{1}{\lambda}-\frac{1}{\mu}\right)\cos\dot\gamma s\,ds \tag{94}$$

The integral in the expression exists [65], and assuming that a termwise integration ($_1F_1$ is given by an infinite series) in Equation 94 can be performed, one can obtain the following dimensionless relation:

$$\frac{\eta(\dot\gamma)}{\eta_0}\left[\frac{\lambda}{\mu}(1+(\lambda\dot\gamma)^2)^{1/2}\right]^\beta = \sum_{n=0}^\infty \binom{\beta}{n}\left(\frac{\lambda-\mu}{\mu}\right)^n \frac{\cos(\beta+n)\arctan\lambda\dot\gamma}{(1+(\lambda_2\dot\gamma)^2)^{n/2}} \tag{95}$$

Similarly, for the primary normal stress coefficient ψ_1, the Equations 90, 92, and 93 yield:

$$\frac{\psi_1(\dot\gamma)\dot\gamma}{2\eta_0}\left[\frac{\lambda}{\mu}(1+(\lambda\dot\gamma)^2)^{1/2}\right]^\beta = \sum_{n=0}^\infty \binom{\beta}{n}\left(\frac{\lambda-\mu}{\mu}\right)^n \frac{\sin(\beta+n)\arctan\lambda\dot\gamma}{(1+(\lambda\dot\gamma)^2)^{n/2}} \tag{96}$$

Since the series appearing in the expression for the viscosity and the primary normal stress co-efficient are convergent for $((\lambda-\mu)/\lambda\mu)^2 - 1 < \dot\gamma^2$ the relations expressed by 95 and 96 cannot be used for arbitrarily low shear rates.

Using the same method, one can also calculate the stress growth and stress relaxation function [65]. In the case of the four-parameter model, given by Equation 88, the method outlined above can be significantly simplified if one introduces the complex material function:

$$\eta^*(\dot\gamma) = \eta(\dot\gamma) - i\frac{\dot\gamma}{2}\psi_1(\dot\gamma) \tag{97}$$

given by Bird et al. [18]. As pointed out by Friedrich [66], the series development is then no longer necessary and one obtains the results discussed in [18]. Other types of constitutive equations can be treated in a similar fashion.

CONCLUSION

The shear relaxation modulus $\Phi(t)$ contains all information on the linear viscoelastic behavior of a fluid. The complex viscosity (or the associated dynamic shear modulus) is more commonly measured and is related to $\Phi(t)$ by a Fourier transform. Some investigators have chosen to present their results in terms of the relaxation spectrum. Such a manipulation of the experimental data by numerical inversion is unnecessary, and it also may introduce additional errors. The behavior of $\eta^*(\omega)$ provides a direct and convenient description of dynamic behavior for viscoelastic fluids. Moreover, the complex viscosity function is directly related to the generalized response function which is the basic tool in studying the dynamic response of physical systems. With the help of η^* one can find the relaxation modulus and construct appropriate constitutive equations. These equations can be generalized or extended to the quasilinear and nonlinear regions of large deformations. Thus, the study of the complex viscosity is just another example of a general physical method for investigating the spontaneous fluctuations about the equilibrium state.

Acknowledgments

Some of our research reported herein was supported by operating grants from the Natural Sciences and Engineering Research Council of Canada.

NOTATION

$a(\omega)$	generalized complex function	i	imaginary unit
a', a''	real and imaginary part of $a(\omega)$	I	intensity of light
		$J(t)(J(\omega))$	output signal (flux)
b	effective bond length	k	Boltzmann constant
c	concentration	$\underline{K}(\underline{k}_i)$	Fresnell tensor (eigenvectors of $\underline{K}$)
$\bar{c}$	speed of light in vacuum		
$\underline{C}_t$	relative Cauchy Green tensor	L	mean square end to end distance
f	distribution function	M	molecular weight
f_0	canonical distribution function	$M_w(M_n)$	molecular weight average; weight average (number average)
$\underline{F}_t$	relative deformation gradient		
		N	number of particles
${}_1F_1(a, b; c)$	degenerate hypergeometric function	N_0	degree of polymerization
		n_i	refractive index
$\underline{g}_i(g_i)$	eigenvectors (eigenvalues) of $\dot{\underline{\gamma}}$	p	momentum
		P	hydrostatic pressure
G_k	spring constant	q	generalized coordinate
G^*	complex modulus	t	time
$G'(G'')$	storage (loss) modulus	T	absolute temperature
$h(t)$	unit step function	V	volume of the system
$H(H_0, H')$	Hamiltonian	$V_x(V_y, V_z)$	velocity components
$H(\lambda)$	relaxation spectrum	Z	partition function

Greek Symbols

β	parameter	η_s	solvent viscosity
$\dot{\gamma}(\dot{\gamma}_{yx})$	shear rate	λ_k	time constant (parameter)
$\dot{\gamma}_0$	constant velocity gradient	λ_d	disengagement time
$\dot{\gamma}^0$	complex amplitude of the complex shear rate	$\Lambda\{\ \}$	functional
		μ_k	time constant (parameter)
Γ	gamma function	$\underline{\pi}$	stress tensor
$\delta(t)$	delta function	$\underline{\tau}(\tau_{ij}, \tau_{yx})$	extra stress tensor (components)
ϵ	real positive number		
$\eta(\dot{\gamma})$	non-Newtonian viscosity	τ^0	complex amplitude of the complex $\underline{\tau}$
η_0	zero shear viscosity		
η^*	complex viscosity	$\tau_I, \tau_{II}, \tau_{III}$	principal stresses
η', η''	real and imaginary parts of η^*	Φ	phase angle
		$\Phi(t)$	relaxation modulus
$\eta^+(t, \dot{\gamma}_0)$	shear stress growth function	Φ_{AB}	response function
		χ	extinction angle
$\eta^-(t, \dot{\gamma}_0)$	shear stress relaxation function	$\psi_1(\psi_2)$	normal stress coefficients
		$\psi_1^+(t, \dot{\gamma}_0)(\psi_2^+(t, \dot{\gamma}_0))$	normal stress growth coefficients
η_k	friction constant of the dashpot	ω	frequency

Symbols

Re	real part	$\langle\ \rangle$	average
P $\int$	principal value	$\{\ \}$	Poisson bracket
$\underline{A}$	tensor	$\underline{\nabla}$	gradient
$\underline{A}^+$	transpose of $\underline{A}$	$\hat{F}(t)$	Fourier transform
$[\ \tilde{}\ ]_{ij}$	matrix	$\dot{A}$	time derivative

REFERENCES

1. Bird, R. B., Stewart, W. E., and Lightfoot, E. N., *Transport Phenomena*, J. Wiley and Sons, Inc., New York (1960).
2. Ashare, E., Ph.D. Thesis, University of Wisconsin (1968).
3. De Kee, D., Ph.D. Thesis, University of Montreal (1977).
4. de Groot, S. R., and Mazur, P., *Nonequilibrium Thermodynamics*, North-Holland, Amsterdam (1962).
5. Prigogine, I., *Nonequilibrium Statistical Mechanics*, Interscience, New York (1962).
6. Tyablikov, S. V., *Methods in the Quantum Theory of Magnetism*, Plenum, New York (1967).
7. Zubarev, D. N., *Nonequilibrium Statistical Thermodynamics*, Consultants Bureau, New York (1974).
8. Goldstein, H., *Classical Mechanics*, Addison-Wesley, Don Mills (1981).
9. Kirkwood, J. G., *J. Chem. Phys.*, *14*, 180 (1946).
10. Callen, H. B., and Welton, T. A., *Phys. Rev.*, *83*, 34 (1951).
11. Kubo, R., *Lectures in Theoretical Physics*, Interscience, New York (1959).
12. Landau, L. D., and Lifshitz, E. M., *Statistical Physics*, Pergamon Press, Oxford (1958).
13. Sansone, G., and Gerretsen, J., *Lectures on the Theory of Functions of a Complex Variable*, Noordhoff, Groningen (1960).
14. Stastna, J., De Kee, D., and Powley, M. B., *J. Rheol.*, *29*, 457 (1985).
15. Levich, B. G., Statistical Physics, *Electromagnetic Processes in Matter*, North-Holland, Amsterdam (1971).
16. Ferry, J. D., *Viscoelastic Properties of Polymers*, Wiley, New York (1970).
17. Truesdell, C., and Noll, W., *The Nonlinear Field Theories of Mechanics*, Handbuch der Physik III/3, Springer, Berlin (1965).
18. Bird, R. B., Armstrong, R. C., and Hassager, O., *Dynamics of Polymeric Liquids*, Vol. I, *Fluid Mechanics*, Wiley, New York (1977).
19. Bird, R. B., Hassager, O., Armstrong, R. C., and Curtiss, C. F., *Dynamics of Polymeric Liquids*, Vol. II, *Kinetic Theory*, Wiley, New York (1977).
20. Astarita, G., and Marrucci, G., *Principles of Non-Newtonian Fluid Mechanics*, McGraw-Hill, New York (1978).
21. Janeschitz-Kriegl, H., *Polymer Melt Rheology and Flow Birefringence* Springer, Berlin (1983).
22. Middleman, S., *The Flow of High Polymers*, Interscience, New York (1968).
23. Ninomiya, K., and Ferry, J. D., *J. Colloid Sci.*, *14*, 36 (1959).
24. Schwarzl, F. R., *Rheol. Acta*, *8*, 6 (1969).
25. Schwarzl, F. R., *Rheol. Acta*, *9*, 382 (1970).
26. Schwarzl, F. R., *Rheol. Acta*, *10*, 166 (1971).
27. Schwarzl, F. R., *Rheol. Acta*, *14*, 581 (1975).
28. Schwarzl, F. R., and Struik, L. C. F., *Adv. Molec. Relaxation Proc.*, *1*, 201 (1967).
29. Staverman, A. J., and Schwarzl, F. R., *Die Physik der Hochpolymeren*, Vol. 4, ed. H. A. Stuart, Springer, Berlin (1956).
30. Gortemaker, F. H., Hansen, M. G., Cindio, B. de, Laun H. M., and Janeschitz-Kriegl, H., *Rheol. Acta*, *15*, 256 (1978).
31. Coleman, B. D., and Markovitz, H., *J. Appl. Phys.*, *35*, 1 (1964).
32. Cox, W. P., and Merz, E. H., *J. Polym. Sci.*, *28*, 619 (1958).
33. Gleissle, W., *Rheology*, Vol. 2, 547, eds. G. Astarita, G. Marrucci and L. Nicolais, Plenum, New York (1980).
34. Gortemaker, F. A., Janeschitz-Kriegl, H., and Nijenhuis, K., *Rheol. Acta*, *15*, 487 (1976).
35.
36. Mach, E., *Ann. der Physik und Chemie*, Ser. II, 146, 313 (1872).
37. Maxwell, J. C., *A Treatise on Electricity and Magnetism*, University Press, Oxford (1873).
38. Born, M., and Wolfe, E., *Principles of Optics*, MacMillan, New York (1964).
39. Coleman, B. D., Hill, E. H., and Toupin, R. A., *Arch. Rational Mech. Analy.*, *5*, 358 (1970).
40. Doi, M., and Edwards, S. F., *J. Chem. Soc. Faraday Trans.*, *II*, *74*, 1789, (1978).
41. Doi, M., and Edwards, S. F., *J. Chem. Soc. Faraday Trans. II*, *74*, 1802, (1978).

42. Doi, M., and Edwards, S. F., *J. Chem. Soc. Faraday Trans. II*, *74*, 1818, (1978).
43. Doi, M., and Edwards, S. F., *J. Chem. Soc. Faraday Trans. II*, *75*, 38 (1979).
44. Curtiss, C. F., and Bird, R. B., *Physica*, *118A*, 191 (1983).
45. Rouse, P. E., *J. Chem. Phys.*, *21*, 1272 (1953).
46. Zimm, B., *J. Chem. Phys.*, *24*, 269 (1958).
47. Tschoegl, N. W., *J. Chem. Phys.*, *40*, 473 (1964).
48. De Gennes, P. G., *Macromolecules*, *9*, 587 (1976).
49. Curtis, C. F., and Bird, R. B., *J. Chem. Phys.*, *74*, 2026 (1981).
50. Bueche, F., *J. Chem. Phys.*, *22*, 1570 (1954).
51. Montfort, J. P., Marin, G., J. Arman and P. Monge, *Polymer*, *19*, 227 (1978).
52. Montfort, J. P., Marin, G., Arman, J., and Monge, P., *Rheol. Acta*, *18*, 623 (1979).
53. Onogi, S., Kato, H., Uebi, S., and Ibaragi, T., *J. Polym. Sci., C*, *15*, 481 (1966).
54. Ballman, R. L., and Simon, R. H. M., *J. Polym. Sci., A*, *2*, 3557 (1964).
55. Lodge, A. S., *Elastic Liquids*, Academic Press, New York (1969).
56. Walters, K., *Quart. J. Mech. Appl. Math.*, *15*, 63 (1962).
57. Spriggs, T. W., Ph.D. Thesis, University of Wisconsin, Madison, Wisconsin, (1966).
58. Carreau, P. J., *Trans. Soc. Rheol.*, *16*, 99 (1972).
59. Roscoe, R., *Brit. J. Appl. Phys.*, *15*, 1095 (1964).
60. Stastna, J., De Kee, D., and Powley, M. B., *J. of Rheology*, *27*, 4 (1983).
61. Powley, M. B., and De Kee, D., Proc. 34th Canadian Chemical Engineering Conference, 331, Quebec (1984).
62. De Kee, D., Stastna, J. and Powley, M. B., Non-Newt. Fluid Mech., *26*, 149 (1987).
63. Utracki, L. A., private communication (1986).
64. Gadshteyn, I. S., and Ryzkik, I. M., *Table of Integrals, Series, and Products*, Academic Press, New York (1980).
65. De Kee, D., and Stastna, J., *Rheol. Acta*, *25*, 564 (1986).
66. Friedrich, C., Private communication (1987).

CHAPTER 21

STATIC EQUILIBRIUM AND MOTION OF SPHERES IN VISCOPLASTIC LIQUIDS

R. P. Chhabra

Department of Chemical Engineering
Indian Institute of Technology
Kanpur, India 208016

and

P. H. T. Uhlherr

Department of Chemical Engineering
Monash University
Clayton, Victoria, Australia 3168

CONTENTS

INTRODUCTION

The literature on the motion of spheres in Newtonian fluids is extensive and a number of reviews are available [1–3]. On the other hand, the motion of spheres in non-Newtonian fluids is less well understood. The growing literature on sphere behavior in time-independent, purely viscous fluids and in viscoelastic fluids has been reviewed recently [4, 5]. One aspect of sphere motion in non-Newtonian media that has received relatively little attention is the influence of yield stress. This chapter focuses on this influence. However, before discussing the behavior of spheres in viscoplastic liquids, a brief summary is given of the rheological equations most commonly used to describe the flow of these liquids. An excellent discussion of these equations and their application to simple flow problems is given by Bird et al. [6].

RHEOLOGICAL EQUATIONS FOR VISCOPLASTIC LIQUIDS

A viscoplastic liquid is one that flows only when the applied stress exceeds a critical value. The critical value of stress is the yield stress. A viscoplastic material thus behaves as a solid so long as the stress level is less than the yield stress; once the stress level exceeds the yield value, the material flows like a liquid. The flow may be localized.

Three simple rheological models are most widely used to describe the flow of viscoplastic liquids—the Bingham, Casson, and Herschel-Bulkley models [6].

Bingham Model

This is the simplest and perhaps the most widely used model. For a simple shear flow it is:

$$\tau_{yx} = \tau_0^B + \mu_B \dot{\gamma}_{yx} \qquad |\tau_{yx}| > \tau_0^B$$
$$\dot{\gamma}_{yx} = 0 \qquad |\tau_{yx}| \leq \tau_0^B$$

$$(1)$$

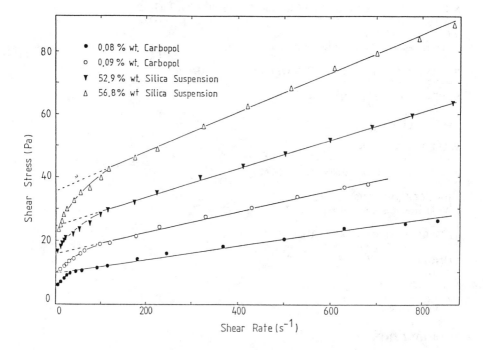

Figure 1. Plot of shear stress as a function of shear rate for two silica suspensions and two aqueous solutions of Carbopol (B.F. Goodrich) showing Bingham-like behavior at large shear rates ($> 40-120 \text{ s}^{-1}$). Extrapolated values of τ_0^B are clearly larger than the corresponding true yield stress values τ_y. The Bingham model parameters are included in Table 1.

where τ_0^B is the Bingham yield stress and μ_B is the plastic viscosity. A comparison of this model with typical experimental data for suspensions and a polymer solution is shown in Figure 1.

For a flow system characterized by the length d and the velocity v, a number of dimensionless groups result:

Reynolds number $Re_B = dv\rho/\mu_B$

Bingham number $Bi = \tau_0^B d/\mu_B v$

The Bingham number is also called the yield number and the plasticity number by some authors. Often a combination of these groups is used:

Hedstrom number $He = Re_B \, Bi = \tau_0^B d^2 \rho/\mu_B^2$

Other combinations are possible, with $Bi/Re_B = \tau_0^B/\rho v^2$ a particularly simple group. This group has also been termed plasticity number.

Casson Model

The Casson model is another two-parameter model which, for a simple shear flow, is:

$$(\tau_{yx})^{1/2} = (\tau_0^C)^{1/2} + (\mu_C \dot\gamma_{yx})^{1/2} \qquad |\tau_{yx}| > \tau_0^C$$
$$\dot\gamma_{yx} = 0 \qquad\qquad\qquad\qquad\qquad |\tau_{yx}| \leqq \tau_0^C \tag{2}$$

The model parameters are the Casson yield stress, τ_0^C and a consistency parameter μ_C.

Experimental data for suspensions and for a polymer solution are compared with this model in Figure 2.

From this model, the dimensionless groups of Reynolds number and Casson number arise. The latter has the same form as the Bingham number, but contains instead the Casson parameters τ_0^C and μ_C.

Herschel-Bulkley Model

This is a generalization of the Bingham model in which the linear shear-rate dependence has been replaced by a power-law behavior. It is a three-parameter model, written for a simple shear flow as:

$$\tau_{yx} = \tau_0^H + m(\dot\gamma_{yx})^n \qquad |\tau_{yx}| > \tau_0^H$$
$$\dot\gamma_{yx} = 0 \qquad\qquad\qquad\qquad |\tau_{yx}| \leqq \tau_0^H \tag{3}$$

This model is more flexible than the two previous ones and generally fits experimental data over a somewhat wider range of conditions. A comparison with experimental data is shown in Figure 3.

Other empirical models containing a yield stress are available, and the relevant literature is referred to by Bird et al. [6].

Bird et al. list 214 references on the flow of viscoplastic liquids. Despite this voluminous literature, the question of whether or not a yield stress exists is far from settled. Thus Barnes and Walters [7] have argued, giving experimental evidence, that the yield stress hypothesis, which has hitherto been a useful empiricism, is no longer needed, and that no yield stress exists. On the other hand, the concept of yield stress is convenient in practice to describe the observed behavior of many materials. The resolution of the argument appears to lie in the choice of a time scale appropriate for the observations, as discussed recently by Cheng [8]. Houwink and de Decker [9] discuss the existence and

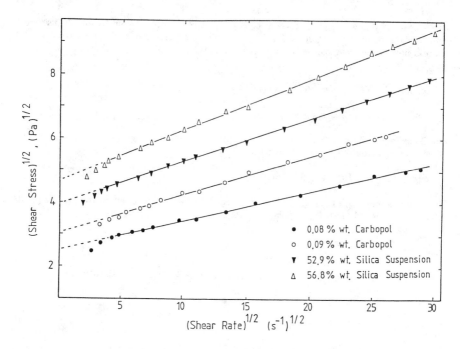

Figure 2. Casson plot, $\tau^{1/2}$ vs. $\dot{\gamma}^{1/2}$ for the two suspensions and two polymer solutions of Figure 1. The Casson model is seen to fail for these fluids at small values of shear rate ($\gamma < 20$ s^{-1}). This represents an improvement over the Bingham model. The Casson model parameters are included in Table 1.

magnitude of the yield stress in terms of material structure and of rate of deformation. They point out, like Barnes and Walters, that the greater the rate of deformation, the greater the yield stress observed.

An indication of the type of behavior on which Barnes and Walters base their arguments can be seen in virtually all flow curves of viscoplastic materials; it is evident in the results shown in Figures 1–3. As the shear rate is reduced, the viscoplastic model equations deviate increasingly from the experimental observations. Thus, not only do many different values of yield stress result for the different rheological models, but different values result for the same model depending on the range of shear rate of the data used. This behavior is typical where parameters are fitted by extrapolation. This ambiguity of yield stress is undoubtedly the cause of much confusion and disagreement among the reported results of various workers. An additional source of disagreement may arise from the method of measuring the yield stress. In the literature cited by Bird et al [6], there is a preponderance of studies using the Couette geometry. The results from this geometry require considerable manipulation, which is model-dependent, in order to extract the true model parameters [6, 10–15]. Yet few authors report whether or not the approrite corrections have been made. For example, the Reiner-Riwlin equation is required if the Bingham model is to be fitted to Couette data. The Reiner-Riwlin equation is [6]:

$$\omega = \frac{T}{4\pi L \mu_B R_2^2}[(R_2/R_1)^2 - 1] + \frac{\tau_0^B}{\mu_B}\ln(R_1/R_2) \qquad (4)$$

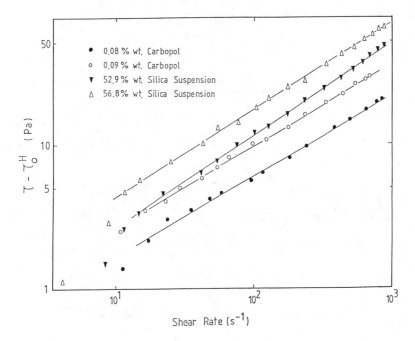

Figure 3. Herschel-Bulkley plot, $\tau - \tau_0^H$ vs. $\dot{\gamma}$ for the two suspensions and polymer solutions of Figure 1. This model is seen to fail for these fluids for small values of shear rate, $\dot{\gamma} < 20 \text{ s}^{-1}$. The Herschel-Bulkley model parameters are included in Table 1.

where ω is the angular speed, T is the measured torque, and R_1 and R_2 are the inner and outer cylinder radii, respectively. This equation is conveniently rewritten as a "correction" factor to be applied to the "yield stress" τ' obtained by extrapolation from large values of apparent shear rate where the latter has been calculated from the rotational speed using the Newtonian expression $2\omega/[1 - (R_1/R_2)^2]$. This expression for the shear rate is the one recommended for general use in many instrument instruction manuals. The correction factor is:

$$\tau'/\tau_0^B = [1 - (R_1/R_2)^2]/2 \ln(R_2/R_1) \tag{5}$$

For most commercial instruments, the ratio of radii is sufficiently close to unity ($R_2/R_1 < 1.4$) for the correction factor to closely approximate R_1/R_2 (within 0.3% for $R_2/R_1 < 1.4$). Thus, if Bingham behavior is assumed, the Bingham yield stress can be obtained from concentric cylinder instrument output using Newtonian calibration and scale factors and the simple multiplier R_1/R_2. The derivation of Equation 5 has been given by Traynis [16].

Figure 4 shows the shear stress-shear rate behavior of a hypothetical Bingham fluid together with the flow curve that would be obtained for this fluid from a concentric-cylinder instrument if the shear rate were calculated using the Newtonian expression. The shape of the instrument curve is discussed by van Wazer et al. [10]. Thus it is not clear, for much published data, whether curvature of the rheogram is due to an instrument artifact or to the true behavior of the fluid.

Despite the many ambiguities that undoubtedly arise in the measurement of yield stress, the assertion of Barnes and Walters [7] that "... no one has ever measured a yield stress, they have only

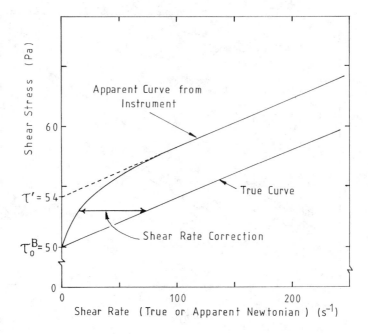

Figure 4. Shear stress-shear rate behavior of a hypothetical Bingham medium ($\tau_0^B = 50$ Pa, $\mu_B = 0.04$ Pa·s) compared with the shear stress-apparent shear rate curve obtained from a concentric-cylinder viscometer ($R_2/R_1 = 1.08$) using the Newtonian shear-rate expression.

extrapolated to it. In effect, yield stress only defines what cannot be measured . . ." appears to be an extreme position. A yield stress measured on a time scale comparable to that of the flow under study still appears to be a very useful empiricism. This is particularly true if the yield stress is measured by a "static" method rather than by extrapolation from a continuously deforming state to one of zero deformation rate. A number of static methods has been described, which are applicable to fluids, and which rely on gradually increasing the applied stress from zero until the yield point is reached [8, 17–24]. The relation between "static" and extrapolated values of yield stress has not yet been systematically investigated. However, agreement appears to be fair with extrapolation of the rheogram by curve-fitting the smallest values of shear rate [22–24]. The value determined in one of these ways—i.e., by a "static" method or by curve fitting low shear rate data—will be termed the "true" yield stress, τ_y, in order to differentiate it from the rheological model parameters τ_0. The two may, of course, be equal.

The model parameters obtained from Figures 1–3 for the two polymer solutions and the two silica suspensions are compared in Table 1. Included in the table are values of yield stress obtained by several "static" methods: vane torsion, stress relaxation, stability on an inclined plane [21–23]. The difficulty of ascribing a value to the yield stress becomes apparent from this table. The difficulty is compounded by the fact that yield stress of real materials is often also a highly time-dependent property [19, 25].

BEHAVIOR OF SPHERES IN VISCOPLASTIC LIQUIDS

There have been relatively few reported studies on the equilibrium and motion of spheres in viscoplastic materials. Table 2 provides a brief summary of available work on this subject. The table

Table 1
Comparison of Yield Stress Determination for Two Polymer Solutions
and for Two Silica Suspensions*

| System of Measurement | Method | Yield Stress (Nm^{-2}) | | | |
| | | Carbopol | | Silica Suspension | |
		0.08 wt%	0.09 wt%	52.9 wt%	56.8 wt%
Haake rotational viscometer	Extrapolation of flow curve (small shear rate)	2.6	6.5	13.1	18.8
	Bingham model	15.0	18.8	26.5	48.9
	Herschel-Bulkley model	4.2	8.8	17.5	20.0
	Casson model	4.8	9.0	16.9	25.0
	Stress relaxation [21]	2.4	5.8	12.7	13.2
	Vane torsion [22]	4.0	6.2	17.5	21.8
Steady flow on plane	Extrapolation of Flow Curve (small shear rate)	2.0	5.8	12.5	
	Bingham Model (small shear rate)	2.0	5.9	12.5	
Stability on Plane [23]		2.0	5.4	11.5	14.3

* *Data from K. H. Park, Ph.D. Thesis, Monash University, Melbourne (1986).*

shows that most effort has been expended on three aspects of sphere behavior:

1. Static equilibrium, and the establishment of a criterion for the initiation of motion under gravity.
2. Qualitative flow visualization studies, attempting to delineate the region of flow.
3. Drag measurements, both in towing tanks and at terminal conditions under gravity, to establish a drag coefficient-Reynolds number relation. Wall effects have been included in some of these studies.

When the behavior of spheres under gravity is studied, an additional dimensionless group can be defined, and this has been done in various ways by different authors. When all arbitrary constants are omitted, the simplest form is a Gravity-Yield group $Y_G = \tau_y/gd(\rho_s - \rho)$. The drag coefficient is defined in the usual way $C_D = 8F_D/\rho\pi v^2 d^2$ which, for steady motion under gravity, reduces to $C_D = 4gd(\rho_s - \rho)/3v^2\rho$. These above two groups may also be combined in the form $Y_G C_D$, which is the same as the combination Bi/Re_B when $\tau_y = \tau_0^B$.

STATIC EQUILIBRIUM

A viscoplastic medium in an unsheared state has the ability, by virtue of its yield stress, to support the weight of an embedded particle. This phenomenon has been utilized in recent years in the design of long-distance slurry pipelines [16, 26, 27]. The criterion for static equilibrium, the condition of incipient motion, has been studied by numerous workers as listed in Table 2 [16–18, 26–36].

Table 2
Summary of Investigations of Sphere Motion in Viscoplastic Media

Author(s)	Ref.	Nature of Work	Conditions	Main Results and Comments
Khomikovskii and Shilov (1946)	28	Experimental	Clay suspensions	Static stability of sand in clay suspensions —recognized a maximum (critical) diameter of grains remaining in suspension; critical diameter increased 10–30 fold with 2–4 fold increase in yield stress.
Tyabin 1949, 1952, 1953	38	Theoretical	Bingham	Integration of equations of viscoplastic motion about a sphere, with simplifying assumptions. The resulting velocity distribution for a viscoplastic medium is the same as that obtained for a viscous medium.
Volarovich and Gutkin (1953) (reply by Tyabin 1953)	37 38	Theoretical	Bingham	First to recognize that the region of flow of the medium due to motion of the sphere is bounded. Beyond this region, shear is not transmitted and only a zone of elastic deformation exists. The boundary is a surface of revolution and moves together with the sphere.
Andres (1960)	29	Experimental	Bingham $0 < \tau_0^B < 4$ Pa	Proposed a stability criterion for a sphere and measured/correlated settling velocity.
Boardman and Whitmore (1960–62)	17 18 40	Experimental	Clay suspensions, $\tau_0^B \sim 4$ Pa	Attempted static measurement of yield stress using immersed bodies, including a sphere, which gave a value "roughly equal to the extrapolated flow-curve value." Other bodies did not; vertical surfaces gave about half, horizontal surfaces about twice the extrapolated value. Verified the applicability of Archimedes principle in the case of viscoplastic media.
Rae (1962)	40			Suggested that bodies immersed in flowing viscoplastic media have solid medium attached to them, so that the yield stress does not act over the body surface but over a much larger surface.
Bulina et al. (1964)	41	Experimental	Clay suspension, Bingham	Experimentally observed a stagnant region of viscoplastic medium at the front of blunt 2-dimensional bodies towed through stationary medium.

Reference	No.	Type	Material / conditions	Description
Valentik and Whitmore (1965)	42	Experimental	Clay suspensions, Bingham, $7.8 < \tau_0^B < 59$ Pa.	in creating sphere fall velocity, postulated a concentric sphere of *unsheared* medium moving with the particle. The diameter of this shell of unsheared medium was obtained by forcing the terminal velocity onto the Newtonian drag curve.
du Plessis and Ansley (1967)	46	Experimental	Kaolin suspensions $1 < \tau_0^B < 3.4$ Pa.	Correlated the drag coefficient of spheres and of sand grains in terms of a combination of Bi and $\mathrm{Re_B}$. Virtually all the results are for $\mathrm{Re_B} \gg 1$.
Ansley and Smith (1967)	30	Experimental	Tomato sauce, $\tau_y = 29$ Pa; clay suspensions, $2 < \mathrm{Re_B} < 130$	Correlated the drag coefficient of spheres with a "dynamic parameter" $\mathrm{Re_B}/(1 + K\,\mathrm{Bi})$ where K was argued to be $7\pi/24$. Postulated the existence of an envelope of sheared medium of toroidal shape and of diameter $\sqrt{2}$ times the sphere diameter. Postulated a criterion for static equilibrium, giving limited experimental support.
Brookes and Whitemore (1968, 1969) Whitmore (1969)	31 44 43	Experimental	Clay suspensions, $16 < \tau_y < 59$ Pa	Measured the residual force on bodies immersed in flowing viscoplastic medium when the flow was stopped. Hence proposed a correlation for static equilibrium. Measured the drag force on spheres in slowly moving viscoplastic media and attempted to correlate their results in terms of an effective viscosity that forces the points to fall on the Newtonian curve. Using flow visualisation, found small stagnant regions at the front and rear of two-dimensional bodies. Cast doubt on the postulate of Valentik and Whitmore [42].
Ito and Kajiuchi (1969)	47	Experimental	Clay suspension, Bingham $0.47 \leq \tau_0^B \leq 2.83$ Pa	Correlated the results of sphere fall tests in terms of a modified Reynolds number, obtained by forcing the results onto the Newtonian drag curve.
Traynis (1970) (English translation 1977)	16	Experimental	Coal suspensions, Bingham.	Postulates an expression for static equilibrium under gravity and claims experimental confirmation but gives no details.
Yoshioka et al. (1971) Adachi and Yoshioka (1973)	35	Theoretical	Bingham	Used variational principles to predict upper and lower bounds on the drag coefficient in creeping motion of a sphere (and of a cylinder) through a Bingham medium of infinite extent. Also showed the sheared zone surrounding the sphere and two small stagnant regions attached to the front and rear of the sphere. First to show up the large discrepancies among published results. Their own bounds agree best with Ansley with Smith [30].

(continued)

Table 2 (continued)

Summary of Investigations of Sphere Motion in Viscoplastic Media

Author(s)	Ref.	Nature of Work	Conditions	Main Results and Comments
Pazwash and Robertson (1971 and 1975)	48 49	Experimental	Clay suspensions, Bingham	Measured the drag force on spheres and discs immersed in a viscoplastic medium in a rotating ring channel. Correlated the deviation of the drag coefficient from the Newtonian value (at Re_B) in terms of He and Re_B in terms of He/Re_B^2, i.e. Bi/Re_B.
Thomas (1977)	26	Discussion	Coal suspensions	Discusses the static equilibrium criterion and the influence of the measure of yield stress used—i.e. static vs. extrapolated; discusses the relation between these measures of yield stress. Discusses the relevance of Archimedes principle.
Wan (1982, 1985)	33 34	Experimental	Bentonite, kaolin suspensions, Bingham.	Allowed plastic beads and sand to be carried up by, or to settle through a uniform upward flow of viscoplastic medium. Correlated the drag coefficient following Ansley and Smith [30]. Experimentally investigated the static equilibrium condition and compared with the criterion of Ansley and Smith.
Hanks and Sen (1983)	50	Experimental	Laponite suspension Herschel-Bulkley; $0.04 \leqq \tau_0^H \leqq 4.5$ Pa $0.57 < n < 0.85$	Measured the terminal settling velocity of spheres and extended the correlation technique of Ansley and Smith [30] to Herschel-Bulkley media, by generalising the Reynolds and Hedstrom numbers.
Beris et al. (1985)	36	Theoretical	Bingham	Finite element solution for creeping motion of a sphere through a Bingham medium of infinite extent. Present velocity distribution, shape and dimensions of sheared zone and of unsheared solid caps as functions of the gravity-yield group Y_G. Also give the static equilibrium criterion in terms of Y_G, by extrapolation. Compare their drag predictions with those of Yoshisha et al [35] and with the experiments of Ansley and Smith [30].
Uhlherr (1986)	32	Experimental	Carbopol solutions $7.3 < \tau_y < 73$ Pa.	Measured the static equilibrium condition using simple pendulum and correlated with static yield stress.
Atapattu et al. (1986)	51	Experimental	Carbopol solutions $3.3 \leqq \tau_y \leqq 25.2$ Pa	Measured the wall effect for creeping motion of spheres under gravity and correlated the wall factor with the gravity-yield group Y_G (based on static yield stress).

In a simple intuitive approach [29, 32] it has been assumed that the buoyant weight of the sphere $\pi d^3(\rho_s - \rho)g/6$ is carried by the vertical component of the yield stress acting over the sphere surface $\pi^2 d^2 \tau_y/4$. This results in the criterion for incipient motion $Y_G = 0.212$. Several authors [18, 30] have recognized that, once motion of spheres ceases, neither the normal nor the shear stress distributions are known over the surface. Pressure may not be hydrostatic and so the buoyant weight of the sphere may not be relevant; the shear stress acting on the sphere surface may not be everywhere the yield stress. However, the results of experiments and of numerical solutions may still be expressed in terms of the gravity-yield number Y_G, which appears to take a critical value for incipient motion. Critical values from the literature are summarized in Table 3.

This table shows a variation in Y_G among different investigators of more than five to one. One contributing factor to this large variation is undoubtedly the uncertainty in the values of yield stress used. However, careful examination of the table indicates that the results fall into two groups. One group, with $Y_G \sim 0.04 - 0.08$, contains the numerical solutions of the equations of motion, those experiments using the observation of motion/no motion in free fall, and the measurement of residual force after cessation of motion of the fluid. The second group, with $Y_G \sim 0.2$, consists of the original postulate of Andres [29] and measurements of static equilibrium of a tethered spheres in a medium which has not been sheared. The similarity of the methods used by Boardman and Whitmore [18] and by Uhlherr [32] and the similarity of their results, together with the large difference between these results and those of all other workers, may indicate a fundamental difference in the processes, which has not been accounted for. Clearly more work is required in this area to establish a reliable criterion for equilibrium.

FLOW FIELD

Volarovich and Gutkin [37] in discussion with Tyabin [38] appear to be the first to have recognized the existence of a restricted zone of flow for the motion of a sphere in a viscoplastic medium. They state, "The solution is complicated by the difficulty in finding the boundaries of the region within which flow of the medium due to motion of the sphere occurs. Beyond the limits of this region, shear is not transmitted and only a zone of elastic deformation exists. This boundary, in any event, is a surface of rotation and moves together with the sphere." Volarovich and Gutkin go further, and state that a first approximation may be reached by "... showing the differential equation of motion for a viscous liquid, taking into account that the flow takes place within a certain region ..." Such an approach has been used for a number of flow problems, not including the sphere, by Lipscomb and Denn [39]. Rae [40] has recognized that, within the region of plastic deformation surrounding a body, there will be quantities of unsheared, i.e., solid medium adhering to certain parts of the body, and that the yield stress does not necessarily act over the body surface but rather over a larger surface consisting of body and the unsheared medium. Bulina et al. [41] have experimentally observed unsheared medium at the front of blunt bodies and moving with the bodies. Whitmore and Boardman, in response to Rae [40], have stated that flow visualization experiments indicate that though a rapid decay in the rate of shearing occurs near the body, no sharp envelope is detected.

The first to take into account a region of solid medium surrounding a moving sphere were Valentik and Whitmore [42]. They postulated the existence of a spherical shell of medium, concentric with the moving sphere and accompanying the sphere. On this basis, they correlated their results. It was subsequently shown by Whitmore [43] and Brookes and Whitmore [44] that this simple model is unrealistic—in some cases the required diameter of the spherical shell exceeded the container diameter in which the experiments were carried out. The model of Valentik and Whitmore leads to a ratio of diameters for the unsheared zone to that of the sphere, of 1.0–1.8 [42] and 8.2–85 [44]. Certainly the predicted dimensions of the shell far exceeded all experimentally-observed dimensions [43].

A more realistic model was postulated by Ansley and Smith [30] based on slip-line theory of solid mechanics. These authors give the clearest statement of sphere motion since that of Volarovich and Gutkin quoted above: "The stress distribution imposed on the plastic material by the motive force on the sphere causes the material to become fluid in an envelope surrounding the sphere. Within the

Table 3

Critical (Upper) Values of the Gravity-Yield Group Y_G for Incipient Motion of a Sphere Under Gravity

Investigator(s)	Ref.	$Y_{G\,max}$ for Motion	Technique	Comments
Andres [1960]	29	0.212	Postulate, τ_0^B	Reports Russian experiments with $Y_{G\,max} = 0.056 - 0.591$
Boardman, Whitemore [1961]	18	0.20	Expt'l. τ_0^B	Spheres which would normally sink, suspended from a cantilever beam in a clay suspension.
Ansley, Smith [1967]	30	~0.068–0.084	Postulate and Expt'l. τ_0^B	Model based on slip-line theory. Observation of motion/no motion in tomato sauce (catsup).
Brookes, Whitmore [1968]	31	0.040	Expt'l. τ_0^B	Direct residual *horizontal* force measurement on stopping the horizontal flow of china clay suspensions. τ_y was observed to be 0.21–0.27 times τ_0^B, from residual stress measurement. Y_G was calculated by equating the residual drag force to the buoyant weight.
Traynis [1977]	16	0.083–0.100 for coal particles. 0.167 for spheres	Postulate and experimental, τ_0^B	No experimental details or results given; states that the postulate has been verified by experiment.
Wan [1982, 1985]	33, 34	0.067 0.056	Postulate Expt'l. τ_0^B	Based on the work of Ansley and Smith [30] Motion/no motion in bentonite suspension by varying concentration.
Beris et al. [1985]	36	0.048	Finite element numerical τ_0^B	Extrapolation of numerical results.
Uhlherr [1986]	32	0.181–0.206	Expt'l. τ_y	Equilibrium of a simple pendulum in carbopol solution.
Atapattu et al. [1986]	51	>0.086	Expt'l. τ_y	Observation of motion under gravity in carbopol solution.

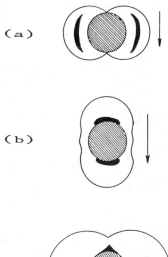

(a)

(b)

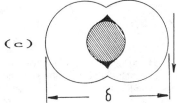

(c)

Figure 5. Shape of the sheared envelope around a sphere in creeping motion through a Bingham medium: (a) postulated by Ansley and Smith [30] on the basis of slip-line theory; (b) calculated by Yoshioka et al. [35] using a variational principle and a trial stress function; (c) calculated by Beris et al. [36] using a finite element technique.

envelope, the motions of the sphere and the displaced fluid are steady as the sphere—envelope system moves through the plastic material causing instantaneous, localized transformation between the plastic and fluid states." The shape of the yield envelope arrived at by Ansley and Smith is "a kind of truncated toroid with its section centred on the surface of the sphere and having diameter $d\sqrt{2}$." The shape of the envelope is shown in Figure 5. Whitmore [43] states that although his visualization technique could not be applied to spheres, none of his experiments showed any "obvious signs of a truncated toroid type of envelope" being present. Whitmore also makes the observation that "a general region of shear or creep appeared to be present," but this was very poorly delineated at its outer edge. This observation is not surprising as the velocity inside the envelope can be expected to approach zero gradually as the outer boundary is approached, and it is zero at and beyond the boundary, which may therefore be quite obscure. This behavior is shown by the velocity profiles calculated numerically by Beris et al. [36], particularly for small values of the gravity-yield group.

The problem of creeping motion of a sphere in a Bingham fluid has been solved numerically using variational principles by Yoshioka et al. [35], and using a finite element technique by Beris et al. [36]. Adachi and Yoshioka have also given a parallel solution for the cylinder [35].

The fluid envelope calculated by Yoshioka et al. from a maximum principle with a trial stress function is shown in Figure 5. Agreement with the postulate of Ansley and Smith is seen to be quite poor. Two small regions of unsheared (solid) medium are seen to be present at the front and rear stagnation points. Bounds on the frontal diameter of the fluid envelope, made dimensionless with respect to the sphere diameter, have been given by Yoshioka et al. as a function of the Bingham number. Their results can be recalculated in terms of the gravity-yield number, as shown in Figure 6.

The finite element solution for creeping sphere motion through a Bingham plastic given by Beris et al. is the most exhaustive study to date. Beris et al. give the shape of the fluid envelope as shown in Figure 5. This is surprisingly close to the shape postulated by Ansley and Smith, and is in relatively poor agreement with the predictions of Yoshioka et al. The frontal diameter ratio obtained by Beris et al. is included in Figure 6 as a function of gravity-yield group. Agreement between the results of Beris et al. and the upper bound (based on a minimum principle and trial velocity function)

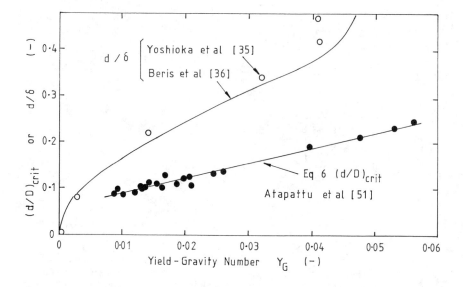

Figure 6. Critical diameter ratio for existence of a wall effect as a function of yield-gravity group Y_G [51]. The ratio of the sphere diameter over the maximum frontal diameter of the sheared zone, as calculated by Yoshioka et al. [35] and by Beris et al. [36] is also shown. This ratio is seen to be about twice the critical sphere/container diameter ratio over a substantial range of Y_G.

of Yoshioka et al. is seen to be quite good. This agreement may be fortuitous, in view of the assumption made by Yoshioka et al. in applying the minimum principle—the envelope was assumed to be ellipsoidal. Beris et al. also give radial profiles of azimuthal velocity at the equator, and these are reproduced in Figure 7. The distributions are seen to be very similar to those observed with shear-thinning power law fluids as presented by Crochet et al. [45], except that the dimensionless velocity does not approach unity asymptotically but rather reaches this value at finite radial distances, depending on the group Y_G. The shape of these curves indicates that visualization experiments are likely to fail in showing the shape of the fluid envelope surrounding a sphere except, perhaps, at large values of Y_G, close to the limit of motion.

Beris et al. also show the dimensions and shape of the solid caps at the front and rear stagnation points of the sphere. Again, it is not surprising that these caps have not been observed experimentally, as they are quite small, except near the limit of motion, extending outwards by only ~ 0.1 sphere radius or less.

WALL EFFECTS

In the experimental determination of particle drag, the presence of container walls frequently complicates the interpretation of results. Of all papers in which drag measurements in viscoplastic fluids are presented [29, 30, 33, 34, 42, 44, 46–50], only two mention wall effects. Ito and Kajiuchi [47] carried out terminal velocity measurements in two tubes of different diameters and found the wall effect to be "negligible." Valentik and Whitmore [42] carried out their measurements in four tubes having different diameters, and obtained the true terminal velocity by extrapolation of the results to infinite tube diameter. They indicate difficulties in reproducibility, particularly for large values of diameter ratio d/D, and they state that "Newtonian-fluid corrections could be applied only

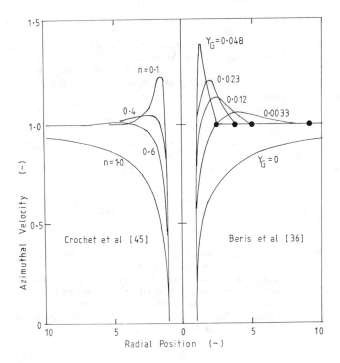

Figure 7. Numerically calculated velocity distributions for creeping motion of a sphere in power law fluids [45] and in Bingham media [36].

to spheres falling at high velocities in Bingham plastics." They presented no results and no correlation for wall effects in viscoplastic media.

Atapattu et al. [51] appear to be the first to have presented a limited but systematic study of the effect of cylindrical walls on the creeping terminal velocity of spheres in viscoplastic media. These authors found that, for a particular fluid-particle combination, the fall velocity was independent of container diameter until a critical value was reached. Beyond this value, the velocity decreased linearly, provided the motion was slow. This linear dependence of velocity on diameter ratio is similar to that observed with Newtonian and pseudoplastic fluids [52]. Atapattu et al. restricted their experiments to small values of Re_B so that creeping motion prevailed (to be discussed shortly), and the wall factor could be expected to be Reynolds number independent. Their results are also limited to relatively small values of diameter ratio, $d/D \leq 0.35$, because above this value spheres tended to fall increasingly off-center. Similar behavior has been observed in other non-Newtonian fluids [5]. Atapattu et al found that, when a wall effect exists, the form of the wall factor is virtually the same as that observed for pseudoplastic fluids [52], the line being simply displaced along the d/D axis by an amount which is a function of the gravity-yield parameter Y_G. Thus, their correlation for wall factor $f = v_D/v$ is shown in Figure 6 and given by:

$$f = 1 \qquad\qquad\qquad d/D < (d/D)_{crit}$$

$$f = 1 - 1.7[d/D - (d/D)_{crit}] \qquad d/D > (d/D)_{crit} \qquad\qquad (6)$$

$$(d/D)_{crit} = 0.056 + 3.32Y_G \qquad 0.0091 \leq Y_G \leq 0.053$$

This correlation is based on the true yield stress τ_y, and was obtained with a number of aqueous Carbopol (B. F. Goodrich) solutions having $3.3 \leq \tau_y \leq 25.2$ Pa.

The critical container diameter appears to be about twice the maximum diameter of the sheared zone surrounding the sphere, as calculated by Yoshioka et al. [35] and by Beris et al. [36], also shown in Figure 6. Thus the stress generated in the medium by the moving sphere is propagated a relatively small distance beyond the sheared fluid zone, as would be expected for an elastic solid. If the unsheared viscoplastic medium were a rigid solid, the critical container diameter would be expected to be equal to the size of the sheared fluid zone. However, this size would be somewhat larger than that predicted for a medium of infinite extent, owing to the backflow of medium which must occur in a bounded geometry and which can only pass through the sheared zone. Preliminary results of flow visualization by Atapattu [53] tend to corroborate this speculation.

Equation 6 may not hold well for other viscoplastic media because the wall effect is expected to be a function of the elastic properties of the solid medium, and this is not included in the correlation.

THE LIMIT OF CREEPING MOTION

In the absence of wall effects, the drag coefficient of a sphere in a Bingham (or in a Casson) fluid is a function of two dimensionless groups: a Reynolds number and the Bingham (or Casson) number, or some combination of these, such as the Hedstrom number. Only a few authors have presented drag data in this form. Thus Brookes and Whitmore [44] give $C_D(Re_B, d)$ for three values of d, but fail to non-dimensionalize the sphere diameter. Pazwash and Robertson [48] present $C_D(Re_B, He)$ for three values of He in the range 920–3,600. Andres [29] has plotted $(Re_B/C_D)^{1/3}$ vs. $(C_D\,Re_B^2)^{1/3}$ for 27 values of He in the range 1–27. Finally, Ansley and Smith [30] give the most comprehensive plot, using $C_D(Re_B, Bi)$. They group their data into 5 ranges of Bi, i.e., 0–5, 5–10, 10–20, 20–100, > 100.

It is not known to what value of Re_B the creeping motion assumption is experimentally satisfied for any value of Bi (or He). For the Newtonian case, $Bi = He = 0$, creeping motion is usually assumed to be satisfied up to Re in the range 0.1–1. It will be assumed here that behavior of the form $C_D\,Re_B = k_1 f_1(Bi)$ can be interpreted as creeping motion; alternatively, this condition corresponds to $C_D\,Re_B^2 = k_2 f_2(He)$. Thus, on a log-log plot of C_D vs. Re_B, a slope less steep than -1 (or -2) implies results beyond the creeping motion regime. The results of Andres, of Brookes and Whitmore, and of Pazwash and Robertson (in terms of He) all reach slopes of -1.6 to -1.8 but not -2. It must be concluded that all these results lie beyond the creeping motion regime. The results of Ansley and Smith, on the other hand, reach a slope of -1 and a considerable number of data points lie in the creeping motion regime. Their results show a very rapid increase in the limiting value of Re_B for creeping motion as Bi increases only slightly from zero. Their results can be very crudely represented by an expression of the form $Re_{B\ limit} \sim 100\ Bi^{0.4}$, based on the mean value for each of the ranges of Bi presented. $Re_{B\ limit}$ is the upper limit for creeping motion.

Beris et al. [36] also observe a very rapid reduction in C_D to the Newtonian value when the gravity-yield parameter Y_G becomes extremely small. It appears that sphere drag is extremely sensitive to very small values of yield stress. This makes it very difficult to extrapolate experimental results in viscoplastic media to the Newtonian case with any accuracy. Conversely, it is difficult to include accurately the Newtonian result as a limit in viscoplastic correlations. This is borne out by most experimental results published so far.

DRAG CORRELATIONS

The cumbersome correlation of Andres [29] can be rewritten in the form:

$$C_D\,Re_B^{1.8} = 10^{(12.26 - 0.78\ He)} \qquad 1 \leq He \leq 27 \tag{7}$$

Andres made no attempt to include Newtonian behavior in his correlation. Subsequent workers have attempted to correlate their results in terms of the Newtonian $C_D(Re)$ behavior. Valentik and Whitmore [42] and later Brooks and Whitmore [44] used the Newtonian drag curve to determine the size of a hypothetical sphere over which the uniform yield stress would generate the observed drag. Thus, they present no predictive equation for sphere drag. More recent authors have used one of two approaches: either to modify the Reynolds number [30, 33, 34, 46, 47, 50]; or to modify the drag coefficient [48, 49]. In either case, the aim is to force the sphere drag curve for viscoplastic media to coincide with that for Newtonian fluids.

Pazwash and Robertson [48, 49] correlate their results (with $920 \leq He \leq 3,600$; $60 < Re_B < 2,000$) in the form of $C_D - C_D^B = 36\, He/Re_B^2$, where C_D^B is the drag coefficient taken from the Newtonian curve at Re_B. They point out that, for small Re_B, $C_D^B \propto 1/Re_B \ll He/Re_B^2$ and so $C_D \sim 36\, He/Re_B^2$. On the other hand, for large Re_B, $C_D \sim C_D^B$. The correlation of Pazwash and Robertson is shown in Figure 8 with their own data, the data of Valentik and Whitmore [42] and of Ansley and Smith [30].

Ito and Kajiuchi [47] give a graphical correlation in the form $Bi = f(Re_B/Re - 1)$ which must be used to obtain Re, which in turn is used to enter the Newtonian curve $C_D = C_D(Re)$ to obtain C_D.

The simple analysis of du Plessis and Ansley [46], who postulated that the drag in a viscoplastic medium consists of Stokes drag plus the yield stress acting over the sphere surface, led them to correlate the drag coefficient in terms of the grouping $(He + Re_B)/Re_B^2$. This grouping is more simply written as $(1 + Bi)/Re_B$. For spheres they propose $C_D = 5.0[(Bi + 1)/Re_B]^{0.49}$. If $Bi \to 0$, $C_D \to 5/Re^{0.49}$ and so this correlation does not approach the Newtonian result. Their work, however, laid the foundation for the model of Ansley and Smith [30] who postulated the correlating

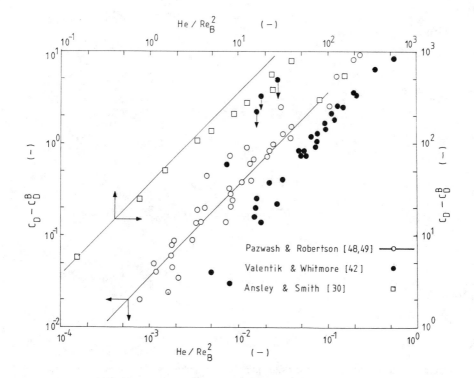

Figure 8. Results from the literature plotted according to the method of Pazwash and Robertson [48, 49].

group $Re_B/(1 + KBi)$, where K was a constant to be determined. Ansley and Smith used slip-line theory to postulate a toroidal sheared envelope around the sphere and hence to find $K = 7\pi/24 = 0.92$. This does not differ greatly from the value of 1.0 used (arbitrarily) by du Plessis and Ansley.

The result presented by Ansley and Smith can be described by:

$$C_D = 34(1 + 7\pi\,Bi/24)/Re_B \tag{8}$$

for values of the dynamic parameter $Re_B/(1 + KB_i)$ smaller than 20; and

$$C_D = 0.4 \tag{9}$$

for values of the dynamic parameter larger than 200. These expressions are not quite additive in the intermediate range not covered by either. Clearly, for the Newtonian case with $(1 + 7\pi\,Bi/24)/Re_B \rightarrow 1/Re$, neither of these expressions agrees well with the Newtonian drag coefficient. The results of Ansley and Smith have been criticized for this shortcoming [50].

Equation 8 is fitted to the majority of the points; there are, however, five points with dynamic parameters smaller than 0.3, which deviate increasingly from equation 8 and which approach the required Stokes line, $C_D = 24(1 + 7\pi\,Bi/24)/Re_B$. The trend of these few points is confirmed by results obtained by Atapattu [53], who has thirty measurements for values of dynamic parameter in

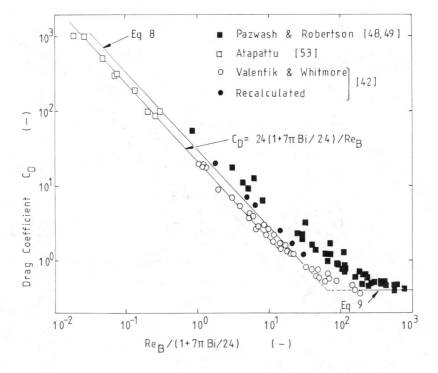

Figure 9. Results from the literature plotted according to the method of Ansley and Smith [30]. For some of the data, the Bingham parameters have been recalculated by Atapattu [53] using the method of Ansley and Smith.

the range $4 \times 10^{-5} - 3 \times 10^{-1}$. Furthermore, Atapattu has recalculated some of the results from the literature as shown in Figure 9. The results of Pazwash and Robertson are seen to be in rather poor agreement with the correlation of Ansley and Smith. The results of Valentik and Whitmore, although in relatively poor agreement with the correlation, agree well with the expected Stokes line up to a value of 20 for the dynamic parameter. If Valentik and Whitmore's results are recalculated by the procedure of Ansley and Smith (a discussion of how these authors obtained τ_0^B and μ_B follows), then agreement with the correlation is better. Clearly the values of the model parameters determine the agreement.

Hanks and Sen [50] have generalized the correlation of Ansley and Smith to account for power law dependence of shear stress on shear rate. They used the Herschel-Bulkley model (Equation 3) to redefine the dynamic parameter of Ansley and Smith. In terms of their generalized dynamic parameter, their results agree well with the Newtonian drag curve. However, their modified dynamic parameter does not approach Ansley and Smith's in the limit of Bingham behavior, an extraneous factor of four remaining. It therefore also does not approach the Reynolds number in the Newtonian limit. The agreement they show for small values of dynamic parameter is only apparent owing to a misplotting of the Newtonian drag curve. Their results for small values of dynamic parameter cross and fall below the expected Stokes line.

Yield Stress Used in Correlations

Much of the disagreement between authors can undoubtedly be ascribed to uncertainties in the values of yield stress used. The value of stress to which a rheogram is extrapolated at zero shear rate depends on the smallest shear rate reached by the measurements. The approximate minimum values of shear rate achieved by various workers are summarized in Table 4. If a flow curve is to be extrapolated, the lowest values of shear rate should at least overlap the processing shear rate. For a sphere moving through a fluid, the rate of deformation is of the order v/d, and this quantity generally takes values rather smaller than 100 s^{-1} and possibly as small as $2-3 \text{ s}^{-1}$.

Hence the fluid characterization of Ito and Kajiuchi [47] is likely to yield Bingham parameter values which have little relevance to the actual fluid properties encountered by their falling spheres.

Ansley and Smith [30] determined the yield stress of tomato catsup with a capillary rheometer and obtained values from 21 to 33 Pa for apparent wall shear rate $Q/2\pi R^3$ in the range 3 to 30 s^{-1}. They used an average value of 29 Pa. For those media where they observed yield-pseudoplastic behavior, they used the intercept and slope of a tangent to the flow curve at a point where $\dot{\gamma} = v/d$. This procedure generates *artificial* values of τ_0^B and μ_B even for simple pseudoplastic fluids having *no measurable true yield stress*. Thus the Ansley and Smith correlation may hold for simple pseudoplastic fluids having no yield stress. This possibility was tested by Atapattu [53] using some of the sphere-fall results of Chhabra [54] obtained with inelastic power-law polymer solutions. The Ansley and Smith dynamic parameter indeed correlated the results of Chhabra almost as well as it did results for media having a true yield stress.

Table 4
Lowest Shear Rate Reached by Various Investigators

Investigators	Ref.	Minimum shear rate (s^{-1})
Ansley and Smith	30	$3 < Q/2\pi R^3 < 40$
Valentik and Whitmore	42	150
du Plessis and Ansley	46	10
Ito and Kajiuchi	47	2000–2500
Pazwash and Robertson	48, 49	5
Hanks and Sen	50	50

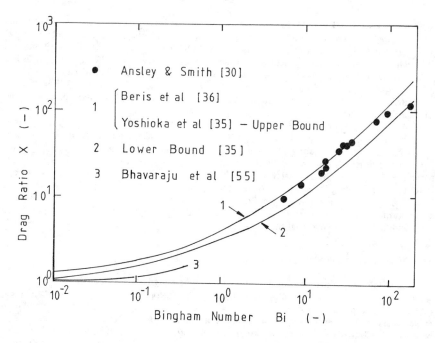

Figure 10. Plot of the drag ratio $X = C_D Re_B/24$ (or $C_D Re_B/16$ for a gas bubble) as a function of Bingham number calculated by Yoshioka et al. [35], Bhavaraju et al. [55] and Beris et al. [36]. Experimental results extracted from Figure 2 of Ansley and Smith [30] are also included.

THEORETICAL DRAG CALCULATIONS

Relatively few theoretical studies of sphere drag in viscoplastic media have been published. Since the early work of 1949, 1952 reported by Tyabin [38], who integrated the equations of viscoplastic flow about a sphere under simplifying assumptions, only three papers have appeared. The first, by Yoshioka et al. [35], gives upper and lower bounds on the drag coefficient in creeping motion as a function of the Bingham number. Their results, in terms of the drag coefficient ratio $X = C_D Re_B/24$, are shown in Figure 10.

A perturbation solution for a spherical gas bubble was given by Bhavaraju et al. [55] for $Bi \leqq 0.4$. They found that the drag coefficient ratio (for a bubble, $X = C_D Re_B/16$) is given by $(1 + 1.61\ Bi)$. This is included in Figure 10. Most recently, Beris et al. [36] have given a finite element analysis of the problem. Their results are included in Figure 10 and compare well with the earlier work of Yoshioka et al. [35]. Beris et al. [36] comment on the sensitivity of the drag coefficient to very small values of yield stress (in the form of the yield-gravity parameter Y_G). Their results are in good agreement with the experiments of Ansley and Smith [30] for small values of Re_B.

CONCLUSION

The drag coefficient of spheres in viscoplastic media is far from well established. Agreement among theoretical results is fair, the recent calculations of Beris et al. [36] being probably the most reliable.

All experimental work is beset by uncertainty in the values of yield stress used. This is probably the greatest source of disagreement among the various correlations proposed in the literature. The correlation of Ansley and Smith [30] appears to be the most extensive and reliable one to date.

Only one correlation is available for wall effect [51] and this must be treated with caution as it was obtained in media all having the same chemical nature.

The flow field about a sphere in creeping motion is available only from the calculations of Beris et al. No experimental confirmation is available yet.

The state of static equilibrium of a sphere suspended in a viscoplastic medium has not yet been clarified, there being two groups of discordant results.

Acknowledgment

The authors are grateful to the Harold Armstrong Memorial Fund and to the Monash University Special Research Fund for financial support.

NOTATION

Bi	Bingham number $\tau_0^B d/\mu_B v$	n	flow-behavior index—parameter of Herschel-Bulkley model
C_D	drag coefficient $8F_D/\rho\pi v^2 d^2$		
C_D^B	drag coefficient at a value of $Re = Re_B$ on the Newtonian drag curve.	Q	volumetric flowrate
		R	pipe radius
d	sphere diameter	R_1, R_2	radii of inner and of outer cylinders in rotating cylinder viscometer
D	container diameter		
$(d/D)_{crit}$	value of diameter ratio below which no wall effect is observed.	Re	Reynolds number for sphere in a Newtonian fluid
f	wall factor v_D/v	Re_B	Reynolds number for sphere in a Bingham medium $dv\rho/\mu_B$
f_1, f_2	function	$Re_{B\,limit}$	maximum value of Re_B for creeping motion
F_D	drag force		
g	acceleration due to gravity	T	torque
He	Hedstrom number	v	sphere velocity in an infinite medium
k_1, k_2	constants	v_D	sphere velocity in a container of diameter D
K	constant		
L	length of inner cylinder in concentric-cylinder viscometer	X	drag ratio $C_D Re/24$
		Y_G	gravity-yield parameter $\tau_y/gd(\rho_S - \rho)$
m	consistency parameter of Herschel-Bulkley model		

Greek Symbols

$\dot{\gamma}_{yx}$	shear rate dv_x/dy	τ_0^B	Bingham yield stress
δ	frontal diameter of sheared zone around a sphere	τ_0^C	Casson yield stress
		τ_0^H	Herschel-Bulkley yield stress
μ_B	plastic viscosity in Bingham model	τ'	intercept on the stress axis of the extrapolation of stress-apparent Newtonian shear rate line from a concentric-cylinder viscometer
μ_C	consistency parameter in Casson model		
ρ	density of medium		
ρ_S	density of sphere	ω	angular speed
τ_y	true yield stress		

REFERENCES

1. Happel, J., and Brenner, H., *Low Reynolds Number Hydrodynamics*, Prentice-Hall, Englewood Cliffs (1965).
2. Clift, R., Grace, J. R., and Weber, M. E., *Bubbles, Drops and Particles*, Academic Press, New York (1978).

3. Hetsroni, G. (ed.) *Handbook of Multiphase Systems*, McGraw-Hill, New York (1982).

4. Leal, L. G. "The motion of small particles in non-Newtonian fluids," *J. Non-Newt. Fluid Mech.*, 5, 33–78 (1979).

5. Chhabra, R. P. "Steady non-Newtonian flow about a rigid sphere," *Encyclopedia of Fluid Mech.* Vol. 1, N. P. Cheremisinoff (ed.), pp. 983–1033 (1986).

6. Bird, R. B., Dai, G. C., and Yarusso, B. J., "The rheology and flow of viscoplastic materials," *Rev. Chem. Eng.*, 1, 1–70 (1983).

7. Barnes, H. A., and Walters, K., "The yield stress myth?" *Rheol. Acta*, 24, 323–326 (1985).

8. Cheng, D. C-H. "Yield stress: a time-dependent property and how to measure it," *Rheol. Acta*, 25, 542–554 (1986).

9. Houwink, R., and de Decker H. K., *Elasticity, Plasticity and Structure of Matter*, 3rd Ed., Cambridge Univ. Press (1971), pp. 19–21.

10. Van Wazer, R. R., et al. *Viscosity and Flow measurement*, Interscience Publishers, New York (1963).

11. Yang, T. M. T., and Krieger I. M., "Comparison of methods for calculating shear rates in coaxial viscometers," *J. Rheol.*, 22, 413–421 (1978).

12. Hanks, R. W. "Couette viscometry of Casson fluids," *J. Rheol.*, 27, 1–6 (1983).

13. Darby, R. "Couette viscometer data reduction for materials with a yield stress," *J. Rheol.*, 29, 369–379 (1985).

14. MacSporran, W. C. "Direct numerical evaluation of shear rates in concentric cylinder viscometry," *J. Rheol.*, 30, 125–132 (1986).

15. Nguyen, Q. D., and Boger, D. V., "Characterization of yield stress fluids with concentric cylinder viscometers," *Rheol. Acta*, in press (1988).

16. Traynis, V. V. *Parameters and Flow Regimes for Hydraulic Transport of Coal by Pipelines*, Terraspace, Rockville, Md. (1977). (Originally published in Russian, 1970.)

17. Boardman, G., and Whitmore, R. L., "Yield stress exerted on a body immersed in a Bingham fluid," *Nature*, 187, 50–51 (1960).

18. Boardman, G., and Whitmore, R. L., "The static measurement of yield stress," *Lab. Practice*, 10, 782–785 (1961).

19. Cheng, D. C-H. "Measurement techniques for thixotropic properties," Brit. Ceramic Soc. Convention, York (1979).

20. DeKee, D., et al. "New method for the determination of yield stress," *J. Text. Studies*, 10, 281–288 (1980).

21. Keentok, M. "The measurement of the yield stress of liquids," *Rheol. Acta*, 21, 325–332 (1982).

22. Nguyen, Q. D., and Boger, D. V., "Yield stress measurement for concentrated suspensions." *J. Rheol.*, 27, 321–349 (1983).

23. Uhlherr, P. H. T., et al. "Yield stress from fluid behavior on an inclined plane," Proc. 9th Internat. Congr. Rheol., Acapulco, 183–190 (1984).

24. Nguyen, Q. D., and Boger, D. V., "Direct yield stress measurement with the vane method," *J. Rheol.*, 29, 335–347 (1985).

25. Nguyen, Q. D., and Uhlherr, P. H. T., "Thixotropic behaviour of concentrated red mud suspensions," Proc. Third Nat. Rheol. Conf., Melbourne, 63–68 (1983).

26. Thomas, A. D. "A rational design philosophy for long distance slurry pipelines," *Chem. Eng. Aust.*, Ch. 2, 22–33 (1977).

27. Duckworth, R. A., et al. "The pipeline transport of coarse materials in a non-Newtonian carrier fluid," Hydrotransport 10, paper C2 (1986).

28. Khomikovskii, P. M., and Shilov, D. I., "The suspending ability of clayey washing liquids used in drilling," *J. Appl. Chem.* (U.S.S.R.), 19, 684–92 (1946) (in Russian).

29. Andres, U. T. "Equilibrium and motion of spheres in a viscoplastic liquid," *Sov. Phys.— Doklady* (USA), 5, 723–726 (1961).

30. Ansley, R. W., and Smith, T. N., "Motion of spherical particles in a Bingham plastic," *AIChE J.*, 13, 1193–1196 (1967).

31. Brookes, G. F., and Whitmore, R. L., "The static drag on bodies in Bingham plastics," *Rheol. Acta*, 7, 188–193 (1968).

32. Uhlherr, P. H. T. "A novel method for measuring yield stress in static fluids," Proc. 4th Nat'l Conf. Rheol., Adelaide, 231–235 (1986).

33. Wan, Z. "Settling velocity of particles in a Bingham fluid," Inst. Hydrodyn. Hydraulic Engng., Tech. Univ. Denmark, Rep. 56, 3–11 (1982).

34. Wan, Z. Bed material movement in hyperconcentrated flow," *J. Hydraulic Engng.*, *111*, 987–1002 (1985).

35. Yoshioka, N., Adachi, K., and Ishimura, H., "On creeping flow of a visco-plastic fluid past a sphere," *Kagaku Kogaku*, *10*, 1144–1152 (1971) (in Japanese). See also Adachi, K., and Yoshioka, N., "On creeping flow of a visco-plastic fluid past a circular cylinder," *Chem. Eng. Sci.*, *28*, 215–226 (1973).

36. Beris, A. N., et al. "Creeping motion of a sphere through a Bingham plastic," *J. Fluid Mech.*, *158*, 219–244 (1985).

37. Volarovich, M. P., and Gutkin, A. M., "Theory of flow of a viscoplastic medium," *Colloid J. U.S.S.R.*, *15*, 153–159 (1953).

38. Tyabin, N. V. Some questions on the theory of viscoplastic flow of disperse systems, *Colloid J. U.S.S.R.*, *15*, 325–331 (1953) (and refs. 2, 3, 10 in this paper, not cited by the authors).

39. Lipscomb, G. G., and Denn, M. M., "Flow of Bingham fluids in complex geometries," *J. Non-Newtonian Fluid Mech.*, *14*, 337–346 (1984).

40. Rae, D. "Yield stress exerted on a body immersed in a Bingham fluid;" and response by R. L. Whitmore and G. Boardman, *Nature*, *194*, 272 (1962).

41. Bulina, I. G., Myasnikov, V. P., and Savin, V. G., "Experimental investigation of flow around blunted bodies by a flat flow of a plastic medium," *J. Appl. Mech. Tech. Phys.*, 203–211, May 1967; translated from *Zh. Prikel. Meth. Tekh. Fiz.* (U.S.S.R.) n5, 1–168 (1964).

42. Valentik, L., and Whitmore, R. L., "The terminal velocity of spheres in Bingham plastics," *Brit. J. Appl. Phys.*, *16*, 1197–1203 (1965).

43. Whitmore, R. L. "Drag forces in Bingham plastics," Proc. 5th Internat. Congr. Rheol., Tokyo, 353–360 (1969).

44. Brookes, G. F., and Whitmore, R. L., "Drag forces in Bingham plastics," *Rheol. Acta*, *8*, 472–480 (1969).

45. Crochet, M. J., Davies, A. R., and Walters, K., *Numerical Simulation of Non-Newtonian Flow*, Elsevier, Amsterdam, 252–257 (1984).

46. du Plessis, M. P., and Ansley, R. W., "Settling parameter in solids pipelining," *J. Pipeline Div.*, Proc. A.S.C.E., *93*, (PL2), 1–17 (1967).

47. Ito, S., and Kajiuchi, T., "Drag force on a sphere moving in plastic fluid," *J. Chem. Eng. Japan*, *2*, 19–24 (1969).

48. Pazwash, H., and Robertson, J. M., "Fluid dynamic consideration of bottom materials," *J. Hydraulics Div.*, Proc. A.S.C.E., *97* (HY9), 1317–1329 (1971).

49. Pazwash, H., and Robertson, J. M., "Forces on bodies in Bingham fluids," *J. Hydraulic Res.*, *13*, 35–55 (1975).

50. Hanks, R. W., and Sen, S., "The influence of yield stresses and fluid rheology on particle drag coefficients," Proc. 9th Internat. Tech. Conf. Slurry Trans., 71–80 (1983).

51. Atapattu, D. D., et al. "The effect of cylindrical boundaries for spheres falling in fluids having a yield stress," Proc. 9th Australasian Conf. Fluid Mech., Auckland, 584–587 (1986).

52. Chhabra, R. P., Tiu, C., and Uhlherr, P. H. T., "Wall effect for sphere motion in inelastic non-Newtonian fluids," Proc. 6th Australasian Conf. Hydraulics Fluid Mech., Adelaide, 435–438 (1977).

53. Atapattu, D. D. Unpublished work, Monash Uni., Melbourne.

54. Chhabra, R. P. "Non-Newtonian fluid-particle systems—sphere drag, Ph.D. Thesis, Monash Univ., Melbourne, 1980.

55. Bhavaraju, S. M., Mashelkar, R. A., and Blanch, H. W., "Bubble motion and mass transfer in non-Newtonian fluids," *AIChE J.*, *24*, 1063–1070 (1978).

CHAPTER 22

EFFECTS OF LONG CHAIN BRANCHING ON POLYMER RHEOLOGY

B. H. Bersted

Amoco Chemicals Company
Naperville, Illinois, USA

CONTENTS

INTRODUCTION

The introduction of branching into polymers can occur either unintentionally, as in high pressure polyethylene or impurities in the monomeric components; or intentionally, as in copolymerization with the introduction of monomers having functionalities greater than two. In general, the rheological behavior for these branched materials of low molecular weight is unremarkable [1], in that the rather minor differences in flow behavior between the branched and linear materials are readily accounted for on the basis of the differing structures. However, when the lengths of the branches exceed a critical molecular weight, the rheological properties can change dramatically [2]. It is these materials, having branches longer than the critical entanglement molecular weight, that are generally referred to as long chain branched polymers. In this chapter, long chain branching will be simply referred to as branching.

Complex behavior can result from the presence of branching. The melt viscosity can be either higher or lower than that of a linear comparator [3–6]. Additionally, the introduction of branching can result in thermorheologically complex behavior, in which the normal shift of rheological measurements with temperature through time-temperature superposition no longer applies [4, 7–9]. Further complications in the rheological behavior of branched polymers are the effects of reversible shear modification [10–15].

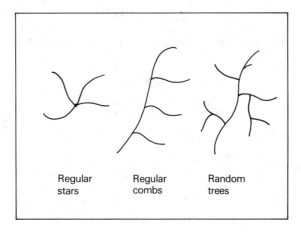

Regular
stars

Regular
combs

Random
trees

Figure 1. Schematic of possible branched structures.

The study of branched polymer systems is complicated by the variety of possible structures, as indicated in Figure 1, and the variation in distribution of molecular weights. Various methods of attempting to study the effect of molecular structure on the rheological behavior of branched polymers have been reported. These involve the study of very narrow molecular weight distribution, star and comb polymers having rather uniform structures [16–29], fractionation and subsequent determination of the structure of the fractions [5, 31, 32], and finally the modeling [33–35], structure determination, and correlation with the rheological behavior of broad MWD commercial polymers.

While most of the efforts to date are related to understanding the effects of branching on rheological behavior, the potential of rheological measurements as a structural tool to detect branching has been largely overlooked. It is the purpose of this chapter to present a review of the literature on the influence of branching on rheological behavior in high molecular weight polymers, with particular emphasis on recent advances in this important field for undiluted systems. The objective of this study will be to review recent advances in our understanding of simple branched model compounds, such as stars, and to advance in complexity to the more difficult to characterize materials, such as commercial randomly branched polymers, with particular emphasis on polyethylene.

OVERVIEW

In order to fully understand the flow behavior of branched polymers, the relationships of the rheological measurements to molecular structure must be examined. Berry and Fox [36] first noted that the viscosity for star molecules below the entanglement threshold molecular weight is similar in magnitude to linear chains of the same radius of gyration, $\bar{S}_0$. This supported the earlier suggestion by Fox & Allen that $\bar{S}_0^2$, the mean squared radius of gyration, be used in the description of melt viscosity. For linear polymers, $\bar{S}_0^2$ is proportional to the molecular weight, M, while in branched polymers:

$$g = (\bar{S}_0^2)_{\text{Br}}/(\bar{S}_0^2)_{\text{lin}} \tag{1}$$

or $(\bar{S}_0^2)_{\text{Br}} \alpha g M$

The branched polymers will have a smaller radius of gyration and intrinsic viscosity than a linear molecule of equivalent molecular weight. The parameter g can be estimated from the structure of the branched molecules by random flight calculations [37] or from solution viscosity as:

$$[\eta]_B/[\eta]_L = g^\alpha \tag{2}$$

where α is generally greater than or equal to 0.5 and less than 1.0. The theoretical expression for g in regular stars is:

$$g = (3f - 2)/f^2 \tag{3}$$

where f is the number of arms. Consequently, in the case of star molecules, knowledge of molecular weight and the number of arms should provide a description of rheological behavior. As the molecular weights increase well beyond the critical entanglement molecular weight, M_c, viscosity enhancement is often seen. In this case, the Newtonian viscosity can be characterized by:

$$\eta_{0(br)} = \eta_L(gM)\Gamma_1 \tag{4}$$

where Γ_1 is a viscosity enhancement factor. This enhancement has been accounted for rather naturally in terms of the reptation concept, where the branch point suppresses reptation along the chain length. Equations 3 and 4 suggest the possibility of either viscosity enhancement by increased intermolecular interaction (larger Γ_1) or a viscosity decrease (smaller $\eta_L(gM)$ relative to a linear sample of equivalent molecular weight), depending on the relative magnitudes of the two factors.

More complex structures, such as regular combs and H-shaped molecules, may also be described by these relationships with some adjustments. The case of regular combs introduces more complexity, in that in addition to the number of branches and the molecular weight of a branch, the backbone molecular weight must be considered.

Knowledge of the molecular structure of branched polydisperse polymers is absolutely necessary for understanding the rheological behavior of these materials. The introduction of branching into polymers either by means of copolymerization, using comonomers having functionalities greater than two in the case of condensation polymers; or random branching, as in the case of free radical processes, e.g., in polyethylene, generally leads to materials with incompletely characterized structures [38]. Because of their complexity, these materials cannot be precisely characterized as in the case of model compounds.

In attempting to establish structure property relationships of randomly branched systems, two approaches have been employed. In the first case, a "known" amount of random branching is introduced [39] to provide model compounds. However, without further characterization, assumptions regarding the distribution of branching in these complex materials is open to question. The other method of structure determination involves either the characterization of fractions [40] or whole polymer methods [33, 41] involving combinations of size exclusion chromatography and solution viscosity. These methods and the models resulting from them will be discussed later in the random branching section of this chapter. It will be shown that empirical models between the structural features and rheological behavior can be obtained for the randomly branched case.

As will be demonstrated later for the case of very low branching levels in polyethylene, impressive enhancement of the viscosity at low shear rates can be described by this concept.

RHEOLOGICAL BEHAVIOR OF MODEL COMPOUNDS

Theory

For linear polymers having molecular weights less than the critical molecular weight for entanglement, M_c, the Newtonian viscosity varies with the first power of the molecular weight. For branched

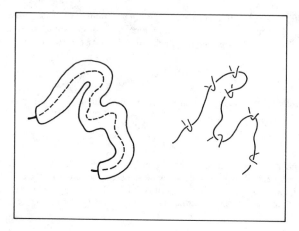

Figure 2. Schematic showing analogy of linear chain in network of fixed obstacles to confinement in a tube, as in the reptation description.

materials, the model of Ham [42] suggested that the viscosity should depend on a similar relationship, except the replacement of molecular weight by $\langle S^2 \rangle_0$, where at the same molecular weight, $\langle S^2 \rangle_0$ for the branched system will be less than that of a linear material.

The description of the differences in rheological behavior of branched and linear systems having molecular weights greater than M_c follows rather naturally from the concept of reptation. A schematic of a linear chain embedded in an entangled polymer melt is schematically represented in Figure 2, where the entanglements are envisioned as togological constraints resulting from the uncrossability of chains. Because of these entanglements, a given polymer chain cannot move, except in a hypothetical tube along its own contour by a process termed reptation [43]. As a result of this

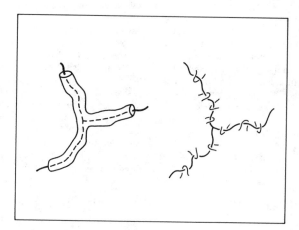

Figure 3. Schematic showing analogy of a branched chain in a network to the tube description in the reptation model.

suppression of movement of the molecule as a whole, one would expect to see enhanced viscosity in an entangled polymer relative to an unentangled system. This accounts for the well known transition of the dependence of the viscosity on the first power of molecular weight for molecular weight less than the critical molecular weight, M_c, to the 3.4 power of molecular weight above M_c.

A similar schematic for a branched molecule embedded in an entangled medium molecule is shown in Figure 3. It would seem intuitively reasonable that the presence of the branch point would effectively suppress reptation along the main chain. This suppression of reptation has in fact been calculated by Graessley [44] to lead to:

$$(n_0)_B/(n_0)_L = K_b exp(\phi M_a/M_e) \tag{5}$$

where K_b depends on the number of branches in the star
M_a = molecular weight of the arm
M_e = molecular weight between entanglements
and ϕ = a constant approximately equal to 1

Prediction of reptation theory for the recoverable compliance J_e^0 gives, for linear polymers [44]:

$$J_e^0 \alpha M^0 \tag{6}$$

where $G_N^0 \alpha M^0$. Predictions of reptation theory for branched systems gives a rather different dependence on molecular weight:

$$(J_e^0)_B = 1.06M/fRT \tag{7}$$

Similar results have been reported [2, 24] in the same form as:

$$J_e^0 = \tfrac{2}{5}(g_2M)RT \tag{8}$$

and $g_2 = (15f - 14)/(3f - 2)^2$

Like g, g_2 is unity for linear polymers and less than one for branched polymers.

J_e^0 is often defined in terms of a reduced compliance J_{cR}, where

$$J_{eR} = J_e^0 RT/M \tag{9}$$

Consequently, theory would predict J_{eR} for branched systems should be independent of molecular weight.

Stars

Stars represent the simplest branched case, in which only two degrees of freedom, the number of arms and molecular weight, are available. A conventional comparison of branched and linear zero-shear viscosities as a function of $\bar{M}_w$ for a polystyrene melt is given [16] in Figure 4. As can be seen, the branched samples show considerably lower viscosities than the linear polymer and the six arm stars show lower viscosities than the four arm stars. Also note the increased slope in the log η_0 vs. log $\bar{M}_w$ curve at higher molecular weights. Similar data for polyisoprene [2] is given in Figure 5. However, comparing the branched and linear viscosities [2] at $(gM)_w$ as in Figure 6 demonstrates that below a critical molecular weight, M_c, this adjustment for molecular size brings both the branched and linear polymers into register, while at higher molecular weights, viscosity enhancement is observed. Equation 5 suggests that the viscosity enhancement relative to the linear system should be compared as in Figure 7. While some differences between stars containing varying numbers of arms is noted, the exponential dependence on the molecular weight of the arm is suggested. Similar viscosity enhancement to that observed in both polystyrene and polyisoprene is shown [9] in Figure 8 for hydrogenated polybutadiene. The generality of viscosity enhancement

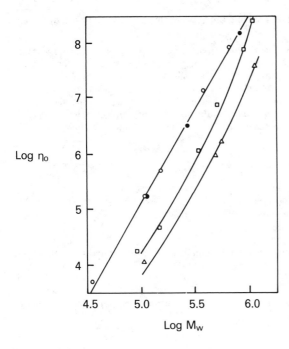

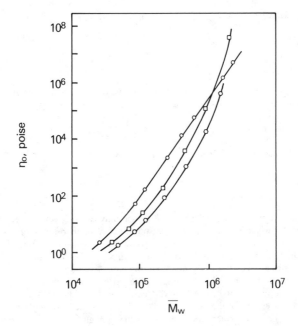

Figure 4. Zero-shear viscosity at 169.5°C vs. molecular, weight: circles, linear polymer; squares, four-arm stars; triangles, six-arm stars [16].

Figure 5. Zero-shear viscosity vs. molecular weight [2] for linear and star-branched polyisoprenes at similar concentrations. The concentrations for all samples are approximately 0.33 g/cm^3. Designations for linear, four-arm star, and six-arm star polymers are as follows: ○-Linear; □-Four-Arm Star; ⬡-Six-Arm Star.

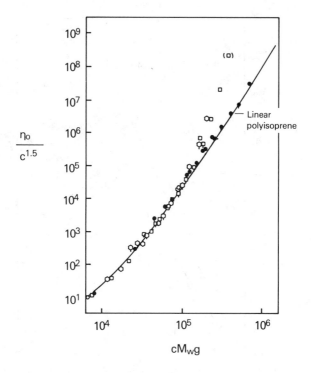

Figure 6. Viscosity data for linear and star-branched polyisoprenes of various molecular weights and concentrations in tetradecane at 25°C. Behavior of linear polyisoprenes was found to correlate [2] with the form $\eta_0 = Kc^{1.5}(c\bar{M}_w)^a$; $\bar{M}_w$ was replaced by $g\bar{M}_w$ for the branched polymers. Solid circles (●) indicate linear polymers, and open symbols indicate star-branched samples.

is therefore demonstrated, if the size differences between linear and branched systems is taken into account.

The elastic properties of stars, while less remarkable than the viscosity, show marked deviations from those of linear molecules. The reduced steady-state shear compliance of both polystyrene and polybutadiene polymers as a function of molecular weight is given [45] in Figures 9 and 10. It is clear that, unlike the linear polymers, the reduced branched compliance is independent of molecular weight, as the tube or reptation theory predicts in Equations 6 and 7.

Comb-Shaped Molecules

While comb-shaped molecules can help bridge the gap between very simple model stars and random branching, as often encountered in commercial polymers, a much smaller number of studies [26–29] on these materials have been reported. The simplest type of comb is that of H-shaped polystyrenes [46], where each of the five subchains are of approximately equal length. As with star-branched polymers, viscosity enhancement (Γ) is also seen for the H-shaped polystyrene melts. This is shown in Figure 11 where the $[n]_\theta$ is proportional to $\langle S^2 \rangle_0$. However, Γ_1, as indicated in Figure 12, increases approximately twice as fast as in the case of H-shaped polystyrenes relative to four-arm stars. Roovers [46] has rationalized this difference in terms of considering the simultaneous

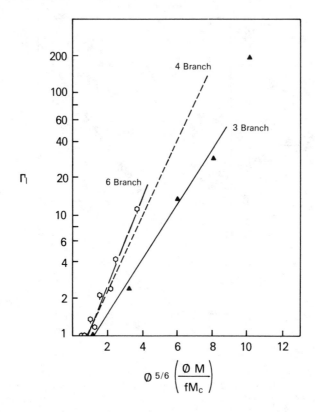

Figure 7. Viscosity enhancement factor for undiluted three-arm star polybutadienes and solutions of six-arm star polyisoprenes [2].

acquisition of a favorable configuration for reptation of the two branch points of the H-shaped molecule.

The zero shear compliance increases with molecular weight, as seen previously for star molecules. The compliance is compared in Figure 13 for H-shaped polystyrenes with the linear molecules. Similar responses to those seen for stars are seen for J_e^0 in H-shaped polystyrene.

Results for regular combs are not as clear as in the H-polymers. In contrast to the H-polymers, in which only molecular weight can vary, molecular weight of the branches, the number of branch points, and the backbone molecular weight can vary in combs. Results for viscosity on combs are unclear, in that viscosity enhancement and the exponential dependence on branch lengths are supported by some data, but not by others [26].

RANDOMLY BRANCHED POLYMERS

General Description

Random branching differs markedly from the study of model compounds in a number of important respects. By definition, random branching follows statistical principles, in which branches along

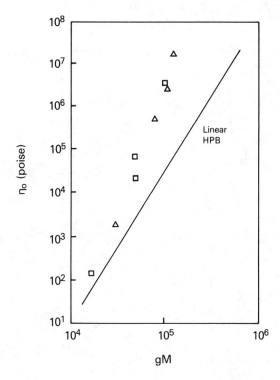

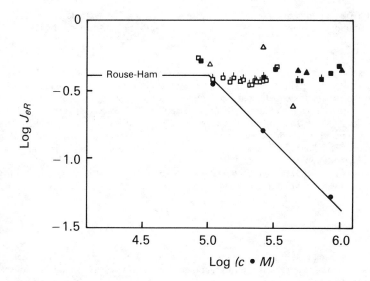

Figure 8. Viscosity of undiluted HPB stars at 190°. △ represents three-arm stars and □ four-arm stars [9].

Figure 9. Dependence of J_{eR} on cM for polystyrene stars. Full symbols for melts, open symbols for solutions. ○-linear polymers; □-four-arm stars; △-six-arm stars [45].

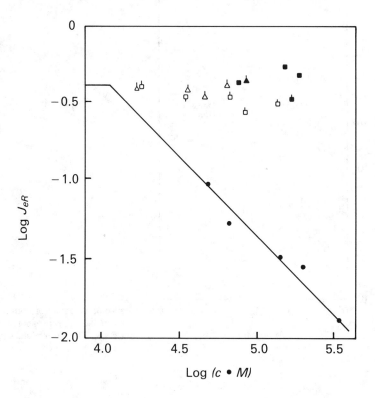

Figure 10. Dependence of J_{eR} on cM for polybutadiene stars. Full symbols for melts, open symbols for solutions. ○-linear polymers, △-three-arm stars, □-four-arm stars, [45].

a polymer backbone, as such, loses its meaning, since the tree-like structures thought to be formed produce statistically varying length chains spanning branch points. Also, unlike model compounds, in which the structure is closely controlled, understanding the rheological behavior of randomly branched systems generally requires careful characterization to correlate the rheological behavior to molecular structure. The majority of random branching studies have involved polyethylene, since polyethylene readily forms branched structures as a result of free radical polymerization or polymer degradation. The following sections are split into high and low levels of branching, for reasons that will become more apparent.

Whole polymer methods of characterization have led to empirical models relating rheological behavior to molecular structure. It has been demonstrated [35] that the Newtonian viscosity can be correlated with $(\bar{g}M)_w$ as:

$$n_0 = K(\bar{g}M)_w^A \tag{10}$$

where A = 3.4 and g = 1 for linear materials and g < 1 and A > 3.4 for branched low-density polyethylenes. Similarly, at any shear rate, a general description of viscosity as a function of shear rate can be represented [35] as:

$$n(\dot{\gamma}) = K[(gM)_w^*]^A \tag{11}$$

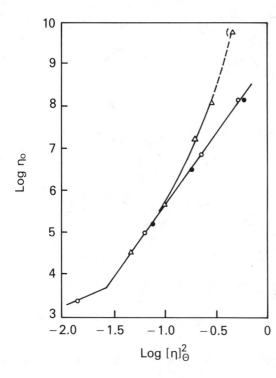

Figure 11. Zero-shear viscosity vs. the square of the Θ-temperature intrinsic viscosity. Circles, linear polystyrene polymers; squares, linear polymers diluted with low MW polystyrene; triangles, H-shaped polystyrene [46].

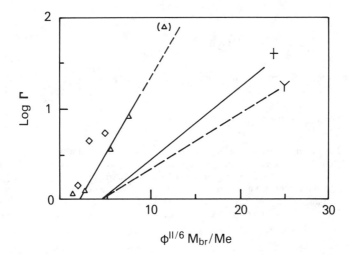

Figure 12. Enhancement of zero-shear viscosity Γ vs. number of entanglements per branch: triangles, H-polymers; diamond, H-polymers diluted with low MW polystyrene [46]. Lines are for regular stars indicated by their symbols.

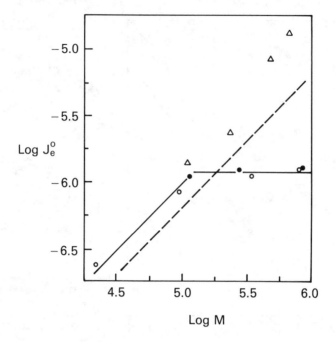

Figure 13. Zero-shear recoverable compliance vs. molecular weight. The solid line represents Equation 6 for linear polymers. The broken lines represent the Rouse-Ham prediction for H-polymers, with $g_2 = 0.677$. Symbols are the same as in Figure 11 [46].

where
$$(g\bar{M})_w^* = \sum_{i=1}^{c-1} w_i(gM)_i + (gM)_c \sum_{i=c}^{\infty} w_i$$

and w_i is the weight fraction of component i in the polydisperse sample. $(gM)_c$ is an empirical shear rate dependent parameter described by:

$$\log(gM)_c = a + b \log \dot{\gamma} \qquad (12)$$

As indicated in the preceding discussion of model compounds, linear and branched samples show different relationships between molecular structure and rheological behavior. At very low branching levels, a situation is encountered which is unparalleled in model compounds. At extremely low levels, not every molecule can contain a branch. This suggests that such a case will be a blend of branched and linear components. In general, it will be shown that this mixture of branched and linear species results in a logarithmic blending law description as:

$$\eta = (\eta_L)^{w_L}(\eta_B)^{w_B} \qquad (13)$$

The branched and linear distributions are assumed to obey equations similar to Equation 11, independent of the presence of the other distribution. It will be demonstrated that this provides a very useful description of the viscosity as a function of shear rate.

High Levels of Branching

Following the earlier convention for model compounds of comparing branched and linear polymers at constant $\langle S^2 \rangle_0$, the mean squared radius of gyration, or gM, it was shown by Mendelson et al. [4] that the exponent in the Newtonian viscosity relationship for branched high pressure polyethylene was equal to 6.56, rather than 3.4 as usually found for linear polymers. In this study the branched samples were regarded as consisting of branched species, with all molecular weights contributing to the rheological behavior as though they were above the critical entanglement molecular weight. In general, there must be a lower limit to molecular weights in a highly polydisperse sample, that can contain branches not capable of forming entanglements. Since for polyethylene M_c is 3,800 [47], molecules having molecular weights less than approximately 7,000 cannot contain branches capable of entanglements. Correcting a series of polydisperse, low-density polyethylene samples for this polymer below 7,000 molecular weight, a relationship between η_0 and $(g\bar{M})_w$ has been found to be as given in Figure 14 [6] such that:

$$\log \eta_0 = 11.44 \log(g\bar{M})_w - 48.79 \tag{14}$$

This figure represents the relationship between the mean squared radius of gyration for polyethylene, having molecular weights high enough that the branches can form entanglements. From the Figure it is seen that over the range examined, the Newtonian viscosity at a given $(g\bar{M})_w$ of the branched polymer is greater than that of the linear. This viscosity enhancement of the branched relative to the linear polymer appears rather similar to the results on model branched systems. Pertinent data on these samples are given in Table 1.

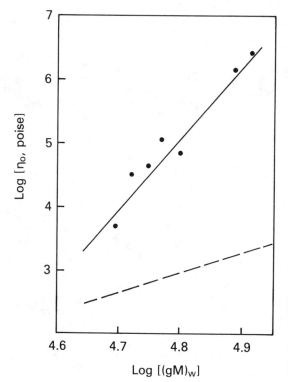

Figure 14. Dependence of Newtonian melt viscosity as a function of molecular size. The solid points and solid line are for conventional low-density polyethylene, and the dashed line for linear polyethylene.

Table 1
Molecular Characterization of Low Density Polyethylene Sample Set Used to Develop Branched Rheological Model

Sample I.D.	$[\eta]$	η_0 (Poise)	η_0 (Poise)[a]	$(gM)_w$	$(gM)_w$[b]	$\bar{M}_w$[c]	# LCB/1000 CH_2[d]
L_1	1.09	1.60×10^6	1.59×10^7	64,636	76,400	167,000	1.16
L_2	1.09	1.35×10^6	2.89×10^7	65,610	82,200	147,000	0.90
L_3	0.77	7.0×10^3	4.95×10^4	40,000	49,500	199,000	2.40
L_4	0.96	2.1×10^5	1.10×10^6	52,800	60,500	184,000	1.60
L_5	0.91	9.60×10^4	4.76×10^5	48,360	55,800	134,000	1.64
L_6	0.88	7.5×10^4	3.24×10^5	45,800	52,500	129,000	1.86
L_7	0.93	5×10^4	3.3×10^5	52,870	63,100	234,000	1.95

[a] Newtonian viscosity of the hypothetical branched component making up the low density polyethylene that is corrected for the presence of linear polymer at low molecular weight.
[b] Corrected for the presence of some linear polymer: $(gM)_w$ is representative of hypothetical branched portion of the low density polyethylene sample.
[c] The corrected [33] (for branching) weight average molecular weight.
[d] Branching level calculated by the Ram and Miltz method. [33].

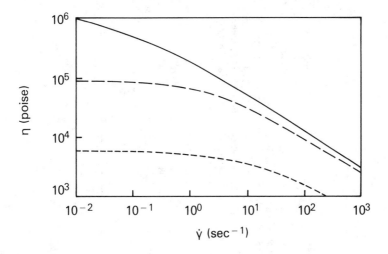

Figure 15. Flow curves for the branched polyethylenes L2, solid line; L5 long dashed line; L3, short dashed line (see Table 1).

The viscosity as a function of shear rate for these samples is given in Figure 15. The non-Newtonian behavior of these branched polyethylenes can be described in terms of molecular structure using [6]:

$$\log(gM)_c = -0.16 \log \dot\gamma + 5.10$$

$$(g\bar{M})_w^* = \sum_{i=1}^{c-1} w_i(gM)_i + (gM)_c \sum_{i=c}^{\infty} w_i \tag{15}$$

and $\log[\eta(\dot\gamma)] = -48.79 + 11.44 \log[(g\bar{M})_w^*]$

Interestingly, from reference to Table 1, the viscosities of the branched systems, having the highest molecular weights, are lowest, in sharp contrast to linear systems.

The elastic properties as monitored by J_e^0 for a series of branched polyethylenes is given [35] in Table 2. Plotting J_e^0 as a function of $(g\bar{M})_z(g\bar{M})_{z+1}/(g\bar{M})_w^2$ gives a good correlation, as shown in Figure 16. This relationship is entirely analogous to that found [47] in linear polymers, except that $(g\bar{M})$ is replaced by M for the linear polymers. A similar correlation with molecular weight in the branched polymers does not show any trends. This, together with the viscosity correlations on the branched polyethylenes, strongly reinforces the suggestion that rheological comparisons of branched and linear systems be made at constant molecular size as indicated by the mean squared radius of gyration.

An important aspect of the elastic response is the swell as an extrudate emerges from a die. The die swell as a function of branches/1,000 CH_2 in low density polyethylene [48] is given in Figure 17. Pertinent data on this group of samples are given in Table 3. The data in Figure 17 clearly show that die swelling increases with branching. Similar results have been reported elsewhere [3], although die swell also was reported to increase with molecular size, $(g\bar{M})_w$. When comparisons are made at constant molecular size, the swell is reported [4] to decrease with branching. In light of the earlier correlations of J_e^0 with $(g\bar{M})_z(g\bar{M})_{z+1}/(g\bar{M})_w^2$, one might intuitively expect the die swell to increase with this size distribution parameter. Unfortunately, no such comparisons have been made to deconvolute the various interdependencies.

Table 2
Molecular Parameters of Branched Polyethylene Samples [35]

Sample	$(g\overline{M})_n$	$(g\overline{M})_w$	$(g\overline{M})_z$	$(g\overline{M})_{z+1}$	$\dfrac{(g\overline{M})_w}{(g\overline{M})_n}$	$\dfrac{(g\overline{M})_z(g\overline{M})_{z+1}}{(g\overline{M})_w^2}$	$J_e^0 \times 10^5$ at 190°C (cm²/dynes)	n_w Index (Number of Branches per Chain Length)
A	1.44×10^4	3.15×10^4	4.61×10^4	5.75×10^4	2.19	2.67	15.4	57.8
B	1.37×10^4	2.43×10^4	3.25×10^4	3.87×10^4	1.77	2.13	5.23	45.8
C	1.09×10^4	1.68×10^4	2.12×10^4	2.45×10^4	1.54	1.84	2.20	53.8
D	7.99×10^3	1.15×10^4	1.42×10^4	1.62×10^4	1.44	1.74	1.08	44.1
E	1.05×10^4	1.90×10^4	2.71×10^4	3.31×10^4	1.81	2.48	9.53	293.3
F	8.66×10^3	1.45×10^4	1.97×10^4	2.39×10^4	1.67	2.24	5.51	361.6
G	6.97×10^3	1.14×10^4	1.55×10^4	1.89×10^4	1.64	2.25	4.55	394.9
H	5.99×10^3	9.27×10^3	1.22×10^4	1.47×10^4	1.55	2.09	2.86	456.9

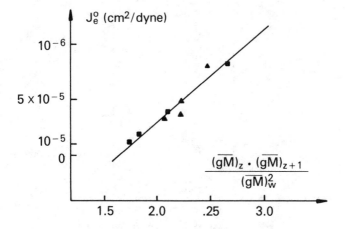

Figure 16. J_e^0 as a function of $(\overline{gM})_{z+1}(\overline{gM})_z/(\overline{gM})_w^2$ T $= 148°$C. $\blacksquare$-Polymer A-D, $\blacktriangle$-Polymer E-H (Table 2) [35]

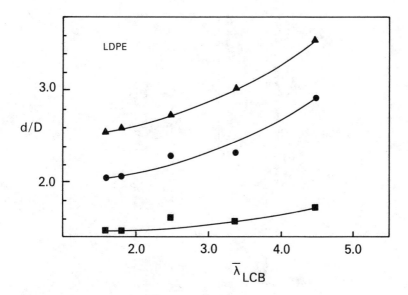

Figure 17. Extrudate swell as a function of the frequency λ_{LCB} of LCB. T $= 180°$C; L/D, $\dot{\gamma}$ (s^{-1}): ($\blacktriangle$) 0,600; ($\bullet$) 2.99, 600; ($\blacksquare$) 24.76, 200 [48].

Table 3
Summary of High Pressure HDPE Properties[a] [48]

Sample	Density	MI	$\bar{M}_n \times 10^{-3}$	$\bar{M}_w \times 10^{-3}$	$\bar{M}_z$	$\bar{M}_{z+1}$	LCB (branches per 1000 C atoms)
A	0.9232	2.24	26.3	110.0	320.3	623.9	1.600
B	0.9230	2.10	16.6	83.9	—	—	1.748
C	0.9186	2.04	21.3	201.6	1258.0	3423.0	2.500
D	0.9210	2.51	22.5	143.1	561.0	1193.0	3.400
E	9.9190	1.80	15.6	243.1	—	—	4.523

[a] All five samples are approximately the same molecular size with $g\bar{M}_w \sim (5.4 \pm 0.5) \times 10^4$, where g is the ratio of mean square radii of gyration for branched (LCB) and linear chains of the same number of repeat units.

Low Levels of Branching

Very low levels of branching present an interesting case for a couple of reasons. At low levels of branching it is evident that not every molecule can contain a branch. The resulting sample must therefore be a mixture of branched and linear molecules. The activation energy for such mixtures of linear and branched polyethylene has been reported [49] to be a linear relationship as shown in Figure 18. This suggests that the Newtonian viscosity of such mixtures are shown to be related by:

$$\eta_0(\text{mixture}) = [\eta_0(\text{Lin})]^{w_L}[\eta_0(\text{Br})]^{w_B} \tag{16}$$

if one assumes an Arrhenius relationship for the viscosity. This expectation is fulfilled, as the data in Figure 19 clearly show. In fact, Equation 16 appears [50] to hold at all shear rates, as indicated in Figure 20 for the blend of low and high density polyethylenes.

The distribution of branching for random branching to give branched and linear molecules, partitioned between the branched and linear distributions of weight fractions, w_L and w_B, must be determined. For this information the statistical probabilities of branching must be considered. If n is the number of branches per molecule, the probability of a molecule remaining linear in the limit of large numbers of molecules has been shown [6] to be:

$$P = \exp(-1.18n) \tag{17}$$

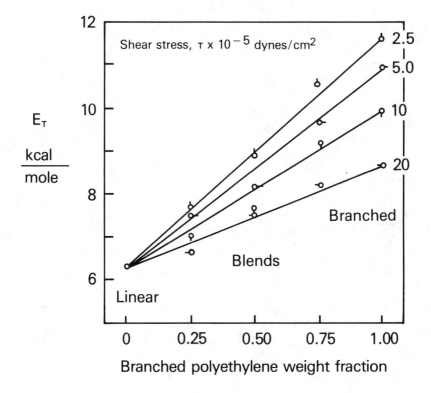

Figure 18. Activation energy for steady-shear viscosity at constant stress vs. blend composition (branched component weight fraction), between 150°C and 190°C at four indicated stress values [49].

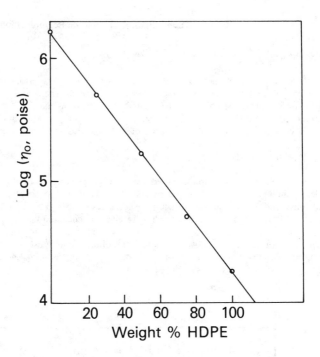

Figure 19. Effect of blend composition (branched LDPE and linear HDPE) on Newtonian viscosity [50]. Reprinted with permission of John Wiley and Sons.

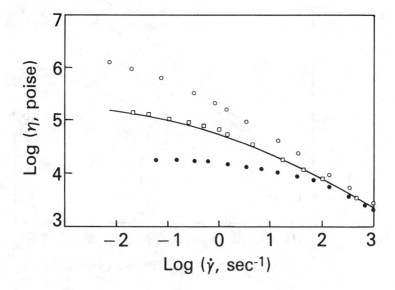

Figure 20. Flow curves for linear polyethylene, solid circles; branched LDPE, open circles; and a $\frac{50}{50}$ blend, squares. The solid line represents predictions from logarithmic blending low [50]. Reprinted with permission of John Wiley and Sons.

for trifunctional branching, and:

$$P = \exp(-1.34n) \tag{18}$$

for tetrafunctional branch points.

For a polydisperse sample, the weight fraction of linear species is:

$$W_L = \sum W_i P_i \tag{19}$$

where W_i are the weight fractions of species of molecular weight M_i. The activation energy, E_a, is related by [49]:

$$E_a = W_L E_L + W_B E_B \tag{20}$$

Using these relationships and experimental data on branching and molecular weight distribution, the activation energy can be calculated [6]. Comparison of a theoretical relationship between activation energy and branching with experimental data is given in Figure 21. The activation energies

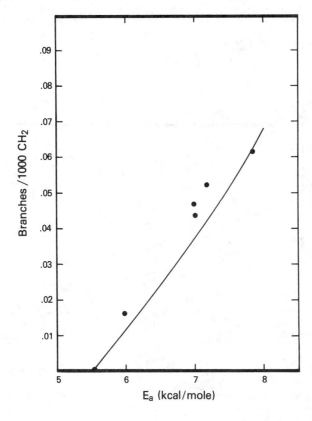

Figure 21. Comparison of theoretical relationships (Equations 18–21) with experimental data on apparent activation energy for samples H_1–H_6 [6]. Reprinted with permission of John Wiley & Sons.

Table 4
Molecular Characteristics and Activation Energy of the Polyethylenes Used [6]

Sample ID	Corrected for LCB × 10⁻³ $\overline{M}_n$	$\overline{M}_w$	$\overline{M}_z$	$\overline{M}_w/\overline{M}_n$	E_a (kcal/mol)	# LCB/1000C	Viscosity at $=10^{-2}$ rad/s (P)
HDPE							
H_1	12.1	129	818	10.6	7.0	0.043ᵃ	6.50×10^5
H_2	17.7	137	801	7.7	7.0	0.046	8.60×10^5
H_3	26.8	163	852	6.1	6.0	0.016	3.70×10^5
H_4	17.7	139	822	7.8	7.8	0.061	1.18×10^6
H_5	12.7	161	891	12.8	7.1	0.052	1.96×10^6
H_6	10.9	161	1070	14.8	5.5	0	1.80×10^5
LDPE							
L_1	21.3	167	630	7.8	12.0	1.16ᵇ	1.60×10^6
L_2	17.6	147	560	8.4	12.0	0.90	1.35×10^6
L_3	15.0	198	1680	13.2	12.1	2.40	7.00×10^3
L_4	20.5	184	1000	9.0	12.3	1.60	2.10×10^5

ᵃ *Branching level calculated by the method in text of comparison of predicted low shear viscosity to experimentally determined data.*
ᵇ *Branching calculated by the Ram-Miltz [33] technique.*

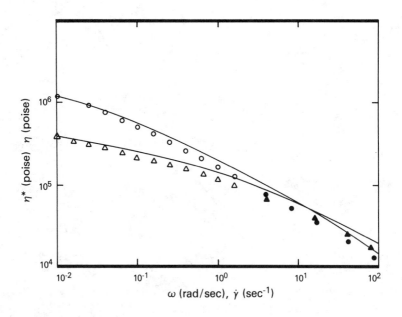

Figure 22. Viscosity as a function of rate for samples H_3 ($\bigcirc$, $\bullet$) and H_4 ($\triangle$, $\blacktriangle$): (—) predicted responses based on Equations 15–18; ($\bullet$, $\blacktriangle$) steady shearing; ($\bigcirc$, $\triangle$) dynamic data [6]. Reprinted with permission of John Wiley and Sons.

for the branched components were assumed to be 12 Kal/mole °K, as found for branched low density polyethylene, since E_a does not appear to vary for large branching levels. Pertinent data on these samples are shown in Table 4. The viscosity as a function of rate for two high-density polyethylenes with different branching levels is given in Figure 22, together with predicted responses based on Equations 15–20. As can be seen from the figure, the effect of branching is most evident at low rates, where the more branched material shows the higher low-rate viscosity, in spite of its having a lower molecular weight. The branching for these polyethylenes is assumed to be trifunctional as the generally agreed upon scheme [51], involving hydrogen abstraction by mechanical or thermal degradation, with the radical termination step resulting in the branch.

A more controlled random branching in polyethylene can be obtained by the addition of peroxides, in which each peroxide molecule leads to one tetrafunctional branch [52]. The characterizations for a group of samples, all prepared from the same precursor, P_0, by the addition of known peroxide levels are given in Table 5. As can be seen from the table, little apparent difference in molecular weight results from these very small branching levels. Comparison of the experimental data (assuming known branching levels from the known added peroxide levels) between activation energy and branching level with the relationship predicted from Equations 18–20 is given in Figure 23. The good agreement suggests the essential correctness of these concepts.

The viscosity as a function of rate for samples $P_0 - P_5$ is given in Figure 24, together with prediction [6] based on Equation 16 and experimental data on molecular size distribution. As can be seen, the predictions are in very poor agreement with the experimental data. Since the predictions were based on the parameters determined for trifunctional branching, it would appear that the effect of a tetra-functional branch is considerably more severe than a trifunctional branching.

To summarize the effects of random branching on the viscosity, we note that simple extrapolation of the effects at high branching levels to low levels does not lead to linear behavior. This is dramatically demonstrated in Figure 25, where a maximum in the low rate viscosity is predicted. This maximum follows from the opposing effects of branching on the concentration of branched molecules, obeying an equation with an exponent exceeding 3.4 for the relation between η_0 and $(g\bar{M})_w$, and the reduction in molecular size with branching. At low branching levels, the low rate viscosity increases with branching content due to the increasing concentration of more viscous branched species, since not every molecule can contain a branch. At higher branching levels, the viscosity decreases due to the increased importance of the reduction in the molecular size with branching. The predicted maximum has been experimentally observed [5] by the fractionation of polyethylene, as shown in Figure 26.

Some interesting differences between model compounds, such as stars, and randomly branched polymers are evident. In model compounds, as molecular weight is increased, the number of branches per molecule remains unchanged, where only branch length varies with branching level. In the limit of very low branching levels, or higher molecular weights, every molecule still contains a branch. This is not the case with random branching, where at low branching levels not every molecule can contain a branch. Consequently, the descriptions must diverge at low branching levels.

SPECIAL CHARACTERISTICS OF BRANCHED SYSTEMS

Shear Modification

Reports over the years have suggested that the rheology of branched systems can be reversibly modified by shearing. The first such report [15] suggested that the viscosity of low-density polyethylene could be decreased by a factor of two by shearing the molten polymer, accompanied by a decrease in the elasticity of the melt. Similar results have been reported [15] for branched acetal polymers. A study of three low-density polyethylenes, the pertinent data of which is given in Table 6, has led to some interesting conclusions [13]. Results on these samples for the shear stress are given in Figure 27. Not only are reversible shear modifications indicated, but these modifications show a strong dependence on molecular weight. The little or no shear modification of the lowest molecular weight material is consistent with the shear modifications more quickly relaxing out in the melt, much like the solvent treated materials; the solvent allowing relaxation to the unsheared

Table 5

Molecular Characteristics and Activation Energy of Tetrafunctional Branched Polyethylenes from Peroxide Degradation [6]

Sample ID	Corrected for LCB			$\bar{M}_w/\bar{M}_n$	E_a (kcal/mol)	#LCB/1000C[a]	Viscosity at $=10^{-2}$ rad/s (P)
	$\bar{M}_n$	$\bar{M}_w$	$\bar{M}_z$				
P_0 (0% peroxide)	24.7	161	625	6.6	5.5	0	2.1×10^5
P_1 (0.01% peroxide)	27.7	177	631	6.4	6.2	0.0103	1.6×10^6
P_2 (0.02% peroxide)	26.2	177	633	6.9	6.3	0.0207	4.2×10^6
P_3 (0.03% peroxide)	27.9	187	672	6.7	7.2	0.0311	8.1×10^6
P_4 (0.04% peroxide)	23.6	185	688	7.9	7.5	0.0415	1.2×10^7
P_5 (0.05% peroxide)	24.1	185	649	7.7	7.5	0.052	

[a] For tetrafunctional branching, two branches per branch point are assumed according to the NMR or infrared conventions and branching calculated based on the assumption that one tetrafunctional crosslink or two branches will be produced from each peroxide molecule, according to the conventions commonly used in NMR or infrared analysis.

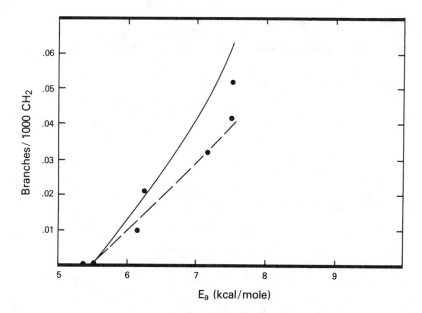

Figure 23. Comparison of theoretical (Equations 18–21) with experimental data on apparent activation energy for samples P_0-P_5 [6]. Reprinted with permission of John Wiley and Sons.

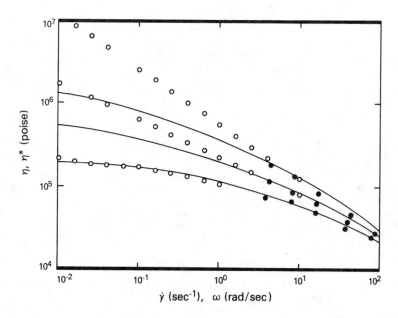

Figure 24. Flow curves for samples P_0-P_1, and P_4: (—) predicted curves based on Equations 15–17 and 19. (●) steady shearing; (○) dynamic data [6]. Reprinted with permission of John Wiley and Sons.

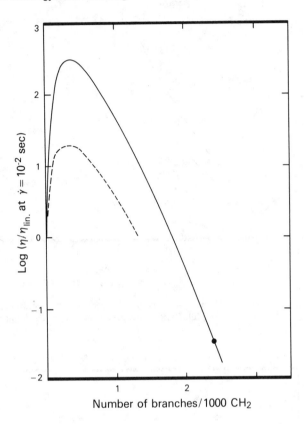

Number of branches/1000 CH$_2$

Figure 25. Predictions of normalized low shear rate viscosity ($\dot{\gamma} = 10^{-2}\,\text{s}^{-1}$) as a function of branch level and molecular weight. The molecular weights are $\bar{M}_w = 200,000$ (——) and 130,000 (- - -) with $\bar{M}_w/\bar{M}_n = 7$. η/η_{lin} is the ratio of the branched to linear viscosity at constant molecular weight distribution. The data points at higher branching levels are experimental data for the sample L$_3$ [6]. Reprinted with permission of John Wiley and Sons.

configurations. Similar behavior is seen in the elastic properties as measured by the die swell ratio. Results for the sample A-O are given in Figure 28, where the swell ratio of the solvent-treated material is always less than the sheared polymer.

While it is not clear that shear modification is unique to branched polymers, it appears that the effect is more dominant (if present at all in linear systems) in the branched polymers.

Thermorheological Complexity

For linear systems, the temperature dependence of rheological properties can be described [47] in terms of a shift factor, a_T, where in the case of the viscosity:

$$n_0(T) = a_T \eta_0(T_0) \tag{21}$$

T_0 being the reference temperature. For these systems, the principle of time-temperature superposition embodied in a_T works with considerable accuracy. The systems are termed "rheologically

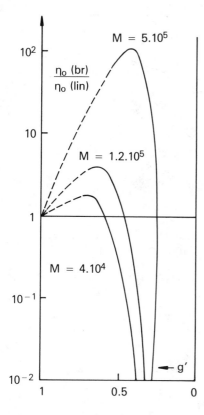

Figure 26. Ratio of Newtonian viscosities of branched and linear fractions having same molecular weight M vs. LCB index g' [5].

Table 6
Characteristics of the Materials Used in Shear Modification Experiments [13]

Sample No.	Melt Index	Density	$\bar{M}_w \times 10^{-5}$	$\lambda \times 10^4$	$\bar{M}_w/\bar{M}_n$	PI[b]
A-0	0.6	0.919	5.31	6.9	17.0	0.58
A-3	8.1	0.914	3.35	12.2	27.7	0.74
C-2	24.0	0.928	0.67	2.1	7.4	0.93

[a] *Branching frequency*
[b] *Die swell of sheared sample/die swell of solution treated material.*

simple." In these cases, simple shifts along the frequency axis provide superposition of dynamic modulus at different temperatures. Some branched polymers, however, behave rather differently in that time-temperature superposition no longer holds [4, 7–9]. An example of this behavior [8] is shown for the dynamic moduli of star-branched hydrogenated polybutadiene in Figure 29, where no single shift in frequency of the curves at the two temperatures can achieve superposition over the entire range. At high frequencies, the shift factor required for superposition is approximately equal to that for linear hydrogenated polybutadiene, while at lower frequencies the shift is greater. The shift, in terms of an apparent activation energy for the star-branched hydrogenated polybutadiene, is graphically illustrated in Figure 30, showing the greater temperature sensitivity of the longer time-

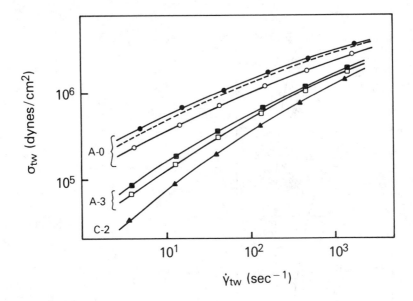

Figure 27. Flow curves of LDPE's with different shearing histories at 160°C: (●, ■, ▲) solvent-treated materials; (○, □, △) full-sheared materials: (–) untreated materials of sample A-O (See Table 6.) [13].

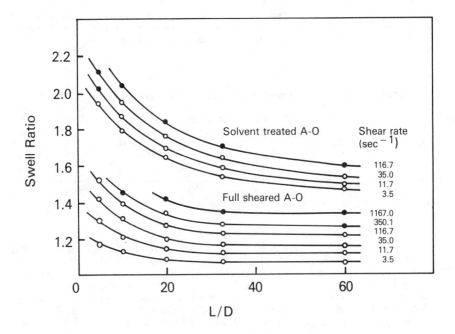

Figure 28. Die swell behavior of sample A-O [13].

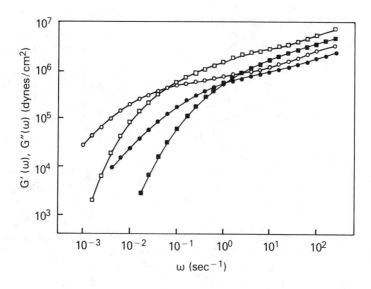

Figure 29. Storage and loss moduli for a star-branched hydrogenated polybutadiene at two temperatures. The sample is 3PHPB-1; open symbols (□ for G, ○ for G″) refer to data at 130°C and closed symbols (■ for G, ● for G″) at 190°C [8].

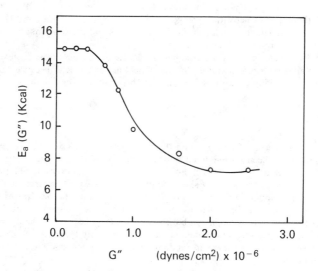

Figure 30. Apparent flow activation energy E_a (G″) as a function of loss modulus for star-branched hydrogenated polybutadiene samples [8].

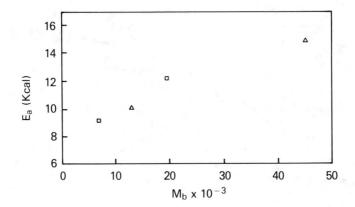

Figure 31. Flow activation energy for star-branched hydrogenated polybutadienes as a function of the molecular weight of the arm [8]. For star polymers

$$\eta_0 = \eta_0(gM)_{\text{Lin}}(\phi M_a/M_e)$$

where ϕ is of the order of unity, M_a = arm molecular weight, and M_e = molecular weight between entanglements ($M_e \simeq M_c/2$).

relaxation processes that dominate at the lower frequencies. Consistent with these results is the dependence of the apparent activation energy on the branch length, since the longer relaxation mechanisms are associated with the larger molecular weights and therefore longer branch lengths. This dependence is illustrated in Figure 31.

Branched polyethylene is by no means unique in displaying thermorheological complexity. Graessley [7] et al. have argued that it is most prominent in polyethylene, because the flow activation energy is small, making departures from time-temperature superposition easy to observe.

CONCLUSION

In this chapter, the effects of branching on the rheological characteristics of polymers are covered. The emphasis has been on undiluted polymer fluids, consisting of star or comb molecules and on random branching polymers such as polyethylene. The reptation or tube theories of the flow of monodisperse branched stars are shown to provide a convenient description of the viscosity enhancement normally found in these systems. While the application of these theories toward describing the flow of randomly branched polydisperse systems has not been reported, the effect of branching appears qualitatively similar in both cases. However, because of the discrete nature of branching, the analogy between model compounds and randomly branched samples is shown to break down at very low branch levels in randomly branched systems, where not every molecule can contain a branch.

Besides the simple viscous and elastic flow behavior, additional unique properties of branched systems are discussed. Shear modification of branched systems and thermorheological complexity are described.

A substantial gap still exists in our basic understanding between model compounds and randomly branched structures. Both the theoretical description and experimental data on more complex model systems are necessary to bridge this gap.

NOTATION

A	exponent in Newtonian viscosity molecular weight relation	M_a	molecular weight of arm in star molecules
a_T	temperature shift factor	M_e	molecular weight between entanglements
f	number of arms in branched star molecules	M_c	critical molecular weight for entanglements
g	The ratio of branched to linear mean squared radius of gyration at a given molecular weight	P	probability of a molecular species being linear
$(\bar{g}M)_w$	weighted average of molecular size parameter proportional to S_0^2	S_0^2	mean squared radius of gyration
		w_L	weight fraction of a polymer sample that is linear
J_e^0	steady-state shear compliance		
J_{eR}^0	reduced steady-state shear compliance	w_B	weight fraction of a polymer sample that is branched
K	constant relating of η_0 and $\bar{M}_w$		
M	molecular weight	n	number of branches per molecule
$\bar{M}_w$	weight average molecular weight		

Greek Symbols

α	empirical exponent relating intrinsic viscosity ratio to mean squared radius of gyration	Γ_1	viscosity enhancement factor
		$\eta(\dot{\gamma})$	viscosity at shear rate $\dot{\gamma}$
$\dot{\gamma}$	shear rate	η_0	Newtonian viscosity
		$[\eta]$	intrinsic viscosity

REFERENCES

1. Schaefgen, J. R., and Flory, P. J., *J. Am. Chem. Soc.*, *70*, 2709 (1948).
2. Graessley, W. W., *Acc. Chem. Res.*; *10*, 332 (1977).
3. Wild, L., R. Ranganath, and Knobelock, D., *Poly. Eng. & Sci.*, *16*, 811 (1976).
4. Mendelson, R. A., Bowles, W. A., and Finzer, F. L., *J. Polym. Sci.*, A-2, *8*, 105 (1970).
5. Constantin, D., *Polym. Eng. & Sci.*, *24*, 268 (1984).
6. Bersted, B. H., *J. Appl. Polym. Sci.*, *30*, 3751 (1985).
7. Carella, J. M., Gotro, J. T., and Graessley, W. W., *Macromol.*, *19*, 659 (1986).
8. Rajiv, V. R., Rachapudy, H., and Graessley, W. W., *J. Polym. Sci.*, *Poly. Phys. Ed.*, *17*, 1223 (1979).
9. Graessley, W. W., and Rajiv, V. R., *J. Polym. Symp.*, No. 71, 79 (1984).
10. Maxwell, B., and Brickwordt, A., *J. of Rheology*, *25*, 55 (1981).
11. Hanson, D. E., *Polym. Eng. Sci.*, *9*, 6 (1969).
12. Rokudai, M., and Fujiki, T., *J. Appl. Polym. Sci.*, *23*, 3289 (1979).
13. Rokudai, M., and Fukiki, T., *J. Appl. Polym. Sci.*, *26*, 1343 (1981).
14. Fukiki, K., *J. Appl. Polym. Sci.*, *15*, 47 (1971).
15. Wissbrun, K., *J. Appl. Polym. Sci.*, *13*, 232 (1969).
16. Graessley, W. W., and Roovers, J., *Macromol.*, *12*, 1959 (1979).
17. Rajiv, V. R., Memenes, E. V., Marin, G., and Graessley, W. W., *Macromol*, *14*, 1668 (1981).
18. Graessley, W. W., Masuda, T. M., Roovers, J. E., and Hadjichristidis, N., *Macromol.* 9, 127 (1976).
19. Masuda, T., Ohta, Y., Yamsuchi, Y., and Onogi, Shigeharw, *Polym. J.*, *16*, 273 (1984).
20. Utracki, L. A., and J. Roovers, *Macromol.*, *6*, 366 (1973).
21. Roovers, J., and N. Hadjichristidis, *J. Polym. Sci.*, *12*, 2521 (1974).
22. Jajiura, H., Ushiyama, Y., Fujimoto, T., and Nagasawa, M., *Macromol.*, *11*, 894 (1978).
23. Kraus, G., and Gruver, J. T., *J. Polym. Sci.*, *A*, *3*, 105 (1965).

24. Rochefort, W. E., Smith, G. G., Rachapudy, H., Raju, V. R., and Graessley, W. W., *J. Polym. Sci., Polym. Phys. Ed.*, *17*, 1197 (1979).
25. Rachapudy, H., Smith, G. G., Raji, V. R., and Graessley, W. W., *J. Polym. Sci., Polym. Phys. Ed.*, 17, 1211 (1979).
26. Roovers, J., and Graessley, W. W., *Macromol.*, *14*, 766 (1981).
27. Fujimoto, T., Narukawa, N., and Nagasawa, M., *Macromol.*, *3*, 57 (1970).
28. Noda, I., Horikawa, T., Kato, T., Fujimoto, T., and Nagasawa, M., *Macromol.*, 3795 (1970).
29. Fujimoto, T., Kajiura, H., Hirose, M., and Nagasawa, M., *Polym. J.*, *3*, 181 (1972).
30. Roovers, J., *Macromol.*, *18*, 1359 (1985).
31. Long, V. C., Berry, G. C., and Hobbs, L. M., *Polymer*, *5*, 517 (1964).
32. Masuda, T., Nagasawa, Y., Ohta, Y., and Onogi, S., *Polym. J.*, *3*, 92 (1972).
33. Miltz, J., and Ram, A., *Polym. Eng. & Sci.*, *13*, 273 (1973).
34. Ram, A., *Polym. Eng. & Sci.*, *17*, 793 (1977).
35. Pedersen, S., and Ram, A., *Polym. Eng. & Sci.*, *18*, 990 (1978).
36. Berry, G. C., and Fox, T. G., *Adv. Polym. Sci.*, *5*, 261 (1968).
37. Zimm, B. H., and Stockmayer, W. H., *J. Chem. Phys.*, *17*, 1301 (1949).
38. Flory, P. J., "Principles of Polymer Chemistry," Cornell Univ. Press, N.Y., 1967.
39. Hughes, J. K., *A.N.T.E.C.* Preprints, Chicago, May 1983.
40. Agarwal, R. K., Horska, J., Stejekal, J., Quadrat, O., and Kratochirl, P., *J. Appl. Polym. Sci.*, *28*, 3453 (1983).
41. Foster, G. N., MacRury, T. B., Hamielec, A. E., *Chromatog. Sci.*, *13*, 143 (1980).
42. Ham, J. S., *J. Chem. Phys.*, *26*, 625 (1957).
43. deGennes, P. G., *J. Chem. Phys.*, *55*, 572 (1971).
44. Graessley, W. W., *Adv. Polym. Sci.*, *47*, 94, Springer-Virlag, Berlin, 1982.
45. Roovers, J., *Polym. Communications*, (1981).
46. Roovers, J., *Macromol.*, *17*, 1196 (1984).
47. Ferry, J. D., "Viscoelastic Properties of Polymers," 2nd Ed., Wiley, New York, N.Y., 1970.
48. Hamielec, L. A., and Vlachopoulos, J., *J. Appl. Polym. Sci.*, *28*, 2389 (1983).
49. R. Porter, Jacovic, M. S., and Pollock, D., *J. Appl. Polym. Sci.*, *23*, 517 (1979).
50. B. H. Bersted, Slee, J. D., and Richter, C. A., *J. Appl. Polym. Sci.*, *26*, 1001 (1981).
51. C. Rideal and Padget, J., *J. Polym. Sci. Symp.*, *57*, 1 (1976).
52. E. R. Howells and Benbow, J. J., *Trans. J. Plastics Inst.*, *30*, 240 (1962).

CHAPTER 23

RHEOLOGY OF HIGHLY FILLED POLYMER MELT SYSTEMS

A. V. Shenoy*

Department of Materials Science and Engineering
University of Florida
Gainesville, Florida, USA

CONTENTS

INTRODUCTION

There is extensive literature on the rheology of filled polymer melt systems [1–60] including comprehensive chapters in a number of books [61–66]. However, the bulk of the literature deals with the rheology of systems in the range of 20 to 40 percent filler loading by volume. Aspects relating to this loading level have been effectively reviewed by Utracki and Fisa [39]. Only recently has there been an enhanced interest in studying the rheology of highly filled polymer melt systems [40, 41, 44, 48, 52, 55–57, 60]. The motivation for such studies has been due to the intended use of polymers as binders during ceramic and metal processing [60, 67–75] as well as for the preparation of functional filler composites [52, 55–57, 76–78]. A summary of the experimental investigations done so far on the melt rheology of highly loaded polymer composites is given in Table 1.

Though there is a wide variety of fillers available for use in polymer composite systems, as can be seen from Table 2, only a few have been used to date in the preparation of highly filled systems. This is mainly because of the difficulties involved in the preparation and characterization of such systems, as well as the limited identified applications of such highly loaded systems. However, the importance of understanding the rheology of these complex systems has been realized and efforts in this direction have been growing during the past few years.

The rheological properties of highly filled polymer composites are dominated by interparticle interactions. The extent of these interactions is dependent on the filler type, its shape, size, size distribution, and amount. Other important factors are the polymer-filler interface and the degree of dispersion. Both of these can be altered by the choice of proper mixing conditions and through the use

---

* Present address: SMART, 64D Girgaum Road, Opera House, Bombay 400004, India.

Table 1

Summary of Investigations Done So Far on the Melt Rheology of Highly Filled Polymer Composites

Polymer Type	Filler Type, Amount	Filler Shape	Surface Modifier Type, Amount	Reference
Polystyrene	Glass Balloon, 50–82%	Spherical	—	10
Low Density Polyethylene	Silas Balloon, 50%	Spherical	—	10
	Steel Powder, 68%	Spherical	—	48
	Alumina Powder, 60%	Particulate	—	48
	Zirconia Powder, 60%	Particulate	—	48
	Steel Powder, 60–70%	Spherical	A1100, 1%	40
			KR38S, 1%	40
			Kemamide E, 1%	40
			W905, 1%	40
	Alumina Powder, 40–60%	Particulate	INT33UDKM, 1%	41
			Kemamide E, 1%	41
			W910, 1%	41
	Zirconia Powder, 69%	Particulate	Kemamide E, 1%	48
	Silicon Nitride, 60%	—	Kemamide E, 1%	48
			W900, 1%	48
	Barium Ferrite, 40–57%	Platelet		55, 57
Polyurethane Thermoplastic Elastomer	Barium Ferrite, 40–57%	Platelet	—	57
Polyester Elastomer	Barium Ferrite, 40–57%	Platelet	—	55, 57
S-I-S Block Copolymer	Barium Ferrite, 40–57%	Platelet	—	55, 57
			KR38S, 1%	52
			KR138S, 1%	52
			KR TTS, 1%	52
			Z6075, 1%	52
			Z6076, 1%	52
High Density Polyethylene	Alumina Powder, 50%	Particulate	—	60

Table 2
List of Different Types of Fillers

Organic			Inorganic		
Cellulosics	**Lignins**	**Proteins**	**Synthetics**	**Carbonates**	**Hydroxides**
• alpha cellulose • cotton flock • sisal • jute • wood flour • shell flour • cotton-seed hulls • cotton linters • cork dust	• processed lignin • ground bark	• soybean meal • keratin	• acrylics • nylons • polyesters	• calcium carbonate • barium carbonate • magnesium carbonate	• calcium hydroxide • magnesium hydroxide

Table 2 (Continued)

Inorganic

Oxides	**Silicates**	**Sulfates**	**Carbon**	**Metals powders/fibers**	**Miscellaneous**
• aluminum oxide • antimony trioxide • zinc oxide • magnesium oxide • quartz • diatomaceous earth • tripoli • hydrogel • aerogel	• calcium silicate • magnesium silicate • clay • talc • mica • asbestos • feldspar • wollastonite • pumice • vermiculite • slate flour • Fuller's earth	• calcium sulfate • barium sulfate	• carbon black • graphite	• aluminium • copper • bronze • lead • zinc • steel	• barium ferrite • magnetite • molybdenum disulfide

of additives which could alter the properties of the polymer matrix or the filler surface. Typical examples of these are given in Tables 3 and 4. Again, the type and amount of these additives as well as the method of treatment does have an effect on the rheology of the highly filled systems. This chapter addresses in detail each of these factors that could affect the rheology of highly filled systems.

PREPARATION OF HIGHLY FILLED SYSTEMS

Filler particles, especially those of submicron size, are available in an aggregated form. At times, this is done on purpose by the suppliers because agglomerates are easier to handle, dustless, and are therefore less hazardous to health. However, due to a variety of forces such as Van der Waals, electostatic, liquid bridges, etc. [79], it is often the strong filler bonds that tend to hold finely divided particles together. In the preparation of highly filled polymer composites, difficulties arise in dispersing the fillers in the polymer matrix due to the basic incompatibility between filler and polymer. Polymers, being organic in nature, have surface tensions that are quite different from those of

Table 3
List of Some Commonly Used Matrix Additives

Matrix Additive Type	Typical Examples
Plasticizers	Acid-modified polyesters
	Alcohol-modified polyesters
	Unmodified polyesters
	Chlorinated paraffins
	Dialphenol phthalate
	Di-2-ethylhexyl phthalate
	Di-isooctyl phthalate
	Dioctyl sebacate
	Tritolyl phosphate
	Trixylyl phosphate
Lubricants	Barium stearate
	Calcium stearate
	Lead stearate
	Ethyl diamino-stearate
	Glyceryl monostearate
	Stearic acid
	Paraffin waxes

most inorganic fillers. They have, thus, a natural tendency to resist wetting of the filler during compounding. Hence, during preparation of highly filled systems, there is certainly a possibility for increased agglomeration in this non-wetting environment, as well as an enhanced probability of forming microvoids around particle clusters.

The presence of agglomerates has a considerable effect on the maximum possible loading of the filler, as can be seen from Table 5. If the agglomerates are all broken down into individual particles, then 63.7 volume percent of the filler can be incorporated into the polymer. However, if a dozen particles are clustered together in each agglomerate, then the maximum loading possible would be only 43 volume percent. At maximum filler loading, the viscosity of the composite is close to a hundred times greater than that of the polymer itself, as can be seen from Figure 1, which shows the viscosity of a composite divided by that of the polymer (η_c/η_p) vs. the volume fraction of the filler relative to the maximum amount that can be incorporated into the composite (41, 80). Agglomerates occlude liquid in their interparticle voids, thereby increasing the relative viscosity value at any given solids loading. Thus, the viscosity would be the same for 43 volume percent of agglomerated filler with a dozen particles in each agglomerate as it is for 63.7 volume percent of non-agglomerated particles. For highly filled polymer systems, it is therefore important to reduce the degree of agglomeration to a minimum level, in order to decrease the system viscosity for easier processing and to increase the extent of filler loading. High shear mixing generates velocity gradients which are normally strong enough to break agglomerates in fillers of micron size or larger. In the case of submicron fillers, the forces holding the particles together are stronger than the shear force created by the velocity gradient. In such circumstances, even high shear mixing does not break the agglomerates or eliminate the microvoids within the composite, and one has to take recourse to filler surface treatment [40, 41, 44, 48, 52] which is capable of altering the interparticle forces, resulting in deagglomeration, better dispersion, and hence lower viscosity with maximum possible loading.

The most common technique for incorporating fillers in polymers has been to make use of internal mixers such as the Banbury mixer for batch mixing and the Twin Screw Mixer/Extruder for continuous operation. In laboratory small-scale processes, the Brabender plasticorder [81] or the Haake torque rheometer [82] is often used for conducting the mixing operation. They have accessories for batch mixing as well as continuous operation, but the batch mixer is most popularly used for laboratory research purposes. The completion of the mixing operation is normally adjudged by the observed constancy of the torque level in the mixer's motor drive unit after a certain length of time.

Table 4
List of Some Typical Surface Modifiers

Surface Modifier Type	Typical Examples	Trade Names	Manufacturers
Silanes	Vinyltrimethoxy silane	A-150/CV4917	M1/M2
	Vinyltriethoxy silane	A-151/CV4910	M1/M2
	Vinyltri(2-methoxyethoxy) silane	VTM050/Z-6082	M3/M4
	Vinyltriacetoxy silane	CV4800/Z-6075	M2/M4
	Vinyltrichloro silane	CV4900/VTC	M2/M3
	Chloropropyltrimethoxy silane	CC3300/CPTMO/Z-6076	M2/M3/M4
	γ-Glycidayloxypropyltrimethoxy	A-187/CG6720/GLYMO/Z6040	M1/M2/M3/M4
	γ-Methacryloxypropyltrimethoxy	A-174/CM8550/MEMO/Z6030	M1/M2/M3/M4
	γ-Aminopropyltriethoxy silane	A-1100/CA0750/AMEO	M1/M2/M3
	N-β-Aminoethyl-γ-Aminopropyltrimethoxy silane	A-1120/CA0700/DAMO-P/X-6020	M1/M2/M3/M4
	Sulfonylazide functional silane	AZ-CUP	M5
Titanates	Isopropyltriisostearoyl titanate	KR TTS	M6
	Isopropyltri(dioctylpyrophospate)	KR 38S	M6
	Titanium di(cumylphenylate) oxyacetate	KR 134S	M6
	Titanium di(dioctylpyrophospate) oxyacetate	KR 138S	M6
	Tetraoctyloxytitanium di(ditridecylphospite)	KR 46B	M6
	Neoalkoxy, tri(dioctylphosphate) titanate	LICA 12	M6
	Neoalkoxy, tri(N-ethylamino-ethylamino) titanate	LICA 44	M6
	Dicyclo(dioctyl)pyrophosphate titanate	KR OPP2	M6
Zirconates	Neoalkyl, trisneodecanoyl zirconate	LZ 01	M6
	Neoalkoxy, trisdodecylbenzene sulfonyl zirconate	LZ 09	M6
	Neoalkoxy, tris(dioctyl)pyrophosphate zirconate	LZ 38	M6
	Neoalkoxy, tris(ethylene diamino) ethyl zirconate	LZ 44	M6

(Continued)

Table 4 (Continued)

Surface Modifier Type	Typical Examples	Trade Names	Manufacturers
Zircoaluminates	Amino functional zircoaluminates	CAVCO MOD A or APG	M7
	Carboxy functional zircoaluminates	CAVCO MOD C or CPG orCPM	M7
	Oleophilic functional	CAVCO MOD F or FPM	M7
	Methacryloxy functional	CAVCO MOD M or MPG orMPM	M7
	Mercapto functional	CAVCO MOD S or SPM	M7
Hydrophobic wetting agents	Polymeric esters	W-900, W-905	M8
	Salt of unsaturated fatty acid	W-910	M8
	Fluorinated alkyl esters	FC-430, FC-431, FC-740	M9
	Perfluoroalkyl sulfonates	FC-93, FC-95, FC-99, FC-120	M9

M1: *Union Carbide Corporation, Old Ridgebury Road, Danbury, CT 06817.*
M2: *Petrarch Systems, Inc., Bartram Road, Bristol, PA 19007.*
M3: *Kay-Fries, Inc., Chemical Div. of Dynamit Nobel of America, Inc., 10 Link Drive, Rockleigh, NJ 07647.*
M4: *Dow Corning Corporation, Midland, MI 48640.*
M5: *Hercules Incorporated, Hercules Plaza, Wilmington, DE 19894.*
M6: *Kenrich Petrochemicals, Inc., 140 East 22nd St., P.O. Box 32, Bayonne, NJ 07002-0032.*
M7: *Cavedon Chemical Co., Inc. Woonsocket, RI 02895.*
M8: *BYK-Mallenckrodt, USA Inc., 19W075 Barbizon, Oak Brook, IL 60521.*
M9: *Commercial Chemicals Division/3M, 223-65E, 3M Center, St. Paul, MN 55144.*

Table 5
Effect of Aggregration on Maximum Filler Concentration ϕ_m [61]

Number of Particles In Aggregated Spheres	Maximum Filler Concentration ϕ_m, Vol. %
1	63.7
3	60
5	53
8	47
12	43
18	39
32	37
57	35
122	34
250	32

A constant torque implies internal homogeneity of the mixture that is achieved within the system's capability limits. A typical torque-time curve generated during a mixing operation [80] of filler and polymer is shown in Figure 2. The major peak represents the moment when the addition of all the filler and polymer to the mixing bowl is complete and when the shearing action begins to disperse the filler into the polymer matrix. As the filler becomes better dispersed, the viscosity of the composite begins to decrease, as exemplified by the recorded torque, till it reaches its equilibrium value beyond which the mixedness would not improve or would improve only marginally due to the system constraints. In fact, it is not advisable to continue mixing once the equilibrium torque level is

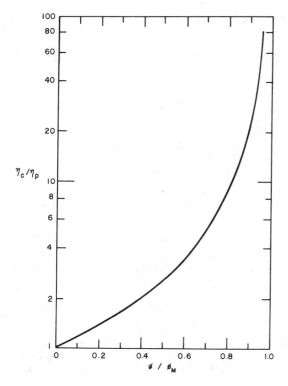

Figure 1. Relative increase in viscosity of a filled polymer as a function of filler volume loading relative to its maximum packing fraction [41, 80].

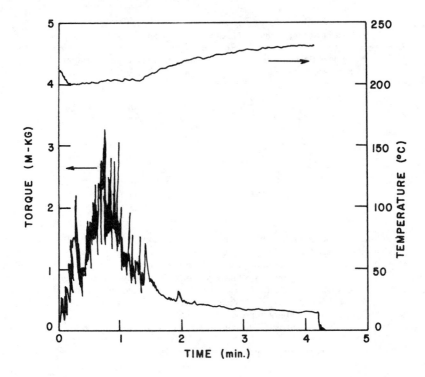

Figure 2. A typical torque-time curve generated in an internal mixer during compounding of fillers into polymers [80].

reached because it could only lead to thermomechanical degradation of the polymer, especially in highly filled systems, where local shear rates between filler particles could be extremely high.

A number of different types of mixer blades are available for the Brabender plasticorder [81] and the Haake torque rheometer [82], such as the roller type, sigma type, cam type or Banbury type, which give different levels of shear during the mixing process. Normally the roller type or the sigma type is preferred for use in the preparation of highly filled composites because of the high level of shear that they give. Bigg [80] found a close similarity in the responses of the two mixers when similar compositions were prepared in a similar manner in the roller blade and the sigma blade mixer. Figure 3 shows the identical rheological response of alumina-filled low density polyethylene at 200°C using different mixer designs.

Besides the type of mixer used, the mixing method plays a significant role in controlling the dispersion level of the polymer composite. The common practice in all low filler loading studies and most high filler loading studies has been to follow a set procedure in terms of the order of addition of filler and polymer, the speed of mixing, and temperature of mixing. This certainly has no adverse effects on the conclusions drawn from the results in studies where only the effect of processing aids or surface treating agents is of interest. But in cases such as ceramic injection molding [60, 67–74], manufacture of flexible or molded magnets [52, 55–57], and preparation of piezoelectric polymer composites [76–78], where the intention is to achieve very high loadings and good dispersion, the mixing conditions must be at the optimum. The effects of mixing conditions has been a rather neglected area in the literature except for the efforts of Lee [83] and Sacks et al. [60]. A cyclic mixing procedure was used by Lee [83] with temperature as a processing variable to reduce the concentration of voids and carbon black agglomerates in the elastomer mix. There are three mixing

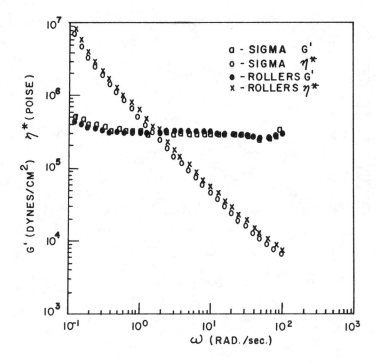

Figure 3. Effect of mixer design on dynamic rheological properties of alumina-filled, low-density polyethylene at 200°C. [80].

variables that could affect the degree of dispersion, namely, the mixing temperature, mixing time, and mixing speed. Sacks et al. [60] also focused on mixing temperature because the effects of mixing time and mixing speed were not as significant as the effect of mixing temperature on the rheology. A plot of dynamic viscosity vs. oscillation frequency for 50 volume percent alumina in 50 volume percent low molecular weight polyethylene at different mixing temperatures of 125, 150, 175, and 220°C is shown in Figure 4. The dispersion in the sample prepared at 150°C is seen to be better than at other temperatures, as adjudged by lower viscosity values and smaller changes in viscosity with increasing frequency. A plot of storage modulus vs. frequency, as shown in Figure 5, also confirms the conclusions. The highest storage moduli values are observed in the sample mixed at 220°C, indicating the presence of extensive particle-particle interactions and poorest dispersion; so also the storage module was independent of frequency, implying the existence of more solid-like behavior due to predominantly strong network formation. The radical effects on dispersion observed due to changes in mixing temperature alone could be attributed to differences in wetting behavior of the polymer and its viscosities at different temperatures. Lower mixing temperatures would preferentially help increase the level of shear during the mixing. However, at temperatures very close to the melting point of the polymer, wettability of the polymer would be the poorest. A moderate balance between these two extremes would thus result in optimum mixing conditions for better dispersion, as indicated by a temperature of 150°C in the case of alumina-polyethylene AC-PE9 system of Sacks et al. [60].

The method of addition of the filler and polymer during the mixing operation could make a difference to the quality of mix because of the differences in the nature of polymer-filler contact. This aspect has not been addressed in the literature yet. In fact, most of the investigators chose their own fixed method of the order of filler and polymer addition during their experiments. For example, Bigg

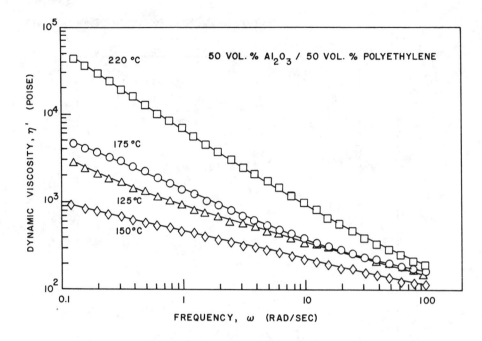

Figure 4. Variation of dynamic viscosity with frequency measured at 125°C for 50 volume percent alumina in polyethylene prepared using different mixing temperatures as indicated [60].

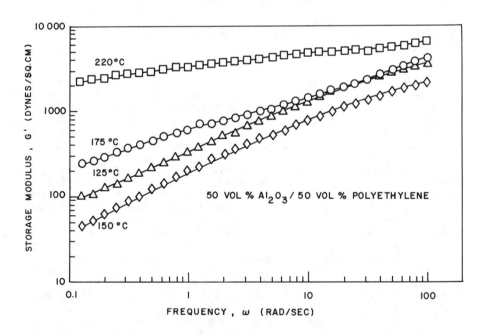

Figure 5. Variation of storage modulus with frequency measured at 125°C for 50 volume percent alumina in polyethylene prepared using different mixing temperatures, as indicated [60].

[40, 41, 48] consistently preheated about one-third of the filler to the mixing temperature of 200°C, then added all the required polymer amount and allowed it to melt while continuing mixing at a moderate rotation speed of 50 rpm. To this premixed polymer-filler system, the remainder of the filler was added and the mixing continued at the same speed until equilibrium torque was reached. Saini et al. [52, 55–57] preheated the entire required filler quantity to the mixing temperature while under rotation at a mixing speed of 50 rpm. The polymer was then added all at once and the rotation increased to 125 rpm. The mixing was then continued till equilibrium torque was reached. Sacks et al. [60] did not preheat the filler, but rather started by first adding all the required polymer quantity to the mixing bowl and letting it melt while in rotation at a high speed of 200 rpm. The filler was then added gradually and the mixing continued for a fixed length of time of 30 minutes.

Preheating the filler certainly has the advantage of much better temperature control throughout the mixing operation. However, when the polymer is added all at once to the preheated filler [52, 55–57], the matrix is suddenly faced with the high loading of the filler that it needs to wet. On the other hand, starting with the polymer melt addition first [60] could make it easier to disperse the filler because the loading occurs in gradually increasing steps as more and more filler gets added. It is probably for this reason that Bigg [40, 41, 48] preheated only one-third of the filler. Hence, this method appears to be a sort of compromise between the two extremes chosen by Saini et al. [52, 55–57] and Sacks et al. [60]. The information in this area is as yet far too limited to make allusions regarding the superiority of one method over the other and hence, no distinct recommendations can be made for the order of filler and polymer addition during the mixing operation. Comparison between the mixing methods is difficult also because different mixing speeds and times were used during the mixing by the different investigators [40, 41, 48, 52, 55–57, 60]. A higher speed [60] would result in higher shear and hence, can be expected to be more beneficial in breaking agglomerates.

However, at the same time, higher speeds are known to induce microbubble formation in the composite melts, which would be extremely difficult to remove and hence, create inhomogeneity in the composite. Lower speeds would certainly help in preventing air entrapment, but would then produce a lower level of shear and would not break agglomerates. Again, a balance has to be achieved and a median speed might be most appropriate depending, of course, upon the polymer-filler combination.

One of the basic problems during compounding of highly filled polymeric systems is the machine wear [84] that occurs due to corrosion and erosion. Often the thermal decomposition of the surface-modifier or other additives can cause corrosive damage. On the other hand, highly filled systems create a very abrasive environment during the high shear mixing and cause considerable wear with time. The wear is directly related to filler hardness, particle size and shape, extent of agglomeration, and level of loading. A suggested method to reduce the wear when mixing highly filled systems is to make use of hardened nitrided steel for the mixing blades or have a special borofuse coating on them and the mixing bowl [82]. The use of matrix additives or filler surface treatment that could reduce the level of torque during mixing due to reduced viscosity [80] as shown in Table 6 would also help in controlling equipment wear.

Table 6
Characteristics of Compounding Al_2O_3 in Low Density Polyethylene
Using a Roller Blade Mixer [80]

Concentration (vol%)	Additive	Equilibrium torque (m·g)
0.32	—	670
0.48	—	1700
0.57	—	3100
0.60	INT-33-UDKH	1400
0.60	Kemamide E	1100
0.60	W-910	1000

RHEOLOGICAL CONSIDERATIONS

For filled polymer systems, knowledge of the degree of dispersion, the extent of matrix-filler affinity, and the behavior of the interfacial region can be obtained from a study of the rheology.

In the past, capillary rheometry has been the most popular technique for obtaining the steady-state rheological response of a material, as it provides information at deformation rates high enough to be close to those encountered during polymer processing. However, the high shear rates achievable in the capillary rheometer do not permit the rheological parameters to remain sensitive to the internal material structure, and hence, the microscopic inhomogeneities get masked. Further, within the capillary tube, there exists a velocity gradient whereby the shear stress at the wall is higher than that at the center of the tube. In filled polymer systems, this leads to migration of the filler particles from the wall towards the center of the tube where the stress is lower, thereby leaving a thin film at the wall which is low in filler concentration or devoid of it. This effect would be more pronounced with large filler particles, especially at higher shear rates. The measured value of apparent viscosity, which is obtained as the ratio of wall shear stress to the shear rate, would not, therefore, be truly representative of the actual rheological characteristic of the material.

One method of overcoming these steady-state measurement problems would be to generate data at lower shear rates, by changing from a capillary rheometer to a cone-and-plate or a parallel-plate viscometer. For filled polymeric systems, the parallel-plate is recommended for use either in steady shear mode or dynamic oscillatory mode. Again, the steady shear mode does not provide very reliable data, especially at higher loadings and for highly agglomerated systems. The internal structure of the material gets broken down during the shearing action, and the centrifugal force developed during the plate rotation throws the sample out of the measuring gap [85, 86], thereby leading to erroneous results. Especially when a thixotropic sweep is used to evaluate the degree of agglomeration, a spurious response may result due to the sample throw-out at the higher end of the shear, thereby giving a lower viscosity in the return curve during this measurement.

The most reliable rheological data on highly filled samples can be obtained through the use of oscillatory measurements. The dynamic rate sweep and the dynamic strain sweep would be the most suitable for assessing the internal structure of the system. During a strain sweep, a plot of storage modulus vs. percentage strain at low frequency would be the best indicator of the level of homogeneity in the system. A decrease in storage modulus with percentage strain would be an indicator of the occurrence of the structural breakdown in the system. During a frequency sweep, it is best to maintain the strain as low as possible within the system constraints, in order to be in the linear viscoelastic region of the material. The response of complex viscosity, storage modulus, loss modulus, and tangent delta that is then obtained would give a measure of the degree of dispersion of the filler in the matrix. A highly agglomerated system would show the existence of a yield at low frequency, the storage modulus would be high and vary minimally with frequency giving a more solid-like response, and the tangent delta would be lower. However, generation of reliable and consistent data in the case of highly filled systems depends to a large extent on the preparation of the sample for the rheological test [87]. Premolding samples under high pressure to a shape and size as would be used for the parallel-plate rheometer test, would ensure that the variation in the observed rheological response is related to the composite characteristics and is not an experimental artifact.

Theoretical equations for modeling the rheological behavior of filled systems have been suggested for low [58] as well as high [55] levels of loading. Shenoy and Saini [58] suggested a form similar to that of Carreau [88] but modified it appropriately for describing the dynamic rheological behavior of low filled systems as:

$$|\eta^*| = |\eta_0^*| [1 + \lambda^2 \omega^2]^{-N} \tag{1}$$

where η_0^* = zero-frequency viscosity function
$\quad\quad\quad \eta^*$ = complex viscosity
$\quad\quad\quad \omega$ = frequency
$\quad\quad\quad \lambda$ = time constant
$\quad\quad\quad N$ = power-law parameter

This equation is ideal for use when the complex viscosity curves show a plateau region in the low frequency range along with a decreasing trend in the higher frequency range. The model given by Equation 1 thus naturally presumes no yield stress. On the other hand, when the filler loading increases, the particle network formed leads to the existence of yield stress in the low frequency region. In such cases of highly filled systems, Saini and Shenoy [55] proposed a modified form of the above equation as:

$$|\eta^*| = \frac{K\omega^{n'-1}}{[1 \pm \omega^2]^{(n'-n'')/2}} \qquad (2)$$

where   K = complex viscosity at frequency of 1 rad/s and at n' = n''
        n' = slope of the $|\eta^*|$ vs. ω curve in the region of $0.1 \le \omega \le 1$
        n'' = slope of the $|\eta^*|$ vs. ω curve in the region of $1 \le \omega \le 10^2$

Equation 2 was suitable for the systems studied by Saini and Shenoy [55] because the complex viscosity in all cases showed the existence of two distinct straight lines—one in the low frequency region below ω equal to 1, and the other in the high frequency region above ω equal to 1. However, in cases where the complex viscosity vs. frequency curves show an initial yield stress followed by a plateau and then a frequency-thinning region, neither of the two equations suggested above can be used. In such circumstances, it might be necessary to break up the curves with two regions and fit two separate equations in each region.

A correlation between complex viscosity η^* and the storage modulus G' was derived [55, 58] by analogously following the method of Wagner [89, 90] for relating the elastic response to the viscous response of the material. The expression obtained [55, 58] was as follows:

$$\frac{G'}{\omega^2} = -\frac{1}{m'} \frac{d|\eta^*|(\omega)}{d\omega} \qquad (3)$$

where m' is an adjustable parameter.

Equations 1 and 3 can be combined to give:

$$\frac{G'}{\omega^2} = \frac{2N\eta_0^*\lambda^2\omega}{m'}(1 + \lambda^2\omega^2)^{-(N+1)} \qquad (4)$$

for low filler loadings.

Equations 2 and 3 can be combined to give:

$$\frac{G'}{\omega^2} = \frac{K}{m'}(1 - n')\omega^{n'-2}[1 + \omega^2]^{(n''-n')/2}\left\{1 + \frac{(n' - n'')\omega^2}{(1 - n')(1 + \omega^2)}\right\} \qquad (5)$$

for high filler loadings.

The loss modulus G'' vs. frequency can be easily predicted from the above equations by using the definition:

$$G'' = \sqrt{(\eta^*\omega)^2 - G'^2} \qquad (6)$$

It was found [55, 58] that the theoretical predictions given by Equations 1–6 agreed well with the experimental determinations for each of the rheological parameters, namely, η^*, G' and G''. All the model parameters with the exception of N varied with filler loading. The adjustable parameter m' itself varied with frequency in one case [55]. Since the model parameter can be correlated with filler compositions, reasonably good estimations of the various rheological characteristics can be made for different filler loadings through the use of Equations 1–6.

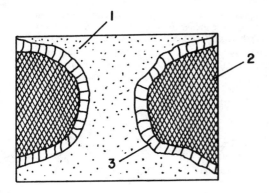

Figure 6. Schematic model of a filled polymer system: (1) polymer, (2) filler, and (3) interphase layer [56].

Effect of Polymer Matrix

Though a filled polymer melt is regarded as a two-phase system, the classical concepts of phases in a material as having clearly distinguishable interfaces is not truly valid. There exists a certain transitional layer (interphase) which includes a layer of the polymeric component altered under the influence of the filler surface (adsorption layer) and a surface layer of the filler which is affected by the polymer matrix [56] as shown in Figure 6. Whereas the properties of the matrix and filler are known before they are compounded, the interphase layer is formed by their interaction and depends largely on their matrix-filler affinity for each other.

The effect of the polymer matrix on the rheology of highly filled polymer composites has been brought out in the work of Saini et al. [55, 57]. The composite systems studied by them consisted of the same filler type; namely, barium ferrite of about 3 micron average particle mixed under the same mixing conditions in four different matrices: S-I-S block copolymer, Hytrel polyester elastomer, thermoplastic polyurethane, and low density polyethylene. The dispersion achieved was determined through steady-state high shear rheology [57] measured in a capillary rheometer and through dynamic low frequency studies [55] measured with parallel-plate geometry.

Figures 7 and 8 show the rheological response of three of the matrices at the same temperature of measurement. It can be seen that S-I-S block copolymer has the highest viscosity while Hytrel polyester elastomer has the lowest. Though low density polyethylene lies in between it is highly shear-thinning in behavior, unlike the other two.

When each of these matrices is filled with 57 volume percent of ferrites, the resulting relative viscosity behavior of the composite is different, as can be seen from Figures 9 and 10. One of the reasons for these differences is that the level of shear during the mixing operation is different in each case due to the differences in the viscosities of the base matrix. On this basis alone, one can expect the relative viscosity in the case of Hytrel polyester elastometer to be the highest. However, there are other reasons such as the matrix-filler affinity that would also contribute to the differences in the composite system viscosity. For example, polyethylene is non-polar and has no affinity for the filler; while S-I-S due to the presence of polystyrene and polyisoprene blocks is polar, and hence, has better affinity to the filler. The result of this affinity is the presence of a greater force to break filler-filler bonds as the polymer pulls the particles away from each other during high shear. This could lead to a better dispersion and lower viscosity. However, when the matrix-filler affinity is high, the system behaves like a bead-spring structure wherein the particles are like beads and the polymer acts as springs. This exemplifies it as a higher viscosity of the composite. The final rheological response is the sum total of the response due to a better dispersion and the restrained deformation behavior due to the bead-spring structure.

Determination of matrix-filler affinity in the melt state has been the subject of a number of investigations [10, 19, 20, 31, 33, 56]. Kataoka et al. [10, 19, 20, 31] used a Maron-Pierce type of

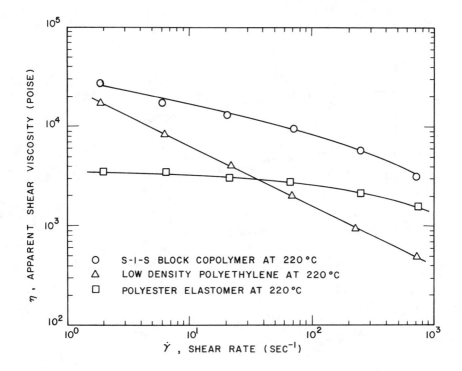

Figure 7. Variation of the apparent steady-shear viscosity with shear rate for unfilled S-I-S block copolymer (○), unfilled low-density polyethylene (△), and unfilled Hytrel polyester elastomer (□) [57].

the following form for relating relative viscosity to volume fraction of filler in order to estimate the thickness of the immobilized polymer adsorbed on the filler surface:

$$\eta_r = \left(1 - \frac{\phi_f}{A}\right)^{-2} \tag{7}$$

where η_r = relative steady shear viscosity of the filled to the unfilled system.
ϕ_f = volume fraction of the filler; and
A = a parameter relating to the packing geometry of the filler,

thus giving a measure of the polymer-filler interaction. Similar studies were carried out by Stamhuis and Loppe [33] wherein the relative steady shear viscosity of the filled and unfilled polymer system plotted against shear stress was taken as a measure of the thickness of the adsorbed layer of the polymer on the filler surface and hence, of the affinity of the polymer for the filler.

Shenoy and Saini [56] used dynamic viscoelastic melt data for quantitative estimation of matrix-filler interaction and postulated that an equation of the following form may be used:

$$\frac{G_c''}{G_p''} = [1 - (\phi_f B)^n]^{-1} \tag{8}$$

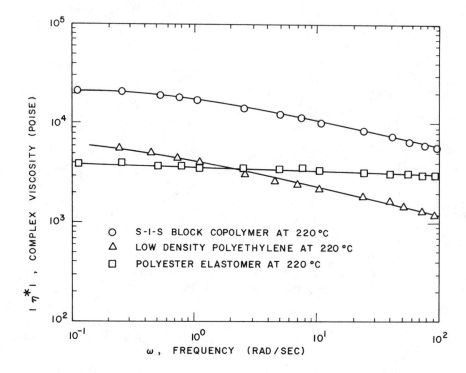

Figure 8. Variation of the complex viscosity with frequency for unfilled S-I-S block copolymer (○), unfilled low-density polyethylene (△), and unfilled Hytrel polyester elastomer (□) [55].

where $G_c^{''}$ and $G_p^{''}$ are the dynamic loss moduli for the filled and unfilled polymer melts, respectively; and ϕ_f is the volume fraction of the filler. The parameter B is related to the filler geometry and the effective thickness ΔR of the interfacial region as follows [91]:

$$B = \left(1 + \frac{2\,\Delta R}{D}\right)^3 \quad \text{for spheres} \tag{9}$$

$$B = \left(1 + \frac{2\,\Delta R}{D}\right)^2 \left(1 + \frac{2\,\Delta R}{L}\right) \quad \text{for rods} \tag{10}$$

$$B = \left(1 + \frac{2\,\Delta R}{D}\right)^2 \left(1 + \frac{2\,\Delta R}{X}\right) \quad \text{for platelets} \tag{11}$$

where   D = diameter of the sphere, rod or platelet
         L = length of the rod
         X = thickness of the platelet

The postulated matrix immobilization at the interphase of the filler given by ΔR is shown schematically in Figure 11.

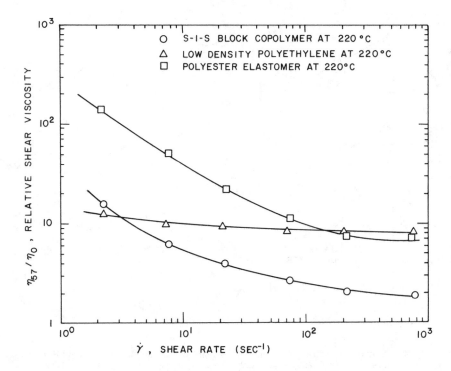

Figure 9. Variation of the relative steady-shear viscosity with shear rate for 57 volume percent barium ferrite filled S-I-S block copolymer (○), low-density polyethylene (△), and Hytrel polyester elastomer (□) [57].

From Equation 8 it is evident that a plot of $(1 - G_p''/G_c'')$ vs. ϕ_f on a log-log scale must yield a straight line, from which the exponent n can be evaluated as the slope and the parameter B from the intercept. ΔR can then be estimated by using the appropriate choice from Equations 9–11.

Effect of Matrix Additives

One method of changing the polymer's interaction with the filler is by the addition of small quantities of matrix additives. Typical examples of these types of additives are the phthalates, fatty acid esters, metallic soaps, paraffin waxes, etc., as shown in Table 3. The main function of most of these additives is to alleviate the attractive forces between the polymer molecules by annulling the dipole-dipole interactions, hydrogen bonding, and other forces existing between polymer molecules. When the intermolecular attractions are disrupted, the polymer molecules flow more easily over each other. This does have an effect on the rheological properties of the composite system.

Figure 12 shows the effect of different types of additives on the viscosity of alumina-filled polyethylene [44, 80]. The lower viscosity is also accompanied by a decrease in the dynamic storage modulus, as shown in Figure 13. It is important when making a choice of the additive to use one that is compatible with the polymer matrix. Incompatible additives can be identified by a sudden drop in the storage modulus at higher frequencies resulting from the migration of the additive to

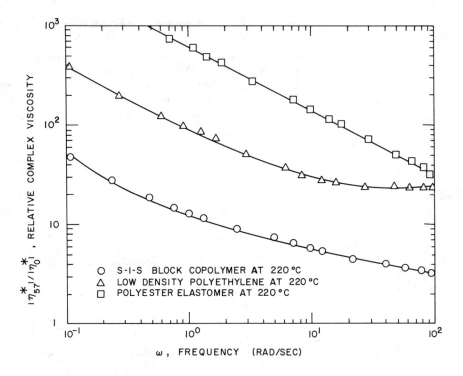

Figure 10. Variation of the relative complex viscosity with frequency for 57 volume percent barium ferrite-filled S-I-S block copolymer (◯), low-density polyethylene (△), and Hytrel polyester elastomer (◻) [55].

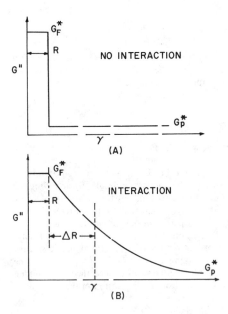

Figure 11. Postulated matrix immobilization at the interface of a dispersed filler with the dynamic complex modulus G^* shown as a function of r, the distance from the center of the filler. ΔR is the effective thickness of the interfacial layer, G_F^* and G_p^* are the complex modulus of filler and matrix, respectively [56].

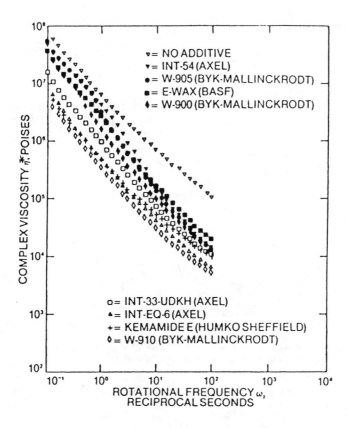

Figure 12. Variation of complex viscosity with frequency showing the effect of wetting agents on the rheology of alumina-filled polyethylene [44].

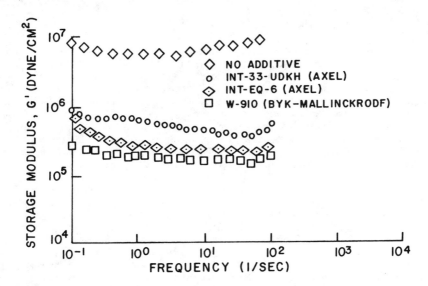

Figure 13. Variation of storage modulus with frequency showing the effect of three of the most effective wetting agents on the rheology of alumina-filled polyethylene [44].

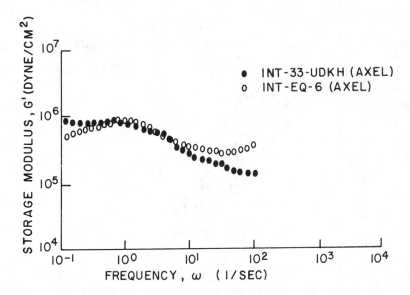

Figure 14. Variation of storage modulus with frequency showing the effect of incompatible additives on the rheology of alumina-filled polystyrene [44].

the measuring tool surface [41, 44] as can be seen from Figure 14. Incompatibility often occurs when the matrix and the additive have different levels of polarity. As these additives are introduced under the influence of heat and are effective at high temperatures, the molecular attractive forces within the polymer get increasingly restored as the system cools down to room temperature. Hence, in many cases, the additive gets forced out of the system when there is a large polarity difference between the polymer and the additive.

Effect of Filler Surface Treatment

Another approach to improving matrix-filler compatibility is the use of surface-modifiers on the filler through a pretreatment process. Surface treatment is meant to help the polymer wet the filler and disperse it. However, the extent of wetting and degree of adhesion are different for each polymer, filler, and surface modifier combination. Some modifiers that will effectively coat the filler surface may not interact with the polymer, whereas others that are compatible with the polymer may not adhere to the filler, and hence, will not effectively modify its surface. Hence, it is very difficult to predict the performance of the surface modifier *a priori* for any filler-polymer combination. It is, therefore, a common practice to select the appropriate surface modifier for a polymer-filler combination rather empirically. One could, of course, refer to the extensive information recently available in the form of books, reports, and papers [92–97] on the various types of surface modifiers listed in Table 4.

Surface modifiers are generally bifunctional molecules with one end capable of adhering to the filler and the other end compatible with the polymer, and at times even capable of reacting with it. There have been extensive studies on the effect of surface treatment on the rheology of filled systems at low filler loadings [8, 14, 16, 32, 34, 35, 37, 42, 43, 47]. The same is not true for highly filled systems. The rheology of highly loaded systems with treated fillers has been studied by Bigg [40, 41, 48], Althouse et al. [44], and Saini et al. [52].

The major thrust of the efforts of Bigg [40, 41, 48] and Althouse et al. [44] was to investigate the influence of a silane A1100 and a titanate KR38S (see Table 4 for chemical description) and to study the effect of the method of surface treatment on the rheology. Polyethylene, which is non-polar, was chosen as the matrix to eliminate the possibility of a chemical reaction with the filler. Spherical steel particles of 15 micron size were used so that they would remain unagglomerated and be devoid of any effects due to variation in particle geometry. The surface modifiers, in one case, were added directly to the polymer melt before adding the filler to the mixer; while, in the other case, a pretreatment step was carried out wherein 5 grams of the modifiers were diluted in 50 ml. of isopropyl alcohol and 500 grams of the steel powder was mixed in it. After drying the powder by evaporating the alcohol under vacuum at 90°C, the treated powder was mixed with the polymer.

The results obtained by the two methods of treatment for the titanate KR38S were different from each other, especially in the low frequency range, wherein it showed a yield stress for the pretreated filler, while showing a viscosity trend similar to the untreated filler when direct addition was used. In the case of silane A1100, the viscosity as well as the shearage modulus curves for the composite prepared by pretreating the filler were almost identical to the curves for the composite prepared by the addition of the surface modifier directly to the melt. Figures 15–18 show the results of the treatment. The titanate KR38S and the silane A1100 both increase the viscosity of the composite over the entire frequency range investigated. It is evident, therefore, that both the surface modifiers couple with the polymer. The organic functionalilty of the surface modifier extends into the polymer phase and creates an apparent increase in the effective radius of the individual filler particles, thus leading to an effective increase in filler loading and hence, an increase in the viscosity and storage modulus of the composite due to greater polymer-filler interaction. A similar effect was observed at lower filler loadings by Luo et al. [47].

Saini et al. [52] used pretreated fillers in their study of the effect of surface modifiers on the melt rheology of styrene-isoprene-styrene block copolymers. The platelet-shaped barium ferrite that was used as filler was not monosized, and had an average particle size of about 3 microns. Two silanes: Z6075 and Z6076; and three titanates: KR 38S, KR 138S, and KR TTS (see Table 4 for chemical description) were used as surface modifiers. The treatment method consisted of using a solution of 95 parts methanol and 5 parts of water by volume for the silanes and 100 parts of xylene for the

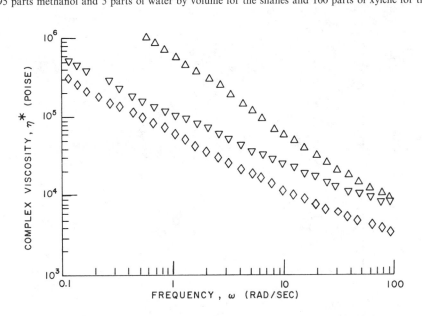

Figure 15. Variation of complex viscosity η^* with frequency ω showing the effect of direct addition of KR 38S ($\triangledown$) and A1100 ($\triangle$) in 60 volume percent alumina-filled polyethylene [40]; ($\diamondsuit$) untreated.

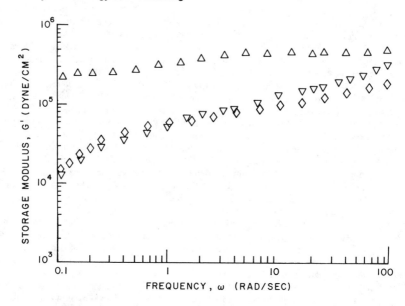

Figure 16. Variation of storage modulus G′ with frequency ω showing the effect of direct addition of KR 38S ($\triangledown$) and A1100 ($\triangle$) in 60 volume percent alumina-filled polyethylene [40]; ($\diamond$) untreated.

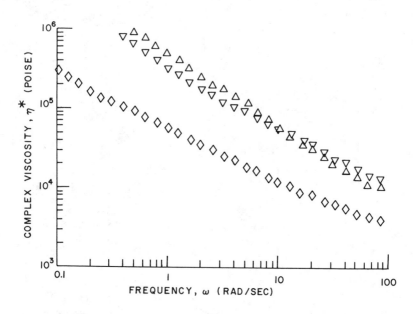

Figure 17. Variation of complex viscosity η^* with frequency ω showing the effect of pretreatment of KR 38S ($\triangledown$) and A1100 ($\triangle$) on 60 volume percent alumina-filled polyethylene [40]; ($\diamond$) untreated.

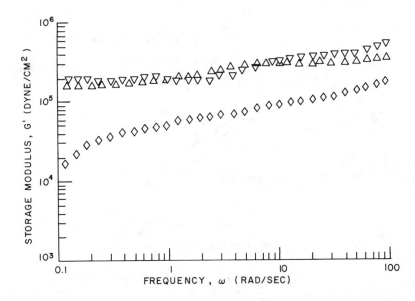

Figure 18. Variation of storage modulus G′ with frequency ω showing the effect of pretreatment of KR 38S (∇) and A1100 (△) on 60 volume percent alumina-filled polyethylene [40]; (◇) untreated.

titanates. Surface modifier of an amount equal to one percent by weight of barium ferrite was dispersed in the solvent. The slurry was formed by wetting the required quantity of barium ferrite with the prepared solution and stirring for about 30 minutes. It was then allowed to stand overnight and the solvent was removed in the oven at 105°C for silanes and 130°C for titanates.

The viscosity vs. shear rate data obtained by Saini et al. [52] for 57 volume percent of barium ferrite pretreated with different surface modifiers is shown in Figure 19. It can be seen that contrary to Bigg [40, 41, 48], the results of Saini et al. [52] show that all the titanates aid in reducing the viscosity of the composite while the silanes show a very marginal effect. Though there have been a number of articles in the literature [7, 8, 14, 32, 34, 40, 92–97] on the mechanism by which surface modifiers act, not all seem to show coherent agreement. Some have postulated [14, 40] that there is a tendency to produce a plasticizing effect, due to the modification of the interfacial characteristics of the filled system. The titanates in the case of Saini et al. [52] could have acted as good dispersing agents, but not as coupling agents, and provided no chemical bridge between the polymer and the filler particles. The scanning electron micrographs shown by Saini et al. [52] give evidence of the fact that the dispersion level is better with the titanates than with the silanes. However, since no low steady shear data or low frequency dynamic data was presented, this conclusion cannot be ascertained with confidence. It is quite plausible that the titanates act as good dispersing agents and provide a plasticizing effect as well, thereby resulting in drastic reductions in viscosity of the composites [52].

The effect of surface modifier concentration was also studied by Saini et al. [52] as shown in Figure 20. It is seen that the optimum concentration is in the range of 0.6–0.8 percent by weight of filler. Then results confirm the range suggested by Monte and Sugerman [93] and Sharma et al. [34]. The exact optimum concentration would, of course, vary for each filler, polymer, and surface modifier combination, and may need to be determined each time.

It must be emphasized here that the method of pretreatment also plays an important role in the final performance of the polymer composite. This point has not been addressed by earlier investigators. The silanes, for example, are known to undergo hydrolysis/condensation reactions, and the

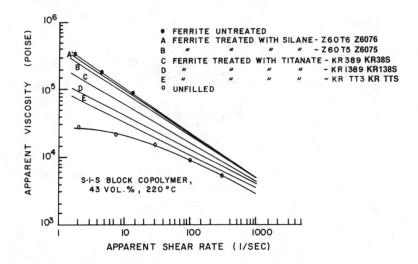

Figure 19. Variation of apparent viscosity with shear rate at 220°C for unfilled, 57 volume percent untreated ferrite filled, and 57 volume percent treated ferrite-filled SIS block copolymer systems [52].

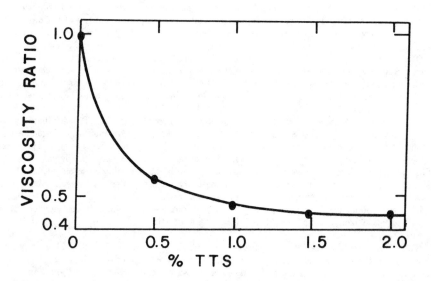

Figure 20. Variation of the viscosity ratio at a shear rate = 100 sec^{-1} of treated to untreated 57 volume percent ferrite-filled SIS with different percentage of KR TTS for determining the optimum treatment level [52].

extent of these reactions is a function of the nature of the solvent phase, silane concentration in solution, pH of the solution, and filler treatment time [91]. Prehydrolysis of the silane is known to be beneficial because the silanols formed in the reaction can then react with the filler surface. However, two silanols can undergo a parallel self-condensation reaction reducing the systems activity toward the filler. By adjusting the pretreatment variables in a favorable manner, it would thus be possible to make either of the possible reactions dominate. This would naturally result in differences in the efficacy of the filler surface modification. Further, it is known that the preferred orientation of a silane molecule at the inorganic filler surface is with the silanol function attached to it and the organofunctional group extending away from it. Deposition of the silane from water or alcohol would naturally assist this favorable orientation, provided the pH is equal to or less than the isoelectric point of the inorganic surface. By altering the pH, it might be possible to deposit the silane in an inverted fashion, as suggested by Plueddeman [92]. This would alter the rheological characteristics of the composite. It is not known to what extent the rheology of the composite could be altered by manipulations in the treating method, and this may need systematic investigation.

Effect of Filler Concentration

With increasing concentration of the filler, the interparticle interactions increase weakly at first and then rather strongly as the concentration becomes higher and higher. The concentration at which particle-particle interactions begin depends on the geometry and surface activity of the filler particles. For example, high aspect ratio fillers would begin to interact at much lower concentrations, while non-agglomerated large size spherical particles would not interact until about 20 volume percent [98]. The final concentration-dependent regime is that when a complete network formation occurs due to particle-to-particle contact, which would occur at concentrations of less than 1 percent for fibers [41] and 40 volume percent for non-agglomerated, randomly dispersed spherical particles [98].

In highly filled systems, as no individual particle can move without disturbing its neighboring particle, the interparticle interactions truly dominate the flow behavior. Saini et al. [57] have shown the variation of relative viscosity with volume fraction of filler for four different polymer matrices at three levels of loadings. One typical plot is shown in Figure 21. The x-axis of the plot is not normalized in a manner similar to Figure 1, because the value of maximum possible loading was not determined for fear of equipment damage due to excessive wear [84] from the abrasive nature of the filler. It is, however, seen that the change in viscosity with filler concentration is exponential and that the major increase in viscosity occurs beyond a filler volume fraction of 0.25 to 0.30. The above conclusions of Saini et al. [57] were based on the rheological data obtained in the high shear region.

In the low shear region, data on the effect of filler concentration were obtained by Bigg [41], and this is shown in Figure 22 for alumina-filled, low density polyethylene composites. The complex viscosity and the storage modulus increase when the filler concentration rises from 32 volume percent to 57 volume percent. It is observed that at filler concentrations of 48 and 57 volume percent, a yield stress shows up at frequencies below 1 rad/s. The storage modulus also begins to depict more solid-like behavior at the higher concentrations, as exemplified by its independence with respect to increasing frequency.

Effect of Filler Size Distribution

The effect of filler size distribution is normally the most difficult to isolate due to added complexities in performing reliable controlled experiments. Hence, it often remains a neglected area. However, in the case of highly filled systems, Bigg [48] has used a very systematic procedure to investigate the effect of different particle size distributions on the packing behavior and the dynamic rheological properties of the composite. Filler particles were chosen very discretely to include both agglomerating and non-agglomerating types, as well as bimodal, narrow, and broad particle size

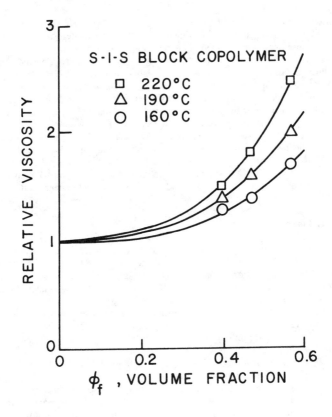

Figure 21. Variation of the relative viscosity with volume fraction of ferrites for styrene-isoprene-styrene block copolymer at three different temperatures [57].

distribution. Table 7 gives the characteristics of the filler particles investigated by Bigg [48] while Table 8 gives the maximum packing fraction of the filler that could be loaded in the polyethylene matrix under the same mixing conditions.

As expected, it was found [48] that using a broad size distribution or a bimodal dispersion improved the level of maximum packing fraction as compared to that using a narrow size distribution. In the case of random shaped alumina and zirconia, which normally exist in agglomerated form, matrix additives were needed to achieve the maximum packing fraction. In the case of unagglomerated spherical steel particles, a bimodal distribution alone could produce the desired effect, as the smaller particles could easily be segregated into the interstices of the larger particles. Of course, its non-random packing is not completely achieveable in a random mixing process. Broadly distributed powders do have a random packing arrangement at their maximum packing fraction. Bigg [48] has shown how the difference between the two packing arrangements can be detected by changes in the shear modulus-frequency response of the composite melt during dynamic measurements in the low strain region. Figure 23 shows that, though the complex viscosity for bimodal distribution of stainless steel spheres and alumina particles is the same, their storage modulus responses are different. Bigg [48] attributed the initial drop in the modulus value at low frequency to the movement of the smaller particles during their flow into the intersticial spaces between the larger particles. The low level of oscillatory motion provides sufficient energy to initiate the movement and create a more

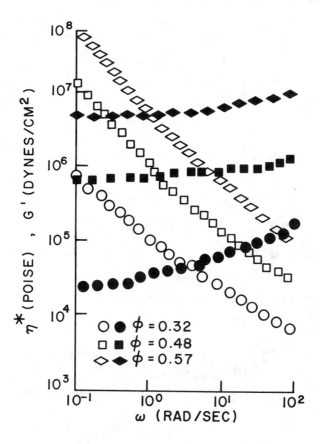

Figure 22. Effect of filler concentration on the complex viscosity and storage modulus variation with frequency for alumina-filled polyethylene [41].

Table 7
Characteristics of Filler Particles Investigated by Bigg [48]

Type	Supplier	Grade	$\bar{d}_1$, μm	$\bar{d}_2$, μm	$d_{84} - d_{16}$	d_{84}/d_{16}	PSD
SS	Amdry	136F	15	—	30 – 9.3	3.2	narrow
SS	—	—	6 (36%)	54 (64%)	—	—	bimodal
Al_2O_3	Alcoa	Al6-SG	0.6	—	1.2 – 0.35	3.4	narrow
Al_1O_3	—	—	2 (30%)	15 (70%)	—	3.4	narrow
ZrO_2	Zircoa	Type C	3	—	8.0 – 1.5	5.3	broad
Si_3N_4	GTE Sylvania	SN 5	<1	—	—	—	—

efficient packing. This occurs favorably for bimodal distribution but fails for broad distribution of zirconia particles, as shown in Figure 24. Even the use of matrix additive does not show the effect observed for the bimodal distribution. Bigg [48] concluded that bimodally distributed powders had the potential of higher loadings than broadly distributed powder, and one cannot achieve the theoretical maximum fraction by the usual random mixing procedures.

Table 8
Maximum Packing Fraction of Various Suspensions [48]

Filler	PSD	ϕ_m	Surface Treatment
stainless steel	narrow	0.63	none
stainless steel	bimodal	0.69	none
Al_2O_3	narrow	0.57	none
Al_2O_3	narrow	0.63	W-910, Kemamide E
Al_2O_3	bimodal	0.70	W-910, Kemamide E
ZrO_2	broad	0.60	none
ZrO_2	broad	0.70	W-910, Kemamide E
Si_3N_4	unspecified	0.62	Kemamide E, W-900, none

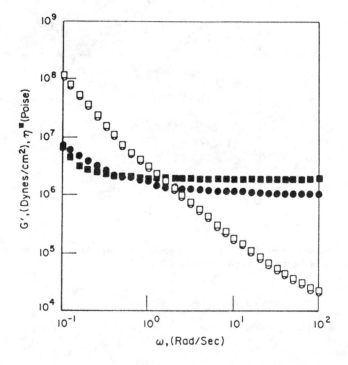

Figure 23. Variation of complex viscosity η^* and storage modulus G′ with frequency ω, showing the effect of bimodal distribution of stainless steel ($\square$, $\blacksquare$; $\phi = 0.68$) and alumina ($\bigcirc$, $\bullet$; $\phi = 0.60$) in polyethylene at 200°C [48].

CONCLUSION

Rheology of highly filled polymer melt systems has received the attention of only a handful of investigators [40, 41, 48, 52, 55–57, 60] during the past few years, as can be seen from Table 1. However, it is an area which is growing rapidly in importance and hence cannot be ignored in the future. In the foregoing sections, a detailed review of the work done until now in this area was presented,

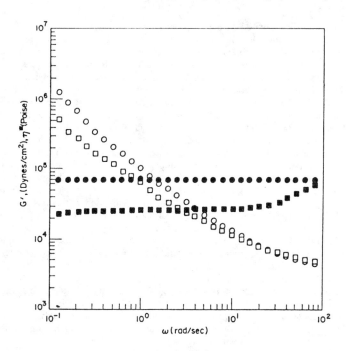

Figure 24. Variation of complex viscosity η^* and storage modulus G' with frequency ω for zirconia-filled polyethylene at 200°C (○, ●; $\phi = 0.69$ for Kemamide E treatment) and (□, ■; $\phi = 0.60$ for no surface treatment) [48].

and a few conclusions that can be drawn even from the limited premises available are summarized below.

During preparation of the composite, care ought to be taken to see that the conditions are favorable for optimum results. Variables such as mixer type, mixing speed, mixing time, mixing temperature, and order of component addition must be studied comprehensively for better performance. Based on existing information [40, 57, 60, 80], it appears that the most sensitive of these variables are the mixing temperature and the order of component addition. The mixing temperature should be chosen such that it is as close to the polymer melt temperature as possible in order to ensure the highest level of shear during mixing, and at the same time, it should be high enough to facilitate proper wetting of filler [60]. As regards the order of component addition during mixing, it is not at all clear which is the preferred route, i.e.: (a) addition of the filler to the melt [60], (b) addition of the polymer to the filler [52, 55–57] or (c) mixing part filler with all polymer and then adding the remainig portion of the filler to the premix [40, 41, 48]. A systematic study in this area in the future would certainly help. With respect to mixer type, mixing speed, and mixing time, a rough guideline would be to choose any type of high shear mixer (sigma or roller type) [80], use the highest possible mixing speed to achieve maximum possible shear within the system constraints [60], and to keep the mixing time to a minimum after equilibrium torque is reached [40, 41, 48, 52, 55–57] in order to minimize polymer degradation and to prevent equipment wear [84].

An idea about the level of dispersion can be gotten from the torque vs. time curve [80] obtained from the mixer, as shown in Figure 2. However, the more sensitive method of adjudging the degree of internal homogeneity of the composite melt is by the rheological response that the mixes depict. Capillary rheometry is not recommended for judging the degree of agglomeration, though it could give useful information regarding the flow behavior of the composite at deformation rates which closely resemble those encountered during the processing operations. Dynamic oscillatory rheological measurements in the low frequency and low strain region would provide the maximum information regarding the agglomeration and the degree of dispersion in the system, and hence, should be preferentially used, taking care to see that the samples for the rheological tests are correctly prepared [87]. The rheological data in terms of η^*, G', and G'' obtained through dynamic rheological tests could be modeled through equations similar in form to those suggested in the literature for filled systems [55, 58]. The advantage of this type of modeling is that the model parameters can be correlated with filler composition, so that reasonable estimates of the rheological characterization can be made at loadings different from those that are studied.

The rheological characteristic of the composite depends to a large extent on the type of polymer matrix; i.e., on its degree of polarity, its molecular weight, its viscosity, and its affinity for the filler. Use of certain select types of additives (see, for example, Table 3), is quite common in order to alter the matrix filler affinity [41, 44, 80]. However, care must be exercised in making the right choice of the additive as incompatible additives are known to migrate [44] to regions of high shear, thereby causing inhomogeneity during the mixing. It is best to choose an additive that has as close a polarity to that of the polymer as possible. The degree of matrix-filler affinity can be judged from the level of increase in the viscosity of the composite relative to the polymer [10, 19, 20, 31, 33]. Another method of quantitatively determining the matrix-filler interaction is by calculating the immobilized polymer layer at the filler surface by using the ratio of the loss moduli of the composite to that of the polymer and determining the interaction radius [56].

Filler surface treatment [92–97] can also be used to improve the affinity of the matrix for the filler. The method of surface treatment [40, 41, 44, 48, 92] could make a difference to the type and level of surface modification that can be achieved. This could, in turn, affect the rheology of the filled system. A detailed study with regard to the method of surface treatment in terms of the treating solvent used, treating time, pH of the treating solution, etc., and its effect on the rheological behavior of the composite formed with treated fillers, would be a useful addition to the existing literature. It has been shown [40, 41, 44, 48, 52] that direct addition of surface modifier to the polymeric melt during mixing, as opposed to pretreatment of the filler before mixing, does make a difference in the rheological response of the composite system. As regards the effect of surface modifier concentration, there seems to be a certain degree of concurrence that a level of about 0.6–0.8 percent by weight of filler is near optimum [34, 52, 93].

Filler concentration certainly has a large effect on the rheology of highly filled systems. The exponential nature of the curve, as can be seen from Figures 1 and 21, clearly indicates that small additions of filler at the higher levels of loading would make large differences in the relative viscosity of the composites. The filler shape, size, and size distribution also have a considerable effect on the rheology of the filled system [48]. A bimodal distribution has a better potential for higher loadings than a broad distribution, though in practice, the theoretical maximum possible loading fraction cannot be achieved by the simple random mixing procedures used for preparing the composites [48].

In conclusion, the rheology of highly filled system is, undoubtedly, a pragmatically important area [52, 55–57, 60, 67–74, 76–78] which is still young and needs a lot of attention from researchers from different disciplines, such as chemists, material scientists, chemical engineers and polymer technologists. The present chapter summarizes all the recent efforts and indicates the untrodden areas where steps could be undertaken to unravel some of the mysteries underlying these rheologically complex systems.

NOTATION

A parameter relating to the packing geometry of the filler in Equation 7.

B parameter related to the filler geometry appearing in Equation 8 and defined by Equations 9–11.

D diameter (m) of sphere, rod, or platelet in Equations 9–11.

G' storage modulus (dynes/sq cm) appearing in Equations 3–6.

G'' loss modulus (dynes/sq cm) defined by Equation 6.

G_c'' loss modulus (dynes/sq cm) of the composite appearing in Equation 8.

G_p'' loss modulus (dynes/sq cm) of the unfilled polymer appearing in Equation 8.

K complex viscosity (poise) at frequency of 1 rad/sec appearing in Equations 2 and 5.

L length (m) of the rod in Equation 10.

m' adjustable parameter appearing in Equations 3–5.

n power-law index in Equation 8.

n' slope of the $|\eta^*|$ versus ω curve in the region of $0.1 \leq \omega \leq 1$.

n'' slope of the $|\eta^*|$ versus ω curve in the region of $1 \leq \omega \leq 100$.

N power-law parameter appearing in Equations 1 and 4.

Greek Symbols

λ time constant (sec) appearing in Equations 1 and 4.

η_r relative steady shear viscosity of the filled to the unfilled system appearing in Equation 7.

η^* complex viscosity (poise) appearing in Equations 1–4.

η_0^* zero-frequency viscosity function (poise) appearing in Equations 1 and 3.

ϕ_f volume fraction of filler appearing in Equations 7 and 8.

ω frequency (rad/sec) appearing in Equations 1–6.

REFERENCES

1. Zakharenko, N. V., Tolstukhina, F. S., and Bartenev, G. M., "Flow of Rubber-Like Polymer With and Without Carbon Black," *Rubber Chem. Technol*, Vol. 35, 1962, pp. 326–334.

2. Chapman, F. M., and Lee, T. S., "Effect of Talc Filler on the Melt Rheology of Polypropylene," *SPE Journal*, Vol. 26, 1970, pp. 37–40.

3. Mills, N. J., "The Rheology of Filled Polymers," *J. Appl. Polym. Sci.*, Vol. 15, 1971, pp. 2791–2805.

4. Nazem, F., and Hill, C. T., "Elongational and Shear Viscosities of a Bead-Filled Thermoplastic," *Trans. Soc. Rheol.*, Vol. 18, 1974, pp. 87–101.

5. Han, C. D., "Rheological Properties of Calcium Carbonate-Filled Polypropylene Melts," *J. Appl. Polym. Sci.*, Vol. 18, 1974, pp. 821–829.

6. White, J. L., and Crowder, J. W., "The Influence of Carbon Black on the Extrusion Characteristics and Rheological Properties of Elastomers: Polybutadiene and Butadiene-Styrene Copolymer," *J. Appl. Polym. Sci.*, Vol. 18, 1974, pp. 1013–1038.

7. Minagawa, N., and White, J. L., "The Influence of Titanium Dioxide on the Rheological Extrusion Properties of Polymer Melts," *J. Appl. Polym. Sci.*, Vol. 20, 1976, pp. 501–523.

8. Boira, M. S., and Chaffey, C. E., "Effects of Coupling Agents on the Mechanical and Rheological Properties of Mica-Reinforced Polypropylene," *Polym. Eng. Sci.*, Vol. 17, 1977, pp. 715–718.

9. Bigg, D. M., "Rheology and Wire Coating of High Atomic Number Metal—Low Density Polyethylene Composites," *Polym. Eng. Sci.*, Vol. 17, 1977, pp. 745–750.

10. Kataoka, T., Kitano, T., Sasahara, M., and Nishijima, K., "Viscosity of Particle Filled Polymer Melts," *Rheol. Acta*, Vol. 17, 1978, pp. 149–155.

11. Kataoka, T., Kitano, T., and Nishimura, T., "Utility of Parallel-Plate Plastometer for Rheological Study of Filled Polymer Melts," *Rheol. Acta*, Vol. 17, 1978, pp. 626–631.

12. Mennig, G., and Hinkelmann, B., "Zum Fliessverhalten von Kurzglasfasergefullten Styrol-Acrylnitril-Copolymeren," *Die Ange. Makromol. Chemie*, Vol. 74, 1978, pp. 249–258.

13. Chan, Y., White, J. L., and Oyanagi, Y., "Influence of Glass Fibers on the Extrusion and Injection Molding Characteristics of Polyethylene and Polystyrene Melts," *Polym. Eng. Sci.*, Vol. 18, 1978, pp. 268–272.

14. Han, C. D., Sandford, C., and Yoo, H. J., "Effects of Titanate Coupling Agents on the Rheological and Mechanical Properties of Filled Polyolefins," *Polym. Eng. Sci.*, Vol. 18, 1978, pp. 849–854.

15. Chan, Yu., White, J. L., and Oyanagi, Y., "A Fundamental Study of the Rheological Properties of Glass Fiber-Reinforced Polyethylene and Polystyrene Melts," *J. Rheol.*, Vol. 22, 1978, pp. 507–524.

16. Monte, S. J., and Sugerman, G., "A New Generation of Age- and Water-Resistant Reinforced Plastics," *Polym. Plastics Tech. Eng.*, Vol. 12, 1979, pp. 115–135.

17. Lobe, V. M., and White, J. L., "An Experimental Study of the Influence of Carbon Black on the Rheological Properties of a Polystyrene Melt," *Polym. Eng. Sci.*, Vol 19, 1979, pp. 617–624.

18. Wu, S., "Order-Disorder Transitions in the Extrusion of Fiber-Filled Poly(Ethylene Terephthalate) and Blends," *Polym. Eng. Sci.*, Vol. 19, 1979, pp. 638–650.

19. Kataoka, T., Kitano, T., Oyanagi, Y., and Sasahara, M., "Viscous Properties of Calcium Carbonate Filled Polymer Melts," *Rheol. Acta*, Vol. 18, 1979, pp. 635–639.

20. Kitano, T., Kataoka, T., Nishimura, T., and Sakai, T., "Relative Viscosities of Polymer Melts Filled with Inorganic Fillers," *Rheol. Acta*, Vol. 19, 1980, pp. 764–769.

21. Kitano, T., Nishimura, T., Kataoka, T., and Sakai, T., "Correlation of Dynamic and Steady Flow Viscosities of Filled Polymer Systems," *Rheol. Acta*, Vol. 19, 1980, pp. 671–673.

22. Crowson, R. J., Folkes, M. J., and Bright, P. F., "Rheology of Short Glass Fiber-Reinforced Thermoplastics and Its Application to Injection Molding I. Fiber Motion and Viscosity Measurement," *Polym. Eng. Sci.*, Vol. 20, 1980, pp. 925–933.

23. Crowson, R. J., and Folkes, M. J., "Rheology of Short Glass Fiber-Reinforced Thermoplastics and Its Application to Injection Molding. II. The Effect of Material Parameters," *Polym. Eng. Sci.*, Vol. 20, 1980, pp. 934–940.

24. Goel, D. C., "Effect of Polymeric Additives on the Rheological Properties of Talc-Filled Polypropylene," *Polym. Eng. Sci.*, Vol. 20, 1980, pp. 198–201.

25. Tanaka, H., and White, J. L., "Experimental Investigations of Shear and Elongational Flow Properties of Polystyrene Melts Reinforced with Calcium Carbonate, Titanium Dioxide, and Carbon Black," *Polym. Eng. Sci.*, Vol. 20, 1980, pp. 949–956.

26. Czarnecki, L., and White, J. L., "Shear Flow Rheological Properties, Fiber Damage, and Mastication Characteristics of Aramid-Glass and Cellulose-Fiber-Reinforced Polystyrene Melts," *J. Appl. Polym. Sci.*, Vol. 25, 1980, pp. 1217–1244.

27. White, J. L., Czarnecki, L., and Tanaka, H., "Experimental Studies of the Influence of Particle and Fiber Reinforcement on the Rheological Properties of Polymer Melts," *Rubber Chem. Tech.*, Vol. 53, 1980, pp. 823–835.

28. Hancock, M., Tremayne, P., and Rosevear, J., "Fillers in Polypropylene. II," *J. Polym. Sci., Polym. Chem. Ed.*, Vol. 18, 1980, pp. 3211–3217.

29. Knutsson, B. A., White, J. L., and Abbas, K. A., "Rheological and Extrusion Characteristics of Glass-Fiber-Reinforced Polycarbonate," *J. Appl. Polym. Sci.*, Vol. 26, 1981, pp. 2347–2362.

30. Hinkelmann, B., "Zum Fliessverhalten Kurzglasfasergefillter Thermoplastchmelzen in Stationaren und Instationaren Bereich," *Rheol. Acta*, Vol. 20, 1981, pp. 561–568.

31. Kitano, T., Kataoka, T., and Shirata, T., "An Empirical Equation of the Relative Viscosity of Polymer Melts Filled with Various Inorganic Fillers," *Rheol. Acta*, Vol. 20, 1981, pp. 207–209.

32. Han, C. D., Van der Weghe, T., Shete, P., and Haw, J. R., "Effect of Coupling Agents on the Rheological Properties, Processability, and Mechanical Properties of Filled Polypropylene," *Polym. Eng. Sci.*, Vol. 21, 1981, pp. 196–204.

33. Stamhuis, J. E., and Loppe, J. P. A., "Rheological Determination of Polymer-Filler Affinity," *Rheol. Acta*, Vol. 21, 1982, pp. 103–105.

34. Sharma, Y. N., Patel, R. D., Dhimmar, I. H., and Bhardwaj, I. S., "Studies of the Effect of Titanate Coupling Agent on the Performance of Polypropylene-Calcium Carbonate Composite," *J. Appl. Polym. Sci.*, Vol. 27, 1982, pp. 97–104.

35. Nakatsuka, T., Kawasaki, H., Itadani, K., and Yamashita, S., "Phosphate Coupling Agents for Calcium Carbonate Filler," *J. Appl. Polym. Sci.*, Vol. 27, 1982, pp. 259–269.

36. Lee, W. M., Abe, D. A., Chipalkatti, M. H., and Liaw, T. F., "Rheological Properties of Particulate-Filled Linear Low Density Polyethylenes," *Proc. Ann. Conf. Reinf. Plast. Compos. Inst., Soc. Plast. Ind.*, 37, 12D, 1982, pp. 7.

37. Juskey, V. P., and Chaffey, C. E., "Rheology and Tensile Properties of Polypropylene Reinforced with Glycerol-Treated-Mica," *Can. J. Chem. Eng.*, Vol. 60, 1982, pp. 334–341.

38. Hinkelmann, B., "Zur Analytischen Beschreibung des Fullstoffein-flusses auf das Fliessverhalten von Kunststoff-Schmelzen," *Rheol. Acta*, Vol. 21, 1982, pp. 491–493.

39. Utracki, L. A., and Fisa, B., "Rheology of Fiber-or Flake-Filled Plastics," *Polym. Composites*, Vol. 3, 1982, pp. 193–211.
40. Bigg, D. M., "Rheological Analysis of Highly Loaded Polymeric Composites Filled with Non-Agglomerating Spherical Filler Particles," *Polym. Eng. Sci.*, Vol. 22, 1982, pp. 512–518.
41. Bigg, D. M., "Rheological Behavior of Highly Filled Polymer Melts," *Polym. Eng. Sci.*, Vol. 23, 1983, pp. 206–210.
42. Shenoy, A. V., Saini, D. R., and Nadkarni, V. M., "Rheograms of Filled Polymer Melts from Melt-Flow Index," *Polym. Composites*, Vol. 4, 1983, pp. 53–63.
43. Suetsugu, Y., and White, J. L., "The Influence of Particle Size and Surface Coating of Calcium Carbonate on the Rheological Properties of its Suspensions in Molten Polystyrene," *J. Appl. Polym. Sci.*, Vol. 28, 1983, pp. 1481–1501.
44. Althouse, L. M., Bigg, D. M., and Wong, W. M., "Evaluating the Effectiveness of Filler Surface Treatments," *Plastics Compounding*, March/April 1983.
45. Shenoy, A. V., and Saini, D. R., "Interpretation of Flow Data for Multicomponent Polymeric Systems," *Colloid Polym. Sci.*, Vol. 261, 1983, pp. 846–854.
46. Lem, K. W., and Han, C. D., "Rheological Behavior of Concentrated Suspensions of Particulates in Unsaturated Polyester Resin," *J. Rheol.*, Vol. 27, 1983, pp. 263–288.
47. Luo, H. L., Han, C. D., and Mijovic, J., "Effects of Coupling Agents in the Rheological Behavior and Physical/Mechanical Properties of Filled Nylon 6," *J. Appl. Polym. Sci.*, Vol. 28, 1983, pp. 3387–3398.
48. Bigg, D. M., "Complex Rheology of Highly Filled Thermoplastic Melts," Proc. IX Intl. Congress on Rheology in Mexico, Adv. in Rheology, Vol. 3, 1984, pp. 429–437.
49. Kitano, T., Kataoka, T., and Nagatsuka, Y., "Shear Flow Rheological Properties of Vinylon- and Glass-Fiber Reinforced Polyethylene Melts," *Rheol. Acta*, Vol. 23, 1984, pp. 20–30.
50. Kitano, T., Kataoka, T., and Nagatsuka, Y., "Dynamic Flow Properties of Vinylon Fibre and Glass Fiber Reinforced Polyethylene Melts," *Rheol. Acta*, Vol. 23, 1984, pp. 408–416.
51. Suetsugu, Y., and White, J. L., "A Theory of Thixotropic Plastic Viscoelastic Fluids with a Time-Dependent Yield Surface and Its Comparison to Transient and Steady State Experiments on Small Particle Filled Polymer Melts," *J. Non-Newtonian Fluid Mech.*, Vol. 14, 1984, pp. 121–140.
52. Saini, D. R., Shenoy, A. V., and Nadkarni, V. M., "Effect of Surface Treatment on the Rheological and Mechanical Properties of Ferrite Filled Polymeric Systems," *Polym. Eng. Sci.*, Vol. 25, 1985, pp. 807–811.
53. Hinkelmann, B., and Mennig, G., "On the Rheological Behavior of Filled Polymer Melts," *Chem. Eng. Comm.*, Vol. 36, 1985, pp. 211–221.
54. Bretas, R. E. S., and Powell, R. L., "Dynamic and Transient Rheological Properties of Glass-Filled Polymer Metls," *Rheol. Acta*, Vol. 24, 1985, pp. 69–74.
55. Saini, D. R., and Shenoy, A. V., "Viscoelastic Properties of Highly Loaded Ferrite-Filled Polymeric Systems," *Polym. Eng. Sci.*, Vol. 26, 1986, pp. 441–445.
56. Shenoy, A. V., and Saini, D. R., "Quantitative Estimation of Matrix Filler Interactions in Ferrite-Filled Styrene-Isoprene-Styrene Block Copolymer Systems," *Polym. Composites*, Vol. 7, 1986, pp. 96–100.
57. Saini, D. R., Shenoy, A. V., and Nadkarni, V. M., "Melt Rheology of Highly Loaded Ferrite-Filled Polymer Composites," *Polym. Composites*, Vol. 7, 1986, pp. 193–200.
58. Shenoy, A. V., and Saini, D. R., "Wollastonite Reinforced Polypropylene Composites: Dynamic and Steady State Melt Flow Behavior," *J. Reinf. Plastics Comp.*, Vol. 5, 1986, pp. 62–73.
59. Mutel, A. T., and Kamal, M. R., "Characterization of the Rheological Behavior of Fiber-Filled Polypropylene Melts Under Steady and Oscillatory Shear Using Cone-and-Plate and Rotational Parallel Plate Geometry," Polym. Composites, Vol. 7, 1986, pp. 283–294.
60. Sacks, M. D., Khadilkar, C. S., Scheiffele, G. W., Shenoy, A. V., Dow, J. H., and Sheu, R. S., "Dispersion and Rheology in Ceramic Processing," *Advances in Ceramics*, Vol. 21, 1987, pp. 495–515.
61. Nielsen, L. E., *Mechanical Properties of Polymers and Composites*, Marcel Dekker, New York, Vol. 2, Ch. 7, 1974, pp. 379–386.

62. Han, C. D., *Rheology in Polymer Processing*, Academic Press, New York, Ch. 7, 1976, pp. 182–188.
63. Nielsen, L. E., *Polymer Rheology*, Marcel Dekker, New York, Ch. 9, 1977, pp. 133–157.
64. Paul, D. R., and Newman, S., *Polymer Blends*, Academic Press, New York, Vol. 1, Ch. 7, 1978, pp. 295–352.
65. Vinogradov, G. V., and Malkin, A. Y., *Rheology of Polymers*, Mir Publishers, Moscow, Ch. 6, 1980, pp. 380–402.
66. Han, C. D., *Multiphase Flow in Polymer Processing*, Academic Press, New York, 1981.
67. Whalen, T. J., and Johnson, C. F., "Injection Molding of Ceramics," Amer. Ceram. Soc. Bull., Vol. 60, 1981, pp. 216–220.
68. Mangels, J. A., "Fabrication of Complex Shaped Ceramic Articles by Slip Casting and Injection Molding," *Progress in Nitrogen Ceramics*, Riley, F. L. ed., Martinus Nijhoff Pub., Boston, 1983, pp. 231–236.
69. Mangels, J. A., and Williams, R. M., "Injection Molding Ceramics to High Green Densities," *Am. Cer. Soc. Bull.*, Vol. 62, 1983, pp. 601–606.
70. Mutsuddy, B. C., "Injection Molding Research Paves Way to Ceramic Engine Parts," *Ind. Res. Development*, July 1983, pp. 76–80.
71. Bandyopadhyay, G., and French, K. W., "Near Net Shape Fabrication and Densification of Silicon Nitride," Proc. of Workshop in Conservation and Substitution Technology for Critical Metals in Bearings and Related Components, Vanderbilt University, Nashville, TN, March 12–14, 1984.
72. Mangels, J. A., and Trela, W., "Ceramic Components by Injection Molding," *Advances in Ceramics*, Vol. 9, 1984, pp. 234–238.
73. Mutsuddy, B. C., "Overview on Organic Binder for Whiteware Ceramics," 39th Pacific Coast Regional Meeting, Washington, Oct. 22–24, 1986.
74. Schurtz, J. F., "Methylcellulose Polymers as Binders for Extrusion of Ceramics," 39th Pacific Coast Regional Meeting, Washington, Oct. 22–24, 1986.
75. Bhattacharya, S. K. (ed.), *Metal-Filled Polymers: Properties and Application*, Marcel Dekker, Inc., New York and Basel, 1986.
76. Runt, J., and Galgoci, E. C., "Polymer/Piezoelectric Ceramic Composites: Polystyrene and Poly(Methyl Methacrylate) with PZT," *J. Appl. Polym. Sci.*, Vol. 29, 1984, pp. 611–617.
77. Runt, J., and Galgoci, E. C., "Piezoelectric Composites of PZT and Some Semi-Crystalline Polymers," *Mat. Res. Bull.*, Vol. 19, 1984, pp. 253–260.
78. Newnham, R. E., and Runt, J. P., "Polymer-Piezoelectric Ceramic Composites," *Polym. News*, Vol. 10, 1984, pp. 132–138.
79. Deryagin, B. V., Krotova, N. A., and Smilga, V. P., "Adhesion of Solids," Consultants Bureau, New York, 1978, p. 282.
80. Bigg, D. B., "Interrelation Among Feedstock Form, Product Requirements, Equipment Type, and Operating Parameters in Polymer Mixing Processes," *Polym. Plast. Technol. Eng.*, Vol. 23, No. 2, 1984, pp. 133–168.
81. Brabender, O. H. G., Duisburg, Postfach 350162, Kulturstrasse 51–55 D-4100 Duisburg 1, FRG.
82. Haake Buchler Instruments, Inc. 244 Saddle River Road, P.O. Box 549, Saddle Brook, NJ 07662.
83. Lee, M. C. H., "The Effects of Degree of Mixing on the Properties of Filled Elastomer," *J. Appl. Polym. Sci.*, Vol. 29, 1984, pp. 499–508.
84. Olmstead, B. A., "How Glass-Fiber Fillers Affect Injection Machines," *SPE J.*, Vol. 26, 1970, pp. 42–43.
85. Connelly, R. W., and Greener, J., "High Shear Viscometry With a Rotational Parallel-Disk Device," *J. Rheol.*, Vol. 29, 1985, pp. 209–226.
86. Kosinski, L. E., and Caruthers, J. M., "The Effect of Particle Concentration on the Rheology of Polydimethylsiloxane Filled with Fumed Silica," *J. Appl. Polym. Sci.*, Vol. 32, 1986, pp. 3393–3406.
87. Rheometrics, Inc., One Possumtown Rd., Piscataway, NJ 08854.
88. Carreau, P. J., "Rheological Equations from Molecular Network Theories," *Trans. Soc. Rheol.*, Vol. 16, 1972, pp. 99–127.

89. Wagner, M. H., "Analysis of Time-Dependent Non-Linear Stress-Growth Data for Shear and Elongational Flow of a Low-Density Branched Polyethylene Melt," *Rheol. Acta*, Vol. 15, 1976, pp. 136–142.

90. Wagner, M. H., "Prediction of Primary Stress Difference from Shear Viscosity Data Using a Single Integral Constitutive Equation," *Rheol. Acta*, Vol. 16, 1977, pp. 43–50.

91. Ziegel, K. D., "Role of the Interface in Mechanical Energy Dissipation of Composites," *J. Colloid Interf. Sci.*, Vol. 29, 1969, pp. 72–80.

92. Plueddemann, E. P., *Silane Coupling Agents*, Plenum Press, New York and London, 1982.

93. Monte, S. J., and Sugerman, G., "Ken-React Reference Manual—Titanate and Zirconate Coupling Agents," Kenrich Petrochemicals Inc., Bayonne, NJ 07002-0032, 1985.

94. Cohen, L. B., "Zircoaluminates Strengthen Premium Ranges of Chemical Coupling Agents," SPE, *Plastics Engineering*, November 1983, pp. 29–32.

95. Cohen, L. B., "Mineral Filled Resins: In Situ Surface Modification with Zircoaluminate Metallo Organic Coupling Agents," SPE ANTEC, paper 636, New Orleans, April 1984.

96. Cohen, L. B., "Adhesion Promotion with Zircoaluminate Coupling Agents," The Adhesion Society, Savannah, GA, February 24–27, 1985.

97. Cohen, L. B., "The Chemistry and Reactivity of Zircoaluminate Coupling Agents for Filled and Reinforced Plastics," SPI RP/C, Atlanta, GA, January 27–31, 1986.

98. Gurland, J., "An Estimate of Contact and Continuity of Dispersion in Opaque Samples," Trans. Met. Soc., AIME, Vol. 236, 1966, pp. 642–646.

CHAPTER 24

ANALYZING STEADY-STATE FLOW OF ELASTOMERS

Nobuyuki Nakajima

Polymer Engineering Center
The University of Akron
Akron, Ohio, USA

and

E. Ray Harrell

BFGoodrich Company Technical Center
Avon Lake, Ohio, USA

CONTENTS

INTRODUCTION

Elastomer is a material that renders large deformation without break and recovers original shape upon removal of the stress. Among the variety of elastomers obtainable from biological source, only natural rubber (Hevea) is commercially important. Also, many synthetic elastomers are produced commercially [1–5].

Elastomer is seldom used as is; it is usually compounded with filler and other additives [3–7]. The compound is shaped and crosslinked to make a final product. Therefore, elastomer processing involves mixing, shaping and crosslinking [3, 8, 9, 10]. Mixing is done with a mill or an internal mixer. Shaping is done by several different methods. Compression molding, transfer molding, or injection molding is used to shape and crosslink simultaneously into the finished product. Extrusion and calendering are used to continuously shape a product for subsequent crosslinking. In the mixing and shaping operation, elastomer is transported through a confining geometry and permanently deformed. In this sense, elastomer processing may be said to involve flow. Therefore, an understanding of rheological behavior is indispensable for interpreting the processability of elastomers [11–15].

Traditionally, thermoplastics have been characterized with steady state flow measurements [16]. However, steady-state flow measurements involving elastomers and compounds are relatively new.

Automation and a need for more precise control of processing require quantitative information on the rheology of compounds. Computer-aided process simulation also requires information on flow. A widespread practice of blending thermoplastics with elastomers requires rheological knowledge of both components [17]. A recent upsurge in the use of thermoplastic elastomers [18, 19] also stimulated the steady-state flow measurements.

THEORY

Basic theories that explain the elastomeric properties utilize network structure as a model [20, 21]. The network junctions are crosslink points, which are connected with flexible polymer chains. The network chain at its relaxed state assumes a random coil configuration; it is sufficiently mobile that it can be stretched to many times its original length. When the stress is removed, it returns to the

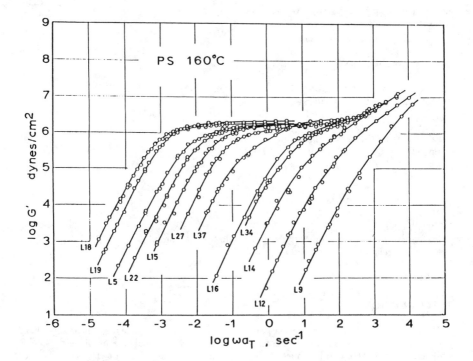

Figure 1a. Master curves of G' for narrow-distribution polystyrenes having different molecular weights. The reference temperature is 160°C. Printed with permission from *Macromolecules*, *3*, 64, copyright 1970, American Chemical Society.

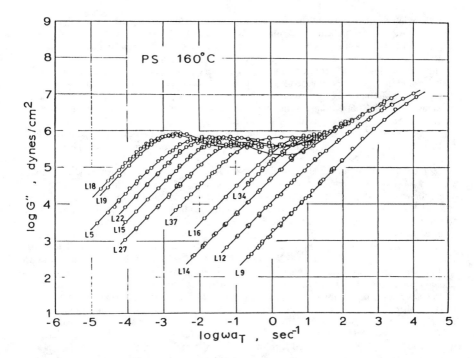

Figure 1b. Master curves of G″ for narrow-distribution polystyrenes having different molecular weights. The reference temperature is 160°C. Printed with permission from *Macromolecules*, *3*, 64, copyright 1970, American Chemical Society.

original relaxed state with the crosslink junction as a "marker." Being a crosslinked network, the material can neither permanently deform nor flow.

Obviously, the discussion on flow must involve uncrosslinked systems. Therefore, the material falling within the present interest is either gum elastomer or compound, but not a crosslinked network. However, even uncrosslinked gum elastomer exhibits elastomeric properties if the condition is appropriate. Such a condition is defined by a temperature-time window. That is, if it is below a certain temperature, the elastomer becomes glassy and brittle. The same occurs at very high rates of deformation, i.e., at a very short time-scale. On the other hand, if either temperature exceeds certain limits or deformation rate is very slow, i.e., at very long time-scale, the uncrosslinked elastomer loses the ability to recover the original shape. Under such a condition, the elastomer flows.

In principle, any flexible chain polymer, if the chain is sufficiently long and available in the amorphous state, may exhibit rubbery behavior within an appropriate temperature-time window. This is illustrated in Figure 1 with dynamic mechanical behavior of polystyrenes having different molecular weights and very narrow molecular weight distribution [22]. In this figure, curves of shear storage modulus, G′, and shear loss modulus, G″ [23], are presented for a sample having the lowest molecular weight at the most right and for a successively higher molecular weight to the left. In the G′ curves, the rubbery region is characterized by the plateau modulus of about 10^6 dynes/cm^2; and in the G″ curves it is signified with an approximately constant modulus value of about 10^5 dynes/cm^2 with a characteristic maximum. The rubbery region is framed in this case at a constant temperature of 160°C with a range of time-scale, i.e., angular frequency, from 10^{-3} to 10^2 rad/s. However, the original data included measurements at different temperatures and were reduced to 160° with the time-temperature correspondence principle [23]. Thus, the illustrated rubbery region is defined by the temperature-time window mentioned previously.

In these figures, it is apparent that below a certain molecular weight, M_e [23], a polymer does not exhibit rubbery region behavior. With molecular weight above M_e, the rubbery region extends further with the increasing molecular weight. The trend indicates that a polymer exhibiting elastomeric properties usually has a very high molecular weight.

Although the above illustrative definition of the rubbery state is simple and lucid, it falls short of real world. First, elastomers, in general, and commercial elastomers, in particular, have some polydispersity of molecular weight. Consequently, the rubbery region does not have a constant elastic modulus. Figure 2 is an example of the modulus-frequency curve of a typical commercial polyacrylate rubber [24]. Rubbery behavior is exhibited over a much wider range of the angular frequency, from 10^{-6} to 10^1 rad/s, because of the very broad distribution extending to a very high molecular weight and because of the long branching structure contained in the high molecular weight fraction.

Another shortcoming in the above definition of rubbery state is more critical. The above data were obtained by measurements with small deformation, e.g., 1%, whereas the unique properties of elastomers involve large deformation, as stated in the beginning of this article.

Smith [25, 26] demonstrated that tensile stress-strain data up to 100% extension may be utilized to construct the modulus-time curve, which was independent of magnitude of strain. The results from various strain-rate experiments formed a master curve, where the rubbery region was indicated.

Actually, gum elastomers often give several hundred percent extension and sometimes more than one thousand percent. Nakajima [27–31] discovered a time-strain equivalence principle, which is obeyed quantitatively by many gum elastomers [32] and semi-quantitatively by some elastomers and compounds [32, 33]. This means that viscoelastic moduli can be plotted against either time-scale, temperature, or magnitude of strain, at the same time holding the other two variables constant.

The rubbery state defined in this manner is different from the basic theories mentioned earlier [20, 21]. Those theories represented deformation at equilibrium only, whereas the present discussion is on the time-dependent state. Nevertheless, at the rubbery state, gum elastomer behaves as if it is crosslinked. This is interpreted with the concept of "entanglement" [23, 34] which is a temporary interchain coupling, whose life is longer than the time-scale of the observation at a given temperature and at a given magnitude of deformation.

In this article, the subject is interpreted to represent either one of two cases. One is that a polymer, normally at rubbery state, is made to flow by changing either temperature, time-scale, magnitude of deformation, or any combination of these. The "flow region" is indicated in Figure 1 at the left of the rubbery region, where the modulus is decreasing steeply with the decrease of frequency. This transformation from rubbery to flow region is observed more often with elevation of temperature than with decrease of frequency. A polymer that is in the rubbery state at room temperature may

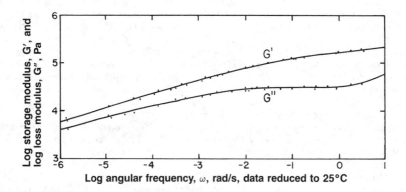

Figure 2. Master curves of G′ and G″ for a commercial polyacrylate having a broad molecular weight distribution.

behave like a thermoplastics melt at the processing temperature, e.g., 100°C. One of the characteristic features of the melt is stickiness, as against absence of it at the rubbery state. A polymer lacking very high molecular weight fraction more readily exhibits flow, as may be expected from Figure 1.

Another case representing steady-state flow of elastomers is related to the use of a particular measuring instrument, whose principle is based on the characterization of fluid behavior. Here, a polymer is handled forcefully, disregarding whether it is in a rubbery state or a flow state. In this case, apparent properties of elastomers are recorded as if they were a fluid. However, the network must be broken somehow in order for it to behave like a fluid. This point will be discussed later.

FLOW PROPERTY MEASUREMENTS

Instruments

Traditionally the properties of elastomer have been characterized with a double-disc rheometer, commonly called the "Mooney Rheometer" [35,–38] (see Figure 3). A typical operation is to charge a sample piece in a cavity, pressing to mold it, preheating for one minute at 100°C, starting rotation at 2 rpm, following the buildup of the torque, and recording the torque after four minutes of rotation. Usually a "large rotor" is used as a standard rotor and the torque value is reported as ML 1 + 4; (M for Mooney, L for large rotor, 1 for 1 minute of preheating, 4 for four minutes of rotation) [39]. This torque value is in an arbitrary scale and is often referred to as "Mooney viscosity." One minute of heating time is inadequate to equilibrate the material temperature. The shape of the torque-time curve depends upon a given sample, but some typical ones are shown in Figure 4 [40]. It is apparent that the steady-state torque is not attained after four minutes. Therefore, the viscoelastic meaning of Mooney viscosity is obscure. The operating procedure given above is for the expediency which is demanded by the production quality control. Therefore, Mooney viscosity is an index which provides only a relative measure without representing a basic property. However, if the

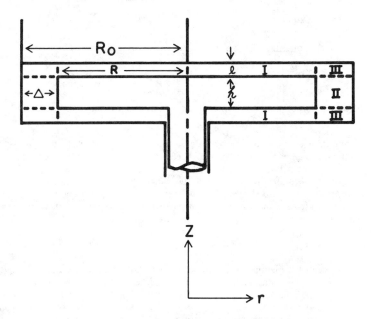

Figure 3. Rotor and stator of a Mooney rheometer.

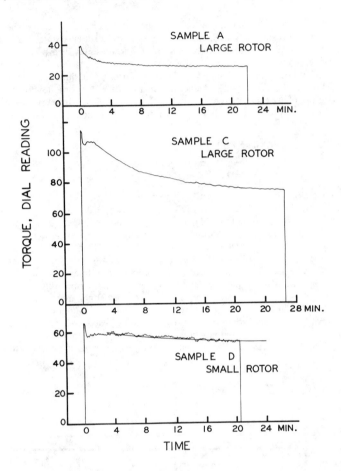

Figure 4. Torque-time curves observed with a Mooney rheometer at 2 rpm.

operating condition is modified, the steady-state flow data may be obtained with this instrument. The curves shown in Figure 5 are examples [28]. The samples were heated for several minutes to attain thermal equilibrium before rotation was started. A particular Mooney rheometer used for this measurement was equipped with a variable speed drive. The rotation was continued until the steady state torque was attained. The value of the steady-state torque and the RPM value may be converted to the steady-state shear stress, τ, and shear rate, $\dot{\gamma}$, respectively [40, 41a]. From these, the steady-state shear viscosity, η, may be calculated as:

$$\eta = \tau/\dot{\gamma} \tag{1}$$

An example is presented in Figure 6 [41b]. The viscosity measured this way is usually in agreement with that by another type of rheometer. However, there are anomalous cases, which will be discussed later. Even though the above procedure uses the steady-state torque, the previously raised question remains as to whether we are really observing "flow" or not. A rotational rheometer other than the Mooney rheometer may be used as long as the instrument is of sturdy construction to handle elastomers [42] and slip between sample and metal fixture is prevented.

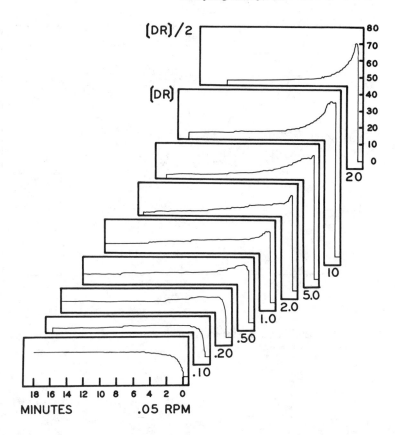

Figure 5. Recorder traces from a variable speed Mooney rheometer with SBR 1500 at 100°C.

A more recent development is a capillary rheometer called the Monsanto Processability Tester (MPT), which is piston-driven to give four levels of constant speed (see Figure 7). The steady-state shear stress, shear rate, and hence shear viscosity, are obtained in the usual manner [43, 44].

In addition to the above parameters, the relaxation of stress after cessation of flow may be recorded. Also, there is a laser device to measure the diameter of the extrudate, often referrred to as "die swell" [45], the significance of which will be discussed later.

The rotational rheometer and capillary rheometer represent the most common types of instrument for the "flow" measurements. The capillary rheometer covers a shear rate range of approximately 1 to 10^3 s^{-1}, and the rotational rheometer range may extend from 1 to 10^{-3} s^{-1}. A special, usually home-made, apparatus is used to measure flow properties at very low shear rates. These may be a "sandwich rheometer" [46] or creep apparatus [23]. Particularly with the latter, the shear rate range may be further lowered by extending the time of observation.

Often, emphasis is placed on the high shear rate flow data on the basis that the processing involves such a rate. Actually, the difference in material behavior is magnified at the low shear rates [47, 55] (Figure 8). In order to fully characterize the steady-state flow behavior of polymers, the shear rate must be low enough to observe Newtonian viscosity. With most commercial elastomers, Newtonian viscosity is not observed at a shear rate as low as 10^{-3} s^{-1}. Graessley and Ver Strate [48] devised a method for evaluating low shear Newtonian viscosity by analyzing the deformation of a strip of polymer under gravitational force.

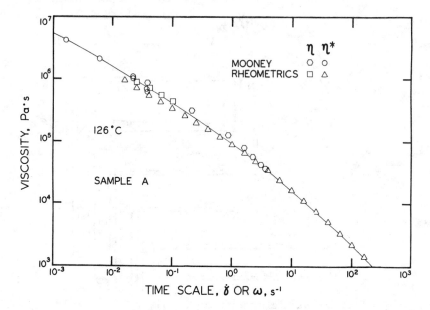

Figure 6. Viscosity master curve of EPDM elastomer derived from Mooney rheometer and Rheometrics mechanical spectrometer.

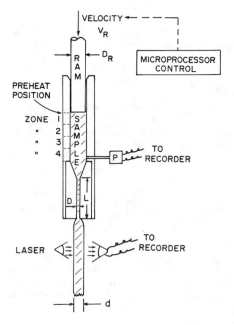

Figure 7. Schematic of a capillary rheometer.

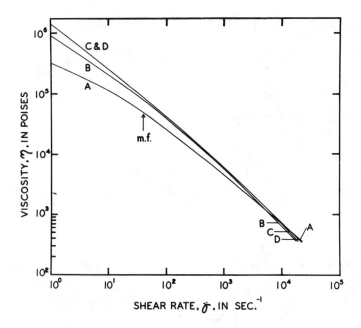

Figure 8. Flow curves of Samples A, B, C, and D at 100°C.

Anomalies and Corrections

The surfaces of the cavity and rotor of the Mooney rheometer are serrated. This is to prevent slippage of elastomer at the metal surface. Sometimes, even with the serrated surface, slippage is suspected; this appears to occur first by developing a fracture plane, which subsequently becomes a slippage surface [49] (Figure 9). It is noticed particularly with a high molecular weight at higher rpm, or lower temperatures.

In Figure 10, illustrating the rotor-cavity arrangement of the Mooney rheometer, the corner sections, designated as section III, cause an "edge effect." If we ignore the edge effect, the steady-state viscosity calculated from the torque-rpm data is usually too high [41]. A method for correcting the edge effect was developed [41]. However, in some cases, the steady-state viscosity turns out to be a more reasonable value without this correction. This occurs with highly loaded compounds, and especially with compounds loaded with short fibers [50].

The capillary rheometer measurements usually involve two corrections, one the previously mentioned "entrance correction," sometimes referred to as Bagley correction [51]. The other is a correction for non-parabolic velocity profile due to non-Newtonian flow, often referred to as Rabinowitch correction [52a]. Figure 11 is an example of Bagley plot, where the pressure difference between the barrel and the exit of capillary is plotted against capillary length-to-diameter ratio, L/D. Substantial pressure drop (intercept of this plot) occurs at the entrance region of the barrel. That correction must be made for calculating shear stress, especially when a short capillary (a small L/D) is used. Actually, the entrance correction determined in this manner contains not only the pressure-loss at the entrance to the capillary but also that in the flow through barrel. With elastomers and compounds, the barrel loss is a significant part of the entrance correction [52b]. That is, the entrance correction depends upon the amount of sample in the barrel. Therefore, in constructing the Bagley plot, experiments must be programmed in such a way as to give the same amount of sample in the barrel at a given shear rate for capillaries of different L/D [53a].

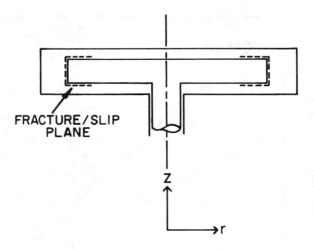

Figure 9. Schematic of observed fracture/slip plane in a Mooney rheometer.

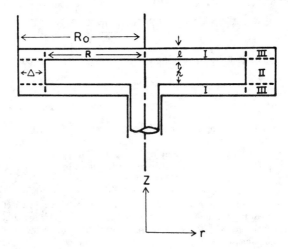

Figure 10. Flow regions considered in edge correction for the Mooney rheometer.

When a long capillary (a large L/D) is used, there is another anomaly; that is, the slope of the Bagley plot is not constant but increases with the increasing L/D. The hydrostatic pressure acting to cause an increase in viscosity is responsible for this behavior [53a].

Sometimes slip is suspected to occur at the interface of capillary and material. Two types of slip have been postulated: one is steady slip and the other unsteady, or slip-stick. For the steady slip, Oldroyd proposed a method of assessing an extent of slip by using capillaries of the same L/D but different diameter (53b). The slip-stick may also be divided into two kinds: one is microscopic and postulated to occur under macroscopically steady flow; the other is macroscopic, unsteady flow associated with a particular type of melt fracture [54]. In the latter case, extremely slow extrusion and very fast slip alternate with high and low pressure of extrusion, respectively.

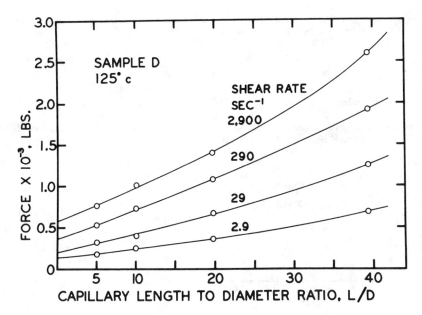

Figure 11. Force vs. capillary L/D at constant shear rate, illustrating the effect of pressure on viscosity.

Shape of Extrudate

With gum elastomers, the shape of the extrudate from a capillary rheometer is usually irregular [53] (see Figure 12). This is in contrast to a cylindrical shape seen with a thermoplastic, which only at high shear rate tends to give irregularly shaped extrudate. The phenomenon is usually called

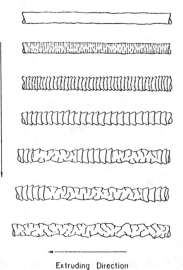

Figure 12. Represents regions of extrudate distortion observed in gum and compounded elastomers. Beginning at the lowest flow rate, the first extrudate sketched is considered smooth. The second, third and fourth extrudates possess increasing levels of "L/D-independent" surface irregularity distortion. The fifth and sixth extrudates exhibit a mixed region of distortion where there are often force oscillations. The sixth extrudate represents a grossly distorted extrudate. Printed with permission from *J. Appl. Polym. Sci., 18,* 1017, copyright 1974, Wiley.

"melt fracture" [54]. With the addition of carbon black, the extrudate becomes a regular cylinder. However, it may develop irregularity when a long capillary is used [55] or diminish irregularity [79].

Most studies on this subject treat thermoplastic melts, but a few works with elastomers have been carried out [55–56].

Swelling of Extrudate

The diameter of an extrudate is usually larger than that of the capillary, as illustrated in Figure 7. This phenomenon is called die swell [45], extrudate swell, or Barus effect. The ratio of extrudate

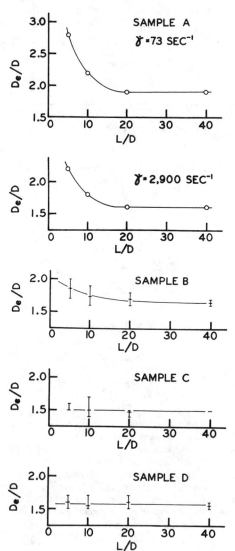

Figure 13. Dependence of die swell on capillary L/D for NBR samples A, B, C, and D.

diameter to capillary diameter is used to characterize this behavior. When the extrudate is irregularly shaped, an average diameter may be used to evaluate die swell. Most studies on this subject have been performed with thermoplastic melts [57, 58].

Extrudate swelling is a recovery of the memory of previous deformation: the swelling ratio at a given shear rate decreases with the increase of L/D, which is proportional to the travel-time through the capillary, Figure 13 [53]. The decrease is caused by the dissipation of memory [57]. With successively larger L/D, the swelling ratio approaches a constant value, which is larger than one. From the above facts it is interpreted that a part of the memory is introduced through the deformation at the entrance of the capillary and another part represents deformational memory present in the steady-state flow [59].

EFFECT OF MOLECULAR STRUCTURE ON STEADY-STATE FLOW

Molecular Structural Variables

Commercial elastomers usually have a broad molecular weight distribution (MWD). This is often coupled with various forms of branching. In some elastomers, gel structure is also present. Gel is a microscopic or macroscopic network structure, generated either by the presence of multifunctional comonomers in the polymerization or by the repeated chain-transfer and branch formation during polymerization. It may also be generated by partial crosslinking of grown chains. Gel is usually characterized as an insoluble fraction separated by a filter or screen [60]. Therefore, the gel content depends upon a choice of solvent, dissolution procedure (temperature, time and agitation, or absence of it), and screen size.

In order to separate the effects of these molecular structural variables on the steady-state flow, model systems must be synthesized.

Effect of Molecular Weight

Kraus and Gruber [61] observed the steady-state viscosity of narrow MWD (so-called monodispersed) linear polybutadienes, which were synthesized to have different molecular weight. Several significant conclusions are (a) at the low shear rate, Newtonian flow is observed, (b) viscosity at this region, η_0, has usual molecular weight M_w dependence above a certain molecular weight, M_c:

$$\eta_0 = KM_w^{3.4} \tag{2}$$

and (c) the shape of flow curve, i.e., shear rate dependence of viscosity, is approximately the same, independent of molecular weight.

Effect of Molecular Weight Distribution

A broadening of the molecular weight distribution can be achieved by adding a lower molecular weight fraction or a higher molecular weight fraction. These do not necessarily have the same effect. The former is relatively insignificant in the commercial elastomers because enhanced generation of low molecular weight fraction is not practiced. On the other hand, variation of the amount of high molecular weight fraction does occur and may be adjusted. The effect of such a broadening of MWD is to keep viscosity increasing with the decrease of shear rate such that Newtonian flow is not observed within a normal range of observation, e.g., down to 1 s^{-1}. With commercial elastomers, the $\eta_0 - M_w$ relation becomes meaningless because the η_0 value is not evaluated [62]. However, viscosity values selected at an arbitrary low shear rate have a quantitative relationship with M_w, usually in the form:

$$\eta = KM_w^\beta \tag{3}$$

where β is smaller than 3.4.

Kraus and Gruber [62] suggested that a molecular weight shift factor α_m may be substituted for η_0:

$$\alpha_m = K'M_w^{3.4} \tag{4}$$

The shift factor α_m corresponds to the amount of shift required to superpose the viscosity-shear rate data, $\eta(\dot{\gamma})$, of a polymer sample onto a viscosity master curve, in a procedure analogous to the time-temperature shift [23]. This presupposes that the $\eta(\dot{\gamma})$ curves of polymer have the same shape; this sets a limitation that there is no significant variation in MWD or in the degree of branching among the samples being compared [63].

A broad MWD polymer generally gives a higher die swell than a narrow MWD polymer.

Effect of Long Chain Branching

One model system for characterizing branched polymer is an "equal-arm-star" molecule, having three or four arms. These are synthesized to have a very narrow distribution [64] in both branch length and molecular weight. Conclusions a–e were drawn from this study. (a) Newtonian flow is observed at low shear rate; (b) Compared at equal M_w, the value of η_0 is, in general, lower than that for the linear, narrow molecular weight distribution polymers; (c) But above a certain M_w, the relative positions change. That is, the η_0 of a branched polymer is higher than that of the linear counterpart (Figure 14); (d) Even in this case, if shear rate dependence of viscosity is examined, the viscosity of a branched polymer becomes lower than that of the linear polymer at higher shear rates. Points (c) and (d) are important in interpreting the behavior of commercial elastomers, even though the branch structure in the latter may be very different. (e) An additional distinction between the

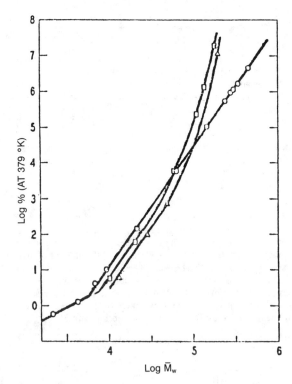

Figure 14. Dependence of Newtonian viscosity on molecular weight: (○) linear; (□) trichain; (△) tetrachain.

star-branched polymer and linear polymer is on the melt fracture behavior. The occurrence of melt fracture is distinct with linear polymers, whereas it is very suppressed with branched polymers [65].

Long Chain Branching in Commercial Polymer

In general, structures of branching are very complex and several different kinds of distribution are conceivable [66]. If we define the longest end-to-end as the backbone chain, there is a length distribution of the backbone chain. Then, with an arbitrarily chosen backbone chain there is a branch point distribution and a branch length distribution. Further, there is a branch-frequency distribution and branch-length distribution over many chains.

It appears hopeless to even attempt to relate branch structure to the flow behavior. However, it is possible to sort out the complexity and select only significant patterns of branching if we know the mechanism of branch formation. Most commercial elastomers are made with either solution polymerization or emulsion polymerization [3]. In the former, the branch formation is much less frequent than in the latter. Therefore, the presence or absence of branching in solution-polymerized chain resembles the previously described model polymers. Information obtainable from dilute solution properties is adequate for characterizing a degree of branching of these polymers [67, 68].

With emulsion polymerization the situation is very different. If a chain transfer is an inherent mechanism, the branch formation is enhanced at higher temperatures of polymerization and with increasing conversion. In this case, the longer chain is more likely to become branched and successive branch formations produce gigantic molecules which eventually become gel [69, 70]. This type of polymerization has been known for a long time, since emulsion polymerization of SBR and NBR was one of the forerunners of synthetic rubber production [71, 72].

For these polymers, dilute solution properties are usually useless because super high molecular weight fractions and gel particles are removed by filtration prior to the property measurements. However, an extent of branch formation may be assessed by gel determination with a filter of appropriate pore size. That is, the higher the gel content the more extensive is the branch formation. An example of the pore size is 300 μm [60]. If the branch formation is less extension, a smaller size pore may be used. Since ultra fine filters are available down to about 0.1 μm, a considerable pore size range is available for the characterization [47]. Since this type of branch formation is unique, the commercial polymer itself may be considered to be a model system. Characteristic flow behavior of these polymers is the enhancement of the low shear viscosity; e.g., Sample D compared to Sample B in Figure 8 [53].

Another type of branching structure has been generated by mechanically treating rubber at a high temperature, sometimes in the presence of peroxide. Exact structure is difficult to determine. However, more or less random branch formation is assumed. Often, it is a result which is a balance of chain scission and branch formation (chain coupling), the latter favoring generation and the former disappearance of the large molecules. Therefore, whether MWD broadens toward higher molecular weight or not depends upon which chemical reaction dominates. Such information can be found from the flow measurements, when the generation or disappearance of the high molecular weight fraction is manifested in the increase or decrease, respectively, of the low shear rate viscosity [65].

Effect of Gel

The term "gel" is somewhat ambiguous. For practical purposes, gel is defined as the insoluble fraction in solvent. As already mentioned, the gel content depends upon a choice of solvent, dissolution condition, and filter size. Gel may not necessarily be a cross-linked network, but rather a densely branched structure which behaves like a network because of its size and the local density of its own chain segment. This type of gel often reaches macroscopic size; therefore it is referred to as macrogel.

When a difunctional comonomer is added in emulsion polymerization, crosslinked microparticles are created. They are referred to as microgel. The presence of both macrogel [73] and microgel [74] increases low shear viscosity. If a large fraction of these gels is present, viscosity may be lowered at the high shear rates [75]. However, macrogel and microgel may not be differentiated in the steady-state viscosity-shear rate relation itself. Microgel is known to suppress melt fracture and decrease die swell [76]. This feature is maintained even after carbon black is compounded [55].

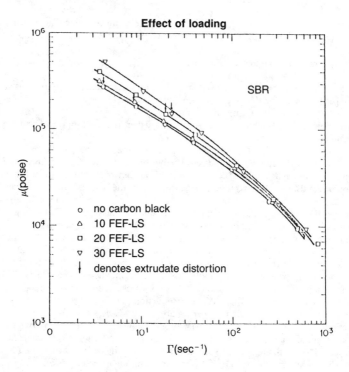

Figure 15. Influence of carbon black loading (parts black per 100 parts of rubber) on the viscosity-shear rate behavior of SBR compounds. The data for the SBR without carbon black are for the milled sample. Printed with permission from *J. Appl. Polym. Sci.*, 18, 10177, copyright 1974, Wiley.

Effect of Carbon Black and other Fillers

Compounding carbon black into gum elastomer has two effects on steady-state flow behavior: Viscosity level is increased over the entire shear rate range of observation (Figure 15) [79]; and elastic behavior, such as melt fracture and die swell, are suppressed. Surface area and structure [78] of carbon black, as well as the loading level, enhance these effects [79]. When a significant amount of carbon black is present, shear stress becomes constant, independent of shear rate, at low shear rates. This is interpreted to be the yield stress [77]. Whether this is truly a yielding behavior or is a result of very long relaxation time is an open question. Steady shear experiments towards extremely low shear rates approaching 10^{-7} s^{-1} indicated that these materials eventually exhibited flow [80] (see Figure 16).

The flow behavior of a compound depends on the degree of dispersion of carbon black. With an increase in the degree of dispersion, viscosity decreases and die swell increases; the latter eventually goes over a maximum and then decreases [81].

Particulate fillers other than carbon black have a semi-quantitatively similar effect on the flow. In detail, however, parameters such as particle size, shape, and surface interaction play an important role. Systematic studies are very few. One quantitative approach is to examine the concentration dependence of viscosity at some selected condition, e.g., at a fixed shear rate, and express it in terms of Guth and Gold's equation [82]:

$$\eta = \eta_G(1 + 2.5c + 14.1c^2) \tag{5}$$

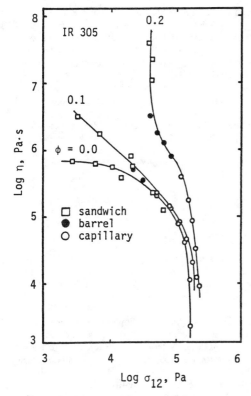

Figure 16. Viscosity-shear stress behavior of the IR 305—carbon black compounds, ϕ = o, 0.1, 0.2.

In general, the coefficients for the concentration dependence are not necessarily the same as those given by the theory, because the theory is for the monodispersed sphere wetted with non-interacting fluid [83]. The differences between theoretical coefficients and observed ones are sometimes used to interpret "shape effect" [84], occlusion of rubber in the cavity of the filler [85], and other interactive effects.

EXAMPLES OF FLOW MEASUREMENTS

In addition to the examples already cited in the structural effects on flow, some measurements are reported for various elastomers, compounds, and blends. Most of the work had been performed with a capillary rheometer. Collins and Oetzel studied flow behavior of NBR, SBR, polyepichlorohydrin, and polychloroprene [86], and examined effects of carbon black [87] and plasticizer [88] on viscosity, die swell, and melt fracture. An extent of shear heating was estimated. Also, the capillary flow behavior was compared to the torque behavior in the miniature internal mixer.

Ramos and Aramburo examined the flow of Guayule rubber and its carbon black filled compounds [89]. Observed results on viscosity, die swell, end correction, and melt fracture were compared to those of natural rubber and synthetic polyisoprene.

Derringer examined flow of SBR and summarized results with a quantitative relationship on the contribution of carbon black and plasticizer on the shear rate dependent viscosity [90].

Folt, Smith, and Wilkes examined flow behavior of natural rubber with particular attention to crystalization of rubber in capillary flow [91–93].

White, Czarnecki, and Tanaka investigated particle-and fiber-filled polystyrene with attention to viscosity and normal stress behavior. Two distinctly different types of flow behavior were observed at low shear rate: In one case the flow approached a Newtonian limit, and in the other the viscosity increased, implying the presence of a yield point. It was indicated that the difference in the behavior was related to the size of the filler [94]. Because the polymer was polystyrene, only an implication may be derived for elastomer behavior in a similar situation.

Folt and Smith examined the mixing behavior of elastomer blends with attendant examination of morphology and flow behavior. The blends were natural rubber/polybutadiene and natural rubber/transpolypentanamer [95].

Ramos-DeValle examined morphology and flow behavior of Guayulethermoplastics blends [96]. The plastics were high-and low-density polyethylene. The effects of carbon black and peroxide added during mixing were examined.

Goettler, Richwine and Wille observed capillary flow and die swell of EPDM and polypropyrene blends which had been crosslinked during mixing [97].

DISCUSSION

Viscoelastic Characterization Methods other than Steady-State Shear Flow

In this paper, the steady-state behavior has been discussed with respect to *shear* flow. In the process involving stretching, the elongational flow is more important. Only limited work exists on the elongational flow of elastomers [98, 99]. Elastomers and compounds tend to break upon stretching before steady-state is reached. Therefore, elongational flow is usually transient behavior rather than steady-state.

There are several typical methods available other than steady-state flow for characterization of deformational behavior of elastomers. These may be creep or stress relaxation [23]. These measurements are usually performed under small deformation. Recently, large deformation-stress relaxation was conducted to compare behavior of different elastomers [100, 101]. Dynamic oscillatory measurement superposed on the large deformation-stress relaxation was used to characterize the behavior of compounds [102, 103a]. Also, stress-growth measurements leading towards steady-state may be effectively used for elastomer characterization [101]. Interpretation of this behavior was reviewed recently by Soong [103b]. Dynamic oscillatory measurements often give numerically the same [104] or similar [23] results to steady-state measurements. Because the dynamic measurement is more expedient, it may be substituted for the steady-state measurement for obtaining essentially the same information. The effect of extending oil in the viscoelastic behavior of elastomer was observed with this method [105]. Graessley and his coworkers [106–109] used this method for evaluating η_0 of a series of narrow molecular weight polybutadienes, both linear and star branched, and confirmed the conclusion of Kraus and Gruber concerning viscosity enhancement by high molecular weight branched molecules [64].

Possible Mechanism of Flow

It was pointed out earlier that elastomers in the rubbery state exist in the form of a network which does not allow the material to flow unless the network is broken. With uncrosslinked elastomers, the network junction exists as an entanglement of neighboring chains that, if deformation is imposed with very slow rate and if sufficient time is allowed, the junction can disentangle. In this case elastomer flows; in the range of such a time scale the elastomer is in the flow state like a thermoplastic melt and not in the rubbery state. When the deformation rate is increased, the response of material becomes more and more elastic; yet, if the deformation is continued under a steady rate, the material response eventually becomes steady-state (see Figure 5). What happens with the network is a matter of conjecture. Mooney and Wolstenholme suggested that supermolecular flow units of the order of magnitude of 1–35 μm are formed [110]. In the course of masticating rubber, the surface texture of rubber sheet indicates as if the material consists of small lumps adhered together. The lumps become

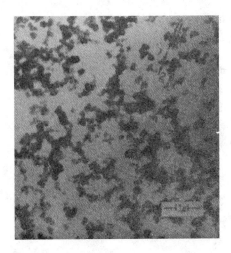

Figure 17. Sizes of rubber domains in the well-dispersed carbon black/rubber mixture.

smaller as mastication progresses. The formation of supermolecular flow units must involve a localized disentangling of chains at the would-be interface of such units.

In the electron micrographs of well-mixed carbon black and rubber, rubber domains of approximately 0.1–1.0 μm size are observed [111] (see Figure 17). Although rubber domains are connected as the matrix, breaking of rubber into smaller and smaller size during mixing is implied [112]. The formation of supermolecular flow units in the steady state flow of elastomers may be a reasonable model. However, detailed mechanisms for the formation of such a flow unit must be investigated further.

REFERENCES

1. Kirk-Othmer, *Encyclopedia of Chemical Technology*, 3rd ed., vol. 8, p. 446. Wiley, New York, 1979, "Rubber, Natural" vol. 20, p. 468, and "Elastomers, Synthetic."
2. *Encyclopedia of Polymer Science and Technology*, Wiley, 1970, "Rubber, Natural" vol. 12, p. 178.
3. *Rubber Technology*, M. Morton ed., 2nd ed., Reinhold, New York, 1973.
4. Stern, H. J., *Rubber: Natural and Synthetic*, 2nd ed., Palmerton, New York, 1967.
5. *The Chemistry and Physics of Rubber-Like Substances*, Bateman, L. ed., Wiley, New York, 1963.
6. "Rubber Compounding," in Reference 1., vol. 20, p. 365.
7. "Rubber Compounding and Processing," in Reference 2., vol. 12, p. 280.
8. "Rubber Processing," in *Encyclopedia of Material Science and Engineering*, Bever, M. B. ed., Pergamon, New York, 1986
9. McKelvey, J. M., *Polymer Processing*, Wiley, New York, 1962.
10. Freakley, P. K., *Rubber Processing and Production Organization*, Plenum, New York, 1985.
11. White, J. L., "Elastomer Rheology and Processing," *Rubber Chem. Technol. 42*, 257 (1969).
12. Norman R. H., and Johnson, P. S., "Processability Testing," *Rubber Chem. Technol.*, Rubber Reviews, 493 (1981).
13. Pearson, J. R. A., *Rubber Chem. Technol. 41*, 23 (1968).
14. Ninomiya, K., and G. Yasuda, *Rubber Chem. Technol. 42*, 714 (1969).
15. Kontos, E. G., *Rubber Chem. Technol. 43* 1082 (1970).
16. "Melt Viscosity," in Reference 1, vol. 8, p. 587.
17. "Polyblends," in Reference 1, vol. 10, p. 694.
18. "Elastomers, Synthetic (Thermoplastic)," in Reference 1., vol. 8, p. 627.
19. *Encyclopedia of Polymer Science and Engineering*, 2nd ed., Wiley 1985, "Elastomers, Thermoplastic," vol. 5, p. 416.

20. Treloar, L. R. G., *The Physics of Rubber Elasticity*, 3rd ed., Clarendon, Oxford, 1975.
21. Flory, P. J., *Principles of Polymer Chemistry*, Cornell Univ. Press, Ithaca, New York, 1953.
22. Onogi, S., Masuda, T., and Kitagawa K., *Macromolecules 3*, 109 (1970).
23. Ferry, J. D., *Viscoelastic Properties of Polymers*, 3rd ed., Wiley, New York, 1980.
24. Nakajima, N., and Harrell, E. R., unpublished data.
25. Smith, T. L., *J. Polm. Sci., 20*, 89 (1956).
26. Smith, T. L., *Trans. Soc. Rheol. 6*, 61 (1962).
27. Nakajima, N., Collins, E. A., and Bowerman, H. H., *Rubber Chem. Technol., 47*, 318 (1974).
28. Nakajima, N., and Collins, E. A., *Rubber Chem. Technol., 47*, 333 (1974).
29. Nakajima, N., Collins, E. A. and Kumler, P. R., *Rubber Chem. Technol., 47*, 778 (1974).
30. Nakajima, N., and Collins, E. A., *Rubber Chem. Technol., 48*, 69 (1975).
31. Nakajima, N., *Polym. Eng. Sci. 19*, 215 (1979).
32. Nakajima, N., *Rubber Chem. Technol., 56*, 1019 (1983)
33. Nakajima, N., Bowerman, H. H. and Collins, E. A., *Rubber Chem. Technol., 51*, 322 (1978).
34. Porter, R. S., MacKnight, W. J., and Johnson, J. F., *Rubber Chem. Technol., 41*, 1 (1968).
35. Mooney, M., *Ind. Eng. Chem.*, Anal. Ed., *6*, 147 (1934).
36. Mooney, M., *Physics, 7*, 413 (1936).
37. Mooney, M., "The Rheology of Raw Elastomers," *Rheology, Theory and Applications*, vol. 2, Eirich, F. Ed., Academic Press, New York, 1958.
38. Wise, R. W., "Rotating Disk Viscometer," in Reference 3., p. 92.
39. ASTM D1646, American Society for Testing and Materials; and also p. 92, Reference 3.
40. Nakajima, N., and Harrell, E. R., *Rubber Chem. Technol., 52*, 9 (1979).
41a. Nakajima, N., and Harrell, E. R., *Rubber Chem. Technol., 52*, 962 (1979).
41b. Nakajima, N., Harrell, E. R., and Collins, E. A., *Rubber Chem. Technol., 50*, 99 (1977).
42. Nakajima, N., and Harrell, E. R., *J. Rheol. 30(2)*, 383 (1986).
43. Leblanc, J. L., *Plastics and Rubber Processing Applications, 1*, 187 (1981).
44. Goettler, L. A., Richwine, J. R., and Wille, F. J., *Rubber Chem. Technol., 55* 1448 (1982).
45. Pliskin, I., *Rubber Chem. Technol., 45*, 1218 (1973).
46. Toki S., and White, J. L., *J. Appl. Polym. Sci., 27*, 3171 (1982).
47. Nakajima, N., and Harrell, E. R., *J. Rheol. 26(5)*, 427 (1982).
48. Graessley, W. W., and Var Strate, G., *Rubber Chem. Technol., 53*, 842 (1980).
49. Harrell, E. R., and Nakajima, N., unpublished observation.
50. Nakajima, N., unpublished results.
51. Bagley, E. B., *J. Appl. Phys. 28*, 624 (1957).
52a. Rabinowitsch, B., *Z. Physik. Chem. A145*, 1 (1929).
52b. McCabe, C. C., *Reinforcement of Elastomers*, Kraus, G., ed., John Wiley and Sons, New York, 1965, pp. 225–245.
53a. Nakajima, N., and Collins, E. A., *Polym. Eng. Sci., 14*, 137 (1974).
53b. Oldroyd, *Rheology, Theory and Applications*, Eirich F. R. ed., Academic Press, 1956.
54. Tordella, J. P., "Unstable Flow of Molten Polymers," *Rheology, Theory and Applications*, vol. 5, p. 57, Eirich, F. R., ed., Academic Press, New York, 1969.
55. Nakajima, N., and Collins, E. A., *Rubber Chem. Technol. 48*, 615 (1975).
56. White, J. L., *Appl. Polym. Symposium No. 20*, 155 (1973).
57. Bagley, E. B., and Schreiber H. P., "Elasticity Effects in Polymer Extrusion." in *Rheology, Theory and Applications*, vol. 5, p. 93, Eirich, F. R., ed., Academic Press, New York, 1969.
58. Mori, Y., and Funatsu, K., Appl. Polym. Symposium *No. 20*, 209 (1973).
59. Nakajima, N., and Shida, M., *Trans. Soc. Rheol. 10:1*, 299 (1966).
60. ASTM D3616-77, American Standard for Testing and Materials.
61. Kraus, G., and Gruver, J. T., *J. Polym. Sci., Part A, 2*, 797 (1964).
62. Kraus, G., and Gruver, J. T., *J. Appl. Polym. Sci. 9*, 739 (1965).
63. Harrell, E. R., and Nakajima, N., *J. Appl. Polym. Sci. 29*, 995 (1984).
64. Kraus, G., and Gruver, J. T., *J. Polym. Sci., Part A, 3*, 105 (1965).
65. Folt, V. L., *Rubber Chem. Technol. 42*, 1294 (1969).
66. Nakajima, N., and Harrell, E. R., *Rubber Chem. Technol. 53*, 14 (1980).
67. Grechanovskii, V. A., *Rubber Chem. Technol. 45*, 519 (1972).

68. Small, P. A., *Adv. Polym. Sci. 18*, 1 (1975).
69. Baker, W. O., *Rubber Chem. Technol. 24*, 935 (1949).
70. p. 347 in Reference 21.
71. Elastomers, Synthetic (Nitrile Rubber), Reference 1., vol. 8, p. 534.
72. Elastomers, Synthetic (SBR), Reference 1., vol. 8, p. 608.
73. Sample D compared to Sample B, Figure 5, Reference 53.
74. Sample C compared to Sample B, Figure 5, Reference 53.
75. Nakajima, N., and Collins, E. A., *J. Rheol. 22*(5), 547 (1978).
76. Sample C in Figure 8 of Reference 53.
77. Montes, S., and White, J. L., *Rubber Chem. Technol. 55*, 1354 (1982).
78. Donnet, J. B., and Voet, A., "Carbon Black, Physics, Chemistry and Elastomer Reinforcement," Marcel Dekker, New York, 1976.
79. White, J. L., and Crowder, J. W., *J. Appl. Polym. Sci., 18*, 1013 (1974).
80. Vinogradov, G. V., Yanovsky, Yu. G., Dreval, V. E., Borisenkova, E. K., Zabugina, M. P., and Barancheyeva, V. V., *Advances in Rheology*, Vol. 3 Polymers, Mena, B., Garcia-Rejon, A., and Rangel-Nafaile C., eds., Universidad Nacional Autonoma de Mexico, 1984, p. 391.
81. Tokita, N., and Pliskin, I., *Rubber Chem. Technol. 46*, 1166 (1973).
82. Guth, E., and Gold, O., *Phys. Rev. 53*, 322 (1938).
83. Einstein, A., *Ann. Physik. 19*, 289 (1906); *34*, 1591 (1911).
84. Guth, E., *Rubber Chem. Technol. 18*, 596 (1945).
85. Medalia, A. I., *Rubber Chem. Technol. 46*, 877 (1973).
86. Collins, E. A., and Oetzel, J. T., *Rubber Chem. Technol. 42*, 790 (1969).
87. Collins, E. A., and Oetzel, J. T., *Rubber Age 102*, 64 (March 1970).
88. Collins, E. A., and Oetzel, J. T., *Rubber Age 103*, 47 (Feb. 1971).
89. Ramos, L. F., and Aramburo, F., *Rubber Chem. Technol. 53*, 388 (1980).
90. Derringer, G. C., *Rubber Chem. Technol. 47*, 828, (1974).
91. Folt, V. L., Smith, R. W., and Wilkes, C. E., *Rubber Chem. Technol. 44*, 1 (1971).
92. Folt, V. L., ibid *44* 12, (1971).
93. Folt, V. L., ibid *44* 29 (1971).
94. White, J. L., Czarnecki, L., and Tanaka, H., *Rubber Chem. Technol. 53*, 823 (1980).
95. Folt, V. L., and Smith, R. W., *Rubber Chem. Technol. 46*, 1193 (1973).
96. Ramos-DeValle, L. F., *Rubber Chem. Technol. 55*, 1341 (1982).
97. Goettler, L. A., Richwine, J. R., and Wille, F. J., *Rubber Chem. Technol. 55*, 1448 (1982).
98. Cotten, G. R., and Thiele, J. L., *Rubber Chem. Technol. 51*, 749 (1978).
99. Nakajima, N., *Rubber Chem. Technol. 53*, 1088 (1980).
100. Nakajima, N., and Harrell, E. R., *J. Rheol. 27*(3), 241 (1983).
101. Nakajima, N., and Harrell, E. R., *J. Rheol. 30*(2), 383 (1986).
102. Arai, K., and Ferry, J. D., *Rubber Chem. Technol. 59*, 241 (1986).
103a. Arai, K., and Ferry, J. D., *Rubber Chem. Technol. 59*, 605 (1986).
103b. Soong, D. S., Rubber Chem. Technol. *54*, 641 (1981).
104. Cox, W. P., and Merz, E. H., *J. Polym. Sci. 28*, 619 (1958).
105. Nakajima, N., and Harrell, E. R., *J. Rheol. 26*(5), 427 (1982).
106. Raju, V. R., Smith, G. G., Marin, G., Knox, J. R., and Graessley, W. W., *J. Polym. Sci., Phys. 17*, 1183 (1979).
107. Rochefort, W. E., Smith, G. G., Rachapudy, H., Raju, V. R., and Graessley, W. W., *J. Polym. Sci., Phys. 17*, 1197 (1979).
108. Rachapudy, H., Smith, G. G., Raju, V. R., and Graessley, W. W., *J. Polym. Sci., Phys. 17*, 1211 (1979).
109. Raju, V. R., Rachapudy, H., and Graessley, W. W., *J. Polym. Sci., Phys. 17*, 1223 (1979).
110. Mooney, M., and Wolstenholme, W. E., *J. Appl. Phys. 25*, 1098 (1954).
111. Hess, W. M., *Reinforcement of Elastomers*, Kraus, G., ed., Wiley, New York, 1965.
112. Nakajima, N., and Harrell, E. R., *Rubber Chem. Technol. 57*, 153 (1984).

CHAPTER 25

TEMPERATURE DEPENDENCE OF LOCAL FLOW IN POLYMERS

Michael-Joachim Brekner

Research and Development, Informationstechnik-Division,
Hoechst AG, Kalle Wiesbaden, Federal Republic of Germany

and

Hans Adam Schneider

Institute of Macromolecular Chemistry
Albert-Ludwigs University of Freiburg
Federal Republic of Germany

CONTENTS

INTRODUCTION

Flow is generally understood as an irrecoverable deformation of a body, while the recovery of its deformation is known as elasticity. If the whole work done by external forces is dissipated via deformation, pure flow is assumed. The case of partially recoverable energy is that of viscoelasticity, a common behavior of polymeric systems.

Characteristic of the viscoelastic behavior of polymers is the time-temperature dependence of the ratio between recoverable and irrecoverable energy during a given deformation. Macroscopic flow in polymeric systems is in fact determined by two phenomena: one is the local flow, i.e., the exchange of locations between various chain units within certain limits of chain topology, and the other is the change of such topological restraints, as for example by chain disentanglement. As long as the temperature dependence of topological restraints in macromolecular materials is negligible, the change with temperature of viscoelastic behavior is due basically to the temperature dependence of local flow.

In order to understand all the implications of molecular characteristics in viscoelastic behavior, it is necessary to make a clear phenomenological delimitation between certain features of visco-elasticity. Local flow, for instance, is bearing such a feature, i.e., a property component of viscoelastic behavior of polymers, in its temperature dependence. This feature is connected to all molecular properties of local character as monomeric structure, conformational chain flexibility, or the glass transition temperature.

An additional important aspect of macromolecular flow discussed in the literature is the existence of several approaches to modeling the flow process in such systems [1–8]. Also in respect to temperature dependence of macromolecular flow, some theories compete for the best description of this phenomenon [9–14].

Our following contribution will deal with most of the above-mentioned aspects of flow, while focusing mainly on the temperature dependence of local flow in polymers.

LOCAL FLOW

Molecular Aspects of Flow in Polymers

Viscoelasticity is a common behavior, typical of amorphous polymeric systems, which we will concentrate on. These systems are usually in a liquid or in a glassy phase. The liquid phase is characterized by high molecular mobility because of conformational rearrangements along the polymer backbone. In the glassy state the backbone conformation is frozen, and the mobility arises basically from possible conformational changes within side or end groups of the polymer.

Flow in amorphous polymers is based on the above-mentioned molecular mobilities, which are activated by external stress. The external stress creates a force that acts on molecular level, producing conformational and positional changes of macromolecular segments. In the glassy state, the occuring conformational changes are very much localized, i.e., they involve mainly chain ends or parts of side chains, and sometimes very small and isolated sequences of the backbone. The increased mobility in the liquid state, on the contrary, offers the possibility of a much more extended cooperative motion on molecular level. But, after all, what is the molecular extent of local flow? In terms of mean field theories, local flow has to be defined as a process of such an extend, that its characteristic parameters are equal to that of the overall flow process of the system. A parameter suitable for this particular case is the activation energy of flow under conditions of constant topological chain restraints. Accordingly, local flow, as a molecular cooperative rearrangement process, should be considered to be of such an extend, that its overall activation energy equals that of macroscopic flow under the mentioned conditions. This activation energy is an experimentally accessible magnitude and will be discussed under various aspects in the following sections.

Local Flow and Models of Viscoelasticity

Before discussing viscoelastic models, it is necessary to refer to the notion of linear viscoelasticity and the Boltzmann superposition principle, two concepts on which these models are based.

A body exhibits linear viscoelasticity while it is deformed only if both the proportionality between stored energy and strain and that between dissipated energy and strain rate, are fulfilled [15–18]. For polymers, such behavior can be achieved experimentally if small deformations and deformation rates are used or if an extrapolation to zero deformation is realized.

The Boltzmann superposition principle [17] states that all impacts of mechanical history on a linear viscoelastic body should be independent and additive.

In accordance with these two concepts, mechanical models have been developed in order to yield a mathematical formulation of linear viscoelasticity. The most well known are the Maxwell and the Kelvin-Voigt models, presented schematically in Figure 1. While the Maxwell model is suitable for simulating relaxation experiments (experiments where strain is controlled and stress is monitored), the Kelvin-Voigt model best simulates reptation experiments (experiments where stress is controlled and strain is monitored). The idea of using such models is based on the perception that

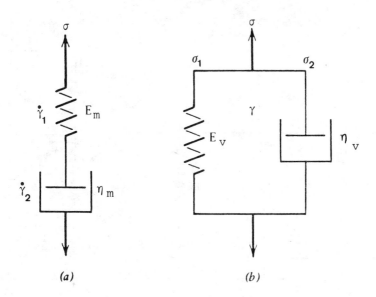

Figure 1. Mechanical models: (a) Maxwell model; (b) Kelvin-Voigt model.

relations between stress and strain for linear viscoelastic materials can be achieved via the solutions of a linear differential equation like:

$$a_0\sigma + a_1(d\sigma/dt) + a_2(d^2\sigma/dt^2) + \cdots = b_0\gamma + b_1(d\gamma/dt) + b_2(d^2\gamma/dt^2) + \cdots \tag{1}$$

The equivalence between the solutions of an equation of this type and those resulting from several linear differential equations corresponding to different viscoelastic model units constitutes the mathematical background for the use of such models. In most cases, however, the number of solutions of Equation 1 is much higher than one, and consequently the corresponding mechanical model has to be composed of several model units. The general case calls for N model units, as presented in Figure 2. These models are therefore called generalized models.

The time it takes each of the viscoelastic units to relax is given by:

$$\theta = \frac{\eta_m}{E_m} \qquad \theta' = \frac{\eta_v}{E_v} \tag{2}$$

The relaxation, θ, and retardation, θ', time, are specific parameters of each viscoelastic unit. The relations between stress and strain for the generalized models are:

$$\sigma(t) = \gamma_0 \sum_i^n E_i \exp(-t/\theta); \qquad \gamma(t) = \sigma_0 \sum_i^n (1/E_i)[1 - \exp(-t/\theta')] \tag{3}$$

For the case of N going to infinity, these relations can be easily transformed into integrals:

$$G(t) = G_e + \int_{-\infty}^{\infty} H(\theta) \exp(-t/\theta)\, d(\ln \theta) \tag{4}$$

$$J(t) = J_0 + \int_{-\infty}^{\infty} L(\theta')[1 - \exp(-t/\theta')]\, d(\ln \theta') \tag{5}$$

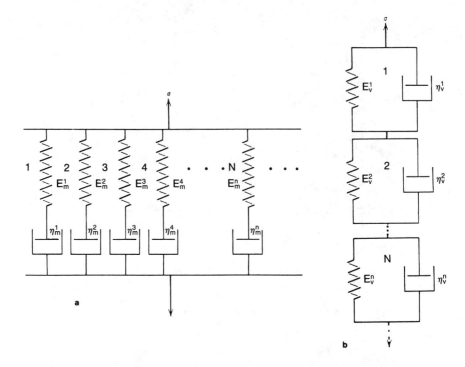

Figure 2. Generalized mechanical models: (a) Generalized Maxwell model; (b) Generalized Kelvin-Voigt model.

Here $H(\theta)$ and $L(\theta')$ represent distribution functions of the E_i values in respect with the other unit characteristics θ and θ', respectively. $G(t)$ and $J(t)$ stand for the relaxation modulus and the compliance, respectively. G_e, i.e., the equilibrium modulus, and J_0, i.e., the instantaneous compliance, have the role of integration constants. Further details on mathematics of viscoelastic functions and their dependence on models are available in text books [19–24] (see also "Temperature Dependence of Local Flow and Viscoelastic Functions" later in this chapter).

In view of our main subject, it is important to point out how local flow in polymers has to be considered in terms of these mechanical models. Taking into account the elements which compose the viscoelastic units, it is obvious that local flow has to be located in the dashpots. In terms of the generalized models, many different dashpots have to exist throughout an amorphous material. Under conditions of unchanged topological chain restraint, which means unchanged E_i values, the hole temperature dependence is due to the temperature dependence of the flow in these dashpots. The fact that all θ_i and θ'_i parameters exhibit the same temperature dependence for most of the macromolecular systems shows that in all considered dashpots similar flow occurs. A formulation of the viscosity of these dashpots as:

$$\eta_i = \frac{\theta_i}{E_i} = \frac{x_i}{E_i} f(T) \tag{6}$$

justifies the perception that each dashpot consists of x_i flow steps of the same temperature dependence $f(T)$. In conclusion, local flow in polymers can be understood in terms of these mechanical models as such a flow step in a dashpot. It also becomes evident that although on a macroscopic scale flow is apparently non-Newtonian, on a molecular level (i.e., the considered local flow), Newtonian flow is still present.

Molecular Statistic Theory

One of the first approaches to a molecular description of polymeric flow processes was presented by Bueche in 1952 [1]. For the first time a cooperative motion of so-called kinetic chain units was taken into consideration. Based on this concept, models have been designed to simulate the relaxation of macromolecules. The most successful model for the case of amorphous polymers became the bead-spring model, presented in Figure 3.

Rouse [3] based his theory on this model. Although the Rouse theory was initially designated for polymer solutions only, it was extended later on to polymer melts too. Today this theory is a cornerstone of many theoretical developments in this field. The most important realization of the Rouse theory is probably its formulation of the flow of macromolecules. Accordingly, each macromolecule can be considered as composed of N submolecules. Each submolecule is thereby supposed as having a Gaussian chain end distribution. During flow, such a macromolecule diffuses because of the imposed entropic unfavorable conformational arrangements. The result is a thermodynamic potential. This potential is always equilibrated by frictional forces acting on the beads, which, in terms of the model presented in Figure 3, represent joints of the submolecules. Finally, the theory yields this relation for relaxation times of macromolecular chains:

$$\theta_p = \frac{a^2 P^2 \zeta_0}{6\pi^2 p^2 k_B T} \qquad (7)$$

where P = degree of polymerization
ζ_0 = monomeric friction coefficient
a = mean-square end-to-end distance per monomer unit
p = the corresponding mode of motion (used in this expression only)

For polymer melts the relation can be transformed, in order to use as parameters the zero shear viscosity η_0 and the molecular weight M:

$$\theta_p = \frac{6\eta_0 M}{\pi^2 p^2 \rho R T} \qquad (8)$$

For details of the calculations, refer to [3, 25–28]. Several modifications of the Rouse theory [29–31] and of the bead-spring model [32] did not essentially change the Rouse concept. This

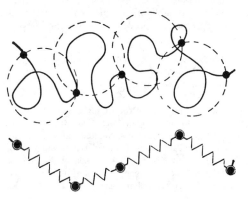

Figure 3. Bead-spring model of the polymer chain.

applies as well to the related theory worked out by Zimm [4, 5], who also accounted for hydrodynamic interactions between chain segments.

However, all the mentioned statistic theories still have difficulties in describing the relaxation of very high molecular polymer species. Thus, they do not explain the power relation, $\eta \sim M^{3.4}$, which is found for these species experimentally. In order to eliminate this lack, subsequent theoretical attempts have been considered in addition to various models of topological restraints. One of the most successful models in this respect is the reptation model [5–7].

Nevertheless, these statistic theories do not give a detailed description of the temperature dependence of flow. This feature is usually included in some of the parameters, such as "a" [33] or "ζ_0".

Important for local flow is one common concept of all these theories, namely the connection of the relaxation processes to certain macromolecular chains. Thus, flow in polymers is viewed as a sum of flow steps along the polymer chain. In terms of this concept, local flow has to be considered as a step in the relaxation process of a macromolecular chain.

Molecular Kinetic Theory

Fundamentals of the kinetic aspect of flow were worked out by Eyring in his molecular theory of deformation kinetics [9], which is based on the absolute rate theory [34–39]. Accordingly, using the transition state concept, the rate constant of flow is expressed as a function of an apparent, Gibbs-type activation energy $\Delta G^{\#}$:

$$k^{\#} = \varkappa(k_B T/h)(Q^{\#}/Q)\exp(-\Delta E^{\#}/k_B T) = \varkappa(k_B T/h)\exp(-\Delta G^{\#}/k_B T) \tag{9}$$
$$= \varkappa(k_B T/h)\exp(\Delta S^{\#}/k_B)\exp(-\Delta H^{\#}/k_B T)$$

where $\Delta S^{\#}$ and $\Delta H^{\#}$ = activation entropy and enthalpy, respectively (for constants in Equation 9 see Notation). They are defining the activated state of the flow process or, in other words, the potential energy barrier which the flowing molecules have to surmount. Applying this approach to the macromolecular flow, Eyring has assumed some representative flow dimensions as λ, the interval between equilibrium positions defined by one single energy barrier, and λ_p, the length of a chain segment. Finally, the theory yields Equation 10 for the relaxation time of a chain segment:

$$\theta_p = \frac{\lambda_p}{2\lambda k^{\#}} \tag{10}$$

Relations for the viscosity can be derived as well [9].

This kinetic approach connects obviously the relaxation time and thus the local flow with molecular dimensions, which, unfortunately, are not accessible experimentally. In terms of this theory, if an equal overall temperature dependence of flow, i.e., equal energy barriers, is taken into account, local flow should be considered as a process of surmounting one of these potential energy barriers or as a single step in the relaxation of a chain segment. In addition, this theory has the merit to create some theoretical tools for approaching the temperature dependence of flow in polymers.

TEMPERATURE DEPENDENCE OF LOCAL FLOW

Temperature Dependence of Local Flow and Viscoelastic Functions

Viscoelastic functions are time dependent magnitudes that were introduced in rheology in order to characterize the mechanical behavior of materials under certain experimental conditions. By defining such magnitudes, exact mathematical relations between stress or strain and time were established. These functions can be derived from those mechanical models that are the most suitable for the mechanical impact under consideration. Thus, the number of existing viscoelastic functions is relatively high (for further details, see [19–24]). However, besides being dependent on the real experimental time, the viscoelastic functions are also related to the polymer-specific relaxation or retardation times, and to the respective distribution functions, as shown in Equation 4 and 5. All yet discussed theories concerning polymeric flow yield relaxation or retardation times related to local flow as the only possible temperature dependent phenomenon under conditions of constant chain restraint. In conclusion, the temperature dependence of local flow and that of relaxation and retardation times are the same. Inserting this temperature dependence of local flow into the expression of the relaxation time:

$$\theta_p = x_p f(T) = \theta_p(T) \tag{11}$$

it can as well be introduced into the relations of the viscoelastic functions. For instance, in the case of some selected dynamic viscoelastic functions one gets [40]:

$$G'(\omega, T) = \int_{-\infty}^{\infty} \frac{H[\theta(T)][\omega\theta(T)]^2}{1 + [\omega\theta(T)]^2} \, d \ln \theta \tag{12}$$

$$G''(\omega, T) = \int_{-\infty}^{\infty} \frac{H[\theta(T)][\omega\theta(T)]}{1 + [\omega\theta(T)]^2} \, d \ln \theta \tag{13}$$

$$\eta(\omega, T) = \int_{-\infty}^{\infty} \frac{\theta(T)H[\theta(T)]}{1 + [\omega\theta(T)]^2} \, d \ln \theta \tag{14}$$

where ω = experimental frequency, i.e., $1/\omega$ = experimental time, and $H[\theta(T)]$ = temperature-dependent relaxation time spectrum.

A similar procedure is applicable for retardation times, as well as for other viscoelastic functions.

The temperature dependence of the selected viscoelastic functions can be illustrated very intuitively by considering the graphical representation of the frequency functions as shown in Figure 4.

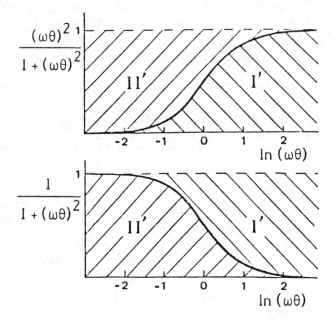

Figure 4. Frequency functions of G′ and η vs. ln($\theta\omega$). Printed with permission of Springer International [40].

Accordingly, the relations:

$$I' = \int_{-\infty}^{\infty} \frac{(\omega\theta)^2}{1 + (\omega\theta)^2} \, d \ln(\omega\theta) \tag{15}$$

$$II' = \int_{-\infty}^{\infty} \frac{1}{1 + (\omega\theta)^2} \, d \ln(\omega\theta) \tag{16}$$

$$I' + II' = \int_{-\infty}^{\infty} d \ln(\omega\theta) \tag{17}$$

are effective, demonstrating how the frequency functions split the distribution function, i.e., the temperature-reduced relaxation time spectrum H' (see next paragraph), into a relaxed and an unrelaxed part. If one assumes that the relaxation time θ is temperature dependent, i.e., $\theta(T)$, the respective displacement of the split in the formally considered relaxation time spectrum can be illustrated as in Figure 5. It becomes evident that whereas the experimental time (or frequency) determines the position of the frequency function along the logarithmic time scale, the spectrum H' itself is shifted unaltered along this scale due to the identical temperature dependence of all relaxation times. This shift is expressed by a function a_T, the so called shift factor:

$$\ln[\theta_p(T_2)] - \ln[\theta_p(T_1)] = -\ln a_T$$

$$\frac{\theta_p(T_1)}{\theta_p(T_2)} = a_T \tag{18}$$

The shift also causes a synchronous change of the areas I and II, and consequently of the value of the respective viscoelastic functions presented by Equations 12–14. A second specified frequency, ω_2, in Figure 5, illustrates how measurement at higher temperatures can approach zero shear conditions, i.e., where area II can be supposed invariant with respect to frequency. The temperature invariance of the distribution function H' is a feature of the relaxation time spectra of polymers and also a requirement of the condition of constant chain restraint. Further details on this aspect follow.

The above introduced temperature dependence of local flow into rheological formulations offers the possibility of viewing viscoelastic behavior not only from the isothermal perspective, but also from the isochronal one [41, 42]. Thus, in accordance with the condition of invariant chain restraint and with the definition of a temperature dependent relaxation time $\theta_p(T)$, some further associations can be defined as suggested in Figure 6. Developing this concept, the reduced reciprocal relaxation temperature spectrum H_r can be derived [42]. Using H_r instead of H_r, the storage modulus, for instance, results as:

$$G_r'(\omega_0, T_0) = (G_e')_r + \int_0^{\infty} H_r[T_p(\omega_0)] \frac{\exp\left[2 \cdot \int_{1/T_p}^{1/T_0} [E(T)/R] \, d(1/T) \right]}{1 + \exp\left[2 \cdot \int_{1/T_p}^{1/T_0} [E(T)/R] \, d(1/T) \right]} d(1/T) \tag{19}$$

where r = temperature reduction. E(T) represents the temperature dependent activation energy of local flow, which will be discussed in detail. If E(T) = E = constant, Equation 19 simplifies to:

$$G_r'(\omega_0, T_0) = (G_e')_r + \int_0^{\infty} H_r[T_p(\omega_0)] \frac{\exp[(2E/R)(1/T_0 - 1/T)]}{1 + \exp[(2E/R)(1/T_0 - 1/T)]} d(1/T) \tag{20}$$

Applying such an isochronal concept, the usual frequency function turns into a temperature function, which for the simple case of Equation 20 is illustrated in Figure 7.

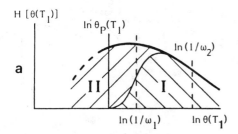

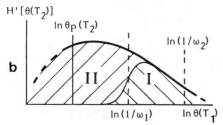

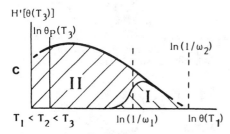

Figure 5. Split of the logarithmic relaxation time spectrum H at different arbitrary temperatures. $T_1 < T_2 < T_3$. $1/\omega$ = experimental time; H' = relaxation time spectrum reduced to T_1; θ_p = relaxation time of a relaxation process, P, i.e., a certain value of H' at each temperature; I = unrelaxed part of the spectrum, and II = relaxed part of the spectrum. Printed with permission of Springer International [40].

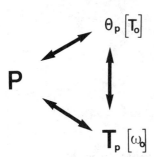

Figure 6. Correlations between the relaxation time, θ_p, and the relaxation temperature, T_p, of an arbitrary relaxation process, P.

In conclusion, it should be pointed out that the presented isochronal extension of the viscoelastic functions enables a uniform rheological description of the viscoelastic behavior in a time-temperature space (for details see [42]).

Temperature Dependence of Local Flow and the Time-Temperature Superposition Principle

Based on experimental observations, the time-temperature superposition principle states that viscoelastic properties measured at different temperatures can be brought to superposition by shifting isothermal property curves along the logarithmic time scale to a reference temperature (see

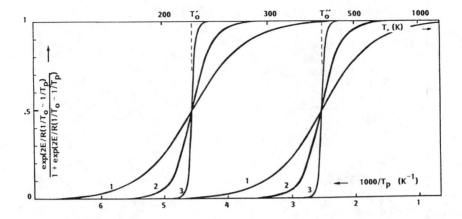

Figure 7. The temperature function of Equation 20 for two arbitrary temperatures, T_0' and T_0'', using different constant E values. (1) E = 10 kJ/mole, (2) E = 25 kJ/mole, and (3) E = 100 kJ/mole. Printed with permission of Springer International [42].

Figure 8). This feature was first mentioned in connection with dielectric measurements [43] and has been discussed in detail by several authors [44-49]. It has also been demonstrated repeatedly that for polymers, this principle holds only up to certain polymer-specific deformations and deformation rates [50].

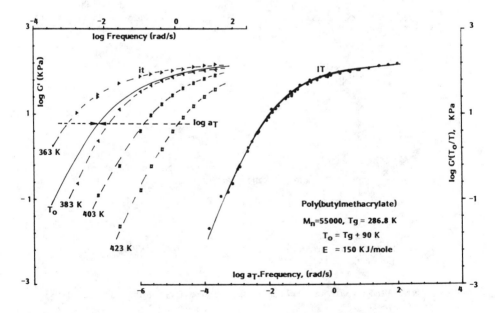

Figure 8. Illustration of the time-temperature superposition using experimental data of the storage modulus, G', of poly(butylmethacrylate) in the terminal zone.
it = isotherm data curve, IT = isotherm master curve at the reference temperature T_0 (eccentric rotating disc data in the terminal zone).

All the properties subjected to such shift procedures have to first be reduced by a factor accounting for modulus variations with temperature as they result from the theory of entropic elasticity of flexible chain molecules [51–54]. Tobolsky [55] used for this reduction initially the ratio T_0/T, with T_0 the reference temperature. The factor $T_0\rho_0/T\rho$ was subsequently applied for the reduction of dynamic [56] and creep [57] data. In the temperature range of the rubber plateau, such reduction affects considerably the shift along the logarithmic time scale [58–60], i.e., the shift factor, and consequently the appearing temperature dependence of the local flow. From the phenomenological point of view, some difficulties arise when the reduction is applied to data of the glass transition temperature range [61–63]. If the impact of an unexact reduction in the glass transition range on the evaluation of the temperature dependence of local flow is not negligible, the best solution is still to use the loss factor, tg $\delta = G''/G'$, a viscoelastic function which is not influenced by the reduction. Reduction and shifting of viscoelastic data is also known as "method of reduced variables" [22].

An analysis of the time-temperature superposition principle on the basis of mechanical models [23] and molecular concepts already discussed, leads to the conclusion that the obedience of viscoelastic data to this principle proves the temperature invariance of the relaxation time spectrum. At the same time, it corresponds to the condition of invariant topological restraints for all superposed properties of the polymer under consideration. Accordingly, the validity of this principle has to be considered a precondition for any evaluation of local flow, as it has been defined here. The reader interested in approaches to the description of changes in topological restraints, under conditions of extreme deformations and deformation rates, is refered to other publications [50, 64–68]. In the determination of the temperature dependence of local flow, the main difficulty resulting from such conditions is to distinguish between changes of topological chain restraints and those of local flow.

In order to verify the validity of the time-temperature superposition principle, one should choose the frequency range such that broad overlapping of extremely different temperatures is achieved. However, once the principle is valid, several simplifications and time-saving methods can be applied for the evaluation of temperature dependence of local flow (see "Applications" later in this chapter).

Experimental Accessibility

The Shift Factor

As pointed out in the previous paragraph, only the temperature dependence of local flow determines the shift along the logarithmic time scale of viscoelastic properties. Validity of the time-temperature superposition principle is, however, the condition. Thus, if this validity is assured, the shift $\log(a_T)$ can easily be estimated and used in the evaluation of the temperature dependence of local flow. The common procedure of determining $\log(a_T)$ is a graphical one (see Figure 8). Its accuracy usually depends on the estimation of the best superposition of the data curves. Consequently, a curve with many data points covering a large time range will provide a higher degree of accuracy. On the other hand, the shift factor can also be defined as a function of limited values of viscoelastic functions in the zero shear range:

$$a_T = \frac{(\eta_0)_T}{(\eta_0)_{T_0}} \cdot \frac{T_0\rho_0}{T\rho} \qquad a_T = \frac{(A_G)_T}{(A_G)_{T_0}} \cdot \frac{T_0\rho_0}{T\rho} \qquad (21)$$

where A_G and η_0 are defined by the relations:

$$A_G = \lim_{\omega \to 0} \frac{G'(\omega)}{\omega^2} \qquad \eta_0 = \lim_{\omega \to 0} \frac{G''(\omega)}{\omega^2} \qquad (22)$$

Finally, combining Equation 18 with Equation 7, a relation between the shift factor and the temperature dependent parameters of the Rouse theory [3] is obtained:

$$a_T = \frac{[a^2\zeta_0]_T \cdot T_0}{[a^2\zeta_0]_{T_0} \cdot T} \qquad (23)$$

Because the molecular statistic theories do not account for temperature dependence of local flow, Equation 23, in fact, is not relating parameters which characterize the temperature dependence of local flow of the respective polymer, and the statement of Equation 23 is equal to that of Equations 21 and 22.

As the temperature dependence was always obtained via more or less empiric shift procedures, the shift factor has acted as a data basis for most of the theories concerning temperature dependence of flow in polymers. Accordingly, the shift factor has been related to polymer specific parameters as well (see "Classic Theories" in this chapter).

The Apparent Activation Energy of Local Flow

The kinetic approach of flow, as developed by Eyring (see Equations 9 and 10), implies the following formulation of the temperature dependence of local flow:

$$\log \frac{\theta(T)}{\theta(T_0)} = \frac{E}{2.303 \ R} \ \frac{1}{T} - \frac{1}{T_0} \tag{24}$$

Equation 24 is an Arrhenius type relation, including accordingly the assumption of E being constant. Data demonstrate, however, that constant apparent activation energies of local flow are exceptions in the case of polymeric flow. Thus the apparent activation energy has to be considered a temperature dependent function:

$$\frac{d[\log \theta_p(T)]}{d(1/T)} = \frac{d[\log a_T]}{d(1/T)} = \frac{E(T)}{2.303 \ R} \tag{25}$$

E(T) is related with the shift factor via integration of Equaion 25:

$$\log(a_T) = \int_{1/T_0}^{1/T} \frac{E(T)}{2.303 \ R} \ d(1/T) \tag{26}$$

A closer analysis of E(T) suggests that in fact it is apparent in a double sense. Firstly, it is apparent [69] because its evaluation in accordance with Equation 25 is similar to the procedure used to determine an Arrhenius-type activation energy; and secondly, because of Eyring's consideration [9]. In order to make a distinction, let us call E(T) the apparent activation energy and $E^{\#}$ the Eyring apparent activation energy. Mathematically, the distinction results from:

$$E(T) = \left[E^{\#} + \frac{dE^{\#}}{d(1/T)} \frac{1}{T} \right] \tag{27}$$

It is evident that as long as E(T), i.e., the experimentally accessible magnitude, is not defined mathematically via some theoretical approach, $E^{\#}$ cannot be evaluated (see "Kinetic Parameters of Local Flow," this chapter).

According to Equation 25, the temperature function E(T) can be computed via derivation of the function $\log(a_T)$. There is, however, also a direct way to determine E(T) using the viscoelastic functions. If the condition of constant topological restraint, i.e., the shift possibility in a $\log(\omega) - 1/T$ plane, is formulated as:

$$dG'(\log \omega, 1/T) = \frac{\delta(G')_T}{\delta(\log \omega)} \ d(\log \omega) + \frac{\delta(G')_\omega}{\delta(1/T)} \ d(1/T) = 0 \Bigg|_{\substack{G' = const \\ 1'\omega = \theta_p(T)}} \tag{28}$$

Equation 29 can be deduced:

$$-\frac{d(\log \omega)}{d(1/T)}\Bigg|_{1'\omega = \theta_p(T)} = \frac{d[\log(a_T)]}{d(1/T)} = \frac{\delta(G')_\omega/\delta(1/T)}{\delta(G)_T/\delta(\log \omega)}\Bigg|_{\substack{G' = const \\ 1'\omega = \theta_p(T)}} = \frac{E(T)}{2.303 \ R} \tag{29}$$

G′ is here representatively chosen for any viscoelastic function and is already temperature reduced. This relation can also be deduced from graphical considerations, as illustrated in Figure 9, where the viscoelastic function is represented in its reciprocal temperature-logarithmic frequency space [40]. If this spacial view of the viscoelastic function is extended for the whole time and temperature range of a master curve, a master surface is the result (see Figure 10). Accordingly, $\log[G'(\log \omega_0, 1/T)]$ in Figure 9 defines one point on such a surface as in Figure 10. It has to be mentioned that this particular surface of Figure 10 is in fact specific for a constant apparent activation energy, which is not valid for most polymers. However, this master surface is consequently less sophisticated and offers a very comprehensive picture of the isothermal and isochronal modulus variations. Considering the representation in Figure 9, the equations:

$$\log[G'(\log \omega_0 + a, 1/T_0)] = \log[G'(\log \omega_0, 1/T_0 + b)]$$

$$\frac{b}{a} = \frac{R \ln 10}{E} = \text{tg } \alpha$$

$$\frac{\log[G'(\log \omega_0 + a, 1/T_0)] - \log[G'(\log \omega_0, 1/T_0)]}{a} = \text{tg } \alpha_1$$ (30)

$$\frac{\log[G'(\log \omega_0, 1/T_0 + b)] - \log[G'(\log \omega_0, 1/T_0)]}{b} = \text{tg } \alpha_2$$

$$\text{tg } \alpha = \frac{\text{tg } \alpha_1}{\text{tg } \alpha_2}$$

can be stipulated and finally a similar relation to Equation 29 results:

$$\text{tg } \alpha = \frac{\text{tg } \alpha_1}{\text{tg } \alpha_2} = \frac{\delta[\log(G')]_{T_0}/\delta(\log \omega)_0}{\delta[\log(G')]_{\omega_0}/\delta(1/T)_0} = \frac{R \ln 10}{E} = \frac{2.303 \, R}{E(T_0)}$$ (31)

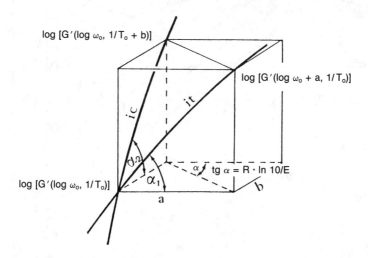

Figure 9. Spatial view of an arbitrary selected intersection point of an isochrone and an isotherm data curve of the storage modulus in the reciprocal temperature—log frequency space. Shown are two possible ways of attaining equivalent values of G′: either along the isochrone curve, ic, by changing the temperature; or along the isotherm curve, it, by changing the frequency.

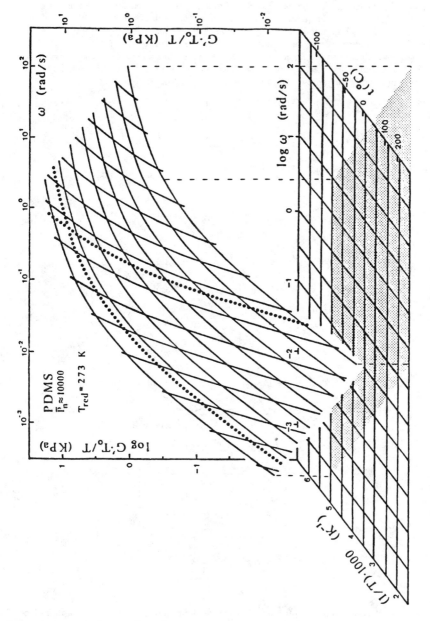

Figure 10. Master Surface of the storage modulus, G′, of poly(dimethylsiloxane) in the terminal zone. T_{red} = reduction temperature. Printed with permission of Springer International [90].

Equations 29 and 31 can as well be extended for the general case with f an arbitrary viscoelastic function:

$$\frac{\delta(f)_\omega/\delta(1/T)}{\delta(f)_T/\delta(\log \omega)} = \frac{E(T)}{2.303 \, R} \tag{32}$$

$(f = G'; G''; J'; J''; \text{tg } \delta)$

For dynamic viscosity, the relation changes somewhat:

$$\frac{\delta[\log(\eta)]_\omega/\delta(1/T)}{1 + \delta[\log(\eta)]_T/\delta(\log \omega)} = \frac{E(T)}{2.303 \, R} \tag{33}$$

$E(T)$ can also be defined from the rheological point of view [42]. Accordingly, under conditions of constant chain restraint and for $T = T_p$, $E(T)$ is defined as:

$$\left[\frac{H_r(T_p(\omega_0))}{H_r(\theta_p(T_0))}\right]_P = \frac{E(T_p)}{R} \tag{34}$$

Finally, it should be pointed out that although the use of reciprocal temperatures is the only physically meaningful way to determine kinetic characteristics, $E(T)$ can also be derived from:

$$\frac{d(\log(a_T))}{dT} = \frac{-E(T)}{2.303 \, RT^2} \tag{35}$$

An analog relation to Equation 26 is then of the form:

$$\log(a_T) = \int_T^{T_0} \frac{E(T)}{2.303 \, RT^2} \, dT \tag{36}$$

For the characterization of the temperature dependence of local flow, both the temperature function $\log(a_T)$ and $E(T)$ are applicable. But, as such, these functions do not directly offer the possibility of a meaningful interpretation related to polymer-specific parameters. Consequently, the temperature dependence of local flow implies a relationship between $\log(a_T)$ or $E(T)$ and rheological parameters. This evaluation step has to be based, however, on some theoretical approaches on which we will be focusing below.

Classic Theories

One of the most well known approaches to an evaluation of the temperature dependence of viscoelastic data is the equation of Williams, Landel, and Ferry (WLF) [12]:

$$\log(a_T) = -\frac{c_1^0(T - T_0)}{c_2^0 + T - T_0} \tag{37}$$

which originally was an empirical relation. Later on, it was supported theoretically by the free volume concept applied to T_g. The reference temperature T_0, usually assumed as $T_0 = T_g + 50$, was also employed instead of T_g. The constants c_1^0 and c_2^0 ($c_1^0 = 8.86$, $c_2^0 = 101.6$ for $T_0 = T_g + 50$) or, in the case of referring to T_g, c_1^g and c_2^g ($c_1^g = 17.44$, $c_2^g = 51.6$) have been considered for a long time universal constants [22]. Lately, it has been generally accepted that these constants are polymer-specific parameters, however, only if T_0 is related with the T_g of the polymer. The validity of this equation is estimated by Ferry as limited to the temperature range between T_g and $T_g + 100$ K.

In order to support the equation theoretically, Ferry started with the Doolittle equation [11]:

$$\ln \eta_0 = \ln A + B\left(\frac{v_0}{v_f}\right) \tag{38}$$

which represents a description of viscosity changes, introducing the free volume v_f as a temperature dependent variable. Considering a free volume fraction defined by $f = v_f/v_0 \simeq v_f/v$, with v representing the volume, v_0 the occupied volume, and v_f the free volume, the shift factor becomes:

$$\log(a_T) = \log\left(\frac{\eta_0}{\eta_0^0}\right) = \frac{B}{2.303}\left(\frac{1}{f} - \frac{1}{f_0}\right) \tag{39}$$

Finally, by assuming a linear temperature dependence of the free volume fraction, i.e., $f = f_0 + \alpha_f(T - T_0)$, the WLF constants can be related to f_0 and α_f according to the following relations:

$$\log(a_T) = -\frac{B}{2.303\, f_0}\left[\frac{T - T_0}{f_0/\alpha_f + T - T_0}\right] \tag{40}$$

$$c_1^0 = B/2.303\, f_0 \qquad c_2^0 = f/\alpha_f \tag{41}$$

In order to use f_0 and α_f for an approximation of the constants, further assumptions are necessary (for details see [22]). The constants which refer to various temperatures, e.g., T_0 and T_1, respectively, are correlated by:

$$c_1^0 = \frac{c_1^1 c_2^1}{c_2^1 + T_0 - T_1} \qquad c_2^0 = c_2^1 + T - T_0 \tag{42}$$

To conclude, it should be pointed out that the WLF equation is based on the idea of referencing the temperature behavior of flow to the glass transition temperature or to a T_g related temperature. The constants are thus dependent on the chosen reference temperature.

Reference temperatures, on which we will focus next, have been under consideration not only for the WLF approach. Fulcher [70], and Tammann and Hesse [71] proposed the equation:

$$\log(a_T) = C' + \frac{B'}{T - T_\infty} \tag{43}$$

which includes as reference temperature the Vogel temperature, T_∞, introduced originally by Vogel [10] into an empirical equation for viscosity. T_∞ is considered a temperature around 50 K below T_g. In terms of the WLF equation [22], T_∞ can be expressed as $T_\infty = T_0 - C_2^0 = T_g - C_2^g$ (see "Generalizing Concept," in the next section of this chapter).

Gibbs and DiMarzio [13] defined, in their thermodynamical approach, the temperature T_2 as a characteristic temperature of local flow. They assumed that at T_2 a second order phase transition is taking place, i.e., a critical configurational entropy S_c^* is exceeded. T_2 is located around $T_g/1.3$ K. For $T > T_2$, Gibbs and DiMarzio formulated a transition probability that is supposed to determine local flow:

$$W(T) = A \exp\left(\frac{-\Delta\mu S_c^*}{k_B T S_c}\right) \tag{44}$$

where S_c = molar configurational entropy and
$\Delta\mu$ = energy barrier between two stable configurations. The shift factor then becomes:

$$-\log(a_T) = \log\frac{W(T)}{W(T_0)} = 2.303(\Delta\mu S_c^*/k_B)\left(\frac{1}{T_0 S_c(T_0)} - \frac{1}{T S_c(T)}\right) \tag{45}$$

Comparing this equation with the WLF equation, Adam and Gibbs [72] found the following correlation between the parameters of the Gibbs DiMarzio theory and the WLF constants:

$$c_1^0 = a_1 = 2.303 \, C/(\Delta c_p T_0 \ln(T_0/T_2))$$

$$c_2^0 = a_2(T) = T_0 \ln(T_0/T_2)/[\ln(T_0/T_2) + (1 + T_0/(T - T_0)) \ln(T/T_0)] \tag{46}$$

Accordingly, a slight dependence of c_2^0 on temperature is predicted, which is obviously not compatible with the WLF approach.

Another well known and for flow phenomena often considered approach is the Arrhenius approach:

$$\log(a_T) = \log A + \frac{E}{2.303 \, RT} \tag{47}$$

The theoretical support of Equation 47 is the Eyring absolute rate theory [34–39]. With respect to reference temperatures, the temperature in this case is 0 K. Both the pre-exponential factor A and the activation energy E are considered constants. The Arrhenius equation is suitable mostly for the description of the flow in very mobile phases, i.e., for polymers probably in temperature ranges far above T_g.

In addition to these theories limited more or less to a certain validity range, attempts have been made toward a general, unified concept of temperature dependence of flow. Thus, Macedo and Litovitz [73] have combined propositions from the absolute rate theory and the free volume concept. Accordingly, the probability of local flow is determined by both the probability of the jumping unit attaining sufficient energy to overcome restraining bonds, P_E [74], and the probability that sufficient local free volume is available to accomodate the jump, P_V [75].

$$\eta = \frac{k}{P_j} = \frac{k}{P_E P_V} \tag{48}$$

This approach yields the concept that at temperatures close to T_g, local flow is determined by the existence of local free volume, whereas at high temperatures an apparent activation energy becomes decisive. The handicap of this approach lies in its relatively high number of parameters and variables.

Evaluation of Experimental Data

Generalizing Concept

In practice, the WLF and Arrhenius approaches are the most frequently applied concepts for the evaluation of temperature dependence of polymeric flow. However, from the theoretical point of view, the Gibbs DiMarzio concept [13] and the concept of Macedo and Litovitz [73] have a lot of significance, as will be shown in the next paragraphs. For example, Macedo and Litovitz's idea to try a generalization and unification of the existing theoretical descriptions will be a basic concept in the following discussion.

As already presented with respect to experimental accessibility of temperature dependence of local flow in polymers, the temperature functions E(T) and $\log(a_T)$, related to each other by Equations 25 and 26, originate from different theoretical approaches. Considering $\log(a_T)$ given by a WLF equation, Equation 25 becomes:

$$\frac{d[\log(a_T)]}{d(1/T)} = \frac{c_1^g c_2^g T^2}{(c_2^g + T - T_g)^2} = \frac{E(T)}{2.303 \, R} \tag{49}$$

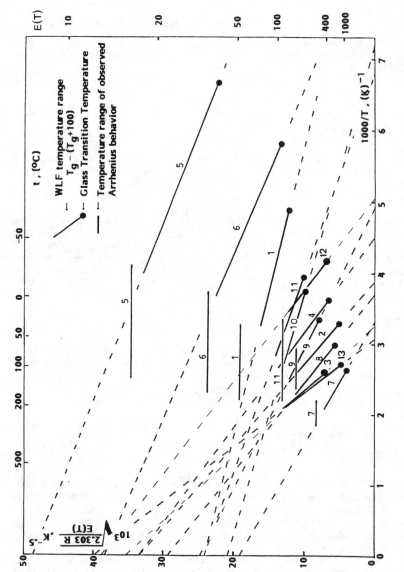

Figure 11. Illustration in accordance with Equations 50 and 51 of the temperature dependences of the activation energy of flow in the ranges of WLF and of Arrhenius behavior (for polymers see Table 1). E(T) is given in kJ/mole. Printed with permission of Springer International [92].

Further transformation yields a linear equation with respect to the reciprocal temperature:

$$\sqrt{\frac{2.303\ \mathrm{R}}{\mathrm{E(T)}}} = \sqrt{\frac{1}{c_1^g c_2^g}}\left(1 + \frac{c_2^g - T_g}{T}\right) \tag{50}$$

$$\sqrt{\frac{1}{\mathrm{E(T)}}} = A^* + B^*\left(\frac{1}{T}\right) \tag{51}$$

According to Equation 51, a WLF-type temperature dependence of local flow can be described by an inclined straight line in the respective plot. In the same plot, the Arrhenius-type temperature dependences correspond to horizontal straight lines. Thus, besides realizing a generalized picture of these two behaviors, a plot based on Equation 51 also gives the possibility to estimate in a simple way the obedience of the local flow temperature dependence to one of the two approaches.

In Figure 11, the temperature dependence of local flow of some polymers listed in Table 1 are presented in such a representation. The Arrhenius-type behavior shown by horizontal straight lines may indicate the rightness of the Macedo-Litovitz concept. A change of the WLF constants with temperature, as reported by Pfandl [93] and presented in Figure 12 from the point of view of Equation 51, may also be considered in this respect. The temperature dependence of local flow, obeying to a WLF-type or to the Arrhenius-type behavior, is marked by approaching the respective linearity in a plot like in Figure 11. Accordingly, in the temperature range where the temperature dependence can be approached by a straight line in such a plot, the respective local flow mechanism should be invariant. The Arrhenius-type behavior appears in terms of Figure 11 as a limiting case of the WLF-type behavior.

Kinetic Parameters of Local Flow

A reformulation of the WLF equation into a relation similar to the Tammann equation [71]:

$$\log(a_T) = -c_1^g + \frac{c_1^g c_2^g}{c_2^g + T - T_g} = C' + \frac{B'}{T - T_\infty} \tag{52}$$

Table 1
Viscoelastic Characteristics of Some Polymers

Polymer	T_g	E_∞^*	T_∞	$T_g - T_\infty$	c_1^g	Ref.
1. Poly(isobutylene)	205.0	33.43	99.6	105.4	17.56	76–78
2. Poly(vinylacetate)	305.0	17.23	255.4	49.6	18.17	79, 80
3. Polystyrene	373.0	12.12	322.6	50.4	12.58	81, 82
4. Poly(methylacrylate)	283.0	17.23	220.0	63.0	14.30	83
5. Poly(dimethylsiloxane)	148.0	8.08	79.8	69.2	6.11	84, 48
6. Polybutadiene	172.0	13.03	118.9	63.1	10.78	85
7. Poly(methylmethacrylate)**	388.0	52.59	299.3	88.7	30.96	86, 87
8. Poly(ethylmethacrylate)	335.0	22.64	267.6	67.4	17.52	88
9. Poly(n-butylmethacrylate)	300.0	31.18	200.7	99.3	16.40	89, 87
10. Poly(n-hexylmethacrylate)	268.0	44.38	137.7	130.3	17.81	89
11. Poly(n-octylmethacrylate)	253.0	31.51	145.9	107.1	16.56	90, 87
12. Poly(vinylmethylether)	237.5	12.74	199.0	38.5	17.28	91
13. Polystyrene	376.0	15.50	309.0	66.5	11.78	91

* *given in kJ/mole*
** *according to c_1 and c_2 data reported by Schwarzl and al.[104] the values are: $E_\infty = 5.5$ kJ/mole and $T_\infty = 360.6$ K*

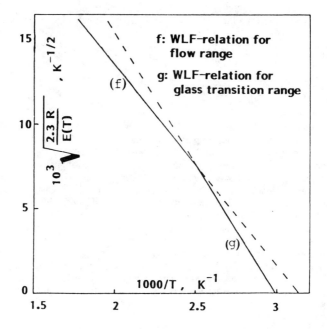

Figure 12. The two temperature ranges of different WLF behavior of polystyrene in accordance with the data published by Pfandl et al. [93]:
f = terminal zone; $c_1^g c_2^g = 706$ K; $T_\infty = 45.7°$C
g = glass transition range; $c_1^g c_2^g = 459$ K, $T_\infty = 60.7°$C.
Printed with permission of Springer International [92].

reveals the following relations between the respective constants:

$$c_1^g c_2^g = B' \qquad -c_1^g = C' \qquad T_g - c_2^g = T_\infty \tag{53}$$

The latter equation states clearly that T_g and the Vogel temperature T_∞ differ just by c_2^g, the second WLF constant. Obviously, the relation is also valid for other reference temperatures, T_0, and the respective constants, c_2^0. A corresponding reformulation of Equation 49:

$$\sqrt{\frac{2.303\ R}{E(T)}} = \sqrt{\frac{1}{c_1^g c_2^g}} \left(1 - \frac{T_\infty}{T}\right) \tag{54}$$

shows that in terms of Figure 11, the extrapolated intersections of the straight lines with the reciprocal temperature axis occur always at $T = T_\infty$. On the other hand, the extrapolated intersections with the apparent activation energy axis in the same plot can be defined as:

$$\lim_{T \to \infty} E(T) = c_1^g c_2^g\ 2.303\ R = E_\infty \tag{55}$$

with E_∞ the apparent activation energy of local flow at infinite temperature.

Using T_∞ and E_∞, i.e., a temperature and an apparent activation energy, as characteristic parameters of the temperature dependence of local flow, Equation 54 becomes:

$$\sqrt{\frac{1}{E(T)}} = \sqrt{\frac{1}{E_\infty}} \left(1 - \frac{T_\infty}{T}\right) \tag{56}$$

For both E(T) and $E^{\#}$ (see Equation 27), the correlation with E_{∞} and T_{∞} is given by:

$$E(T) = \frac{E_{\infty} T^2}{(T - T_{\infty})^2} \tag{57}$$

$$E^{\#} = E_{\infty} \frac{T}{T - T_{\infty}} \tag{58}$$

Due to the fact that $E^{\#}$ and E(T) are based on a kinetic approach of polymeric flow, E_{∞} and T_{∞} can be referred to as kinetic parameters of local flow in polymers. A secured, exact association of E_{∞} and T_{∞} with certain phenomenological characteristics is not possible yet. However, it is obvious that the T_{∞} temperatures are very close to the T_2 temperatures predicted by the Gibbs DiMarzio approach, which is based on a thermodynamic concept of a critical configurational entropy at T_2. The conformational entropy, in fact a thermodynamic function approachable from thermoanalysis, is supposed to become zero in a temperature range also very close to the T_{∞} range [94]. Accordingly, it seems reasonable to consider T_{∞} a temperature determined by entropic factors. On the other hand, E_{∞} is an activation energy with values in the range of the potential barriers of conformational changes, i.e., C—C bond rotation. These interpretations of E_{∞} and T_{∞} also seem reasonable because of the generally accepted view of polymeric flow as a conformational rearrangement process of macromolecular chains.

Considering Erying's formulation of the relaxation time and Equation 58, the relaxation time of an arbitrary relaxation process P can be expressed by:

$$\theta_p(T) = P^* \exp\left(\frac{E_{\infty}}{R(T - T_{\infty})}\right) \tag{59}$$

with P^* a pre-exponential factor characteristic of the process P, and in terms of Equation 10 proportional to the number of flow barriers associated with P. Equation 59 offers another option in the definition of E_{∞} and T_{∞}. Thus, E_{∞} is a real Erying apparent activation energy and T_{∞} is a temperature that splits the intensive thermal energy into two parts, one part corresponding to $R(T - T_{\infty})$, which is used for surmounting the energy barrier E_{∞}, and the second part RT_{∞} that contributes to create a certain critical free volume, necessary to render molecular dislocation. From this point of view, Arrhenius behavior represents only a special case of that formulated in Equation 58, namely that of $T_{\infty} = 0$. Then, the whole intensive thermal energy is invested in surmounting the energy barrier E_{∞}.

On the basis of this view, some generalizing equations can be formulated with $T_{\Delta} = T - T_{\infty}$:

$$\theta_p(T) = P^* \exp\left(\frac{E_{\infty}}{RT_{\Delta}}\right) \tag{60}$$

$$\log(a_T) = A + \frac{E_{\infty}}{2.303\, RT_{\Delta}} \tag{61}$$

$$\frac{d[\log(a_T)]}{d(1/T_{\Delta})} = \frac{E_{\infty}}{2.303\, R} = \text{constant} \tag{62}$$

Besides the phenomenological background of these parameters, it should be made clear that they are real polymer-specific parameters, not dependent on reference temperatures like the WLF constants. Williams, Landel, and Ferry had to introduce the respective constants in their semiempirical equation only because they were referring to T_g or to a T_g-related temperature. In fact, on the basis of the generalizing concept illustrated in Figure 11, and of Equations 54–59, it is evident that the only justified reference temperature for temperature dependence of local flow is T_{∞}, and not T_g as it is usually believed. However, some general correlations between T_g and T_{∞} exhibiting a scatter

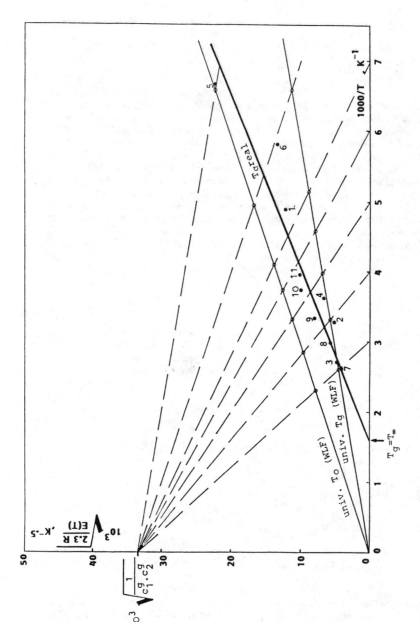

Figure 13. The "universal" WLF behavior in terms of Equation 54. (○) "universal" T_g or T_0 values as predicted by the "universal" WLF constants; (●) experimental T_g data (polymers as in Figure 11). Solid line-suggested $T_g - T_\infty$ correlation.

of up to 40 K can be established. Figure 13 illustrates such a correlation, which in this case is considered linear in terms of the generalizing plot. In Figure 13 are also indicated glass transitions, as predicted by the older WLF concept claiming universality for the constants.

An important aspect of Figure 13 is the fact that an extrapolation of the considered linear correlation between T_g and T_∞ exhibits an intersection with the reciprocal temperature axis at a temperature between 600 and 750 K [95, 96]. At this limiting temperature, T_g and T_∞ apparently coincide, and in addition it is obvious that thermal degradation of polymers with C—C backbone bonds occurs just in this temperature range. It might be worthwhile to reflect on this observation!

In order to exemplify the evaluation of the temperature dependence of local flow via the kinetic parameters E_∞ and T_∞, Figure 14 presents a plot according to Equation 51 for poly(styrene), (PS), poly(vinylmethylether), (PVME), and some of their compatible blends [92]. The resulting kinetic parameters of local flow are plotted vs. composition in Figure 15. The differences between the parameters of blends with high molecular PS and those with oligomeric PS can be interpreted according to the phenomenological background associated with the respective parameters. Thus, the more pronounced increase of E_∞ in the case of oligomeric PS is probably due to a better energetic interaction, i.e., better coupling of conformational rearrangements, while the more pronounced decrease of T_∞ of this type of blends might be due to the higher mobility, i.e., more free volume, introduced into this system by chain ends. These arguments happen to be in accordance with other

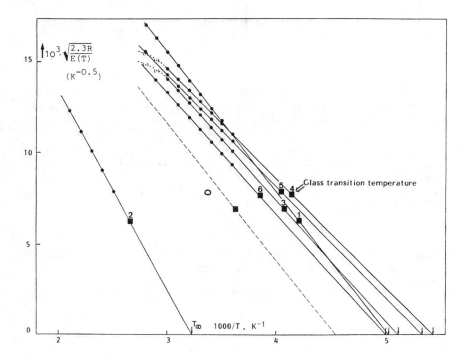

Figure 14. Plot of the E(T) values of the local flow process in PS-PVME blends. 1 = PVME; 2 = $PS_{75,000}$; 3 = $PS_{75,000}$/PVME, 24.1 w/w% PS; 4 = PS_{800}/PVME, 8.6 w/w% PS; 5 = PS_{800}/PVME, 24.2 w/w% PS; and 6 = PS_{800}/PVME, 75.4 w/w% PS. Dashed line = local flow behavior of PS_{800} derived from extrapolated E_∞ and T_∞ data; ○ = single experimental value of E(T) of PS_{800}; straight lines = characterizing the local flow process; dotted line = deviations at high temperatures, tendency of Arrhenius behavior; ● = experimental values of the E(T) function. Printed with permission of Springer International [92].

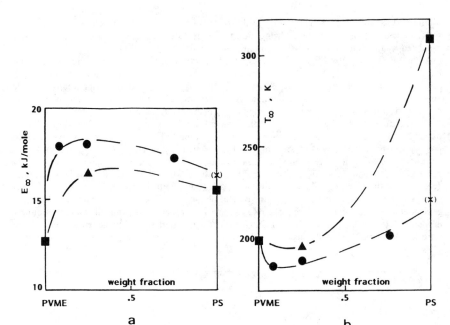

Figure 15. Composition dependence of the kinetic parameters of the local flow process. ■ = homopolymers; blends with ● = PS_{800} and ▲ = $PS_{75,000}$; x = extrapolated values of T_∞ and E_∞ for PS_{800}. Printed with permission of Springer International [92].

investigations of such blends like T_g-determination [91, 97] or FTIR-spectrometry [98]. The opposed changes of E_∞ and T_∞ of the blends might also be viewed as a compensation effect [99]. In addition, Figures 14 and 15 also indicate the possibility to evaluate local flow behavior of materials by extrapolation from the behavior of their blends.

Glass Transition and Local Flow

As pointed out in the previous paragraph, not T_g but T_∞ is a characteristic parameter of the temperature dependence of local flow in polymers. In terms of a local flow mechanism, defined by a straight line in Figure 11 for any temperature higher than T_∞, relaxations are characterized by the relaxation times expressed in Equation 59. Thus, the relaxation time at T_g becomes:

$$\log \theta_p(T_g) = \log P^* + \frac{E_\infty}{2.303\ R(T_g - T_\infty)} \tag{63}$$

The shift factor with respect to T_g is then:

$$\log(a_T) = \log[\theta_p(T)] - \log[\theta_p(T_g)] \tag{64}$$

It is interesting to observe that, if considering Equations 52 and 64, the first WLF constant results as:

$$c_1^g = \frac{E_\infty}{2.303\ R(T_g - T_\infty)} \tag{65}$$

Interpreting Equation 65 on the basis of Erying's absolute rate theory, c_1^g represents a reduced logarithmic flow time of a flow unit at T_g. This physical meaning of c_1^g is totally different from that of Equation 41, which is based on the free volume concept. The fact that for various polymers c_1^g has values more or less grouped around an average value of 17 indicates, in terms of flow time considerations, that the molecular motions detected at T_g with the usual, thermo-analytical or thermo-mechanical, techniques lie within a certain experimental time window. This interpretation leads to the concept of glass transition as an iso-time phenomenon, which differs from the iso-free volume concept [100, 101], but corresponds with the generally accepted view of glass transition as a kinetically determined process.

Besides these considerations about glass transition based on kinetic parameters of local flow, there exist some other aspects of polymeric flow at T_g. Thus, for example, arises the question concerning the validity of the time-temperature superposition principle when temperature approaches T_g. If the only freezing mobility during glass transition is the conformational rearrangement process of the macromolecular backbone, i.e., α-relaxation, generally the time-temperature superposition principle can be supposed as valid. This applies, for example, to poly(vinylchloride) [95, 102] and poly(methylmethacrylate) [95, 103, 104]. Some polymers exhibiting a pure α-relaxation show deviations from WLF behavior near T_g [103]. Typical then is a drop of the apparent activation energy, E(T), near T_g; i.e., it shows deviations from linearity in a generalizing plot. Figure 16 illustrates the case of poly(methylmethacrylate) [87]. The resulting branch of the E[T] curve below T_g (see Figure 16) coincides reasonably well with the value of $E_\beta = 88$ kJ/mole and $T_\beta = 318$ K reported by Boyer [105] for the β-relaxation of this polymer (β-relaxation stands for an additional change of molecular mobility in the polymeric glass, based mainly on the freeze of conformational rearrangement processes of side chains and chain ends). From the theoretical point of view, such a development of the E(T)-curve in the glass transition range has been substantiated by Bueche [103] and Kovacs [106]. The latter based his considerations on the Macedo-Litovitz approach. Lately, after observing a similar behavior in the case of poly(propylene), McCrum [107, 108] tried to explain this phenomenon by means of the compensation law, and by considering the existence of an iso-kinetic point somewhat above T_g. In terms of the generalizing plot in Figure 11, however, the deviation from linearity, caused by the E(T) decrease, has to be viewed as a change in local flow mechanism.

The case of the time-temperature superposition principle not being valid has not yet been mentioned. This usually occurs when the β-relaxation overlaps with the α-relaxation, like in the T_g range of poly(n-butylmethacrylate). Figure 17 illustrates, for example, by contour lines of a G'' surface of poly(n-butylmethacrylate) projected in a reciprocal temperature-logarithmic time plane, how superposition becomes impossible near T_g. Accordingly, all evaluation methods of temperature dependence of local flow based on the validity of the time-temperature superposition principle fail for such behavior. The straight contour lines at higher temperatures and lower frequencies indicate an Arrhenius-type temperature dependence of local flow in that range.

Applications

Optimization of Data Collection

Experimental data collection for the determination of viscoelastic behavior of polymers is usually a time consuming process, especially if the Newtonian flow range is approached. The already mentioned time-temperature superposition principle gives the possibility to use "temperature" as a time spearing procedure, i.e., recording isotherm data curves at different temperatures. However, as long as the temperature dependence of local flow of the respective polymer is unknown, the determination of viscoelastic behavior implies the application of shift procedures, which require overlapping of isotherms, and thus the use of a broad experimental time or frequency window. In terms of these mentioned aspects, optimization of data collection means reduction of experimental time, reduction of the number of data points, and reduction of the overall experimental effort, but all this without diminishing the quality of the final result.

If it is justified, by whatever information or experience, to assume for a particular polymer the validity of the time-temperature superposition principle, and if the measurements are kept strictly

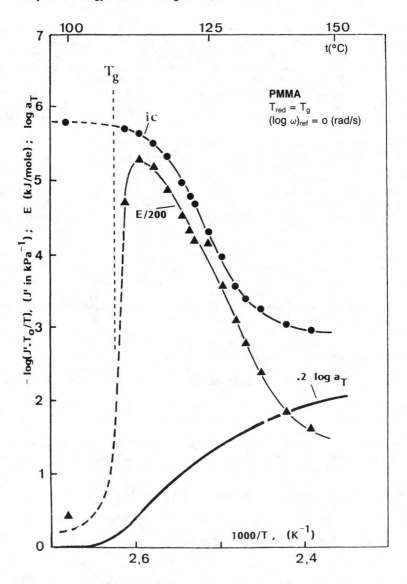

Figure 16. Temperature dependence of E(T) and log(a_T) data of poly(methylmethacrylate) in the glass transition region. Isotherm compliance data of Schwarzl et al. [104] reanalyzed via master surface representation in accordance with Equations 32 and 26. ic = isochrone representation of "it" data of Schwarzl.

within the range of linear viscoelasticity, some alternatives for the optimization of data collection should be considered. First of all, there is the possibility to use the apparent activation energy as a function representing the temperature dependence of viscoelastic behavior. E(T) is an experimentally accessible magnitude and offers the advantage that its determination does not require overlapping

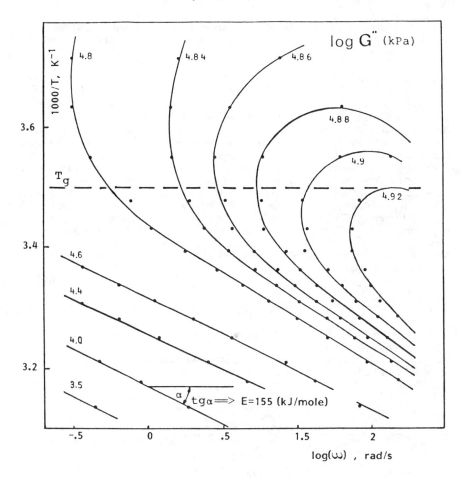

Figure 17. Contour representation of the loss modulus, G″, of poly(n-butylmethacrylate) in an experimentally accessible section of the viscoelastic surface in the glass transition range. 4.88 = Contour line for G″ = $10^{4.88}$ KPa (oscillatory bar data in the glass transition range).

of isotherms (see Equations 31–33). Accordingly, the experimental time interval can be considerably reduced. The temperature dependence can then be evaluated by means of the generalizing plot in Figure 11. Subsequently, composite curves of viscoelastic functions are obtained via shift procedures according to $\log(a_T)$ functions, as will be presented in the next paragraph.

There is also the possibility to minimize the number of E(T) values in terms of Figure 11. Accordingly, depending on the degree of certainty with respect to a pure WLF- or Arrhenius-type behavior, the number of E(T) values needed for the determination of the temperature dependence of viscoelastic behavior over the respective temperature range can be considerably reduced. The most extreme numbers are "two" for pure WLF-type and "one" for pure Arrhenius-type behavior.

The applier of such optimization is urged to consider carefully the particular case with respect to the information he is expecting from his experiment. He should be able to estimate up to what degree of optimization he can proceed without affecting the accuracy of the required information. The great advantage of these optimization results is the possibility of a quick estimation of viscoelastic behavior of a polymer.They are suitable mostly for routine measurements or for detecting systematic changes of a particular viscoelastic feature of the polymer, as, for example temperature dependence or modulus changes with the gradual variation of a molecular structure element.

Representation of Viscoelastic Functions

For the representation of viscoelastic functions as a function of experimental time, or temperature, or both, it is neccessary to determine first of all the temperature dependence of the viscoelastic behavior, i.e., of local flow, of the respective polymer. If time is not a limiting factor, and the interest is focused on isothermal behavior at certain temperatures, the determination of the temperature, dependence may be avoided by using long-time experiments and classic shift procedures.

The applicability and the advantage of using the apparent activation energy $E(T)$ as a temperature function characterizing the temperature dependence of local flow have been pointed out earlier in this chapter. In order to use $E(T)$ for the representation of viscoelastic properties, it has to be converted into its integral form, which is the shift factor. According to Equation 26, any experimentally determined $E(T)$-function can be transformed into a $\log(a_T)$-function. The integration can be performed numerically or via fitting the experimental $E(T)$-values to a function suitable for integration. An example of such a fitted $E(T)$-function is given in Figure 16. If WLF or Arrhenius behavior is detected, the following relation between the shift factor and the kinetic parameters of local flow should be used:

$$\log(a_T) = \frac{E_\infty}{2.303 \, R(T - T_\infty)} - \frac{E_\infty}{2.303 \, R(T_0 - T_\infty)} \tag{66}$$

E_∞ and T_∞ result from a plot like that in Figure 11. Referring to a reciprocal temperature-logarithmic frequency plane, $E(T)$ determines the slope of the curve, i.e., of the $\log(a_T)$-function, along which each data point can be shifted in this plane [102]. An illustration of such shift curves is presented in Figure 18. The shift of viscoelastic properties in this plane offers the possibility to construct

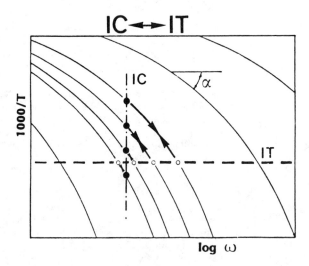

Figure 18. IC — IT shift procedures for temperature-dependent activation energy of flow. tg α = E(T)/2.303R. Printed with permission of Steinkopf Verlag [102].

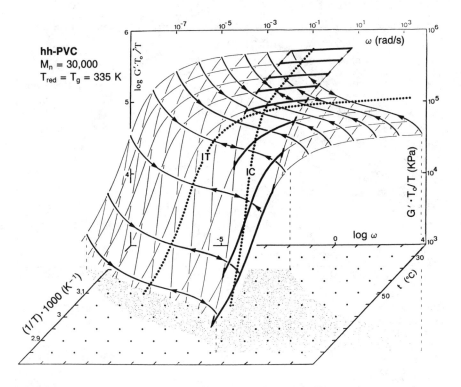

Figure 19. Master surface of the storage modulus of hh-PVC in the glass transition region. Solid lines = experimental "it" data curves; dotted lines = master curves: IT = isotherm and IC = isochrone. Printed with permission of Steinkopf Verlag [102].

master surfaces, which give a very comprehensive picture about time and temperature variations of viscoelastic properties, including the temperature dependence of local flow. An example of a master surface for head-head poly(vinylchloride) in the glass transition range is presented in Figure 19. It indicates very clearly how the isotherm and isochrone master curves are part of the master surface. As illustrated in Figure 18, for any temperature dependence of local flow differing from the Arrhenius-type, isochronal data have to be shifted individually, whereas isothermal data can be shifted grouped as isotherm curves. Applying this shift procedure, the isotherm and isochrone master curves of Figures 20 and 21 have been constructed. The master curves of Figure 21 are based on data often cited in the literature [22, 90] for poly(n-octylmethacrylate). Figure 20 presents the master curves marked also on the master surface of Figure 10 for poly(dimethylsiloxane) [40], and constructed using a constant apparent activation energy of 15.5 kJ/mole. It is also an example of Arrhenius behavior which offers the possibility to shift isochronal data in groups, i.e., as a whole isochrone curve [41, 102].

An additional way of representing viscoelastic properties results from Equations 60–62. These relations suggest that the use of $1/(T - T_\infty)$ as temperature axis might offer interesting possibilities of direct comparison of viscoelastic behavior of polymers.

All the above-described ways of presenting viscoelastic behavior represent the practical aspect of the previously mentioned isochronal extension of viscoelastic functions. The given examples demonstrate, however, the applicability of the shift procedures illustrated in Figure 18.

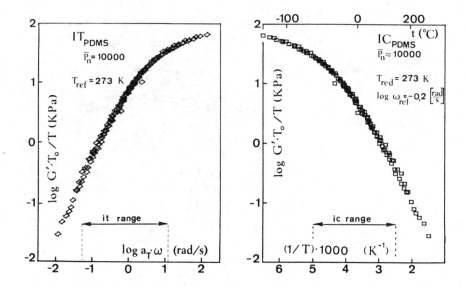

Figure 20. IT and IC master curves of the storage modulus of PDMS in the terminal zone, shifted by using calculated E(T) and log(a_T) values via master surface presentation and application of Equations 32 and 26.

CONCLUSION

The temperature dependence of local flow in polymers exhibits many aspects that are still controversial because of their complexity and also because of the existence of different approaches and phenomenological theories in this field. The above-proposed concepts are meant to overcome some of these conceptual differences and to improve the possibilities of interpretation and representation of viscoelastic behavior of polymers. An extension of the rheological formulations of viscoelasticity by an additional temperature dimension creates a basis for uniform description of viscoelastic properties in a time-temperature space. This offers, in return, ways to directly convert isothermal properties into isochronal ones, and vice-versa. Advantages result as well for the experimental part of viscoelastic property determination.

With respect to the interpretation of local flow in terms of molecular parameters, the presented generalizing concept of characterization of the temperature dependence of local flow by kinetic parameters offers theoretical and practical advantages. From the theoretical point of view, it has the advantage that the parameters are not depending on a reference temperature, and that they have a clear physical meaning. Additionally, it constitutes a general approach applicable to the WLF-type, the Arrhenius-type, and also to transitions between various types of temperature dependence of local flow. On the other hand, due to the linear representation of the two basic types of behavior in the generalizing plot, some practical advantages result for the efficient and accurate determination of the kinetic parameters.

An additional aspect, which is of theoretical as well as of practical relevance, represents the possible improvement of the "method of reduced variables" by using $\log(a_T) = E_\infty/2.303\ R(T - T_\infty)$ for shifting. Thus, any dependence of the reduced time coordinate on another phenomenologically irrelevant temperature, as for example T_g, is avoided. According to:

$$\log[(\theta_p(T)] = \log P^* + \frac{E_\infty}{2.303\ R(T - T_\infty)} \tag{67}$$

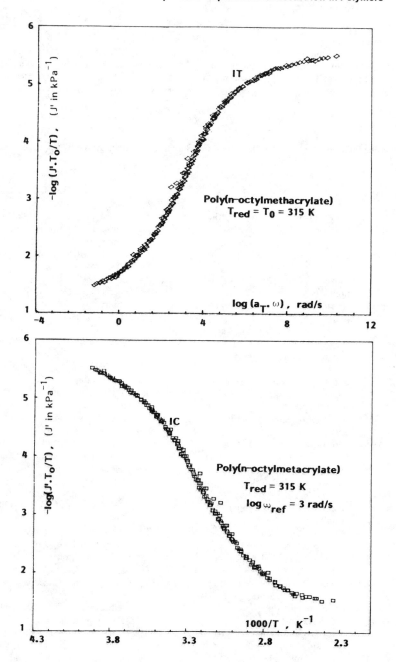

Figure 21. IT and IC master curves of the storage compliance of poly(n-octylmethacrylate) in the glass transition region using calculated E(T) and log(a_T) values. Data of Ferry et al. [90] reanalyzed via master surface presentation.

the reduced logarithmic time coordinate would be $\log(P^*)$ or $-\log(P^*)$. The here-proposed reduced time coordinate exhibits no dependence on any reference temperature.

Some unanswered questions still exist. They are basically related to attempts to find some additional molecular flow features, common or limiting for certain classes of polymers. The availability of more and accurate data in this field will probably be decisive for the successful encounter of this challenge.

Acknowledgment

Generous financial support from the Sonderforschungsbereich 60 is gratefully acknowledged.

NOTATION

A	pre-exponential factor of the Doolittle, Erying, Gibbs-DiMarzio, and related equations
A_G	characteristic viscoelastic constant
B	constant of the Doolittle equation
B', C'	constants of the Tammann equation
E	Young modulus; Arrhenius-type activation energy
$E(T)$	apparent activation energy of local flow
E_∞	apparent activation energy of local flow extrapolated to infinite temperature
$E^\#$	Eyring apparent activation energy
$\Delta E^\#$	activation energy of the transition state theory; height of the energy barrier at 0K
G'	storage modulus
G''	loss modulus
$G, G(t)$	relaxation modulus
G_e	equilibrium modulus
$\Delta G^\#$	activation Gibbs energy
H	relaxation time spectrum
H_r, H'	reduced relaxation time spectrum
H_r	reduced reciprocal relaxation temperature spectrum
$\Delta H^\#$	activation enthalpy
IC	isochrone master curve
IT	isotherm master curve
$J, J(t)$	retardation compliance
J'	storage compliance
J''	loss compliance
J_0	instantaneous compliance
L	retardation time spectrum
M	molecular weight

P	degree of polymerization; arbitrary relaxation process
P^*	pre-exponential factor associated with an arbitrary relaxation process
P_j	flow probability
P_E	energetic determined flow probability
P_V	"free volume" determined flow probability
Q	partition function of the ground state
$Q^\#$	partition function of the transition state
R	universal gas constant
S_c	molar conformational entropy
S_c^*	critical conformational entropy
$\Delta S^\#$	activation entropy
T	absolute temperature
T_∞	Vogel temperature; extrapolated temperature for infinite activation energy
T_2	critical conformational transition temperature of Gibbs-DiMarzio
T_g	glass transition temperature
T_p	temperature of an arbitrary relaxation process
T_{ref}, T_0, T_1	arbitrary reference temperature
T_{red}	reduction temperature of viscoelastic function
T_Δ	temperature of the generalized Eyring relation
$W(T)$	conformational transition probability
a	mean-square end-to-end distance per monomer unit; frequency step along the it data curve in the master surface presentation

a_T	shift factor	ic	isochrone data curve
$a_1, a_2(T)$	constants of the Gibbs-Di-Marzio equation	it	isotherm data curve
		$k^{\#}$	unilateral rate constant of the transition state theory
a_i, b_i	coefficients of the linear differential viscoelastic function	k	rate constant of the flow process
b	reciprocal temperature step along the ic data curve in the master surface presentation	k_B	Boltzmann constant
		p	mode of motion
		t	experimental time
c_1^g, c_2^g	WLF-constants for T_g as reference temperature	v_0	specific occupied volume
		v_f	specific "free" volume
c_1^0, c_2^0	WLF-constants for T_0 as reference temperature	x_i	local flow step
f	fractional free volume; viscoelastic magnitude		

Greek Symbols

θ	relaxation time	η	dynamic viscosity
θ'	retardation time	χ	transmission coefficient of the transition state theory
α_f	thermal expansion coefficient of the fractional "free" volume	λ	interval between equilibrium positions in flow direction
$tg\,\alpha_1$	slope of the viscoelastic it data curve	λ_p	length of a flow chain segment
$tg\,\alpha_2$	slope of the viscoelastic ic data curve	$\Delta\mu$	energy barrier between stable conformations
γ	deformation; strain; shear	σ	stress
ζ_0	monomeric friction coefficient	ω, ω_0	experimental frequency, reference
η_m, η_v	Newtonian viscosities		
η_0	zero shear viscosity		

Subscripts

m	refers to the Maxwell model	r	refers to temperature reduction
p	refers to a certain relaxation process	v	refers to the Kelvin Voigt model

REFERENCES

1. Bueche, F., *J. Chem. Phys.*, 20, 1959 (1952).
2. Bueche, F., *J. Chem. Phys.*, 25, 599 (1956).
3. Rouse, P. E., Jr., *J. Chem. Phys.*, 21, 1272 (1953).
4. Zimm, B. H., *J. Chem. Phys.*, 24, 269 (1956).
5. Zimm, B. H., and Kilby, R. W., *J. Polym. Sci.*, 37, 19 (1959).
6. de Gennes, P. G., *Macromolecules*, 9, 587, 594 (1978).
7. Doi, M., and Edwards, S. F., *J. Chem. Soc. Faraday Trans. 11*, 74, 1789, 1802, 1818 (1978).
8. Doi, M., and Edwards, S. F., *J. Chem. Soc. Faraday Trans. 11*, 75, 38 (1979).
9. Krausz, A. S., and Eyring, H., *Deformation Kinetics*, Wiley, New York, 1975.
10. Vogel, H., *Phys. Z.*, 22, 645 (1921).
11. Doolittle, A. K., *J. Appl. Phys.*, 22, 1417 (1951).
12. William, M. L., Landel, R. F., and Ferry, J. D., *J. Am. Chem. Soc.*, 77, 3701 (1955).
13. Gibbs, J. H., and DiMarzio, E. A., *J. Chem. Phys.* 28, 373 (1958).
14. Macedo, P. B., and Litovitz, T. A., *J. Chem. Phys.*, 42, 245 (1965).

15. Weber, W., *Pogg. Ann.*, (2) 4, 247 (1835).
16. Kohlrausch, R., *Pogg. Ann.*, (3) 12, 393 (1847).
17. Boltzmann, L., *Wied. Ann.*, 5, 430 (1878).
18. Zener, C., *Elasticity and Anelasticity of Metals*, Chicago University Press, Chicago, 1948.
19. Gross, B., *Mathematical Structure of the Theories of Viscoelasticity*, Hermann, Paris, 1953.
20. Alfrey, T., *Mechanical Behavior of High Polymers*, Interscience Publishers, New York, 1948.
21. Tschoegl, N. W., *The Theory of Linear Viscoelastic Behavior*, Academic Press, New York, 1980.
22. Ferry, J. D., *Viscoelastic Properties of Polymers*, Wiley, New York, 1980.
23. Vinogradov, G. V., and Malkin, A. Ya. *Rheology of Polymers*, Springer, Berlin, 1980.
24. Eirich, F. R., *Rheology–Theory and Applications*, Academic Press, New York, 1956.
25. Berry, G. C., and Casassa, E. F., *Macromol. Rev.*, 4, 1 (1970).
26. Yamakawa, H., *Modern Theory of Polymer Solutions*, Harper and Row, New York, 1971.
27. Osaki, K., *Adv. Polym. Sci.*, 12, 1 (1973).
28. Bird, R. B., Hassager, O., Armstrong, R. C., and Curtiss, C. F., *Dynamics of Polymeric Liquids*, Vol. II, Wiley, New York, 1977.
29. Chompff, A. J., and Prins, W., *J. Chem. Phys.*, 48, 235 (1968).
30. Ferry, J. D., Landel, R. F., and Williams, M. L., *J. Appl. Phys.*, 26, 359 (1955).
31. Bueche, F., *J. Appl. Phys.*, 26, 738 (1955).
32. Marvin, R. S., and Oser, H., *J. Res. Nat. Bur. Stand.*, 66B, 171 (1962).
33. Flory, P. J., Hoeve, C. A., and Ciferri, A., *J. Polym. Sci.*, 34, 337 (1959).
34. Eyring, H., and Polanyi, M., *Z. Phys. Chem.*, 12, 279 (1931).
35. Eyring, H., and Polanyi, M., *J. Am. Chem. Soc.*, 53, 2537 (1931).
36. Eyring, H., *J. Chem. Phys.*, 3, 107, (1935).
37. Wynne-Jones, W. F. K., and Eyring, H., *J. Chem. Phys.*, 3, 492 (1935).
38. Eyring, H., Walter, J., and Kimball, G. E., *Quantum Chemistry*, Wiley, New York, 1944.
39. Ree, T., and Eyring, H., *J. Appl. Phys.*, 26, 793 (1955).
40. Brekner, M.-J., Cantow, H.-J., and Schneider, H. A., *Polym. Bulletin*, 10, 328 (1983).
41. Schneider, H. A., and Cantow, H.-J., *Polym. Bulletin*, 9, 361 (1983).
42. Brekner, M.-J., Cantow, H.-J., and Schneider, H. A., *Polym. Bulletin*, 13, 51 (1985).
43. Wagner, K. W., *Elektrotech. Z.*, 36, 135, 163 (1915).
44. Leaderman, H., *Elastic and Creep Properties of Filamentous Materials and Other High Polymers*, The Textile Foundation, Washington, 1943.
45. Müller, F. H., *Kolloid-Z.*, 114, 2 (1949).
46. Bischoff, J., E. Catsiff, and A. V. Tobolsky, *J. Am. Chem. Soc.*, 74, 3378 (1952).
47. Schwarzl F., and Stavermann, A. J., *J. Appl. Phys.*, 23, 838 (1952).
48. Tobolsky, A. V., *J. Appl. Phys.*, 27, 673 (1956).
49. Nakada, O., *J. Phys. Soc. Jpn.*, 12, 1218 (1957).
50. Malkin, A. Ya., *Advances in Polymer Rheology* (in russian), edited by Vinogrodov, G. V., Khimiya Publishers, Moscow, 1970.
51. Flory, P. J., *Chem. Rev.*, 35, 51 (1944).
52. Tobolsky, A. V., *Properties and Structure of Polymers*, Wiley, New York, 1960.
53. Ward, I. M., *Structure and Properties of Oriented Polymers*, Applied Science Publishers LTD., London, 1975.
54. Elias, H.-G., *Macromolecules* (in german), Hüthig Wepf, Basel, 1981.
55. Tobolsky, A. V., and Andrews, R. D., *J. Chem. Phys.*, 11, 125 (1943).
56. Ferry, J. D., *J. Am. Chem. Soc.*, 72, 3746 (1950).
57. Dahlquist, C. A., and Hatfield, M. R., *J. Colloid. Sci.*, 7, 253 (1952).
58. Hopkins, I. L., *J. Appl. Phys.*, 24, 1300 (1953).
59. Philipoff, W., *J. Appl. Phys.*, 25, 1102 (1954).
60. Plazek, D. J., Dannhauser, W., and Ferry, J. D., *J. Colloid Sci.*, 16, 101 (1961).
61. Ferry, J. D., and Fitzgerald, E. R., *J. Colloid. Sci.*, 8, 224 (1953).
62. Barlow, A. J., Lamb, J., Matheson, A. J., Padmini, P. R. K. L., and Richter, J., *Proc. R. Soc.*, A298, 467 (1967).
63. Barlow, A. J., Erginsay, A., and Lamb, J., *Proc. R. Soc.*, A298, 481 (1967).
64. Graessley, W. W., *J. Chem. Phys.*, 43, 2696 (1965); 47, 1942 (1967).

65. Graessley, W. W., *J. Polym. Sci.*, A-2, 6, 1887 (1968).
66. Graessley, W. W., *Macromolecules*, 2, 49 (1969).
67. Shroff, R. N., and Shida, M., *J. Polym. Sci.*, C, 35, 153 (1971); Trans. Soc. Rheol. 21, 327 (1977).
68. Cote, J. A., and Shida, M., *Trans. Soc. Rheol.*, 17, 401 (1973).
69. Ferry, J. D., *Viscoelastic Properties of Polymers*, Wiley, New York, 1980, p. 289.
70. Fulcher, G. S., *J. Am. Chem. Soc.*, 8, 339, 789 (1925).
71. Tammann, G., and Hesse, G., *Z. Anorg. Allg. Chem.*, 156, 245 (1926).
72. Adam, G., and Gibbs, J. H., *J. Chem. Phys.*, 43, 139 (1965).
73. Macedo, P. B., and Litovitz, T. A., *J. Chem. Phys.*, 42, 245 (1965).
74. Wehmann, H. D., *Kolloid-Z.*, 138, 41 (1954); Kolloid-Z. Polymere, 181, 131 (1962).
75. Cohen, M. H., and Turnbull, D., *J. Chem. Phys.*, 31, 1164 (1959).
76. Baumann, G. F., and Steingiser, S., *J. Polym. Sci.* Part A-1, 1, 3395 (1963).
77. Fitzgerald, E., Gradine, L. D., Jr., and Ferry, J. D., *J. Appl. Phys.*, 24, 650 (1953).
78. Schneider, H. A., unpublished data.
79. Ferry, J. D., and Landel, R. F., Kolloid-Z., 148, 1 (1956).
80. M. L. Williams and Ferry, J. D., *J. Colloid Sci.*, 9, 479 (1954).
81. Endo, H., Fujimoto, T., and Nagasawa, M., *J. Polym. Sci.*, 7, 1669 (1969).
82. Odani, H., Nemoto, N., Kitamura, S., Kurata, M., and Tamura, M., *Polym. J.*, 1, 356 (1970).
83. Williams, M. L., and Ferry, J. D., *J. Colloid Sci.*, 10, 474 (1955).
84. Barlow, A. J., Harrison, G., and Lamb, J., *Proc. R. Soc.*, A 282, 228 (1964).
85. Maekawa, E., Mancke, R. G., and Ferry, J. D., *J. Phys. Chem.*, 69, 2811 (1965).
86. Berry, G. C., and Fox, T. G., *Adv. Polym. Sci.*, 261 (1967).
87. Schneider, H. A., Cantow H.-J., and Brekner, M.-J., *Polym. Bulletin*, 11, 383 (1984).
88. Ferry, J. D., Child, W. C., Jr., Zand, R., Stern, D. M., Williams M. L., and Landel, R. F., *J. Colloid Sci.*, 12, 53 (1957).
89. Child, W. C., Jr., and Ferry, J. D., *J. Colloid Sci.*, 12, 327, 389 (1957).
90. Dannhauser, W., Child, W. C., Jr., and Ferry, J. D., *J. Colloid Sci.*, 13, 103 (1958).
91. Brekner, M.-J., Cantow, H.-J., and Schneider, H. A., *Polym. Bulletin*, 14, 17 (1985).
92. Brekner, M.-J., Cantow, H.-J., and Schneider, H. A., *Polym. Bulletin*, 14, 9 (1985).
93. Pfandl, W., Link, G., and Schwarzl, F. R., *Rheol. Acta*, 23, 277 (1984).
94. Miller, A. A., *J. Polym. Sci.*, A-2, 4, 415 (1966); *J. Chem. Phys.*, 49, 1393 (1968); *Macromolecules*, 2, 355 (1969); 3, 674 (1970).
95. Brekner, M.-J., Thesis, University Freiburg, 1985.
96. Schneider, H. A., M.-J. Brekner, and H.-J. Cantow, *Polym. Bulletin*, 14, 479 (1985).
97. Schneider, H. A., and Leikauf, B., *Thermochim Acta*, 114, 165 (1987).
98. Holary, J. L., Numai, J. M., and Monnerie, L., *Polymer*, 25, 956 (1984).
99. Schneider, H. A., Jishan, W., Cantow, H.-J., Auman, B. C., and Percec, V., *Polymer*, 28, 132 (1987).
100. Fox, T. G., and Flory, P. J., *J. Appl. Phys.*, 21, 581 (1950).
101. Simha, R., and Boyer, R. F., *J. Chem. Phys.*, 37, 1003 (1962).
102. Brekner, M.-J., Cantow, H.-J., and Schneider, H. A., *Progr. Colloid & Polym. Sci.*, 71, 173 (1985).
103. Bueche, F., *Physical Properties of Polymers*, Wiley, New York, 1962.
104. Schwarzl, F. R., and Zahardnik, F., *Rheol. Acta*, 19, 137 (1980).
105. Boyer, R. F., *Rubber Chem. Technol.*, 36, 1303 (1963).
106. Kovacs, A. J., *J. Polym. Sci.*, 30, 131 (1958).
107. McCrum, N. G., Pizzoli, M., Chain, C. K., Treurnicht, J., and Hutchinson, J. M., *Polymer*, 23, 473 (1982).
108. McCrum, N. G., *Polymer*, 25, 299 (1984).

CHAPTER 26

PRINCIPLES OF POLYMER MIXING AND EXTRUSION

N. P. Cheremisinoff

Exxon Chemical Co.
Linden, New Jersey, USA

CONTENTS

INTRODUCTION

Mixing and extrusion are two primary unit operations in the processing and manufacturing of elastomeric and plastic articles. In this volume of the encyclopedia various authors describe the hydrodynamics of these operations from the viewpoint of fundamental principles which may be generalized to design and scale-up methodology. Before applying the design principles outlined in successive chapters, an appreciation of the mechanics of mixing and extrusion, along with the practical limitations of these unit process operations, must be gained. This chapter provides detailed practical operating and design guidelines for the processing of elastomers, plastics, and various industrial pastes and non-Newtonian solutions, as well as description of the hardware. Although the design methodology is emperical, it is based on well established practices developed by industry and reported in the open literature.

OVERVIEW OF MIXING PRACTICES

The mixing of non-Newtonian materials such as pastes, plastics, resins, etc., involves factors distinctly different from those involved in the mixing of Newtonian fluids. A rotating propeller immersed in a paste-like material or a viscous liquid affects only a small portion of the total mass, leaving the greater part of it relatively undisturbed. Semi-solids, viscous liquids, and heavy pastes require the mixing services of devices which are capable of affecting every portion of the material and achieving a homogeneous state by pushing one portion of the mass into another portion. Factors requiring special attention are the physical preparation of the materials, the behavior of the material under flow, and the effect of the order in which the ingredients are introduced into the mix. For highly viscous materials such as elastomers, equipment is often selected on the basis of its ability to shear material at low speed, or to wipe, smear, fold, stretch, or compress the mass being processed.

Of primary importance in the selection of a particular type of mixer for processing non-Newtonian materials is the behavior of that material while it is undergoing flow or shear. Many non-Newtonian materials exhibit different resistances to shear at different rates of shear. Some of these materials have greater resistance to shear, or flow, at high shear rates, while others show greater resistance at low rates of shear. The behavior of non-Newtonian materials in regard to these properties determines the type of equipment used for mixing and the amount of power that must be used to achieve a desired degree of mixing.

Consider a thin layer of fluid between two parallel plates a distance dy apart, as m in Figure 1. One plate is stationary, and a shearing force F is applied to the other. When conditions are steady the force F will be balanced by an internal force in the fluid due to its viscosity. For a Newtonian fluid in laminar motion, the shear stress is proportional to the velocity gradient, i.e.:

$$F/A = \tau \propto du/dy$$

This equation may be written as:

$$\tau = \mu \, du/dy = \mu \dot{\gamma} \tag{1}$$

where Newtonian viscosity, μ, is the tangential force per unit area exerted on layers of fluid a unit distance apart and has a unit velocity difference between them. The Newtonian viscosity depends only on temperature and pressure and is independent of the rate of shear. The diagram relating shear stress and rate of shear for Newtonian fluids, referred to as the *flow curve*, is therefore a straight line of slope μ_1. The single constant μ, in this case, completely characterizes the fluid. Newtonian behavior is exhibited in fluids (gases, liquids, and various solutions) with comparatively small molecular mass. Liquids having a greater molecular mass show marked deviations from Newtonian behavior.

In contrast, the flow curve of a non-Newtonian fluid is non-linear. That is, the "viscosity" of a non-Newtonian fluid is not constant at a given temperature and pressure but depends on other factors such as the rate of shear in the fluid, the apparatus in which the fluid is contained, or even on the previous history of the fluid.

These fluids may be classified into three broad types:

1. Fluids for which the rate of shear at any point is a function of the shearing stress at that point and depends on nothing else.

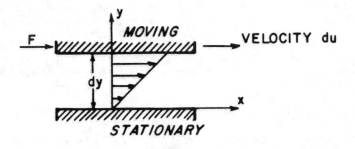

Figure 1. Fluid sheared between two plates.

2. More complex systems for which the relation between shear stress and shear rate depends on the time the fluid has been sheared or on its previous history.
3. Systems which have characteristics of both solids and fluids and exhibit partial elastic recovery after deformation (so-called viscoelastic fluids).

Fluids of the first group, where properties are independent of time, are described by rheological equation of the form:

$$\dot{\gamma} = f(\tau) \tag{2}$$

This equation implies that the rate of shear at any point in the fluid is a simple function of the shear stress at that point. These materials are termed *non-Newtonian viscous fluids* (or time-independent fluids).

Such fluids may be subdivided into three distinct types depending on the nature of the function in Equation 2:

1. Bingham plastics
2. Pseudoplastic fluids
3. Dilatant fluids

A *Bingham plastic* is an idealized fluid, although some materials can be approximated by this description. The flow curve is a line having an intercept τ_y on the shear-stress axis. The rheological equation for such a liquid may be written as:

$$\tau = \tau_y = \eta_p \dot{\gamma}; \qquad \tau > \tau_y \tag{3}$$

where τ = shear-stress
$\dot{\gamma}$ = gradient of shear
η_p = plastic viscosity (i.e., the slope of the flow curve)

The properties of real liquids (e.g., slurries, concentrated suspensions, oil paints) can be approximated by this equation. The Bingham plastic at rest contains a three-dimensional structure of sufficient rigidity to resist any stress less than the yield stress value τ_y. Upon exceeding this stress, the structure completely disintegrates and the system behaves as a Newtonian fluid under a shear stress $\tau - \tau_y$ (a straight-line relationship between shearing stress and rate of shear). When the shear stress falls below τ_y (i.e., $\tau < \tau_y$) the structure is said to be reformed.

Pseudoplastical fluids are frequently encountered in industrial practice. Among the most common materials are polymers. Their flow curve, as in the case of Newtonian liquids, starts at the origin. That is, these fluids have no yield stress. The typical flow curve for these materials reflects the ratio of shear stress to the rate of shear, which is termed the apparent viscosity, μ_a.

The curve for pseudoplastic fluids represents materials for which the required increase in shear stress to cause flow becomes smaller as the rate of shear increases. A decrease in the required shear stress is caused by the fact that the resistance to shear has decreased. Hence, the curve also indicates that the resistance to shear decreases as the shearing rate increases. A logarithmic plot of shear stress and shear rate is often found to be linear, with a slope between zero and unity. As a result, an empirical functional relation known as the *power law* is widely used to characterize these fluids. This relation, which was originally proposed by Ostwald [1] and has since been fully described by Reiner [2], may be written as:

$$\tau = k\dot{\gamma}^n \tag{4}$$

where k and n are constants with n < 1, for the particular fluid; k reflects a measure of the consistency of the fluid with the higher values representative of more viscous materials. Exponent n is a measure of the degree of non-Newtonian behavior, and the greater the departure from unity the more pronounced are the non-Newtonian properties of the fluid. It is important to remember that although n is nearly constant in many cases over wide ranges of shear rate, it is not a true constant for real fluids over all possible ranges of shear. This is not a great disadvantage, since all that is needed is a rheological equation that describes the fluid over the particular range of shear rate encountered in a particular problem. Over such a range, n may often be regarded as constant.

The dimensions of k depend on the index n, and this fact has led to many objections to the use of the power law (see [2]). However, in most engineering calculations, these objections are not serious. The apparent viscosity, η_a, for a power law fluid may be expressed in terms of n since:

$$\eta_a = \tau/\dot{\gamma}$$

$$\eta_a = k\dot{\gamma}^{n-1} \tag{5}$$

Since n < 1 for pseudoplastics, the apparent viscosity decreases as the stress rate increases. This type of behavior is characteristic of suspensions of asymmetric particles or solutions of high polymers such as cellulose derivatives. This suggests that the physical interpretation of this phenomenon is probably that with increasing rates of shear, the asymmetric particles or molecules are progressively aligned. That is, instead of the random intermingled state which exists when the fluid is at rest, the major axes are brought into line with the direction of flow. The apparent viscosity continues to decrease with increasing rate of shear until no further alignment along the streamlines is possible and the flow curve then becomes linear.

Since pseudoplastic fluids are time-independent, this implies that the alignment of molecules suggested above occurs instantaneously as the rate of shear is increased or, at any rate, so quickly that the time effect cannot be detected using ordinary viscometric techniques.

Other empirical equations that have been used to describe pseudoplastic behavior are summarized below (see Wilkinson [3] for a review of engineering models):

Prandtl	$\tau = A \sin^{-1}(\dot{\gamma}/C)$	(6A)
Eyring	$\tau = \dot{\gamma}/B + C \sin(\tau/A)$	(6B)
Powell-Eyring	$\tau = A\dot{\gamma} + B \sinh^{-1}(C\dot{\gamma})$	(6C)
Williamson	$\tau = A\dot{\gamma}/(B + \dot{\gamma}) + \mu_\infty\dot{\gamma}$	(6D)

Coefficients A, B, and C are constants, specific to the particular fluid. These equations are considerably more difficult to apply than the simple power law expression.

Dilatant fluids are similar to pseudoplastics in that they show no yield stress. In contrast, the apparent viscosity for these fluids increases with increasing rates of shear. In the process industries dilatant fluids are much less common than pseudoplastics, but when the power law is applicable, the treatment of both types is much the same. The dilatant-curve represents materials (such as starch slurries, pigment-vehicle suspensions) for which the required increase in shear stress to cause flow increases as the rate of shear increases. This also indicates that the resistance of shear increases as the rate of shear increases.

The power law equation is again often applicable, but in this case the index n has values greater than unity. The phenomenon of dilatancy may be explained as follows [4]: The mixture consists of solid particles in intimate contact and of an amount of liquid just sufficient to fill up the voids between the particles. At low flow velocity, the internal friction in such a mixture is small, as the liquid present acts as lubricant between the shifting solid particles. At higher flow velocity, the solid particles are no longer in close contact. The voids between them enlarge and cannot be filled up by the liquid, whereby the internal friction in the mixture increases.

Some general comments on time-dependent fluids are necessary. Many real fluids cannot be described by a simple rheological expression such as Equation 2. The apparent viscosity of more complex fluids depends not only on the rate of shear, but also on the time the shear has been applied. Recall that these fluids may be subdivided into two classes; namely thixotropic and rheopectic, according as the shear stress increases or decreases with time when the fluid is sheared at a constant rate.

Thixotropic materials are those whose consistency depends on the duration of shear as well as on the rate of shear. They are encountered more often than rheopectic fluids. When a thixotropic material is sheared at a constant rate after a finite period of rest, the structure progressively disintegrates and the apparent viscosity decreases with time. The rate of structure breakdown during shearing at a given rate depends on the number of linkages available for breaking, and must therefore decrease with time. The simultaneous rate of reformation of structure will increase with time as the number of possible new structural linkages increases. Eventually, a state of dynamic equilibrium is achieved when the rate of build-up of structure equals the rate of breakdown. This equilibrium position depends on the rate of shear and moves toward greater breakdown at increasing shear rates.

A common example is material confined in a Couette viscometer. After the material has been resting for a long time, one of the cylinders is rotated at a constant speed. The torque on the other cylinder would then decrease with time as shown in Figure 2A. The rate of decrease and the final torque would both depend on the speed, i.e., on the rate of shear. This behavior produces a hysteresis loop on the curve of shear-stress plotted against rate of shear, if the curve is plotted first for the

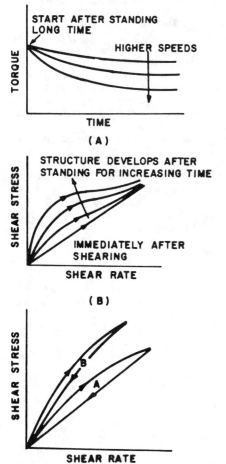

Figure 2. Development of hysteresis loops for thixotropic fluids.

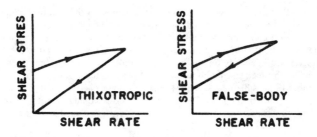

Figure 3. Types of hysteresis loops.

rate of shear increasing at a constant rate and then for the rate of shear decreasing at a constant rate. This is illustrated in Figures 2B and C, where the curves A and B in Figure 2C are drawn for fluids of the Newtonian and pseudoplastic types which exhibit thixotropy.

Flow curves of increasing height can be obtained by applying shear for increasing lengths of time before making the return path. A single curve can be obtained by continuing the shearing process to equilibrium before returning. Pryce-Jones [5] introduced the term "false body" to distinguish types of thixotropic behavior of Bingham plastics. True thixotropic materials break down completely under the influence of high stresses and behave like true liquids even after the stress has been removed, until such time as the structure has reformed. False-bodied materials, on the other hand, do not lose their solid properties entirely and can still exhibit a yield value, even though this might be diminished. The original yield value is only regained after resting for a long time period. Figure 3 shows the hysteresis loop on the flow curve for these two materials.

Consider a liquid in a vessel with a cylinder on a torsion wire immersed in it whereby the cylinder is deflected and the liquid stirred. If stirring is then stopped and the cylinder released, the torsion in the wire would then vary with time as in Figure 4 for the two types of material.

With the false-bodied materials there would be a residual torsion in the wire, indicating that the material can offer permanent resistance to shear immediately after stirring. That is, it retains a finite yield value. A true thixotropic material would show a residual torsion only if some time elapsed after stirring had ceased before the cylinder was released, to allow the structure to build up.

Similarly, false-bodied materials can retain elasticity. This would result in a recoil of the cylinder in the above experiment.

For *rheopectic fluids* the viscosity increase is a result of gradual formation of structure in the limits of low shear rates; reaching these rates, the structure may be destroyed and the fluid will behave as a thixotropic fluid.

The two curves plotted in Figure 5 represent time-dependent non-Newtonian fluids. Curve A represents a rheopectic fluid whose shear stress increases as the time of shear (mixing time) increases. An increase in shear stress means that the shearing force F must be increased to produce flow. Since for any given rate of shear, the consistency is the property that influences the amount

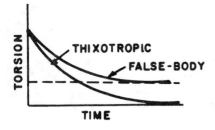

Figure 4. Comparison of true thixotropic to false body behavior.

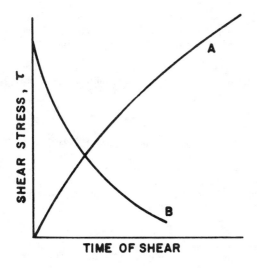

TIME OF SHEAR

Figure 5. Plots of shear stress vs. time-of-shear for non-Newtonian fluids.

of force required, an increase in shear stress must mean an increase in consistency. Hence, the material of curve A also exhibits an increase in consistency, or apparent viscosity, when the time of shear is increased.

Curve B is typical of a thixotropic liquid, exhibiting a decrease in shear stress with increase in time of shear. Hence, as the mixing time is prolonged, the consistency or apparent viscosity of the fluid decreases. Steady-state flow permits the use of equations of pseudoplasticity for systems displaying "time-effects." It should be noted that the "time effects" are reversible, and after eliminating the stress, the structure is completely reformed. "Time-effects" have an important role in batch operations, where as a result of long-time action of shear, after starting the machine there is a decrease in the apparent viscosity of materials to be mixed. For this reason, the theoretical calculation of the energy balance is difficult especially for the starting period.

Thixotropic behavior is similar to pseudoplasticity from the standpoint that the time required for the alignment of particles is not negligible. Further, rheopectic fluids are superficially similar to their time-dependent counterparts (dilatant fluids) whereby the time for structure build-up is negligibly small. The analogy in the latter case is not so close because with rheopectic fluids, structure build-up is brought about by small shearing rates only. That is, there is an upper limit to the shear rate beyond which the analogy is no longer valid.

Viscoelastic fluids are those that possess both elastic and viscous properties. In other words, although the material may be viscous, it exhibits a certain elasticity of shape. An example of a viscoelastic fluid is pitch. For a simplified description, we consider Newton's law for the viscous component and Hooke's law for the elastic component. In steady-state flow under a shear stress τ the rate of shear will be τ/μ_0, where μ_0 is a constant Newtonian viscosity coefficient. If the shear stress is increased to $\tau + \delta\tau$ very rapidly, the material will be sheared through an additional angle $\delta\tau/G$, where G is the modulus of rigidity. There is therefore an additional rate of shear proportional to the rate of change of stress at any instant, and the total rate of shear is given by:

$$\dot{\gamma}\tau/\mu_0 + \dot{\tau}/G \tag{7}$$

or in terms of a time constant λ_1:

$$\tau + \dot{\lambda}_1\dot{\tau} = \mu_0\dot{\gamma}, \text{ where } \gamma_1 = \mu_0/G \tag{8}$$

Equation 8 is Maxwell's equation, and fluids described by it are usually referred to as "Maxwell fluids."

The parameter λ_1 is the time constant of the exponential decay of stress at a constant strain. Observe from Equation 8 that if the motion is stopped, the stress will relax as $\exp(-t/\lambda_1)$. Consequently, λ_1 is known as the relaxation time. Schofield and Scott-Blair [6] have applied the Maxwell equation to flour doughs.

Oldroyd [7] investigated the elastic and viscous properties of emulsions and suspensions of one Newtonian liquid in another and derived theoretically the differential equation relating the shear stress τ and the rate of shear $\dot{\gamma}$ in the following form:

$$\tau + \lambda_1 \dot{\tau} = \mu_0(\dot{\gamma} + \lambda_2 \ddot{\gamma}) \tag{9}$$

The constants μ_0, λ_1, and λ_2 depend on the physical properties of the mixture. The elastic strain energy is stored during flow by virtue of the fact that interfacial tension provides the restoring force which makes the individual drops resist changes of shape. The same equation was also derived by Frölich and Sack [8] for a dilute suspension of solid particles in a viscous liquid. Elastic strain energy is stored because the solid elastic particles are deformed by the flow of the surrounding liquid. Elastic strain energy is stored because the solid elastic particles are deformed by the flow of the surrounding liquid.

The constant μ_0 is the viscosity at low rates of shear in the steady state, i.e., when $\dot{\tau} = \ddot{\gamma} = 0$. The constant λ_1 is a relaxation time and the physical significance of this is that if the motion is suddenly stopped, the shear stress will decay as $\exp(-\tau/\lambda_1)$; λ_2 is called a "retardation time" and reflects that if all stresses are removed, the rate of strain decays as $\exp(-\tau/\lambda_2)$.

Toms and Strawbridge [9] found that the behavior of dilute solutions of poly-methylmethacrylate in pyridine and some bitumens can be described by a similar expression. We conclude that the rheological equation for a viscoelastic fluid contains the time derivatives of both τ and γ in general. The general case is:

$$f_1(D)\tau = f_2(D)\gamma \tag{10A}$$

or alternatively, as a polynomial in D:

$$\sum_{n=0}^{N} a_n D^n \tau = \sum_{m=0}^{M} \beta_m D^m \gamma \tag{10B}$$

where D is the differential operator, d/dt.

MIXING PRACTICES

Irrespective of the individual ingredients comprising a non-Newtonian material (i.e., liquid, solid particles in suspension, plastics), the objective of mixing is to decrease the concentration gradient to a desired minimum. In some cases this is accompanied by a decrease in the thermal gradient in processes involving heat transfer.

The minimum gradient of concentration (or temperature) is achieved when the infinitesimal samples of the mixture randomly extracted from any location within the mixing system have the same composition. In some processes mixing is accompanied by dispersion, i.e., by a phenomenon by which there is a change in the physical characteristics of the components (e.g., intrusion of solid fillers into a resin mass, decreasing the particle size of a filler, etc.). In addition, mechanical mixing may be accompanied by physico-chemical processes of plasticization.

The mixing methods and the design of mixing machines depend on the physical properties of the components to be mixed. The mixing of non-Newtonian materials is basically carried out by different mechanical devices which both combine ingredients and provide intensive agitation. Common devices used are Sigma-Blade mixers, Banbury mixers, Roller Mills, Anchor agitators, centrifugal Disk-Type Mixers, and others.

Heavy pastes and materials with pronounced plastic properties require heavy machinery in order to achieve satisfactory mixing. Natural flow of materials and momentum effects are negligible and as such, the mixing must be forced. Sections of the mix must be separated from the whole mass and then forced back into a different part of the mixture volume by means of shearing, kneading, or wiping actions.

Highly viscous liquids and pastes can be mixed in either batch or continuous operations. A *batch mixing process*, as a rule, is performed in a closed volume of a mixing device. The principle parameter affecting mixing efficiency in this case is the minimum mixing time necessary for providing the desired homogenity of the mixture. The capacity of the mixing device depends on the mixing time, the times of loading ingredients, starting, stopping, and unloading. Mixing time is established not only by the available volume of the mixing device, the design of the working elements, rotational velocity, and the properties of components to be mixed, but also, to a large degree by the initial orientation of components and the order in which they are introduced.

The rationally designed mixer must provide an equal mixing time independent of the initial location of components. Periodic reorientation of material during mixing will decrease the basic mixing time. In general, batch mixers are not very efficient at handling large capacities mainly because of difficulties encountered when attempting to automate operations. Over the course of a batch cycle, the properties of the mixture may change considerably.

During mixing and plastification of polymer materials, the power consumption, as a rule, decreases. This often requires the installation of a motor drive of higher capacity, which must be selected in accordance with the initial characteristics of the mixture. However, there is a need to use batch mixers in many cases, especially if required mixing times are too long.

Continuous mixing operations involve the continuous loading and unloading of components. In this case there is a drastic variation in the concentration of components at the inlet. When properly performed, mixing decreases these variations at the exit to the desired minimum. Continuous operations have the advantage of providing a stable process. Also, the power consumption is both lower and constant. The parameters of the mixture, as they move from inlet to outlet, vary, even though the volume of the mixer remains constant. Despite the advantages, continuous mixing operations are difficult to justify in many cases because of long mixing time requirements. Long mixing times are somewhat compensated for in continuous mixers by increasing process intensity (i.e., operating at higher rotational velocity). This may, however, result in uneconomical increases in the dissipation of mechanical energy and thermal destruction.

The mixing action imposed by turbine, propeller, paddle, and anchor impellers results in complicated streamlines of fluid motion when applied to non-Newtonian materials. Recommended geometries for these types of mixers are summarized in Table 1 and detailed design practices are given by Azbel and Cheremisinoff [10]. In this process, the power consumption depends not only on machine design, but also on the physical condition of the material.

Power consumption for mixing Newtonian materials cannot be determined from a purely theoretically basis even for the simplest of working devices. Therefore, the problems of scale-up and design must be addressed using as a basis similarity theory, whereby carefully planned experiments in model equipment are necessary. Non-Newtonian mixing is even more complex due to the interrelationships between fluid consistency, temperature, and shear. Fluid behavior of non-Newtonians during mixing is further complicated due to the large dissipation of mechanical energy which results in considerable variations in the temperature level of the process. Under actual process conditions there is little or no possibility of assessing the instantaneous viscosity of the material.

When a non-Newtonian fluid is processed in a mixing vessel, the variations in shear rate with distance from the impeller give rise to corresponding variations in fluid consistency. To allow for this, Metzner and Otto [11] and Magnusson [12] identified an average shear rate $(du/dr)_A$ in the vessel. The apparent viscosity μ_A corresponding to $(du/dr)_A$ is defined as the viscosity of that Newtonian fluid which would show exactly the same power consumption for agitation under identical conditions, at least in laminar flow. An empirical correlation that describes this is:

$$\dot{\gamma}_A = \left(\frac{du}{dr}\right)_A = k_s N \qquad (11)$$

Type of Mixer	Size Ratios	Sphere of Application
Two Blades	$\dfrac{d}{D} = 0.5\text{--}0.7$ $\dfrac{h}{d} = 0.1\text{--}0.3$ $\dfrac{h_1}{d} = 0.14\text{--}0.2$ $\dfrac{b}{D} = 0.08$	For mixing of liquids with viscosities up to 15 N-s/m² and dissolution of solid particles, u = 1.5–3 m/s
Four Blades	$\dfrac{d}{D} = 0.2\text{--}0.4$ $\dfrac{h}{d} = 0.2\text{--}0.4$ $\dfrac{h_1}{d} = 0.4\text{--}0.8$ $\dfrac{b}{D} = 0.08$	For mixing of liquids of medium viscosity and dissolution of solid particles, u = 1.5–3 m/s
Anchor	$\dfrac{H_\varphi}{H} = 0.75\text{--}0.85$ $\dfrac{h}{H} = 0.56$ $\dfrac{b}{d} = 0.07$ $\delta = 25\text{--}40$ mm	For mixing of liquids of viscosities up to 200 N-s/m² in tanks with heating elements, u = 1–3 m/s
Framed	$\dfrac{H_\varphi}{H} = 0.75\text{--}0.85$ $\dfrac{h}{H} = 0.6$ $\dfrac{h_0}{H_0} = 0.56$ $h_1 = 190\text{--}275$ mm $\delta = 25\text{--}40$ mm $\dfrac{b}{d} = 0.07$	See anchor mixers

(Continued)

Table 1 (Continued)

Type of Mixer	Size Ratios	Sphere of Application
Turbine	$\dfrac{d}{D} = 0.3$ $\dfrac{H_\varphi}{H} = 0.75-0.85$ $\dfrac{h}{d} = 0.2-0.3$ $\dfrac{l}{d} = 0.25$ $\dfrac{h_1}{d} = 0.5-1.5$ $\dfrac{d_1}{d} = 0.65$ $\dfrac{b}{D} = 0.08$	For intensive mixing of suspensions, dissolution and dispersion of liquids and gases. May operate in the media with viscosities up to 25 N-s/m², $u = 3-8$ m/s
Shrouded Turbine	$\dfrac{D}{d} = 2.4$ $\dfrac{h}{d} = 0.25$ $\dfrac{h_1}{d} = 0.85$ $\dfrac{d_1}{d} = 1.1;\ \dfrac{d_2}{d} = 1.6$ $\dfrac{H_\varphi}{d} = 1.75$	
Propeller	$\dfrac{D}{d} = 2-4$ $\dfrac{H_\varphi}{d} = 2-4$ $\dfrac{h_1}{d} = 0.7-1.6$ $\dfrac{b}{D} = 0.08$ $\dfrac{t}{d} = 1-2$	For mixing of liquids with viscosities up to 4 N-s/m², dissolution and suspending of solid particles

Table 2
Description of Curves in Figure 6 as Recommended by Rushton et al. (1950)

Curve	Impeller	Baffles	D, ft	D_t/D	n	$k_s (n < 1)$
A-A	Single turbine with 6 flat blades	4, $J/D_r = 0.1$	0.167–0.67	1.3–5.5	0.05–1.5	11.5 ± 1.5
A-A$_1$	Single turbine with 6 flat blades	None	0.167–0.67	1.3–5.5	0.18–0.54	11.5 ± 1.4
B-B	2 turbines, each with 6 flat blades and $D_r/2$ apart	4, $J/D_r = 0.1$	—	3.5	0.14–0.72	11.5 ± 1.4
B-B$_1$	2 turbines, each with 6 flat blades and $D_r/2$ apart	4, $J/D_r = 0.1$ or none	—	1.023–1.18	0.14–0.72	11.5 ± 1.4
C-C	Fan turbine with 6 blades at 45°	4, $J/D_r = 0.1$ or none	0.33–0.67	1.33–3.0	0.21–0.26	13 ± 2
C-C$_1$	Fan turbine with 6 blades at 45°	4, $J/D_r = 0.1$ or none	0.33–0.67	1.33–3.0	1.0–1.42	13 ± 2
D-D	Square-pitch marine propellers with 3 blades (downthrusting)	None, (i) shaft vertical at vessel axis, (ii) shaft 10° from vertical, displaced R/3 from center	0.417	2.2–4.8	0.16–0.40	10 ± 0.9
D-D$_1$	Same as for D-D but upthrusting	None, (i) shaft vertical at vessel axis, (ii) shaft 10° from vertical, displaced R/3 from center	0.417	2.2–4.8	0.16–0.40	10 ± 0.9
D-D$_1$	Same as for D-D	None, position (ii)	1.0	1.9–2.0	0.16–0.40	10 ± 0.9
D-D$_1$	Same as for D-D	None, position (i)	1.0	1.9–2.0	0.16–0.40	10 ± 0.9
E-E	Square-pitch marine propeller with 3 blades	4, $J/D_r = 0.1$	0.5	1.67	0.16–0.60	10
F-F	Double-pitch marine propeller with 3 blades (downthrusting)	None, position (ii)	—	1.4–3.0	0.16–0.40	10 ± 0.9
F-F$_1$	Double-pitch marine propeller with 3 blades (downthrusting)	None, position (i)	—	1.4–3.0	0.16–0.40	10 ± 0.9
G-G	Square-pitch marine propeller with 4 blades	4, $J/D_r = 0.1$	0.392	2.13	0.05–0.61	10
G-G$_1$	Square-pitch marine propeller with 4 blades	4, $J/D_r = 0.1$	0.392	2.13	1.28–1.68	—
H-H	2-bladed paddle	4, $J/D_r = 0.1$	0.283–0.416	2–3	0.16–1.68	10 (n < 1)
—	Anchor	None	0.927	1.02	0.34–1.0	11 ± 5
—	Cone impellers	0 or 4, $J/D_r = 0.08$	0.33–0.5	1.92–2.88	0.34–1.0	11 ± 5

Metzner and Taylor [13] confirmed Equation 11 independently. The experimental determination of parameter k_s for a given geometry is as follows:

1. N_P is measured for a particular N.
2. The corresponding Reynolds number is obtained from the appropriate plot for Newtonian fluids on a chart provided by Rushton [14].
3. The apparent viscosity, μ_A, for these conditions is computed from the Reynolds number. (Laminar flow is used for maximum sensitivity to changes in μ_A).
4. The shear rate, $(du/dr)_A$, is obtained from the flow curve for the particular fluid under consideration, since $\mu_A = \tau/(du/dr)_A$.
5. The constant k_s is then evaluated from Equation 11. The procedure is repeated for various N values to give an average k_s.

A compilation of experimental k_s values for a variety of geometries is given in Table 2 and Figure 6.

The prediction of power consumption in a particular non-Newtonian agitation system for a given impeller speed proceeds in the following manner:

1. Compute $(du/dr)_A$ from Equation 11, using the appropriate k_s value from Table 2.
2. Evaluate the corresponding μ_A from the flow curve as $\tau/(du/dr)_A$.
3. Calculate the Reynolds number, $D^2N\rho/\mu_A$, and read the Power number, $P/D^5N^3\rho$, from the appropriate curve in Figure 6. P is then computed from N_P.

Calderbank and Moo-Young (1961) give the following relation for computing k_s for power law fluids:

$$k_s = B\left(\frac{4p}{3n + 1}\right)^{n/(1-n)} \tag{12}$$

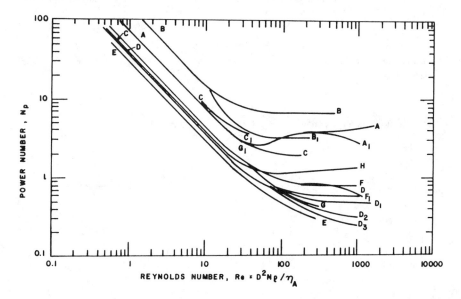

Figure 6. Correlation of the power number in the agitation of non-Newtonian fluids (based on data of Rushton, et al. 1950).

In this expression, n is the fluid's flow behavior index. Equation 12 can be used with Equation 11 to compute $(du/dr)_A$. The following empirical relationships were recommended by the investigators for the constant B:

a. For high-speed impellers:

(i) $n < 1; \dfrac{D_T}{D} > 1.5; R = 4; \dfrac{J}{D_T} = 0.1$

$$B = 11 \pm 10\% \tag{13}$$

(ii) $n > 1; \dfrac{D_T}{D} < 3.0; R = 4; \dfrac{J}{D_T} = 0.1$

$$B = \frac{22(D_T/D)^2}{(D_T/D)^2 - 1} \pm 15\% \tag{14}$$

b. For anchor agitators, $n < 1; D_T/D < 1.4$

$$B = 9.5 + \frac{9(D_T/D)^2}{(D_T/D)^2 - 1} \pm 10\% \tag{15}$$

The term involving n in Equation 11 has the value $0.84 \pm 8.5\%$ for $0.05 < n < 1.68$ and may therefore be considered a constant for practical calculations. This means that a linear relationship between $(du/dr)_A$ and N is predicted by both Metzner and Otto and Calderbank and Moo-Young, with only minor dependence on the flow behavior index.

As already noted, the viscous behavior of numerous non-Newtonian fluids can be represented by a power law equation of the general form:

$$\tau = K(\dot{\gamma})^n \tag{16A}$$

This expression is applicable over a limited range of shear rates. Applying this to a viscoelastic material where:

$$\eta_a = K(\dot{\gamma})^{n-1} \tag{16B}$$

with the Reynolds number defined as:

$$Re = \frac{D^2 N_p}{\eta_a(\dot{\gamma})} \tag{17}$$

then, with Equation 11, we have:

$$Re = \frac{D^2 N \rho}{K(\dot{\gamma}_A)^{n-1}} = \frac{D^2 N \rho}{K(k_s N)^{n-1}} = \frac{D^2 N^{2-n} \rho}{k_s^{n-1} K} \tag{18}$$

and from $\sigma_1 = h(\dot{\gamma})^{m-2} \tag{19}$

and $N_{W_i} = \dfrac{\sigma_1(\dot{\gamma})}{\eta_a(\dot{\gamma})} N \tag{20}$

and combining with Equations 16A and 11 we obtain:

$$N_{W_i} = \frac{b(\dot{\gamma}_A)^{m-2}}{K(\dot{\gamma}_A)^{n-1}} N = \frac{h}{K} (k_s N)^{m-n-1} N = \frac{h}{k_s K} (k_s N)^{m-n} \tag{21}$$

Perhaps the simplest non-Newtonian fluid to describe is the Bingham plastic, being that it is a linear relationship. Adopting the procedure used for Newtonian fluids, the power for mixing a Bingham plastic is:

$$\frac{P}{\rho N^3 D^5} = \phi \left(\frac{\mu_p}{\rho N D^5}, \frac{\tau_y}{\rho N^2 D^2}, \frac{N^2 D}{g} \right) \tag{22A}$$

Note that the second group is the ratio of yield stress to inertia forces. This can be expressed in terms of the Hedstrom number (He $= \tau_y \rho D^2/\mu_p^2 = Re^2 \tau_y/\rho N^2 D^2$). Thus:

$$P/\rho N^3 D^5 = \phi(Re, He, Fr) \tag{22B}$$

Design procedures for estimating power requirements for mixing non-Newtonian materials are sparce. One procedure that appears useful for highly pseudoplastic materials is that of Metzner and Otto, applicable to flat-blade turbines. The procedure is as follows:

1. Find μ_a at a given N from the measured power coefficient and the appropriate correlation between power coefficient and Reynolds number used for Newtonian fluids, i.e., measure $P/\rho N^3 D^5$ for the non-Newtonian system, and find $\rho N D^2/\mu_a$ from the correlation at this value of the power coefficient. This gives μ_a, knowing $\rho N D^2$ for the system, if μ_a is defined above, i.e., the viscosity of a Newtonian fluid which gives the same power coefficient in the same apparatus at the same speed.
2. Find the shear rate, $\dot{\gamma}$, which gives the value of μ_a from the flow curve of the non-Newtonian fluid.
3. Find K by substituting the values of $\dot{\gamma}$ and the speed, N, in the equation:

$$(\dot{\gamma})_{av} = KN \tag{23}$$

4. Repeat for different fluids at different speeds using various sizes of apparatus to determine the best value of K. All the experiments must be confined to the laminar flow region, since outside this region viscosity is not an important factor.

The value of K so obtained by Metzner and Otto was 13 where N is in r.p.m. and $(\dot{\gamma})_{av}$ in min^{-1}. Metzner and Otto's [11] results are shown plotted in Figure 7. The difference between the two curves is that the laminar region for non-Newtonian pseudoplastic fluids extends further than that for Newtonian fluids. The reason for this is that μ_a increases with increasing distance from the impeller (regions of lower shear rate) which tends to depress eddies and delay the onset of turbulence.

Calderbank and Moo-Young [15] have extended this work for a wide variety of sizes and types of impellers and found that for Bingham and pseudoplastic fluids the value of K was 10 rather than 13. For dilatant fluids, the relative size of the impeller and mixing vessel has an influence on the shear rate and therefore on the effective value of K. Calderbank and Moo-Young found in their work that for these fluids, K could be represented by $12.8(D_1/D_T)^{1/2}$, where D_1 and D_T are the diameters of the impeller and tank, respectively.

Discussion is now directed to the problem of turbulent heat transfer to non-Newtonian fluids. For slightly non-Newtonian materials such as dilute suspensions, numerous data on the heat transfer characteristics are reported in the literature (see Winding et al. [16] and Orr et al. [17] for examples). For non-Newtonian fluids in this category, the flow behavior index, n, does not differ greatly from unity. The two most widely used correlations are the Dittus-Boelter equation for

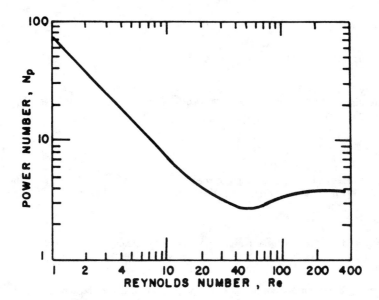

Figure 7. Power coefficient vs. Reynolds number for non-Newtonian fluids (based on the work of Metzner and Otto [11]).

forced convection in circular tubes and that of Sieder and Tate which incorporates a viscosity correction term:

$$\frac{hD}{k} = 0.023 \left[\frac{\rho u_m D}{\mu}\right]^{0.8} \left[\frac{\mu C_p}{k}\right]^{x} \tag{24}$$

where exponent $x = 0.4 - 0.3$.

$$\frac{hD}{k} = 0.023 \left[\frac{\rho u_m D}{\mu}\right]^{0.8} \left(\frac{\mu C_p}{k}\right)\left(\frac{\mu}{\mu_w}\right)^{0.14} \tag{25}$$

These equations are most often applied to heat exchanger calculations.

For heat transfer to highly non-Newtonian fluids, dimensional analysis has produced several correlations which have limited applicability. Metzner, Vaughn, and Houghton [18] suggest the following correlation:

$$\frac{\mu_a C_p}{k} = \frac{C_p m}{k} (u_m/D)^{n'-1}$$

where the generalized Reynolds number is defined as:

$$Re' = D^{n'} u_m^{2-n'} \rho/m;$$

$$m = k' 8^{n'-1}$$

and the apparent viscosity, μ_a, is defined by relating the Newtonian Reynolds number to the generalized one:

$$\rho u_m D / \mu_a = D^{n'} u_m^{2-n'} \rho / m$$

or $\quad \mu_a = m(u_m/D)^{n'-1}$

Incorporating this into the Seider-Tate equation gives:

$$\frac{hD}{k} = 0.023 \left(\frac{D^{n'} u_m^{2-n'} \rho}{m}\right)^{0.8} \left(\frac{mC_p}{k}(u_m/D)^{n'-1}\right)^{0.4} \left(\frac{m}{m_w}\right)^{0.14} \tag{26}$$

Equation 26 has been found useful for order of magnitude estimates of the turbulent heat transfer coefficient.

Skelland and Dimmick [19] studied heat transfer between coils and pseudoplastic fluids with propeller agitation in baffled vessels. The pseudoplastic fluids studied obeyed the power law, with $0.528 \le n \le 0.910$. Various sizes of axially mounted marine-type propellers were used, each with three blades and square pitch. Various sized coils were also tried, and both downthrusting and upthrusting agitation was employed. The correlation obtained from this study is:

$$\frac{h_c D_e}{k} = 0.258 \left(\frac{D^2 N \rho}{\mu_A}\right)^{0.62} \left(\frac{c_p \mu_A}{k}\right)^{0.32} \left(\frac{\mu_A}{\mu_{AW}}\right)^{0.2} \left(\frac{D}{D_T}\right)^{0.1} \left(\frac{D_e}{D_T}\right)^{0.5} \tag{27}$$

where h_c is the individual heat transfer coefficient on the agitated side of the coil, and D_e is the external diameter of the coil tube. In the case of a power law fluid:

$$\tau = K\left(\frac{du}{dr}\right)_A^n$$

$$\mu_A = \frac{\tau}{(du/dr)_A} = \frac{K(du/dr)_A^n}{(du/dr)_A} = \frac{K}{(du/dr)_A^{1-n}}$$

Substituting Equation 11 for $(du/dr)_A$:

$$\mu_A = \frac{K}{(k_s N)^{1-n}} \tag{28}$$

Thus, for power law fluids:

$$\frac{h_c D_e}{k} = 0.258 \left(\frac{D^2 N^{2-n}}{k_s^{n-1} K}\right)^{0.62} \left(\frac{c_p K}{k(k_s N)^{1-n}}\right)^{0.32} \left(\frac{K}{K_w}\right)^{0.2} \left(\frac{D}{D_T}\right)^{0.1} \left(\frac{D_e}{D_T}\right)^{0.5} \tag{29}$$

The form of Equation 27 is not restricted to power law materials, but applies in general to any time-independent non-Newtonian fluid over the limits $332 \le D^2 N \rho / \mu_A \le 2.6(10^5)$. Furthermore, it reduces exactly to the recommended Newtonian correlation with regard to the effects of the six key variables (D, N, D_T, D_e, μ, μ/μ_w).

Since the temperature of the fluid varies during the heating or cooling process, the temperature at which to evaluate μ_A in Equation 27 (or K in Equation 29) becomes an issue of concern. Skelland and Dimmick [19] showed that evaluation of μ_A at the mean run temperature, $(T_1 + T_2)/2$, was adequate throughout their work. An additional study worth noting is that of Hagedorn and Salamone [20] for heat transfer in the simpler geometry of a jacketed vessel. Their mildly non-Newtonian results ($0.69 \le n \le 1.0$) were correlated with an average deviation of $\pm 14\%$, whereas for their highly non-Newtonian data ($0.36 \leq n \leq 0.69$) the average deviation from their correlation increased to $\pm 20\%$.

A practical design problem is that of scale-up in coil-heated, baffled vessels with propeller agitation. Skelland [21] presented the example where the following criteria are required to duplicate some product characteristic when scaling up using power law fluids:

1. Equal rates of heat transfer per unit surface of coil are to be maintained in the model and prototype equipment.
2. Equal volumes of heat transfer per unit volume of vessel contents are to be maintained.

For power law fluids, Equation 29 may be expressed as follows:

$$h_c = \phi D_e^{-0.5} D^{1.34} D_T^{-0.6} N^{0.92 - 0.3n} \tag{30}$$

where parameter ϕ is defined as:

$$\phi = 0.258 k^{0.68} \rho^{0.62} C_p^{0.32} (K/K_w)^{0.2} k_s^{0.3(1-n)s} K^{-0.3} \tag{31}$$

From similarity, the ratio of impeller speeds in the two vessels is written for criterion A:

$$\frac{N_1}{N_2} = \left[\left(\frac{D_{e_1}}{D_{e_2}} \right)^{0.5} \left(\frac{D_2}{D_1} \right)^{1.34} \left(\frac{D_{T_1}}{D_{T_2}} \right)^{0.6} \frac{\Delta T_{1m_2}}{\Delta T_{1m_1}} \right]^{1/(0.92 - 0.3n)} \tag{32}$$

Equation 32 assumes the same fluid is handled over temperature ranges with the same mid-point and that the tube wall temperatures have the same average value in the two different vessels. That is:

$$\phi_{av,1} = \phi_{av,2}$$
$$h_{c_1} \Delta T_{1m_1} = h_{c_2} \Delta T_{1m_2} \tag{33}$$

Subscripts 1 and 2 refer to the different size vessels.

For criterion B we write:

$$\frac{q_1}{V_1} = \frac{q_2}{V_2}$$
$$\frac{h_{c_1} \pi D_{e_1} L_{c_1} \Delta T_{1m_1}}{H_1 (\pi D_{T_1}^2 / 4)} = \frac{h_{c_2} \pi D_{e_2} L_{c_2} \Delta T_{1m_2}}{H_2 (\pi D_{T_2}^2 / 4)} \tag{34}$$

where L_c = length of submerged coil
         H = height of liquid in vessel

Substituting Equation 30 for h_c and solving for the ratio of shaft speeds required to meet criterion B:

$$\frac{N_1}{N_2} = \left[\frac{H_1}{H_2} \left(\frac{D_{T_1}}{D_{T_2}} \right)^{2.6} \left(\frac{D_{e_2}}{D_{e_1}} \right)^{0.5} \frac{L_{c_1}}{L_{c_2}} \left(\frac{D_2}{D_1} \right)^{1.34} \frac{\Delta T_{1m_2}}{\Delta T_{1m_1}} \right]^{1/(0.92 - 0.3n)} \tag{35}$$

To simultaneously duplicate both criteria, Equations 32 and 35 give the following:

$$\frac{H_1}{H_2} = \frac{D_{e_1}}{D_{e_2}} \left[\frac{D_{T_2}}{D_{T_1}} \right]^2 \frac{L_{c_1}}{L_{c_2}} \tag{36}$$

Note that Equation 36 cannot be satisfied when strict geometrical similarity prevails in the two size vessels. Consequently, criteria A and B cannot both be achieved in this example.

Jackets are frequently used instead of coils for heating or cooling. Baker and Walter [22] give one correlation predicting the heat transfer coefficients inside jackets fitted to provide jetting action of the heating and/or cooling medium.

Helical ribbon impellers are widely used in promoting heat transfer to non-Newtonian fluids of high consistency, when operation is confined to the laminar and transitional flow regimes. For heat transfer in jacketed vessels agitated by double helical ribbon impellers, and when $D^2N\rho/\mu_A$ is below 1,000, Nagata [23] recommends the following correlation:

$$\frac{h_j D_T}{k} = 1.75 \left(\frac{D^2 N\rho}{\mu_A}\right)^{1/3} \left(\frac{c_p \mu_A}{k}\right)^{1/3} \left(\frac{\mu_A}{\mu_{AW}}\right)^{0.2} \left(\frac{D_T - D}{D_T}\right)^{-1/3} \tag{37}$$

where μ_A has the same definition as given earlier for non-Newtonian power consumption and μ_{AW} is the viscosity at the wall temperature. h_j is the individual agitated-side heat transfer coefficient to or from the jacket.

Scraped surface heat exchangers are widely used for processing non-Newtonian fluids of high consistency which may tend to adhere to the heat transfer surface. Such devices are comprised of rotating blades which continually scrape material from the surface and are exemplified by the Votator, the Dopp Kettle, and the helical ribbon impeller fitted with rubber scrapers (see Skelland [22], Huggins [24], and Nagata [23]).

To analyze the heat transfer in such units, consider the fluid in the vicinity of the heat transfer surface between scrapings by two consecutive blades. It can be assumed that:

1. Plug flow exists in the fluid over the depth of heat penetration.
2. The fluid thickness exceeds the depth of heat penetration.
3. There is complete mixing of the fluid displaced by the scraper blade with the bulk fluid after each displacement from the vicinity of the heat transfer surface.

A standard approach to analyzing these systems is to first develop the unsteady-state three-dimensional conduction equation, and then reduce it to that for one-dimensional thermal transport.

Consider a fluid volume element in the vicinity of the heat transfer surface, awaiting removal by the next scraper blade as shown in Figure 8. Unsteady-state conduction may occur through all six faces of the element, depending on the symmetry of the temperature field.

Fourier's law describes the rate at which heat enters through the left face of the element by conduction:

$$-k \frac{\partial T}{\partial z} \, dx \, dy$$

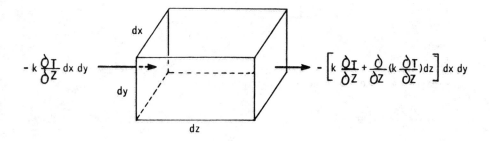

Figure 8. Analysis of heat transfer.

The rate at which heat leaves by conduction through the right face is:

$$-\left(k \frac{\partial T}{\partial z} + \frac{\partial}{\partial z}\left(k \frac{\partial T}{\partial z}\right) dz \right) dx\, dy$$

The rate of accumulation of heat within the volume element from these two sources is therefore:

$$\frac{\partial}{\partial z}\left(k \frac{\partial T}{\partial z}\right) dx\, dy\, dz$$

From the top and bottom faces the accumulation rate is:

$$\frac{\partial}{\partial y}\left(k \frac{\partial T}{\partial y}\right) dx\, dy\, dz$$

and from the front and rear faces it is:

$$\frac{\partial}{\partial x}\left(k \frac{\partial T}{\partial x}\right) dx\, dy\, dz$$

Another expression for the rate of accumulation of heat in the volume element is:

$$dx\, dy\, dz\, c_p \rho \frac{\partial T}{\partial t}$$

Thus, for constant thermal conductivity k:

$$\frac{\partial T}{\partial t} = \alpha \left(\frac{\partial^2 T}{\partial x^2} + \frac{\partial^2 T}{\partial y^2} + \frac{\partial^2 T}{\partial z^2} \right) \tag{38}$$

where α is the thermal diffusivity, $k/\rho c_p$.

For one-dimensional conduction in the z direction for example, this equation reduces to:

$$\frac{\partial T}{\partial t} = \alpha \frac{\partial^2 T}{\partial z^2} \tag{39}$$

Equation 39 is the basic equation for unsteady-state conduction in the radial (or z) direction. The boundary conditions for this system are as follows:

$$T(z, 0) = T_\infty$$

$$T(0, t) = T^* \tag{40}$$

$$T(\infty, t) = T_\infty$$

The temperature at the heat transfer surface $(z = 0)$ is constant at T^*, as is the temperature T_∞ at z effectively equal to infinity. Equation 39 may be expressed as follows:

$$\frac{\partial T'}{\partial t} = \alpha \frac{\partial^2 T'}{\partial z^2} \tag{41}$$

where
$$\begin{aligned} T' &= T - T_\infty \\ T^{*\prime} &= T^* - T_\infty \end{aligned}$$

The boundary conditions then become:

$$T'(z, 0) = 0$$

$$T'(0, t) = T^{*'} \tag{42}$$

$$T'(\infty, t) = 0$$

The Laplace transform of both sides is taken with respect to time t:

$$\int_0^\infty e^{-pt} \frac{\partial^2 T'}{\partial z^2} \, dt = \frac{1}{\alpha} \int_0^\infty e^{-pt} \frac{\partial T'}{\partial t} \, dt$$

$$\frac{d^2 F}{dz^2} = \frac{1}{\alpha} pF - T'(z, 0) = \frac{P}{\alpha} F$$

where $F(z, p) = L_t[T'(z, t)]$

whence $\dfrac{d^2 F}{dz^2} - \dfrac{p}{\alpha} F = 0 \tag{43}$

The second boundary condition transforms to $F(0, p) = T^*/p$. The solution of the ordinary differential equation for F, subject to $F(0, p) = T^*/p$ and F remains finite as $z \to \infty$, is:

$$F(z, p) = \frac{T^{*'}}{p} e^{-\sqrt{pz^2/\alpha}}$$

Skelland [21] obtained the function having this as its Laplace transform, thus providing an expression that gives the temperature in the fluid near the heat transfer surface as a function of position Z and time t. The instantaneous heat flux from the surface is:

$$\frac{q}{A} = -\alpha c_p \left(\frac{\partial T}{\partial z} \right)_{z=0} \tag{44}$$

Evaluating $(\partial T/\partial z)_{z=0}$ from Skelland's solution:

$$\frac{q}{A} = (T^* - T_\infty) c_p \rho \left(\frac{\alpha}{\pi t} \right)^{1/2}$$

The total thermal energy penetrating the fluid in an exposure time t_e is therefore:

$$\int_0^{t_e} \frac{q}{A} \, dt = (T^* - T_\infty) c_p \rho \left(\frac{\alpha}{\pi} \right)^{1/2} \int_0^{t_e} t^{-1/2} \, dt$$

$$= 2(T^* - T_\infty) c_p \rho \left(\frac{\alpha t_e}{\pi} \right)^{1/2} \tag{45}$$

and the average rate of transfer during exposure is obtained by dividing the last expression by t_e:

$$\left(\frac{q}{A} \right)_{av} = 2(T^* - T_\infty) c_p \rho \left(\frac{\alpha}{\pi t_e} \right)^{1/2} \tag{46A}$$

or $\dfrac{(q/A)_{av}}{T^* - T_\infty} = h = 2 \left(\dfrac{c_p \rho k}{\pi t_e} \right)^{1/2} = 1.1284 \left(\dfrac{c_p \rho k}{t_e} \right)^{1/2} \tag{46B}$

The time of exposure, t_e, is the time between passage of two consecutive blades. For n_b scraper blades rotating at N rps, $t_e = 1/n_b N$ where the blades are uniformly distributed around the shaft. Then the scraped surface heat transfer coefficient h is given by:

$$h = 1.1284(c_p \rho k n_b N)^{1/2} \tag{47}$$

And in dimensionless form:

$$\frac{hD}{k} = 1.1284 \left(\frac{D^2 N \rho}{\mu_A} \cdot \frac{c_p \mu_A}{k} \cdot n_b \right)^{1/2} \tag{48}$$

Equation 48 shows that the heat transfer coefficient varies with rotary shaft speed N raised to the 1/2 power which has been confirmed by Skelland [22] using water data in the Votator obtained by Houlton [25]. Other investigators [26, 27] have studied fluids of low to moderate consistency or viscosity and obtained an exponent close to 0.5. With high consistency or viscosity fluids Skelland [22], Bott and Azoory [27], and Ramdas, Uhl, et al. [28] found lower values for the exponent on N (0.113 − 0.18).

For *helical ribbon impellers* fitted with two rubber scrapers, Nagata [23] gives the following correlation:

$$\frac{h_j D_T}{k} = 5.4 \left(\frac{D^2 N \rho}{\mu_A} \right)^{1/3} \left(\frac{c_p \mu_A}{k} \right)^{1/3} \left(\frac{\mu_A}{\mu_{AW}} \right)^{0.2} \tag{49}$$

This was developed from data obtained in a vessel having a diameter of 30 cm.

Mass transfer of gas-liquid non-Newtonian systems is reasonably well correlated by the following empirical equation:

$$\frac{k_L a D^2}{D_L} = 0.060 \left(\frac{D^2 N \rho}{\mu_A} \right)^{1.5} \left(\frac{D N^2}{g} \right)^{0.19} \left(\frac{\mu_A}{\rho D_L} \right)^{0.5} \left(\frac{\mu_A V_s}{\sigma} \right)^{0.6} \left(\frac{ND}{V_s} \right)^{0.32} \left[1 + 2(N'_{wi})^{0.5} \right]^{-0.67} \tag{50}$$

where N'_{wi} is the Weissenberg number (N'_{wi} = characteristic material time/characteristic process time), $k_L a$ is the liquid phase mass transfer volumetric or capacity coefficient, a is the interfacial area per unit volume, V_s is the superficial gas velocity (length/time), and μ_A is the average apparent viscosity, obtained from the flow curve as described earlier:

$$\mu_A = \tau/(du/dr)_A = \tau/k_s N \tag{51}$$

For Newtonian fluids, μ_A becomes μ and the Weissenberg number equals zero. The numerator of the Weissenberg number is essentially the reciprocal of the shear rate at which the reduced complex viscosity, i.e., the ratio of the apparent viscosity μ'_A to the zero-shear viscosity μ_0, is 0.67.

For *liquid-liquid systems*, Skelland and Seksaria [29] report visual observations revealing the minimum impeller speed N_m at which one phase was completely dispersed as droplets in the other. This study produced the following empirical correlation:

$$\frac{D^{1/2} N_m}{g^{1/2}} = C_1 \left(\frac{D_T}{D} \right)^{a_1} \left(\frac{\mu_c}{\mu_d} \right)^{1/9} \left(\frac{\Delta \rho}{\rho_c} \right)^{0.25} \left(\frac{\sigma}{D^2 \rho_c g} \right)^{0.3} \tag{52}$$

The values of C_1 and a_1 are tabulated by the investigators for different impeller types and location. Depending on the type impeller and its position, the average percent deviation between predicted and observed N_m ranged from 4.28% to 18.15%. However, almost all the average deviations were below 12% for nearly 200 data points.

For agitation of two-phase Newtonian fluids, Treybal [30] showed that the Power number-Reynolds number plot coincides with that for single-phase liquids when the Power and Reynolds numbers are defined as follows:

$$\rho_M = \rho_c \phi_c + \rho_d \phi_D \tag{53}$$

$$\mu_M = \frac{\mu_c}{\phi_c} \left(1 + \frac{1.5 \mu_d \phi_D}{\mu_d + \mu_c} \right) \tag{54}$$

where ϕ_c and ϕ_D are volume fractions of the continuous and disperse phases.

The effects of a non-Newtonian disperse phase have not been extensively studied, although if the drops behave as rigid particles (high surface tension σ, low $\Delta\rho$, small diameter) then the effects of μ_d may not be important. In this regard, Harriott [31] and Calderbank [32] experimentally, and Azbel [33] theoretically, state that small drops and bubbles behave as rigid spheres when suspended in agitated liquids.

Dynamics of Impellers

The pumping capacity of an impeller is primarily responsible for the overall flow around a vessel, generating fresh interface even within a single-phase liquid. The action of mixing is thus promoted by molecular and eddy diffusions. The pumping or circulation capacity may be measured, by velocity traverses across the stream ejected by the impeller. More often, and with less accuracy, it is estimated by determining the average time for some suitable small size particle, of neutral buoyancy, to complete one circulation loop within the vessel, as established by visual observations and stopwatch measurements.

In either case, the results are correlated as the dimensionless circulation number, N_{Ci}, defined as:

$$N_{Ci} = \frac{q}{ND^3} \doteq \frac{V}{\theta_c ND^3} \tag{55}$$

where q is the volumetric discharge rate of the impeller, V is the volume of liquid in the vessel, and θ_c is the time for one circulation loop to be completed.

Many non-Newtonian mixing systems are confined to the laminar or transitional flow regimes. In these cases, forms of helical ribbon or helical screw and draught tube devices are most often used.

Carreau et al. [34] measured both circulation times (θ_c) and mixing times (θ_m) in high consistency Newtonian, pseudoplastic, and viscoelastic fluids stirred with helical ribbon impellers. The ratio θ_m/θ_c was about 3.5 for the Newtonian fluids, increasing by a factor of two or three for slightly elastic solutions, and increasing markedly for the highly elastic fluids (up to seven-fold).

Carreau and coworkers [34] showed that the mixing time θ_m increased by factors of 3 to 7 as the elastic characteristic time increased. The pumping capacity of the helical ribbon was correspondingly reduced by increasing elasticity. Furthermore, in the absence of significant stagnation zones, it was found that the mixing effectiveness (defined as $V/ND^3\theta_m = 1$/dimensionless mixing time), is directly related to the axial pumping capacity of the ribbon impeller.

For a *helical screw inside a draught tube*, Chavan and Ulbrecht [35] examined axial discharge rates, circulation times, and axial velocities for Newtonian, pseudoplastic, and viscoelastic fluids. Again, the circulation number N_{Ci} was found to be independent of impeller speed, Reynolds number, and the rheology in the laminar region for Newtonian and pseudoplastic fluids ($D^2N^{2-n}\rho/K \leq 10$ or 100, depending on geometry), where power law behavior was observed. Elastic effects, however, reduced the circulation number by up to 50%, in a way that also depended on geometry. A straightforward correlation is provided by Chavan and Ulbrecht [35] for the circulation number in terms of the geometry of the screw and draught tube unit. The empirical nature of the expression requires its application within the tabulated ranges of a large number of geometrical variables used in the study.

Ford and Ulbrecht [36] obtained an empirical correlation for the dimensionless blending time, $N\theta_B$, using a helical screw in a draught tube. The end point for blending was assessed by optical means in systems comprised of blending equal amounts of polymer solutions having different rheological properties. The fluids included Newtonian, pseudoplastic, and viscoelastic materials, and the correlation takes the form of a plot of $N\theta_B(\mu_{0M}/\mu_{0L})^{-z}(1 + 0.52N_{Wi})^{-1.25}$ vs. $Re = D^2N\rho/\mu_a'$ with:

$$\mu_a' = \mu_0 - mN^{b-1} \tag{56}$$

where μ_0, m, and b are parameters of the flow curve of the *final* mix.

The exponent z on the ratio (μ_{0M}/μ_{0L}) in the ordinate is related to the initial orientation of the two components to be blended, with a value $z = 0.059$ when the more viscous liquid is initially in the upstream position in the draught tube, $z = 0.17$ when the more viscous liquid is initially in the downstream position in the draught tube. Also, μ_{0M} and μ_{0L} are the zero-shear viscosity of the more and less viscous components, respectively. Skelland [21] provides further discussion.

Chavan et al. [37] examined the influence of pseudoplasticity and viscoelasticity on mixing. In the laminar region $(D^2N^{2-n}\rho/K < 10)$ they found that $N\theta_c$ and $N\theta_M$ were constants for a given geometry, unaffected by the shear thinning viscosity behavior. Mixing time was observed to be a factor of two for viscoelastic materials. The interaction between shearing and normal stresses in viscoelastic fluids caused substantial reduction in the axial velocity component, with substantial increase in the angular component of velocity.

Ribbon-screw combinations were studied by Coyle et al. [38] who found the mixing time of nonelastic liquids to be independent of the apparent viscosity, μ_A, above 15 poises, with $N\theta_M$ being constant for a given geometry in laminar flow. Measurements of both circulation and mixing times showed that $\theta_M \doteq 3\theta_C$.

In some cases the range of applicability of fan turbines and of helical impellers overlap, depending upon the fluid consistency involved and the degree of mixing considered satisfactory. Coyle et al. [38] have compared the economics of alternative forms of agitation when satisfactory results are obtainable from either source. The relative cost data, based on 1970 dollars, are summarized in Table 3.

The flow patterns generated in Newtonian and purely viscous non-Newtonian fluids by axial and radial flow impellers (e.g., propellers and turbines), are qualitatively well known, consisting of recirculation loops described in standard mixing textbooks. With viscoelastic fluids, however, secondary flows not encountered with purely viscous fluids may arise. This is particularly true for rotating turbines (Kelkar, et al. [39] has simulated this behavior using rotating spheres). The competing influence of shearing and normal stresses may cause a toroidal vortex to form above and below the rotating body, the vortices becoming segregated at a particular numerical combination of Weissenberg and Reynolds numbers (for examples see Chavan and Mashelkar [40] and Ulbrecht [41, 42]. Fluid trapped in these vortices fails to mix with the bulk of the material in the vessel, thereby reducing overall mixing efficiency and diffusion of ingredients.

In contrast, no such segregated vortices have been observed with propeller agitators. In this case, the screw propulsion process apparently is enhanced by the viscoelasticity, thus accentuating the usual axial recirculation pattern as described by Ulbrecht [42]. This constitutes an advantage for axially thrusting propellers over turbines and paddles when agitating viscoelastic materials.

We shall now turn attention to the hardware of mixing non-Newtonian fluids.

Table 3
Relative Cost Comparison Between Axial Flow Turbines and Helical Impellers
For Equal Blend Times and Equal Heat Transfer Characteristics

Impeller Type	Relative Values			Initial Cost
	hp	Speed	Torque	
Axial flow turbine	1	1	1	1
Helical impeller	1/3–1/10	1/15–1/6	1.5–3.0	2.5–3.5

Blade Mixer Operation

Blade mixers are used to promote kneading and mixing action accompanied with heating or cooling of different deformable or plastic solids and high consistency pastes. It involves compressing the fluid mass flat, folding it over on itself, and then compressing it again. The material is usually torn apart and high shear is produced between the moving and stationary fluid elements. The mixing is usually performed by two Z-shaped heavy blades rotating in opposite directions at different speeds on parallel horizontal shafts.

Typical blade designs are illustrated in Figure 9. Figure 9(A) shows the widely used sigma-blade employed for general purpose kneading. The blade designs that are commercially available vary greatly, ranging from lightweight to heavyweight constructions. Selection of the specific design depends on the consistency of the mix. The size of the mixer is limited primarily by considerations of power input, weight, speed of mixing, materials of construction, and methods of mix discharge. Many machines are equipped with a tilting mechanism which facilitates the discharge of the batch while the blades are turning. For special mixing requirements, the sigma-blade mixer may incorporate special construction features, such as jackets for heating or cooling the troughs, dust-tight or vacuum-tight lids, and linings of special alloys for the mixing of corrosive or abrasive materials. Capacities of the equipment for handling heavy-consistency materials range from laboratory-sized batches to several hundred gallons with capacities for lighter-consistency material that are much larger. In general, these mixers require very heavy drive mechanisms and motors.

The agitator blades in the sigma-blade mixer may be mounted so that their paths are either tangential or overlapping. In the tangential mounting arrangement, the two blades rotate side by side with their circular paths of rotation not quite touching. In the overlapping mounting, the paths of rotation overlap; and consequently, the blades must be designed and the speed of rotation adjusted so that the blades always clear each other. In the tangential type, the blades can have any

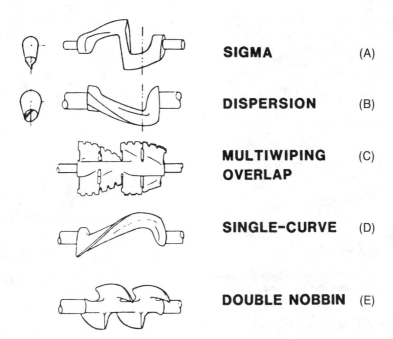

SIGMA	(A)
DISPERSION	(B)
MULTIWIPING OVERLAP	(C)
SINGLE–CURVE	(D)
DOUBLE NOBBIN	(E)

Figure 9. Different agitator blades for double—arm kneaders.

relative speed because their paths of rotation do not overlap. Many modifications may be made in the shape of blades to meet specific mixing requirements. Many manufacturers provide double-arm mixers with interchangeable blades.

Examples of materials handled by double-arm kneaders of the sigma-blade type are resins, putty, adhesives, baker's dough, and cellulose additives. Sigma-type agitator blades are best for general purpose use.

The single-curve (or spiral agitator blade) shown in Figure 9(D) provides the same smooth blending and folding action as the dispersion blade (Figure 9(B)), but has been designed for larger overlapping-type mixers. The dispersion agitator blades provide excellent mixing for fiber-reinforced products. They do not have the same heavy shearing action of other types, and therefore, produce a smooth homogeneous mix with no fiber breakdown.

The double nobben agitator blade produces extra shearing action required on certain materials. This agitator design resists blade distortion from stresses in the mixing load. Commercial designs are available in both overlapping and tangential action mixers. These units are most often used for heavy plastic materials.

By optimizing important process parameters, any mixing system has the potential of providing high-quality mixing at minimum power consumption per unit volume of materials production. A proper mixer should also be of a low weight, compact and durable. To optimize a design, we first require a system of equations that will enable parametric calculations or sensitivity studies to be made.

Following the analysis of Pikovsky, et al. [43], consider a particle of material or fluid positioned on a mixer blade located at angle α to the plane of rotation. This fluid particle is under action of gravity force G and centrifugal force P:

$$P = \frac{G}{g} \omega^2 x \tag{57}$$

where x is the particle's distance from the axis of rotation, (m); and g is the gravitational acceleration (m/s^2); and P has units of kg_f. Under the action of these two forces there arise in the plane of particle motion the following forces:

A friction force of the opposing material against the bottom of the trough:

$$W_1 = \left(G \sin \varphi + \frac{G}{g} \omega^2 x \right) f, \quad kg \tag{58}$$

A component of the gravity force:

$$W_2 = G \cos \varphi, \quad kg \tag{58A}$$

A friction force against the blade:

$$W_3 = W_1 f \cos \alpha, \quad kg \tag{58B}$$

A friction force due to the gravity force:

$$W_4 = W_2 f \cos \psi \cotang \alpha, \quad kg \tag{58C}$$

where ψ = angle of blade rotation, radians
         ω = blade angular velocity, rad/sec
         f = friction coefficient of particle against the metal

The total resistance is thus:

$$W = W_1 + W_2 + W_3 + W_4 = G(1 + f \cotang \alpha) \cdot \left(\frac{w^2 f x}{g} + f \sin \psi - \cos \psi \right), \quad kg \tag{59}$$

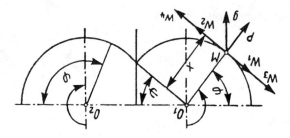

Figure 10. Forces acting on particle.

Figure 10 summarizes the forces acting on the particle.

An elemental amount of work, dA, spent for passing over the total resistance at the blade's rotation at an angle $d\psi$ is:

$$dA = (W_1 + W_3)R \, d\psi - (W_2 + W_4)x \, d\psi, \quad (kg\text{-}m) \tag{60}$$

The total work at the blade rotation from $\psi = 0$ to $\psi = \pi - \psi$ is:

$$A = G(1 + f \cotang \, \alpha)[fR(0.24\omega^2 x + 1.71) - 0.71x] \tag{61}$$

where   R = blade radius, m
             ψ = extension angle of the blade from the bottom zone, rad.

To compute the power, with respect to the dimensions of the blade, the following formula is recommended:

$$N = 0.105nzb\gamma' \sin \alpha(1 + f \cotang \, \alpha)(CR^3 - r^3) \times (0.0009fRn^2 - 0.24) + 0.86fR(R^2 - r^2) \tag{62}$$

where   N = power, kg-m/sec
             r = initial radius of the blade, m
             b = blade width, m
             n = rotational velocity, rot/min
             z = number of blades
             γ' = specific gravity of material, kg/m^3

The motion of a blade during mixing can be visualized by the analogy of a slab moving through a viscous liquid. Consider an elemental area dF (shown in Figure 11) where dF = b dx, m^2; b is the length of the elementary area, and dx is the width. According to Newton's law, the resistance acting on the elementary plane is:

$$dP = C\frac{\gamma'}{g} dFv^2, \quad kg$$

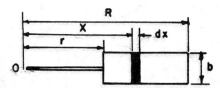

Figure 11. Slab moving through a viscous fluid.

where γ' = liquid specific weight, kg/m^3
         $v = xw$, rotational velocity of the plate, m/sec
         C = drag coefficient

Then:

$$dP = C \frac{\gamma'}{g} b\omega^2 x^2 \, dx, \quad kg_f$$

and after integration:

$$P = C \frac{\gamma'}{g} b\omega^2 \int_r^R x^2 \, dx = C \frac{\gamma'}{3g} b\omega^2 (R^3 - r^3) \tag{63}$$

The power required to rotate the blade is:

$$N = \int_r^R dPv$$

or:

$$N = \int_r^R C \frac{\gamma'}{g} b\omega^3 x^3 \, dx = C \frac{\gamma'}{4g} b\omega^3 (R^4 - r^4), \quad kg\text{-}m/sec$$

If the number of blades is Z = 2, then for a drive efficiency η_{eff} the required horsepower is:

$$N = C \frac{\gamma'}{g} \cdot \frac{\omega^3 (R^4 - r^4)}{410\eta_{eff}} \tag{64}$$

Kharkhuta, et al. [44] have experimentally determined that the coefficient C for asphalt-concrete mixtures is a function of the blade velocity n. At n = 60 to 70 rpm, C = 6; at n = 70 to 80 rpm, C = 5. From dimensional analysis, the following formula was derived for high-way mixers:

$$N = 150d^{4.56} n_0^{2.78} \left(\frac{\gamma'}{g}\right)^{0.78} \mu_a^{0.22}, \quad kg\text{-}m/sec \tag{65}$$

where   d = circle diameter traced out by the blade
         n_0 = rotational blade velocity, rot/sec
         μ_a = apparent mixture viscosity, $kg\text{-}sec/m^2$

For approximate calculations of power, Kharkhuta, et al. [44] recommend the following formulas:
For Q_M < 1,400 kg

$$N = 0.035Q, \quad kW \tag{66A}$$

For Q_M > 1,400 kg

$$N = 30 + 0.01Q, \quad kW \tag{66B}$$

where Q_M = mass of the mix, kg
    The capacity of a batch mixer is:

$$G_M = \frac{Q_M}{T} \tag{67}$$

where T = time for a single mix.

The capacity of a continuous mixer is:

$$G_c = \frac{Q_M}{t_m} \tag{68}$$

where $Q_M = V\rho$, the mass of material in the mixer, kg, determined by the mixer volume V and fluid density ρ; t_m = mixing time.

Because the capacity is equal to the product of the cross-sectional area of the mixer F and its length l, the capacity expression may be restated as follows:

$$G_c = FS_d\rho, \quad kg/hr \tag{69}$$

where   F = cross-sectional area of material in the mixer, m^2
          S_d = material displacement, m/hr
          ρ = density of the mixture, kg/m^3

Capacity is the main parameter determining the basic elements of the mixer. From the capacity, the mass of the mix (Equations 67 and 68) can be computed. Further, from the mass of the mix Q_M, the volume of mixer trough can then be determined. For batch mixers, the following formulas are used for computing the unit's dimensions of length L, width B, and height H:

$$L = 750 + 0.67 \, Q_M, \, mm$$

$$B = 830 + 0.37 \, Q_M, \, mm \tag{70}$$

$$H = 448 + 0.385 \, Q_M, \, mm$$

The blade radius as a function of mix mass is determined from the following equation:

$$R = \sqrt[3]{\frac{Q_m}{12.6\rho K_f}} \tag{71}$$

where ρ = density of mixture, kg/m^3
          K_f = filling coefficient
          Q_M = mix mass, kg

The length of trough can be computed from:

$$L = 4.25R, \quad m$$

The width b_b and height h_b of the blades can be computed from:

$$b_b = 0.42R, \quad m; \qquad h_b = 0.5R, \quad m$$

The blade pitch is normally established by the manufacturer, and a typical value is:

$$t = 0.75, \quad m$$

The blade velocity is:

$$n_b = \frac{45.3}{\sqrt{R}}, \quad rpm$$

The size of a continuous mixer as a function of the mix mass is:

$$R = \sqrt[3]{\frac{Q_m}{(1.21 \sim 1.41)\gamma'zk_c}}, \quad m \tag{72}$$

Figure 12 shows the recommended dimensions of a blade mixer where the distance between two blade shafts is set at $l = 1.5R$, the trough width is generally $B = l + 2R$, the height of the part of the trough over the blade is $h = 1.35R$, and the height of the trough is $H = h + R = 2.35R$.

The length of the trough can be computed from the following formula:

$$L = \frac{Q_M}{\rho K_d F}, \quad m \tag{73}$$

where the area of mixing chamber is:

$$F = R^2 \left[\pi - 0.5 \left(\frac{\pi\psi}{90°} - \sin 2\psi \right) \right], \quad m^2 \tag{74}$$

The shafts of mixers are designed for combined deformation from bending and torque moments. Increasing the rotational speed n_0 is practical only up to a certain limit; beyond this limit any increase in n_0 does not provide appreciable increases in mixing efficiency. The critical rpm is typically 180–200 for blade mixers. The approximate rpm can be estimated from the following relationships, developed by Kharkhuta, et al. [44]:

For a mix with $40 - 160$ kg

$$n_0 = \left(\frac{100}{m} + 54.5 \right), \quad rpm$$

For a mix with $160 - 360$ kg

$$n_0 = \left(\frac{180}{m} + 46 \right), \quad rpm$$

For any size mixer

$$n_0 = \left(\frac{9,600}{m} + 52 \right), \quad rpm$$

where m = mass of the mix, kg.

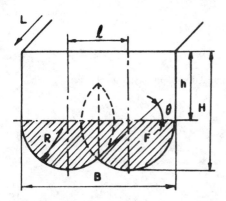

Figure 12. Recommended dimensions of a blade mixer.

The rotational speed and the distance from the blade tip to the axis R_m establishes the velocity of the blade tip in the mixing material, which thus influences mixing efficiency, where R_{max} is typically 270 to 300 mm.

The area of one blade is $S = 225$ to 275 cm^2 for batch mixers, and $S = 150$ cm^2 for continuous mixers.

The value of ψ and the distance between blades along the shaft determines the character of the helical surface and the rate of material displacement along the mixer. The smaller the value of ψ, the faster the material will pass through the mixer. For materials requiring substantial mixing time, $\psi = 90°$.

The formulas presented in this subsection can be used to establish preliminary dimensions for blade mixers. Parametric calculations can be made to establish a range of mixer sizes that will provide high-quality mixing at acceptable or minimum power consumption.

Banbury Mixers

There are a variety of kneading machines where the trough or container is open, so the contents may be unloaded by tilting. Some designs however, have an enclosed mixing chamber, in which case the units are known as *internal mixers*. This type of mixer is often used for dissolving rubber and for dispersing rubber in liquids. The Banbury mixer illustrated in Figure 13 is a typical example. It is a heavy-duty double arm mixer in which the agitators are in the form of interrupted spirals.

The Banbury mixer resembles a double-arm kneader in that it has two adjoining cylindrical sections which meet tangentially. In the Banbury design, however, the rotating agitators are much more rugged in construction and are able to apply considerably more power per gallon of working volume. Following Figure 13, two rotors (1) turn slowly toward each other at slightly different speeds. Each rotor has a blade which extends along the length of the rotor, roughly in the form of a spiral. Each rotor is cored to permit cooling or heating by the passage of cooling water or an appropriate heating agent. The mixing chamber (2) may also be cooled or heated, by means of the sprays (3). The materials to be mixed are fed into the mixing chamber through the feed hopper (4). A floating weight (5) is operated by compressed air and rests on top of the feed, serving to confine the material to the mixing space and to exert pressure on it. The mixed batch is discharged by a power-operated sliding discharge mechanism (6). The saddle (7) between the two rotors, which is attached to the sliding mechanism, slides out from under the rotors, leaving an opening through which the mix discharges.

Because of the high degree of agitation, a Banbury mixer can complete a mix in a relatively short time. It is capable of reducing to a matter of minutes mixing operations requiring hours in other types of mixers. Examples of applications include the mixing of wood flour and linseed oil in linoleum manufacture, and the incorporation of fillers, softeners, and accelerators into rubber stock. The mixing of viscoelastic polymeric materials such as rubber with different ingredients is considered a mechanical process where under different shear deformations the dispersion of ingredients takes place. In addition to the mechanical processes of mixing, physio-chemical processes take place between the material, fillers, and other ingredients.

The mixing process is normally carried out under laminar conditions of material flow, created by the rotating parts of the machine. During this action the non-Newtonian material is subjected to different stresses and strains. The selection of the mixing regime depends on several parameters, such as the amounts of materials loaded, the order of loading, and the loading times; the time of a mix, the rotational speed of the blades, and the pressure in the chamber. By varying these parameters, the process may be considerably intensified. However, the basic source of intensification is an increase of blade velocity and an increase of the pressure in the mixing chamber. An increase in the rotational velocity of the blades increases the shear velocity, which leads to more frequent dividing of the mass and renewal of its surface. This promotes rapid distribution of ingredients in the mass. An increase in the rotational velocity leads to temperature rises in the mixture, as well as pressure exerted against the walls of the chamber.

The largest amounts of mixing energy are consumed in applications involving viscous components and when adding filler materials in the form of powders to viscous solutions. The energy consumption in these cases is variable. It depends on various technological factors as well as the

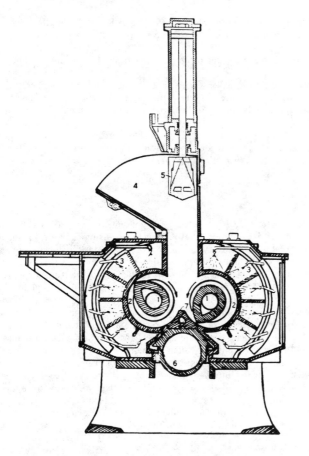

1-ROTORS OR AGITATORS

2-MIXING CHAMBER   3-COOLING SPRAYS   4-FEED HOPPER

5-FLOATING WEIGHT   6-SLIDING DISCHARGE   7-SADDLE

                                                    DISCHARGE OPENING

Figure 13. Details of a Banbury mixer.

physio-chemical properties of components. Figure 14 shows a typical time plot of mixer power consumption. The area limited by the power consumption curve and x-axis is equal to the energy consumption per mixing cycle. A plot such as Figure 14 provides an evaluation of the intensity of the process as well as an indication of the distribution of the ingredients in the paste. The energy consumption for a given amount of mixture of specified composition and temperature is constant and independent of the rotational velocity of the blades.

For Newtonian fluids, a good approximation is to assume that the drive horsepower is proportional to the rotational velocity. For non-Newtonian materials, however, this is not a valid assumption because non-linear relationships exist between shear stress and shear rate. Furthermore, at increased speeds the rate of shear deformation also increases, which promotes temperature rises

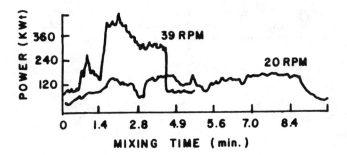

Figure 14. Time plot of mixer power consumption.

due to energy dissipation. Heat transfer promoting mixture cooling is generally poor, and as such, an increase in temperature of the mixture results in a lowering of the fluid's viscosity. This, in turn, decreases the energy consumption of mixing. It should be noted that the power of the drive and the energy consumption depend on the order of loading mixture components. For materials loadings in succession, a decrease in the time intervals between loadings of discrete portions demands power increases due to a shortening of the mixing cycle. The maximum power of the drive occurs when all materials are loaded simultaneously. Pressure increases over the mixture influences the energy consumption upon totally filling the chamber. This is especially true when loading hard mixtures. At the same time, energy consumption increases, but not proportionally with pressure increases. Pressure rises cause temperature increases in the mixture, resulting in delaying of the power consumption. During this action, the specific energy consumption does not undergo significant changes, but rather, gradually decreases with mixing time.

Mixing theory of non-Newtonian materials is complex and not completely understood. Consequently, a calculation procedure for establishing the drive horsepower cannot be recommended. As a rule, this parameter must be established on the basis of experimental data and information obtained from mixers of similar designs.

Attempts at establishing guidelines for the power consumption in closed mixers were made by Bernhardt [45] who considered the deformation process of viscous liquids when shear takes place between the tip of a blade and the wall of the chamber. The material was assumed to be of constant viscosity, the radius of the chamber was large in comparison to the gap, and the process was isothermal.

These assumptions, particularly constant viscosity and temperature, prohibit an accurate evaluation of the power consumption. They do, however, enable the system evaluation to be made qualitatively.

In the case where the gap h between the blade tip and chamber wall is constant, the velocity distribution along the gap is:

$$v = u\left(1 - \frac{u}{h}\right) \tag{75}$$

where   u = peripheral velocity of the blade tip
         y = coordinate

The velocity varies linearly from $v = 0$ at $y = h$ (at the wall of the chamber) to $v = u$ at $y = 0$ (at the blade surface). In this case, the shear stress is:

$$\tau = \mu \frac{dv}{dy} = -\mu \frac{u}{h} = 2\mu \frac{Q}{h^2} \tag{76}$$

where Q = volumetric rate related to a unit length of blade in the axial direction. As h = constant, the shear stress is also constant along the channel. The power per unit length is the product of the resistance force to the blade motion and velocity:

$$N = u \int_0^L \tau \, dx = \mu u^2 \, \frac{L}{h} \qquad (77)$$

where L = blade width.

Thus, the power for a rectilinear channel per unit length of blade is:

$$N = 4\mu Q^2 \, \frac{L}{h^3} \qquad (78)$$

Assuming the gap varies linearly along the length L(x), then:

$$h = h_0(1 - cx) \qquad (79)$$

the shear stress will be:

$$\tau = 2\mu \, \frac{Q}{h_0^2} \left(\frac{1}{1 - \beta\rho} \right)^2 \qquad (80)$$

where $\beta = \dfrac{\alpha - 1}{\alpha};$

$\zeta = \dfrac{x}{L}$

$\alpha = \dfrac{h_L}{h_0}$

and the power is:

$$N = 15.5\mu Q^2 \, \frac{L}{h_0^3} \qquad (81)$$

Thus, the shear stress and power consumption are considerably higher in an inclined channel. Equation 78 may be rewritten as:

$$N = 4\mu u^2 \, \frac{L}{h_0} \qquad (82)$$

It is assumed in this case that the channel has a constant depth, from which the shear stress is:

$$\tau = \mu \, \frac{u}{h_0^3} \qquad (83)$$

The product μu may be assumed to be a constant. Using the above equations, Bernhardt et al. [45] assumed that the shear stress in the closed mixer depends only on the gap size between the blade and the wall. However, the assumption that μu = constant is valid only as a first approximation. As an alternative approach for estimating the power consumption, Guber [46] recommends an exponential law for the shear stress:

$$\tau = K\dot{\gamma}^n \qquad (84)$$

where τ = shear stress, kg/cm^2
k and n = rheological constants
$\dot{\gamma}$ = shear rate in sec^{-1}

Equation 84 has been found to represent rubber mixtures over moderate ranges of shear rate reasonably well. Keeping in mind that the shear rate in the mixer is proportional to the rotational rate of the blades, and an average stress is proportional to the power consumed, the following analysis can be applied to estimating the power consumption of the mixer.

The specific energy spent in the deformation of a unit volume of material is:

$$N_{sp} = \tau\dot{\gamma} \tag{85}$$

The total power of the drive is:

$$N = N_{sp} \times V \tag{86}$$

And from Equations 84, 85, and 86, we obtain:

$$N = k\dot{\gamma}^{n+1}V \tag{87}$$

where N = horsepower, kg-cm/sec
V = volume of mixture, cm^3
$\dot{\gamma}$ = average shear rate, sec^{-1}

The average shear rate of the material in the gap is:

$$\dot{\gamma} = \frac{u}{h} \tag{88}$$

where u = peripheral velocity of the blade's ridge, cm/sec
h = gap between the blade tip and chamber wall, cm

Guber [46] has verified this relation experimentally. Guber also developed the following set of equations for Banbury mixers that can be used for parametric calculations. The section of material in the gap is divided into a series of elements; then the power is determined for each element and summed as follows:

$$N = 2K\left(\frac{\pi n_{av}}{60}\right)^{n+1}\{[l_1(0.5^{n+1} + 0.865^{n+1}) + 2l_2 \times 0.705^{n+1}]F'$$
$$+ (D_r/h_0)^{n+1}h_0\delta(l_1 + l_2)\}, \quad kg\text{-}cm/sec \tag{89}$$

where n_{av} = average velocity of rear and front blades, rpm
l_1 = length of the long blade ridge, cm
l_2 = length of the short blade ridge, cm
D_r = diameter of blade ridge, cm
h_0 = gap between the blade ridge and the chamber, cm
δ = width of the blade ridge

Parameter F' is given by:

$$F' = \sum_{i=1}^{j}\left(\frac{D_k}{h_i} - 2\right)^{n+1}f_i \tag{90}$$

where   i = number of elements in which the deforming volume is divided into, or the width of deformation zone of the material in the gap between the blade and the chamber

D_k = chamber inside diameter, cm

h_i = gap between the blade ridge and the chamber for an element, cm

f_i = cross-sectional area of the ith-element, cm^2

Guber [46] gives values of F' as a function of the deformation zone width for different rheological constants n. For geometrically similar equipment, the following relationship applies:

$$\frac{N''}{N'} = \frac{k''\left(\frac{\pi n''_{av}}{60}\right)^{n''+1} U^3 \alpha}{k'\left(\frac{\pi n'_{av}}{60}\right)^{n'+1}} \tag{91}$$

where   u = geometrical scale

α = F''/F' coefficient considering the rate of filling (space factor)

The prime (') denotes the model and ('') denotes the prototype. When both mixers are filled with the same mixture and operated at the same temperature, Equation 91 simplifies to the following:

$$\frac{N''}{N'} = \left(\frac{n''_{av}}{n'_{av}}\right)^{n+1} \alpha u^3 \tag{92}$$

Experiments have shown that the pressure in the mixer develops between the gap and that the maximum mixture pressure arises for the minimum gap. At any point along the gap, the pressure is approximately three times as great as the shear stress at the corresponding point. The following equations were obtained for determining these variables:

$$P_{av} = 3\tau_{av} = 3K\dot{\gamma}^n_{av}$$

$$\tau_{av} = \frac{2M_t}{3V} = \frac{10N}{\pi n_{av} V} \tag{93}$$

$$P_{av} = \frac{2M_t}{V} = \frac{30N}{\pi n_{av} V}$$

where P_{av} = average mixture pressure in the chamber, kg/cm^2

τ_{av} = average shear stress of deforming mixture, kg/cm^2

M_t = blade torque moment, kg-cm

V = volume of deforming mixture, cm^3

n_{av} = average blade velocity, rpm

For rubber mixtures of different compositions, the horsepower vs. velocity and floating weight is approximately linear, as shown by Zakharkin, et al. [47] and Starov [48]. However, in power-velocity coordinates, the slope of the approximating curve exceeds that in the coordinates of power-pressure. Thus, mixing intensity shows a greater dependency on velocity than pressure. From a mixture containing 30% carbon black and 30% chalk as fillers, the following empirical relation was obtained:

$$W = A + Bp$$

and $W = C + Dn_0$ \tag{94}

Table 4
Values of Coefficients in Equation 94

Rear Blade Velocity (rpm)	Velocity Limits (rpm)	Specific Pressure on Mixture (km/cm^2)	Limits of Specific Pressure (km/cm^2)	A	B	C	D
32	32–100	0.66	.66–1.32	4.05	0.57	1.25	0.1
50	32–100	0.88	.88–1.32	5.26	1.41	1.8	0.1
80	32–100	1.32	.88–1/32	7.76	2.41	1.25	0.12

where W = horsepower, kW
$\quad\quad\quad p$ = pressure on the mixture, kg/cm^2
$\quad\quad\quad n_0$ = rotational velocity of the rear blade, rpm

The values of the coefficients in Equation 94 are given in Table 4.

From a series of experiments, the horsepower calculation of any similar type mixer, where it is necessary to change the operating regime, may be made by using the following relationship:

$$N = N_0 + \frac{\Delta P_g}{\Delta P_d} \Delta N_p + \frac{\Delta n_g}{\Delta n_d} \Delta N_d \tag{95}$$

where N = horsepower at the new operating regime, kW
$\quad\quad\quad N_0$ = horsepower at the existing operating regime
$\quad\quad\quad \Delta N_d$ = increase in horsepower in the model
$\quad\quad\quad \Delta P_g, \Delta n_g$ = the prototypes degree of increase in pressure and rpm, %
$\quad\quad\quad \Delta P_d, \Delta n_d$ = the model's degree of increase in pressure and rpm, %.

The following example problem illustrates some of the principles outlined above:

Example 1

The blade speed of a 140 liter mixer is 30 rpm, and the pressure in the mixture is 5 kg$_f$/cm^2. The horsepower is 630 kW.

Determine the horsepower required to operate in a different mixing regime, where the speed is 40 rpm and the pressure is 6.65 kg/cm^2.

Solution

From the graph developed by Starov [48] of $N = f(P)$ for a model mixer, we determine the horsepower increase (ΔN) and pressure increase (ΔP), in %:

$$\Delta P = \frac{P_2 - P_1}{P_1} \, 100 = \frac{1.32 - 0.88}{0.88} \times 100 = 50\%$$

$$\Delta N = \frac{N_2 - N_1}{N_1} \, 100 = \frac{4.8 - 4.5}{4.5} \times 100 = 6.67\%$$

The pressure coefficient is:

$$K_p = \frac{\Delta N}{\Delta P} = \frac{6.67}{50} = 0.133$$

From a plot of $N = f(n)$ for the model:

$$\Delta n = \frac{n_2 - n_1}{n_1} \times 100 = \frac{40 - 30}{30} \times 100 = 33.3\%$$

$$\Delta N' = \frac{N_2' - N_1'}{N'} \times 100 = \frac{8 - 6}{6} \times 100 = 33.3\%$$

The velocity coefficient is:

$$K_n = \frac{\Delta N'}{\Delta n} = \frac{33.3}{33.3} = 1$$

The change in pressure for the new regime is:

$$\Delta P_d = \frac{6.65 - 5}{5} \times 100 = 33\%$$

The required horsepower of the prototype for this increase in pressure is:

$$\Delta N_d = \Delta P_d K_d = 33 \times 0.133 = 4.4\%$$

i.e., the required increase in horsepower for an increase in pressure of 33% is 28 kW.
The change in rotational velocity in the prototype is:

$$\Delta n_d = \frac{40 - 30}{30} \times 100 = 33.3\%$$

The increase in horsepower corresponding to this increase in velocity is:

$$\Delta N_d = \Delta n_d \times k_n = 33.3 \times 1.0 = 33.3\%$$

Thus, the horsepower for the new regime is:

$$N = 630 + 28 + 210 = 868 \text{ kW}$$

This is an approximate calculation; a more accurate estimate of the horsepower can be made by using Equation 95. To intensify mixing at the expense of greater velocity and pressure requires more powerful drives, and consequently, greater power consumption. With large capacity machines, the main portion of energy introduced is dissipated, and provisions must therefore be made for the evacuation of large amounts of heat. As such, calculation of a thermal regime is of great importance. The primary reason for a thermal design is to ensure that the mixture temperature does not exceed a pre-specified level that may harm the process or the products.

The largest portion of heat generated during mixing arises from the intense shearing action imposed on the viscous material. It is often assumed that the heat generation is constant during the mixing cycle for a fixed rotational velocity. This assumption must, however, be applied with reservations, because as mixing proceeds the properties of the viscous mass change. Kapitonov [49] reports that the temperature of the mixture first increases sharply, then stabilizes due to an equilibrium established between heat generation and evacuation by an appropriate cooling medium (e.g., water).

Most of today's commercial mixers operate in an intensive regime, and thus the mixing cycle is shorter than the time needed to arrive at a stable or equilibrium-state regime. Calculations must therefore be based on the principles of unsteady heat transfer. For design purposes, a relationship between the mixture temperature t_m, heat transfer coefficient h, and cooling water flow rate, G_w, is needed. The temperature interval can be assumed to be so small that the mean arithmetic temperature can be applied under the condition that:

$$\frac{\Delta t_{fin}}{\Delta t_{in}} < 2$$

where Δt_{in} and Δt_{fin} are initial and final temperatures of the mixture and cooling medium. The temperature of the mixture at the end of the ith-time interval is:

$$t_{m_i} = \frac{Q_g - Q_{ev_i}}{M_m C_m} + t_{m_{(i--1)}} \tag{96}$$

The amount of heat evacuated by the cooling medium from the mixture in time $\Delta \tau_i$ is:

$$Q_{ev} = KF\Delta\tau_i(t_{m_i} - t_{w_i}) \tag{97}$$

After some transformations, the following expressions are obtained:

$$Q_{ev} = \frac{\Delta\tau_i hFM_m C_w(t_{m_i} + t_{m_{(i-1)}} - 2t_{w_i}}{2M_w C_w + \Delta\tau_i hF} \tag{98}$$

and

$$t_{m_i} = \frac{Q_g(2M_w C_w + \Delta\tau_i hF) + 2\Delta\tau_i hFM_w C_w t_{w_i}}{M_m C_m(2M_w C_w + \Delta t_i hF) + \Delta t_i hM_w C_w}$$
$$+ \frac{M_m C_m(2M_w C_w + \Delta\tau_i hF) - \Delta\tau_i hM_w C_w}{M_m C_m(2M_w C_w + \Delta\tau_i hF) + \Delta\tau_i hFM_w C_w} t_{m_{(i-1)}} \tag{99}$$

where Q_g = amount of generated heat in the mixture for $\Delta\tau_i$ − time interval
   $\bar{h}$ = average heat transfer coefficient from the mixture to the water
   F = total heat transfer area
   M_w = water flow rate for $\Delta\tau_i$
   C_w = specific heat of water
   t_{w_i} = initial water temperature

Denoting the polynomials in Equation 99 as A and B, respectively, the equation for the first time interval is simply:

$$t_{m_1} = A + Bt_{min} \tag{100A}$$

For the second time interval $t_{m_{(i-1)}} = t_m$:

$$t_{m_2} = A + AB + B^2 t_{min} \tag{100B}$$

and for the nth-time interval:

$$t_{m_n} = A(B^0 + B^1 + B^2 + \cdots + B^{n+1}) + B^n t_{m_i} \tag{100C}$$

From Equation 99, the maximum mixture temperature at steady-state, considering the given cooling regime, can be determined as follows:

$$t_{m_{max}} = Q_g \left(\frac{1}{\Delta\tau_1 hF} + \frac{1}{2M_w C_w} \right) t_{w_i} \tag{101}$$

The output of a Banbury mixer is determined by the mass of loaded mixture, which in turn depends on the mixing chamber volume:

$$M = 60 \frac{V_\rho}{\tau} \psi, \quad \text{kg/hr} \tag{102}$$

where V = volume of loading, m^3 (typically 55–60% of the chamber volume)
         ρ = density of the mixture, kg/m^3
         ψ = operation factor (assumed to be equal to 0.8–0.9)
         τ = cycle duration, min.

The cycle duration is:

$$\tau = \tau_1 + \tau_2 + \tau_3 + \tau_4 + \tau_5 + \tau_6 + \tau_7 \tag{103}$$

where τ_1 = loading time
         τ_2 = time for closing feed hopper
         τ_3 = time for opening of hopper gate
         τ_4 = mixing time
         τ_5 = time for opening of discharge mechanism
         τ_6 = time for closing of discharge mechanism
         τ_7 = unloading time

Mixing time τ_4 is the main component and depends on the process technology and its intensity. All other components of the mixing cycle are considered to be auxiliary operations. The smaller the mixing time, the more severe are the demands for auxiliary operations. If the mixing time is 3 minutes, the auxiliary operations should not exceed 30–40 sec.

To increase loading operations, mechanical transportation and automatic techniques for dosing ingredients are employed. These mixers are provided with pneumo- or hydro-drives.

Consider the design of a *hydraulic drive gate*. The equation describing the gate motion is:

$$m \frac{dv}{dt} = P_d - P_{r.c.} - P_r \tag{104}$$

or $$m \frac{d^2y}{dt^2} = P_d - P_{r.c.} - E' \tag{105}$$

where   m = mass of moving parts

$$v = \frac{dy}{dt} = y' - \text{gate velocity}$$

         y = gate path
         d^2y/dt^2 = gate acceleration
         P_d = driving force from the pressure of the working liquid on the piston of the hydrocylinder
         $P_{r.c.}$ = constant component of resistance forces of the gate
         P_r = variable component of resistance forces of the gate.

The driving force is:

$$P_d = P_1 \frac{\pi}{4} (D^2 - d_1^2) \tag{106}$$

where P_1 = pressure of working liquid in the cylinder
         D = inside diameter of the cylinder
         d_1 = piston rod outside diameter

Pressure d_1 is determined from Bernoulli's equation, which is applied over two sections: the section at the pump discharge at nominal pressure P and the section at the outline in the gate-cylinder space at P_1; then:

$$P_d = A' + v_1^2 C' \tag{107}$$

where A' and C' = coefficients from Kapitonov [49]; v_1 = speed of the cylinder. The constant component of forces which resists the gate motion $P_{r.c.}$ arises from friction forces in the guides, and the friction force of the mixture against the sliding gate is:

$$P_{r.c.} = \mu_1 P_0 (1 - y)s + \mu_2 [G + P_0 (1 - y)s] = B \tag{108}$$

where P_0 = pressure of the mixture in the chamber
μ_1 = mixture friction against the gate
μ_2 = friction against the guides
s = width of sliding gate
G = weight of gate moving parts
y = length of the path covered by the gate

Despite variation in mixture loadings (which is equal to $P_0(1 - y)s$), it is common practice to assume the load to be constant both during mixing and mixture unloading.

During unloading operations, there are no sharp reductions in mixture level, and the amount of the mixture to be unloaded is proportional to the increasing area of the discharge opening. The variable component of the resistance force P_2 is determined by hydraulic resistances:

$$P_2 = E' + F' u_1^2 \tag{109}$$

where E' and F' = coefficients.

Taking into account Equation 109, we rewrite Equation 105 as follows:

$$\frac{G}{g} y'' = (C' - F')(y')^2 = A' - B' - E' \tag{110}$$

or $y'' + A'(y')^2 = B'$ \hfill (111)

where $A' = \dfrac{g}{G} (F' - C') = \text{constant}$

and $B' = \dfrac{g}{G} (A' - B' - E')$

Solving Equation 111 relative to time, we obtain:

$$\tau = \sqrt{\frac{A'}{B'}} \, L, \quad \text{sec} \tag{112}$$

and the gate velocity becomes:

$$y' = v_1 = \sqrt{\frac{B'}{A'}} = \text{constant} \tag{113}$$

To decrease the time of auxiliary operations (in this case the time of gate work), an increase in the pressure of the working liquid, a decrease in the hydraulic resistances, friction factor of the mixture against the gate, and friction factor of the guides as well as the weight of the moving parts of the gate are recommended.

Mixing Rolls

Mixing rolls subject pastes and deformable solids to intense shear by passing them between smooth or corrugated metal rolls that revolve at different speeds. These machines are widely used in the rubber and plastics industries. The principle design consists of two horizontal rolls or cylinders, arranged side-by-side and rotating toward each other at different speeds. The ratio of the peripheral speeds of the rolls, known as the friction ratio, ranges from 1 to 2 but is usually around 1.2. The higher friction ratios lead to greater heat generation. Friction, speed, and the sizes of rolls influence the cooling of the material mass and the intensity of its treatment. As such, data obtained from a unit are specific to that machine and cannot be applied to a different one.

Figure 15 illustrates the basic mixing operation. The material enters the mixing rolls in the form of lumps, powder, or friable laminated materials. As a result of rotation, adhesion, and friction, the material is entrained into the gap between the rolls, and upon discharge it sticks to one of the rolls depending on their temperature difference and velocities. The rolls are temperature controlled. The rolling process is also influenced by the gap between the rolls. In batch mixing rolls the mass after loading passes through the gap between the rolls several times, and is mixed due to their different speeds of rolls (Figure 15A). In continuous mixing rolls, the mass enters continuously from one side of the machine and passes between the rolls in rotational and forward motion along the unit's axis. The mix is continuously discharged in narrow strips (see Figure 15B). Both the shearing action and entrainment material into the gap are very important to the mixing process and in transporting the material through the unit.

Shearing strain is required in order to mix initially regular or isolated systems consisting of two components. The objective of this strain is to mix the system as a determined statistical variation of any of the properties of a series of samples to a minimum. According to mixing theory, three basic principles may be formulated:

1. The total component surface contact area should increase during mixing.
2. The elements of surface contact area should be evenly distributed in the mixing mass.
3. Mixture components must be distributed such that for any element of volume, the relative content of components is the same as in the total system.

Parametric calculations of mixing rolls enable one to estimate the basic parameters of the machine: namely, its productivity, the thrust forces between rolls, torque, and horsepower. The calcu-

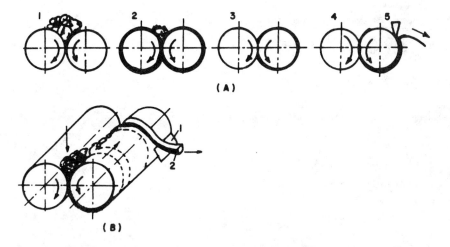

Figure 15. Operation of mixing rolls: (a) batch operation (1-loading, 2-rolling, 3-end of rolling, 4-mass shear, 5-knife); (b) continuous operation (1-knife, 2-continuous discharge of mass).

lation of these parameters marks the starting point of the structural design of mixing rolls. The questions of time and quality of mixing, the required number of passes of the mixture through the rolls, as well as the other mixing characteristics, must be established from industrial and laboratory experiments.

The issues outlined below are related to deformation and flow of polymeric non-Newtonian materials between the gap of the mixer rolls. An examination of the flow behavior in this region will provide insight into computing the basic parametric values which characterize the operation of mixing rolls. Figure 16 shows the basic scheme of the rolling process. The rolls act on the material by compressing and pushing it along the machine's horizontal axis. We define the rolls as having radius R, located at a distance $2h_0$ from each other, and rotating at velocity v. The material wedge thickness at the gap entrance is $2h_2$, and at discharge, $2h_1$. The hydrodynamic theory of this process is covered by Bernhard [45], Soroka, et al. [50], Bekin and Nemytkov [51], and Lukach, et al. [52], where it is shown that the streamline equation is obtained by integration of the following stream function:

$$\psi = \int v_x \, dy \tag{114}$$

where ψ = streamline (ψ = const)
$\quad\quad\quad v_x$ = velocity component in the x-axis direction
$\quad\quad\quad v_y$ = velocity component in the y-axis direction determined from the continuity equation:

$$\frac{\partial v_x}{\partial x} + \frac{\partial v_y}{\partial y} = 0 \tag{115}$$

Defining the following dimensionless parameters [45, 52]:

$$\left.\begin{aligned}
\rho &= \frac{x}{\sqrt{2Rh_0}} = \pm\sqrt{\frac{h}{h_0} - 1} \\[2ex]
\text{and}\quad \eta &= \frac{y}{\sqrt{2Rh_0}}
\end{aligned}\right\} \tag{116}$$

The velocity in the x-axis direction is:

$$v_x = \frac{3v}{2}\left\{\left[\frac{\rho^2 - \rho_1^2}{(1+\rho^2)^3}\right]\frac{4h^2}{C^2} + \frac{2 - \rho^2 - 3\rho_1^2}{3(1 + d^2)}\right\} \tag{117}$$

where ρ_1 = value of ρ at the gap outlet; and $C = \sqrt{2h_0 R}$ = constant.

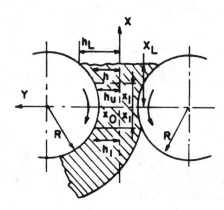

Figure 16. Mechanisms governing rolling process.

Substituting the value of v_x from Equation 117 into Equation 114 and integrating using the boundary conditions ($\psi = 0$ at $v_x = y = 0$), we obtain:

$$\psi = \frac{vh_0\mu}{C}\left[\frac{4h^2(\rho^2 - \rho_1^2)}{C^2(1 + \rho^2)} + \frac{2 + 3\rho_1^2 - \rho^2}{1 + \rho^2}\right] \tag{118}$$

The results of this expression are presented in Figure 17 for a series of ρ and η values. As shown in Figure 17, near the roll surface, the material flows parallel and the roll surface itself is the streamline. At the central zone located at the wedge entrance, countercurrent flow is observed. For a wedge of a final size, the countercurrent pattern takes the form of two closed eddies. This is the amount of material which may be observed in rolls of equal peripheral velocities. The material passing out of the gap sticks to one of the rolls rotating with it and again touching with the portion of the wedge where rotational motion takes place in order to enter in the gap.

The contact area increases very slowly for part of the material. As shown by Figure 17(A), the streamline $\psi = 0$ forms a closed contour which passes through the countercurrent zone where the velocity gradient is very small. Beyond the stagnation point the velocity gradient for $\psi = 0$ is equal to zero. Thus, for the case considered, the interface of one part of the material increased considerably slower than the one on the streamlines which pass through the zones of high velocity gradients. The elements of the interface are not evenly distributed in the mass. Since only the interface is oriented along the streamlines, the material stops to change its orientation because there is no motion across the streamlines. The existence of closed streamlines, as well as the absence of a distinct motion along z-axis parallel to roll generatrix are the reasons why the elements are not distributed evenly in the mixing mass. Even if it is assumed that the components are evenly distributed along the roll axis, there will always be some non-broken interfaces. Thus, the symmetrical rolling process does not provide satisfactory distribution of the ingredients.

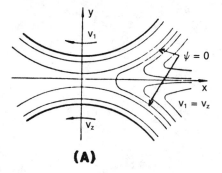

(A)

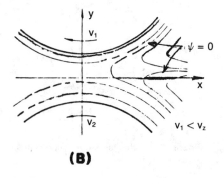

(B)

Figure 17. Streamlines in the gap of a double-roll type mixer: (a) rolls at the same peripheral velocities; (b) rolls at different peripheral velocities.

The mixing process may be intensified by imposing different velocities and temperatures on the rolls. The equations describing the flow in the gap between the rolls may be obtained by essentially the same method described by Lukach, et al. [52]. In this latter situation, a double integration of Equation 117 is made over the limits of $v_x(h) = v_1 > v_x(-h) = v_2$, where v_1 and v_2 are the peripheral velocities of the front and rear rolls. The equation of streamlines for rolling with friction is:

$$\psi = \frac{v_0 h_0 \eta}{C} \left[\frac{4\eta(\rho^2 - \rho_1^2)}{C^2(1 + \rho^2)} + \frac{2 + 3\rho_1^2 - \rho^2}{1 + \rho^2} + \frac{2\lambda\eta}{3C(1 + \rho^2)} \right] \tag{119}$$

where $\quad v_0 = \dfrac{v_1 + v_2}{2}; \lambda = \dfrac{v_1 - v_0}{2v_0}$

As follows from Equation 119, there is a closed streamline $\psi = 0$ at $\eta = 0$ (Figure 17(B)). In this case, the countercurrent zone is displaced to the roll with a lower peripheral velocity. It is important in this case that beyond the stagnation point, the streamlines pass through the zone of definite shear strain, and in comparison to the symmetrical rolling, the shear of material increases. However, even for this case, the streamlines are closed and the rolling with friction does not satisfy the requirements of perfect mixing, because the interfaces oriented along the streamlines maintain their positions.

To eliminate these drawbacks, the operator uses the technique of material undercut, and then introduces it again to the gap from the other side of the roll. The closeness of streamlines is violated and the material is displaced along the axial direction. The material undercut is a necessary part of the process in two-roll mixers, where in the case of a continuous process they are provided with a special automatic device.

The methods for evaluating thrust forces are based on the hydrodynamics of rolling, the theories of elastic and plastic deformation, and the theory of similarity. The Soviet literature gives detailed analytical treatment of this subject [51, 53].

Polymer materials mixed by rolling undergo both combined and total deformation:

$$\varepsilon = \varepsilon_{el} + \varepsilon_{h \cdot el} + \varepsilon_{pl} \tag{120}$$

where $\quad \varepsilon$ = total deformation
ε_{el} = elastic deformation
$\varepsilon_{h \cdot el}$ = high elastic deformation
ε_{pl} = plastic deformation

The plastic deformation of a polymer involves viscous flow with irreversible mutual displacement of molecules. The plastic deformation is highly sensitive to temperature.

Note that the relationships between the temperatures of different components and total deformation play different roles. From these points of view there are three different amorphous states of polymers: glassy, in the zone of lowest temperatures (in this case elastic deformation prevails); high elastic, in the zone of medium temperatures (in this case high elastic deformation prevails); and the viscous-flowing state, in the zone of high temperature (in this case the deciding factor is plastic deformation). The lower regions of elastic and high elastic deformation are best suited for processing polymers by the rolling method.

The law of viscous flow depends on the properties of the materials, and may be written as follows:

For a Newtonian fluid, $\quad \tau = \mu_a \dfrac{dv}{dx}$ $\hfill$ (121A)

For a Bingham material, $\quad \tau = \tau_0 + \mu_a \dfrac{dv}{dx}$ $\hfill$ (121B)

For a pseudoplastic fluid, $\quad \tau = K \left(\dfrac{dv}{dx} \right)^n$ $\hfill$ (121C)

where τ = shear stress
          μ_a = apparent viscosity
       dv/dx = velocity gradient
          τ_0 = limiting shear stress
   K and n = rheological constants of the flow (n — tangent of linealized section of the curve)

To determine the flow curve of a non-Newtonian material, the rheological parameters K and n must be known. Flow curves may appear linear on logarithmic coordinates over a portion of the shear rates. This means that the material may be more viscous over a portion of the shear rates and less viscous over others. These properties are accounted for through the coefficient of apparent viscosity:

$$\eta = \mu_a = \frac{\tau}{\dfrac{dv}{dy}} = K\left(\frac{dv}{dy}\right)^{n-1} \tag{122}$$

We now consider the method based on the *hydrodynamic theory of rolling*. The behavior of a polymer material approaches that of a non-Newtonian (quasi-viscous) fluid; therefore, polymers may be considered as a viscous fluid entrained in the gap by rotating rolls. In deriving design equations, the following assumptions are applied:

1. The flow regime in the gap is laminar.
2. The material sticks to the roll surface, i.e., there is no slip between the relative motion of the polymer and the walls, which limits the flow (the layers of material adjacent to the rolls are in motion at the same velocity as the rolls).
3. The gravitational and inertial forces are small compared to surface forces, and thus may be neglected.
4. The flow of material is assumed to be one-dimensional, i.e., the material passes mostly through the gap ($v_z = 0$; $v_x \geq v_y$ and $\partial v_x/\partial y \leq \partial v_y/\partial y$) as illustrated in Figure 18.

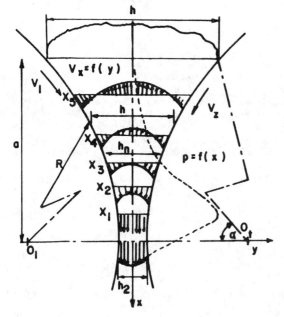

Figure 18. Pressure and velocity distribution of material in the roll section.

5. Hydrodynamic pressure at the polymer gap entrance and at the outlet from the rolls is zero. The pressure in the plane parallel to the roll axis does not change in the y- and z-directions, i.e.:

$$\frac{\partial P}{\partial y} = \frac{\partial P}{\partial z} = 0$$

The Navier-Stokes equations are the starting point in the analysis. Considering the system to consist of a steady plane-parallel flow of viscous liquid in the gap between the rolls and applying the above assumptions we write:

$$\left. \begin{array}{l} \dfrac{\partial^2 v_x}{\partial y^2} = \dfrac{1}{\mu_a} \times \dfrac{\partial P}{\partial x} \\[3mm] \dfrac{\partial P}{\partial y} = 0 \end{array} \right\} \tag{123}$$

where P = pressure.

In the zone of maximum pressure $\partial P/\partial x = 0$ (i.e., $\partial v/\partial y$ = constant). In this zone, the flow rate of polymer changes uniformly from v_1 to v_2 (taking into account that material sticks to the roll surface).

Upon integration of Equation 123, we obtain:

$$v_x = \frac{1}{\mu_a} \times \frac{\partial P}{\partial x} \times \frac{y^2}{2} + C_1 y + C_2 \tag{124}$$

Substituting the friction value $f = v_2/v_1$ into Equation 124 and applying the boundary conditions $(v_{-h/2} = v_1; v_{h/2} = v_2 = fv_1)$, we obtain (after determining and substituting C_1 and C_2):

$$v_x = \frac{1+f}{2} v_1 + \frac{1}{2\mu_a} \times \frac{\partial P}{\partial x} \left(y^2 - \frac{h^2}{4} \right) + (1+f) \frac{v_1}{h} \tag{125}$$

where h = moving coordinate (the distance between the rolls).

Using Equation 125 and determining the flow rate in the gap, the differential equation of pressure becomes:

$$\frac{\partial P}{\partial x} = \pm \frac{1+f}{2} 6\mu_a v_1 \sqrt{2} \frac{h - h_1}{h^3 \sqrt{h - h_k}} \tag{126}$$

After integration, we obtain a formula for determining the specific thrust force:

$$P = \frac{1+f}{2} 2.22 \frac{\mu_a v_1 R}{h_K}, \quad \text{kg/cm} \tag{127}$$

where μ_a = apparent dynamic viscosity, kg-sec/cm^2
v_1 = peripheral velocity of the roll, cm/sec
R = roll radius, cm
h_k = minimum gap between rolls, cm

The thrust force acting between the rolls is:

$$P = pL \tag{128}$$

where   p = specific thrust force from Equation 127
         L = length of the roll

The coefficient of apparent viscosity μ_a, may be approximately determined from the velocity gradient formula:

$$\frac{\partial v}{\partial y} = \frac{2v_1}{h_k} \tag{129}$$

From either literature data or rheological testing, a flow curve of $\mu_a = f(\partial v/\partial y; t°C)$ can be constructed and a value for μ_a obtained.

From the laws of plastic deformation of material between the rolls, the average specific pressure on the roll is:

$$P_{av} = K\sigma_T \frac{2h_{n.l.}}{(\delta - 1)\,\Delta h}\left[\left(\frac{h_{n.l.}}{h_k}\right)^\delta - 1\right] \tag{130}$$

where   K = coefficient, ($\simeq 1.15$)
         σ_T = yield limit of rolling material, kg/cm^2
         $h_{n.l.}$ = neutral layer thickness

$$\delta = \mu \left/ \tan\frac{\alpha}{2}\right., \text{coefficient}$$

         $\Delta h = 2R(1 - \cos \alpha)$, $-$ linear rolling reduction
         α = angle of material seizure

The thrust force is:

$$P_{th} = P_{av}B_{in}l_s, \quad kg \tag{131}$$

where $l_s = \sqrt{R\,\Delta h}$, the arch of seizure (see Figure 19A).

According to the laws of elastic deformation of materials, the thrust force between rolls is:

$$P_{th} = \frac{4ERb_H}{h_H} \sin \alpha(1 - \cos \alpha), \quad kg \tag{132}$$

where E = elastic modulus of material, kg/cm^2; b_H, n_H (from Figure 19B).

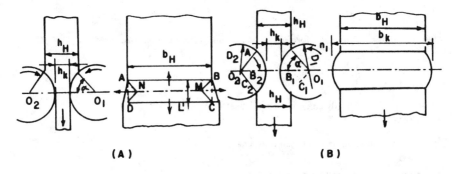

(A)   (B)

Figure 19. Deformation of material between rolls: (a) at plastic deformation; (b) elastic deformation.

From similarity theory, the following empirical equations which may be used for evaluating the thrust forces in rubber mixtures were obtained by Lukach et al.

$$\frac{P}{\gamma D^3} = C_1 B^{x_1} \left(\frac{h_k}{D}\right)^{y_1} \left(\frac{L}{D}\right)^{z_1} \left(\frac{D_1}{D}\right)^{k_1}$$

$$\frac{P}{\gamma D^3} = C_2 M^{x_2} \left(\frac{h_k}{D}\right)^{y_2} \left(\frac{L}{D}\right)^{z_2} \left(\frac{D_1}{D}\right)^{k_2}$$

(133)

where B and M = reducibility and softness of mixture
δ = specific gravity of mixture
D = diameter of the roll
L = length of material band on rolls
h_k = minimum gap between rolls

Coefficients $C_1, C_2, x_1, x_2, y_1, y_2, z_1, z_2, k_1, k_2$ are determined from experiments. Design equations for some synthetic and natural mixtures are also reported by Lukach, et al. [52]. For example, for butadiene acrylonitrile blends:

$$\left. \begin{array}{l} P = C_1 \gamma D^{1.4} L^{0.7} h_k^{0.1} B^{-0.4} \\ P = C_2 \gamma D^{1.4} L^{0.7} h_k^{0.1} M^{-1.8} \end{array} \right\}$$

(134)

The values for C_1 and C_2 are as follows:

	C_1	C_2
CSN-40	260	71
CSN-26	180	54

Determination of horsepower. As in estimating thrust forces, different methods of calculating torque and horsepower are available. The principle methods are: that based on the theory of plastic or elastic deformation, on hydrodynamic theory of rolling, or on the theory of similarity. The power consumed by mixing rolls depends on several factors, including the properties and temperatures of materials, the peripheral velocities of the rolls, the rate of friction, and the gap size.

The influence of some of these factors on the energy consumption of the mixing rolls can be made through the theory of plastic deformation. An increase in the peripheral velocity leads to an increase in the volume of material that can be deformed between the rolls. This results in an increase in the work of deformation. Changes in the peripheral velocity also influence the rate of deformation. Elastic deformation, which does not depend on time, does not play an important role. For highly elastic and particularly for plastic deformation, a decrease in the time of deformation results in an increase in the necessary load on the rolls, which in turn leads to higher horsepower requirements.

Greater friction results in an increase in the volume of material undergoing deformation, as well as in the rate of deformation, and consequently the horsepower consumed.

Enlarging the gap between rolls leads to an increase in horsepower requirements; however, the horsepower increase falls behind the gap increase. This can be explained by the fact that for larger gaps, an increase in the material volume passing through requires more work of deformation. On the other hand, as the gap is enlarged, a decrease in the linear rolling occurs which reduces the work of deformation. The opposite may also occur, whereby the role of relative deformation becomes determinant.

The energy consumption in batch operations may change significantly with time, due to the variation in the material's plastic properties. The resistance torque to the rotation of the rolls may be assumed to consist of two components:

$$M = M_p + M_f, \quad kg_{f-m}$$

(135)

810   Polymer Rheology and Processing

where M_p = the torque required for overcoming the resistance of the material deformation, as determined by thrust forces.

M_f = the torque for overcoming friction in the bearings with respect to gravity and thrust forces.

The torque for overcoming thrust forces in:

$$M_p = PD \sin \frac{\alpha}{2}, \quad \text{kg-cm} \tag{136}$$

where   P = thrust force determined from Equation 128
D = roll diameter
α = angle of seizure

The torque attributed to friction is:

$$M_f = \mu(P + G)d, \quad \text{kg-cm} \tag{137}$$

where μ = friction coefficient in bearings
G = roll gravity force
d = diameter of journal of roll

The horsepower can be computed from the following formula:

$$N = \frac{(M_p + M_f)}{9700\eta}, \quad \text{kW} \tag{138}$$

where   n = rotational velocity of the roll, rpm
η = efficiency of the drive

The electric power of mixing rolls reaches its maximum value only for a short time (within the first 2–3 min.). Therefore, the horsepower of an electric motor may be 1.5–2.0 times less than the value computed from Equation 138.

Based on the hydrodynamic theory of rolling, the horsepower consumed by the mixing rolls is established by the shear stresses arising in the material. The change of shear stress in the direction of deformation for a roll which rotates slowly is [51]:

$$\tau_{+h_{k/2}} = \mu_a \left[\frac{3(1-f)(\delta-\delta_0)}{\delta^2 h_k} + \frac{(1-f)}{\delta h_k} \right] \tag{139}$$

For rapidly rotating rolls:

$$\tau_{-h_{k/2}} = -\mu_a \left[\frac{3(1-f)(\delta-\delta_0)}{\delta^2 h_k} - \frac{(1-f)}{\delta h_k} \right] \tag{140}$$

where μ_{ap} = apparent dynamic viscosity;
v_1 = peripheral velocity of slow rotating roll;
f = friction;

$$\delta = \Delta = \frac{h}{h_k} - \text{dimensionless parameter}$$

$$\delta_0 = \frac{h_1}{h_k} - \text{dimensionless parameter}$$

h = moving width of the gap;
h_k = minimum width of gap (see Figure 17)

The corresponding section modulus from the forces of viscous friction is:

$$M_{+h/2} = \frac{3C_1 K\alpha_{ap}^n (1 + f) R \sqrt{RL} v_1^n}{\alpha_{ap_1} \sqrt{h_k}}$$

$$M_{-h/2} = \frac{3C_2 K\alpha_{ap}^n (1 + f) R \sqrt{RL} v_1^n}{\alpha_{ap_2} \sqrt{h_k}}$$

(141)

where α_{ap} = coefficient determined from the following formulas:

$$\alpha_{ap_1} = \frac{(1 + f)\sqrt{RT_1}}{1\sqrt{h_k}}$$

$$\alpha_{ap_2} = \frac{(1 + f)\sqrt{RT_2}}{1\sqrt{h_k}}$$

(142)

$$\alpha_{ap} = \frac{3(1 + f)\sqrt{RT}}{21\sqrt{h_k}}$$

where C_1, C_2, T_1, T_2 = experimental constants.

l = length of the roll

The total torque is:

$$M = \frac{6CK\alpha_{ap}^n v_1^n (1 + f)^2 \sqrt{RL}}{\alpha_{ap} \sqrt{h_k}}$$

(143)

The total technological horsepower is:

$$N = \frac{3EK\alpha_{ap}^n v_1^n (1 + f)^2 \sqrt{RL}}{\alpha_{ap} \sqrt{h_k}}$$

(144)

where E = constant
        L = length of the roll

The third method available for establishing horsepower requirements is based on similarity theory. The following equations were obtained for basic marks of butadiene acrilonitrile caoutchoucs:

$$\left. \begin{array}{l} N = K_1 \gamma \omega D^2 L^{0.6} h_k^{0.1} f^{-0.2} B^{-0.7} \\[2mm] N = K_2 \gamma \omega D^2 L^{0.6} h_k^{0.1} f^{-0.2} M^{-2.5} \end{array} \right\}$$

(145)

and for styrene-butadiene rubbers:

$$\left. \begin{array}{l} N = K_1 \gamma \omega D^{2.3} L^{0.6} h_k^{0.1} f^{-0.2} B^{-0.7} \\[2mm] N = K_2 \gamma \omega D^{2.3} L^{0.6} h_k^{0.1} f^{-0.2} M^{-2.5} \end{array} \right\}$$

(146)

where values of the parameters K_1 and K_2 are:

	K_1	K_2
Caoutchouc AN-40	0.11	0.0192
AN-26	0.1	0.02
Styrene butadiene rubber SBR-30	0.115	0.0145
SBR-10	0.084	0.014

Equations 145 and 146 were obtained on the basis of experiments where parameters were varied over the following limits: $h_k = 0.6 - 2.5$ mm; $v_1 = 6.28 - 18$ n/min; $f = 1 - 3$; $L = 150 - 1050$ mm; $D = 200 - 400$ mm; initial caoutchouc plasticity $\eta_a = 0.06 - 0.15$; the temperature of rolls and caoutchouc was kept constant over all plastification regimes (rolls were $45 \pm 5°C$; caoutchouc $80 \pm 5°C$).

Considering rolls as a double energy contour, the friction gear will transfer power that is slightly greater than that obtained by the driving roll. Part of horsepower may be transferred due to friction from a slower moving roll to the faster one. As a result, the horsepower required for the rapidly moving roll may exceed that consumed by the drive.

Torques exerted on the rolls are not equal. The total torque may be estimated from the following formula:

$$M = M_{d_2}\left(1 \pm \frac{K_{ci_2}}{f}\right) + M_f\left(1 + \frac{1}{f}\right) \tag{147}$$

where M = total torque
M_{d_2} = torque on driving roll
M_f = torque of friction on the bearing of one roll
K_{ci_2} = coefficient of circulation determined from the graph developed by Lukach, et al. [52]

In addition to the above, the influence of circulation patterns must also be included in the structural design of mixing rolls.

Another area important to parametric evaluations is the roll productivity. Rolls may operate in either batch (multiple passing of material through rolls), or continuous processes (single-pass of material through the gap of the rolls). The productivity design of mixing rolls should be done correspondingly.

Batch mixing rolls. The productivity of batch mixing rolls depends on a single-time volume loading of the machine, the processing cycle, the size of the rolls, and the operational factor. Productivity may be calculated from the following formula:

$$Q = \frac{60q_1\rho\eta_e}{\tau}, \quad \text{kg/hr} \tag{148}$$

where q_1 = volume of mixture for one-time loading, dm^3
ρ = mixture density, kg/dm^3 ($\rho = 0.9 - 1.1$ kg/dm^3)
η_e = operation factor ($\eta_e = 0.8 - 0.9$)
τ = time cycle, min.

The one-time volume q_1 is determined from experiments for each material and roll size. Preliminary calculations can be made using the following correlation:

$$q_1 = (0.0065 \sim 0.0085)DL, \quad dm^3 \tag{149}$$

where D = rear roll diameter, cm.

Continuous mixing rolls. Productivity may be determined from:

$$Q = 60\pi Dnhb\rho v_e, \quad kg/hr \tag{150}$$

where D = rear roll diameter, dm
   v_e = rear roll velocity, rpm
   h = thickness of material band leaving the gap
   b = width of material band leaving the gap

The average velocity of the material is determined from:

$$v_m = \frac{Q}{bh\rho}, \quad n/min \tag{151}$$

where Q = productivity of rolls, kg/min.
   b and h = width and height of band from the gap, dm

Complicated heat processes occur during the treatment of plastic materials in mixing rolls. Depending on the operating regime and material properties, heat flow may either be introduced or evacuated from the machine. The requirements for cooling or heating are determined by a heat balance over the machine:

$$G_m i_{in} + Q_N + G_c C_c t_{w \cdot in} = G_m i_{out} + G_{w \cdot in} C_w t_{w \cdot out} + Q_l \tag{152}$$

where G_m = amount of material to be treated per unit time
   i_{in} = enthalpy of material at initial temperature
   i_{out} = enthalpy of material at final temperature
   Q_N = amount of heat obtained due to transformation of mechanical energy into thermal energy
   G_c = amount of cooling water entering the rolls
   $C_c, t_{w \cdot in}$ = specific heat and temperature of water entering rolls
   $t_{w \cdot out}$ = temperature of water leaving rolls
   Q_l = heat losses of rolls

From Equation 152, the amount of heat absorbed by the cooling water is established.

$$Q_w = G_c C_c(t_{in} - t_{out}) = Q_N - Q_l - G_m(i_{in} - i_{out}) \tag{153}$$

The amount of heat due to energy dissipation is:

$$Q_N = 860N\eta_e \tag{154}$$

where N = average horsepower consumed by the rolls
   η_e = drive efficiency

The heat losses consist of losses by convection and radiation:

$$Q_l = (q_c + q_R)F \tag{155}$$

$q_c = \bar{h}_c(t_w - t_a)$, the specific heat flow by convection
$\bar{h}_c$ = heat transfer coefficient from a roll to air
t_w = temperature of wall of roll; it is assumed to be equal to the temperature of the material to be treated
t_a = temperature of ambient air

q_R = specific heat flow by radiation

$$q_R = \varepsilon C_0 \left(\frac{T_w}{100} \right)^4 \tag{156}$$

where ε = emittance, and accounts for the fact that one roll is covered with material
 T_w = absolute temperature of the wall of the roll
 C_0 = radiation constant of an absolute black body

According to calculations, depending on material properties, the amount of heat spent in raising the temperature of the mass from t_{in} to t_{out}, including heat losses, can be as high as 10 to 25% of the total heat generation Q_N. The amount of heat absorbed by the cooling water is determined from a heat balance equation:

$$Q_w = UL \, \Delta t_{av} \tag{157}$$

where U = heat transfer coefficient through the cylindrical wall.

$$U = \frac{1}{\dfrac{1}{2\pi K} \ln(d_{out}/d_{in}) + \dfrac{1}{\bar{h}\pi d_{in}}} \tag{158}$$

where   K = conductivity of roll material
 d_{out} = outside roll diameter
 d_{in} = inside roll diameter (diameter of roll hollow or average diameter of a circle passing through the centers peripheral channels)
 $\bar{h}$ = heat transfer coefficient from internal roll space to the moving water (determined by one of the equations of forced convection depending on the flow regime)
 L = roll length
 Δt_{av} = average temperature difference, defined as:

$$\Delta t_{av} = t_w - \frac{t_{w \cdot out} - t_{w \cdot in}}{2} \tag{159}$$

The method of heat calculations of rolls amounts to the following procedure:
First, determine Q_1 and G_c (a temperature difference can be assumed; typically $t_{w \cdot out} - t_{w \cdot in} = 5 - 7°C$). Knowing the size of the roll hollow (or the sizes of peripheral channels), it is then possible to determine the velocity of the cooling water in order to estimate the heat transfer coefficient U.
From Q_w, U, and L, determine Δt_{av}, and from Equation 159, calculate $t_{w \cdot out}$ or $t_{w \cdot in}$. For specified $t_{w \cdot out}$ and $t_{w \cdot in}$, apply Equation 157 to establish whether the length is sufficient for evacuation of the given amount of heat, Q_w.

PRINCIPLES OF RUBBER COMPOUNDING

Properties of Carbon Black and Reinforcement of Rubber

Carbon black belongs to an important class of industrial carbons employed as reinforcing agents in rubber and as black pigments in inks, coatings, and plastics. The large majority of carbon black manufactured for use in the rubber industry is used in tire production. The remainder is used in a variety of other rubber products such as inner tubes, conveyor belts, wire and cable covering, motor mounts, fan belts, hose, gaskets, rubber heels, and a variety of specialty elastomeric products for the consumer market. Type and loading of carbon black vary with the application and service demands to which that product is to be subjected. In a tire tread, for example, the resistance to abrasive wear is of major concern, and hence, highly reinforcing blacks are required. In contrast, in tire sidewalls and ply compounds, a minimum of hysteresis and low heat generation is essential, and semireinforcing blacks are generally preferred. Extruded articles, such as automotive stripping and glass-run channels, require blacks with structure that provides a minimum of shrinkage and close adherence to die dimensions during extrusion.

The preparation of carbon black-rubber "masterbatches" is common practice in the industry. Masterbatching consists of adding the appropriate loading of carbon black in the form of a slurry to the rubber prior to coagulation.

In plastics applications, medium- and high-color channel blacks are employed for tinting and to provide maximum jetness at low loadings. Carbon black is also used as anti-photo and thermal-oxidation agents in polyolefins. As an example, clear polyethylene cable coating is susceptible to crazing or cracking, accompanied by rapid loss in physical properties and dielectric strength when exposed to sunlight for extended periods of time. The carbon black essentially serves as a black-body which absorbs ultraviolet and infrared radiations. It also serves to terminate free radical chains, and hence, provides good protection against thermal degradation. Hawkins [54] has shown that clear polyethylene cable jackets degrade to brittleness after a 2-year outdoor exposure, whereas the same compound containing 2% carbon black (medium-color channel) shows no change after the equivalent of twenty years' exposure.

Carbon black is also employed in the paper industry in the manufacture of black papers, including album paper, leatherboard, wrapping and bag papers, opaque backing papers for photographic film, highly conducting and electrosensitive paper, and black tape for wrapping high-voltage transmission cables. This industry refers to channel black as "Paris" black. Both channel blacks and furnace blacks of appropriate jetness and wetting characteristics are widely used. The use of these blacks is particularly significant when conducting black papers are desired.

Black loadings vary with application, but a range of 2–8% by weight of pulp is typical. To obtain adequate dispersion, the black is generally employed in the fluffy form, and it is commonly added directly to the beater in a dispersible bag to avoid dusting of carbon black to the atmosphere. In other applications it may be added in the form of an aqueous slurry.

Carbon blacks are commonly used as pigments in the preparation of paints, lacquers, enamels, and industrial finishes (classified as high, medium, and standard color). In these applications, jetness or masstone is of primary concern. Jetness depends upon particle size; therefore, the coating industry uses a wide range of channel and furnace carbon blacks varying from 100 to 4,000 Å in diameter. High-color blacks provide exceptional jetness and gloss for automobile finishes and high-grade enamels. Medium-color blacks are used in industrial enamels, and the standard grades of black are used in general utility and industrial paints. The high- and medium-color blacks are prepared by the channel process, and the standard color blacks may be either channel or furnace blacks. Lampblacks and large particle size furnace and thermal blacks are also used in paints and other coatings. These are deficient in jetness; however, they provide a desirable blue "tone" to the coating. Color blacks are available in pelleted or beaded form, since the grinding techniques employed in the coating industry are adequate to ensure good dispersion of the pigment. Carbon black is also used in the lacquer industry in the form of masterbatch "chips." These chips consist of a high loading of carbon black dispersed in an appropriate resin.

Printing inks typically employ 10–12% black in petroleum oil. These inks are relatively fluid, and dry by penetration of the oil into the fibers of the paper. Both channel blacks and HAF grades of oil-furnace black are used for newspaper ink production. Inks for coated papers, such as those used in large circulation publications, employ flash-drying inks which consist of a volatile solvent, a resin, and from 15–20% carbon black. The ink in this application is dried by passing over a heat source such as steam or gas flames. In book printing, offset or lithographic inks are employed. These inks are characterized by maximum tinting strength and covering power. The oils used for dispersion are usually linseed varnishes, which are relatively viscous and can employ black loadings as high as 25%. Flow in these ink dispersions is induced by increasing the combined oxygen or volatile matter on the black's surface to about 12%, which reduces the yield stress of the ink. Other examples of carbon black applications in this industry are pigments in carbon papers, typewriter ribbons, and various synthetic fibers.

Carbon black is elemental carbon that is differentiated from commercial carbons such as coke and charcoals by the fact that it is in particulate form. Particles are spherical, quasi-graphitic in structure, and of colloidal dimensions. Carbon blacks are manufactured either by a partial combustion process or by thermal decomposition of liquid or gaseous hydrocarbons. There are many commercial classifications of carbon black, but all blacks can be generally characterized by their method of production; i.e.:

- Lampblacks. Produced via combustion of petroleum or coal tar residues in open shallow pans (typical sizes 600–4,000Å).
- Channel Blacks. Produced by impingement of underventilated natural gas flames (100–300Å).
- Furnace Combustion Blacks. Produced by partial combustion of natural gas or liquid hydrocarbons in retorts or furnaces (400–800Å; coarsest variety 1,400–4,000Å).
- Thermal Blacks. Produced by the thermal decomposition of natural gas.
- Acetylene Black. Produced by the exothermic decomposition of acetylene.

The various commercial grades and the specific properties imparted to end-use products via their incorporation depend on particle size (i.e., surface area), chemical composition and relative activity of the particle surface, and the degree of particle-to-particle association.

Carbon black essentially remains as a discrete phase when dispersed in mediums such as rubber. The extent of mixture reinforcement imparted to the rubber, or for example, the intensity of color imparted to a coating formulation, mainly depends on the particle size or surface area.

The definitions used for characterizing average particle size vary. Arithmetic averages are defined as:

$$D_n = \sum nd / \sum n \qquad (160)$$

where n = number of particles of diameter d.

A more meaningful definition is the surface-average diameter:

$$D_A = \sum nd^3 / \sum nd^2 \qquad (161)$$

Particle size distributions of commercial grades can vary from Gaussian to skewed.

Specific surface areas are evaluated by absorption techniques, and the arrangement of carbon atoms within a carbon black particle has been extensively studied by x-ray diffraction methods. Carbon black displays two-dimensional crystallinity, which is a structure defined as mesomorphic. Smith (1964) provides detailed discussions of the molecular and chemical properties of carbon blacks and graphite.

One of the most important properties of carbon black is its surface activity. Carbon itself has proven extremely useful as an adsorbent. All carbon blacks possess a distribution of energy sites, whereby those of highest energy are first occupied by adsorbate. As the adsorption process continues, less active sites become filled and the differential heat of adsorption decreases, eventually approaching the heat of liquefaction of the adsorbate at monolayer coverage. High-energy sites can be progressively reduced by heat treatment. At 3000°C, all high-energy sites are reduced, and the substance displays characteristics of a homogeneous surface of uniform activity. Carbon adsorption is treated in detail by Cheremisinoff and Ellerbusch [55].

Chain structure is another property of importance, particularly in terms of the properties imparted to rubber. In particular, extrudability, elastic modulus, and electrical conductivity of rubber vulcanizates are sensitive. As general comments, lampblack and acetylene black have a high degree of structure, whereas channel and low blacks are typically low in chain structure.

In the rubber industry, reinforcement by fillers, especially carbon black, is a major part of the technology. The relevant properties of carbon black include particle size/surface area, particle porosity, aggregate structure (i.e., bulkiness), the amount of carbon per aggregate, surface activity, and surface chemistry. Examples of widely used elastomers are SBR, BR, acrylonitrile-butadiene copolymers, and EPDMS. These are examples of polymers in which the molecular chains are not highly oriented when their gum vulcanizates are stretched. Gessler, et al. [56] sites examples where upon stretching a gum vulcanizate, the tensile strengths are 0.4 to 0.6 MPa, whereas when the same elastomer is compounded with 50 php of a selected carbon black, a vulcanized tensile strength as high as 6.5 MPa is measured.

The usefulness of elastomers greatly depends on the ability of fillers such as carbon black to impart reinforcement properties. The property of reinforcement is characterized in terms of the vulcanizates' stiffness, modulus, tear strength, rupture energy, cracking resistance, fatigue stress, and abrasion resistance. It is important to note that some fillers are non-reinforcing, but are instead used as extenders in rubber formulations to reduce raw material costs. Fillers of this type are usually chemically inert and have large particle sizes. Reinforcing fillers are the opposite, i.e., they are typically small in particle size and chemically active. Gessler, et al. [56] define fully-reinforcing fillers as those solid additives having mean particle sizes below 50 nm. The two principle additives are carbon blacks and silica. Solid fillers having sizes greater than 50 nm are clays, silicates, calcium carbonates, SFR carbon blacks, and a range of semi-reinforcing blacks that are usually derived via thermal oxidation.

It is important to make a distinction between the carbon black-rubber interactions of uncured and vulcanized materials. The effects of carbon black on such properties as resilience and stiffness will be different for these two states of the material. In the uncured state, the incorporation of carbon black results in viscoelastic changes in the rubber system. In the vulcanized state, carbon black incorporation causes viscoelastic property changes, which in fact directly alter the rubber network. The specific properties affected in the vulcanizate are modulus, dynamic properties, and hysteresis.

Commercial carbon blacks used in rubber compounding applications are usually classified in terms of their morphology (i.e., particle size/surface area, vehicle absorptive capacity). The ASTM nomenclature system for carbon black is strictly used in the U.S., where the first digit is based on the mean particle diameter as measured with an electron microscope. Other commonly used methods to test for classifying blacks by size are iodine number, nitrogen adsorption, and tinting strength. Important also are the shapes of individual particles and of aggregates. DBP absorption is the principle technique employed for measuring the irregularity of the primary aggregates.

The term "structure" characterizes the bulkiness of individual aggregates. Often when carbon black is mixed into rubber, some of the aggregates fracture. In addition to fracturing, the separation of physically attracted or compacted aggregates (microagglomerates) can occur. Aggregates can be held together fairly rigidly because of the irregular nature of their structures. Microagglomerates can also be formed during mixing. That is, high shear forces can cause micro-compaction effects wherein several aggregates can be pressed together. Excessive microagglomeration can lead to persistent black network structures, which can affect extrusion and ultimately vulcanizate properties.

Baranival [57] and Cotton [58] have studied aggregate breakdown in ball milling and roll mill operations. Both investigators report methods of predicting breakdown.

The relationship of carbon black morphology to the failure properties of rubber vulcanizates has been extensively studied. Strength properties are usually enhanced with increasing black surface area and loading. There are, however, limiting values. The upper limit of black loading for maximum tensile strength and tear resistance depends on carbon black fineness and structure, with the former usually having the greater effect. Coarser, lower-structure blacks generally show peak strength properties at higher loadings. In terms of the ultimate level of strength reinforcement for different blacks, structure is significant as a dispersing aid which may be attributable to better bonding between black and polymer. High structure is also important at lower black loadings, particularly for tear resistance.

There is some evidence that the strength reinforcing properties of fillers are directly related to modulus development. These properties are derived from the large stresses held by the highly extended polymer chains attached to the immobile particles. Boonstra [59] has related high tensile strength to energy dissipation by a slippage mechanism at the filler surface. This is supported by the fact that high-surface-area, inactive (partially graphitized) carbon blacks give very high tensile strength under standard testing conditions. Under more severe conditions, however, adhesion between black and polymer become important.

Andrews and Walsh [60] have shown that the path of rupture through a filled vulcanizate passes from one filler aggregate to another, which are sites of high stress concentration. One approach to increasing strength is to lengthen the overall rupture path. The finer the filler and the higher the loading, the greater the effective increase in total cross section. There is a limiting point, however, when the packing of the filler aggregates becomes critical and they are no longer completely separated by the polymer. Preferential failure paths between aggregates may then be formed. These, combined with the fact that a smaller amount of polymer is being strained, can result in failure. The level of filler-polymer adhesion is important, especially as the upper limits of loading (aggregate packing) are reached.

Filler-polymer adhesion is important to the amount of elastic energy released by internal failure. Strongly adhering fillers enlarge the volume of rubber that must be highly strained during the process of rupture. It is worth noting that the relative importance of different carbon black parameters that influence vulcanizate properties greatly depends on the conditions of testing.

Carbon black fineness is the dominant factor governing vulcanizate strength properties. Tensile strength, tear resistance, and abrasion resistance all increase with decreasing black particle size. Cyclic processes such as cracking and fatigue are more complex because they may involve internal polymer degradation caused by heat build-up. Beatty [61] points out that it is important to note whether or not the end-use application represents constant energy input or constant amplitude vibrations. The latter mode of service greatly reduces the fatigue life of rubber compounds containing fine or high-structure blacks. Beatty has reported no significant particle-size effect on fatigue on the basis of equal energy input.

The relationship of carbon black fineness to failure properties is not straightforward, since it is difficult to separate the effects of aggregate size and surface area. It is likely that both are important, since aggregate size relates to the manner in which the surface area is distributed. In general, decreasing aggregate size and increasing black loading reduce the average inter-aggregate spacing, thereby lowering the mean free rupture path. Increasing black fineness and loading can be viewed in terms of either increased interface between black and polymer, or increased total black cross-section (lower aggregate spacing). Both show a strong effect on tensile strength up to the maximum tensile value that can be achieved. Gessler et al. [56] measured the tensile strength properties of five blacks (SRF, HAF, HAF-LS, SAF, SAF-LS) in SBR-1712 over a loading range of 40–140 phr (optimum cure, room temperature). Figure 4A shows the positive correlation with total surface area and Figure 4B shows an inverse relationship with the average inter-aggregate spacing ($\bar{D}$). The values were derived from the volume fraction (ϕ) and the average aggregate volume ($V^{1/3}$) as measured in rubber. A simple cubic packing model was employed. Only the values up to the maximum tensile of each black are plotted; therefore, the actual loadings vary for the different blacks. The tread blacks exhibited maximum tensile in the range of 70–80 phr, while the SRF sample showed a peak at about 100 phr.

The ultimate value for tensile strength across all blacks appears to be determined by either aggregate size or specific surface area. Tensile strength can be improved to a limiting value by increasing the loading. It is not possible, however, to match the ultimate tensile of a fine black by increasing the loading of a coarse one, at least not without other modifications (e.g., improving the ultimate dispersion or the bonding between black and polymer).

Blends of two or more elastomers are used in a variety of rubber products. The compatibility of elastomers in terms of their relative miscibility and response to different fillers and curing systems is of great importance to the rubber compounder. From the standpoint of carbon black reinforcement, certain combinations of polymers can give less than optimum performance if the black is not proportioned properly between them. Note that equivalent volume proportionality of the black is not always desirable. This depends on the nature of the polymers and their relative filler requirements in terms of strength reinforcement.

The compatibility of elastomer blends has been studied by a variety of different techniques, including optical and electron microscopy, DTA, GPC, solubility, thermal and thermochemical analysis, and X-ray analysis. These and other methods have been discussed by Corish and Powell [62].

Microscopical methods are especially useful in studying the phase separation (zone size) of different polymer combinations and in determining the relative amounts of filler in each blend component. Walters and Keyte [63] studied elastomer blends by means of phase-contrast optical microscopy, where the contrast mechanism is based on differences in the refractive indexes of the polymers. Their work covered blends that included NR/SBR, NR/BR, and SBR/BR. Their results indicated that few, if any, elastomers can be blended on a molecular scale. They also provided direct evidence that fillers and curing agents do not necessarily distribute proportionately.

The term "compatibility" can be defined in terms of the glass transition temperature (T_g). Blends that have T_g values of the individual polymer components are considered incompatible, while those that result in a single, intermediate T_g can be viewed as compatible. Also, solubility parameters (δ) are considered a prerequisite to compatibility. In the category of compatible blend combinations, Corish [64] lists NR/SBR, NR/BR, and SBR/BR. Incompatible blends are NR/NBR, NBR/BR, and NR/CR.

The compatibility of elastomer blends can also be defined from the standpoint of interfacial bonding between the different polymer phases. The technique of differential swelling, using solvent systems and temperatures such that one elastomer is highly swollen and the other is below its θ temperature with the polymer chains remaining tightly coiled, can be used. Thus, the polymer below its θ temperature could be treated in the same manner as a filler with respect to the way it restricts the swell of the other polymer. A high degree of swelling restriction is indicative of interfacial bonding between phases, while the reverse is analogous to the dewetting that occurs with non-reinforcing mineral fillers in elastomeric networks. Also, the type of curing system is important in achieving interfacial bonding.

The importance of the proper curing system in blends of low-functionality rubber with more unsaturated or polar elastomers must also be emphasized. Large amounts of polymer can be extracted from blends when unsatisfactory curing systems (e.g., sulphur-ZnO alone) are employed. This can be attributed to curative diffusion, because it occurs whether or not the curatives are added to the blend or to the low-functionality rubber alone.

Good blending is favored by a similarity of solubility parameters and viscosity. For polymers varying in unsaturation or polarity, cure compatibility must be considered in terms of both properly crosslinking each polymer component and achieving satisfactory interfacial bonding. In contrast, the addition of fillers to elastomer blends can significantly alter the state of the polymer phases. Where large differences in unsaturation exist between the polymers in a blend, staining methods may be used to render the high-unsaturation polymer more opaque, to provide contrast for either light- or electron-microscope analysis.

To the point, the contributing aspects of reinforcement are dispersion, aggregate breakdown and interactions, and distribution between the separate phases of a polymer blend. For blends of dissimilar elastomers (e.g., in unsaturation, polarity, crystallization, or viscosity), problems can arise in achieving optimum black distribution in the end product. When fillers are added to elastomer blends, one very obvious change is a reduction in the size of the separate polymer zones. In other words, there is a preferential location of the black in one of the blend components. This phenomenon may be related to both molecular structure and relative viscosity. The great mobility and possibly more linear structure of one of the blend component molecules apparently enables better wetting of the black surface. This characteristic is often observed in SBR/BR blends. The lower initial viscosity of the BR would also tend to favor the acceptance of the black. It is, however, possible to alter the normal pattern of distribution in terms of how the filler is added, along with mixing conditions. Other polymer factors which favor preferential filler adsorption in elastomer preblends are higher unsaturation and polarity.

Another phenomenon contributing to reinforcement is carbon black transfer. This is the ability of a carbon black to migrate from one polymer to another during mixing. Transfer is favored by low heat history and high extender-oil content. Both these parameters minimize interaction between black and polymer. Hence, solution or latex masterbatches tend to favor transfer, while hot mixing in a Banbury does not. Black transfer also occurs when a masterbatch of a low-unsaturation rubber is cutback with a high-unsaturation polymer. Polarity is also a factor.

Carbon Black Mixing

As previously noted, carbon black is widely used as a reinforcing filler; however, the unique property of improving tear and abrasion resistance in rubber vulcanizates, particularly in synthetic rubber of the butadiene-styrene type, is not fully understood. It is likely that carbon black surface and rubber interact both chemically and by physical adsorption. The parameters important to this interaction are capacity, intensity, and geometry. The total interface between polymer and filler is expressed in units of square meter per cubic centimeter of vulcanizate or compound. The intensity of interaction is determined by the specific surface activity per unit area. It should be noted that adsorptive energies vary greatly in different locations on the black surface, and it is likely that this distribution is responsible for the variability in properties among different types of carbon blacks. Geometrical properties are characterized by the structure, which is basically anisometry, and particle shape and porosity. Greater anisometry results in looser particle packing. The void volume is used as a measure of the packing density.

Carbon black particles form irregular structures, which tend to break down during intensive mixing. It is therefore a combination of carbon black reactivity, rubber and black chemical, physical and rheological properties, and the conditions of mixing, which establish the final strength properties of the vulcanizate. As a rule-of-thumb, high-structure blacks (e.g., ISAF) impart a higher modulus (at 300% elongation) than a corresponding normal black. The high modulus is determined both by the anisometry and surface activity. The separate influence of these properties can be observed by heat treating these blacks at 2000–3000°C. The crystalographic structure of carbon black is altered by heat treatment and properties approach that of graphite. Through recrystallization, highly active sites on the carbon black surface lose their high activity. In this situation, the entire surface area becomes homogeneous, and adsorption energies approach their lowest state. Heat treatment typically results in a minor decrease in surface area and further reductions in tear resistance. Modulus and elongation can be decreased by a factor of 3 or 4. The decrease in properties can be attributed to the removal of highly active sites from the surface. Boonstra [65] shows that this is accompanied by a decrease in water adsorption and propane adsorption.

Microscopic examinations of thin sections of vulcanizate, in which carbon black or other fillers and polymer were mixed for a short time, only reveal that this additive exists as coarse agglomerates in a nearly pure rubber matrix, almost without any colloidal dispersion of the additive. It is only after mixing has been continued, either at greater intensity and/or for longer time periods, that one can observe how these agglomerates gradually disappear, making room for an increasing amount of additive. In all cases, the initial product of mixing is comprised of an agglomerate which is formed by the penetration of rubber in the voids between carbon black particles or other additives such as mineral fillers (e.g., clays) under the pressure and shear which builds up during Banbury mixing and on a roll mill. Once these voids are filled, the additive is incorporated but not yet dispersed. As soon as the agglomerates are formed, continuous mixing exposes them to shearing forces, which breaks them up and eventually disperses them. In other words, both agglomerate formation and break-down take place almost simultaneously.

The composition of the carbon black agglomerates is established by the void volume per gram or per cubic centimeter carbon black (or filler). This is the volume determined during an oil adsorption experiment. This value is determinant for the carbon black concentration in the primary agglomerants.

Boonstra [65] notes that blacks which are compatible in size and total surface area, but vary in structure and hence, void volume, require different mixing times to achieve the same level of dispersion. The reason for this is that since during mixing the voids between particles are filled, a greater void volume would require a longer time to be filled. Note also that for most commercial blacks, increasing structure is associated with increasing surface activity. Lower adsorption activity in graphitized blacks promotes slippage of rubber molecules on the particle surface, when filling interstices during black incorporation. This shortens the time needed for this process as compared to the original blacks. Easy incorporation, however, does not necessarily ensure good dispersibility. After a black has been completely incorporated, additional dispersibility depends on structure and adsorption activity. As a general rule, high-structure blacks tend to require more incorporation energy; however, once they are incorporated, less energy for dispersion is needed compared to lower-structure blacks.

An important consideration during the mixing and dispersion of carbon black and rubber is the degree of interaction between these two species, which can lead to the formation of bound rubber. These bonds are both of a physical nature (i.e., adsorption onto highly active sites) and of a chemical nature. The latter is described as a reaction of free rubber radicals with reactive carbon black surface groups, promoted by high shearing energy. A parallel relationship exists between the formation of bound rubber and shearing forces in a mixer. Figure 20 shows a torque-time response curve obtained from a Haake rheocord mixer. It is observed that bound rubber can be formed almost immediately during mixing. The maxima observed in torque during mixing typically signi-

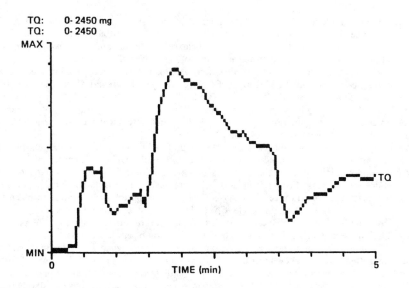

TQ: 0- 2450 mg
TQ: 0- 2450

Figure 20. Torque-time response curve obtained on a rheocord, suggesting formation of bound rubber.

fies that degrading forces exist. It is not clear to what extent bound rubber influences vulcanizate properties. Usually, cross-linking in bound rubber gel tends to be low. The formation of bound rubber is accompanied by an increase in viscosity. During bound rubber formation, shearing forces at constant rotor speeds increase due to this rise in viscosity. These shearing forces will affect both further dispersion of the carbon black and breakdown of the rubber. Vulcanizate properties eventually degrade after continued mixing due to a breakdown of the polymer.

The effect of fillers on crosslink density in vulcanizates can be characterized by either modulus or swelling measurements. A common problem in selecting the proper black is the difficulty of knowing whether the black interferes with the vulcanization, causing higher crosslink density. It may also lower the degree of swelling due to physical reasons, while the crosslink density in the rubber compound remains unchanged. A distinction can be made between adhering and non-adhering fillers, depending on their degree of interaction with the polymer in the vulcanizate state. Adhering fillers (most carbon blacks) tend to reduce the swelling of their vulcanizate in a manner that is proportional to the filler content. In contrast, non-adhering fillers (e.g., $CaCO_3$, glass beads) tend to increase swell through the formation of voids surrounding the filler particles.

Considering a noncrystallizing, unfilled elastomer, during elongation of the unfilled vulcanizate, the most highly elongated polymer chains reach their maximum elongation first and then break. When this occurs, those chains no longer carry any tension and hence, no longer contribute to tensile strength. As elongation continues, the next most highly elongated chains break next. This process continues until eventually only a few chains contribute to the final tensile strength. It can be concluded, therefore, that those materials displaying low tensile strength experience unequal distribution of loading. This heterogeneous distribution can be improved by wetting or slippage. For example, if the most highly elongated molecular chains do not break down and retain their part in the elongation, a more uniform stress distribution will result and the final material will be stronger. The mechanism of mobile adsorption can contribute to homogeneity of stresses. Elastomer chains that are adsorbed onto the carbon black surface will remain in two-dimensional motion on the surface without being separated from it. At excessive elongation, they tend to slip along the surface. In this case, the amount of energy per chain segment required for the process is lower than that needed for complete separation from the surface. Adsorptive energies are additive, and hence they can attain considerable values if a large number of successive segments are adsorbed. At the same time, while chains slip along the surface during elongation, distributed segments line up sequentially on the surface, building up tension that balances the elastic forces at a given elongation. The greatest contribution is derived from the points of high adsorptive activity.

The phenomenon parallels that of crystallization, which is naturally occurring in rubbers. Pure gum vulcanizates of crystallizing elastomers display greater tensile strength than elastomers that are noncrystallizing (amorphous). As such, crystalline polymers show only slight reinforcement through carbon black incorporation. Carbon black vulcanizates display a permanent set after elongation. In contrast, pure gum vulcanizates show little, if any, permanent set. This permanent set tends to increase with increasing filler loading.

As noted earlier, incorporation refers to the wetting of carbon black with rubber. During this operation, entrapped air is squeezed out between the voids of the rubber and carbon black particles. Early stages of mixing reveal that as the carbon black becomes incorporated, relatively large agglomerates, on the order of $10 \sim 100$ um, form. Cotten [66, 67] suggests that the time required for full carbon black incorporation can be determined by measuring the time required to reach the second power peak during a mixing cycle. Cotten [67] performed mixing studies in a Banbury mixer, observing from microscopic examination of rubber/carbon black compounds, the progression of black dispersion at different times. The rates of carbon black dispersion in this study were computed from the maximum torque data. A typical power curve generated by the author in reproducing Cotten's work is shown in Figure 21 using an oil-extended EPDM. Following Cotten, the rubber was first masticated for about 2 minutes, and then the rotors were stopped. Carbon black was charged in the chute and the mixer ram inserted, and rotors started again. Mixing times were measured from the instant when the rotors were restarted. The carbon black incorporation time was taken to be the time required to attain the second power peak shown in Figure 21.

Bound rubber in studies such as this can be measured by standard solvent extraction techniques. For example, toluene at room temperature or boiling heptane or hexane extractions can be used with a known alliqust of rubber sample. From a measurement of the residue weight, one can calculate the percentage of insoluble polymer.

The percentage (by volume) of unincorporated (nonwetted) carbon black can be estimated from density measurements. The volume of air in the batch (V) at time t can be computed from the

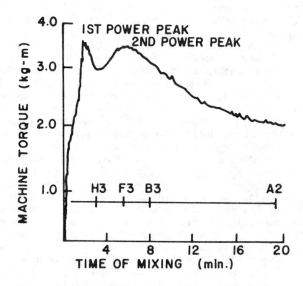

Figure 21. Typical torque response curve for the rubber mixing in a Brabender.

difference in densities (ρ' and ρ) at time t and the time at the termination of mixing when carbon black dispersion is better. The formula used for this calculation is:

$$V = (B/\rho' - B/\rho) \tag{162}$$

where B = batch weight (phr).

The first power peak corresponds to the ingestion of the batch into the mixing chamber. This coincides with the instant that the ram in the loading chute reaches the bottom of its flight and thus removes any additional hydrostatic pressure from the mixing chamber. Cotten has found that the fraction of undispersed carbon black decreases linearly with the time of mixing at the point where the second power peak occurs. At shorter mixing times, the compound can appear inhomogeneous and crumbly. Figure 22 illustrates some typical correlations for SBR. The mixing times can be observed to be inversely proportional to the rotor speed. When normalized, data tend to collapse to a single linear correlation. Cotten's work shows that there is a strong correlation between incorporation time and the rate of incorporation as computed from the slope of regression lines for change of densities with time for carbon black compounds in a single polymer.

The existence of a double power peak depends in part on the properties of the carbon black itself. Using pelletized carbon black will result in an absence of the first power peak, because no additional hydrostatic pressure is applied when the mixer chute is lowered (hence, the measured torque is no longer affected). The time to reach the second power peak, however, remains the same. Cotten notes that with fluffy carbon black, the time to reach the second power peak increases if no pressure is applied. Large agglomerates of carbon black form during the initial mixing stages, regardless of the type of carbon black used.

Other studies by Turetsky, et al. [68] and Smith [69] have shown good correlation between the measured black incorporation time (BIT) and weight average molecular weight, $\overline{MW}$, of polymers. Incorporation times will increase sharply with increasing polymer molecular weight. This effect tends to mask expected decreases in incorporation times when the Mooney viscosity is decreased through the addition of oil.

Decreasing concentrations of carbon black and increasing oil loading tends to reduce incorporation time. This is generally thought to be related to a lowering of the polymer viscosity.

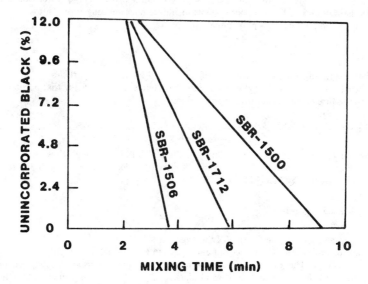

Figure 22. Correlation of unincorporated black with mixing time.

Typical filler-reinforced elastomers contain, in the rubber, filler, curatives, plasticizers, and stabilizers. After mixing and curing a masterbatch, both physical and chemical cross-linking processes transform the system into a network structure. The structure is composed essentially of two networks, namely, a stationary and a transient network. The stationary network comprises chemical crosslinks that are formed by both curatives and fillers. This network also includes permanent crystalline structures from crystallizable polymers. In contrast, the transient network comprises trapped entanglements and transient ordered structures. Payne and Watson [70] and Lee [71] have proposed two mechanisms that explain the reinforcing effects of filler in elastomers. The first of these mechanisms can be described as a hydrodynamic interaction in which the filler particles are responsible. The second mechanism is that of strong chemical interactions between the filler and the matrix. Both of these reinforcing interactions contribute to the mechanical properties of filler reinforced polymers. As noted earlier, the mechanical properties of engineering importance are the tensile modulus, tensile strength, and the ultimate stretch ratio. Tensile modulus is mathematically defined as the slope of the stress-strain curve at zero strain for a given masterbatch. Tensile strength is defined as the force at break per unit area of the original sample. The ultimate stretch ratio is the uniaxially fractured gage length divided by the original gage length of the filler-reinforced polymer specimen.

A problem in designing polymer structures for a particular reinforced elastomeric application is a lack of quantitative physical relationships, which define reinforcing effects of fillers on mechanical properties. Such constitutive expressions should ideally account for both the effects of fillers on the detailed structure and for the degree of mixing or dispersion of the masterbatch. Lee [71] has tackled this problem somewhat by attempting to develop a mixing rule to correlate these effects. Lee's study focused on establishing a relationship for the tensile modulus and the ultimate stretch ratio of the filler-reinforced elastomer system.

Smallwood [72] developed a simple relationship for the elastic modulus of filled rubber, in terms of the modulus of the gum E_1:

$$E = E_1(1 + 2.5\phi) \tag{163}$$

where ϕ = volume fraction of filler.

This expression is in fact the universal viscosity relation of Einstein. The relation accurately describes the modulus of filled rubber systems for dilute filler concentrations (up to 1%). A more accurate expression, based on a polynomial relation, is:

$$E = E_1(1 + 2.5\phi + 14.1\phi^2) \tag{164}$$

This relation accounts for the increase in stiffness caused by spherical particles.

For particles which tend to agglomerate into chain-like clusters, a factor that accounts for the asymmetric nature of the cluster must be introduced:

$$E = E_1(1 + 0.67f\phi + 1.62f^2\phi^2) \tag{165}$$

where f is the geometric factor defined simply as the ratio of cluster length to width.

From the concepts of occluded volume and effective occluded volume, a slightly more complex relation was presented by Lee [71]:

$$E = E_1(1 + 2.5\phi'_{aggr} + 14.1\phi'^2_{aggr}) \tag{166}$$

where ϕ'_{aggr} = effective volume fraction of the aggregates.

In the above expressions, the values of f and ϕ'_{aggr} can be deduced from a polynomial regression of the modulus data. The literature provides some working correlations for projecting compounding properties. For heat-treated and thermal blacks, $1.3 < \phi'_{aggr}/\phi < 2.4$. For the ultimate stretch ratio of filled polymers, λ_b, a 1/3 power law relation (i.e., $\lambda_b \sim \phi^{1/3}$) is applicable for some filled plastics.

From thermodynamics, the entropy of mixing defines the tensile modulus and the ultimate stretch ratio. For a given elastomer composition, different mixing histories give rise to different states of entropy. Therefore, a logical basis for defining tensile properties of filled reinforced elastomers is in terms of thermodynamic mixing rules.

As noted earlier, conventional mixing practices of fillers into different rubbers results in the formation of filler-rubber structures (e.g., bound rubber for carbon black filled elastomers). The specific filler-rubber structures formed affect the thermodynamic state of the elastomer system. This means that the reinforcement properties of the filler change due to the formation of these rubber-filled structures. Entropy of mixing for an ideal system can be computed from the Flory-Huggins equation

$$\Delta S'_m = -k_B(N_1 \ln \phi_1 + N_2 \ln \phi_2) \tag{167}$$

where k_B = Boltzman constant
ϕ_1 = volume fraction of gum
ϕ_2 = volume fraction of filler
N_1, N_2 = numbers of effective polymer chain segments and effective filler particles, respectively

The entropy of mixing for a real system is:

$$\Delta S^R_m = -k_B(N_1 \ln \phi_1 + N_2 \ln \phi'_2) \tag{168}$$

where ϕ'_2 = volume fraction of filler actually wetted by polymer matrix

Figure 23 illustrates schematically the difference between ideal and real mixing in terms of a hard spheres model. For real mixing, not all the fillers are incorporated into the polymer-filler wetting process due to the formation of filler agglomerates. Following Lee's [71] development, the excess entropy due to the heterogeneous distribution of the ith type filler in the rubber matrix after mixing is:

$$\overline{\Delta S}_{p-i} = \overline{\Delta S^R_m} - \overline{\Delta S'_m}; \qquad i = 2, 3, \ldots \tag{169}$$

And combining expressions, Lee obtains:

$$\overline{\Delta S}_{p-2} = \frac{\Delta S_{p-2}}{N_2} = -k_B \ln(\phi'_2/\phi_2) \tag{170}$$

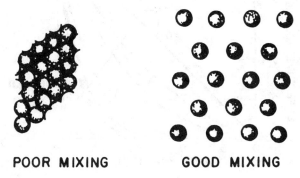

POOR MIXING   **GOOD MIXING**

Figure 23. Hard sphere-model illustrating good and poor mixing dispersion.

For an ith component system, $\phi_i' = \phi_i$, $\overline{\Delta S}_{p-i} = 0$, and hence:

$$\overline{\Delta S}_{p-i} = -k_B \ln(\phi_i'/\phi_i) \tag{171}$$

Equation 171 defines the case of perfect mixing.

Using the effective volume fraction of the filler, Lee proposes a semiempirical mixing rule to describe the relative tensile modulus of filled elastomers:

$$\ln E^{rel} = \ln(E/E_1) = \phi' \ln K \tag{172}$$

where   E = modulus of filled elastomer
$\quad\quad$ E_1 = modulus of gum
$\quad\quad$ ϕ' = effective volume fraction of filler
$\quad\quad$ ln K = reinforcement effectiveness factor

Equation 172 can also be written as:

$$E^{rel} = \exp\{(\ln K)\phi \exp[A(\phi - 1)]\} \tag{173}$$

where A is an index defining the degree of mixing.

The parameters ln K and A can be evaluated via a non-linear regression of E^{rel}, ϕ data. Figure 24 shows the relationship between the effective volume fraction (ϕ_2') and the actual volume fraction (ϕ_2) of the filler computed for different mixing indices, A, and zero strain. Lee [71] has shown that Equation 12 provides a good fit of the modulus data for different rubbers and carbon blacks. Different rubbers evaluated in this study were chlorosulfonated polyethylene (CSPE), ethylene-propylene-diene rubbers (EPDM), and polychloroprene (CR).

The effective volume fraction of aggregate, ϕ_{aggr}', can be correlated with the effective volume fraction of filler:

$$\phi_{aggr}'/\phi = \left(\frac{\ln K}{2.5}\right)\exp[A(\phi - 1)] \tag{174}$$

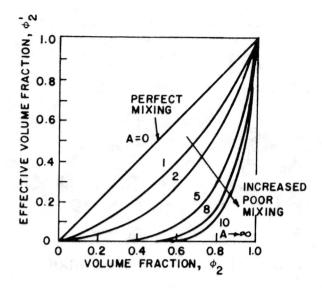

Figure 24. Relationship between A, ϕ_2, and ϕ_2'.

Using tensile modulus data, the relative mixing index for different elastomers can be determined (e.g., through A). This is a useful approach to assessing the degree of mixing of carbon black in different polymers, and hence, is practical for both the end-user in developing compound formulations for different applications, as well as for the polymer technologist in developing elastomeric products for customers. The mixing index A, based on tensile modulus data, is found to correlate qualitatively with morphological studies using the SEM (scanning electron microscope). Hence, the effective volume fraction of filler, ϕ', can be used for characterizing the nonideal mixing behavior of filled elastomers.

Increasing the concentration of carbon black results in a decrease of the ultimate stretch ratio of the compound stock. Also, laboratory tests show that the ultimate stretch ratio of a good mixing system is higher than that of a poorer mixing elastomer system. The reason for this is that the poor degree of mixing of the filler produces weak spots, which lead to premature failure (see Lee [71]). A relationship for the ultimate stretch ratio of filled elastomers based on a power-law expression is:

$$\frac{\lambda_b}{\lambda_{b_1}} = \lambda_b^{rel} = (1 - \phi')^{J/3} \tag{175}$$

where λ_b = ultimate stretch ratio of filled elastomer
   λ_{b_1} = ultimate stretch ratio of gum
   J = fracture coefficient
   ϕ' = effective volume fraction of filler

Nielson [72] gives the following expression for the relative percent ultimate strain:

$$\varepsilon_b/\varepsilon_{b_1} = (1 - \phi^{1/3}) \tag{176}$$

where ε_b = percent ultimate strain of filled elastomer (i.e., $\varepsilon_b = (\lambda_b - 1) \times 100$)
   ε_{b_1} = percent ultimate strain of the gum
   ϕ = volume fraction of filler

The problem with this correlation is that it does not account for the effect of the degree of mixing on the ultimate stretch ratios.

Lee [71] derived a power-law relationship between the mixing index A and the fracture coefficient J for conventionally mixed CSPE, CR, and EPDM:

$$J = 3.89A^{2.87}, \qquad \text{for } A \geq 1 \tag{177}$$

This correlation can be combined with Equation 17 to give:

$$\frac{\lambda_b}{\lambda_{b_1}} = \{1 - \phi \exp[A(\phi - 1)]\}^{1.30A^{2.87}} \tag{178}$$

This correlation is applicable for the range: $1 \leq A \leq 3$ (i.e., reasonably well mixed elastomer systems).

Latex-black masterbatching is another mixing technique where polymer and black are brought together, but in this case, both materials are in a finely divided colloidal syspension in water. SBR latex black masterbatches were first introduced about 45 years ago. Early masterbatches used dispersing agents to keep the black in an aqueous suspension state. Today, a continuous dispersant-free latex masterbatching technique is used where the black is maintained in aqueous suspension under high turbulence, while being brought into contact with the latex. Since the black has an inherently high surface area, it also serves as a creaming agent, which results in the production of a porous crumb that can be readily washed and dried.

In the dispersant-free latex production method, the parameters of importance are dry carbon black, oil, latex, and stabilizer emulsion. The initial procedure involves grinding the carbon black.

The black is then slurried in water and blended with the latex, stabilizer emulsion, and oil emulsion under high speed agitation. Oil is normally added separately to the mixer. From the mix tank, the material is sent into an acid coagulant step where rapid coagulation is promoted. The crumb then passes through a series of dewatering screens, filter presses, and driers, prior to being baled and packaged for customer shipping.

Critical to producing a good latex masterbatch is the ability to achieve thorough wetting of the black by the polymer. Good wetting also results in a finer subdivision of the carbon black agglomerates. The presence of large dry agglomerates (i.e., poor polymer penetration) of black leads to poor physicals, and subsequently, detrimental end-use performance.

It should be noted that although latex masterbatching conceptually results in very good filler dispersions, it does not necessarily provide a better-performing product. With adequate mixing, dry batch masterbatching procedures can produce compounds that are equivalent to latex masterbatching. One advantage of latex masterbatching, however, is the reduced need for costly mixing equipment.

Solution masterbatching differs from the latex process in that the polymer starts out in a hydrocarbon solution. In this case, water is added to this solution to form small droplets, which are brought into contact with an aqueous slurry of carbon black. The aqueous carbon black slurry is prepared using the conventional latex procedure. The two suspensions are contacted under high agitation conditions, and rapid phase transfer occurs as the organophilic black aggregates interact with the polymer-solvent droplets. The finishing end of the process is essentially that of latex masterbatching (i.e., crumb formation, dewatering, and drying stages). The process does, however, require an additional step of solvent recovery. Solution masterbatching (also referred to as hydrosolution masterbatching) has been claimed to offer easy final processing with better product uniformity over the latex process. In comparison to latex masterbatching, solution mixing of black has some advantages over dry mixing in terms of operational maintenance and less costly processing equipment. Scott and Eckert [73] and Burgess, et al. [74, 75] describe the process in detail.

SCREW MIXERS AND EXTRUDERS

Basic Design Formulas

Screw-type mixers, or extruders, of which there are numerous design configurations, are widely employed for the extrusion of molten or plasticized polymers to semi- and final-product forms. These machines are also used for preparing additives, such as resins for plastification, pigments, and others. Components to be mixed are normally doped with additives in a feed tunnel to the machine, thus providing a relatively homogeneous mass which is then extruded in the main working chamber (screw channel). Mixing and material extrusion can be accomplished in single or double rotating screw machine.

In single screw machines, mixing quality is established by the total shear of deformation for a given material volume. Shear deformation is a measure of the relative particle displacement, and as such, is equal to the product of the velocity gradient and the material's residence time. The total shear deformation may be increased by decreasing the height of the screw channel, by varying the angle of the pitch helix, and/or by increasing the countercurrent or sinks through an increase in the head resistance.

The shearing strain of any material element (e.g., a polymer melt) depends on its initial location in the screw channel. The streamlines of material displacement, and consequently the residence time and shear rate, depend on the element's location in the channel's cross-section. Material elements at the center of the channel undergo less mixing than elements near the screw's periphery or the channel walls. The reason for this is a smaller residence time for material located at the center of the channel. This can be illustrated by examining the velocity distribution in the working chamber.

There are two types of flows in the channel of a single screw-mixer: longitudinal (along the helical axis of the channel) and transverse (circulatory). Figures 25 and 26 show typical material velocity profiles in the longitudinal and transverse mixing directions, respectively. In the "melt zone,"

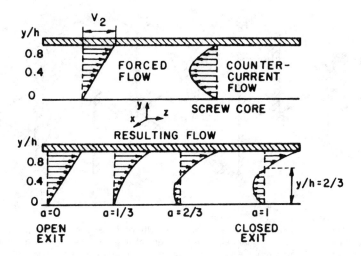

Figure 25. Velocity profiles along channel axis.

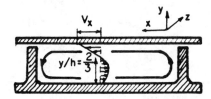

Figure 26. Velocity profiles for circulation flow.

there are four components of motion:

1. A forward motion of melt along the screw axis due to the screw's motion relative to the cylinder (working chamber).
2. A second component which characterizes the braking of the forward motion due to head resistance against the primary flow direction. This component, referred to as the velocity of countercurrent motion, is essentially an idealized phenomenon that will be shown later to simplify analysis of the mixer's productivity and flow patterns.
3. A component which characterizes the flow of sink taking place in the gap between the body and the external surface of the screw.
4. The last component characterizes material circulation in the normal plane of the channel, i.e., in the plane parallel to the horizontal axis. The circulation flow is in fact a transverse flow. The velocity distribution of the transverse flow does not depend on pressure in the head, but rather on the channel geometry and rotational velocity of the screw.

To realistically represent the velocity distribution in three-dimensions, it is necessary to vectorially sum the velocity components at each point. Figure 27 shows the velocity distribution in the flow region of a screw in a rectangular cross section. Given are values of the forward motion for the melt at the closed exit, open exit, and at an intermediate section. The plots reveal an insignificant displacement along the axial direction. Bernhardt [45] and Lukach, et al. [52] recommend Moore's equation, among others, for determining the shearing strains in the planes parallel or perpendicular to the screw axis. These equations can be used to evaluate the shearing strain as a function of

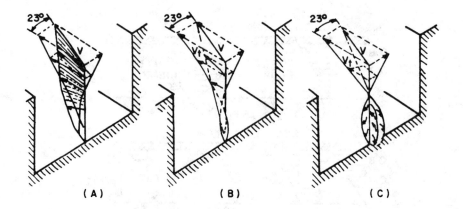

Figure 27. Three-dimensional representation of velocity vector and its two component at melt flow of polymer in the screw channels: (a) free exit; (b) intermediate regime; (c) closed exit (v-velocity vector of particle; v_t-vector velocity component, tangent to the axis helix channel; v_b-vector velocity component normal to helix channel axis).

material element location along the height of the channel (i.e., along the y-axis):

$$D_z = \frac{L}{h}\left(A - \frac{B}{1-a}\right) \tag{179}$$

$$D_x = \frac{L}{h}\left(\frac{A}{\tan\psi} + \frac{B\tan\psi}{1-a}\right) \tag{180}$$

where D_z = shearing strain in the plane parallel to the screw axis
 D_x = shearing strain in the plane perpendicular to the screw axis
 L = screw length
 h = height of the screw channel
 ψ = helix angle
 a = ratio of countercurrent rate to that of forced flow
 A and B = dimensionless functions of the ratio to the thread base and height of the channel y/h.

By integrating these equations over the flow's cross-sectional area, an average value of the shearing strain is obtained. Different configuration and size mixing nozzles are provided at the exit of screw mixers in order to increase the shearing strain on the extruded material.

Twin-screw mixers are more effective because they process material by the action of intermeshing screws. The material streamlines are interrupted when they pass through a zone of low velocity gradients with low mixing effects. However, overall, the bulk of the material volume enclosed between the wall of the casing and screw surfaces undergoes a highly efficient form of mixing. A successful modification of the screw-mixer consists of the working member comprising one of the screws and an interrupted helix (the teeth and gaps are located on the helix). These teeth on the rotating screw pass between the stationary teeth on the casing. Material between the meshing teeth is thus subjected to longitudinal, axial, and radial shears.

Another variation is the "KO-kneader," which can handle light and medium stiff pastes. In this design, a worm runs along a horizontal casing fitted with teeth. The worm is interrupted at regular intervals by gaps. The shaft not only turns, but reciprocates in the axial direction, so that the teeth periodically clean the gaps on the casing. This periodic reciprocation minimizes the material flow in one direction only. Note, however, that the intensive shearing strain in this machine is periodic, and the gaps tend to reduce the effective shear stress. The large surface areas of material exposed are a result of shear stresses generated by great torques. This limits the viscosity or rigidity of material to be mixed.

The first parameter of interest in design calculations for screw-type mixers is the rated capacity. In the case of polymers, this requires knowledge of the material's non-Newtonian behavior in the dosing zone, i.e., in its molten state. In some applications, separate estimates of the capacity of the feeding zone are needed. This is important in the prevention of pulsating flows through the machine, whereby the designer must establish a feed capacity to exceed that in the dosing zone. Standard design calculations are outlined below.

The first case of interest concerns establishing the *capacity of the feeding zone of a single-screw mixer for polymer processing*. In this zone of the machine, the polymer is normally introduced in solid granular or crumb form. The entrainment and transportation of solid granular material in this region depends not only on the equipment's geometry (pitch, rpm, helix angle), but also on the friction between the process material and working metal parts. The friction coefficient of plastics that are in contact with hot metal surfaces increases with increasing temperature up to the plastic's melting point and then decreases. Figure 28 defines the principal dimensions of interest in the transporting zone. The capacity in this zone may be computed from the following formula:

$$Q = \frac{\pi^2 D^2 \tan^3 \psi}{4} (F - \tan \rho'T)n, \quad cm^3/min. \tag{181}$$

where D = screw outside diameter, cm
   ρ' = friction angle of material against metal
   n = rotational velocity, rpm

The coefficients F and T are defined as follows:

$$F = 4.6 \log \frac{\sin \psi_1}{\sin \psi} + (\cos^2 \psi - \cos^2 \psi_1) \tag{182}$$

$$T = \frac{\sin(\psi_1 - \psi)}{\sin \psi \sin \psi_1} + \cos(\psi_1 + \psi) + \sin(\psi_1 - \psi)\frac{\pi}{90°} \tag{183}$$

where ψ = helix angle based on the outer diameter of the coil;

$$\tan \psi = \frac{t}{\pi D} \tag{184}$$

ψ_1 = helix angle based on the core diameter;

$$\tan \psi_1 = \frac{t}{\pi(D - 2h_0)} \tag{185}$$

$$\tan \rho = f \tag{186}$$

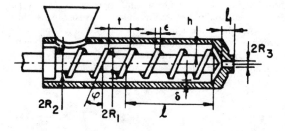

Figure 28. Important geometric relations for single screw-mixer extruders.

where   t = helix pitch, cm
         f = friction coefficient between material and metal.

The volumetric efficiency of the transport zone can be calculated from the following formula:

$$\eta_v = \frac{\pi D^3 \tan^3 \psi}{(D^2 - d^2)t}\,(F - T \tan \rho) \tag{187}$$

There are few data in the literature for establishing the optimum screw size and specific dimensions. Ryabinin and Lukach [76] report some specific criteria for this purpose, along with the following formula for determining the screw's critical rotational velocity in the feeding zone:

$$n_{cr} = \frac{42.4 \cos \rho}{\sqrt{D} \sin \psi \sin(\psi + \rho)} \tag{188}$$

The capacity of the dosing zone characterizes the rated capacity of the machine. However, this zone depends not only on the screw's geometry and rotational velocity, but also on the arrangement of the head. Capacity calculations for the dosing zone are recommended as follows: First, determine the geometric characteristics of the screw; then, design the capacity of passage through the head.

Capacity of dosing zone for constant size screws. For steady-state laminar flow of an isotropic non-compressible liquid, the equation of motion in the Z-direction may be written as follows:

$$\frac{\partial p}{\partial z} = \mu_a \left(\frac{\partial^2 v_z}{\partial x^2} + \frac{\partial^2 v_z}{\partial y^2} \right) + \frac{\partial v_z}{\partial x} \cdot \frac{\partial \mu_a}{\partial x} + \frac{\partial v_z}{\partial y}\frac{\partial \mu_a}{\partial y} \tag{189}$$

From Equation 189, the material's viscosity is a function of the location of each fluid element in the channel, and consequently, depends on both the temperature and velocity gradients.

If we assume that the fluid's viscosity varies insignificantly over the channel's cross section, which is reasonable for many cases, then $(\partial \mu_a / \partial x) = 0$, and Equation 189 simplifies to:

$$\frac{\partial p}{\partial z} = \mu_a \left(\frac{\partial^2 v_z}{\partial x^2} + \frac{\partial^2 v_z}{\partial y^2} \right) + \frac{\partial v_z}{\partial y} \times \frac{\partial \mu_a}{\partial y} \tag{190}$$

Equation 190 describes non-isothermal flow of a non-Newtonian fluid through the channel of the screw. Unfortunately, no analytical solution to Equation 190 has been reported in the literature.

If we further assume the viscosity to be constant along the channel height, the last term in Equation 190 is eliminated; i.e., $(\partial \mu_a / \partial y) = 0$. The equation then becomes:

$$\frac{\partial p}{\partial z} = \mu_a \left(\frac{\partial^2 v_z}{\partial x^2} + \frac{\partial^2 v_z}{\partial y^2} \right) \tag{191}$$

Further simplifying assumptions are needed in order to develop a working formula. Consider a fixed point on the surface of a screw. As the screw rotates, the position of this point changes relative to the cylinder, and the material is displaced along the helix line which may be considered as the screw's mirror image. From the standpoint of material transport, this situation is easier to visualize by considering the screw to be stationary and the cylinder to rotate in the direction opposite to the actual rotation of the screw. The cylinder's velocity, U, may be expanded in two components: T, perpendicular to the direction of the screw thread; and V, parallel to it. All three velocity vectors can be related to each other through the angle of the helix slope of the screw:

$$T = U \sin \psi \tag{192}$$

$$V = U \cos \psi \tag{193}$$

If the material's density does not vary under pressure, then capacity may be defined as:

$$Q = Q_0 - Q_c - Q_1 \tag{194}$$

where Q_0 = volumetric capacity of longitudinal flow
          Q_c = volumetric capacity of countercurrent flow
          Q_1 = volumetric capacity of sinks

The transverse velocity component (Equation 192) does not contribute to the system's overall capacity. However, where heat transfer is important, it does promote forced convection between flat layers of materials. In layers of high viscosity, natural convection is insignificant. The transverse velocity component is also important in applications involving the addition and mixing of fillers in polymer melts.

When the material is subjected to pressure, an additional flow pattern due to "leakage" arises. In this case, the material flows through a very narrow ring between the screw and the internal surface of the mixer case. Considering this ring to be an infinitely long narrow gap, Equation 191 may be restated to describe one-dimensional liquid flow under pressure:

$$\frac{\partial^2 v_z}{\partial y^2} = \frac{1}{\mu_a} \times \frac{dp}{dz} \tag{195}$$

Equation 195 is a second order homogeneous differential equation.

The constants of integration, C_1 and C_2, can be obtained from the following boundary conditions:

$$y = 0, \; v_z = 0; \quad \text{at } y = \delta, \; v_z = 0$$

From the first boundary condition, we find that $C_2 = 0$.
Using the second condition, we obtain:

$$C_1 = \frac{1}{2\mu_a} \times \frac{dp}{dz} \delta \tag{196}$$

where δ = height of the gap.

Substituting the expression for C_1 into the integrated form of Equation 195, the velocity distribution is obtained:

$$V = \frac{1}{2\mu_a} \times \frac{dp}{dz} y^2 + \frac{1}{2\mu_a} \times \frac{dp}{dz} \delta y \tag{197}$$

or $$V = \frac{1}{2\mu_a} \times \frac{dp}{dz} (\delta y - y^2) \tag{198}$$

To determine the volumetric rate, or the amount of leakage for a single-start thread, Equation 198 is integrated along the gap height. The obtained equation is then multiplied by the gap width $D/\cos \psi$ to give:

$$Q_y = \frac{\pi D}{\cos \psi} \times \frac{1}{2\mu_a} \times \frac{dp}{dz} \times \frac{\delta^3}{6} \tag{199}$$

or $$Q_y \, dz = \frac{\pi D \delta^3}{12\mu_a \cos \psi} dp \tag{200}$$

Integrating Equation 200 over the following limits: For the left-hand side, from 0 to l cos ψ (i.e., the gap length); and for the right-hand side, from p_1 to p_2, where p_1 and p_2 are the pressures on the sides of screw ridge:

$$Q_y \, l \cos \psi = \frac{\pi D \delta^3}{12 \mu_a \cos \psi} (p_2 - p_1) \tag{201}$$

$$\text{or} \quad Q_y = \frac{\pi D \delta^3 \varepsilon}{12 \mu_a \cos^2 \psi} \Delta p \tag{202}$$

where ε = eccentricity; $\varepsilon = 1$ for ideal centering of the screw in the casing. ε may vary up to a value of 2.5, depending on the friction of the screw against the casing.

For practical calculations, ε may be assumed to have a value of 1.2. The pressure drop across a single-start thread can be estimated from the total pressure drop across the unit (Δp_0):

$$\Delta p = \frac{\pi D \tan \psi}{L} p_0 \cos^2 \psi \tag{203}$$

Substituting Equation 25 into Equation 24 for $\varepsilon = 1.2$, we obtain:

$$Q_y = \frac{\pi^2 D^2 \delta^3 \tan \psi \sin \psi}{10 \mu_a e^{lo}} \Delta p_0 = \gamma \frac{\Delta p_0}{\mu_a} \tag{204}$$

The gap will typically account for about 10% of the countercurrent flow rate.

Depending on the size of the gap, the mean bulk temperature of the melt can be affected. As a rough guideline, the gap height should be approximately 0.2 to 0.3 mm in order to minimize thermal gradients. For radial gaps larger than 0.2 mm, the peaking layer of polymer will experience a temperature rise usually no greater than 10°C. For very narrow gaps, temperature gradients are more pronounced. For example, at a gap size of 0.1 mm, the temperature increase can be as high as 40°C, and at 0.05 mm, it may be 100°C. The designer should always check the gap size in screw mixers, particularly for those materials that are susceptible to thermal destruction.

The radial gap has no influence on the total horsepower requirements. However, if leakage rates exceed 10% of the countercurrent flow, mixer capacity suffers. It is the forced flow along the axis of the screw that basically establishes the unit's capacity. This flow is strongly dependent on the conditional countercurrent flow. Both flows are described by the following differential equation:

$$\frac{d^2 v}{dy^2} + \frac{d^2 v}{dx^2} = \frac{1}{\mu} \frac{dp}{dz} \tag{205}$$

As shown by Equation 205, the material's velocity at any point along the screw axis depends on the local depth (i.e., the flowing fluid's free surface profile). The two-dimensional velocity distribution given by this equation is difficult to solve, even for the simplest of screw geometries, due to the complexity of flow patterns. To simplify the expression, we may assume that the channel walls do not influence the velocity distribution. This is a limiting case assumption, analogous to flow between infinite parallel plates. Equation 205 then reduces to a one-dimensional expression for the velocity profile. For relatively shallow channels, this is a good approximation. For aspect ratios (i.e., ratio of channel width to mean depth) greater than or equal to 10, the absolute error between predicted and measured profiles is no more than 10 percent.

To derive the one-dimensional velocity distribution, the second derivative along the x-axis in Equation 205 is taken to be zero:

$$\frac{d^2 v}{dy^2} = \frac{1}{\mu_a} \frac{dp}{dz} \tag{206}$$

The equation is solved to give:

$$v = \frac{1}{\mu_a} \times \frac{dp}{dz} \times \frac{y^2}{2} + C_1 y + C_2 \qquad (207)$$

The boundary conditions for C_1 and C_2 are:

at $y = 0$, $v = 0$;   at $y = h$, $v = v_0$

Thus $C_1 = \dfrac{v_0}{h} - \dfrac{1}{\mu_a} \dfrac{dp}{dz} \times \dfrac{h}{2}$ (208)

and $v = \dfrac{v_0 y}{h} + \dfrac{(y^2 - hy)}{2\mu_a} \times \dfrac{dp}{dz}$ (209)

The first term in Equation 209 is the longitudinal or forced flow velocity. The second term describes the countercurrent flow.

The forced flow follows a linear law, whereas the countercurrent flow is defined by a parabolic relationship. The volumetric velocity in this case is:

$$Q = \int_0^h bv \, dy \qquad (210)$$

where b = channel width:

$b = (t - e) \cos \psi$

$t = $ helix pitch   (211)

$\psi = $ helix angle

or $Q = \dfrac{bh}{2} v_0 - \dfrac{bh^3}{12\mu_a} \times \dfrac{dp}{dz}$ (212)

The first term on the right-hand side of Equation 212 is the volumetric rate of longitudinal (forced) flow, and the second term is the volumetric counter current flow.

The linear velocity at rotation is $U = (\pi Dn)/60$, and its component is:

$$v_0 = \frac{\pi Dn}{60} \cos \psi, \quad \text{cm/sec} \qquad (213)$$

where   D = outside diameter of the screw, cm
             n = rotational velocity, rpm

Taking into account the relations for v_0 and b, we obtain:

$$Q = \frac{\pi Dnh(t - e) \cos^2 \psi}{120} - \frac{h^3(t - e) \cos \psi}{12\mu_a} \times \frac{dp}{dz} \qquad (214)$$

where z = axis along the helical channel of the screw; it is convenient to change it by the longitudinal axis of the screw; x. Then:

$$dz = \frac{dx}{\sin \psi} \qquad (215)$$

The volumetric capacity thus becomes:

$$Q = \frac{\pi Dn(t-e)\cos^2\psi}{120} - \frac{h^3(t-e)\sin^2\psi}{24\mu_a} \times \frac{dp}{dz} \tag{216}$$

The volumetric capacity of a multithreaded screw having constant size is expressed by the following equation:

$$Q = \frac{i\pi Dnh\left(\frac{t}{i}-e\right)\cos^2\psi}{120} - \frac{ih^3\left(\frac{t}{i}-e\right)\sin^2\psi}{24\mu_a l_0}\,p_0 \tag{217}$$

or $\quad Q = \alpha n - \beta \dfrac{\Delta p_0}{\mu_a} \tag{218}$

Taking into account leakage:

$$Q = \alpha n - \beta \frac{\Delta p_0}{\mu_a} - \gamma \frac{\Delta p_0}{\mu_a} \tag{219}$$

where   i = number of threads
        D = outside diameter of the screw
        h = thread depth
        n = rotational velocity of the screw
        t = helix pitch
        e = thread width
        ψ = helix angle
        l_0 = zone length
        α = coefficient of the injection flow
        β = coefficient of countercurrent flow
        γ = coefficient of leaking

Equation 219 characterizes the flow in a screw channel of constant dimension and geometry.

Dosing zone capacity of screws of variable pitch. The efficiency of a screw mixer varies with the volume of the pitch in the helical channel of the screw. The volume reduces in the direction from the inlet hopper to the extruder head. Capacity can be computed from the following formula:

$$Q = \alpha_1 n - \frac{\beta_1 + \gamma_1}{\mu_a}\Delta p_0, \quad cm^3/min \tag{220}$$

where α_1 = coefficient of flow injection:

$$\alpha_1 = \frac{\pi^3 D(D-h)^2 hJ_1}{2\pi^2(D-h)J_2 - J_3} \tag{221}$$

β_1 = coefficient of countercurrent flow:

$$\beta_1 = \frac{h^3\pi(D-h)\,\Delta t}{3|4\pi^2(D-h)^2J_2 - J_3|} \tag{222}$$

γ_1 = coefficient of leaking:

$$\gamma_1 = \frac{\pi D^2 \delta^3 \, \Delta t}{5e(D - h)\{\pi(D - h)J_4 + tJ_5\}} \tag{223}$$

where
n = rotational velocity
μ_a = apparent viscosity
Δ_{po} = pressure drop over the screw
D = screw outside diameter
h = depth of screw thread

Δt = pitch increment along screw length, defined as $\Delta t = \dfrac{t_{in} - t_{out}}{m - 1}$

δ = gap between screw threads and case
J_1, J_2, J_3, J_4, J_5 = coefficients characterizing a screw design having variable pitch

$$J_1 = t_{in} - t_{out} + \Delta t \cdot 2.3 \log(t_{in}/t_{out}) \tag{224}$$

$$J_2 = \frac{\Delta t + 2e}{2e} \cdot 2.3 \log\left(\frac{t_{in} - e}{t_{out} - e}\right) - \frac{\Delta t}{2e} \cdot 2.3 \log\left(\frac{t_{in}}{t_{out}}\right) \tag{225}$$

$$J_3 = (t_{in} - t_{out})(t_{in} - t_{out} + 2\,\Delta t + 6e) + 4.6e(\Delta t + 2e) \log\left(\frac{t_{in} - e}{t_{out} - e}\right) \tag{226}$$

$$J_4 = 2.3 \log\left(\frac{\tan \psi_{in}/2}{\tan \psi_{out}/2}\right) + 2 \frac{\sin \dfrac{\psi_{in} + \psi_{out}}{2} \sin \dfrac{\psi_{in} - \psi_{out}}{2}}{\cos \psi_{in} \cos \psi_{out}} \tag{227}$$

$$J_5 = 2 \frac{\cos \dfrac{\psi_{in} + \psi_{out}}{2} \cos \dfrac{\psi_{in} - \psi_{out}}{2}}{\sin \psi_{in} \sin \psi_{out}} - 2.3 \log\left\{\frac{\tan \dfrac{90 - \psi_{in}}{2}}{\tan \dfrac{90 - \psi_{out}}{2}}\right\} \tag{228}$$

where
t_{in} = initial screw pitch
t_{out} = outlet screw pitch
ψ_{in} = initial helix angle
ψ_{out} = outlet helix angle

m = number of pitches; $m = \dfrac{2e}{t_{in} + t_{out}}$

e = width of screw thread
l = total length of the screw

Dosing zone capacity of screws with variable depth. The volume of material in the mixer chamber decreases along the length of the helical pitch due to a decrease in depth. A decreasing material profile is observed in mixer designs where the conical core diameter of the screw is a maximum at the head of the mixer. The channel depth along the axis of the mixer can be approximated by the following linear relation:

$$h_x = h_1 - (h_1 - h_2)\frac{x}{l} \tag{229}$$

where h_1 = depth of helix channel at $x_2 = 0$, i.e., at the entrance to the zone where the material starts melting

h_2 = depth of helix channel at $x_1 = 1$, i.e., at the end of the channel, near the head.

Defining the rate of compression as:

$$i' = \frac{V_{in}}{V_{out}} \qquad (230)$$

and $h_1 = 0.155D \qquad (231)$

The available chamber volume per screw pitch at the loading funnel is then:

$$V_{in} = \frac{\pi(D^2 - d_1^2)}{4}(t - e) \qquad (232)$$

where D = outside diameter of the screw
d_1 = core diameter

The available chamber volume per screw pitch at the head is:

$$V_{out} = \frac{\pi(D^2 - d_2^2)}{4}(t - e) \qquad (233)$$

where d_2 = core diameter at the head; $d_2 = D - 2H_2$
The rate of compression is given as:

$$i' = \frac{h_1(D - h_1)}{h_2(D - h_2)} \qquad (234)$$

The total capacity of the screw with variable core depth is:

$$Q = \alpha_2 n - \frac{(\beta_2 + \beta_2)}{\mu_a}\Delta p, \quad cm^3/min \qquad (235)$$

where n = screw's rotational velocity
μ_a = apparent viscosity
Δp = pressure drop over the limits of the screw
α_2 = coefficient of injecting flow

$$\alpha_2 = \frac{\pi^3(t - \lambda e)\sigma}{a + t^2 b}, \quad cm^3 \qquad (236)$$

σ = constant based on screw dimensions:

$$\sigma = 1 - \frac{6.9D}{2(h_{out} - h_2)}\log\frac{h_{out}}{h_2} + \frac{D^2}{2h_{out}h_2} \qquad (237)$$

β_2 = coefficient of countercurrent flow:

$$\beta_2 = \frac{\pi t(t - \lambda e)}{12L_{in}(a + t^2 b)}, \quad cm^3 \qquad (238)$$

γ_2 = coefficient of leaking:

$$\gamma_2 = \frac{\pi D\, \delta t^2}{10 e L_{in} \sqrt{\pi D^2 + t^2}}, \quad cm^3 \tag{239}$$

a, b are coefficients characterizing a mixer with variable core dimensions:

$$a = \frac{\pi^2}{h_{in} h_z}\left(\frac{D(h_{in} + h_z)}{2 h_{in} h_z} - 1\right), \quad cm^{-2} \tag{240}$$

$$b = \frac{2.3}{(h_{in} - h_z)} \log \frac{h_{in}(D + d_2)}{h_z(D + d_1)} + \frac{2 h_{in} h_z + (h_{in} + h_z)D}{2 D^2 h_{in}^2 h_2^2}, \quad cm^{-4} \tag{241}$$

$$h_{in} = h_1 - \frac{h_1 - h_z}{L} L_0 = h_1(0.6 \sim 0.4)(h_1 - h_2) \tag{242}$$

ψ = helix angle based on the screw's outer diameter

Dosing zone capacity and head resistance. A screw mixer's operation depends not only on the geometry of working parts and their boundaries, but also on the geometry of the head and profiling elements.

The volumetric flow capacity through the head or some other device at the mixer's inlet is directly proportional to pressure drop and inversely proportional to the material's dynamic viscosity:

$$Q = K \frac{\Delta p}{\mu} \tag{243}$$

Combining Equation 243 with Equations 219, 220, and 235, we obtain:

$$Q = \frac{\alpha K}{k + \beta + \gamma} n \tag{244}$$

$$Q = \frac{\alpha_1 K}{k + \beta_1 + \gamma_1} n \tag{245}$$

$$Q = \frac{\alpha_2 K}{k + \beta_2 + \gamma_2} n \tag{246}$$

where K = coefficient depending on head geometry, cm^3.

From information on K for different screw mixer heads, the capacity of a screw mixer can be readily determined. Figure 5 shows the relationships for volumetric capacity in terms of different process parameters. Figure 29A shows that the capacity of the head and screw increases as a function of pressure induced by the screw. The working point A is the intersection of the head characteristics (line 1) with the screw characteristics (line 2). Figure 29B shows that the capacity of the head and screw is process dependent. Curves 1 and 4 characterize an adiabatic process, and curves 2 and 3 show the change in capacity for an isothermal process. The region limited by curves 1, 2, 3, and 4 represents a polytropic mixer operation.

Figure 29C shows the location of the working points of the mixer which depend on the head resistance (curves K_1 and K_2) and rotational velocity (curves n_1 and n_2). Figure 29D shows the influence of material temperature on mixer capacity. In this plot, the characteristics of the screw and head are represented at temperatures T_1 and T_2 (where $T_2 > T_1$). If the melt temperatures in the screw and head are the same and equal to T_2, the regime of the mixer is determined by point

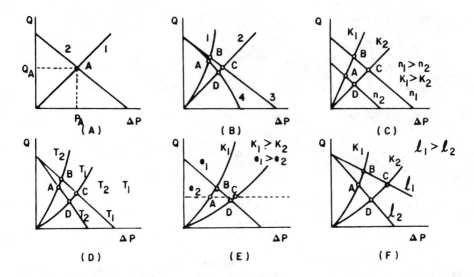

Figure 29. Relationship between capacity and pressure drop.

1. By simultaneously decreasing the melt temperature in the screw and the head to value T_1, the pressure in the head will increase up to point C. The capacity in this case will remain unchanged. However, if the melt temperature in the screw is T_2, but the temperature in the head is decreased to T_1, capacity will decrease to some value as denoted by point D. On the other hand, if the melt temperature in the screw is T_1 and the head is heated to the higher temperature T_2, the mixer's capacity is increased slightly and is given by point B.

Figure 29E illustrates capacity in the screw and the head as a function of the depth of the helical channel (e_1-deep channel, e_2-shallow channel) and head resistance. For the head having the larger cross-sectional area, i.e., smaller resistance coefficient, point A denotes the operating regime for a shallow channel, and point B denotes that of a deep channel. In this case, the screw having a deeper channel provides a higher capacity. For a head with a higher resistance (i.e., smaller cross-sectional area), point C determines the operating regime for a shallow channel, and point D that of a deep one. In the example shown, the screw having a shallow channel and higher pressure provides greater capacity.

For each head there corresponds an optimum screw channel geometry which provides maximum capacity. Figure 29F shows the influence of length on the discharge zone. An increase in screw length results in a decrease in capacity.

Design of heads. The forming elements of heads are orifices of specified geometries through which polymer can be extruded, thus producing a finished part. The design method for these forming elements consists of specifying a flow area to meet maximum capacity at a given pressure. That is, the design should be based on a predetermined resistance coefficient for the head or an inverse value of K, referred to as the shape factor. From this information, the geometry and size of the forming elements required to deliver the desired product can be established. Forming elements can be classified into two groups according to the flow patterns of the melt:

1. Head forming elements where the melt is in one-dimensional flow, i.e., the flow velocity varies only in one direction (simple section).
2. Head forming elements where the flow is two- or three-dimensional, i.e., the velocity varies in two or more directions (sections of complex profiles).

In forming elements having two-dimensional flow, the acting forces distort the shape of the extruded profile in comparison to the profile of the forming elements, due to different extrusion velocities in sections of different sizes. The shape factor is defined as:

$$K = \frac{Q\mu_a}{\Delta p} \tag{247}$$

where Q = volumetric capacity, cm^2/sec
Δp = pressure drop across the head, kg/cm^2
μ_a = apparent viscosity, $kg \times sec/cm^2$

Neglecting time, local temperature variations due to adiabatic effects, and changes in viscosity, the shape factor K (cm^3) can be considered a constant. In addition, several approximating assumptions can be made in order to establish a design basis. First, the melt may be considered to be in laminar flow.

Secondly, we assume that the melt "wets" the inside walls of the head casing. Thus, the outer film of the flow sticks to the walls and the flow velocity on them is zero. The equilibrium equation between the pressure of extrusion and shear stress is:

$$\int p \, dq = \int \tau \, dF \tag{248}$$

where p = exit melt pressure, kg/cm^2
q = channel cross-sectional area, cm^2
τ = shear stress, kg/cm^2
F = boundary area between the two layers of laminar flow, cm^2

The flow expression is:

$$\frac{dv}{dl} = -\frac{1}{\mu_a} \times \frac{\tau}{\tau_0} \tag{249}$$

where v = velocity at a specified point, cm/sec
l = linear size, cm
μ_a = melt viscosity, $kg \times sec/cm^2$
τ = shear stress between two adjacent layers, kg/cm^2
τ_0 = shear stress, kg/cm^2

For many non-Newtonian thermoplastics, a modified form of Newton's law may be applied:

$$\frac{dv}{d\rho} = -\frac{1}{\mu_a}\left(\frac{\tau}{\tau_0}\right)^n \tag{250}$$

where n = exponent (1 < n < 4)
ρ = flow coordinate, cm

The extrusion rate is obtained by integrating this expression:

$$v = \int \frac{dv}{d\rho} \, d\rho \tag{251}$$

A second integration yields an expression for the extrusion capacity:

$$Q = \int v \, dq \tag{252}$$

Table 5
Screw Mixer Channel Shape Factors K (cu.cm) and Shear Rates S (1/sec)

CHANNEL SHAPE	DESIGN SCHEME	DESIGN FORMULAS
ROUND CYLINDRICAL		$K_c = \dfrac{\pi d^4}{128 L_c}$; $S_c = \dfrac{32Q}{\pi d^3}$
ROUND CONICAL		$K_k = \dfrac{3\pi D^3 d^3}{128 L (D^2 + Dd + d^2)}$ $$S = \dfrac{256Q}{\pi (D-d)}$$
ROUND CIRCULAR		$K = \dfrac{\pi}{8L}\left[R_{out}^4 - R_{in}^4 - \dfrac{(R_{out}^2 - R_{in}^2)^2}{\ln(R_{out}/R_{in})} \right]$ $$S = \dfrac{5.58Q}{\pi (R_{out} + R_{in})(R_{out} - R_{in})^2}$$
CONICAL CIRCULAR WITH A CONICAL GAP		$K_6 = \dfrac{\pi(R_0 b_2 - R_1 b_1)}{6Lm}$ $m = \dfrac{(R_0 - R_1)^2}{(R_2 b_2 - R_1 b_1)^2} \ln(R_0 b_2 / R_1 b_1) - \dfrac{(R_0 - R_1)(b_1 - b_2)}{(R_0 b_1 - R_1 b_1) b_1 b_1} - \dfrac{b_1^2 - b_2^2}{2 b_1^2 b_2^2}$ $S = \dfrac{22.32Q}{\pi(R_0 + R_1)(b_1 + b_2)^2}$
FLAT GAP		$K_{f.g.} = \dfrac{bh^3}{12L}$; $S = \dfrac{5.58Q}{bh^2}$
WEDGE GAP		$K_{wg} = \dfrac{b\, h_1^2 h_2^2}{6L(h_1 + h_2)}$ $S_{wg} = \dfrac{11.16Q}{6(h_1 + h_2)^2}$
ANY CROSS-SECTION		$K = \dfrac{F}{2LP^2}$; $S = \dfrac{2QP}{F^2}$

where   q = cross section of the flow, cm^2
          v = velocity at a specified point along the channel, cm/sec

Typical channel shapes and design formulas for their coefficients are given in Table 5.
    The head profile may be considered to consist of channels of simple shapes. Then the total shape factor may be calculated as:

$$K = \frac{1}{\dfrac{1}{K_1} + \dfrac{1}{K_2} + \cdots + \dfrac{1}{K_i}} \tag{253}$$

This simplified method of calculating profile elements of heads is satisfactory for specifying head profiles for mixing, and can be used for granulation or semi-product manufacturing. In addition to the shape factor, the head must be specified. The following formula can be used:

$$\Delta p = \frac{Q\mu_a}{K} \tag{254}$$

where   Q = capacity, cm^3/sec
          μ_a = viscosity, kg × sec/cm^2
          K = shape factor of the head, cm^3

Capacity of twin-screw mixers. The flow of molten material in this type of machine is more complex than in single-screw mixers. Design specifications are primarily based on experimental data. The mixer's capacity is determined by both forced and countercurrent flows, as defined by the following equation:

$$Q = n(2\pi - d')(\pi D \tan \psi - b')(D - h)h - \frac{(2\pi - \alpha')D\delta^3 \tan \psi \, \Delta p}{12\mu_a b'} \tag{255}$$

where   n = screw rotational velocity

α' is an angle determined from the following formula:

$$\cos \alpha' = 1 - \frac{2h}{D - h} + \frac{h^2}{2(D - h)^2}$$

where   h = depth of helix channel
          D = screw diameter
          ψ = helix angle
          b' = thickness of the thread
          δ = radial gap between the coils and core of the screw
          Δp = mass pressure difference on both sides of the coil
          μ_a = apparent viscosity of the mass

    The effective capacity, as computed from Equation 255, does not account for the geometric compatibility of the screws. Consequently, the formula given below is recommended for characterizing the capacity of double-screw mixers with the screw rotation in one direction:

$$Q = 2Kn\left[\pi h(t - by)(Df + Df_d \frac{\cos^2 \psi}{2} - DF_c f - hf - F_3 t \right] \tag{256}$$

where   K = coefficient considering the influence of the mixing cam; s, K $\simeq 0.6$;
        n = rotational velocity, rpm
        h = depth of helix channel
        t = helix pitch
        b_y = conditional width of coil ridge
        D = outside diameter, cm
        ψ = helix angle
        F_d = coefficient considering the influence of the side walls, $F_d \simeq 0.64$
        F_c = coefficient considering the influence the channel curvature; $F_c \simeq 1.05$
        f = correction coefficient, f $\simeq 0.28$
        F_3 = area of segment gearing, cm^2

Screw mixer capacity for rubber processing. The capacity of screw mixers employed in processing rubber mixtures can be computed from the following correlation:

$$Q = 60 v_c n i \rho \beta, \quad \text{kg/hr} \tag{257}$$

where v_c = volume between two coils of one-screw mixer, m^3
        n = screw rotational velocity, rpm
        i = number of screw threads
        ρ = mixture density, kg/m^3
        β = space factor between coils; $\beta = 0.05 \sim 0.3$ (for a single-screw mixer with constant pitch and for double-screw mixers with variable pitch)

In this case, the force acting on the screw is:

$$P_z = \frac{91,700 N}{n r_0 \tan(\alpha + \rho)}, \quad \text{kg} \tag{258}$$

where P_z = axial force in the helix channel
        N = horsepower transmitted by the screw, kw
        n = rotational velocity, rpm
        r_0 = average coil radius, cm
        α = helix angle
        ρ = friction angle of rubber mixture, $\rho = 26 \sim 38°$

Further details on this design case are given by Ryabinin and Lukach [16].

Horsepower drive. The horsepower consumed by screw mixers is expended on material displacement along the channel and for material shear in the gap between the screw ridge and the internal wall of the case:

$$N = \frac{N_1 + N_2}{\eta} \tag{259}$$

where N_1 = horsepower spent for forced displacement along the screw channel
        N_2 = horsepower spent on material shear in the gap between coil ridge and wall of the case
        η = efficiency, $\eta = 0.4 \sim 0.6$.

$$N_1 = \frac{\pi^3 (t - e) L J \mu_a \times 10^{-4}}{36 t} n^2 + \frac{\alpha_2 \Delta p n \times 10^{-3}}{6}, \quad \text{kg-m/sec} \tag{260}$$

where J = coefficient obtained from the following formula:

$$J = \frac{\pi^2 D^2 - 4t^2}{\pi^2} + \frac{(D - d)^3 - (D + d_1)^3}{3(d_2 - d_1)} + \frac{2.3\pi^2 D^5}{(t^2 + \pi^2 D^2(h_{in} - h_{out}))} \log\left(\frac{h_{in}}{h_{out}}\right) \tag{261}$$

where   n = rotational velocity, rpm
      p = pressure drop across the head, kg/cm^2
      α_2 = constant for a specified flow, cm^3
      d_1 = core diameter at the inlet of the dosing zone, cm
      d_2 = core diameter at the outlet, cm
      h_{in} = thread depth at inlet of the dosing zone, cm
      h_{out} = thread depth at the screw outlet, cm

The following formula can be used to estimate the shear rate in the screw helix, which in turn can be used to evaluate the material's dynamic viscosity:

$$S = \frac{\pi^2(D - h_{th})(D - 2h_{th})^n}{60h_{th}\sqrt{\pi^2(D - 2h_{th})^2 - t^2}}, \quad 1/\text{sec} \tag{262}$$

where h_{th} = average depth of the thread:

$$h_{th} = \frac{h_1 + h_2}{2} \tag{263}$$

h_1 = thread depth at the inlet of the dosing zone, cm

h_2 = thread depth at the end of the screw, cm

$$N_2 = \frac{10^{-4}\pi^3 D^3 eL\mu_a n^2}{36\,\delta t}, \quad \text{kg} \times \text{m/sec} \tag{264}$$

where   D = screw outside diameter, cm
      e = width of a ridge, cm
      L = length of dosing zone, cm
      δ = radial gap, cm
      t = helix pitch of the channel, cm
      n = screw rotational velocity, rpm
      μ_a = apparent viscosity, kg $\times$ sec/cm^2

The apparent dynamic viscosity can be determined from the relationship between shear rate and viscosity. The rate of shear can be computed from the following formula:

$$S = \frac{\pi^2 D^2 n}{60\delta\sqrt{\pi^2 D^2 + t^2}}, \quad \text{sec}^{-1} \tag{265}$$

The temperature rise due to the transformation of mechanical energy into thermal energy may be approximated from the following formula:

$$\Delta t = \frac{860\left(N - \frac{Q\,\Delta p}{36 \times 10^4}\right)}{QC_p\rho} \tag{266}$$

where   N = horsepower consumed by a screw, kwt
          Q = capacity, m³/hr
          Δp = pressure drop in the head, kg/m²
          C_p = heat capacity, kcal/kg × °C
          ρ = density, kg/m³

The value of density used in this calculation should be based on the material's melt temperature, since density decreases with increasing temperature.

Horsepower calculations for twin screw mixers in plastics processing. The principle design equation for this example is:

$$N = Pv = \frac{\mu v^2 F}{a} \qquad (267)$$

where   p = shear force during the motion of the working surface and acting on the mass, g
          F = area of working surfaces (shear surface), cm²
          v = relative velocity between adjacent working surfaces, cm/sec
          a = distance between adjacent working surfaces, cm

The ratio of P/F is a shear stress, and v/a is a gradient or shear rate. Equation 88 may be rewritten in an alternate form:

$$N = \frac{\mu}{a} \int v^2 \, dF \qquad (268)$$

The power consumption in wedged sections for screws rotating in one direction is:

$$N_{Zone} = Z\frac{\mu}{a} \times \frac{\alpha}{2}(2\pi h)^2(D - h + \delta)\frac{2\alpha'}{2}(D - h)h \qquad (269)$$

where Z = total amount of wedge-shaped sections, depending on the number of coils in gearing; $\delta = \delta_1 - \delta_2$ — radial gap between coils; a = side gap between coils.
   The drive horsepower spent on the work in the radial gap may be determined considering this gap to be parallel between two coils, i.e., the same as in the rolls. In this case, there is a great inaccuracy, because in contrast to rolls in the given gap before and after, there is the pressure of the mass. For counter-rotating screws, the following formula is applicable:

$$N_{counter} = \mu\pi^2 n^2(D - h)^3\left(\frac{1}{\delta} - \frac{1}{\omega}\right)L \qquad (270)$$

where ω = material thickness before entering the gap.

Horsepower calculation of screw mixers for processing rubber mixtures. The energy transmitted to the screw is spent for overcoming the following resistances:

● Extrusion forces, T_1
● Friction forces of material against the screw, T_2
● Friction forces of material against the machine case
● Friction forces in the bearings of the drive, T_4

Taking into account these forces, the horsepower is:

$$N = \frac{1}{60 \times 102}\sum_1^4 Tv = \frac{1}{6120}\sum_1^3 Tv\frac{1}{\eta}, \quad kW \qquad (271)$$

where η = drive and bearing efficiency which is accounted for by T_4
         v = extrusion velocity, m/min

The extrusion force is:

$$T_1 = pF_0 \times 10^{-2}, \quad kg \tag{272}$$

where p = pressure of the mixture at extrusion, kg/cm^2.
The friction force of the mixture against the screw is:

$$T_2 = \frac{\tan(\alpha + \rho) - \tan \alpha}{\tan \alpha} T_1, \quad kg \tag{273}$$

The friction force of the mixture against the casing walls is:

$$T_3 = \frac{\pi DLfpv_1}{2v}, \quad kg \tag{274}$$

where   D = diameter of the cylindrical working part, cm
         L = length of the cylinder working section, cm
         f = friction factor of the mixture against the cylinder
         v = velocity of the helix motion; v_1 = tni
         ρ = friction angle; $\rho = \tan^{-1} f$; $f = 0.3$
         n = rotational velocity of the screw
         t = distance between coils
         i = number of screw threads

The overall efficiency of a screw mixer is:

$$\eta_0 = \frac{\eta T_1}{T_1 + T_2 + T_3} \tag{276}$$

or $\eta_0 = \dfrac{\eta}{\dfrac{\tan(\alpha + \rho)}{\tan \alpha} + \dfrac{\pi DLfv_1}{2F_0v \times 10^{-2}}}$ \hfill (277)

Substituting average values for variables in the denominator of Equation 277, it is observed that the two terms differ by only 5%, and hence, we may write:

$$\eta_0 = \frac{2F_0v\eta \times 10^{-2}}{\pi DLfv_1} \tag{278}$$

Substituting this expression into the horsepower formula, we obtain:

$$N = \frac{T_1 v}{6,120\eta} = \frac{pDLfni}{3,900\eta}, \quad kht \tag{279}$$

The horsepower of a small screw mixer for processing rubber mixtures may be computed from the following formula:

$$N = \frac{T_1 v}{6,120\eta_0} \tag{280}$$

where η_0 = efficiency.

Substituting into Equation 280:

$$T_1 v = F_0 p v \times 10^{-2} = \frac{pG}{60\gamma_0}$$

then $$N = \frac{Gp}{3.68 \times 10^5 \gamma_0 \eta_0} \qquad (281)$$

As shown by Equation 281, horsepower is proportional to the pressure and extrusion capacities. The energy of extrusion transformed into heat is calculated from the following formula:

$$Q_T = N\eta_T 860, \quad Kcal/hr \qquad (282)$$

or $$Q_T = GC_p(t_2 - t_1), \quad Kcal/hr \qquad (283)$$

where the temperature of the mixture increases to:

$$t_2 = t_1 + \frac{810\eta_T}{GC_p} \qquad (284)$$

where t_1 = temperature of the mixture before extrusion
C_p = heat capacity of the mixture, Kcal/kg × °C
η_T = heat efficiency for heating the mixture, $\eta_T = 0.9$

The horsepower of an electric motor may be approximated from:

$$N = 0.00353D^2 n, \quad kht \qquad (285)$$

where   D = outer screw diameter, cm
n = screw velocity, rpm

Determination of forces acting on the screw. Two calculation procedures are available for estimating the specific pressure at the end of the screw (i.e., near the head). The first consists of computing forces transmitted by the screw, and the second is based on the determination of the maximum specific pressure generated at the closed opening in the head.
From the first method we have:

$$P_Z = \frac{97,000N}{nr_s \tan(\alpha + \rho)}, \quad kg \qquad (286)$$

where P_Z = axial force developed in the screw thread, kg
N = horsepower transmitted by the screw, kht
n = screw velocity, rpm
r_s = average thread radius, cm
α = helix angle at r_s
ρ = friction angle, $= 26 - 38°$.

and specific pressure $$P = \frac{P_Z}{F_Z} = \frac{P_Z}{\pi(R^2 - r^2)} \qquad (287)$$

where F_Z = cross-sectional area of screw thread, cm^2
R = outside thread radius, cm
r = inside thread radius, cm

The axial force acting from the forming head side is:

$$A = F_s p \tag{288}$$

where   A = axial force, kg
        F_s = screw cross-sectional area, cm^2
        p = specific pressure at the screw end

The total axial force acting on the thrust bearing is the sum of the axial forces and the tangential component of material friction against the screw surface:

$$K = A + T \tag{289}$$

where   K = total axial force, kg
        A = axial force, kg
        T = tangential component of friction; $T = F2\pi r_s \tan \rho$

$$F = \text{specific force; } F = \frac{1}{3} P \frac{1}{2} = \frac{pl}{6} \tag{290}$$

        l = length of the filled screw thread (assumed half of threaded part)
        p = specific pressure at the screw end, kg/cm^2
        r_s = average radius of the screw thread, cm
        $\tan \rho = f -$ friction factor (for rubber against steel $\rho = 26 \sim 30°$C)

Heat balances. The heat balance about a screw mixer may be written as follows:

$$G_m C_m t_{in} + Q_N + Q_K + Q_H + G_w C_w t_{w_1} = G_m C_m t_{out} + G_w C_w t_{w_2} + Q_l + Q_3 \tag{291}$$

where G_m = amount of material entering the machine, kg/hr
        C_m = heat capacity of the material, Kcal/kg × °C
        t_{in} = initial temperature of material, °C
        t_{out} = final temperature of material, °C
        Q_N = amount of heat due to energy transformation, Kcal/hr
        Q_K = amount of heat introduced to the machine (by steam, heated water or electrical heaters), Kcal/hr
        Q_H = amount of heat introduced to the head (by steam, heated liquid, or electrical heaters), Kcal/hr
        G_w = amount of water for cooling the screw, kg/hr
        C_w = heat capacity of water, Kcal/kg × °C
        t_{w_1}, t_{w_2} = initial and final temperature of cooling water, °C
        Q_l = heat losses by the screw mixer, Kcal/hr
        Q_3 = amount of heat introduced in feeding zone, Kcal/hr

Solving for the temperature of the material leaving the mixer, we obtain:

$$t_{out} = \frac{Q_N + Q_K + Q_H - G_w C_w (t_{w_2} - t_{w_1}) - Q_l - Q_3}{G_m C_m} + t_{in} \tag{292}$$

The components of the heat balance are determined as follows:

$$Q_N = 860N, \quad \text{Kcal/hr} \tag{293}$$

where N is determined from Equation 80 for the entire machine.

The amount of heat, Q_K, introduced to the mixer from outside depends on the system of heating, which may be electric, liquid, or by steam.

Since the material discharge temperature is known, Q_K may be determined from Equation 113:

$$Q_K = G_m C_m(t_{out} - t_{in}) + G_w C_w(t_{w_2} - t_{w_1}) + Q_1 + Q_3 - Q_N - Q_H \qquad (294)$$

The machine's capacity is determined from parametric calculations. Selecting an average heat capacity $\bar{C}$, we determine the amount of heat absorbed by the cooling water:

$$Q_x = G_w C_w(t_{w_2} - t_{w_1}) \qquad (295)$$

The proper size of the screw channel can be detemined from design considerations, and the cooling water pipe diameter is established by the water channel cross section. Assuming a water velocity of $0.1 \sim 0.8$ m/sec, we obtain:

$$G_w = f \times v \times 3600\rho, \quad kg/hr \qquad (296)$$

where f = cross-sectional area, mm^2
v = water velocity, m/sec
ρ = water density, kg/m^3

The temperature differential $(t_{w_2} - t_{w_1})$ can be assumed to be around $5 \sim 10°C$ for preliminary calculations.

Heat losses from the mixer are:

$$Q_1 = F\alpha(t_b - t_w), \quad Kcal/hr \qquad (297)$$

where F = outside surface of the mixer, m^2
α = heat transfer coefficient at free convection
t_b = temperature of outside surface of the mixer (insulated); $t_b = 50$ to $80°C$.

The amount of heat absorbed in the feeding zone, Q_3, is calculated similarly to that of screw cooling, provided that the cooling medium is water.

The amount of heat introduced to the head is:

$$Q_H = G_m C_m(t_{out} - t_h) \qquad (298)$$

where t_{out} = temperature of the material after the head, °C
t_h = temperature of the material before the head, °C

The amount of heat for heating the body and head of the mixer for liquid heating agents is:

$$Q = G_T C_T(t_{in} - t_{out}), \quad Kcal/hr \qquad (299)$$

where G_T = amount of heating agent, kg/hr; $G_T = 3,600Fv\rho$, kg/hr
F = cross-sectional area for introducing the heating agent, m^2
C = heat capacity of the agent, Kcal/kg $\times$ °C   (300)
v = velocity of the agent in the channel, m/sec
ρ = density of heating agent, kg/m^3

Knowing Q, C_T, and ρ, and selecting the velocity of the heating agent, we may determine the temperature difference necessary for heat transfer Q.

For saturated steam as the heating agent:

$$Q = G(i_s - i_c), \quad Kcal/hr \qquad (301)$$

where   G = amount of steam entering the mixer, kg/hr
         i_s = enthalpy of steam, Kcal/kg
         i_c = enthalpy of condensate, Kcal/kg

The steam pressure is determined by the temperature needed for processing the material. The use of steam is limited by the available pressure drop rather than by temperatures. For example, a steam temperature of 250°C is possible at a pressure of about 40 kg/cm², which makes the design of the mixer heavier and more complicated. The method considered above is related to determining the thermal characteristics of screw mixers, associated with a heat balance. However, provisions should also be provided for the transfer of quantities of heat. During the final stages of design, it is necessary to check whether the obtained heat transfer surface provides the necessary amount of thermal energy.

From the basic equation of heat transfer:

$$Q = KL\,\Delta t_{av} \tag{302}$$

it is possible to determine the desired heat transfer zone length (surface), or from a known length, to determine the amount of heat transferred, Q, from information on the heat transfer coefficient K and average temperature difference Δt_{av}.

If electric energy is used for heating, the heat transfer coefficient for a cylindric wall is determined from the following equation:

$$K = \frac{1}{\dfrac{1}{\pi d_{in}\alpha_1} + \dfrac{1}{2\pi\lambda}2.3\log\dfrac{d_{out}}{d_{in}}}, \quad \text{Kcal/m} \times \text{hr} \times \text{°C} \tag{303}$$

If steam or a liquid carrier is used, then:

$$K = \frac{1}{\dfrac{1}{\pi d_{in}\alpha_1} + \dfrac{1}{2\pi\lambda}2.3\log\dfrac{d_{out}}{d_{in}} - \dfrac{1}{\pi d_{out}\alpha_2}} \tag{304}$$

where d_{out} = outside diameter of cylindrical body where the heater is mounted or comes in contact with the heating agent, m
         d_{in} = inside diameter in contact with the material, m
         λ = conductivity of the mixer body
         α_1 = heat transfer coefficient from case surface to the material, Kcal/m² × hr × °C
         α_2 = heat transfer coefficient from the carrier to the case outside surface, Kcal/m² × hr × °C

Note that in the feeding zone, heat transfer from the wall to the surrounding air, as well as partially to the granular material, takes place. Because the size of this zone is small and heat transfer is not intensive, its importance to the above calculations is small. Physical constants, used in the formulas, should be based on the material's average melt temperature and the wall temperature. Because the material moves through the screw channel, the determining size is equivalent to the diameter of the screw channel:

$$d_{eq} = \frac{2\left[(t-b)\cos\alpha\dfrac{d_{out}-d_{in}}{2}\right]}{\left[(t-b)\cos\alpha+\dfrac{d_{out}-d_{in}}{2}\right]}, \quad \text{m} \tag{305}$$

where t = helix pitch, m
        b = coil width, m
        d_{out} = screw outside diameter
        d_{in} = screw inside diameter
        α = helix angle

The material's velocity is:

$$v = \frac{Q_v}{F \times i}, \quad \text{m/sec} \tag{306}$$

where Q_v = volumetric capacity of the mixer, m³/sec
        i = number of threads
        F = cross-sectional area of screw channel, m²;

$$F = \left[(t - b) \cos \alpha \frac{d_{out} - d_{in}}{2} \right] \tag{307}$$

For heating calculations for the head, the following equations are used:

$$d_{eq} = \frac{4F}{P'} \tag{308}$$

$$v = \frac{Q_v}{F} \tag{309}$$

where F = cross-sectional area of discharge opening in the head, m²
        P' = perimeter of discharge opening, m

The thermal regime of the mixer can be checked on the basis of the heat balance equation, i.e., if Q_K is determined from a heat balance, then the amount of heat calculated from Equation 302 should be equal to Q_K. If such an equality is not realized, the process of heat transfer should be intensified or the heat transfer area F (for the case $F = \pi d_{in}L$) increased, i.e., the size of the mixer or its head should be enlarged. Eqaution 302 should be used for determining the screw's cooling process, where the heat transfer coefficient is determined from the following fomula:

$$K = \cfrac{1}{\cfrac{1}{\pi d_{in}\alpha_1} + \cfrac{1}{2\pi\lambda} 2.3 \log \cfrac{d_{out}}{d_{in}} + \cfrac{1}{\pi d_{in}\alpha_2}} \tag{310}$$

where d_{out} = outside diameter of screw cylinder, m
        d_{in} = inside diameter of screw cylinder, corresponding to the surface reached by the water stream moving in the circular gap, m
        α_1 = heat transfer coefficient from material to the screw surface, Kcal/m²-hr-°C
        α_2 = heat transfer coefficient from internal surface of the screw to the cooling water moving in the circular channel between the water feeding pipe and inside surface of the screw, kcal/m² × hr × °C

Coefficient α_1 is calculated similarly to that in Equation 304, where d_{eq} is obtained from Equation 305, and the material velocity is obtained from Equation 306.

Coefficient α_2 (for flowing cooling water) is calculated from a dimensionless expression which depends on the flow regime. The determining size for this calculation is:

$$d_{eq} = d_{in} - d_{out} \tag{311}$$

where d_{in} = internal diameter of screw cylinder, corresponding to the surface reached by water, m.

If the machine case is insulated, then the thickness of the insulated layer is calculated by using the formulas of conductivity through a flat or cylindrical surface. In this case, the heat flux through the insulation layer is determined from the following equation:

$$Q = \alpha F(t_{out} - t_a), \quad Kcal/hr \tag{312}$$

where α = heat transfer coefficient from an outer surface of insulation to the air (use formulas of free convection)
F = outside surface of insulation, m^2
t_{out} = temperature of outside surface of insulation which should be assumed
t_a = temperature of air

The required insulation layer thickness may be determined from the heat flux and conductivity. In performing this calculation, the temperature difference $\Delta t = t_{in} - t_{out}$ (where t_{in} = temperature of internal surface of insulation layer) can be obtained by assuming t_{in} to be equal to the temperature of the surface that is to be insulated.

Single-Screw Modeling

The principles of similarity and modeling are widely used in the design of different unit operations. The study of the flow of polymer materials can be based on the following dimensionless relation:

$$Eu = CRe^n \left(\frac{l}{d}\right)^m \tag{313}$$

where $Eu = \dfrac{\Delta p}{\rho v^2}$, the Euler number

$Re = \dfrac{Vd}{\nu}$, the Reynolds number

Δp = pressure drop in the channel
ρ = density of the polymer melt
v = average velocity of polymer
d = channel diameter
l = channel length
ν = kinematic viscosity

Silin [77] applied similarity theory to developing design correlations for screw mixers. For a basis of design, the process parameters of a well defined system must be known. A defined system is one where the mixer's dimensions, the screw's rotational velocity n_0, horsepower N_0, etc. are known and the performance and limits of operation have been examined. From this basic information, a system of equations characterizing the process and design sizes of the prototype can be developed. The principle forms of these equations for dynamically similar machines are as follows:

Capacity

$$Q = Q_0 \left(\frac{D}{D_0}\right)^{3 - 2\psi} \tag{314}$$

Screw rotational velocity

$$n = n_0 \left(\frac{D}{D_0}\right)^{-\psi} \tag{315}$$

Depth of screw channel

$$h = h_0 \left(\frac{D}{D_0}\right)^{1-\psi} \tag{316}$$

Pressure at the screw end

$$p = p_0 \left(\frac{D}{D_0}\right)^{1-\psi} \tag{317}$$

Horsepower

$$N = N_0 \left(\frac{D}{D_0}\right)^{3-\psi} \tag{318}$$

Resistance factor of the head

$$K = K_0 \left(\frac{D}{D_0}\right)^{3-(1-\psi)} \tag{319}$$

Equations 314 through 319 were developed from successive model and prototype experimental units, and define the principal design parameters in terms of the diameter ratio of prototype to model, and an additional parameter ψ defined as:

$$\psi = \frac{1}{2}\frac{T_1 - T_0}{T_2 - T_0} \tag{320}$$

where T_0, T_1, and T_2 are the temperatures of the materials in the three screw zones, respectively.

In certain applications it is necessary to maintain nearly identical design specifications between the prototype and model (e.g., constant screw length to diameter, and/or rate of compression). Parameter ψ is dependent on the thermal process in the mixer; that is, it is a function of the ratio between the energy introduced to the material via transformation of mechanical energy of the drive into thermal energy, and energy introduced by outside heaters due to heat transfer. The extremes of operation are isothermal, where $\psi = 0.5$, and adiabatic, where $\psi = 0$.

Twin-Screw Modeling

Four scaling groups, each consisting of different forces acting in a screw mixer, were studied by Silin [77]. The first group relates to the scales of inertia forces, centrifugal forces, and head resistance. The second group concerns the scales of gravity forces. The third comprises the scales of internal friction, and the fourth refers to the scales of strength and elasticity of the polymer. The principal forces acting in plastics processing between two parallel screws are those of compression, rupture, shear, and elasticity (i.e., the fourth group of forces). The scale equality of these forces is expressed by the following equation:

$$C_\rho' = C_\rho^{IV} = \frac{\rho_0 C_e^4}{\rho_m D_e^2} = \frac{E_0 C_e^2}{E_m} \tag{321}$$

As follows from Equation 321, for equal elastic moduluses $E_0 = E_m$ and densities $\rho_0 = \rho_m$ of processed materials (in the model and prototype) the geometric (linear) scale is equal to the time scale:

$$C_e = C_t \qquad (322)$$

Thus, as a basis of similarity for double-screw mixers, the Cochy number $C_o = \rho v^2 / E$ can be used for corresponding scales of modeling. As follows from the scales of modeling, for two similar double-screw mixers, the product of rotational velocity and the height of the screw coils is constant:

$$C_n C_h = \frac{n_0 h_0}{n_m h_m} = \frac{C_e}{C_e} = 1 = C_e^a C_e^b \qquad (323)$$

For the proper selection of modeling scales for the coil height and screw rotational velocity, it is necessary to maintain equality of the principle forces. In addition, it is necessary to maintain conditions of viscosity at critical corresponding points in the model prototype. The latter criterion may be achieved by maintaining the same temperature regimes and velocity gradients of the melt flow at corresponding points along the screw channels in both the prototype and model:

$$C_r = \frac{r_0}{r_m} = \frac{\pi D_0 n_0 h_0}{\pi D_m n_m h_m} = \frac{C_e C_n}{C_h} = 1 \qquad (324)$$

$$\mu_0 = \mu_m$$

Upon substitution of the modeling scale, velocity gradient, and coil heights, we obtain:

$$C_r = \frac{C_e C_e^b}{C_e^a} = C_e^{1+b-a} = C_e^0 = 1 \qquad (325)$$

Hence, from Equation 325:

$$1 + b - a = 0$$

Simultaneously solving Equations 323 and 325, we obtain:

$$a = 0.5; \qquad b = -0.5$$

Thus, the modeling of twin-screw mixers is achieved through the equality of modeling scales, height of coils, and rotational velocities between the model and prototype:

$$C_h = \frac{h_0}{h_m} = C_e^{0.5}$$

$$\qquad (326)$$

$$C_n = \frac{n_0}{n_m} = C_e^{-0.5}$$

The coil height of the screws $(h_0 = h_m \sqrt{C_e})$ at $n_0 = n_m / \sqrt{C_e}$ corresponds to the optimum modeling case.

The geometrical scale of coil and channel widths between coils is equal to the linear scale of diameter modeling:

$$C_e = \frac{b_0}{b_m} = \frac{a_0}{a_m} = \frac{L_0}{L_m} = \frac{D_0}{D_m} \qquad (327)$$

It follows then that the proper scale of capacity is:

$$C_Q = \frac{Q_0}{Q_m} = \frac{\pi D_0 h_0 H_0 n_0 K_0 \eta_0 \psi_0 \gamma_0}{\pi D_m h_m H_m h_m K_m \eta_m \psi_m \gamma_m} = C_e^2 \qquad (328)$$

where K_0 and K_m are overlapping factors in the model and prototype.

The inter-axial distances are determined from the conditions of equal velocity gradients and viscosities of material flow between the coil ridges and their cores in the model and prototype. Because in the gaps δ_0 and δ_m (see Figure 30) the material is subject to the largest strains and stresses, the following criteria must be maintained:

$$r_0 = r_m; \qquad \mu_0 = \mu_m$$

The scale for velocity gradients in the gaps between the coil ridges and screw cores can be computed from the following equation:

$$C_r = \frac{r_0}{r_m} = \frac{\dfrac{\pi D_0 n_0}{\delta_0}}{\dfrac{\pi D_m n_m}{\delta_m}} = C_e^{0.5} \frac{\delta m}{\delta_0} = 1 \qquad (329)$$

where $n_0/n_m = C_e^{0.5}$; the scale of velocity modeling at the coil height is $h_0 = h_m C_e^{0.5}$.

Hence:

$$\delta_0 = \delta_m C_e^{0.5} \qquad (330)$$

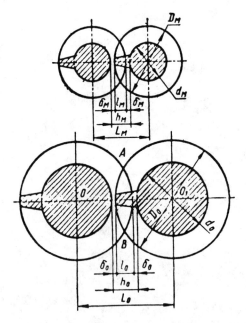

Figure 30. Cross sections of twin-screw mixers for scale-up developments.

After establishing the coil height h_0, and the gap δ_0, the distance between the screw axes in the prototype can be computed as follows:

$$L_0 = D_0 - B_0 = D_0 - B_m C_e^{0.5} \tag{331}$$

where B_0 = width of coil overlapping, which is equal to:

$$h_0 - \delta_0 = h_m C_e^{0.5} - \delta_m C_e^{0.5} = B_m C_e^{0.5}$$

Oscillating Screw Mixers

Universal oscillating screw mixers are used for processing a variety of polymer materials. These machines are characterized by a reciprocal motion of screws in the axial direction with simultaneous rotation. For intensive mixing, plastification, homogenation, and degassing of different plastics, the screw coils are interrupted in definite order, forming clearances in which three rows of teeth, located on the internal surface of the mixer cylinder, enter these clearances. Due to variable axial and radial screw motion between the teeth of the mixer, the material is exposed to shear, compression, rupture, and mixing at different planes over small volumes between the coils.

A high degree of mixing is achieved in these designs as compared to other machines, and at relatively low energy consumption (from 0.02 to 1.0 kwt per 1 kg of mixture). Depending on the properties of the material, three design variations are possible. Figure 31 shows the three principal types. The P-type mixer is employed in processing very viscous materials (rigid and mild polyvinyl chloride, polystyrene, and other polymers). K-type mixers serve for processing different pastes and viscous materials (for manufacturing carbon electrodes, chocolate, dough). M-type mixers are used for processing different dry materials. The primary design differences between the three lies in the shape and size of the teeth.

Mechanical similarity of oscillating screw mixers is achieved through geometric, kinematic, and dynamic similarities. Geometric similarity is reproduced by maintaining equality of ratios between the corresponding geometrical sizes of discontinuous screws and teeth of the cylinders of the model and prototype. Comparison of commercial and laboratory size mixers have revealed that geometric similarity is important. This implies the following constant geometric ratios:

1. Pitch of the left double-start thread (see Figure 32):

$$H_1 = 0.6D \tag{332}$$

where D = outside screw diameter

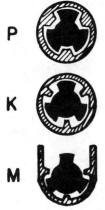

P

K

M

Figure 31. Types of oscillating screw mixers.

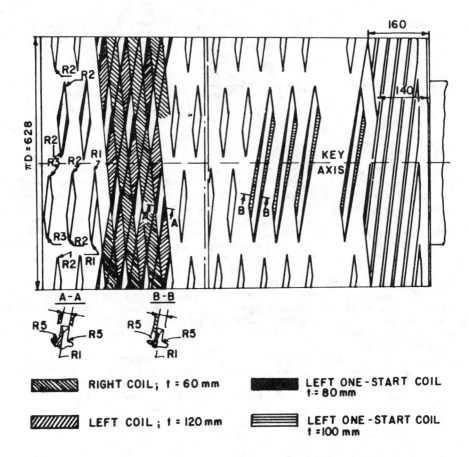

Figure 32. Involute of discontinuous coils of the screw of an oscillating mixer. Section A-A: 1-tooth section along normal to plane is formed by the right coil with pitch t = 60 mm and the left two-start coil with pitch t = 120 mm; 2-tooth section along normal to plane by left one-start coil with pitch t = 80 mm through 4 teeth with individual treatment of each tooth. Section B-B: 1-tooth section along normal to plane formed by left two-start coil with pitch t = 120 mm; 2-section of tooth along normal to plane formed by left one-start coil with pitch t = 100 mm with individual treatment of each tooth.

2. Pitch of right single-start thread:

$$H_2 = \frac{H_1}{2} = 0.3D \tag{333}$$

3. Height of the thread:

$$h = 0.175D \tag{334}$$

4. The number of longitudinal grooves of the screw, m, is equal to the number of forming teeth, K, located on the internal cylinder surface:

$$m = K = \frac{H_1 + H_2}{H_2} = 3 \tag{335}$$

5. Number of left-hand start threads:

$$Z = K - 1 = 2 \tag{336}$$

6. Length of screws, width of coils and grooves of thread, are proportional to the diameter of the screws:

$$\left. \begin{array}{l} L_0 = L_m C_e \\[2mm] b_0 = b_m C_e \\[2mm] a_0 = a_m C_e \end{array} \right\} \tag{337}$$

where L_0, L_m = screw lengths of the prototype and model

$$C_e = \text{geometric scale}, \frac{D_0}{D_m}$$

b_0, b_m = coil width of the screw for prototype and model
a_0, a_m = groove width, for prototype and model

7. Teeth are located on the internal surface of cylinders between discontinuous screw coils in three rows; the angles between the teeth are $\alpha_0 = \alpha_m = 120°$.
8. The pitch between the teeth in each row on the cylinder surface is equal to the pitch of the right one-start screw thread:

$$H_{tooth} = H_2 = 0.3D \tag{338}$$

9. The forming teeth of mixers have different shapes, depending on their location along the cylinder length: For the cylinder, the tooth height is $h_{tooth} = 0.1D$, and its shape is $h_{tooth} = 0.15D$.
10. The axial path of the screw is equal to one-half of the pitch of a one-start thread of the screw:

$$1 = \frac{H_2}{2} = 0.15D \tag{339}$$

11. For free passage of discontinuous coils of the screw between the forming teeth of the cylinder during reciprocal and rotational screw motion, the coils should be undercut with a milling cutter. The undercutting pitch in the feeding zone is $H_3 = 0.5D$, and in the compression and plastification zones is $H_4 = 0.4D$.

The second condition of similarity of oscillating mixers is kinematic similarity, which is realized in the case when in each compatible point of similar screws, the direction of velocities of moving particles of material to be mixed are parallel and proportional to each other. With this in mind, kinematic of reciprocal motion together with the rotation of the screw is considered.

For simplifying calculations, the teeth motion can be considered relative to a stationary screw. As we see from the involute of the surface of discontinuous coils of the screw and teeth (see Figure 33) at the first half turn and forward motion of the screw, the forming tooth 1 is moving along the helix line 1-1'. In this case, tooth 1 crosses screw coil B in the slit between the coil (teeth) parts B_1

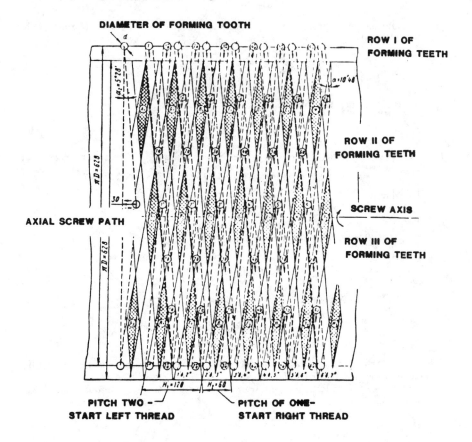

Figure 33. Geometric explanation of kinematic of discontinuous screw coils between forming teeth of an oscillating screw mixer.

and B_2. At the second half turn and reciprocal motion of the screw (backward), the forming tooth 1 is moving along helix line 1-1″ without crossing screw coils. The same motions relating to discontinuous screw coils B, F, D, etc., have forming teeth 2, 3, 4, etc., located in the same row with tooth 1 of the mixer cylinder.

For one turn of the screw, they move along helix lines 2-2′-2″, 3-3′-3″, 4-4′-4″, etc., crossing the screw coils B, F, and D in the slits between the teeth (sections) of coils B_1 and B_2, F_1 and F_2, D_1 and D_2. The forming teeth of the second row of the mixer, 1a, 2a, 3a, etc., in the first half turn of the screw and its forward motion pass the path along their helix lines 1a-1′a, 2a-2′a, 3a-3′a, etc., through coils B, F, and D in slits between the teeth (parts) of coils B_2 and B_3, Γ_2 and Γ_3, D_2 and D_3. In the second half turn, the forming teeth 2a, 3a, 4a, etc., pass the path (1′a − 1″a) + (1″a − 1a); (2′a − 2″a) + (2″a − 2a), etc., between coil teeth Γ_2 and Γ_3, D_2 and D_3 . . . Similar relative motions have the forming teeth of the third row of the mixer 1b, 2b, 3b, etc. Thus, sinusoidal reciprocal and rotating motion of the screw is due to the regular location of forming teeth in the coil slits of the screw and exactly limited axial displacement of the screw. The axial screw displacement (forward and backward) is equal to one-half of the pitch of a one-start right thread:

$$1 = 0.5H_2 \tag{340}$$

In this case, the helix angle relative to the motion of each forming tooth is equal to the helix angle of the right thread of the screw:

$$\psi = \tan^{-1} \frac{2l}{\pi D} = \psi_2 = \tan^{-1} \frac{H_2}{\pi D} \tag{341}$$

The number of longitudinal screw paths m which is equal to the number of rows of forming teeth K in the mixer cylinder is determined from the ratio of pitches of left and right threads of the screw:

$$m = K = \frac{H_1 + H_2}{H_2} = \frac{2H_2 + H_2}{H_2} = 3 \tag{342}$$

The number of starts of the left thread is:

$$Z = K - 1 = 2 \tag{343}$$

The capacity of an oscillatory mixer is:

$$Q = \frac{\pi(D^2 - d^2)HKA \cos \alpha n \eta \rho}{4\pi D} \tag{344}$$

where
  D = screw outside diameter, cm
  d = screw inside diameter, cm
  H = pitch of left thread of the screw, cm
  K = number of teeth in one coil of the screw, which is equal to number of rows of forming teeth
  A = length of one tooth of screw coil, cm

  α = helix angle of left thread of screw, $\alpha = \tan^{-1} \dfrac{H}{\pi D}$

  n = screw velocity, rpm
  η = volumetric capacity efficiency, depending on head counter pressure, coefficient of charge, slit width between coils of screw, and properties of material to be processed
  $\eta = 0.1 \sim 0.25$
  ρ = density of material processed, kg/cm^3

The third condition of similarity of oscillating mixers is dynamic similarity. This is reproduced when the acting forces (pressure, gravity, inertia, elasticity, viscosity, friction, centrifugal, etc.) in the model and prototype are proportional and parallel to each other. Similarity is determined by the three scales: geometric, C_e; time scale, C_t; and force scale, C_p. To achieve similarity between prototype and model based on all the acting forces corresponding to Froude, Reynolds, and Cochy numbers is impossible. The qualities of scales are based on the forces of axial pressure acting on the oscillating screw, centrifugal and inertial forces corresponding to the first group of forces, as well as on elastic forces and compressive strength, tensile strength and shear of material at mixing, plastification and strain between discontinuous coils and forming teeth corresponding to the fourth group of forces, and friction forces which are derivatives of the mentioned forces.

The equality of scales of these forces is expressed by the following equation:

$$C_\rho^I = C_\rho^{IV} = \frac{\rho_0 C_e^4}{\rho_m C_e^2} = \frac{E_0 C_e^2}{E_m} \tag{345}$$

which corresponds to a Cochy number defined as:

$$C_0 = \frac{\rho v^2}{E} \tag{346}$$

Thus, the modeling scales of oscillating mixers are the same as those for screw mixers if geometric similarity is maintained. At equal rotational velocities in model and prototype units, the capacity and horsepower of the prototype are increased correspondingly by the values established by the modeling scales:

$$C'_Q = C_Q C_e = C_e^3$$

$$C'_N = C_N C_e = C_e^3$$

(347)

NOTATION

A	area; mixing index; axial force	J	heat transfer coefficient; also fracture coefficient
A, B	dimensionless functions of ratio of thread base and channel height	J_i	coefficient characterizing screws of variable pitch
A'B'	constants	k', k	constants
B	batch weight	k_B	coefficient
a	exponent or variable; also ratio of countercurrent rate to forced flow rate	k_n	power number
		k	overall heat transfer coefficient
a'	interfacial area	L	length; carbon black loading
b	channel width	L_p	turbulent mixing length
b'	thickness of threads	l_0	zone length
c	velocity, constant	M	torque moments
C	concentration	M_w	weight average molecular weight
C_e	geometric scale factor	N_p	mixer power
C_w	heat capacity of water	N_t	mixing number
C_p	heat capacity at constant pressure	N_1, N_2	number of effective polymer chain segments and filler particles, respectively
c_1, c_2	coefficients		
D, d	diameter; also degree of carbon black dispersion	N_L	modified power number
$D_{x,z}$	shearing strain	N, n, n_0	rotational speed
E	elastic modulus	P	pressure; also centrifugal force
E_u	Euler number	P_r	Prandtl number
e	elasticity coefficient; also thread width	p	power input; also perimeter
		Q	volumetric rate or pumping capacity
F	area; also shape factor	Q_n	heat flow to extruder head
$F_{c,d}$	friction and geometric screw coefficients	q	mass or volumetric throughput; channel cross section
F'	force	R_e	Reynolds number
F_2	cross section of threads	R, r	radius
F_r	Froude number	S	entropy
f	ratio of cluster length to width	s	pitch; also swelling factor
G	modulus of rigidity; also gravitational force or mass throughput	T	absolute temperature; also parameter
G_a	Galileo number	t	temperature or time; helix pitch
G_w	cooling water mass rate	U	overall heat transfer coefficient velocity
g	gravitational acceleration		
H	depth or head; pitch of left thread of screw	u	velocity
		V	velocity or volume
h	height of screw channel or thread depth	W	dimension
		W_e	Weber number
h_e	heat transfer coefficient	W	particle width
i	number of threads	z	axial distance

Greek Symbols

α	heat transfer coefficient		and disperse phases, and emulsions,
α, β	angle or coefficients		respectively
$\dot{\gamma}$	shear rate	η_e	drive efficiency
γ	specific weight or concentration	θ	characteristic time
γ_{123}	elastic deformation	τ_i, τ'	mixing time
δ	clearance	τ	shear stress
ε	deformation	τ_y	yield stress
ε_b	percent ultimate strain of filled	ρ	density; also friction angle
	elastomer	v	velocity; kinematic viscosity
θ	temperature	φ	parameter or angle; also volume
λ	friction		fraction of filler
λ_1	time constant	φ_2^1	volume fraction of filler wetted by
λ_v	heat of vaporization		polymer
λ_b	stretch ratio	ψ	angle, stream function; also helix
μ	Newtonian viscosity		angle
η_0	efficiency	ψ'	void fraction
η_p	plastic viscosity	ψ_0	angle
η_c, η_d, η'	effective viscosities of continuous		

REFERENCES

1. Otswald, W., *Kollaidzchr*, 38, 26 (1926).
2. Reiner, M., *Deformation and Flow*, Lewis Pub., London (1949).
3. Wilkinson, W. L., *Non-Newtonian Flow*, Pergamon Press, N.Y. (1960). •
4. Metzner, A. B., "Non-Newtonian Technology," *Fluid Mechanics, Mixing and Heat Transfer, Advances in Chemical Engineering*, Vol. 1, 77–153, Academic Press, N.Y. (1956).
5. Pryce-Jones, J., *Coll. Zeits.*, 96, 129 (1952).
6. Schofield, R. K., and Scott-Bair, G. W.., Proc. Roy. Soc., A138, 707, (1932).
7. Oldroyd, J. G., Proc. Roy. Soc., A128, 122 (1953).
8. Frohlich, H., and Sack, R., Proc. Roy. Soc., A185, 415 (1946).
9. Toms, B. A., and Strawbridge, D. J., Trans. Faraday Soc., 49, 1225 (1953).
10. Azbel, D. S., and Cheremisinoff, N. P., *Fluid Mechanics and Unit Operation*, Ann Arbor Sci., Ann Arbon, Mich. (1983).
11. Metzner, A. B., and Otto, R. E., *AICHE J.*, 3,3 (1957).
12. Magnusson, K., *IVA*, 23, 2, 86–99 (1952).
13. Metzner, A. B., and Taylor, J. S., *AICHE J.*, 6, 109 (1960).
14. Rushton, J. H., Costich, E. W., and Everett, H. J., *Chem. Process Des. and Dev.*, 8, 267 (1969).
15. Calderbank, P. H., *Mixing*, Vol. 2 Uhl, V. H., and Gray, eds., Academic Press, N.Y. (1967).
16. Winding, C. C., Dittmann, F. W., and Kranich, W. L., Cornell Univ. Report, Ithaca, N.Y. (1944).
17. Orr, C., and Dalla Valle, J. M., Chem. Eng. Progr. Symp., Service No. 9, 50, 29 (1954)
18. Metzner, A. B., Vaughn, R. D., and Houghton, G. L., *AICHE J.* 3, 92 (1957).
19. Skelland, A. H. P., and Dimick, G. R., *Ind. Eng. Chem. Process Des. and Dev.*, 8, 267 (1969).
20. Hagedorn, D., and Salamone, J. J., *Ind. Eng. Chem. Process Des.* and Dev., 6, 46 (1967).
21. Skelland, A. H. P., Chapter 7, "Mixing and Agitation for Non-Newtonian Fluids," 179–211 in *Handbook of Fluids in Motion*, Cheremisinoff, N. P., and Gupta R., eds., Ann Arbor, Mich. (1983).
22. Baker, C. K., and Walter, G. H., Heat Transfer Engineering, 1, 2, 28 (1966).
23. Nagata, S., Mixing Principles and Application, John Wiley & Sons, N.Y. (1975).
24. Huggins, R. E., *Ind. Eng. Chem.*, 23, 749 (1931).
25. Houlton, H. G., *Ind. Eng. Chem.*, 36, 522 (1944).
26. Harriott, P., Chem. Eng. Prog. Symp. Ser., 55, 29, 137 (1959).

27. Bott, T. R., and Azoory, S., *Chemical and Process Engineering*, 50, 1, 85–90 (1969).
28. Ramdas, V., Uhl, V. W., Osborne, M. W., and Ortt, J. R., *Heat Transfer Engineering*, 1, 4, 38–46 (1980).
29. Skelland, A. H. P., and Seksaria, R., *Ind. Eng. Chem. Process Des. and Dev.*, 17, 56 (1978).
30. Treybal, R. E., *Liquid Extraction*, 2nd Ed., McGraw-Hill Co., N.Y., (1963).
31. Harriott, P., *AICHE J.*, 8, 93 (1962).
32. Calderbank, P. H., *Mixing*, Vol. 2 Uhl V. H., and Gray, eds., Academic Press, N.Y. (1967).
33. Azbel, D. S., Two-Phase Flows in Chemical Engineering, Cambridge Univ. Press, N.Y. (1981).
34. Carreau, P. J., Patterson, I., and Yap, *Can. J. Chem. Eng.*, 54, 135 (1976).
35. Chavan, V. V., and Ulbrecht, J., *The Chem. Eng. Journ.*, 6, 213–223 (1973).
36. Ford, D. E., and Ulbrecht, J., *AICHE J.*, 21, 1230 (1975).
37. Chavan, V. V., Armugam, M., and Ulbrecht, J., *AICHE J.*, 21, 613 (1975).
38. Coyle, C. K., Hirschland, H. E., Michal, B. J., and Oldshue, J. Y., *AICHE J.*, 16, 903 (1970).
39. Kelkar, J. V., Mahelkar, R. A., and Ulbrecht J., *J. Trans. Inst. Chem. Engrs.*, London, 50, 343 (1972).
40. Chavan, V. V., and R. A., Mashelkar, in *Advances in Transport Processes*, Mujudar, A. S., ed., Vol. 1, pp. 210–252, John Wiley & Sons, N.Y. (1980).
41. Ulbrecht, J., *The Chem. Eng.*, London, 347–353, 367 (1974).
42. Ulbrecht, J., *The Chem. Eng.*, London, 347–353, 367 (1974).
43. Pivosky, Ya. M., Polosin-Nikitin, S. M., and Votschinia, N. N., Dorozhnye mashiny i Oborudovanie, M. Mashgiz, USSR (1960).
44. Kharkhuta, N. Ya., Kapustin, M. I., and Semenov, V. P., Dorozhnye Mashiny i Oborudovanie, Mashgiz, M., USSR (1968).
45. Bernhardt, E., Pererabotka Termoplasticheskikh marerialov, M. Goshkhinisdat, USSR (1962).
45a. Bingham, E. C., *Fluidity and Plasticity*, McGraw-Hill, N.Y., (1922).
46. Guber, F. B., Kauchik i Resina, 9, 28, USSR (1966).
47. Zakharkin, O. A., et al., Kauchuk i Resina, 7, 8–11, USSR (1966).
48. Starov, I. M., et al., Kauchuk i Resina, 6, 19, USSR (1961).
49. Kapitonov, E. N., Kauchuk i Resina, 4, 20, USSR (1968).
50. Soroka, B. S., and B. A., Khimichestioe Mashinostroenie, 2, 15–19, Kiev, Tekhnika, USSR (1965).
51. Bekin, N. G., and V. A. Nemytkov, Kauchiek i Resina, 10, 31, USSR (1966).
52. Lukach, Yu. E., Ryabinin, D. D., and Metlov, B. N., Valkovye mashinydlia Pererabotki Plastmass i Resinovykh Smesey, M. Mashinostroenie, USSR (1967).
53. Karpachev, P. S., Maisel, M. M., and Plevako, N. A., Mashiny i Apparaty Proisvodstv iskustvenoy kozhy i Plenochnykh MMaterialov, M. Legkay Industria, USSR (1964).
54. Hawkins, W. L., *Rubber Plastics Weekly*, London, 142, 291 (1962); Hawkins, W. L., Rubber Plastics Weekly, London, 142, 291 (1966).
55. Cheremisinoff, P. N., and Ellerbusch, F., *Carbon Adsorption*, Ann Arbor.
56. Gessler, A. M., Hess, W. M., and Medalia, A. I., "Reinforcement of Elastomers with Carbon Black," paper 1164, Plastics and Rubber Processing (1978).
57. Baranival, K. C., Die makromolekulare Chemie, 100, 242 (1967).
58. Cotten, G. R., Paper No. 1 to A.C.S., Rubber Division, Cleveland, OH (May 1975).
59. Boonstra, B. B., in *Rubber Technology*, Morton, M., Ed., Litton Educational Pub. Inc., NY, 1973.
60. Andrews, E. H., and Walsh, A. J., *J. Pol. Sci.*, 33, 39 (1958).
61. Beatty, J. R., *Rubber Chem. and Tech.*, 37, 1341 (1964).
62. Corish, P. J., and Powell, B. D. W., *Rubber Chem. and Technol.*, 47, 3, 481 (1974).
63. Walters, M. H., and Keyte, D. N., Trans. I.R.I., 38, 40 (1962).
64. Corish, P. J., *Rubber Chem. and Technol.*, 44, 3, 814 (1971).
65. Boonstra, B. B., *Journ. of Appl. Polym. Sci.*, Vol. 11, 389–416, 19.4 (1967).
66. Cotten, G. R., Paper presented at Rubber Division Meeting, American Chemical Soc., Los Angeles, CA, April 23–26, 1985.
67. Cotten, G. R., *Rubber Chem. Technol.*, 57, 118 (1964).
68. Turetsky, S. B., Van Bushirk, P. R., and Gurberg, P. F., *Rubber Chem. Technol.*, 49, 1 (1976).

69. Smith, B. R., *Rubber Chem. Technol.*, 49, 278 (1976).
70. Payne, A. R., and Watson, W. F., *Rubber Chem. Technol.*, 36, 147 (1963).
71. Lee, M. C. H., *J. Appl. Polym. Sci.*, 29, 499 (1984).
72. Nielson, L. E., Vol. 2, Chapters 7 and 8 in *Mechanical Properties of Polymers and Composites*, Marcel Dekker Pub., NY, (1974).
73. Scott, C. E., and Eckert, F. J., *Rubber Chem. and Technol.*, 36, 147 (1963).
74. Burgess, K. A., and Hirshfield, S. M., and Stokes, C. A., *Rubber Age*, 98, 9, 85 (1965).
75. Burgess, K. A., Thune, S. S., and Palmese, E., *Rubber World*, 149, 4, 34 (1974).
76. Ryabinin, D. D., and Lukach, Yu. E., Cherviachnye Mashiny dlia Pererabotki Resinovykh smesei i Plasticheskikh mass, M. Mashinostroenie, USSR (1965).
77. Silin, V. A., Modelirovanie Chervyachnyk Mashin. sb. Trudov Ukrniplastmash, Oborudovanie dlia Pererabotki Polymerov, Kiev, Tekhnika, USSR (1964).

CHAPTER 27

MIXING OF NON-NEWTONIAN LIQUIDS WITH HELICAL RIBBON IMPELLERS

Koji Takahashi

Department of Chemical Engineering
Yamagata University
Yonezawa, Japan

CONTENTS

INTRODUCTION

The largest class of non-Newtonian fluids handled in the chemical and food industries are pseudo-plastic. They include nearly all polymer solutions, suspensions of solid in liquid media, and fermentation broths. For the mixing of pseudoplastic liquids, the use of a small impeller is quite inefficient, because the high apparent viscosities at the low shear fields distant from the impeller easily create the stagnant regions. To eliminate such regions, the close-clearance impellers are commonly used. These impellers require high power input and are operated at quite low agitation speeds. The impellers which produce mainly tangential flow, such as the anchor, gate, and large paddle impellers, provide poor top-to-bottom mixing. For this reason, the impellers of more complex designs such as the helical ribbon and helical screw impeller are used. This chapter discusses the mixing of pseudoplastic liquids in a helical ribbon agitated vessel.

POWER CONSUMPTION

Power consumption provides a useful basis for comparison in the evaluation of the impellers with different geometrical variables for mixing time.

For Newtonian liquids, power consumption in the laminar flow region can be expressed as [2, 11, 16, 19, 22]:

$$NP \cdot Re = C_1 \tag{1}$$

where C_1 is a geometrical constant.

Table 1

Summary of Power Correlation Based on Modified Reynolds Number

Authors	Reference	Correlation
Bourne and Butler	2	$N_P \cdot Re_m = \pi^2 \left(\dfrac{h}{d}\right)\left(\dfrac{D}{d}\right)^2 \left(\dfrac{4\pi}{n\{(D/d)^{2/n} - 1\}}\right)^n$
Chavan and Ulbrecht	5, 6	$N_P \cdot Re_m = 2.5\pi a \left(\dfrac{de}{d}\right)\lambda^2 \left\{\dfrac{4\pi}{n(\lambda^{2/n} - 1)}\right\}^n$
		where $a = \pi(h/d)(w/d)/(s/d)$
		$\lambda = D/de$
		$\dfrac{de}{d} = \dfrac{D}{d} - \dfrac{2(w/d)}{\ln\left(\dfrac{(D/d) - \{1 - 2(w/d)\}}{(D/d) - 1}\right)}$
Sawinsky, Havas and Deak	22	$N_P \cdot Re_m = 19\left(\dfrac{L}{d}\right)^{0.45}\left(\dfrac{D}{d}\right)\left(\dfrac{D}{c}\right)\exp\left\{(n-1)\left(4.2\dfrac{d}{D} - 0.5\right)\right\}$
		where $\dfrac{L}{d} = \left(\dfrac{h}{d}\right)\sqrt{1 + \pi^2\left(\dfrac{d}{s}\right)^2}$

For non-Newtonian liquids, a similar relation has been obtained by several investigators [2, 5, 6, 11, 16, 20, 22]:

$$Np \cdot Re' = C_1' \tag{2}$$

where C_1' is a function of the liquid properties adding to the geometrical variables.

They used two different types of the Reynolds number: the modified Reynolds number, Re_m[2, 5, 6, 22]; and the apparent Reynolds number, Re_a[11, 20], and recommended a different correlation for each geometry.

The power-law model is simple and has been widely used to describe the flow behavior of the pseudoplastic liquids:

$$\tau = K \cdot \dot{\gamma}^n \tag{3}$$

where K and n are consistency and flow behavior indexes, respectively. By substitution of Equation 3 into the definition of the Reynolds number, the modified Reynolds number is expressed for pseudoplastic liquids:

$$Re_m = d^2 N^{2-n} \rho / K \tag{4}$$

The power correlations using this modified Reynolds number are summarized in Table 1 [2, 5, 6, 22].

Metzner-Otto Method

A method widely used for power correlation in the mixing of non-Newtonian liquids is the "Metzner-Otto" method [13]. They assumed that there is an effective shear rate for a mixer which describes power consumption, and that this shear rate is directly proportional to impeller speed:

$$\dot{\gamma}_e = k_m N \tag{5}$$

where k_m depends on geometrical variables and the flow behavior index for power law liquids. If k_m in Equation 5 is given in advance, the apparent viscosity for non-Newtonian liquids is evaluated from the measurement of the flow curve by using the following equation:

$$\mu_a = \tau / \dot{\gamma}_e \tag{6}$$

Thus, the apparent Reynolds number is defined as follows:

$$Re_a = d^2 N \rho / \mu_a = (d^2 N^{2-n} \rho / K) / (k_m)^{n-1} \tag{7}$$

Assuming that the relation expressed by Equation 1 is valid for the non-Newtonian liquids as well, the power for non-Newtonian liquids can be calculated by replacing the Reynolds number in Equation 1 with the apparent Reynolds number.

Reversing the above-mentioned procedure, the values of k_m are determined. That is, from the power measurement at a specified rotational speed of the impeller for pseudoplastic liquids, and the power number characteristics of Newtonian liquids expressed by Equation 1, the apparent viscosity for the pseudoplastic liquid is calculated:

$$\mu_a^* = d^2 N \rho \, N_p^* / C_1 = P^* / d^3 N^2 C_1 \tag{8}$$

The effective shear rate corresponding to this apparent viscosity can be estimated from the measurement of flow curve. Therefore, the value of k_m is calculated from Equation 5. Figure 1 shows graphically this procedure for getting the value of k_m [10, 14].

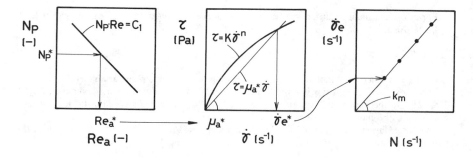

Figure 1. Determination of shear rate constant k_m.

The author and co-workers [26] have carried out the measurements of the power consumption for helical ribbon impellers of different geometrical variables and determined the values of km. The general configuration of a helical ribbon impeller is shown in Figure 2. Table 2 summarizes the geometrical variables of impellers used. The typical geometrical variables taken into account are the clearance between blades and wall, c, the impeller pitch, s, and blade width, w. Aqueous solutions of corn syrup were used as Newtonian liquids to obtain the values of C_1 in Equation 1. Aqueous solutions of carboxymethyl cellulose and mixtures of these solutions and corn syrup were used as pseudoplastic liquids. The rheological behavior of the pseudoplastic liquid could be expressed by the power law model given in Equation 3. The values of consistency and flow behavior indexes are shown in Table 3. The relations between the effective shear rate and the rotational speed are shown in Figure 3. This figure shows that the value of k_m is independent of the liquid properties. The values of k_m determined experimentally are also summarized in Table 2. The values of k_m recommended in papers of other workers and the geometries of helical ribbon impellers used are tabulated in Table 4.

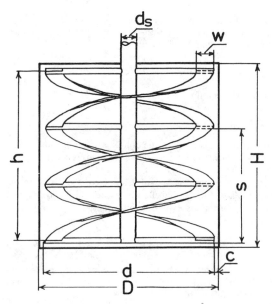

Figure 2. General configuration of a helical ribbon impeller.

Table 2
Geometrical Variables and Measured k_m for Helical Ribbon Impellers

Geometry No.	c/D	s/D	w/D	km
DH1	0.0227	0.914	0.102	37.9
DH2	0.0623	0.966	0.101	24.7
DH3	0.0970	0.956	0.102	19.3
DH4	0.0583	0.643	0.102	32.7
DH5	0.0502	0.452	0.102	37.7
DH6	0.0404	1.26	0.102	28.2
DH7	0.0457	1.89	0.102	24.3
DH8	0.0448	0.912	0.0771	24.3
DH9	0.0449	0.916	0.128	28.8
DH10	0.0416	0.932	0.153	31.5
DH11	0.0431	0.914	0.203	30.5

$D = H = 128$ mm $n_p = 2$ $d_s/D = 0.0938$

Table 3
Properties of Test Liquids

Liquid No.	n [−]	K [Pa · sⁿ]
1.0 wt% CMC	$0.768 \sim 0.770$	$2.22 \sim 2.46$
2.5 wt% CMC	$0.543 \sim 0.566$	$1.20 \sim 1.72$
3.0 wt% CMC	$0.443 \sim 0.473$	$4.12 \sim 6.33$

Several investigators [9, 11, 23, 24] have proposed the power correlations for Newtonian liquids applicable to the various geometries of helical ribbon impellers. Thus, the accurate estimation of km makes it possible to predict the power consumption for non-Newtonian liquids precisely.

Correlation of km

The relation between the experimental values of k_m listed in Tables 2 and 4 and each of three geometrical ratios, c/D, s/D, and w/D, is shown in Figure 4. A decrease in c/D or s/D and an increase in w/D both increase the value of k_m. This figure indicates that k_m can be correlated by the following equation [26]:

$$k_m = 11.4(c/D)^{-0.411}(s/D)^{-0.361}(w/D)^{0.164} \tag{9}$$

The four constants in Equation 9 were determined by a multiple non-linear regression using the experimental data shown in Table 2.

Some investigators have reported the effects of geometrical variables for helical ribbon impellers on the value of k_m as well. The correlations for km proposed are summarized in Table 5. The relationship between the modified Reynolds number. Re_m, and the apparent Reynolds number, Re_a, can be expressed as follows:

$$Re_a = Re_m/(k_m)^{n-1} \tag{10}$$

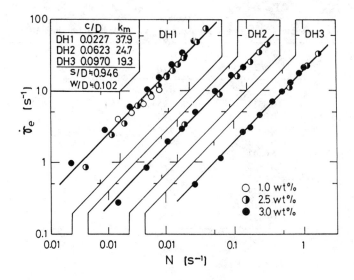

A. effect of clearance

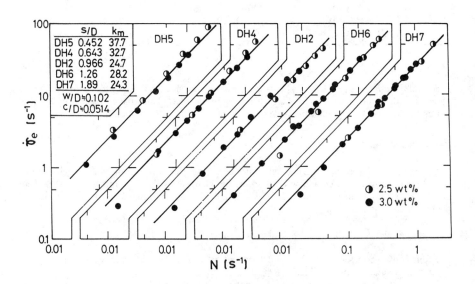

B. effect of impeller pitch

Figure 3. Relations between effective shear rate and rotational speed. (A) effect of clearance; (B) effect of impeller pitch; (C) effect of blade width.

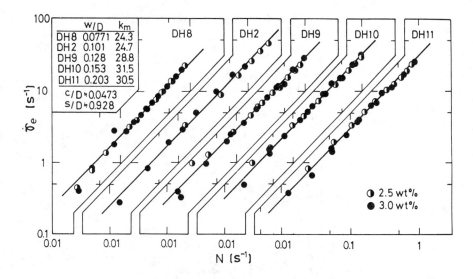

C. effect of blade width

Figure 3. *continued*

Combining Equation 10 and the power correlations based on the modified Reynolds number listed in Table 1, the correlations for k_m can be obtained. These are tabulated in Table 5 as well. Some of them indicate that k_m depends on the flow behavior index in addition to the geometrical variables, but the variation of the value of k_m with the changes in flow behavior index is very small for the correlations obtained by Bourne and Butler [2] and Chavan and Ulbrecht [5.6] except for that proposed by Yap, Patterson, and Carreau [28] as reported elsewhere [21].

Every correlation listed in Table 5 takes into account the effect of the clearance between blades and vessel wall on k_m, but rarely the effects of impeller pitch and blade width. Only the correlations proposed by Chavan and Ulbrecht [5, 6] and Yap, Patterson, and Carreau [28] include the blade width and the impeller pitch, respectively, as one of the geometrical variables. Carreau et al. [4] have indicated the important roles of these geometrical variables, especially blade width, in the mixing of Newtonian and pseudoplastic liquids. The correlation derived by the author and co-workers incorporates these three geometrical variables. The relation between k_m calculated from the correlations and each geometrical variable is compared in Figure 5. Figure 5(a) shows that the correlations proposed by Sawinsky, Havas, and Deak [22]; Kuriyama, Arai, and Saito [12]; Edwards and Ayazi-Shamlou [9]; and the author and co-workers [26] can represent the effect of clearance on k_m approximately. Figure 5(b) and 5(c) show that only the correlation obtained by the author and co-workers agrees with the experimental results.

Figure 6 shows the comparison of calculated values of k_m from Equation 9 and experimental ones. The agreement between them is satisfactory. Since Chavan and Ulbrecht [6] have reported that the elasticity has no influence on the power consumption in the laminar flow region, Equation 9 may also be applicable for the viscoelastic liquids.

MIXING [27]

In a helical ribbon agitator, mixing proceeds mainly in the clearance between blades and wall where the liquid is subjected to very high shearing, but the overall mixing appears to be controlled

Table 4

Geometrical Variables and Values of k_m from Literature

Authors	Reference	D[m]	n_p	c/D	s/D	w/D	H/D	k_m
Hall and Godfrey	11	0.042	1	0.051	0.464	0.121		
		0.287	1	0.044	0.451	0.0886		
		0.287	2	0.044	0.912	0.0886	1.02	27
		0.287	2	0.049	0.902	0.0885		
		0.559	2	0.045	0.91	0.091		
Nagata, Nishikawa, Tada and Gotoh	17	0.200 0.300 0.400	2	0.0250	0.950	0.100	—	30.0
Rieger and Novak	20	0.101 0.148	2	0.0250	0.950	0.0950	—	36.73 ± 1.45
Kuriyama, Arai, and Saito	12	0.160	2	0.024 0.048 0.070	0.900	0.100	1.00	32 25 21

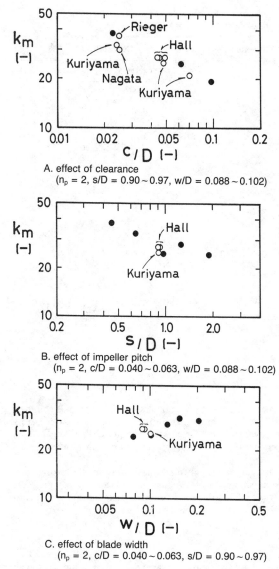

A. effect of clearance
($n_p = 2$, s/D = 0.90 ~ 0.97, w/D = 0.088 ~ 0.102)

B. effect of impeller pitch
($n_p = 2$, c/D = 0.040 ~ 0.063, w/D = 0.088 ~ 0.102)

C. effect of blade width
($n_p = 2$, c/D = 0.040 ~ 0.063, s/D = 0.90 ~ 0.97)

Figure 4. Relation between experimental values of shear rate constant and each of three geometrical ratios (● author ○ others). (A) effect of clearance ($n_p = 2$, s/D = 0.90 ~ 0.97, w/D = 0.088 ~ 0.102); (B) effect of impeller pitch ($n_p = 2$, c/D = 0.040 ~ 0.063, w/D = 0.088 ~ 0.102); (C) effect of blade width ($n_p = 2$, c/D = 0.040 ~ 0.063, s/D = 0.90 ~ 0.97).

by the flow pattern which permits the renewal of liquid in the clearance and distributes the liquid flowing out of the clearance region to the low-shear region of the vessel. The flow pattern may be easily affected by small changes of liquid properties adding to those of impeller geometrical variables. Thus, the mixing of non-Newtonian liquids in a helical ribbon agitated vessel is a much more complex topic than power consumption, and the amount of data and theory available is relatively small.

Several investigators [3, 4, 15] have carried out the measurements of the mixing time of pseudoplastic liquids with helical ribbon impellers in the small range of Reynolds number and reported that the dimensionless mixing time is constant in the laminar flow region, as well as that for

Table 5
Summary of Correlations of k_m

Authors	Reference	Correlation
Bourne and Butler	2	$k_m = 4\pi \left\{ \dfrac{[n\{(D/d)^{2/n} - 1\}]^n}{(D/d)^2 - 1} \right\}^{1/(1-n)}$
Chavan and Ulbrecht	5, 6	$k_m = 4\pi \left\{ \dfrac{[n(\lambda^{2/n} - 1)]^n}{\lambda^2 - 1} \right\}^{1/(1-n)}$
Sawinsky, Havas and Deak	22	$k_m = \exp\left\{ 4.2\left(\dfrac{d}{D}\right) - 0.5 \right\}$
Yap, Patterson and Carreau	28	$k_m = 4^{1/(1-n)}\left(\dfrac{d}{D}\right)^2\left(\dfrac{L}{d}\right)$
Edwards and Ayazi-Shamlou	9	$k_m = 34 - 114\left(\dfrac{c}{d}\right)$
Kuriyama, Arai and Saito	12	$k_m = 8.9\left(\dfrac{c}{D}\right)^{-1/3}$
Takahashi, Yokota and Konno	26	$k_m = 11.4\left(\dfrac{c}{D}\right)^{-0.411}\left(\dfrac{s}{D}\right)^{-0.361}\left(\dfrac{w}{D}\right)^{0.164}$

Newtonian liquids. That is:

$$N \cdot t_m = C_2 \tag{11}$$

where C_2 is a function of liquid properties and geometrical variables. However, there is considerable confusion about the effect of non-Newtonian properties on the value of C_2. Carreau et al. [3, 4] reported the value up to 5 times longer than that for Newtonian liquids, while Nagata et al. [15] reported that C_2 is almost independent of the material properties for both Newtonian and non-Newtonian fluids.

In a wide range of Reynolds number, the author and co-workers have measured the mixing times of pseudoplastic liquids in agitated vessels equipped with various types of helical ribbon impellers by means of the liquid crystal method [25]. The properties of test liquids and the geometrical variables of impellers are summarized in Tables 6 and 7, respectively.

Correlation of Mixing Time

The patterns of the primary circulation flows are almost the same as mentioned for Newtonian liquids by previous investigators [1, 4, 18], and the mixing patterns are approximately similar in spite of the different liquid properties and impeller geometries.

Figure 7 shows the relations between the dimensionless mixing time. $N\,t_m$, and the apparent Reynolds number, Re_a, of different liquid properties for each impeller. With the widest clearance impellers, DH3, the stagnant zones are detected at both the top and bottom corner near the wall, even after 500 impeller revolutions. Mixing time was determined in the region without the stagnant zones. In each figure, the broken line represents the data for Newtonian liquid reported by the author and co-workers [25].

The data shown in Figure 7 indicate that the mixing times of pseudoplastic liquids are almost the same as those for Newtonian liquids, but increase slightly with an increase in Reynolds number.

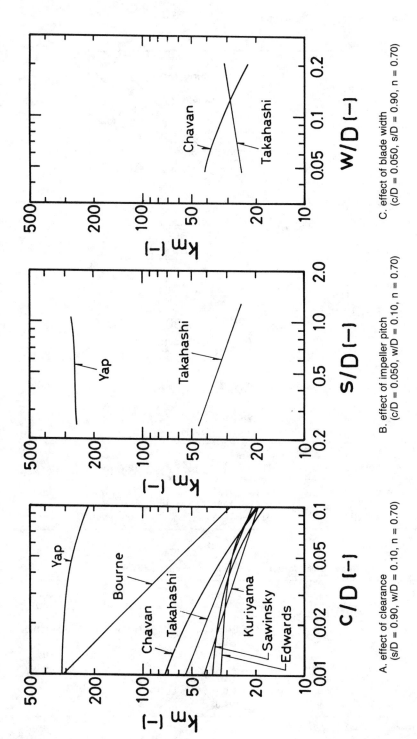

Figure 5. Comparison of correlations of shear rate constant from literature. (A) effect of clearance (s/D = 0.90, w/D = 0.10, n = 0.70); (B) effect of impeller pitch (c/D = 0.050, w/D = 0.10, n = 0.70); (C) effect of blade width (c/D = 0.050, s/D = 0.90, n = 0.70).

A. effect of clearance
(s/D = 0.90, w/D = 0.10, n = 0.70)

B. effect of impeller pitch
(c/D = 0.050, w/D = 0.10, n = 0.70)

C. effect of blade width
(c/D = 0.050, s/D = 0.90, n = 0.70)

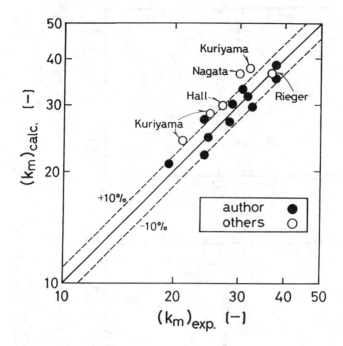

Figure 6. Correlation of k_m.

Table 6
Properties of Test Liquids

Liquid No.	n [−]	K [Pa · Sⁿ]
3 wt% HEC	$0.768 \sim 0.832$	$0.724 \sim 1.56$
4 wt% HEC	$0.718 \sim 0.761$	$2.76 \sim 4.60$
5 wt% HEC	$0.686 \sim 0.735$	$7.06 \sim 14.1$

Table 7
Geometrical Variables for Helical Ribbon Impellers

Geometry No.	d[mm]	c/D	s/D	w/D
DH1	95.9	0.0208	0.926	0.100
DH2	88.5	0.0574	0.909	0.100
DH3	82.0	0.0900	0.912	0.100
DH4	91.0	0.0450	0.621	0.100
DH5	90.3	0.0482	0.455	0.100
DH6	90.4	0.0482	0.930	0.152
DH7	91.9	0.0405	0.921	0.200

$D = H = 100\,mm$ $n_P = 2$ $d_s/D = 0.0938$

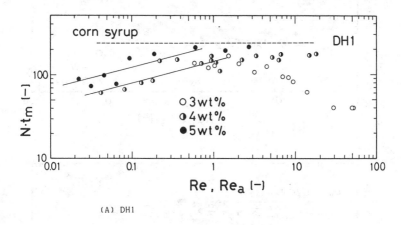

(A) DH1

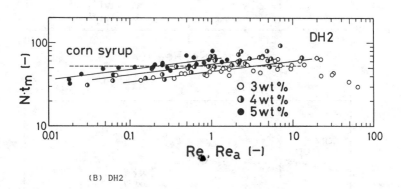

(B) DH2

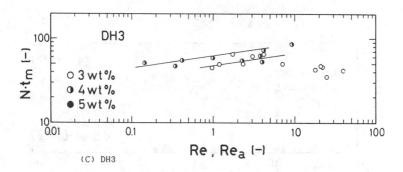

(C) DH3

Figure 7. Relation between dimensionless mixing time and apparent Reynolds number of different pseudoplastic liquids for each impeller. (A) DH1, (B) DH2, (C) DH3, (D) DH4, (E) DH5, (F) DH6, (G) DH7.

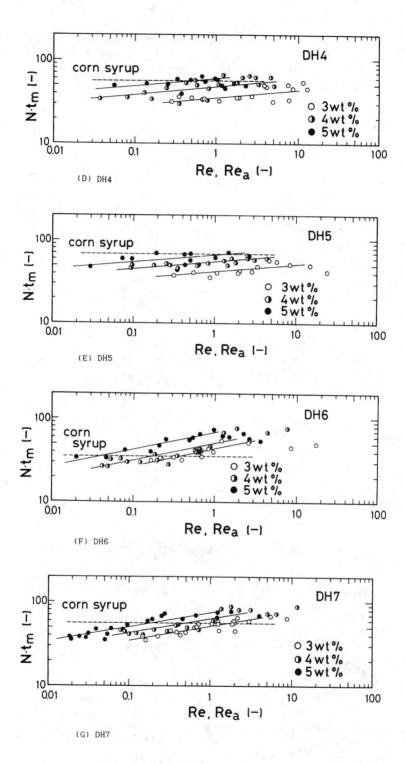

Figure 7. (Continued)

Geometry No.	α			β	Q_1/Nd^3
	3 wt%	4 wt%	5 wt%		
DH1	—	145	221	0.256	0.108
DH2	45.1	55.0	63.5	0.123	0.112
DH3*	47.7	62.4	—	0.146	0.123
DH4	35.5	47.6	59.6	0.0928	0.0732
DH5	42.1	54.9	65.9	0.0832	0.0708
DH6	43.0	49.2	67.5	0.205	0.185
DH7	51.3	62.9	74.5	0.171	0.137

* measured in the region without stagnant zones

The most plausible equation for the mixing time of pseudoplastic liquid is:

$$N \cdot t_m = \alpha \, Re_a^{\beta} \tag{12}$$

This expression differs from Equation 11 recommended by the previous investigators.

Using a least square method, the two constants α and β in Equation 12 were determined. It was found that the value of β is almost independent of liquid properties, but dependent on the geometries of the system. Therefore, for each impeller, the average value of β of three pseudoplastic liquids was calculated, and another constant α of each liquid was redetermined. The values of α and β are listed in Table 8. The calculated results of $N \cdot t_m$ are shown as solid lines in Figure 7.

For each impeller, the value of α increases as the test liquids become more non-Newtonian. Because of the small difference in the flow behavior indexes of pseudoplastic liquids used in this work, it was difficult to estimate precisely the effect of liquid properties on the value of α. Carreau [3] has reported the dimensionless mixing time of non-Newtonian liquids with a helical ribbon agitator measured by a decoloration method in a small range of the Reynolds number, according to the relation represented by Equation 11. The relation between the mixing time and the flow behavior index is shown in Table 9. The data also indicate that the mixing time increases drastically as the liquid shear-thinning property increases, in spite of the different impeller geometries and measurement methods of mixing time.

Figure 8 shows the relation between the value of β and each of the three geometrical ratios. The value of β increases with both a decrease in clearance and an increase in impeller pitch, and has a maximum at a certain w/D. For Newtonian liquids, the author and co-workers have reported the circulation flow rate calculated from the time required for the tracer liquid to complete one circuit [25]. The values of circulation number, $Q_1/(Nd^3)$, are also summarized in Table 8. It is clearly

Table 9
Influence of Liquid Properties on Mixing Time Reported by Carreau [3]

Liquid	$N\,t_m$	n
85% and 100% glycerol	45	1
2.1% CMC	105	0.41
2.5% CMC	123	0.41
0.5% Separan	143	0.27
1.5% Separan	258	0.20

D = 144 mm   c/D = 0.0495   s/D = 0.648   w/D = 0.0874

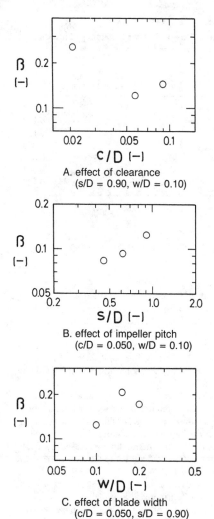

Figure 8. Relation between value of β and each of three geometrical ratios. (A) effect of clearance (s/D = 0.90, w/D = 0.10); (B) effect of impeller pitch (c/D = 0.050, w/D = 0.10); (C) effect of blade width (c/D = 0.050, s/D = 0.90).

seen that the value of β is nearly proportional to the circulation number. Pseudoplastic liquids have a lower viscosity in regions of high shear, as near an impeller, and a higher viscosity in regions of low shear, as distant from an impeller. Therefore, a large viscosity distribution may be created in a vessel equipped with the impeller, which creates a strong circulation flow rate. This distribution may change with the impeller speed and lead to flow pattern and mixing behavior dependent on the Reynolds number.

In order to investigate the dependency of flow pattern on Reynolds number, the axial circulation times, t_c, were measured by following a tracer particle in a wide range of Reynolds number for the DH2 impeller. The circulation times were measured at least 30 times for every rotational speed. The average values of circulation numbers were plotted against Reynolds numbers and shown in Figure 9. With an increase in Reynolds number, the dimensionless circulation time increases slightly. Note that similar results have been obtained by Chavan et al. [7, 8] for pseudoplastic liquids with helical screw impellers at a low Reynolds number. The dependency of the dimensionless circulation time on Reynolds number is smaller than that of the dimensionless mixing time. It

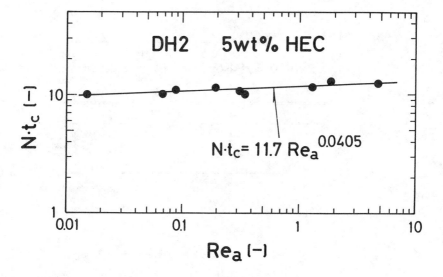

Figure 9. Relation between circulation number and apparent Reynolds number.

may be explained by the assumption that the tangential flow rate increases with an increase in Reynolds number as well. However, more quantitative information about flow patterns is necessary for detailed discussion.

Mixer Selection

Figure 10 shows the comparisons of the calculated mixing times of each pseudoplastic liquid between the different impellers. The results of those of Newtonian liquids reported elsewhere [25] are also shown in Figure 10. For optimum performance in terms of mixing time, the DH6 impeller seems best for Newtonian liquids. On the other hand, the most efficient impeller for the mixing of pseudoplastic liquids is the DH6 impeller in the region of $Re_a < 0.5$, and the DH4 impeller in the region of $0.5 \leqq Re_a$, in spite of different flow behavior indexes covered in this work. In the mixing process of pseudoplastic liquids, the recommended values of c/D, s/D, and w/D, are 0.050, 0.60, and 0.15, respectively. These values differ from those proposed by the author and co-workers for Newtonian liquids, i.e, 0.060, 0.90, and 0.15. A large pitch impeller has a relatively large region of low shear between blades where pseudoplastic liquids have a higher viscosity, and therefore, is not suitable for the mixing of pseudoplastic liquids.

NOTATION

a	dimensionless surface area, $(-)$	H	height of vessel, m
c	clearance between blades and vessel wall, m	h	height of impeller, m
		K	consistency index, $N \cdot s^n/m^2$
C_1, C_1', C_2	geometrical constants in Equations 1, 2 and 11, respectively, $(-)$	k_m	shear rate constant in Equation 5, $(-)$
D	vessel diameter, m	L	length of blade, m
d	impeller diameter, m	N	rotational speed of impeller, s^{-1}
de	equivalent diameter in power correlation by Chavan et al., m	NP	power number $(=P/\rho d^5 N^3)$, $(-)$
		n	flow behavior index, $(-)$
d_s	shaft diameter, m	n_p	number of blades, $(-)$

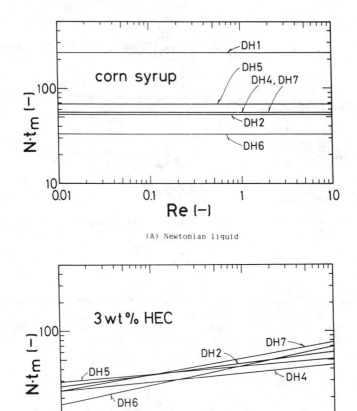

(A) Newtonian liquid

(B) 3wt% HEC

Figure 10. Influence of impeller geometry on mixing time of Newtonian [25] or each pseudo-plastic liquid between different impellers. (A) Newtonian liquid (B) 3 wt% HEC (C) 4 wt% HEC (D) 5 wt% HEC

P	power consumption, W
Q_1	axial circulation flow rate calculated from the time required for tracer liquid to complete one circuit, m^3/s
Re	Reynolds number $(=d^2N\rho/\mu)$, $(-)$
Re_a	apparent Reynolds number $(=d^2N\rho/\mu_a)$, $(-)$

Re_m	modified Reynolds number $(=d^2N^{2-n}\rho/K)$, $(-)$
Re'	apparent or modified Reynolds number, $(-)$
s	impeller pitch, $(-)$
t_c	axial circulation time, s
t_m	mixing time, s
w	blade width, m

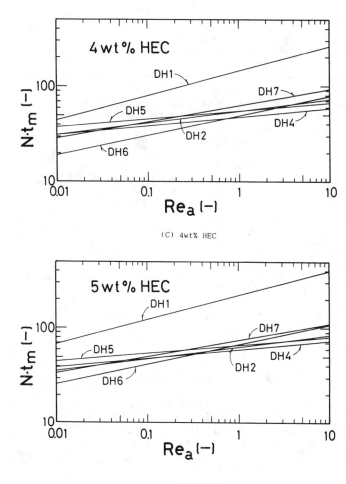

(C) 4wt% HEC

(D) 5wt% HEC

Figure 10. (Continued)

Greek Symbols

α, β	constants in Equation 12, $(-)$	μ	viscosity, Pa·s
$\dot{\gamma}$	shear rate, s^{-1}	μ_a	apparent viscosity, Pa·s
$\dot{\gamma}_e$	effective shear rate, s^{-1}	ρ	density, kg/m^3
λ	parameter in power correlation by Chavan et al., $(-)$	τ	shear stress, Pa

REFERENCES

1. Bourne, J. R., and Butler, H., "An Analysis of the Flow Produced by Helical Ribbon Impellers," *Trans. Inst. Chem. Engrs.*, Vol. 47 (1969), pp. T11–T17.
2. Bourne, J. R., and Butler, H., "Power Consumption of Helical Ribbon Impellers," *Trans. Inst. Chem. Engrs.*, Vol. 47 (1969), pp. T267–T270.

3. Carreau, P. J., "Mixing of Rheologically Complex Fluids," *Proceedings of Second World Congress of Chemical Engineering*, Montreal, Canada, (1981), pp. 379–382.
4. Carreau, P. J., Patterson, I., and Yap, C. Y., "Mixing of Viscoelastic Fluids with Helical-Ribbon Agitators. I-Mixing Time and Flow Patterns," *Can. J. Chem. Eng.*, Vol. 54 (1976), pp. 135–142.
5. Chavan, V. V., and Ulbrecht, J., "Power Correlation for Helical Ribbon Impellers in Inelastic Non-Newtonian Fluids," *Chem. Eng. J.*, Vol. 3 (1972), pp. 308–311.
6. Chavan, V. V., and Ulbrecht, J., "Power Correlation for Close-Clearance Helical Impellers in Non-Newtonian Liquids," *Ind. Eng. Chem. Process Des. Develop.*, Vol. 12 (1973), pp. 472–476.
7. Chavan, V. V., and Ulbrecht, J., "Internal Circulation in Vessels Agitated by Screw Impellers," *Chem. Eng. J.*, Vol. 6 (1973), pp. 213–223.
8. Chavan, V. V., Ford, D. E., and Arumugam, M., "Influence of Fluid Rheology on Circulation, Mixing and Blending," *Can. J. Chem. Eng.*, Vol. 53 (1975), pp. 628–635.
9. Edwards, M. F., and Ayazi-Shamlou, P., *Low Reynolds Number Flow Heat Exchangers*, Hemisphere Publishing Corpn., 1983.
10. Godfrey, J. C., *Mixing in the Process Industries* (Harnby, N., Edwards, M. F., and Nienow, A. W., Eds.), Butterworth & Co. Ltd., 1985, pp. 185–201.
11. Hall, K. R., and Godfrey, J. C., "Power Consumption by Helical Ribbon Impellers," *Trans. Inst. Chem. Engrs.*, Vol. 48, (1970), pp. T201–T208.
12. Kuriyama, M., Arai, K., and Saito, S., "Mechanism of Heat Transfer to Pseudoplastic Fluids in an Agitated Tank with Helical Ribbon Impeller," *J. Chem. Eng. Japan*, Vol. 16, (1983), pp. 489–494.
13. Metzner, A. B., and Otto, R. E., "Agitation of Non-Newtonian Fluids," *AIChE J.*, Vol. 3, (1957), pp. 3–10.
14. Nagata, S., *Mixing: Principles and Applications*, Halstead-John Wiley, New York, 1975.
15. Nagata, S., Nishikawa, M., Katsube, T., and Takaishi, K., "Mixing of Highly Viscous Liquids," *Kagaku Kogaku*, Vol. 35, (1971), pp. 794–800.
16. Nagata, S., Nishikawa, M., Gotoh, S., and Nakajima, M., "Power Consumption of Helical Mixer for the Mixing of Highly Viscous Liquid," *Kagaku Kogaku*, Vol. 34, (1970), pp. 1115–1117.
17. Nagata, S., Nishikawa, M., Tada, H., and Gotoh, S., "Power Consumption of Mixing Impellers in Pseudo-plastic Liquids," *J. Chem. Eng. Japan*, Vol. 4, (1971), pp. 72–76.
18. Nagata, S., Yanagimoto, T., and Yokoyama, T., "A Study on the Mixing of High-Viscosity Liquid," *Kagaku Kogaku*, Vol. 21, (1957), pp. 278–286.
19. Novak, V., and Rieger, F., "Homogenization Efficiency of Helical Ribbon and Anchor Agitators," *Chem. Eng. J.*, Vol. 9, (1975), pp. 63–70.
20. Rieger, F., and Novak, V., "Power Consumption of Agitators in Highly Viscous Non-Newtonian Liquids," *Trans. Inst. Chem. Eng.*, Vol. 51, (1973), pp. 105–111.
21. Saito, S., Arai, K., Takahashi, K., and Kuriyama, M., *Encyclopedia of Fluid Mechanics Vol. 2 Dynamics of Single-Fluid Flows and Mixing* (Cheremisinoff, N. P., Ed.), Gulf Publishing Co., 1986, pp. 927–948.
22. Sawinski, J., Havas, G., and Deak, A., "Power Requirement of Anchor and Helical Ribbon Impellers for the Case of Agitating Newtonian and Pseudoplastic Liquids," *Chem. Eng. Sci.*, Vol. 31, (1976), pp. 507–509.
23. Takahashi, K., Arai, K., and Saito, S., "Power Correlation for Anchor and Helical Ribbon Impellers in Highly Viscous Liquids," *J. Chem. Eng. Japan*, Vol. 13, (1980), pp. 147–150.
24. Takahashi, K., Arai, K., and Saito, S., "An Extended Power Correlation for Anchor and Helical Ribbon Impellers," *J. Chem. Eng. Japan*, Vol. 15, (1982), pp. 77–79.
25. Takahashi, K., Sasaki, M., Arai, K., and Saito, S., "Effects of Geometrical Variables of Helical Ribbon Impellers on Mixing of Highly Viscous Newtonian Liquids," *J. Chem. Eng. Japan*, Vol. 15, (1982), pp. 217–224.
26. Takahashi, K., Yokota, T., and Konno, H., "Power Consumption of Helical Ribbon Agitators in Highly Viscous Pseudoplastic Liquids," *J. Chem. Eng. Japan*, Vol. 17, (1984), pp. 657–659.
27. Takahashi, K., Yokota, T., and Konno, H., "Mixing of Pseudoplastic Liquid in an Agitated Vessel Equipped with a Variety of Helical Ribbon Impellers," *J. Chem. Eng. Japan*, Vol. 21, (1988), pp. 63–68.
28. Yap, C. Y., Patterson, W. I., and Carreau, P. J., "Mixing with Helical-Ribbon Agitators—Part III. Non-Newtonian Fluids," *AIChE J.*, Vol. 25, (1979), pp. 516–521.

CHAPTER 28

MIXING IN CONTINUOUS PROCESSORS

Dilhan M. Kalyon

Department of Chemistry and Chemical Engineering
Stevens Institute of Technology
Hoboken, New Jersey, USA

CONTENTS

GENERAL BACKGROUND

Introduction

Mixing of various ingredients is an important task in polymer processing. Mixing operations include the blending of a number of polymeric resins together, reactive processing, and the introduction of various solid and liquid additives. Some of the commonly used additives are processing aids, cross-linking, foaming and slip agents, stabilizers, antioxidants, and pigments. Various fillers and reinforcements are also incorporated into polymers to improve costs, ultimate properties, or appearance of final product.

The diverse mixing tasks encountered in polymer processing are carried out with either batch or continuous mixers. Batch mixers include paddle, double arm, planetary, intensive internal mixers, and roll mills [1, 2]. Continuous mixers include single screw and twin screw extruders, single shaft kneaders, and co-rotating disc extruders. Continuous mixers have the following advantages:

- They generally come with interchangeable parts and are thus versatile.
- They hold only a fraction of the load of a batch mixer at any time, while producing at the same rate.
- They facilitate better heat transfer due to their greater surface to volume ratio in comparison to batch mixers.
- They allow for better control of product quality.
- Uninterrupted operation is possible with continuous mixers.

In this chapter, various continuous mixers and their salient features will be discussed. However, first an introduction to quantitative description of the mixing quality will be made, to be followed by a review of the basic mechanisms of mixing. These concepts will be utilized in evaluation of various types of continuous mixers.

Description of Mixing Quality—"Goodness of Mixing"

Quantitative means are desirable for describing the mixing quality or goodness of mixing of a given mixture. The mixture will be taken to consist of one minor and one major component, which can be solid or liquid. When more than two components are involved, analysis can be facilitated by considering the operation as concurrent mixing of each component with the rest [3]. Quantitative descriptions can be developed upon comparison of the mixture to the most complete mixing state attainable. This "complete mixing" corresponds to statistical randomness of the ultimate particles (distinct blobs of fluid, individual particulates, etc.) of the ingredients being mixed. Mixtures can thus be described by their deviation from a completely random mixture employing conventional statistical parameters, tests of confidence, and distributions.

The approach to the quantitative description of a mixture basically involves the following steps:

- Determine whether the mixture is random.
- If results indicate that the mixture cannot be considered as random, characterize the scale and intensity of segregation of the mixture. These parameters describe the average distance between clumps of the same component and the average deviation of the concentration from the mean concentration.

The distribution in the randomly mixed system is given by the binomial distribution, which describes the probability, P_n, of finding x particles of the minor component in each sample consisting of n particles:

$$P_n(x) = \binom{n}{x} \Phi^x (1 - \Phi)^{n-x} \tag{1}$$

where Φ is the volume fraction of the minor component in the random mixture and the binomial coefficient is given by:

$$\binom{n}{x} = \frac{n!}{x!(n-x)!} \tag{2}$$

The variance, τ^2, and the coefficient of variation, β, for the binomial distribution are given by:

$$\tau^2 = \frac{\Phi(1 - \Phi)}{n} \tag{3}$$

and $\quad \beta = \frac{\sqrt{\tau^2}}{\Phi} = \sqrt{\frac{(1 - \Phi)}{n\Phi}} \tag{4}$

To determine whether a mixture is random or not, N samples of n particles each are taken from all parts of the mixture. The concentration of each sample is then determined through analytical, spectroscopic, or optical means. The mean of the samples, $\bar{c}$, and their variance, s^2, are then determined:

$$\bar{c} = \frac{1}{N} \sum_{i=1}^{N} C_i \tag{5}$$

$$s^2 = \frac{1}{N} \sum_{i=1}^{N} (C_i - \Phi)^2 \tag{6}$$

Obviously, significant deviation of $\bar{c}$ from Φ indicates a sampling error. The ratio s^2/τ^2 is computed and compared with tabulated values of χ^2/f, chi square over degree of freedom, to test the hypothesis that the system is a random mixture. If the mixture is found not to be random, two parameters, i.e., intensity and scale of segregation, are necessary to characterize the mixture.

The intensity of segregation, I, may be defined as the coefficient of variation of the concentration in the system, defined as the quotient of the limiting value of the standard deviation of the concentration of one component divided by the average concentration, Φ [3]:

$$I = \sqrt{\tau_1^2}/\Phi \tag{7}$$

$$\text{where} \quad \tau_1^2 = \lim_{N \Rightarrow \infty} \frac{1}{N} \sum_{i=1}^{N} (C_i - \Phi)^2 \tag{8}$$

In practice, only a sufficient number of samples need to be collected and analyzed to bring the variance of the samples s^2 defined by Equation 8 to the limiting value τ_1^2. Naturally, the value of I will decrease as the goodness of mixing improves. The lowest value of I corresponds to that of a random mixture given by:

$$I \text{ random} = \beta \text{ random} = \sqrt{\frac{(1 - \Phi)}{n\Phi}} \tag{9}$$

On the other hand, the scale of segregation, which describes the average distance between clumps of the same component, can be defined as the average distance between like interfaces in the mixture. This distance is the striation thickness, r, defined as:

$$r = \frac{V}{(A/2)} \tag{10}$$

where V is the volume and A is the interfacial area. The scale of segregation should decrease as mixing progresses, and as the interfacial area between components, A, increases. The reduction in striation thickness of a fluid system located between parallel plates and with interfaces initially oriented perpendicular to the fluid streamlines is illustrated in Figure 1 [4]. The initial striation thickness before shearing is r_i. As angle ϕ increases, with the displacement of the top plate by a distance L to the right, the striation thickness decreases to:

$$\frac{r}{r_i} = \sin(\phi) \tag{11}$$

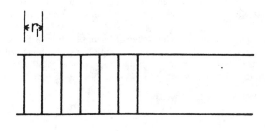

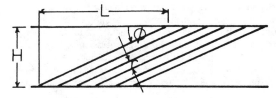

Figure 1. Reduction in striation thickness upon the introduction of total strain L/H in simple shear [4].

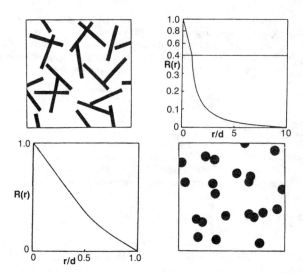

Figure 2. Correlograms for scale of segregation describing mixtures of uniform sized spheres and strips. Diameter of spheres and width of strips are d, and length of strips is 10d.

Danckwerts [5] has proposed another measure of the scale of segregation, analogous to the "scale of turbulence" used in fluid mechanics. This measure is based on the coefficient of correlation R(r) defined as:

$$R(r) = \frac{1}{Ns^2} \sum_{i=1}^{N} (C'_{Ai} - \bar{C}_A)(C''_{Ai} - \bar{C}_A) \qquad (12)$$

where N is the number of pairs of volume fractions (C'_{Ai}, C''_{Ai}) which are determined at a constant distance of separation r in the mixture, and $\bar{C}_A$ is the average volume fraction of component A. If R(r) is determined vs. the distance of separation r, a correlogram of a sample may be obtained. Typical correlograms are shown in Figure 2, for clumps of the minor component with various shapes. As mixing proceeds, the number and sizes of clumps will decrease, thus diminishing the area under the correlogram.

The analysis of a mixture for uniformity requires prior knowledge of the application of the mixture. The scale of examination or the level of scrutiny thus corresponds to the largest volume, within which a high degree of homogeneity is desired. For example, in the production of multi-vitamin pills, the mixture of vitamins is required to be homogeneous at the scale of the volume of individual pills.

Basic Mixing Mechanisms

The mixing step may be extensive (distributive) or intensive (dispersive) in character. In extensive mixing, two or more starting components are interspersed in space with one another. On the other hand intensive (dispersive) mixing, describes a multitude of processes in which some intrinsic change takes place in the physical character of one or more components during processing. The extensive and intensive mixing modes are illustrated in Figures 3 and 4 with two components, A and B. In Figure 3, two initially segregated liquids are shown to be mixed by distribution. Figure 4 shows schematically the process of dispersive mixing where the solid agglomerates are ruptured into their

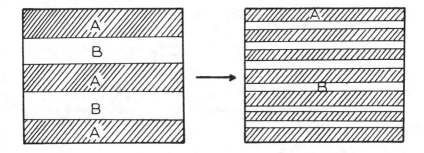

Figure 3. Extensive mixing and distribution of a minor component.

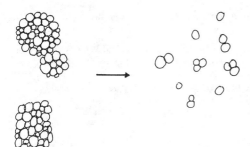

Figure 4. Intensive mixing and dispersion of solid agglomerates.

aggregates and ultimate particles. The bulk convection mixing of powder, chunks of materials, etc., will not be considered here.

The extensive and dispersive mechanisms of mixing of polymeric viscous fluids in polymer processing differ considerably from the mixing modes available to chemical technologies for mixing of low viscosity liquids. Diffusion and turbulence provide randomizing phenomena in the process of mixing of low viscosity materials, which are not available to viscous liquids. On the other hand, distributive and dispersive mixing operations of viscous liquids rely on complex, continuous deformations. Thus, the mechanisms of mixing of polymeric viscous liquids are inherently different in character from the mixing of inviscid fluids, and necessitate special mixers.

Extensive Mixing

In extensive mixing, the total strain introduced through various types of deformation, i.e., shear, squeezing, and extensional flow, induce an increase of the interfacial area between components. The interfacial area increase, in turn, reduces the striation thickness on the basis of Equation 10.

The mechanism of extensive mixing can be understood by following a simplified analysis [3, 6]. Figure 5 shows a surface element that has been confined between two vectors $\vec{r}_1$ and $\vec{r}_2$ at time $t = 0$. The area of the surface element is given by:

$$A_0 = 1/2(C_x^2 + C_y^2 + C_z^2)^{1/2} \tag{13}$$

where C_x, C_y, C_z are the components of the vector $\vec{C}$, normal to the surface element; i.e., $\vec{C} = \vec{r}_1 \times \vec{r}_2$, and its orientation in space is specified by its three directional cosines defined by:

$$\cos \alpha_x = C_x/|\vec{C}|, \cos \alpha_y = C_y/|\vec{C}|, \cos \alpha_z = C_z/|\vec{C}| \tag{14}$$

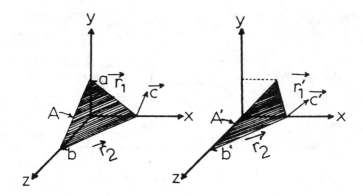

Figure 5. Change in interfacial area upon unidirectional shear strain [4].

This surface element is subjected to simple shear flow. In simple shear only one velocity component exists, and this component of velocity changes only in one direction. In Figure 5, $\partial V_x/\partial y = \dot{\gamma}_{xy}$ and $V_x = \dot{\gamma}_{yx}y$.

As shown in Figure 5, after a certain elapsed time, Δt, the new interfacial area is confined between position vectors $\vec{r}_1'$ and $\vec{r}_2'$, and the ratio of the new interfacial area A to the previous area, A/A_0, becomes:

$$\frac{A}{A_0} = (1 - 2\cos\alpha_x \cos\alpha_y\gamma + \cos^2\alpha_x\gamma^2)^{1/2} \tag{15}$$

where γ is the total strain imposed on the element during Δt, i.e.:

$$\gamma = \int_0^{\Delta t} \dot{\gamma}_{yx}(t')\,dt' \tag{16}$$

Equation 15 suggests that:

• Deformed surface is proportional to the undeformed surface.
• The total strain imposed during deformation, γ, increases the interfacial area.
• The growth of the interfacial area depends on the orientation of the surface prior to deformation.

For large deformations where $\cos^2\alpha_x\gamma^2 \gg 1 - 2\cos\alpha_x \cos\alpha_y\gamma$, the interfacial area growth becomes a linear function of the total strain as:

$$\frac{A}{A_0} = |\cos\alpha_x|\gamma \tag{17}$$

Effect of Initial Orientation on Mixing Efficiency

As suggested by Equations 15–17, the initial orientation of the interface between various components relative to the flow streamlines in the mixer is of paramount importance [3]. With some processing equipment, mixing efficiency can be improved drastically by proper initial placement of the components. The initial placement should be such as to provide the maximum rate of increase of the interfacial surface by the flow streamlines. Thus, the striation thicknesses are reduced more rapidly.

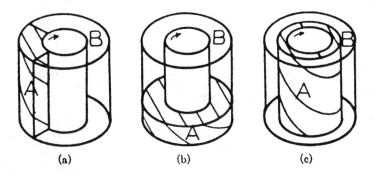

(a)   (b)   (c)

Figure 6. Effect of initial orientation on extensive mixing [3].

This is illustrated in Figure 6, where Couette flow is considered. In this geometry, the inner shaft is rotating and the outer cylinder is stationary. Two fluids labeled A and B fill the annular gap. If the minor component, Fluid A, is placed as in Figure 6A, the shearing rapidly increases the interfacial area. For this initial orientation, $\cos \alpha_x$ is unity, thereby producing rapid increase in interfacial area with increasing total strain. On the other hand, Figures 6B and 6C show initial orientations of Fluid A in which $\cos \alpha_x$ is zero. Subsequent shearing does not produce any increase in interfacial area. Both fluids move in closed streamlines, and thus mixing relies solely on diffusion, which is a very slow process for viscous polymeric fluids.

Improvements of Interfacial Area Growth

Extensive mixing should occur more readily in shear if the simple shear flow described above is interrupted and the fluid reoriented [7]. As shown in Figure 7, where the interfacial area is determined experimentally by striation thickness measurements in a Couette geometry, the interfacial area increases with the number of times the interface is reoriented favorably for subsequent shear. The optimum reorientation of the interface is to be perpendicular to the shearing plane, as suggested by Equation 17. For a simple shear mixer with $N - 1$ mixing sections, each of which optimizes the interfacial orientation for subsequent shear, and having N shearing sections each of equal shearing

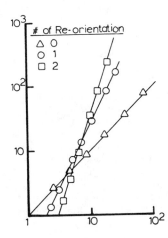

Figure 7. Effect of interface reorientation on mixing efficiency [7].

magnitude (γ/N), the growth of the interfacial area is given by [8]:

$$\frac{A}{A_0} = \left(\frac{\gamma}{N}\right)^N \tag{18}$$

Upon comparison with Equation 17, one notes that the rate of mixing with shear increases substantially by reorientations incorporated in a mixer.

So far, we have dealt with only simple shear flow. Another class of flows that one can consider is the shear free flow, for which it is possible to select for every fluid element an orthogonal set of unit vectors fixed in the element. Referred to these axes, the rate-of-strain tensor has only diagonal components [9].

$$\dot{\gamma} = \begin{pmatrix} \dot{\gamma}_{11} & 0 & 0 \\ 0 & \dot{\gamma}_{22} & 0 \\ 0 & 0 & \dot{\gamma}_{33} \end{pmatrix} \tag{19}$$

The uniaxial elongational flow is defined with:

$$\dot{\gamma}_{11} = 2\dot{\varepsilon}; \quad \dot{\gamma}_{22} = -\dot{\varepsilon}; \quad \dot{\gamma}_{33} = -\dot{\varepsilon}$$

where $\dot{\varepsilon}$ is the uniaxial Hencky strain rate, given by:

$$\dot{\varepsilon} = \frac{1}{L(t)} \frac{dL(t)}{dt} \tag{20}$$

and $L(t)$ is the change in total length of stretched sample.

The total strain is given by:

$$\varepsilon = \ln \frac{L(t)}{L_0} = \ln \lambda_x \tag{21}$$

where λ_x is the extension ratio in stretch direction.

The interfacial area grows with increasing extensional strain ε as [3, 7]:

$$\frac{A}{A_0} = \left(\lambda_x + \cos^2 \alpha \left(\frac{1}{\lambda_x} - \lambda_x\right)\right)^{1/2} \tag{22}$$

If the interface is oriented with $\cos \alpha = 0$, then:

$$\frac{A}{A_0} = \lambda_x^{1/2} = e^{\varepsilon/2} \tag{23}$$

Thus extensional flows, which occur in mixing principally when the material is forced through contractions, give rise to improved efficiency in extensive mixing, compared to shear flows.

In summary, the goal of extensive mixing is to generate composition uniformity of the ingredients throughout the mixture. In this mode of mixing, large strains need to be imposed upon the fluid. Furthermore, the interfacial elements (or the solid additives) need to be distributed throughout the system. The initial orientation of the phases and the subsequent orientation of the interface are critical for achieving efficient extensive mixing. Extensional flows improve the efficiency of extensive mixing processes.

It should be noted that so far we have employed a very simplified analysis in which viscoelasticity of phases, interfacial tension, filled liquid systems, and liquid drop/wall and drop/drop interactions are ignored. Information on these aspects may be found elsewhere [10–23].

Intensive Mixing, Dispersion

The mixing of solid additives into a polymeric matrix, i.e., filled or reinforced plastics or rubbers, generally involves the rupture of agglomerates of the solid particulates and the further separation of the closely packed particles after rupture [24, 25]. These operations constitute dispersive mixing operations in which some intrinsic change takes place, i.e., in shape and size of the particulates of solid phase.

It can be assumed that the agglomerates rupture when internal stresses, induced by viscous drag on the particles, exceed a certain threshold value [26]. This threshold may be considered as the cohesive force holding the agglomerate together. The simplified dynamics of dispersive mixing is illustrated next by considering two rigid beads of radii r_1 and r_2, present in a homogeneous flow field as shown in Figure 8 [4, 27–29]. For low Reynolds number flows, as typical in polymer processing, the viscous drag force exerted on each spherical rigid particle of radius r_i by the Newtonian fluid of shear viscosity, η, is $6\pi\eta r_i$, according to Stokes Law. In simple shear flow of an incompressible, Newtonian fluid with shear rate $\dot{\gamma}$, the force between the particles can be shown to be [29]:

$$F = \frac{6\pi\eta\dot{\gamma}X_zY_z}{L}\left(\frac{r_1r_2}{r_1 + r_2}\right) \tag{24}$$

where X_z and Y_z = coordinates of the second bead with the coordinate system placed at the center of bead 1
   L = the center-to-center distance between the particles
   η = the Newtonian viscosity of the fluid dragging the particles

The force between the particles vanishes when X_z or Y_z are zero; i.e., if the line connecting the centers of the two spheres are parallel or perpendicular to the flow field (1), emphasizing as in extensive mixing the significance of the initial orientation of the agglomerate. For the case of the two rigid spheres in contact with each other, the maximum force acting to separate the spheres is:

$$F_{max} = 3\pi\eta\dot{\gamma}r_1r_2 \tag{25}$$

Equation 25 indicates that the maximum force acting to rupture an agglomerate of solid particles will be proportional to the shear stress ($\eta\dot{\gamma}$) acting on the agglomerate. Simply put, this suggests

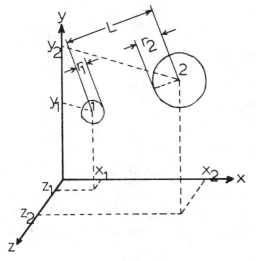

Figure 8. Two particles of radii r_1 and r_2 being separated during dispersive mixing [1].

that high shear stresses promote dispersion. With a given system, there is a critical value of shear stress below which no dispersion will occur. When the shear stress is above the critical value, only those which are favorably oriented with their long axis perpendicular to the streamlines will be dispersed [4]. Maximum force is also seen to increase with increasing product of radii, $(r_1 r_2)$. This indicates that it is easier to break two large particles apart in comparison to one large and one small or two small particles. It should be noted, however, that this simplified analysis ignores the effects of the agglomerates on the flow kinematics and the surface chemistry and interactions between agglomerates.

Figures 9 and 10 show the comparison of the rheological behavior of a surface-treated $CaCO_3$ filler vs. an untreated silica-based filler under simple shear flow between a cone and plate. Both fillers are incorporated at 30% by weight into a low density polyethylene matrix, LDPE employing similar compounding procedures. Figure 9 shows the shear stress growth. The $\tau_{12,r}$ indicates that the shear stress values are normalized by division, with the steady shear stress value exhibited by neat LDPE at 0.1 s^{-1}. On the other hand, Figure 10 drawn on a semi-log graph shows the first normal stress growth material function, $\Psi_{1,r}^{+}$ normalized by division with the first normal stress coefficient of the LDPE resin at 0.1 s^{-1}. Both fillers exhibit similar particle size distribution.

The surface-treated $CaCO_3$ filled samples behave similarly to the neat polymer, characterized by reaching of steady torque and normal force. On the other hand, steady-state shear stress and first normal stress difference values are not reached with the silica-based filler. Especially the first normal stress difference exhibits a spectacular rise with time of deformation. This suggests that agglomeration and strong interaction occur between agglomerates of the silica-based filler. These

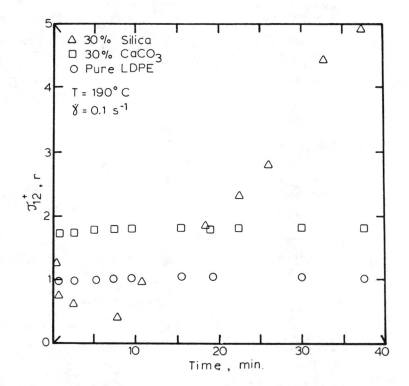

Figure 9. Shear stress growth function of a polyethylene resin filled with two different fillers [30].

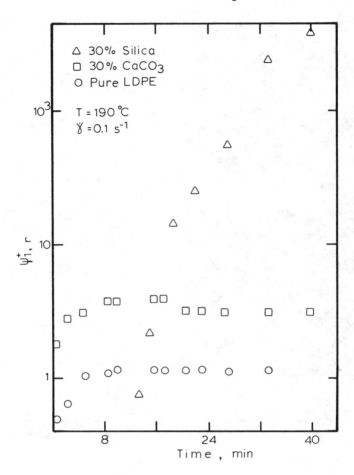

Figure 10. First normal stress difference growth function of a polyethylene resin filled with two different fillers [30].

interactions convert the structure during simple shear into a network that approaches solid-like behavior [30], suggesting strong ramifications on the processing requirements of this filled system.

Particle attrition deserves special attention, especially in the compounding of highly filled or re-inforced systems. An example of particle attrition is shown in Figure 11. Ammonium sulfate particles were compounded into a polybutadiene matrix employing a co-rotating twin screw extruder. The ultimate particles of ammonium sulfate are shown to be ground-up during mixing, as revealed by the scanning electron micrographs. Also in the introduction of reinforcements, fiber attrition occurs readily and is highly undesirable, because it results in decreases in various ultimate properties.

Demixing

Demixing is an important aspect of every mixing operation. The selected geometry and flow kinematics for compounding of various ingredients may, under certain situations, give rise to the demixing of the ingredients. A simple example can be seen from Equation 15, which was utilized

Figure 11. Scanning electron micrographs of samples filled with ammonium sulfate particles (a) compounded properly, (b) compounded under conditions which resulted in particle attrition.

to describe the growth of the interfacial area with increasing strain during extensive mixing. For small strains and for various initial orientations which give rise to the following condition:

$$2 \cos \alpha_x \cos \alpha_y \gamma > 1 + \cos^2 \alpha_x \gamma^2 \tag{26}$$

the applied strain would reduce the interfacial area, contrary to our general intuitive expectations.

Demixing may occur in the blending of two incompatible liquids with differing shear viscosities, if the blend is made to undergo pressure flow. The most common situation is pressure flow through a die, where the two fluids may segregate [31–33]. This would involve the migration of the lower molecular weight, and thus lower viscosity resin to the high shear rate region, i.e., toward the wall in Poiseuille flow. The higher viscosity resin will occupy the low shear rate region, located at the center of the tubular die.

In mixing of suspensions, rigid particles have been observed to migrate across planes of shear in directions which depend on the rheological behavior of suspending liquid [34]. In the mixing of suspensions, incorporating a distribution of particle size of the solid phase, the smaller particles may migrate to the wall of the die, whereas the greater particles occupy the low shear rate region of the die (Segre-Silberberg effect [35–37]). Furthermore, in the mixing of highly filled suspensions, if the suspension is forced through a contraction with a steep degree of approach, the solid particulates may establish a solid bed, which effectively filters out the polymer matrix [38–39]. Upon depletion of the polymer, the pressure builds up. This results eventually in the rupture of the solid bed with a slip at the wall. This will give rise to a product with a concentration varying as a function of time.

Components of a mixture may also demix upon the completion of the mixing and the shaping operation. Examples include the exudation of the slip additives to the surface of polymeric films, a phenomenon used to promote slip between film layers and film/metal surfaces [40, 41]; and the undesired, but commonly occurring exudation of the plasticizers from PVC articles with time. In general, the geometry and operating conditions should be selected to minimize the segregation of components during and after the mixing operation. Obtaining a good mixture at one point of the process is no guarantee that the state of the mixture will be conserved during the rest of the process.

CONTINUOUS MIXERS

Basic Single Screw Plasticating Extruder

The single screw plasticating extruder is one of the most widely used machines in polymer processing. A plasticating extruder consists of an Archimedean screw rotating in a heated barrel, with a "head" or die attached as shown in Figure 12. Solids in the form of pellets or powder, etc., can be fed into a plasticating extruder either through a hopper, i.e., "flood feeding," or by "starved" feeding. In flood feeding of an extruder, the feed hopper is filled with solid particles. Under the influence of gravity and the interparticle and particle/wall friction forces, the particles are fed into the extruder feed throat, where they are picked up by the rotating screw. On the other hand, solid feed can be metered into the extruder feed throat by a feeding device at controlled rates, i.e., starved feeding [42–44].

For polymer processing operations involving large aspect ratios and low Reynolds numbers, the system can be modeled as a stationary channel, with the upper plate moving diagonally across the top at helix angle θ, as shown in Figure 13. The solids are conveyed in the down-channel direction through particle/barrel frictional drag.

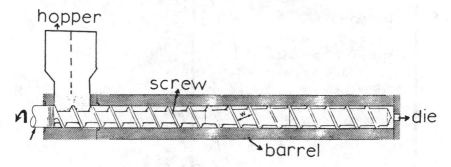

Figure 12. Plasticating single-screw extruder.

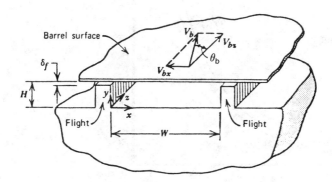

Figure 13. Schematics of unwound single-screw extruder geometry [1].

The conveying of the solids by frictional drag at the barrel is accompanied by the compaction of the deformable solid bed and increase in pressure. Friction generates heat mainly at the barrel/ solid bed interface, proportional to the developed pressure and the friction coefficient of the barrel [45]. The heat generation plus the heat flux conducted through the barrel increases the temperature of the solids at the barrel/solid plug interface to above the melting temperature for semi-crystalline polymers and above the glass transition temperature for amorphous polymers.

At this location, the frictional drag mechanism is converted into a viscous drag mechanism, whereby the solid bed is conveyed further by shear stresses generated in the molten film, sandwiched between the barrel and the solid plug. Examples of pressure and heat generation rate vs. down-channel distance and the temperature distribution in the solid bed during solid conveying are shown in Figures 14–16, as a function of screw speed and mass flow rate related to the com-pounding of a thermoset powder [46].

As shown schematically in Figure 17, the pushing flight scrapes the molten layer off the barrel, and the melt starts accumulating at the pushing flight. As melting proceeds, the relative width of the solid bed, X/W, gradually decreases.

Neglecting the leakage flow through the flight clearance, δ, the Equation of Motion for the melt pool in the cross-channel direction x for fully developed, isothermal flow of an incompressible Newtonian fluid is:

$$\frac{\partial P}{\partial x} = \eta \frac{\partial^2 V_x}{\partial y^2} \tag{27}$$

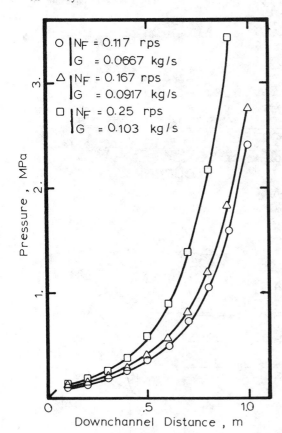

O | N_F = 0.117 rps
G = 0.0667 kg/s
△ | N_F = 0.167 rps
G = 0.0917 kg/s
□ | N_F = 0.25 rps
G = 0.103 kg/s

Figure 14. Pressure in the down-channel direction [46].

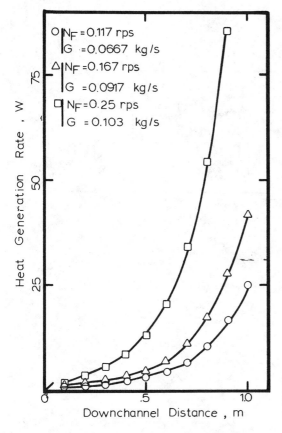

Figure 15. Heat generation rate at barrel/solid interface in down-channel direction [46].

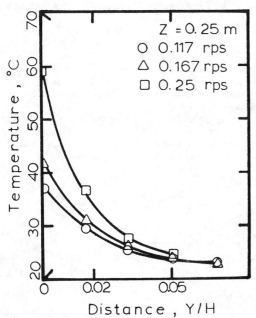

Figure 16. Temperature distributions in solid bed in down-channel direction [46].

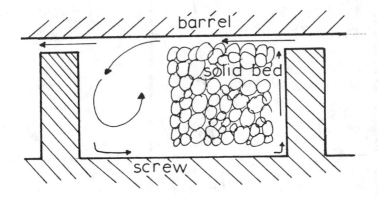

Figure 17. Schematics of melting in a single-screw extruder.

which can be easily solved [4] with $V_x(0) = 0$ and $V_x(H) = -V_{bx}$, and with zero net flow rate in the x-direction:

$$\int_{y=0}^{y=H} V_x \, dy = 0 \tag{28}$$

The cross-channel velocity profile becomes:

$$V_x = V_{bx} \frac{y}{H} \left(2 - 3 \frac{y}{H} \right) \tag{29}$$

where V_{bx} is the x-component of barrel velocity, V_b, i.e., $V_b \sin \theta b$, with θb the helix angle at barrel surface and H the channel depth.

The described velocity profiles obtained with Newtonian fluids under fully-developed, isothermal conditions are instructional. However, for detailed calculations, one can resort to numerical techniques. The typical and realistic cross-channel velocity profile in the channel are shown in Figures 18, and 19 and describe the circulation of the melt in the melt pool while being pumped in the down-channel direction. The length of the arrow indicates the magnitude of the velocity. The curvature of the screw geometry has been taken into consideration by applying a finite element based numerical technique in conjunction with various types of fluids [47].

The melt pool is conveyed forward in the down-channel direction by the axial component of the drag flow induced by motion of the barrel, V_{bz}. Pressure builds up in the forward direction, due to the resistance offered by the die at the outlet of the extruder. The net volumetric flow rate in the axial direction can be given for fully-developed, isothermal flow of a Newtonian fluid in a constant channel depth, H channel:

$$Q = \frac{V_{bz} WH}{z} F_d + \frac{WH^3}{12\eta} \left(\frac{-\partial P}{\partial z} \right) F_p \tag{30}$$

where F_d and F_p are "shape factors" for the pure drag and pure pressure flows, respectively. The values of shape factors are less than one and depend on the aspect ratio H/W. The net flow rate in the axial direction, V_1, becomes:

$$V_1 = V_x \cos \theta + V_z \sin \theta \tag{31}$$

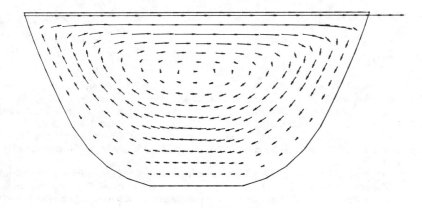

Velocity Vectors
Newtonian Fluid

Figure 18. Cross-flow in a single-screw extruder channel with Newtonian fluids [47].

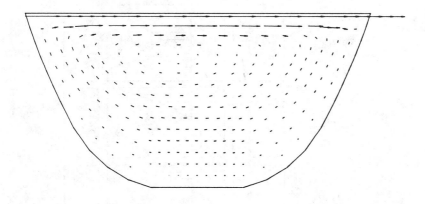

Velocity Vector
Bingham Fluid

Figure 19. Cross-flow in a single-screw channel with Bingham plastic [47].

The ratio of pressure to drag flow rates is given by:

$$\frac{-Q_p}{Q_d} = \frac{H^2}{6\eta V_{bz}}\left(\frac{\partial p}{\partial z}\right)\frac{F_p}{F_d}$$

(32)

The net flow rate, Q, is obtained by linear superposition of drag, Q_d, and pressure, Q_p, flow rates [4], valid for isothermal, fully developed, Newtonian flow. The velocity profiles corresponding to various Q_p/Q_d values are shown in Figure 20. From those velocity profiles, one can deduce the path of fluid particles in the channel. For closed discharge, $(Q_p/Q_d) = -1$, the fluid advances and re-treats in the x- and z-directions. Overall, as shown in Figure 21, the fluid particles move in a helical path through the helical channel, "helix in a helix," the helix angle at any point being determined by local velocity field.

Obviously, fluid particles experience different strain histories according to their initial geometrical location between a screw and barrel [1, 4, 48, 49], indicating that the extrudate leaving the extruder will not be uniformly mixed. Taking into consideration the residence time distribution of the melt, a weighted average strain, γ_{av}, can be defined [49] as:

$$\gamma_{av} = \frac{\int_{t_0}^{t} \gamma f(t)\, dt}{\int_{t_0}^{t} f(t)\, dt}$$

(33)

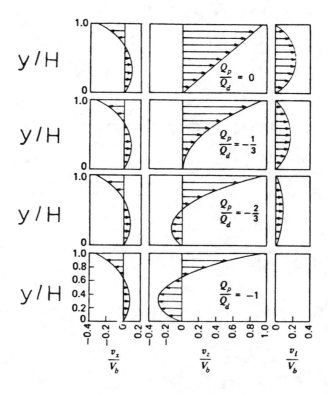

Figure 20. Cross-channel, down-channel, and axial velocity profiles for various Q_p/Q_d values in shallow, square pitched screws [4].

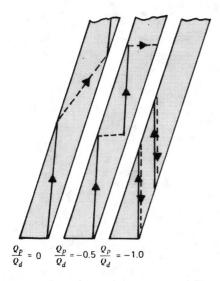

$$\frac{Q_p}{Q_d} = 0 \qquad \frac{Q_p}{Q_d} = -0.5 \qquad \frac{Q_p}{Q_d} = -1.0$$

Figure 21. The path of a fluid particle in the screw channel [1].

where f(t) dt is the fraction of the fluid, at the exit, that has spent a time between t and t + dt in the extruder; and t_0 is the minimum residence time pertaining to the fluid located initially at $y/H = 2/3$. The experimental and theoretical cumulative residence time distribution function, F(t), which represents the fraction of the material which has spent the time, t or less in the single screw extruder, is shown in Figure 22 [50]. The mean residence time, $\bar{t}$, is given by:

$$\bar{t} = \int_{t_0}^{\infty} t f(t)\, dt \tag{34}$$

The residence time distribution in a melt extruder is quite narrow, and only 5% of the flow rate stays more than twice the mean residence time in the single screw extruder. The typical strain distribution function across the channel is shown in Figure 23 as a function of the back pressure, i.e.,

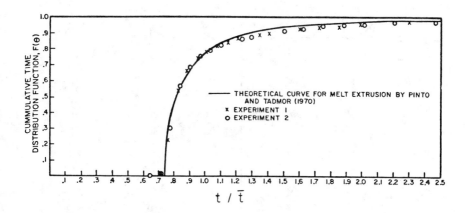

Figure 22. Experimental and theoretical cumulative residence time distribution in a single screw [50].

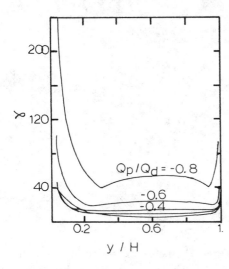

Figure 23. Strain distribution function across the channel as a function of Q_p/Q_d ratio [49].

Q_p/Q_d ratio. The strain increases at every point as the back pressure increases [49]. The effect of helix angle on the weighted average strain is shown in Figure 24. The average strain goes to infinity at 0° and 90° helix angles. The minimum is rather flat and covers a significant helix angle range.

It should be noted that although large strains can be imposed in single screw extrusion through the flow kinematics described above, the lack of effective orientation of the material elements at the flights causes the bulk of the interfacial area to be oriented parallel to the channel bottom in a relatively short downstream distance, regardless of initial orientation of the components to be mixed [51]. Consequently, the extensive mixing achieved in single screw extruders is generally poor. Furthermore, there is no dispersive mixing capability that can rupture agglomerates in a general-purpose single screw extruder except for leakage flow over small flight clearance, δ. For better mixing, either special mixing sections are incorporated into the single screw, i.e., screw modifications, or the design is radically altered to introduce gaps through which portions of the melt are repeatedly forced through, i.e., single shaft kneaders.

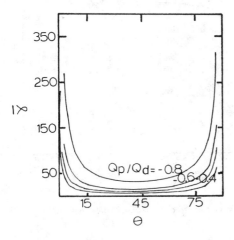

Figure 24. The weighted average total strain, γ, as a function of helix angle at various Q_p/Q_d values [49].

Single Screw Extruders Modified for Better Mixing

The rapid orientation of the interfacial area parallel to the channel bottom regardless of initial orientation, and the lack of effective reorientation of the interfacial area are identified as causes for the poor mixing in single screw extruders. This has led to the design and incorporation of mixing sections. Mixing sections obstruct and disrupt the flow, thus redistributing the streamlines and re-orienting the interfacial area [52–55]. Both obviously improve the extensive mixing efficiency of single screw extruders.

The simplest mixing section that can be incorporated into plasticating extrusion is a series of mixing pins as shown in Figure 25. Each mixing pin divides the helical flow into two streams, which are again combined into one upon passing the pin. The growth of the interfacial area upon the division and combination of the flow upon passing around a mixing pin is shown in Figure 26

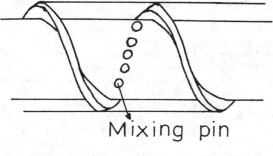

Figure 25. Mixing pins.

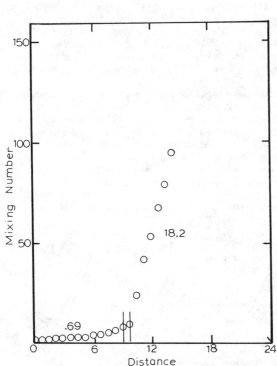

Figure 26. Growth of interfacial area upon passage around a mixing pin [52].

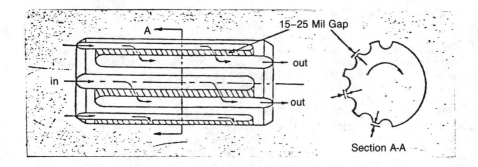

15–25 Mil Gap

out

in

out

Section A-A

Figure 27. Fluted mixing sections.

[52]. On the other hand, the introduction of the mixing pin introduces further velocity gradients and thus should also increase the total strain imposed on the material.

Fluted mixing sections in single screw extruders are devices also employed to redistribute the melt, as shown in Figure 27. These barrier-type restrictions basically introduce gaps which all melt elements need to pass through [53]. The barrier may take a number of forms. A simple form is the dam or series of dams of almost the full channel height welded across the channel at selected locations. This continuous distribution of the melt, reorientation of the interface, and further shearing obviously improve the efficiency of extensive mixing in a single screw extruder.

Potential problems with fluted mixing sections are hold-up of material and dead spots [54, 55], which can be minimized by proper selection of the helix angle of this section, by tapering the inlet channel to zero depth, and by reversing the depth profile in the outlet channel. There should also be considerable pressure drop as the material is forced from the wide screw channel into a number of narrow inlet channels, as shown in Figure 27. Overall, the fluted mixing sections force the material to pass through narrow, albeit short, gaps at relatively high shear rates. This should reorient the interfacial area, redistribute the streamlines, increase the total strain imposed, and furthermore subject the mixture to high shear stress values at the gaps, also introducing some dispersive mixing action.

Another example of a barrier-type device is the Maillefer transition section, shown in Figure 28. This is a spiral barrier or secondary screw flight extending over the entire length of the transition section. Many variations of the basic system shown in Figure 28 are possible. Additional barriers or flights can be introduced to split the flow into two or more streams, which in the limit arrives at a series of longitudinal grooves or flutes spaced around the circumference of a cylinder. Mass and force balances on the Maillefer screw are given by Pearson [56].

Dynamic mixing sections, like the cavity transfer mixer, can also be incorporated to the single screw extruder. The cavity transfer mixer facilitates the transfer of the material continuously between the barrel, the "stator," and the screw, the "rotor." This is achieved by the presence of flighted grooves in the barrel, which act as a secondary screw. Over a mixing section, the root diameter of

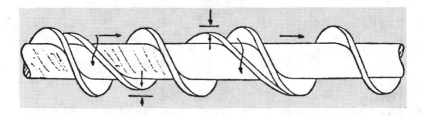

Figure 28. Maillefer transition section.

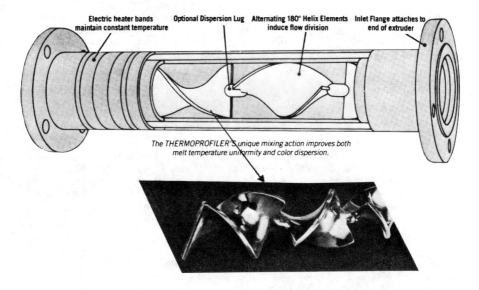

Electric heater bands maintain constant temperature

Optional Dispersion Lug

Alternating 180° Helix Elements induce flow division

Inlet Flange attaches to end of extruder

The THERMOPROFILER'S unique mixing action improves both melt temperature uniformity and color dispersion.

Figure 29. Motionless mixer (courtesy of Luwa Corp.).

the rotor gradually decreases from full depth to zero depth, while the opposite occurs in the stator, forcing the mixture from rotor to stator and vice versa. This concentric screw effect increases the residence time and the total strain, and further continuously reorients the interfacial area, increasing the efficiency of the extensive mixing.

It is also possible to incorporate distributive mixing sections which do not contain moving parts, i.e., "motionless mixers," to the single screw. The motionless mixers are generally placed between the screw and the die, and consist of a string of alternating right- and left-handed helical elements fixed in a tubular housing, as shown in Figure 29. The energy for mixing is derived from the pressure loss incurred as the process fluids flow through the motionless mixer. The splitting and recombination of streams results in a predicted increase in the number of striations. The increase in the number of striations with an increasing number of elements is shown in Figure 30, with a Luwa

Flow Division   Elements

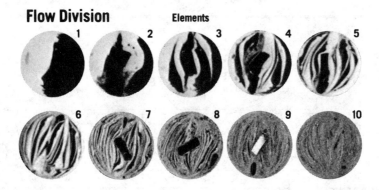

Figure 30. Decrease of striation thickness upon passage through increasing number of elements of a motionless mixer (Courtesy of Luwa Corp.).

Motionless Mixer. Various types of mixers and their mixing characteristics were recently reviewed [57], where the performances of various motionless mixers were also compared. For example, the number of striations, N_δ, produced with the number of elements present, σ, vary as the following for various designs:

Kenics Mixer $N_\delta = 2^\sigma$

ISG $N_\delta = 4^\sigma$

Lightnin $N_\delta = 3(2)^{\sigma - 1}$

In spite of their inherent limitations, single screw extruders are popular mixers mainly because of favorable economics. They are ideal for low volume compounding jobs, including filling, reinforcing, and coloring of mainly commodity plastics [58]. For tougher applications, including compounding of engineering plastics and blending of incompatible polymers, twin screw extruders or single shaft kneaders with interactive screw and barrel elements are generally employed.

Single Shaft Kneaders

For dedicated mixing operations like compounding of poly(vinylchloride) formulations, molding powders, and reinforced or filled systems, various designs which operate on the basis of a single shaft but are radically different than the conventional plasticating or melt extruder are employed. The common denominators in these single shaft dedicated compounding extruders are the various protrusions, the grooves or the profiles built into the barrel sections with corresponding elements in the screw sections. Examples include the Buss and Baker-Perkins Ko-Kneaders, and Sterlex Transfermixer. These mixers are equipped for dispersive mixing, induced through narrow gaps, i.e., high shear stress zones and repeated passages through these high shear stress zones.

The Ko-Kneader-type continuous kneaders are characterized by a kneading screw which rotates and oscillates in a barrel, as shown in Figure 31 [46, 59, 60]. Fluffy feeds (molding powder, etc.) are introduced into the kneader by means of a feeding/cramming screw, which compacts, conveys, and pressurizes the feed into the kneader. The geometry of the kneading screw involves a regular flighted, cooled, conveying section adjacent to the hopper exit. The conveying section is followed by the "kneading section." The kneading section involves interrupted flight kneading elements on the screw and barrel surfaces. These are screw flight elements formed by the interruption of the screw spiral, usually by three gaps per turn and the kneading teeth, which are fixed on the barrel

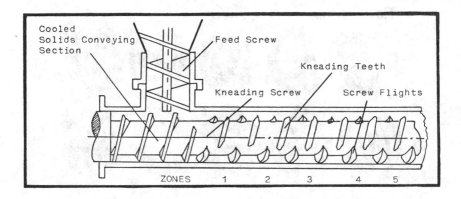

Figure 31. Schematics of a Ko-Kneader.

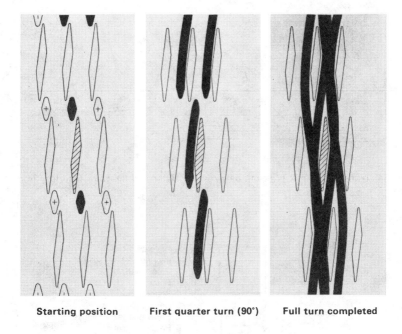

Starting position   **First quarter turn (90°)**   **Full turn completed**

Figure 32. Kneading action in a Ko-Kneader (courtesy of Buss Corp.)

surface. Dispersion and homogenization take place in between the rotating and oscillating screw flights and kneading teeth.

The kneading action is illustrated in Figure 32, whereby the interactions of the interrupted screw flights and the barrel kneading teeth are described during one complete screw revolution. Four kneading teeth wipe off all four flanks of a flight during one full turn, and the material is thus subjected to high deformation rates, i.e., dispersive mixing in the small gap between the flight flank and the barrel teeth. Ko-Kneaders are applied in a multitude of processes, including compounding of thermosetting powder coatings, i.e., epoxy, polyester, acrylic, and polyurethane based, thermosetting molding compounds, reinforced engineering plastics with matrices including PA, PBT, PC, PPS, PPO, POM, and rigid and plasticized PVC for producing film and sheet.

A mixer that is designed on the cavity mixing principle is the Sterlex Transfermix [61], a double concentric screw extruder. It consists of a rotor within a sectionalized grooved barrel. As shown in Figure 33, the rotor is deep in the feeding section. The pre-warming section consists of a smooth barrel section, and the melt-mix section incorporates the "transfer and mix" principle illustrated in

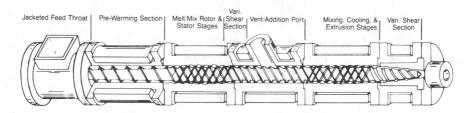

Figure 33. Double concentric screw extruder (courtesy of Sterling Corp.).

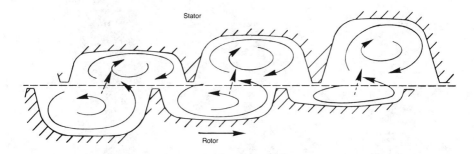

Figure 34. Transfer and mix principle between the stator and the rotor (courtesy of Sterling Corp.).

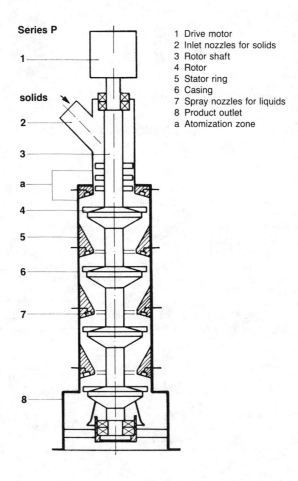

Series P

1 — Drive motor
2 — Inlet nozzles for solids
3 — Rotor shaft
4 — Rotor
5 — Stator ring
6 — Casing
7 — Spray nozzles for liquids
8 — Product outlet
a — Atomization zone

solids

1
2
3
a
4
5
6
7
8

1 Drive motor
2 Inlet nozzles for solids
3 Rotor shaft
4 Rotor
5 Stator ring
6 Casing
7 Spray nozzles for liquids
8 Product outlet
a Atomization zone

Figure 35. Turbine mixer by Buss (courtesy of Buss Corp.).

Figure 34. There is a conical section at the end of the rotor. The position of the conical section relative to a female bushing is adjustable. The material is forced through the small gap between the rotor and the bushing, thus facilitating dispersive mixing. This mixer is applied in compounding operations, including color concentrates and masterbatches; glass, mica, and talc filled thermoplastics; plasticized formulations, pre-charged foamable pellets, and hot melt adhesives.

A turbine rotor and stator-based continuous mixer produced by Buss is presented here as an example of mixers applicable to the preparation of solutions, suspensions, pastes, and emulsions. This mixing turbine is shown in Figure 35. It basically involves the inlet and atomization of the solid particles, the whirling of the particles outward, where they are sprayed with liquid components, and continuous downward motion due to the streamlined shapes of the stator and rotor elements and gravity.

Twin Screw Extruders

There are various types of twin screw extruders available commercially. They differ in their design and operating principles, thus in their abilities for distributive and dispersive mixing, and hence in their application areas. The available twin screw extruders can be classified as co-rotating and counter-rotating, on the basis of the direction of the rotation of the screws. The counter-rotating extruders can again be classified on the basis of the degree of intermesh of the screws, ranging from fully intermeshed, where the flight of one screw fits into the channel of the other screw, to non-intermeshing "tangential," where the two screws rotate freely in their barrel sections. The co-rotating screw extruders are not produced in the non-intermeshing mode.

Figure 36 shows the mechanisms of different types of twin screw extruders [62]. Here distinction is made between the axially open machines, where there is continuous passage between the inlet and outlet, and the axially closed machines, where the passage is interrupted at regular intervals. The twin screw extruders are also classified on the basis of whether material exchange between the two screws is possible or not, neglecting the leakage flows.

The right-handed, "forward," regular flighted elements shown in Figure 36 are only one type of element employed in twin screw extruders. As will be discussed in individual sections, twin screw extruders can also be equipped with other types of elements, including left-handed, "reverse," regular flighted elements, forward and reverse kneading discs, shearing discs, etc. Thus, most twin screw extruder screws can be assembled with the "building block" principle. Depending on the requirements of the compounding task at hand, proper screw elements can be selected and assembled.

Counter-Rotating Intermeshing Twin Screw Extruders

The available counter-rotating intermeshing twin screw extruders are designed as "conical" and "cylindrical" extruders [63]. Conical twin screw extruders allow for more space for the installation of thrust bearings. On the other hand, cylindrical counter-rotating twin screw extruders enjoy the ability to be built by the "building block" method.

Schematic representation of the cylindrical intermeshing counter-rotating screws is shown in Figure 37. The bulk of the material is conveyed in the down-channel direction in isolated C-shaped segments, with the flights acting as positive displacement pumps [62–67]. The unwound channel is shown in Figure 38 [1], whereby the material circulates both in the down-channel, z, and cross-channel, x, directions. Neglecting leakage flow, the volumetric flow rate, Q, is given as a function of screw speed, N, and the geometry alone [1]:

$$Q = \pi N \bar{D} L_s H \left[1 - \frac{1}{2\pi} \left(\frac{D_f}{\bar{D}} \right) \left(\frac{D_f}{H} \right) \cos^{-1} \left(1 - \frac{H}{D_f} \right) \right.$$
$$\left. + \frac{1}{2\pi} \left(\frac{D_f}{\bar{D}} \right) \left(1 - \frac{H}{D_f} \right) \sqrt{\frac{2D_f}{H} - 1} \right] \tag{35}$$

Engagement		System	Counter rotating screw	Co-rotating screw
intermeshing	fully intermeshing	lengthwise and crosswise closed	1. 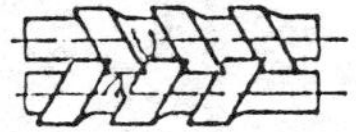	2. theoretically not possible
		lengthwise open and crosswise closed	3. theoretically not possible	4. screws
		lengthwise and crosswise open	5. theoretically possible practically not realized	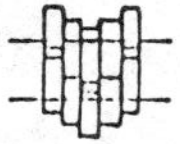 6. kneading discs
	partially intermeshing	lengthwise open and crosswise closed	7. 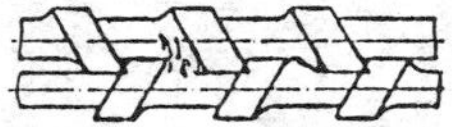	8. theoretically not possible
		lengthwise and crosswise open	9a. / 9b.	10a. / 10b.
not intermeshing	not intermeshing	lengthwise and crosswise open	11. 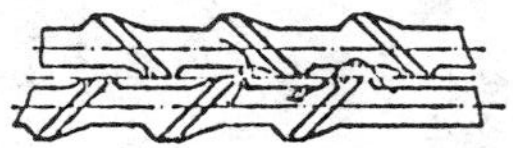	12. 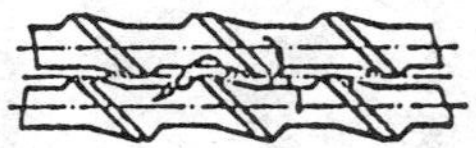

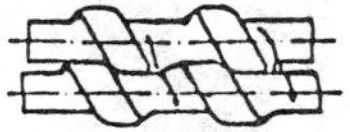

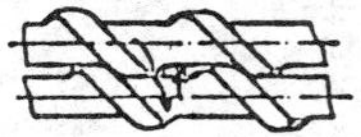

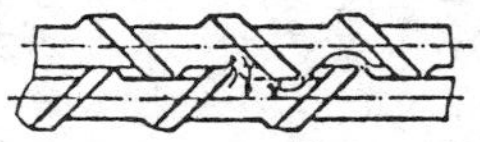

Figure 36. Types of twin screw extruders [62].

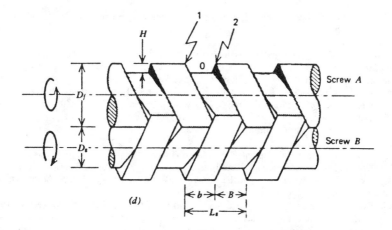

Figure 37. Schematic representation of intermeshing counter-rotating twin-screw extruder [1].

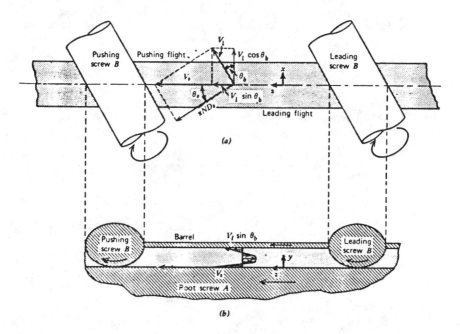

Figure 38. The unwound channel of a counter-rotating screw [1].

where L_s is the screw lead, H is the channel depth, D_f is the diameter at the tip of flights, and $\bar{D}$ is the mean diameter, $D_f - H$. Thus, in the absence of leakage flow, the residence time distribution in the intermeshing counter-rotating mode should be very narrow, with the average residence time, θ, becoming:

$$\theta = Q/V \tag{36}$$

where V is the volume of the extruder. The volumetric flow rate, Q, is commonly controlled through starve feeding in twin screw extruders. Flood feeding generally requires prohibitively high torque and power.

The typical circulatory flow pattern is shown in Figure 39, and suggests continuous extensive mixing of the material as it is being pushed by the screw flight and is being dragged by the barrel and the screw root. It should be noted further that leakage flows exist in intermeshing counter-rotating twin screw extruders [65, 67], and are shown schematically in Figure 40. The leakage flows occur through the screw flight and the barrel, Q_f; between the flanks of the flights, Q_t and Q_s; and between the tip of the flight of one screw and the root of the second screw, Q_c.

The leakage flows induce the following:

- Intermingling of the material elements located in different C-shaped segments at the same screw and in between different screws. This should generate backmixing and broaden the residence time.
- The passage of the material through the narrow gaps during leakage, where the deformation rates are relatively high, generates dispersive mixing.
- The leakage flow, between the tip of one screw flight and the root of the second screw, whereby the material is calendered, generates normal stresses which tend to push the two screws apart. The parting forces can generate considerable wear and thus limit the intermeshing counter-rotating twin screw extruders to relatively low screw speeds, typically less than 200 rpm [68].

Current applications of counter-rotating twin screw extruders include tasks which require narrow residence times; for example, PVC profile extrusion, applications including color-concentrate preparation, and reactive processing, as with drag induced flow reactors [69].

Counter-Rotating Non-Intermeshing (Tangential) Twin Screw Extruders

The schematics of the regular flighted, forward screw elements in tangential extruders are shown in Figure 41. The two screws rotate at the same frequency, and the respective flights can be placed

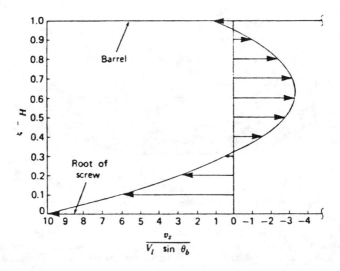

Figure 39. Velocity profile in the down-channel and cross-channel direction in regular forward-flighted counter-rotating twin screw [1].

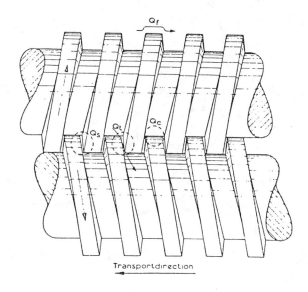

Figure 40. Leakage flows in intermeshing, counter-rotating twin screw [65].

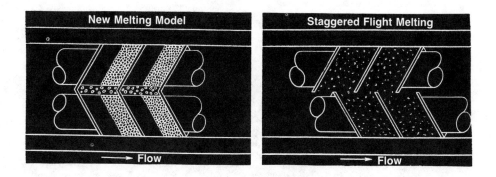

Figure 41. Matched and staggered screw-flight positions in tangential twin screw [70].

either facing each other or in a staggered fashion. The kinematics of the flow are not very different from the one in the single screw extruder, except for one important difference: the interaction between the two screws. The unwound channel is shown in Figure 42, with a corresponding three-plate model [70]. The lower and upper plates represent the two screws, and the moving slitted center plate represents the barrel surface for both screws. At the slit, the presence of a pressure gradient will act as a driving force for interchange of material between the two screws with pressure flow. The design equation for the tangential extruder for isothermal flow of Newtonian fluids in shallow channels becomes:

$$Q = \frac{1}{2} WHV_{bz}F_1 - \frac{WH^3}{12\eta} \left(\frac{\Delta P_T}{\Delta Z_T} \right) F_2 \qquad (37)$$

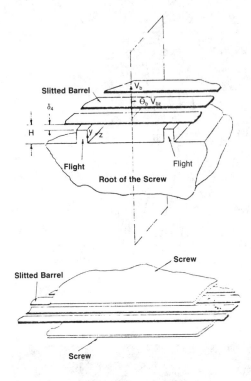

Figure 42. Unwound channel in non-intermeshing, counter-rotating twin-screw extruder [70].

where W = channel width
H = depth
ΔP_T = pressure change over total helical distance, ΔZ_T
η = Newtonian viscosity
F_1 and F_2 = correction factors to account for the slit opening

The meeting of the streams at the interface between the two screws increases the efficiency of extensive mixing in the counter-rotating twin screw extruders, in comparison to single screw extruders. It has been shown experimentally that the leakage flow at the nip can penetrate and form reoriented regions across the depth of the channel [71]. If the flights are further staggered as shown in Figure 41, this mode should give rise to better extensive mixing at the expense of decrease in pumping efficiency. The residence time distribution of a non-intermeshing twin screw extruder is determined experimentally to be broader than the single screw [72], presumably due to excessive leakage flows outlined above.

Other types of elements applicable to tangential extruders are shown in Figure 43, and include reverse flighted and cylindrical elements [73]. The reverse flighted elements should induce extensive mixing in the longitudinal direction, and cylindrical elements are used for sealing purposes close to liquid addition ports.

Counter-rotating non-intermeshing tangential twin screw extruders are employed for applications which do not necessitate dispersive mixing. The applications include polymerization reactions, blending of some polymers, compounding for hot melt adhesives, pigment concentrates, incorporation of glass fiber reinforcements into engineering plastics, and devolatilization.

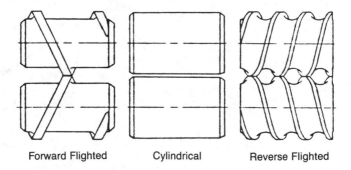

Forward Flighted   Cylindrical   Reverse Flighted

Figure 43. Various types of elements used in non-intermeshing, counter-rotating twin-screw extruders [73].

Co-Rotating Intermeshing Twin Screw Extruders

Co-rotating twin screw extruders are commonly produced only on the fully intermeshing mode and operate on the building block principle. Screw elements are selected and assembled, depending on the requirements of the mixing task at hand. Some of the employed screw elements are shown in Figure 44. Commonly employed elements include right-handed and left-handed (forward and reverse) regular flighted elements, forward and reverse kneading discs, and mixing and shearing pins. Obviously, various elements come in with various shapes and dimensions also. Reviews of the operation principals and comparisons to especially the counter-rotating twin screw extruders are available [62, 74–79].

For regular flighted elements, fully intermeshing co-rotating screws are open length-wise, but are closed cross-wise, except for leakage over the flights. The analysis of right-handed regular flighted elements of the intermeshing co-rotating twin screw extrusion process is not different from the single screw except for the nip regions, where the two screws intermesh. The schematic of the process is shown in Figure 45, where the two flights are assumed to move vertically up and down at the nip region [80].

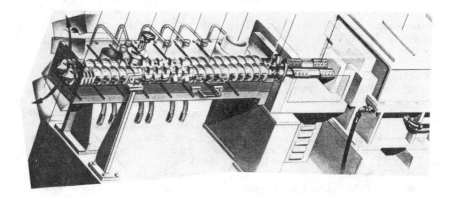

Figure 44. Co-rotating twin-screw extruder (courtesy of Baker-Perkins).

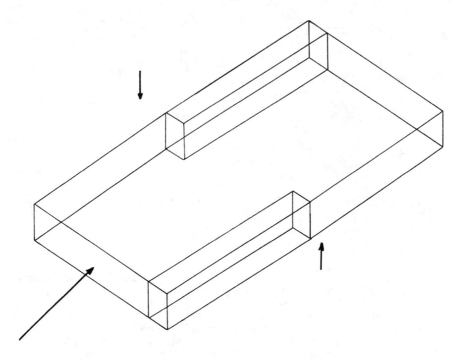

Figure 45. Schematics of flow in regular flighted co-rotating twin screw section [80].

Our three dimensional finite difference based solution of the continuity and momentum conservation equations suggests that the nip area serves to:

1. Change the direction of the shearing planes, thus reorienting the interfacial area for better
   extensive mixing.
2. Impart relatively high rates of shear. The relative velocity at the interface is relatively high
   given by $2\pi N(R_s + R_f)$, where N is rotational speed of the screws, and R_s and R_f are the radii
   at the screw root and at the tip of the flights, respectively.

The change in direction at the nip area and the distribution of deformation rate, i.e., the second
invariant of deformation rate tensor at a location away from the nip area and at the nip area, are
shown in Figures 46 and 47. The lengths of arrows are proportional to the value of the second
invariant. The deformation field can be affected significantly if the widths of the flights are changed.
Some of the "lenticular shape" kneading discs [81] which can be incorporated into the screw
are shown in Figure 48. The discs are self wiping. Depending on the stagger angle neutral, forward
or reversing screw sections can be generated. In the neutral mode, the material is transferred from
one half of the barrel to the other half in figure-8 form before being pressured to move on in the
axial direction by the following melt elements. The calendering action, i.e., passage of the material
through the high shear rate gap between the two discs, generates excellent dispersive mixing. The
introduction of reverse elements will generate further extensive mixing in the axial direction.
Co-rotating twin screw extruders are currently in wide use for a multitude of applications, including incorporation of fillers and reinforcements to commodity plastics and engineering resins,
mixing in production of powder coatings, additive concentrates, color concentrates, thermosetting

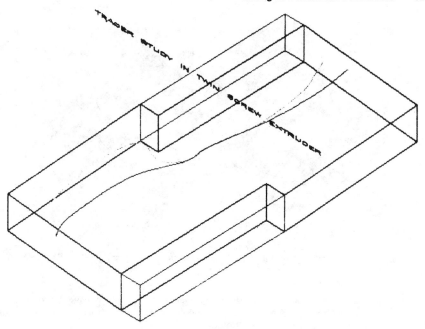

Figure 46. Change in direction in the nip region in co-rotating flow [80].

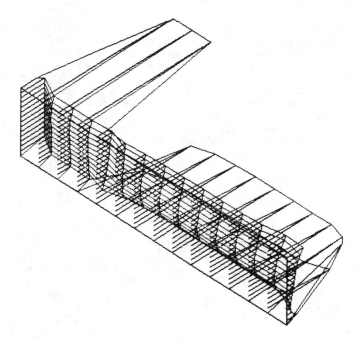

Figure 47. Rate of deformation in the nip region in co-rotating flow [80].

Figure 48. Kneading disks in co-rotating twin-screw extruders (courtesy of Werner & Pfleiderer).

molding compounds, thermoplastic rubbers, blowing agent compounding, polymer blending, PVC formulations, and reactive extrusion. They are also employed widely in other industries, including the cooking, mixing, and processing of food products.

Other Continuous Mixers

The common feature of all the continuous mixers reviewed is the presence of one moving boundary and one stationary surface in the channel (the screw and the barrel). One continuous mixer, the Farrell Diskpack, is a co-rotating disk extruder and has two moving drag inducing surfaces [82–85]. The machine, schematically shown in Figure 49, consists of a single rotor with toroidal (doughnut-shaped) processing chambers, which fit in a circular housing. Between the inlet and outlet openings of each chamber, a channel block is positioned as a stationary element. It diverts the polymer through the outlet. Processing chambers may be connected in parallel, in series or in combination, and are assembled on the building block principle. Elements can be introduced through the housing to enhance mixing, polymer film spreading, and liquid injection.

The flow kinematics in the chamber can be analyzed on the basis of Newtonian, isothermal, fully-developed flow. The analysis is similar to that developed for unwound single screw extruder channels, except now both walls are moving with velocity V_0. Including the pressure flow, which arises due to the presence of a flow restriction, i.e., the die downstream, the design equation becomes [1]:

$$q = V_0 H - \frac{H^3}{12\eta}\left(\frac{dp}{dz}\right) \tag{38}$$

where q is the volumetric flow rate per width; H is depth of the channel, which has both walls moving at velocity V_0; and dp/dz is the pressure gradient due to the presence of a restriction. The ratio of the drag and pressure induced flow rates are given by:

$$\frac{q_p}{q_d} = \frac{H^2}{12\eta V_0}\frac{dp}{dz} \tag{39}$$

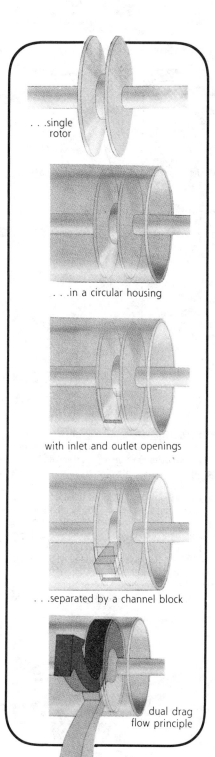

. . .single rotor

. . .in a circular housing

with inlet and outlet openings

. . .separated by a channel block

dual drag flow principle

Figure 49. Co-rotating disk extruder (courtesy of Farrel Corporation).

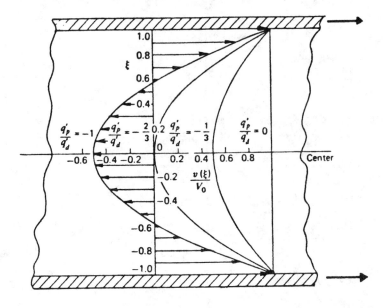

Figure 50. Velocity profiles in co-rotating disk extruder [1].

The velocity distribution for this simplified analysis is shown in Figure 50, for various values of q_p/q_d. As expected, the presence of the restriction generates a circulatory flow in the axial direction. At the same pressurization capability, the shear rates with two walls moving are considerably smaller than with only one wall moving. Thus, mixing pins are necessary to impose high strains and to reorient the melt. High shear stress regions may be introduced also for dispersive mixing. This type of compounder is applied in the compounding of commodity and engineering plastics with fillers, reinforcing agents, in preparation of concentrates, and in polymer blending and alloying.

Finally, the Farrel continuous mixer is a twin-rotor internal mixer [86] and is based upon the transformation of the popular Banbury batch mixer into a continuous mode. Perpendicular to the axis of rotation of the rotors, the cross section of this continuous mixer resembles the batch Banbury mixer [1]. This mixer, shown in Figure 51, basically involves a conveying section, which propels the ingredients and an intensive mixing section. In the intensive mixing section, the material is dispersed by passage through small gaps found between the rotors and the chamber walls, coupled with kneading between the rotors and a rolling action of the material, itself. This continuous mixer is applied in polyolefin homogenization and masterbatching, cross-linking of polyethylene, compounding of PVC, polyamid, ABS, SAN, carbon electrode stock, TRP, rubbers, and in preparation of concentrates and additives.

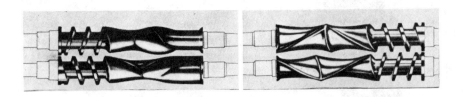

Figure 51. Twin-rotor internal mixer (courtesy of Farrel Corporation).

Acknowledgment

The financial support of ONR through contract #N0001486-K-0620, which made some of our own findings possible, is gratefully acknowledged.

REFERENCES

1. Tadmor, Z., and Gogos, C. G., "Principles of Polymer Processing," John Wiley, N.Y. (1979).
2. Manas-Zloczower, I., Nir, A., and Tadmor, Z., *Rubber Chem. Techn.*, 57, 583–620 (1984).
3. Mohr, W. D., *Processing of Thermoplastic Materials*, Bernhardt, E., ed., R. Krieger Publishing Comp., Malabar (1959).
4. McKelvey, J. M., *Polymer Processing*, John Wiley, New York (1962).
5. Danckwerts, P., *Applied Science Research*, 3A, 279–296 (1952).
6. Spencer, R. S., and Wiley, R. M., *J. Colloid Sci.*, 6, 133–145 (1951).
7. Ng, K., and Erwin, L., *Polym. Eng. Sci.*, 21, 212–217 (1981).
8. Erwin, L., *Polym. Eng. Sci.*, 18, 572 (1978).
9. Bird, B., Armstrong, R., and Hassager, O., *Dynamics of Polymeric Liquids*, Volume 1, John Wiley, N.Y. (1977).
10. Taylor, G., *Proc. Roy. Soc.*, A138, 41–48 (1932).
11. Taylor, G., *Proc. Roy. Soc.*, A146, 501–523 (1934).
12. Rumscheidt, F., and Mason, S., *J. Colloid Sci.*, 16, 238–261 (1961).
13. Bartok, W., and Mason, S., *J. Colloid Sci.*, 6, 354 (1961).
14. Chaffey, G., and Mason, S., *J. Colloid Interface Sci.*, 21, 254 (1966).
15. Karam, H., and Bellinger, J., *Ind. Eng. Chem. Fundam.*, 7, 576 (1968).
16. Cox, R., *J. Fluid Mech.*, 37, 601 (1969).
17. Torza, S., Cox, R., and Mason, S., *Phil. Trans. Roy. Soc.*, 269, 295 (1971).
18. Torza, S., Cox, R., and Mason, S., *J. Colloid and Interface Sci.*, 38, 395–411 (1972).
19. Flumerfelt, R., *Ind. Eng. Chem. Fundam.*, 11, 3, 312–318, (1972).
20. Van Oene, H., *J. Colloid and Interface Sci.*, 40, 448–467 (1972).
21. Acrivos, A., and Lo, T., *J. Fluid Mech.*, 86, 4, 641–672 (1978).
22. Chan, D., and Powell, R., *J. Non-Newtonian Fluid Mechanics*, 15, 165–179 (1984).
23. Kitano, K., Kataoka, T., and Nagatsuka, Y., *Rheologica Acta*, 23, 408–416 (1984).
24. Manas-Zloczower, I., Nir, A., and Tadmor, Z., *Rubber Chem. Techn.*, 55, 1250 (1982).
25. Hold, P., *Adv. Polym. Techn.*, 2, 141–151 (1982).
26. Bolen, W., and Colwell, R., *Soc. Plast. Eng. J.*, 14, 24–28 (1958).
27. Dizon, E., Micek, E., and Scott, C., *Rubber Chem. Techn.*, 48, 339 (1975).
28. Bird, R., Warner, H., Jr. and Evans, D., "Kinetic Theory and Rheology of Dumbbell Suspension with Brownian Motion," Fortsch. Hochpolymeren Forch, Springer Verlag, Berlin, 8, 1–90 (1971).
29. Tadmor, Z., *Ind. Eng. Chem. Fundam*, 15, 346 (1976).
30. Kalyon, D., and Yu, D., Unpublished Results, January (1986).
31. White, J., Ufford, R., Dharod, K., and Prise, R., *J. Appl. Polym. Sci.*, 16, 1313–1330 (1972).
32. Akay, G., *Rheol. Acta*, 18, 256–267 (1979).
33. Jones, R., *Rheol. Acta*, 14, 397–401 (1975).
34. Gauthier, F., Goldsmith, H., and Mason, S., *Trans. Soc. Rheol.*, 15, 297–330 (1971).
35. Segre, G., and Silberberg, A., *Nature*, 189, 209 (1961).
36. Segre, G., and Silberberg, A., *J. Fluid Mech.* 14, 115 (1962).
37. Denson, C., Christiansen, E., and Salt, D., *AIChE J.*, 12, 589–595 (1966).
38. Seshadri, V., and Sutera, P., *Trans. Soc. Rheol.*, 14, 3, 351–373 (1970).
39. Metzner, A., *J. Rheology*, 29, 739–775 (1985).
40. Kalyon, D., and Khemis, M., *SPE ANTEC Technical Papers*, 30, 136–140 (1984).
41. Kalyon, D., and Khemis, M., "Role of Slip Additives in Blown Film Extrusion of Low Density Polyethylene," accepted for publication in *Plastics and Rubber Processing and Applications*, 8, 3, 157–164 (1987).

42. Nichols, R., and Kinder, G., *SPE ANTEC Technical Papers*, *20* (1974).
43. McKelvey, J., *Plastics Engineering*, June, 45–49 (1978).
44. Lopez-Latorre, L., and McKelvey, J., *Adv. Polym. Techn.*, *3*, 4, 355–364 (1983).
45. Tadmor, Z., and Broyer, E., *Polym. Eng. Sci.*, *12*, 5, 379 (1972).
46. Kalyon, D., and Hallouche, M., *Adv. Polym. Techn.*, *6*, 237–249 (1986).
47. Gotsis, A., Kalyon, D., Gogos, C., and Tsenoglou, C., unpublished results (1987).
48. Mohr, W., Saxton, R., and Jepson, C., *Ind. Eng. Chem.*, *49*, 1855 (1957).
49. Pinto, G., and Tadmor, Z., *Polym. Eng. Sci.*, *10*, 5, 279–288 (1970).
50. Wolf, D., and White, D., *AIChE J.*, *22*, 122–131 (1976).
51. Chella, R., and Ottino, J., *Ind. Chem. Fund.*, *24*, 170–180 (1985).
52. Mokhtarian, F., and Erwin, L., *Polym. Eng. Sci.*, *23*, 49 (1983).
53. Maddock, B., *SPE Journal*, July, 23 (1967).
54. Rauwendaal, C., *SPE ANTEC Techn. Papers*, *30*, 62 (1984).
55. Espesito, R., *Plastics Eng.*, October, 39 (1986).
56. Pearson, J., "Mechanics of Polymer Processing," p. 662, Elsevier Applied Science Publishers, London (1985).
57. Godfrey, J., "Static Mixers" in "Mixing in the Process Industries," Harnby, N., Edwards, M., and Nienow, A., Editors, Butterworths (1985).
58. Wigotsky, V., *Plastics Engineering*, February, 19–23 (1986).
59. Stade, K., *Polym. Eng. Sci.*, *17*, 50 (1977).
60. Stade, K., *Polym. Eng. Sci.*, *18*, 107 (1978).
61. Parshall, C., and Geyer, P., U.S. Patent 2,744,287 (1956).
62. Herrmann, H., Burkhardt, U., and Jakopin, S., SPE Technical Papers, Montreal (1977).
63. Rauwendaal, C., *Polym. Eng. Sci.*, *21*, 16, 1092–1100 (1981).
64. Wyman, C., *Polym. Eng. Sci.*, *15*, 606–611 (1975).
65. Janssen, L., Mulders, L., and Smith, J., *Plastics and Polymers*, June, 93–98 (1975).
66. Schenkel, G., "Plastics Extrusion Technology and Theory", Illife Books, London (1966).
67. Doboczky, Z., *Plast. Verarb.*, *16*, 57–67 (1965).
68. Nichols, R., *Modern Plastics*, September, 90–94 (1986).
69. Janssen, L., and Schaart, B., *2nd World Congress of Chemical Engineering*, *6*, 543, Montreal (1981).
70. Kaplan, A., and Tadmor, Z., *Polym. Eng. Sci.*, *14*, 58–66 (1974).
71. Howland, C., and Erwin, L., *SPE ANTEC Technical Papers*, (1983).
72. Walk, C., *SPE ANTEC Technical Papers*, *28*, 423 (1982).
73. Nichols, R., and Yao, J., *SPE ANTEC Technical Papers*, *28*, 416 (1982).
74. Mack, W., and Herter, R., *Chemical Engineering Progress*, January, 64–70 (1976).
75. Eise, K., Herrmann, H., Werner, H., and Burkhardt, *Adv. Plast. Techn.*, *1*, 2, 1–22 (1981).
76. Todd, D., *Polym. Eng. Sci.*, *15*, 6, 437–443 (1975).
77. Todd, D., and Baumann, D., *Polym. Eng. Sci.*, *18*, 4, 321–325 (1978).
78. Karian, H., *J. Vinyl Techn.*, *7*, 4, 154–159 (1985).
79. Booy, M., *Polym. Eng. Sci.*, *18*, 973 (1978).
80. Du, C., and Kalyon, D., Unpublished Results, March (1987).
81. Loomans, B., and Brennan, A., U.S. Patent 3,195,868 (1965).
82. Tadmor, Z., Hold, P., and Valsamis, L., *SPE ANTEC Technical Papers*, *25*, 193–204 (1979).
83. Tadmor, Z., Hold, P., and Valsamis, L., Ibid., 205–211 (1979).
84. Tadmor, Z., U.S. Patent 4,142,805 (1979).
85. Tadmor, Z., U.S. Patent 4,194,841 (1980).
86. Hold, P., U.S. Patent 3,154,808 (1969).

CHAPTER 29

COMPUTER MODELING AND ANALYSIS OF EXTRUSION OPERATIONS

Donald H. Sebastian

Stevens Institute of Technology
and
Polymer Processing Institute
Hoboken, New Jersey, USA

CONTENTS

INTRODUCTION

In this era of high technology, design and operation of polymer processing equipment remains as much an art as a science. More often than not, a new design is guided by past experience, empirical wisdom, and a fair amount of trial and error. As in so many areas of today's technology, the pace of change brought on by exploration of new techniques, and application of existing technology to new materials, is sufficiently rapid that aids must be found to accelerate the accumulation of information and to extend the basis of knowledge. A number of professions have turned to computer-based analysis in one form or another as a means to facilitate exploration of new frontiers of industrial practice.

The tool and die industry was perhaps the earliest to draw upon the advantages offered by combining computer computations with interactive video displays so as to streamline the process of new product design. The act of conceptualizing parts as images on a computer graphics terminal, and then directly generating instructions for automatic milling and cutting equipment was the genesis of CAD/CAM, the first of the acronyms which now populate the "alphabet soup" of computer jargon. The first operation, tagged Computer Aided Design, and the second, Computer Aided Manufacturing, have been followed by a seemingly endless procession of computer aided hybrids including: Computer Aided Instruction (CAI), Computer Aided Engineering (CAE), Computer Aided Process Control (CAPC), Computer Aided Process Design (CAPD), and Computer Integrated Manufacturing (CIM).

Expansion of capabilities within each of these fields has resulted in a certain amount of overlap in roles; nevertheless, each has identifiable origins in some professional practice which are responsible for the unique aspects of the approach. The term CAE became popularized when design software began to do more than simply emulate visual appearance of a finished article. Computer hardware engineers recognized the practical application for their own products. Not only could complex computer chip layouts be schematically represented on the screen, but simulating their performance by computer models allowed prototype evaluation in advance of actual part fabrication. This integration of design and simulation is the distinction of CAE, and is by no means limited in utility to the electronics industry. It is, in fact, especially pertinent to the process related industries, where creation of a process is of fundamentally equal importance to creation of the product ultimately generated by the process.

Not all engineering professions have made a heavy committment to computerized design procedures. Routine computer usage implies the ready availability of software that addresses the major bottlenecks in the design process. Development of commercial software still rests primarily in the hands of computer software professionals. The extent to which their own education, training, and background meshes with the needs of any given profession governs the rate at which quality software will evolve. The process industries, including chemical, petroleum, and polymer processing, have not received the same level of concentrated attention that software developers have placed on other application areas. It falls, then, upon some segment of these industries to contribute to the development of appropriate computer tools. In the field of polymer processing, which draws its members from those trained in mechanical, chemical, and material engineering, it is a chemical engineering background that offers the most direct connection to this task. The approach of using balance equations for heat, mass, and momentum, which is fundamental to this profession, as well as the systems perspective implicit in any large scale process design, are necessary adjuncts to the high level programming skills required to make a contribution in this area.

The ability to develop process models is not, in itself, adequate justification to warrant radical transitions in design methodology. There are many things which can be, but prehaps should not be, done on a computer; sometimes computerization does not offer sufficient advantages over conventional approaches to merit investment in new technology. This argument is frequently applied to polymer processing design models. An engineer with twenty to thirty years of experience can trust intuition empiricism, and experience to be as reliable as the results of the current crop of computer simulation packages. Such a person is not the audience for simulation software. But these individuals are few in numbers, and the problems facing the industry are increasing faster than new experts can be trained. The gestation period for developing expertise has to be shortened if the industry is to face the challenge of foreign competition, and realize sustained growth.

Computer simulation has direct benefits in the areas of training and formal design on several levels. One can compress the time scale for normal cause and effect learning by exposure to a number of design situations in a simulated environment. Even when the response of the simulation is more qualitative than quantitative, the user can acquire considerable knowledge from the trends observed. A more powerful dimension of simulation is its ability to provide a window into the equipment, revealing the fundamental processes responsible for shaping system performance. Learning which is leveraged in this fashion builds the foundations necessary to confidently tackle situations which do not lie within the bounds of previous experience. Computer simulations can, and will, become more accurate and more accessible; it is only a matter of time.

As compelling as the motivations for engaging in computer aided design may be, the challenges to construction of a working process model are equally foreboding. Polymer processing operations combine all the complexities imaginable in a modeling exercise: materials with non-ideal, non-linear thermodynamic and transport properties; complicated, irregular flow geometries which frequently require full three dimensional flow analysis; transient behavior, free surfaces, phase changes, heterogeneous systems, and more. Successfully overcoming these obstacles, and providing routine access to the resultant software, requires advances by hardware and software engineers, process rheologists, and numerical analysts in conjunction with the polymer processing expert. The current pace of evolution in the computer industry, the adoption of standards in areas of software functionality, and concentrated academic research on the key problems of numerical analysis all suggest that polymer process modeling is about to come of age as a serious design tool.

ELEMENTS OF A PROCESS MODEL

Computer design software of any type is a system of software components, each with a specific mission in accomplishing the overall goal of the design exercise. One may select from a number of different techniques or algorithms to fulfill the functional requirements of a particular routine. The activity of software design involves the balance of optimizing individual operations against the primary objective of optimizing of overall system performance. The basic components of a polymer processing simulation are shown in Figure 1.

Mathematical Models

At the heart of a simulation package is a process model which must emulate the true performance of the operation to be analyzed. It is commonplace to lump together the process model with the numerical analysis technique when discussing a simulation; however, they are distinctly different components. The model represents a visualization of the real polymer process. It is the mathematical expression of this abstraction, which attempts to draw out the most important features of operation, while presenting a form capable of solution by analytical methods, or one or more numerical algorithms.

Models can be loosely categorized as empirical or rigorous. An empirical model often serves as a vehicle for interpolating or extrapolating experimental information. Such models can be useful in multi-variable problems, but can be limited in applicability if one relies on the predictive powers of extrapolation. Major changes in rate-controlling mechanisms can take place over relatively narrow regions of parameter values. Extrapolation of data from one regime to another would fail to account for such changes. Rigorous models, based upon the mathematical expression of the fundamental principles of conservation of mass, energy, and momentum, can provide a platform for examination of conditions beyond those already encountered in practice.

Process analysis through use of balance equations has become a standard approach in academic settings over the last twenty years. Use of material and energy balances, and the "Transport Phenomena" approach have dominated chemical engineering education since the introduction of the text of that name by Bird, Stewart, and Lightfoot in 1960 [1]. The microscopic conservation equations

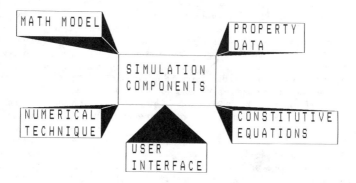

Figure 1. Components of a processing simulation.

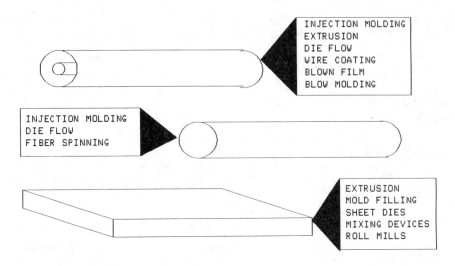

Figure 2. Elementary flow geometries: annular, circular, and rectangular.

provide the framework for a rigorous description of any polymer processing operation; however, without further simplification, they generally lead to an intractable set of relationships. It is incumbent upon the modeler to reduce complexity by eliminating expressions pertaining to second-order effects, and concentrating on those phenomena responsible for imparting the characteristic behavior of the process. There is a certain degree of subjectivity in such reduction, and the success of a model in terms of accuracy, sensitivity, and extensibility hinges upon these hypotheses.

Suprisingly, simple geometries serve as visualizations for a number of polymer processing steps. Shown in Figure 2, rectangular, circular, and annular flow passages are the building blocks for analysis of die flow, extrusion, and injection molding. In some instances, the simple geometry suffices as an analog to more complex processes. Pressure drop-flow rate characteristics of a pipe die or wire coating dies can be captured by annular flow approximations. Flow in injection molding runner systems can be captured as circular pipe flow. Most models of single and twin screws are based upon a visualization of flow in a rectangular channel, with one boundary moving transversely, and longitudinally, in relation to the channel.

When such models are too simplistic, one can often splice together simple flow geometries to approximate more complex fields. The nature of polymer flows is such that variations in geometry in the direction of flow can be legitimately approximated in stair-step fashion. By virtue of this, the "lubrication approximation," flow through a tapered annular section can be modeled as connected annular elements of successively increasing dimension (see Figure 3). Flow through a mandrel die can be successfully simulated by combining circular and annular elements along with the lubrication approximation to describe the die's varying flow geometry [2, 3]. One popular approach to modeling injection mold filling requires projection of the mold cavity onto a planar figure (called a "lay-flat"). The projection is then broken into a series of connected elements of regular cross-section, such as those shown in Figure 2, and progression of the flow front during various stages of fill can be computed.

Greater accuracy can be obtained by reducing the size of the region over which an approximation to the local geometry is expected to hold. When a flow field has one dimension that is substantially smaller than the other two, as in molds and many dies, for example, the flow path can be visualized as a series of connected parallel plates of varying separation. This visualization is the cornerstone of a solution technique known as Flow Analysis Network (FAN) which has been applied to molds, dies, and extrusion channels [4–6]. The ultimate, of course, is full three-dimensionality along with

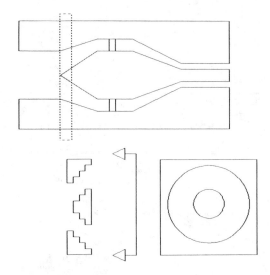

Figure 3. Visualization of a Mandrel pipe die as connected annular and circular cross sections.

proper description of transient effects. The flow element modeled would then be the same "differential" element of volume used in the derivation of the basic flow balance equations. The number of degrees of freedom in such an approach, even for a relatively small flow region, would be prohibitively large to be accomodated on modern computing equipment. Thus, even with the ability to formulate a rigorous description, and numerical techniques capable of solving the posed equations, there are motivations for seeking simplifications. Typically, temperature gradients, secondary flows, and normal stress component are among the items neglected in computational models for polymer processing.

Single Screw Extrusion

Single screw extrusion of polymers predates multi-screw techniques, and remains the most widespread of operations for polymer plastication and melt pumping to supply downstream operations for sheet, tube, and profile forming. Efforts to develop mathematical models of the full single screw plasticating process date back to the mid-sixties [4]. Many investigators [4–17] have contributed to improving the sophistication and accuracy of these models in the intervening twenty years. The focus of research has been primarily upon improvements to the analysis of melting in the screw channel, where a significant amount of visualization is required to render the rigorous balance equations simple enough to be solved. The full plasticating process, however, is comprised of a series of unit operations which combine to transform solid resin in pellet or granular form at room temperature to a molten mass at elevated temperatures, and at pressures which are sufficiently high to drive flow through downstream shaping devices. Different sections of the screw are designated to accomplish this sequence of events. In truth, these events may overlap functional segments of the screw design, but the diagram in Figure 4 provides a loose definition of the zones and their respective locations along the machine axis. Each operation is subject to a modeling visualization.

Hopper

There are a number of polymer processes that are directly fed melt streams. Reactor effluent may be compounded or devolatilized prior to pelletizing, or the extruder may be part of a multi-stage operation. The most common use of single screws involves the digestion of feeds containing virgin resin, sometimes in combination with regrind of scrap material, rather than melt-fed systems. These

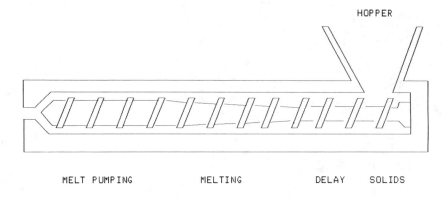

Figure 4. Functional zones of a plasticating single-screw extruder.

materials are supplied to the extruder "throat from conical hoppers. The hopper geometry, the height of fill, and the physical properties of the particulate solids dictate the rate of delivery of solids to the screw, as well as the pressure under the hopper. The goal of modeling the hopper is to ensure that flow rates to the screw do not limit attainable throughput, and to provide the initial conditions of pressure at the screw entrance. Current models [18–20] cannot predict aberrations such as arching, piping, or funnel flow in the hopper. The major conclusion from the model analysis is that the base pressure reaches a limiting value in spite of an increasing height of solids in the hopper, and that the base pressure is proportional to the bin diameter and inversely proportional to the coefficient of friction between solids and hopper wall. Experimentally measured base pressures for polystyrene feed material confirm the model predictions [21].

Screw Visualization

The true flow path of solids and melt in the screw channel is a complicated one. The flow channel is the helical groove in the screw, and melt actually travels in a helical path within this helix. At the heart of most screw simulations is the visualization of the flow path as a long rectangular channel which might result if one could "upwrap" the material contained in the screw channel, and stretch it out as a long continuous ribbon. Furthermore, it is convenient to analyze the flow from a frame of reference attached to the screw root, so the screw root and flights appear motionless, and the barrel appears to move across the top of the open channel. As a result, the visualization is that of a long rectangular channel with a plate moved across the upper surface at an angle to the channel axis (see Figure 5). Correction for the effects of channel curvature in both the axial and transverse directions are featured in some models. Their importance depends upon the ratio of channel depth to screw diameter [22].

Solids Conveying

The particulate solids delivered to the screw from the hopper are conveyed down the screw channel by the dragging action of the barrel. As they move downstream, they are pressurized and compacted. The shearing action of the barrel on the solid surface in combination with the heat conducted from the barrel, raises the temperature of the polymer and ultimately induces melting. The creation of molten polymer is not instantaneous, and so there are generally several turns characterized as solids conveying sections which precede the melting zone. The model visualization traditionally applied to this zone is one whereby the solids are assumed to fuse in the form of a rigid, non-deformable mass, which may isotropically reduce in volume through application of ex-

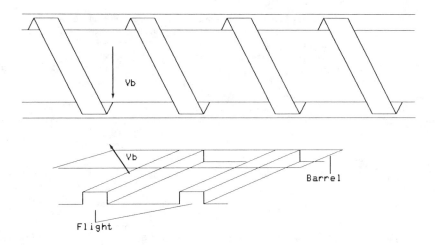

Figure 5. Visualization of single screw channel.

ternal pressure. Screw pulling experiments [22, 23] have shown that some materials do indeed behave in this fashion, while others remain loose particles which do not behave in unison.

Solid conveying capacity is then analyzed by virtue of a force balance on a differential element of the solid bed, taken from along the helical screw path, as shown in Figure 6. The major conclusions of such an analysis are:

1. Pressure will increase exponentially in the flow direction.
2. Maximum flow rates occur with large barrel friction factors and small screw surface frictional resistance.
3. Further increase in flow rate can be achieved if the barrel friction factor in the tangential direction is much larger than in the longitudinal direction.
4. There exists an optimum helix angle for conveying of solids which depends on other screw geometry and frictional resistances.

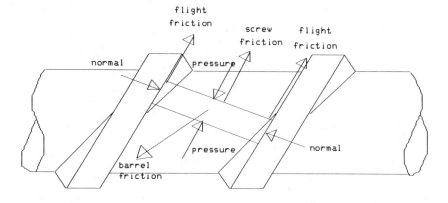

Figure 6. Forces acting on a section of the polymer solid bed.

The second conclusion is justification for polishing screw surfaces while leaving a rough finish on the barrel, while the third suggests advantages are to be gained from grooved feed throat sections for maximizing pressurization of the solids [22, 24]. The last conclusion arises from the competing effects of increasing solids conveying angle and decreasing throughput as helix angle increases. The optimum angle for properties typical of many commercial polymers lies in the range of 17–20 degrees, which confirms the usual selection of a "square pitched" screw (helix angle = 17.23° when lead is equal to diameter) common in many designs.

It should be noted that the friction factors used in force balance equations are extremely difficult to determine. The nature of the solid bed surface changes from an irregular array of solid particles to a smoothed, semi-tough exterior. Steady-state experiments performed on blocks of solid resin below processing temperatures cannot capture the dynamic nature of change in the solids [25]. It has been suggested that actual screw performance data might provide more reasonable estimates of friction factors than laboratory testing [26].

Melting

The most challenging aspect of screw modeling is an accurate description of the melting process from the onset of a melt film at the solid bed surface through the complete consumption of the solids. One must contend with a multi-phase system; one must deal with solids behavior ranging from loose particulates to fused solid, treat flow geometries that vary from narrow deep channels to wide shallow channels, and allow for the potentially unsteady-state nature of the solid bed break-up. The complexity of the process forces the modeler to make a series of assumptions relative to the mechanism by which melting develops in the screw channel.

The onset of melting cannot be precisely defined. At first, as melt is created by the combination of shear and heat transfer at the barrel, the melt which is generated can penetrate irregularities in the solid bed, or be dragged across the flight clearance. This phase, prior to the development of a melt pool in the channel, is referred to as the "Delay Zone," and may last for several turns. A semi-empirical correlation which unites experimental results for several polymers is shown in Figure 7 [22], and is employed in simulations.

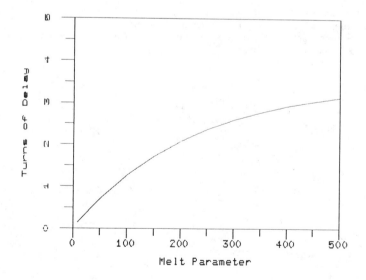

Figure 7. Length of delay zone as a function of dimensionless melt parameter.

Once there is sufficient melt generation to lead to an accumulation in the channel, an analysis of the two-phase melt/solid system is required. The simplest of models might be categorized as "one-dimensional" models, because they do not allow for cross-channel variations, and step in the axial direction an increment of length at a time. As a result, at any given point, only gradients normal to the barrel are considered. In light of these assumptions, one must also presuppose the placement of the solid bed in the channel cross section. Based upon screw pulling experiments [22] it was noted that a wide variety of resins conformed to the "Maddock Melting Mechanism" [23]. Shown in Figure 8, the solid bed is located against the trailing flight, the melt pool accumulates along the pushing flight, and a thin melt film, of constant depth, separates the barrel and solid bed. As melting proceeds, the fraction of channel width occupied by the solid bed decreases. Presumption of this mechanism in a model generally confines melting to the barrel-solid bed interface, and cannot allow for dissipative melting which occurs if there is substantial melt penetration in the solid bed. Enhancements to the original model allow for melt films surrounding the entire solid bed, non-Newtonian melt flow with associated non-linear temperature profiles in the melt film, solid bed acceleration, and temperature profiles in the solid bed.

A subsequent generation of models have evolved which are "two-dimensional" in character [11–16]. They still step in the axial direction, and are therefore incapable of anticipating downstream conditions, or the apparent backflow (see melt pumping) which can arise due to backpressure. They do permit variations in the channel cross section parallel and normal to the barrel surface. In general, these models allow the melt film to completely surround the solid bed. The location of the solid bed may shift in response to the pressures and drag forces exerted by the various melt films and pools on the solid bed surface, and melting can take place along all of the solid bed surfaces. Two fundamentally different model approaches are based on opposing visualizations of the solid bed behavior: deformable vs. rigid. Deformable models assume the most extreme case of behavior whereby the solids freely rearrange their shape to accomodate local forces. In a sense, the behavior of the solid is assumed to be fluid-like. This is in contrast to rigid bed models in which only solid body translations are permitted. Although both approaches have been shown to yield reasonable estimates of melting rate, the deformable bed models have not been as reliable in providing quantitative estimates of pressure build up during melting [27].

The most ambitious melting model in the literature is a full three-dimensional model [17]. This model eliminates the downstream stepping in favor of simultaneous solution of all points in the flow domain. The solid bed "rheology" was treated as an extension of the melt, that is, it was assumed to be a melt of "infinite viscosity rather than applying a separate description of the solid bed mechanics. The location of the solid bed was noted by the temperature field (all temperatures below the melting point were assumed to indicate solid). The model appears capable of reproducing a variety of different melting mechanisms without a priori assumption of a mechanism.

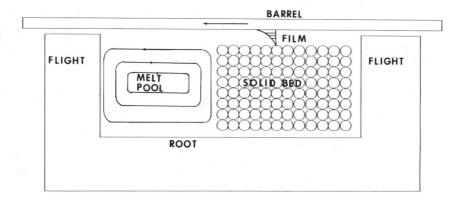

Figure 8. Visualization of melting mechanism.

Most of the different melting models appear to give reasonable estimates of the length of screw necessary to complete melting. Predictions of pressure are somewhat less successful. A number of phenomena are yet to be fully incorporated in the modeling process. A rigorous description of the solid bed dynamics which could account for the varying response of different particulates, including feeds containing regrind, is still not available. Also, experimental observations [22] indicate that the solid bed does not steadily diminish in size along the screw axis. It reaches a point where break-up becomes a transient process, necessitating even more complex analysis than yet attempted. The viscoelastic nature of polymer melt is not accounted for, and the full three-dimensional nature of the melt pool flow field, with associated thermal gradients, is generally omitted, or approximated by open channel models. Other factors omitted from analysis are the kinetics of melting, for crys-

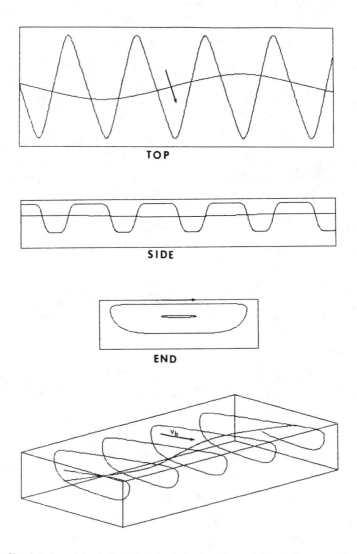

Figure 9. Simulated particle trajectories for extruder channel flow with no axial pressure gradient.

talline materials, and degradation kinetics. Extensions of modeling techniques to multi-flighted screw designs have been reported [28, 29], and follow the same visualizations applied to conventional designs.

Melt Pumping

The flow of melt in the screw channel is the aspect of numerical models which can be treated in the most rigorous fashion of all the extrusion steps, although a number of simplifications are still made in modeling visualizations. Melt flow in the channel follows a complicated pattern often referred to as a "helix within a helix". Figure 9 shows a simulated tracer experiment, which reveals the helical path within the unwound channel confines. The parallel plate visualization of extruder flow is often applied (independently) to the cross and down channel components of flow. Cross-channel flow is always under "closed-discharge" conditions, giving rise to a velocity profile similar to that shown in Figure 10, Line 1. Depending upon the axial conditions, flow may be due solely to drag, may be impeded by a pressure rise, or aided by a pressure drop. The axial flow profile may be any of those shown in the figure. It is the profile associated with an axial pressure rise (Line 1), which causes many to describe this condition as one of reverse flow. This is actually a misnomer; material does not flow from the die back to the hopper. Material on the lower streamlines is ultimately swept up to the top by the cross channel components of flow, and moved downstream. An example of the effect of an axial pressure rise is shown in the three-dimensional perspective of Figure 11. It should be apparent that the helical paths have been compressed, much like a spring recoiling after extension, but that fluid elements ultimately move toward the channel exit. In the limit of closed discharge conditions in the axial direction, fluid streamlines would be closed loops; fluid elements would orbit in the direction of the barrel motion, never advancing down the screw axis.

The fact that fluid elements on the outer streamlines must traverse a longer circumferential path than inner ones results in a residence time distribution in the melt at the reactor exit [30, 31]. The distribution in retention times may also imply distribution in other properties resulting from streamline flow, such as temperature and imposed shear deformation. Screw-end mixing devices which homogenize the extruder output, but provide no back-mixing, cannot remove the residence time distribution.

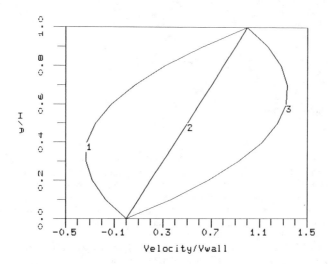

Figure 10. Various superpositions of pressure and drag flow: (1) pressure gradient opposes drag, (2) no pressure gradiennt, (3) pressure gradient aids drag.

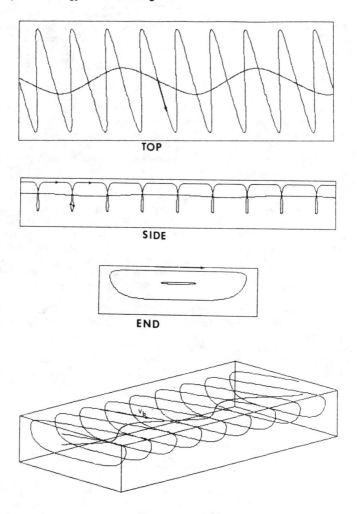

Figure 11. Simulated Particle trajectories for extruder channel flow with axial pressure gradient which opposes the barrel drag.

When the channel is sufficiently broad relative to the channel depth, recirculation is confined to the regions close to the screw flights, and thus the bulk of the cross channel flow can be approximated by flow between parallel plates. This is not the case for channels which are square or deep and narrow, as shown in the cross channel recirculation patterns given in Figure 12. Note the development of multiple recirculation fields in the narrow channel. The metering section, or melt pumping zone of commercial screw designs, typically has a channel aspect ratio in excess of 10:1, so the latter case is not to be expected in the metering zone. However, the flow in the melt pool adjacent to the solid bed during the course of melting will certainly have a low aspect ratio at the outset, and this condition must prevail for a significant portion of the melting process.

The errors engendered by assumption of "fully developed" cross-channel flow appear to be minor relative to other assumptions implicit in the melting model. It is in the consideration of heat transfer effects that neglect of the full recirculation could pose problems. Material encounters a spectrum

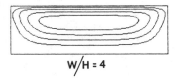

W/H = 4

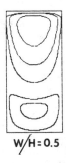

W/H = 0.5

Figure 12. Recirculation patterns for a wide and narrow channel.

of heat transfer conditions as it circles from the barrel to the screw root and back again. Some models have attempted to account for this phenomena by modifying open channel flow equations using an algorithm to shift material from streamlines above the flow symmetry point to streamlines below.

The approximations to the flow field necessitate additional approximations to account for the non-isothermal nature of the flow. Ideally, the full distributed parameter system should be considered, but it is conventional to model heat flux from the melt pool to the barrel by using the product of the difference between local barrel and average melt temperature, and a heat transfer coefficient [32, 33]. This coefficient may simply reflect the thermal resistance of the melt layer which is not wiped by the passage of the flights, or may include the effect of heat input due to viscous energy dissipation which is created by the shearing action of the flight [33].

Mixing Devices

There are a number of custom screw elements, created with the design purpose of breaking up the normal flow pattern of melt in order to homogenize the contents of the channel cross section. The subject of most modeling efforts has been fluted mixing elements [34–36]. These are screw sections in a variety of configurations, but all with a basic design principle of operation which finds pairs of parallel channels separated by a flight with a greater clearance than the flights isolating the pair from neighboring channels. Melt enters the mixing section through the opening of only one of the channels, and is forced to pass over the intervening flight in order to pass out the discharge end of the other channel. In different designs, the channels may or may not have a helix angle, an axial taper, and axial variations in the relative channel widths. The modeling visualizations are similar to those applied to conventional screw channels and barrier screw designs.

Twin Screw Extrusion

All the complexities associated with single screw analysis are manifest in the description of twin screw equipment, while additional factors come into play as well. The ability to model the full range of behavior in twin screws (either co-rotating or counter-rotating) has not progressed to the level of integration now realized in single screw analysis. There are, however, some commonly used visualizations which are useful in understanding behavior of isolated zones within these devices. There are three major categories of twin screw device, each requiring special analysis: counter-rotating fully intermeshing, counter-rotating tangential non-intermeshing, and co-rotating fully intermeshing twin screw extruders.

Counter-Rotating

The fully intermeshing twin screw is a positive displacement device. The intermesh isolates fluid elements along the screw axis, and the rotation conveys these segments along the screw axis. Figure 13 shows one such segment, and the resulting visualization of the flow field, as a rectangular box with several moving walls [37, 38]. The resulting analysis differs from that of a single screw under closed discharge conditions. Both upper and lower plates appear to move relative to the end planes (which are the intermeshing flights from the opposing screw). The axial flow field develops two recirculating paths, and its maximum velocity is at the stagnant point of the cross channel pattern, as seen in the velocity profiles of Figure 14. The net result is a flow path that is highly randomized, and leads to good convective mixing within the closed cell. It is not uncommon to simplify analysis to a "plug flow" visualization; that is, to assume the content of each "c-section" is completely uniform, and all variations occur axially.

The non-intermeshing, tangential counter-rotating twin screw can be viewed as two parallel single-screws. At regular intervals along the screw axis, the flow paths from the two independent screws meet. The analysis of "unwound" flat channels is still applied to each screw individually, but the apex region where the two channels meet must be accounted for. The arrangement shown in Figure 15 presents a framework for this analysis which is a straightforward extension of single screw analysis [39, 40]. Variations hinge on the treatment of the plate separation geometry in the region where the flow path from each screw converges [40–42].

Co-Rotating

Self-wiping, intermeshing co-rotating twin screws present some of the most difficult problems in visualization. This is particularly true for sections with substantial leakage flows, and especially

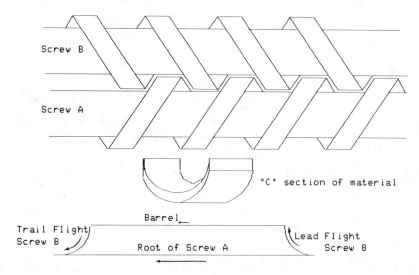

Figure 13. Visualization of counter-rotating, fully inter-meshing twin-screw extruder.

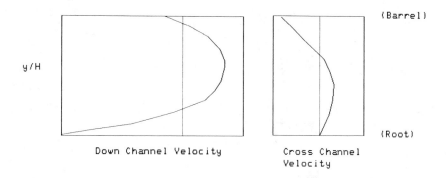

Figure 14. Down channel and cross channel velocity profiles in twin screw "C" section.

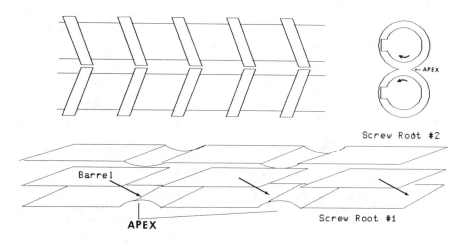

Figure 15. Visualization of counter-rotating tangential twin-screw extruder.

true for the mixing and kneading sections characteristically used on these twin screws. Most attempts to quantify flow behavior are confined to melt pumping in conventional flighted sections. An analog to the other unwound channel visualizations is presented in Figure 16 [43]. Detailed analysis of the flow in mixing sections where elements have no pitch remains to be undertaken.

Properties and Constitutive Equations

Proper representation of the flow field is insufficient for design use of a model. Material properties such as heat capacities, transition temperatures, viscosity as a function of shear rate and temperature, and thermal conductivity are all required to characterize the polymer to be processed. In representing material behavior, one is faced with choices which parallel selection of a modeling technique. Given sufficient experimental measurements, one might simply use regression correlations to provide estimates of property values called for in the computation. Regression fits may, however, show substantial deviation from the true material response when extrapolated beyond the bounds of original experimentation. A relationship which has some grounding in molecular

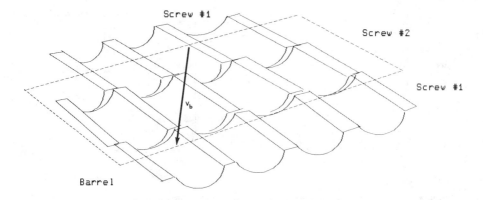

Figure 16. Visualization of flow in flighted section of co-rotating twin-screw extruder.

theory is preferable in that its response to variations in system parameters will be qualitatively correct, even when it might lack the accuracy to precisely duplicate experimental measurements. There are a number of fundamental models to choose from in representing the shear rate and temperature dependence of viscosity. There is not the same level of accord in model selection when one looks for a methodology for describing elastic flow behavior, both in response to shear and elongational deformations. Such flows are of more than academic curiosity. They dominate aspects of blow molding, blown film, fiber spinning, coating, and profile extrusion. Selection of the best constitutive equation currently depends greatly on the particular algorithm used to solve the flow equations.

Flow is of such fundamental importance to polymer processing operations that it is easy to overlook the importance of non-idealities in other polymer properties. Properties such as density, thermal conductivity, and heat capacity, routinely taken as constants for conventional petrochemicals, can undergo significant changes during the course of processing. Of particular importance to processors is the melting or softening transition in polymer solids. Amorphous polymers do not melt, per se, and crystalline polymers melt over a range of temperatures rather than at a single precise value. There has not been the same level of interest in developing equations of state to predict such behavior, and curve-fitting experimental data is the typical route taken by modelers.

If there is one point that should rise above all others, it is the realization that accurate models require substantially more information than is generally supplied by commercial resin manufacturers. The picture is further muddled by variations from lot to lot of base resin, and the effect of additives, modifiers, and fillers. If models are to have the steady stream of reliable property data they require, then any one or all of the following must occur:

1. Development of simple experimental devices for real time property measurement.
2. Creation of centralized information banks with full up-to-date property data.
3. Research on general multi-phase predictive equations (mixing rules).

Numerical Techniques

Prior to computerization, simulation required use of classical mathematics to produce closed-form solutions to the balance equations. Generally, only the simplest of visualizations could be solved in this manner. In early work, computing was used to facilitate iterative solution of analytical expressions where explicit dependencies could not be isolated from highly non-linear terms. It was also useful in evaluating solutions which contained infinite series as part of the solution. The presence of computing did not influence the calculation or analysis procedures; it simply reduced the labor-intensive aspects of obtaining an answer.

Most modern simulation techniques are based upon discrete mathematics, since these are more closely aligned with the digital nature in which computers operate [44, 45]. The continuum of real space is discretized into small domains. In some techniques, the derivatives of the balance equations are replaced by difference equations linking point to point in the solution domain. This is the approach used in Finite Difference (FD) formulations. The main difficulty with FD approaches has been their limitations in handling irregular geometries. Variations on the basic approach which allow for variable mesh sizes and coordinate transformations have had some success in coping with this problem, but lack generalizability. The most widely used methods are now based upon variational calculus, particularly the Finite Element Method (FEM) which has been adapted from its commonly used form in mechanical stress analysis to serve as a tool for viscous flow analysis [45]. FEM techniques approximate the solution to the equations as polynomials which apply in the small region of a single discretization point. The solution technique must then find the coefficients of these polynomials such that they conform to the constraints of the governing balance equations and boundary conditions. These techniques have become the dominant tool for numerical research in polymer processing in the last five years. They are adept at handling complicated flow geometries, although they have not been highly successful in addressing the problems of elastic flow behavior, and tend to require extremes in computing power even for problems of moderate size.

Increased computer processor speed and expanded memory capacity have made practical a host of numerical analysis techniques that were formerly too cumbersome for routine use. Furthermore, new hardware technologies such as array processors, supercomputers, and parallel processing systems are stimulating whole new fields of investigation. Rediscovery of the old and development of the new may combine to bring about solution algorithms capable of removing the computational barriers that exist today.

User Interface

Up until now, our discussion has focused on the needs of the computer model. Of equal practical importance are the needs of the model user. Sophisticated design software can be rendered useless if it demands a level of computing expertise which is not likely to be held by the typical user. The growth of personal computing has done a great deal to stimulate interest in developing methodologies for human interaction with computer software that seek to emulate more natural forms of communication. Special command languages modeled on traditional computer operating system interfaces have given way to more conversant "menu" and "forms" oriented approaches. These present the user with lists of available options, requiring nothing more than "point-and-do," or "fill-in-the-blank" to effect an action. Window systems, popularized by Apple's MacIntosh microcomputer, were the natural progression from menu systems. They provide the user with simultaneous views of concurrent activities resident on the computer, and take advantage of the power of pictorial metaphors for operational commands as an easily mastered medium of dialog. Figures 17 and 18 are examples of interactive computer screens used in a commercial extrusion simulation package for program control, and data entry [46, 47].

It is particularly difficult to find simple and efficient means for describing the complicated geometries encountered in die and mold design. Ideally, one would like the computer to take the three-dimensional description and generate any approximations required by the analysis. This is the fundamental problem of traditional CAD/CAM, and has been the focus of a great deal of development. Recent strides in perfecting "solids modeling" may go a long way toward resolving this issue. By adding together geometrical shapes developed from simple section geometries, or revolution of simple profiles, one can build a complicated object on the video screen and modify it until the image appears just as the final part would. Custom computer hardware dedicated to the task of three-dimensional projection and transformation, and display of naturally shaded imagery has provided the breakthrough necessary to use such approaches.

EXTRUDER DESIGN EXERCISES

One can regard the simulation as an adjunct to experimentation in the design process. It provides a convenient means for examining a variety of changes, and for isolating the effects of manipulating key parameters. The major classes of design problem ammenable to computer aided analysis can

```
          Single Screw Plasticating Extrusion Simulation
                        Program Control Options

Locate the desired option(s) using the <ARROW> keys (^,v,<-,->) to
position the cursor. Select or De-select the option by using <SELECT>.
When you have chosen the desired options enter <DO>.

=>1.  Recall Saved Resin, Equipment, or Operating Parameters
   2.  Change Operating Conditions
   3.  Change Equipment Specifications
   4.  Change Resin Property Constants
   5.  Change Die Equation Constants
   6.  Change Simulation Specifications
   7.  Go to Results Display Menu
   8.  Proceed with Extruder Simulation


<DO>    To execute the desired option
<EXIT>  To terminate execution of the program


<<<< PASS-1 >>>>              Polymer Processing Institute  1985
```

Figure 17. Choice or option menu used in Polymer Processing Institute's extruder simulation system.

Single Screw - Plasticating Extruder Simulation

Operating Conditions Input Menu

Please enter the specified information concerning the extruder feeds.
Use the <SELECT> to choose the state of the feed. You may use the unit
conversion utility by simply specifying the alternate units after your
input, and enclosing them in braces - { }.

Feed Pressure {Psi}: 14.7
Feed Temperature {F}: 80   <SELECT> If Screw reciprocates
Coolant Temperature {F}: 80   <SELECT> If Screw is cooled
Screw Speed in RPM: 60   State of Feed : SOLID
Through-put {Lbm/hr}: 190   MELT
                                                        MIX

<NEXT SCREEN> To go to the Barrel Temperature Set Point menu.
<DO> To return to the Main Option menu.
<EXIT> To stop this program.

                                        Polymer Processing Institute   1985

<<<< PASS-1 >>>>

Figure 18. Data entry form used in Polymer Processing Institute's extruder simulation system.

be broadly classified as:

1. New equipment design. Computer analysis can be used to specify the geometrical parameters, and configuration information based on simulated performance. In screw design, channel depths, lengths of feed, compression and metering zones, screw lead, flight clearances, and addition of mixing elements can be varied to meet desired performance criteria.
2. Optimization of operating conditions. For a fixed set of equipment parameters, the effects of varying RPM, feed conditions, and barrel temperature can be examined for influence on process behavior and process sensitivity to fluctuations.
3. Evaluation of sensitivity to changes in material characteristics. For a given set of operating parameters, and a fixed equipment design, the process can be examined from the standpoint of variation in resin properties. Variations can be a reflection of lot to lot variations in rheology of a single resin, variations caused by selection of a different vendor's resin of a generic type, or exercises in changeover of a line from one resin to another.

All of the data, as well as all of the plots for the following examples, were generated by the extrusion simulator in the PASS-1 software system developed at the Polymer Processing Institute [46, 47].

Screw Selection

A typical screw design exercise revolves around specification of appropriate screw geometry so that the design will melt and pump the target resin at sufficient pressure to flow through an attached die. Matching the screw's pressure generation capability to the die's pressure drop-flow characteristics leaves open many degrees of freedom. Pressurization is the result of a complex interaction between the progress of melting, the changes in screw channel cross section, and the variations of material properties in response to local temperature, pressure, and shear rate.

The results of a simulation exercise are illustrated in Figures 19 and 20. The simulation is used to examine the effect of the relative lengths of compression and metering zones on the performance

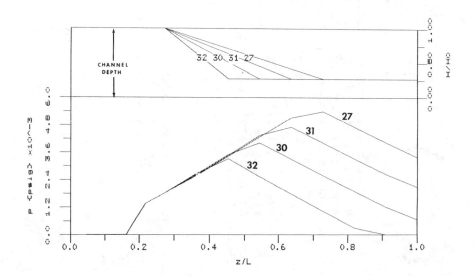

Figure 19. Simulated pressure profiles for polystyrene extrusion in a 2.5″ screw of overall length 55″, operating at 60 RPM, with output of 120 lb/hr.

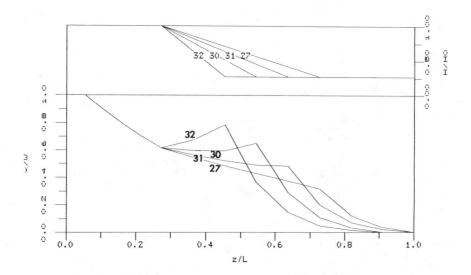

Figure 20. Simulated solid bed profiles for polystyrene extrusion in a 2.5″ screw of overall length 55″, operating at 60 RPM, with output of 120 lb/hr.

of a screw to be used for processing a commercial polystyrene resin. There is a clear trade off in the improvement of melting rate vis a vis the ability to deliver material to the screw end at a useful working pressure. The most rapid compression yields the fastest melting, but results in the lowest pressure build up in the compression zone. At the specified operating conditions, the drag flow capacity of the screw is insufficient to convey the melt through the metering zone, and as a result, there is a pressure loss in this region. For the shorter compression lengths, this pressure loss is comparable to or in excess of the pressure rise in the previous zones. An optimum appear to lie between the extremes.

A similar route might be used to size a two stage screw for devolatilization. The design objective is to fully melt the resin in the first stage, but to deliver it to the second stage at so low a pressure that the second stage feed section will be partially empty (allowing for the pulling of a vacuum, and associated foaming). If one considers the previous example as the first stage of a two stage screw, the negative characteristics of the short transition zone now become a virtue. It is the only design which accomplishes early melting, and zero discharge pressure. The other designs would need some form of obstruction, such as a blister section, to provide the added pressure drop prior to the second stage. The drawback of such a solution is that the excessive shear encountered in such a section could damage the material and could cause undue temperature peaks.

It is important to bear in mind that the conditions and information required by a simulation are dictated by the solution algorithm. Most simulations "march" from hopper to die, so that all entrance conditions must be known, and exit conditions are predicted. It is customary in designing a screw to seek the throughput attainable for a given discharge pressure (which corresponds to the pressure drop through the attached die). A simulation cannot answer such a question in one pass, since it requires the user to specify throughput, and then predicts the discharge pressure. The procedure for such an analysis requires the user of the program to step through a number of possible throughputs, and develop the pressure drop flow rate curve for the screw. Figures 21 and 22 show the detailed axial pressure profiles, and related discharge pressure-flow rate curves for a single screw processing polyethylene. Notice from the axial profiles, the transition from pressure rise to pressure drop across the metering section as output rates increase. In principle, one should be able to increase flow rate until the exit pressure drops to zero; however, the melting characteristics are

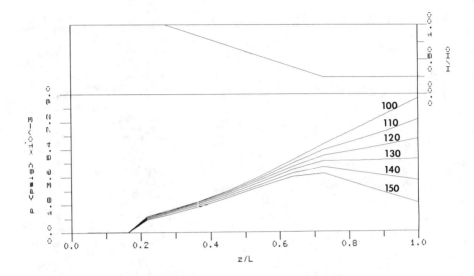

Figure 21. Simulated axial pressure profiles for low density polyethylene extrusion in a 2.5″screw, with 4:1 compression ratio. Parameter is output in pounds per hour.

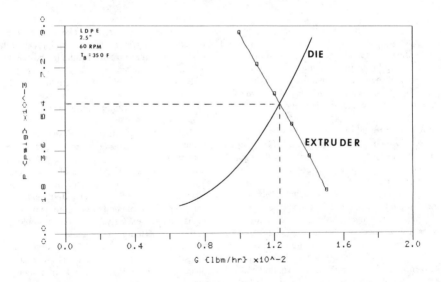

Figure 22. Pressure drop flow rate characteristic curves for extruder of Figure 21 mated with a mandrel pipe die.

also dependent upon throughput. The highest throughput rate in the figure corresponds to the last case in which complete melting could be achieved by the midpoint of the metering zone. Higher throughput rates would bring the likelihood of unmelted pellets reaching the die. Specification of the operating point for the extruder-die combination can be found by the intersection of the pressure drop flow rate characteristic for the die with that of the screw, as shown in Figure 22.

Effect of Operating Conditions

One does not always have the luxury of custom cutting a new screw in order to solve every processing problem. Manipulation of screw speed, barrel temperature settings, and feed rate and temperature are all possible remedies for operations that have gone astray from design expectations. The operation of the screw is dictated by a number of competing processes, each with a different response to changes in operating parameters. The ultimate behavior of the system is not always easy to forecast without some computational aid.

Selection of barrel temperatures is an example of a process which may be counter-intuitive. Logic suggests that increasing the barrel temperature results in increasing the melting rate, but this is frequently untrue. A major portion of the heat for melting is produced by viscous energy dissipation in the thin film of melt between the barrel and solid bed surface. Increasing the barrel temperature decreases the melt viscosity, and therefore decreases the amount of heat produced by this mechanism. Melting must then rely upon the inefficient process of heat conduction through the melt film. The point of greatest efficiency depends upon all of the process variables, and can be computed dynamically. Figures 23 and 24 contrast a screw operating at a single setting of barrel temperature with one that is operated optimally. The fixed case uses a temperature equal to the desired exit temperature, while the optimal barrel profile is one that uses low temperatures during melting, and higher temperatures in the metering zone (to reduce melt viscosity and thus pressure drop). The improvement in discharge pressure is evident, and the length required to achieve melting is reduced by three turns.

Some operating conditions are not under the designer's control. The flight clearance, for example, may change during the lifetime of the screw as a result of wear. The increase in clearance can cause a loss of pumping efficiency, and a decrease in the melting rate. Figure 25 illustrates the magnitude of the performance changes in response to substantial increases in flight clearance. For this design the sensitivity to such a change is minimal for normal tolerances due to wear.

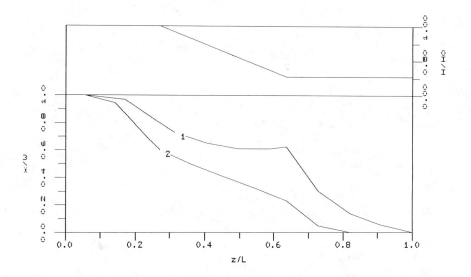

Figure 23. Effect of barrel temperature optimization on performance of high-density polyethylene extrusion. Extruder in Curve 1 is operated at 100 lb/hr with fixed barrel temperature of 450°; Curve 2 represents optimal settings and a throughput of 125 lb/hr.

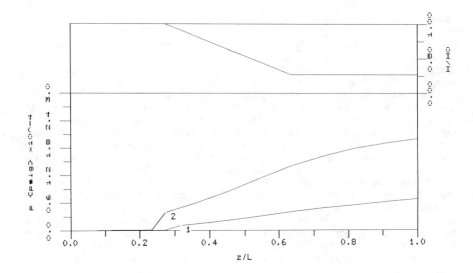

Figure 24. Pressure profiles for extruders used in Figure 23.

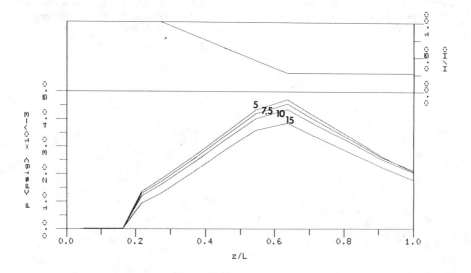

Figure 25. Effect of flight clearance on a 2.5″ screw used for polystyrene extrusion. Parameter is clearance in mils.

Effect of Resin Changes

Resin rheology and thermodynamic properties are the factors that shape the material's response to the imposition of machine conditions. Polymer resins are frequently blends of virgin polymer with a variety of additives, any of which may vary in chemical nature or proportion. Even "virgin resin" is a blend of sorts; most polymers possess a distribution of chain lengths, and the fine struc-

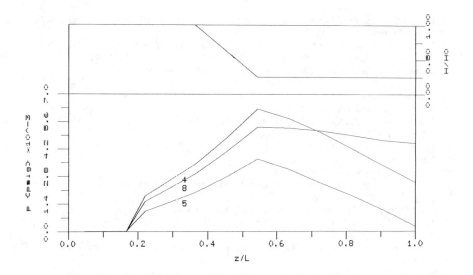

Figure 26. Performance of 2.5″ screw with two different high-density polyethylene resins (curves 4 and 5). Curve 8 represents the effect of temperature optimization on the conditions used for curve 5.

ture of this distribution as well as the gross average properties may vary from lot to lot. A good screw design must be flexible enough to allow compensation for these fluctuations through alteration of operating conditions. In shops where a small library of screws must accomodate a wide array of resins, flexibility of design is of particular importance.

The pressure profiles in Figure 26 show the simulated effect of changing grades of resin. The two high density polyethylenes are from the same manufacturer, and sold for the same end-use market. Their primary difference is in rheology, and although melting rate is the same, the pressure characteristic of the screw is quite different for the substitute resin. The added curve suggests one possible remedy, use of barrel temperature optimization as described in the preceding section. Other process variables could also be manipulated to attempt to compensate for the different processing characteristics of the new material.

CONCLUSION

Polymer processing draws its roots from both the tool and die industry and the chemical process industry. Computer software dedicated to the needs of the polymer processing industry must draw upon this dual heritage. The full design process involves mechanical part design as well as process specification, and both aspects must be addressed. Injection molding design and analysis have led the way for the polymer processing industry, but other processing steps must develop analogous capabilities. As the computer hardware industry presents new tools at a dizzying pace, it is now our foremost challenge to harness the potential that is offered, and grow with the technology into the next century.

REFERENCES

1. Bird, R. B., Stewart, W. E., and Lightfoot, E. N., *Transport Phenomena*, John Wiley and Sons, New York, (1960).
2. Sebastian, D. H., and Rakos, R., *Adv. in Polymer Tech.*, 5(4), 333, (1985).

3. Rao, N. S., *Designing Machines and Dies for Polymer Processing with Computer Programs*, MacMillan Publishing, New York, (1981).
4. Tadmor, Z., Broyer, E., and Gutfinger, C., Polym. Eng. Sci., 14, 660, (1974).
5. Wang, V. W., Heiber, C. A., and Wang, K. K., J. Polymer Eng., 7(1), 22 (1986).
6. Takahashi, H., and Matsuoka, T., *Tecnho Japan*, 19(2), 38, (1986).
7. Tadmor, Z., *Polym. Eng. Sci.*, 6, 185 (1966).
8. Tadmor, Z., Duvdevani, I. J., and Klein, I., *Polym. Eng. Sci.*, 7, 198 (1967).
9. Chung, C. I., *Mod. Plast.*, 45, 178, (1968).
10. Donovan, R. C., *Polym. Eng. Sci.*, 11, 247 (1971).
11. Edmonson, I. R., Fenner, R. T., *Polymer*, 16, 49, (1975).
12. Carlille, D. R., and Fenner, R. T., *J. Mech. Eng. Sci.*, 20, 73, (1978).
13. Lindt, J. T., *Polym. Eng. Sci.*, 16, 284, (1976).
14. Lindt, J. T., *Polym. Eng. Sci.*, 21, 1162, (1981).
15. Shapiro, J., Halmos, A. L., and Pearson, J. R., *Polymer*, 17, 905, (1976).
16. Lindt, J. T., Elbirli, B., *Polm. Eng. Sci.*, 25, 412, (1985).
17. Viriyayuthakorn, M., and Kassauhun, B., 42nd ANTEC Soc. Plast. Eng., New Orleans, 81 (1984).
18. Janssen, H. A., and Vereinschr. Z., *Dtsch. Ing.*, 39(35), 1045, (1895).
19. Walker, D. M., *Chem. Eng. Sci.*, 21, 975, (1966).
20. Brown, R. L., and Richards, J. C., *Principles of Powder Mechanics*, Pergamon Press, Oxford (1966).
21. McCabe, W. L., and Smith, J. C., *Unit Operations of Chemical Engineering*, McGraw Hill, New York (1956).
22. Tadmor, Z., and Klein, I., *Engineering Principles of Plasticating Extrusion*, Van Nostrand Reinhold, New York, (1970).
23. Maddock, B. M., *SPE.J.*, 15, 383, (1959).
24. Rauwendaal, C., 42nd ANTEC Soc. Plast. Eng., New Orleans, 85, (1984).
25. Schneider, K., *Kunstoffe*, 59, 97, (1969).
26. Derezinski, S., 43rd ANTEC Soc. Plast. Eng., Washington D.C., 69, (1985).
27. Lindt, J. T., 42nd ANTEC Soc. Plast. Eng., New Orleans, 73, (1984).
28. Elbirli, B., Lindt, J. T., Gottgetreu, S. R., and Bab, S. M., 40th ANTEC Soc. Plast. Eng., San Francisco, 472, (1982).
29. Rauwendaal, C., 43rd ANTEC Soc. Plast. Eng., Washington D.C., 59, (1985).
30. Tadmor, Z., and Lidor, G., *Polym. Eng. Sci.*, 16, 450 (1976).
31. Sebastian, D. H., and Biesenberger, J. A., 41st ANTEC Soc. Plast. Eng., Chicago, 121, (1983).
32. Jepson, C. H., *Ind. & Eng. Chem.*, 45(5), 992, (1953).
33. Hold, P., Sebastian, D. H., and Kumar, R., *Adv. Polym. Tech.*, 2(4), 259, (1982).
34. Tadmor, Z., and Klein, I., *Polym. Eng. Sci.*, 13, 382 (1973).
35. Elbirli, B., Lindt, J. T., Gottgetreu, S. R., and Baba, S. M., 41st ANTEC Soc. Plast. Eng., Chicago, 104, (1983).
36. Rauwendaal, C., 42nd ANTEC Soc. Plast. Eng., New Orleans, 59, (1984).
37. Tadmor, Z., and Gogos, C., *Principles of Polymer Processing*, John Wiley and Sons, New York, (1979).
38. Herrmann, H., Burkhardt, U., and Jakopin, S., 35th ANTEC, Soc. Plast. Eng., Montreal (1977).
39. Kaplan, A., and Tadmor, Z., *Poly. Eng. Sci.*, 14, 59, (1974).
40. Nichols, R. J., and Yao, J., 40th ANTEC Soc. Plast. Eng., San Francisco, 416, (1982).
41. Nichols, R. J., 41st ANTEC Soc. Plast. Eng., Chicago, 130, (1983).
42. Nichols, R. J., 42nd ANTEC Soc. Plast. Eng., New Orleans, 6, (1984).
43. Eise, K., Werner, H., Herrmann, H., Burkhardt, U., *Adv. Plastics Tech.*, 1, 1 (1981).
44. Carnahan, B., Luther, H. A., and Wilkes, J. O., *Applied Numerical Methods*, John Wiley and Sons, New York, (1969).
45. Pearson, J. A., and Richardson, S. M., *Computational Analysis of Polymer Processing*, Applied Science Publishers, New York, (1983).
46. Sebastian, D. H., *Plastics World*, 43(6), 96, (1985).
47. Sebastian, D. H., *Adv. Polym Tech.*, 5(4), 333, (1985).

CHAPTER 30

CONTROL OF SINGLE SCREW EXTRUSION

Sandra L. Harris

Department of Chemical Engineering
Clarkson University
Potsdam, New York, USA

CONTENTS

INTRODUCTION

Extrusion is probably the most important polymer processing operation. One half of all polymeric materials are extruded at least once in the route to finished product [1]. Although at one time plastic products were considered cheap, this is no longer so, and the standards for products are high, both aesthetically and dimensionally. Each year polymers are used for new applications, such as weight reduction in automobiles and replacement of materials that easily corrode. The polymer processing industry is thus required to produce more, higher quality plastics, under reasonable safety standards, and still keep operating costs low. To make these improvements in processing efficiency, either the equipment design must be changed or the controls must be improved. It is the latter that is addressed here.

An extrusion process typically consists of an extruder, a die, a cooling line, and a take-up device. An extruder can also be a part of another process, such as injection molding. However, the following discussion deals primarily with the extruder. A typical single-screw plasticating extruder is shown in Figure 1. Solid polymer granules or pellets are fed into a hopper at one end, usually fall by gravity into a long heated barrel, and are transported down the barrel by a constantly rotating screw. The polymer melts due to heat conducted through the barrel and shearing caused by the rotation of the screw. The melt is forced through a die at high pressures, and the final product is created. The polymer itself within the screw region is at first solid granules, then a mixture of molten polymer and solid, and finally a melt. A typical extruder is divided into several zones, and the barrel temperature of each is individually controlled so that a desired barrel temperature profile can be established. Indicators for screw speed, power consumption, and temperature and pressure at various locations along the barrel and at the die are usually present.

The goals of extrusion are to produce a high-quality product, at a high output, and at a reasonable cost. "Quality" must be defined. As discussed by Maddock [2], "quality" usually means that the item has a certain visual appearance (no streaking or roughness, a certain color, a certain gloss, etc.), has dimensional accuracy (meets certain size tolerances), and/or meets certain chemical, physical, or performance specifications. Although these characteristics are easily determined by offline measurements or tests, some means of assessing quality online is needed as part of the implementation of a control system.

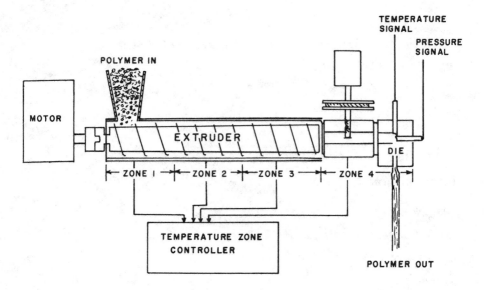

Figure 1. Single-screw plasticating extruder.

Most researchers in the field seem to be in agreement that if melt temperature and pressure at the die are constant, then quality is constant [2, 3, 4]. Instability in the delivery rate leads to dimensional variation and variability in melt temperature, and degree of mixing is manifested as visual or mechanical imperfections. Rate instability and surging are detectable in pressure measurements. Both temperature and pressure measurements reflect mixing problems.

Maddock [2] further states that for film manufacture, quality is adequate with a temperature variation of less than $\pm 0.1°$C and a pressure variation of less than ± 10 psi ($\pm 0.4\%$). He states that if temperature variations exceed $\pm 1.0°$C and/or pressure variations exceed $\pm 1\%$, there is usually some sort of quality defect in the finished product. Dennis-Germuska et al. [5] state that narrower tolerances for melt temperature could be necessary for specific applications, and Tadmor and Klein [6] state that often it is the large temperature fluctuations that cause significant problems with product quality.

Relatively little attention has been paid to extrusion control because the extrusion process is inherently stable. There are generally PID or simpler controllers for each zone heater, but often screw speed and other input variables are changed manually. It is only in the last decade or so, coinciding with the availability of inexpensive and reliable microcomputers, that there has been much interest in designing more sophisticated control systems. Before applying more extensive controls, some understanding of the dynamics of the extrusion process must be gained. And before that can be done, the variables of interest as controlled and manipulated variables must be determined.

Melt temperature and pressure at the die are of interest as controlled variables. In addition, especially if take-up equipment is used, extrudate thickness might also be considered as a controlled variable. Griffith and Tsai [7] show the high correlation of extrudate measurements and that one measurement can be used to size the entire extrudate. This was also confirmed by Stevenson [9]. Although of these three measurements, thickness is the only one that is a direct indicator of quality, the others have been shown to indirectly indicate quality, as referenced above. In addition, temperature and pressure are easy and inexpensive to measure continuously online. Thickness is more expensive and difficult to measure online, but it is possible (e.g., see [5, 9]). Output rate is another possible controlled variable.

The question of which variables to use as manipulative variables is an important one. The response time of the system must be fast. For example, a natural choice would be to manipulate barrel temperature profile to maintain melt temperature at the die. However, the time constant for the melt temperature-barrel profile system is large. Fingerle [10] states that it takes more than 20 minutes to compensate a disturbance by changing the barrel temperature. Thus, by the time control action was complete, whatever disturbance had caused the change in melt temperature would likely have passed, particularly if it was a disturbance in the feed stock. Input variables having smaller time constants associated with them include screw speed, die restriction, and take-up rate. Take-up rate has the additional complication that using it as a manipulated variable introduces dead time into the system. If the feed was by some other method than by gravity, it would be possible to use feed rate as a manipulated variable as well.

Disturbances will be discussed later, but these include variations in polymer feed quality, periodic bed breakup, and environmental changes (line voltage fluctuations, cooling water changes, etc.).

DYNAMIC MODELING

Extrusion is a very complex process. It is distributed and nonlinear. The physical properties such as viscosity, density, and thermal diffusivity change continuously along the barrel. Heat transfer occurs both radially and in the axial direction. Determining a model that is based on first principles would require the simultaneous solution of mass, energy, and momentum balances, and an equation of state for a non-Newtonian fluid. Even if such a model could be determined, it is unlikely that all the physical property data needed for the parameters would be available. However, the first principle approach has been successful for steady state modeling.

Although dynamic models are of interest from a controls standpoint, steady-state models show the affect of geometric parameters and operating conditions on extruder performance. In addition, some early dynamic models were based on steady-state models. An early set of papers covering steady-state behavior of extrusion include Carley and Strub [11] (Newtonian; described fluid behavior in extruders but neglected the die); Carley et al. [12] (expanded the former; included the die); and McKelvey [13] (tested the former).

Kirby [14] attempted to explain surging and used a glass walled extruder in his studies. He presented a simple dynamic surging equation. Krueger [15] also conducted experiments using a glass-walled extruder to study dynamic behavior. He included non-Newtonian effects in his analysis. Neither Kirby nor Krueger considered the die in their studies.

White and Schott [16] were the first to apply classical control techniques to the study of an extruder. They used step and pulse tests. The step in screw speed used was 40 to 60 rpm, which is probably too large; that is, the extruder would not be linear over such a large range of screw speeds, and the transfer function models used would not be valid. The resulting data seemed to indicate a second order underdamped process, and they in fact suggested a transfer function relating pressure to screw speed which was fourth order in the numerator and second order underdamped in the denominator. While the experiments are interesting, the model is physically unrealizable because the order of the numerator is higher than the order of the denominator, thus implying prediction.

Reber et al. [17] presented a lumped macroscopic model. Step tests in screw speed, barrel temperature profile, and back pressure were done in order to obtain data to fit the model. The model is for a specific extruder and a specific polymer. Tadmor et al. [18] presented a more complex dynamic model, using steady-state models to calculate instantaneous values of some variables. Simulation results are presented.

Parnaby et al. [19] and Kochhar and Parnaby [3] found that the extruder could not be identified using normal operating records and so employed a pseudorandom binary sequence (PRBS). Stochastic models relating temperature and pressure to screw speed were presented. However, the sampling time used to obtain these models was too large (it is larger than one of the time constants they report), and so the resultant model cannot adequately describe the process. The delay for the pressure-screw speed model is given as being less than one, which is inconsistent with a digital process representation (at least one sample time is required before an output response to an input perturbation can be detected). Also, Costin et al. [20] pointed out that the temperature-screw speed model contains a common pole and zero, so that a lower order model would suffice. In spite of these failings, the work is of interest because it suggested the use of stochastic models.

Patterson and de Kerf [21] perturbed a 25 mm L/D = 20:1 extruder using PRBS signals. Screw speed was perturbed and melt temperature at the die, pressure at the die, and output rate were measured. Data plots but no models are presented. Time constants are reported and possible model orders indicated. The response to screw speed change was rapid. In a second paper, Patterson et al. [22] perturbed valve position (die restriction) with a PRBS. Data plots and discussion were again presented. Response of pressure was very fast. Temperature at the die showed no change. They concluded that use of the die restrictor is a viable means of controlling output flow.

Nelson et al. [1] and Chan et al. [23] performed step tests on a 25 mm L/D = 24:1 extruder. Steps up and down in screw speed and back pressure were made. Changes in material fed were also examined. Time constants are given and some discussion of possible models. Typical data plots are shown. They found that all data could be fit to first-order, second-order, or lead-lag transfer functions. The inputs were related to pressure, temperature.

Costin et al. [4] and Bezanson and Harris [24] have performed step tests to obtain preliminary information on their extruders. Costin et al. then used PRBS perturbations to obtain data for a time series model relating pressure and screw speed. Bezanson and Harris used a binary multifrequency perturbation and obtained stochastic models relating temperature and pressure to screw speed and die restriction. In both cases, the models were obtained for control purposes. Bezanson and Harris found that any of several model forms would adequately fit the data (goodness tested by examination of the loss function, F-test results, etc.).

It would seem that the primary value of detailed physical models from a controls point of view is to provide physical insight into the process. Models based on simple experimentation are very machine and material specific, but are easy to obtain and provide sufficient information to design many control systems. In particular, the stochastic models used with adaptive algorithms look attractive, because in such cases, the simple linear models are updated frequently. The models are local and are only expected to apply for a small operating region. A reasonable procedure would be to first perform step tests to obtain information regarding major time constant and dead time. Based on that information, appropriate sampling times may be selected and a more sophisticated identification implemented.

Most of these papers give time constants for various output/input pairs. When screw speed is the input, the smallest time constant usually results with pressure at the die as output, then thickness as output, and the largest with melt temperature as output. Any system having barrel profile or temperature of one zone of the barrel the input has a much larger time constant. When thickness/take-up is considered, there is a time delay involved, and this time delay varies with take-up rate.

CONTROL

The single screw extruder is subject to many disturbances. These are classified and discussed in detail by Tadmor and Klein [6]. Disturbances appear to occur within three frequency bands. The lowest frequency disturbances are caused by heater power controller cycling, plant voltage fluctuations, variations in feed quality, and other situations external to the extruder. Disturbances in the intermediate frequency range, one to 15 cycles per minute, are caused by periodic breakup of the solid bed in the melting region. This results in irregular blocks of polymer which melt at different rates, and causes periodic pressure surging. The highest frequency disturbances occur at the same frequency as the screw rotation. These are caused by periodic changes in the feedrate associated with passage of a screw flight near the hopper opening, by an excessively cooled screw, or when extruding at low back pressure.

The high frequency disturbances can be eliminated by increasing back pressure or screw temperature, and no process control is really required (Nelson et al. [1]). The low frequency disturbances can generally be handled using conventional feedback control. The disturbances in the midfrequency range are the main cause of poor product quality. Maddock [2] and Fenner et al. [25] have said that the surging can be reduced by cooling the screw. However, this seems to be more of a steady-state or design solution. The time constant involved in screw cooling should be on the order of time constant involved in heating the barrel: too large to use that particular input for dynamic compensation. In addition, screw cooling has the effect of reducing throughput, so there is some incentive for eliminating surging via improved controls rather than by screw cooling.

Several papers regarding control of single screw extruders have appeared in the last decade or so; some use classical approaches and some apply modern control techniques. All use a computer, most as a means of implementing the desired control algorithm.

Dormeier [36] used digital PID control and a deadbeat algorithm for control of heat input to the die, to regulate long-term drifts of the melt temperature. These were tested on a 45 mm extruder. The PID algorithm worked well. The parameters were tuned offline.

Fingerle [10] regulated the melt temperature of a 60 mm extruder by manipulating heat generated by viscous dissipation. This was done by using an adjustable tube to change the length of an annular section at the die tip. The Dahlin algorithm [26] was used. The sample time used (15 s) was too long to handle the intermediate frequency range disturbances, but long-term temperature disturbances were eliminated. In this case, pressure was unaffected; had the control action affected pressure, screw speed would have been manipulated to regulate pressure.

Frederickson [9] used a distributed system which maintained a specific closed loop time constant, kept a history of past control moves, and used knowledge of the transport delay. The thickness was controlled by changing the take-up rate. (The screw speed was used to control thickness only when a specific line speed was needed.) Throughput was controlled by changing screw speed, and then also the take-up rate was changed so thickness remained constant. A variation of the Dahlin algorithm was used. Offset and long-term drift were eliminated. Rastogi [27] discusses the same system. A first-order with dead time model was used for each part of the process, and a Dahlin controller implemented. A 60 to 70% reduction in thickness variation was achieved, but high frequency variations could not be regulated.

Brauner et al. [28] presented a simplified version of the model of Tadmor et al. [18], more suitable for controller design purposes, and have used it for simulation experiments. They suggest use of this simplified model in a supervisory control scheme. Flow rate and melt temperature at the die would be measured and screw speed and temperature of the last barrel zone would be used as manipulated inputs in a feedback algorithm. These values would be used in the simulator to evaluate the effect on extruder state, and the results would be used to supervise barrel temperature profile. They also suggest the possibility of adjusting flow rate by manipulating a restriction at the die.

Parnaby et al. [19] and Kochhar and Parnaby [3] suggest that steady-state control of the barrel wall temperature be used in conjunction with dynamic screw speed manipulation, to regulate temperature and pressure at the die. Since a second manipulated variable would be necessary to keep both temperature and pressure at desired set points, Kochhar and Parnaby suggest use of the die restrictor. Hassan and Parnaby [29] use a computer control system that samples temperature and pressure at the die and they use an autoregressive moving avarage (ARMA) model for one-step-ahead forecasts. These are then used in a feedback mode and results compared with tolerable operating bands. Then the algorithm determines necessary changes in screw speed, wall temperature, and die restriction, and may also change setpoints. Experiments showed an improvement in the temperature standard deviation by less than a factor of 2, and an improvement in pressure standard deviation by a factor of 3.

Costin et al. [4] applied a digital PI controller and a single variable minimum variance self tuning regulator (STR) (see [30]) to a 38 mm L/D = 24:1 extruder. Pressure was regulated and screw speed was manipulated. The PI controller gave better results. The reason for the poor results of the STR was poor location of the pressure sensor. The work was continued by Dennis-Germuska et al. [5]. Three output/input pairs were considered: melt pressure/screw speed, thickness/take-up rate, and melt temperature/die heater power. The last pair has a very slow time constant compared to the other two. Dahlin algorithms were used for the three feedback loops, and feedforward and a decoupler were used for the loops involving pressure and temperature. Screw speed changes were fed forward to the thickness/take-up rate loop so that two loops wouldn't take action against the same flowrate disturbance. Oscillations and slow drifts in melt pressure and temperature were eliminated. The three setpoints could be moved independently. The thickness loop did not significantly improve the steady-state thickness variations. The paper states that this is due to noisy thickness measurements (measured by passing the extrudate over a light source and focusing the image on a photo-diode array).

Harris and Bezanson [31] used three single-variable algorithms (digital PI, minimum variance STR, and a state space STR) to maintain, by screw speed manipulation, temperature or pressure at the die of a 19 mm L/D = 25:1 extruder. The best results were for pressure regulation using the minimum variance STR. The standard deviation of the pressure was reduced by 83% over the uncontrolled case, and the standard deviation of the temperature by 85%. Multivariable algorithms were also applied [24], using melt temperature and pressure as the controlled variables and screw speed and die restriction as the manipulated variables. Since the multivariable ARMA model was slightly nonminimum phase, a quadratic STR had to be used in place of the minimum variance STR [32]. The state space regulator with fixed parameters was also used. Best results were obtained using the STR, which reduced the standard deviation of the pressure by 76% and the temperature by 88%. Use of the die restrictor was difficult. It had no effect on temperature at the die (as noted by others) and the pressure effect was to climb to a peak and then level off at a steady state just a little different than the original steady state. This general trend is evident in the data of Patterson and de Kerf [21]; however, their new steady-state was closer to the peak value. Also, the die restrictor seemed somewhat fragile under normal operation; this was also noted on another larger (38 mm) extruder by Gillenwater [33].

Yang and Lee [34] used feedback control on a 63.5 mm L/D = 24:1 extruder. Thickness was the controlled variable and take-up rate the manipulated variable. Preliminary open loop tests were performed and then a PI controller was implemented (tuned using IAE (integral of absolute error) criterion). Finally a Smith predictor was applied. Both controlled systems were tested using a setpoint and a load change. Based on the IAE, the Smith predictor was judged to be slightly superior.

Yang and Lee [35] also applied feedforward control to the extruder discussed above. Two algorithms were tried: feedforward plus feedback (FFC) and adaptive feedforward plus feedback (AFFC). The load variables used in the feedforward portion were melt temperature and pressure at the die. First-order transfer functions were used. The FFC system was tested under the same conditions as a PI controller. Based on the ISE, the FFC performed better. The AFFC was not tested under the same circumstances; however, it appears not to have behaved significantly better. The authors attribute some problems to model mismatch.

DISCUSSION

As in any control system, selection of the variables to be manipulated and the variables to be regulated is one of the first considerations. It is generally agreed that maintaining a constant temperature and pressure at the die will yield a good quality extrudate. Since these variables are also easy to measure, they should certainly be included on the list of controlled variables. Thickness is more difficult and expensive to measure, but the measurement is feasible. Thus it can also be included on the list of controlled variables. In some special cases, variables such as color or brightness (as in the paper industry) may be included. The major criteria for inclusion on the list of regulated variables are that the variables be representative of quality and that they be measurable online.

Screw temperature and barrel wall temperature profile are important processing parameters. However, because of the long time constants involved, these should be controlled at some desired operating point using PI controllers and left alone as far as quality variations are concerned. Screw speed is easy to manipulate, as is take-up rate, and these have short time constants associated with them. Thus they should certainly be used as manipulated variables. A more questionable variable is die restriction. Some researchers highly recommend it and others have had trouble using it. Thus there is some incentive to determine another manipulative variable, or perhaps improve on the design of remotely controlled die restrictors.

If the interest is primarily on control, then very little dynamic modeling needs to be done. In many instances a simple second-order, perhaps with dead time, model would suffice. Step tests need to be performed to determine dead times, time constants, and linear operating regions. The next task depends on the type of controller to be used. If an STR is to be used, then a preliminary identification might be performed on a binary signal perturbation. If a control design is to be used that requires a transfer function, then another experiment should be run, using the step test results to design a signal having a more desirable power spectrum than a step.

Selection of the sampling time is important, and many of those reporting experimental results in the polymer processing area have not done this properly. A time constant and dead time can be obtained using information from the step tests, and one of the guidelines presented by Isermann [38] can be used, for example, setting sampling time equal to 0.22 to 0.35 times the dead time. Care should also be taken with the type of signal used for identification experiments. Many researchers have Fourier transformed step test data to obtain transfer functions. However, the step input signal does not have adequate power at higher frequencies, and so the resulting transfer functions may not adequately represent the process. Care must also be taken to select the amplitude of the perturbation low enough so that the process remains in a linear region.

In many cases, a properly tuned PI algorithm would seem to be adequate, but there is some evidence that controllers in the STR family give improved performance. The Dahlin algorithm and variations also seem to be promising. It is not yet clear whether or not those techniques eliminate the troublesome midfrequency range of disturbances. If not, then perhaps feedforward control, in combination with feedback, would have to be used. In this case, a little more emphasis would need to be placed on obtaining an accurate dynamic model.

REFERENCES

1. Nelson, R. W., Chan, D., Yang, B., and Lee, L. J., "Dynamic Behavior of a Single Screw Plasticating Extruder. Part I: Experimental Study," *Polymer Eng. Sci.*, *26*, no. 2, 144 (1986).
2. Maddock, B. H., "Measurement and Analysis of Extruder Stability," *Soc. Plastics Engrs. J.*, *20*, 1277 (1964).
3. Kochhar, A. K., and Parnaby, J., "Dynamic Modeling and Control of Plastics Extrusion Processes," *Automatica*, *13*, 177 (1977).
4. Costin, M. H., Taylor, P. A., and Wright, J. D., "On the Dynamics and Control of a Plasticating Extruder," *Polymer Eng. Sci.*, *22*, 1095 (1982).
5. Dennis-Germuska, D., Taylor, P. A., and Wright, J. D., "Adaptive and Multivariable Control of a Single Screw Extrusion System," *The Canadian Journal of Chemical Eng.*, *62*, 790 (1984).
6. Tadmor, Z., and Klein, I., *Engineering Principles of Plasticating Extrusion*, Van Nostrand Rheinhold, New York (1970).
7. Griffith, R. M., and Tsai, J. T., "Shape Changes During Drawing of Non-Circular Extruded Profiles," *Polymer Eng. Sci.*, *20*, 1181 (1980).
8. Stevenson, J. F., "Analysis of Size and Shape Changes Along an Extrusion Line," *SPE ANTEC*, *30*, 93 (1984).
9. Frederickson, A. A., "A Flat Die Extruder Control System Using Distributed Digital Processors," *SPE ANTEC*, *24*, 561 (1978).
10. Fingerle, D., "Autogenic Melt Temperature Control System for Plastic Extrusion," *J. Elastomers and Plastics*, *10*, 293 (1978).
11. Carley, J. F., and Strub, R. A., "Basic Concepts of Extrusion," *Industrial and Engineering Chemistry*, *45*, 970 (1953).
12. Carley, J. F., Mallouck, R. S., and McKelvey, J. M., "Simplified Flow Theory for Screw Extruders," *Industrial and Engineering Chemistry*, *45*, 974 (1953).
13. McKelvey, J. M., "Experimental Studies of Melt Extrusion," *Industrial and Engineering Chemistry*, *45*, 982 (1953).
14. Kirby, R. B., "Process Dynamics of Screw Extruders," *SPE J.*, 1273 (Oct. 1962).
15. Krueger (1962).
16. White, D. H., and Schott, N. R., "Dynamic Testing of Plastics Extrusion Systems," *SPE ANTEC*, 797 (1972).
17. Reber et al. (1973).
18. Tadmor, Z., Lipshitz, S. D., and Lavie, R., "Dybanuc Model of a Plasticating Extruder," *Polymer Eng. Sci.*, *14*, 112 (1974).

19. Parnaby, J., Kochhar, A. K., and Wood, B., "Development of Computer Control Strategies for Plastic Extruders," *Polymer Eng. Sci.*, *15*, 594 (1975).

20. Costin, M. H., Taylor, P. A., and Wright, J. D., "A Critical Review of Dynamic Modeling and Control of Plasticating Extruders," *Polymer Eng. Sci.*, *22*, 393 (1982).

21. Patterson, I., and T. de Kerf, "The Dynamic Behavior of Extruders," *SPE ANTEC*, *24*, 483 (1978).

22. Patterson, W. I., Branchi, P., and J. Paris, "Valve Control of Extruder Output," *SPE ANTEC*, *25*, 166 (1979).

23. Chan, D., Nelson, R. W., and Lee, L. J., "Dynamic Behavior of a Single Screw Plasticating Extruder. Part II: Dynamic Modeling," *Polymer Eng. Sci.*, *26*, no. 2, 152 (1986).

24. Bezanson, L. W., and Harris, S. L., "Identification and Control of an Extruder Using Multivariable Algorithms," *IEE Proc. Pt. D.*, *133*, no. 4, 145 (1986).

25. Fenner, R. T., Cox, A. P. D., and Isherwood, D. P., "Surging in Screw Extruders," *SPE ANTEC*, *24*, 494 (1978).

26. Dahlin, E. B., "Designing and Tuning Digital Controllers," *Instruments and Control Systems*, *41*, no. 6, 77 (1968).

27. Rastogi, L., "A Flat Die Extruder Control System Using Distributed Microcomputers," *JACC*, Philadelphia, *1*, 375 (1978).

28. Brauner, N., Lavie, R., and Tadmor, Z., "Control of a Plasticating Extruder," 3rd *IFAC Conference on PRD*, Brussels (May 1976).

29. Hassan, G. A., and Parnaby, J., "Model Reference Steady-State Adaptive Computer Control of Plastics Extrusion Processes," *Polymer Eng. Sci.*, *21*, 276 (1981).

30. Astrom, K. J., and Wittenmark, B., "On Self-Tuning Regulators," *Automatica*, *9*, 185 (1973).

31. Bezanson, L. W., and Harris, S. L., "Identification and Digital Adaptive Control of a Single-Screw Extruder," *IASTED J., Control & Comput.*, *13*, no. 1 (1985).

32. Clarke, D. W., and Gawthrop, P. J., "Self-Tuning Controller," *Proc. IEE*, *122*, 457 (1975).

33. Gillenwater, W., "Control of a Single-Screw Extruder," MS Thesis, Clarkson University (1977).

34. Yang, B., and Lee, L. J., "Process Control of Polymer Extrusion. Part I: Feedback Control," *Polymer Eng. Sci.*, *26*, no. 3, 197 (1986).

35. Yang, B., and Lee, L. J., "Process Control of Polymer Extrusion. Part II: Feedforward Control," *Polymer Eng. Sci.*, *26*, no. 3, 205 (1986).

36. Dormeier, S., "Digital Temperature Control—A Way to Improve the Extrusion Process," *SPE ANTEC*, *25*, 216 (1979).

37. Dormeier, S., "Extruder Control," *IFAC Conf. on Instrum. and Autom. in the Paper, Rubber, Plastics and Polymerisation Industries*, Ghent, Belgium, *4*, 551 (1980).

38. Isermann, R., *Digital Control Systems*, Springer-Verlag, 103–107 (1981).

CHAPTER 31

PRACTICAL APPLICATIONS OF RHEOLOGY TO POLYMER PROCESSING

A. V. Shenoy*

Department of Materials Science and Engineering
University of Florida
Gainesville, Florida, USA

CONTENTS

INTRODUCTION

One of the objectives of polymer rheology and study of non-Newtonian fluid flow has been to develop an understanding of the responses of complex systems to various types of deformations so that useful information is generated for the practical processor. However, more often than not, the theoretical rheologist works with complicated mathematical approaches which are beyond the comprehension of the common processor, and the experimental rheologist works on simplified flow systems and situations which are too ideal and have little importance in actual practice. Therefore, the practical processor resorts to simple rules of thumb based on prior experience in order to get answers to processing problems. What is desirable is an acceptable compromise between the complex though accurate mathematical approach and the crude estimates of the simple thumb-rule approach. Then the work of the rheologists and the practical processor would not remain compartmentalized, thereby leading to methods for practical applications of rheology to polymer processing.

Polymer processing operations such as injection molding, compression molding, calendering, and extrusion involve deformation of polymeric material over a wide range of temperatures (170–320°C) and a broad range of shear rates (see, for example, Table 1). For process optimization and product quality, it often becomes absolutely necessary to get an idea about certain specific aspects during processing, as, for example:

● The minimum pressure drop during cavity-filling as well as the minimum clamping force to prevent mold opening in an injection molding operation.

* Present address: SMART, 64D Girgaum Road, Opera House, Bombay 40 0004, India.

Table 1
Shear Rate Ranges Encountered in Common Polymer Processing Operations

Process	Typical Shear Rates (sec^{-1})
Compression Molding	1–10
Calendering	$10–10^2$
Extrusion	$10^2–10^3$
Injection Molding	$10^3–10^4$

- The compaction force in a compression molding operation.
- The pressure distribution, torque, and power input to each roller in a calendering operation.
- The pressure losses through dies of complex cross section during extrusion.
- The viscous heat dissipation during various processing operations.

In order to generate information like the above, a detailed understanding of the rheological behavior of the polymer melt is necessary, and this involves the use of highly sophisticated and expensive rheological equipment which is beyond the financial and technical capabilities of the common processor. In this chapter, a novel approach is discussed which combines the science and the art in order to provide a via-media path for practical applications of rheology to polymer processing.

BASIC CONCEPTS OF THE NOVEL APPROACH

During polymer product fabrication, the only flow parameter that the processor has ready access to is the Melt Flow Index (MFI), which is defined as the weight of the polymer (in grams) extruded

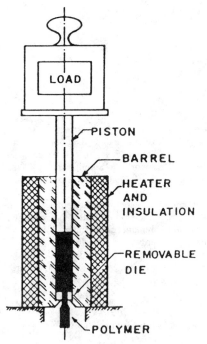

Figure 1. Schematic diagram of the melt flow index apparatus showing a cross-sectional view of the important parts.

in ten minutes through a capillary of specific diameter and length by pressure applied through dead weight under prescribed temperature conditions as per ASTM D1238 specifications. A schematic diagram of a typical melt flow indexer is shown in Figure 1.

MFI is basically a single point viscosity measurement at relatively low shear rate and at a temperature different from those encountered in actual large scale processes, and hence does not correlate directly with processing behavior. In actual processing, rheological data at low as well as high shear are important, and in most cases what is desirable is the entire viscosity vs. shear rate curve at the relevant temperature. The processor, however, does not have as easy an access to this information as he has to MFI. Hence, the basic concept in the novel approach is to use MFI for developing correlations with fundamental rheological parameters and thus predict processing behavior through this simple parameter.

From MFI to Rheogram

Recently, a method has been provided by Shenoy et al. [1] for estimating the rheogram of a polymeric material from the knowledge of its MFI at the appropriate temperature and load condition. Their method involves the generation of unified curves by coalescing rheograms of various grades of a resin at various temperatures using a plot of $\eta \cdot$ MFI and $\dot{\gamma}/$MFI. Based on mechanistic considerations, it has been shown that the curves are unique for each generic type of polymer, as can be seen from Figure 2 for polypropylene. Unified curves have been provided for a large number of homopolymer types, such as polyolefins and styrenics [1, 2], cellulosics [3], vinyls [4], vinylidene fluorides [5], engineering thermoplastics [6], liquid crystalline polymers [7], and some specialty polymers [8]. The technique has been shown to be effectively applicable to filled polymers [9, 10], polymer blends [11], and copolymers [12].

The viscosity vs. shear rate behavior for any polymer grade at any temperature of interest can be obtained from the master curves given by Shenoy et al. [1–12] using the following procedure:

- Firstly, it is essential to get the MFI of the polymer for the particular grade under consideration. This could be done either by making an actual measurement under standard test load and temperature conditions, or by obtaining the MFI value directly from the polymer manufacturer.
- It may happen that the test load condition of the obtained MFI is different from that specified in the unified curve. Under such circumstances, a new MFI value ought to be calculated using the following equation by Shenoy et al. [1]:

$$\frac{MFI_{L_2}}{MFI_{L_1}} = \left(\frac{L_2}{L_1}\right)^{1/n} \tag{1}$$

where n is the slope of the master curve in the straight portion covering the MFI range while L_1 and L_2 are two test load conditions.

It may also happen that the temperature at which the η versus $\dot{\gamma}$ curve is desired is different from that at which the MFI value was determined. In such cases, one of the following two equations ought to be used for estimating the correct MFI value:

Modified WLF-type equation [1]

$$\log \frac{MFI_{T_2}}{MFI_{T_1}} = \frac{8.86(T_2 - T_s)}{101.6 + (T_2 - T_s)} - \frac{8.86(T_1 - T_s)}{101.6 + (T_1 - T_s)} \tag{2}$$

Modified Arrhenius-type equation [13]

$$\frac{MFI_{T_2}}{MFI_{T_1}} = \exp\left[\frac{E}{R}\left(\frac{1}{T_2} - \frac{1}{T_1}\right)\right] \tag{3}$$

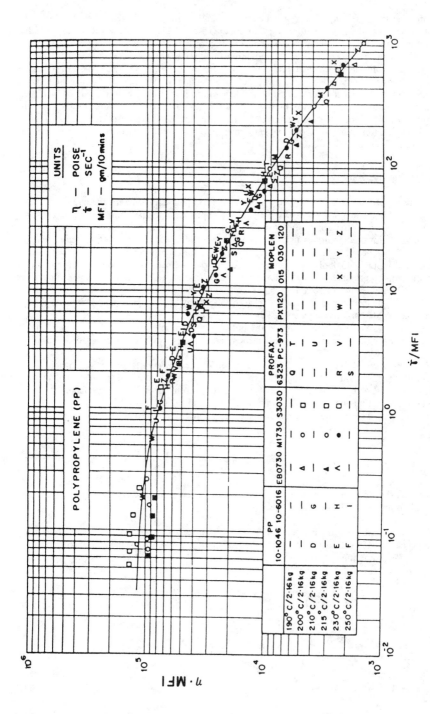

Figure 2. Unified curve for polypropylene at 2.16 kg test load condition for MFI using viscosity vs. shear rate data for 11 grades and 6 different temperatures (from Shenoy et al. [1, 14]).

where T_1 = ASTM recommended test temperature, °K
T_2 = temperature at which the MFI value is to be determined, °K
T_s = a standard reference temperature taken to be equal to $T_g + 50$, °K
T_g = glass transition temperature, °K
R = gas constant equal to 1.9874
E = activation energy for viscous flow

The choice of which equation is to be used for determining the temperature dependence of MFI is mainly governed by whether T is less than or greater than $T_g + 100$ (°K). At temperatures relatively nearer to T_g, it could be expected that free volume and its changes with temperature play a predominant role and hence, the WLF-type equation, Equation 2, could provide better estimates. At temperatures greater than $T_g + 100$ (°K), the temperature dependency of MFI is decisively affected by overcoming of the forces of intermolecular interactions, in which case the Arrhenius type equation, Equation 3, would give better estimates.

Once the correct MFI value is determined at the temperature of interest and under the appropriate load condition as required, then the plot of η vs. $\dot{\gamma}$ can be readily obtained by substitution of this MFI value.

Rheological Model for Unified Viscosity-MFI Curves

The final step in the above procedure for generating the viscosity vs. shear rate curve from MFI involves the reading out of appropriate values from the unified curves. This could induce errors and cause a certain degree of inconvenience. In order to avoid this, Shenoy and Saini [14] fitted appropriate rheological models to each of the unified curves. They modified the well-known Carreau model, Ellis model, and the Ostwald-de Waele model, which are commonly used to describe the flow behavior of non-Newtonian fluids. The forms of the rheological models proposed by Shenoy and Saini [14] are given below:

Modified Carreau Model

$$\eta \cdot \text{MFI} = \eta_0 \cdot \text{MFI}[1 + (\lambda \cdot \text{MFI})^2 \cdot (\dot{\gamma}/\text{MFI})^2]^{-N} \tag{4}$$

Modified Ellis Model

$$\eta \cdot \text{MFI} = \eta_0 \cdot \text{MFI}/[1 + |\tau/\tau_{1/2}|^{\alpha-1}] \tag{5}$$

Modified Ostwald-de Waele Power-Law Model

$$\eta \cdot \text{MFI} = K(\dot{\gamma}/\text{MFI})^{n-1} \tag{6}$$

where $\eta_0 \cdot \text{MFI}$ = modified zero-shear viscosity function
$\eta \cdot \text{MFI}$ = modified non-Newtonian viscosity function
$\dot{\gamma}/\text{MFI}$ = modified shear rate function
$\lambda \cdot \text{MFI}$ = modified time constant
K = consistency index
N, α, and n = dimensionless parameters associated with power-law behavior
τ = shear stress given by the product of $\eta \cdot \text{MFI}$ and $\dot{\gamma}/\text{MFI}$
$\tau_{1/2}$ = value of shear stress at $\eta \cdot \text{MFI} = \eta_0 \cdot \text{MFI}/2$

Tables 2–4 give the model constants for most of the polymers studied based on the modified Carreau model, the modified Ellis model, and the modified Ostwald-deWaele model, respectively.

Table 2
Rheological Parameters of the Modified Carreau Model (Equation 4) for Polymers
of Different Generic Type

Polymer Type	η_0 MFI	λ MFI	N	Applicability Range of Shear Rate (s^{-1})	ASTM Test Load Condition Used in the Master Curve (kg)
Linear Low Density Polyethylenes	9.6×10^4	6.0	0.11	0.01–2	2.16
High Density Polyethylenes	2.1×10^5	24.0	0.15	0.1–1	2.16
Low Density Polyethylenes	3.0×10^5	25.3	0.17	0.1–1	2.16
Polypropylenes	1.2×10^5	4.6	0.13	0.1–1	2.16
Polystyrenes	4.0×10^6	46.4	0.30	0.01–10	5.00
Cellulose Esters	8.5×10^4	0.72	0.06	1–10	2.16
Cellulose Ethers	8.5×10^4	5.0	0.18	1–10	2.16
Acrylics	2.1×10^5	2.4	0.16	1–10	3.80
Nylons	9.5×10^4	11.6	0.03	0.1–1	2.16
Polyesters	8.0×10^4	0.3	0.10	4–50	2.16
Polycarbonates	4.2×10^4	0.19	0.11	5–40	1.20
Poly(vinyl chloride)s	1.2×10^6	3.9	0.36	0.01–200	20.00
Poly(vinylidene fluoride)s	6.0×10^5	0.77	0.3	1–2000	12.50
Poly(phenylene oxide)s	2.2×10^5	0.2	0.34	3–7000	5.00
Poly(phenylene sulfide)s	3.4×10^5	0.26	0.36	2–700	5.00
Poly(ether ether ketone)s	4.5×10^5	1.7	0.24	0.1–1000	5.00
Poly(ether imide)s	1.4×10^5	0.038	0.33	5–10000	5.00
Polyarylates	1.3×10^5	0.04	0.38	1–10000	5.00
Styrene-butadiene-styrenes	2.2×10^5	1.00	0.12	0.1–10	5.00
Acrylonitrile butadiene-styrenes	1.7×10^6	12.8	0.31	0.01–100	5.00
Ethylene-vinyl acetate copolymer	3.0×10^5	13.7	0.21	0.01–10	2.16
Polyester elastomer	9.0×10^4	1.0	0.11	10–1000	2.16

From the range of applicability given for each of the models, it is clear from Tables 2–4 that the Carreau and Ellis models best fit the data in the low to medium shear rate regions. In most industrial polymer processing operations, the shear rate ranges (as given in Table 1) fall within the domain of the Ostwald-de Waele power-law model. Hence, this model will be more frequently used during further discussion. However, the low shear region covered by the Carreau and Ellis models is certainly of interest from a fundamental viewpoint. It is in this region that effects of differences in molecular weight distribution would show out rather blatantly. MFI itself is insensitive to subtle changes in molecular parameters, as has been shown by Smith [15], Borzenskii [16] and Shida et al. [17]. Hence, the coalesced curves of Shenoy et al. [1–12] which are formed by normalizing viscosity and shear rate via MFI would also be insensitive to changes in molecular parameters like molecular weight distribution, long chain branching, etc.

From a fundamental point of view, it would be desirable to relieve the MFI to rheogram technique of this inherent limitation so that even ambitious correlations of estimating zero-shear viscosity from MFI such as those attempted by Boenig [18], Busse [19], and Dutta [20] could become more meaningful. Shenoy and Saini [21] suggested the use of a correction factor $(\bar{M}_z/\bar{M}_w)^{1.7}$ when coalescing low shear viscosity data for polymer grades with widely different molecular weight distributions. They found that two distinct unified curves were generated, as shown in Figures 3 and 4, when $\eta \cdot$ MFI vs. $\dot{\gamma}$/MFI plots were made for eight different polypropylenes with widely different molecular weight distributions. Samples B, C, E, and F, with broad and regular molecular weight distributions, coalesced on one curve (Figure 3), while samples A, D, G, and H, with narrow mo-

Table 3
Rheological Parameters of the Modified Ellis Model (Equation 5) for Polymers
of Different Generic Type

Polymer Type	η_0 MFI	$\tau_{1/2}$	α	Applicability Range of Shear Stress (Dynes/ cm^2)	ASTM Test Load Condition Used in the Master Curve (kg)
Linear Low Density Polyethylenes	1.0×10^5	2.00×10^5	2.00	10^3–4×10^5	2.16
High Density Polyethylenes	2.1×10^5	3.67×10^4	1.85	10^4–10^6	2.16
Low Density Polyethylenes	3.0×10^5	6.00×10^4	2.14	3×10^3–10^6	2.16
Polypropylenes	1.2×10^5	1.54×10^4	2.89	6×10^3–10^6	2.16
Polystyrenes	4.0×10^6	8.00×10^4	2.53	4×10^4–10^6	5.00
Cellulose Esters	8.5×10^4	1.27×10^6	2.13	10^5–4×10^6	2.16
Cellulose Ethers	8.5×10^4	3.82×10^5	2.63	10^5–10^6	2.16
Acrylics	2.1×10^5	4.09×10^5	2.23	10^5–10^7	3.80
Nylons	9.5×10^4	1.18×10^6	2.24	10^4–10^7	2.16
Polyesters	8.0×10^4	3.00×10^6	2.28	10^5–10^7	2.16
Polycarbonates	4.2×10^4	2.73×10^6	1.82	4×10^5–10^7	1.20
Poly(vinyl chloride)s	1.2×10^6	1.32×10^5	2.75	10^5–10^7	20.00
Poly(vinylidene fluoride)s	8.5×10^5	1.40×10^6	3.00	10^5–10^7	12.50
Poly(phenylene oxide)s	3.5×10^5	9.0×10^5	2.40	4×10^4–5×10^6	5.00
Poly(pheylene sulfide)s	3.8×10^5	7.6×10^5	2.70	4×10^3–7×10^6	5.00
Poly(ether sulfone)s	2.2×10^5	2.2×10^6	2.10	10^4–10^7	5.00
Poly(ether ether ketone)s	6.0×10^5	2.8×10^5	2.10	10^4–3×10^6	5.00
Poly(ether imide)s	1.8×10^5	3.6×10^6	2.56	10^5–10^7	5.00
Polyarylates	2.0×10^5	2.3×10^7	1.50	10^4–10^7	5.00
Styrene-butadiene-styrenes	1.8×10^5	2×10^6	2.50	2×10^4–4×10^6	5.00
Acrylonitrile-butadiene-styrenes	2.0×10^6	1.00×10^5	2.25	10^4–10^6	5.00
Ethylene-vinyl acetate copolymer	3.5×10^5	3×10^4	1.85	3×10^3–4×10^6	2.16
Polyester elastomer	8.7×10^4	1.6×10^6	2.10	10^4–3×10^6	2.16

lecular weight distribution coalesced on a separate curve (Figure 4), which as such did not super-impose. However, when a plot of $(\eta \cdot \text{MFI})/(\bar{M}_z/\bar{M}_w)^{1.7}$ vs. $(\bar{M}_z/\bar{M}_w)^{1.7}$ $(\dot{\gamma}/\text{MFI})$ was made as shown in Figure 5, the differences in molecular weight distribution were automatically taken into account, resulting in a single curve. For such a curve, the rheological model that can be fitted is a modified form of Equation 4 given as follows:

$$\frac{\eta \cdot \text{MFI}}{(\bar{M}_z/\bar{M}_w)^{1.7}} = \frac{\eta_0 \cdot \text{MFI}}{(\bar{M}_z/\bar{M}_w)^{1.7}} \left\{ 1 + \frac{(\lambda \cdot \text{MFI})^2}{(\bar{M}_z/\bar{M}_w)^{3.5}} \left[\left(\frac{\bar{M}_z}{\bar{M}_w}\right)^{1.7} \cdot \left(\frac{\dot{\gamma}}{\text{MFI}}\right)^2 \right]^{-N} \right\} \tag{7}$$

It is worth noting that molecular weight distribution is often expressed as one of the following ratios, namely, $\bar{M}_w/\bar{M}_n$, $\bar{M}_z/\bar{M}_w$, $\bar{M}_{z+1}/\bar{M}_z$, etc. Van Krevelen et al. [22] have suggested an approximate interrelationship between the various expressions based on the analysis of data for a

Table 4

Rheological Parameters of the Modified Ostwald-de Waele Power-Law Model (Equation 6) for Polymers of Different Generic Types

Polymer Type	K (g/cm sec^{2-n})	n	Applicability Range of Shear Rate (s^{-1})	ASTM Test Load Condition Used in the Master Curve (kg)
Linear Low Density Polyethylenes	2.0×10^5	0.36	1–100	2.16
High Density Polyethylenes	9.0×10^4	0.54	4–1000	2.16
Low Density Polyethylenes	1.3×10^5	0.46	4–1000	2.16
Polypropylenes	1.4×10^5	0.34	4–1000	2.16
Polystyrenes	3.5×10^5	0.39	0.4–1000	5.00
Cellulose Esters	3.2×10^5	0.47	10–1000	2.16
Cellulose Ethers	1.1×10^5	0.38	3–100	2.16
Acrylics	3.2×10^5	0.44	100–1000	3.80
Nylons	2.8×10^5	0.44	50–1000	2.16
Polyesters	5.0×10^4	0.43	50–1000	2.16
Polycarbonates	1.5×10^5	0.52	40–1000	1.20
Poly(vinyl chloride)s	4.6×10^5	0.36	2–200	20.00
Poly(vinylidene fluoride)s	1.0×10^6	0.4	5–2000	12.50
Poly(phenylene oxide)s	1.0×10^6	0.25	40–9000	5.00
Poly(phenylene sulfide)s	3.0×10^5	0.44	40–700	5.00
Poly(ether sulfone)s	3.0×10^5	0.60	30–20000	5.00
Poly(ether ether ketone)s	6.0×10^5	0.32	20–1000	5.00
Poly(ether imide)s	1.0×10^6	0.34	200–10000	5.00
Polyarylates	2.2×10^5	0.85	100–10000	5.00
Polyarylates	2.2×10^5	0.30	10–1000	5.00
Styrene-butadiene-styrenes	8.0×10^5	0.30	10–1000	5.00
Styrene-acrylonitriles	3.0×10^5	0.33	3–2000	3.80
Acrylonitrile-butadiene-styrenes	3.5×10^5	0.38	1–1000	5.00
Vinyl chloride-vinyl acetate copolymer	4.0×10^5	0.33	1–600	20.00
Ethylene-vinyl acetate copolymer	1.0×10^5	0.58	2–500	2.16
Polyester elastomer	2.5×10^5	0.47	100–3000	2.16

number of polymers, as follows:

$$\frac{\bar{M}_w}{\bar{M}_n} = \bar{Q}, \qquad \frac{\bar{M}_z}{\bar{M}_w} \simeq \bar{Q}^{0.75}, \qquad \frac{\bar{M}_z}{\bar{M}_n} \simeq \bar{Q}^{1.75}$$

$$\frac{\bar{M}_{z+1}}{\bar{M}_z} = \bar{Q}^{0.56}, \qquad \frac{\bar{M}_{z+1}}{\bar{M}_n} \simeq \bar{Q}^{2.31} \tag{8}$$

$$\frac{\bar{M}_z \cdot \bar{M}_{z+1}}{\bar{M}_w^2} \simeq \bar{Q}^{2.06}, \qquad \frac{\bar{M}_z \cdot \bar{M}_{z+1}}{\bar{M}_n^2} \simeq \bar{Q}^{4.06}$$

Any of the above expressions could thus be used in place of $(\bar{M}_z/\bar{M}_w)^{1.7}$ in the unified curve after proper conversion.

Further, it is obvious that zero-shear viscosity could be more effectively predicted than by the methods of Boenig [18], Busse [19] and Dutta [20] considering that $(\eta_0 \cdot \text{MFI})(\bar{M}_z/\bar{M}_w)^{1.7}$ would be fairly constant for each generic type of polymer.

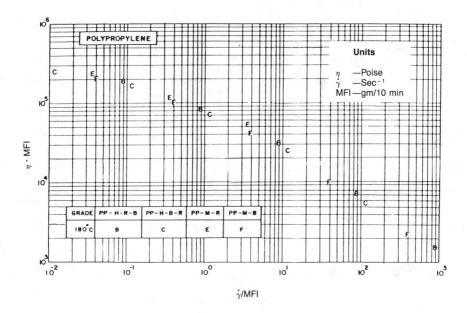

Figure 3. Coalesced shear viscosity curve for broad and regular molecular weight distribution polypropylene at 2.16 kg test load condition for MFI (from Shenoy and Saini [21]).

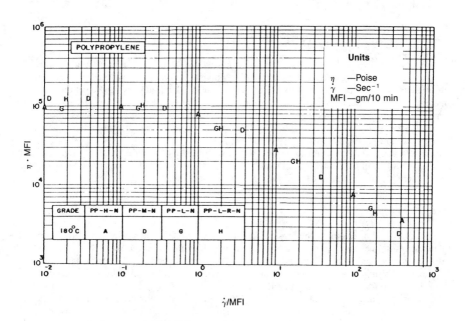

Figure 4. Coalesced shear viscosity curve for narrow molecular weight distribution polypropylene at 2.16 kg test load condition for MFI (from Shenoy and Saini [21]).

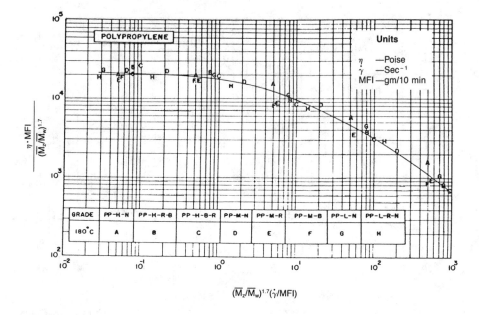

$$(\overline{M}_z/\overline{M}_w)^{1.7}(\dot{\gamma}/MFI)$$

Figure 5. Coalesced shear viscosity curve for broad, regular, and narrow molecular weight distribution polypropylene at 2.16 kg test load condition for MFI; (—) predictions of Equation (7) (from Shenoy and Saini [21]).

PRACTICAL APPLICATIONS OF THE NOVEL APPROACH

It has been shown in the earlier section how a novel approach can be used to obtain unified viscosity vs. shear rate curves for each generic type of polymers. The unified curve when fitted with appropriately modified forms of well-known rheological models lends an easy way to get the rheogram merely through mathematical calculations, knowing the value of MFI under correct temperature and load conditions. The other advantage of fitting such rheological models to the unified curves lies in the fact that calculations involving entrance length estimates, heat transfer, die design, mold design, etc., are greatly simplified.

The following sections demonstrate how this novel approach could be effectively used for determining a number of parameters useful in polymer processing operations within reasonable accuracy limits merely using the knowledge of the MFI of the material.

Injection Molding

Injection molding is one of the most widely used processes for the fabrication of thermoplastic materials. It is, in essence, an operation which involves high pressure squeezing of a polymeric melt through a very small hole into a cold cavity and then packing additional material into the cavity to allow for shrinkage as the material cools. The injection molder as well as the mold designer have known the importance of operating under minimum pressure drop conditions during cavity filling in order to minimize frozen-in stresses, and also of working under minimum clamping force conditions to prevent mold opening. The effect of a cooled mold on the pressure vs. flow rate curve must be known for calculating the minimum pressure requirements. But this involves non-trivial equations to be solved through computer programs using numerical techniques. Besides this, a knowledge of the complete flow curve depicting the variation of melt viscosity over the relevant range of shear rates (30–$3,000$ sec^{-1}) and temperatures (190–$320°C$) is also essential for design calculations. Such requirements provide an ideal ground for using the earlier-discussed approach. Saini and Shenoy [23] worked along these lines to develop a method for simplified calculations in mold filling during non-isothermal flow of polymer melts. They based their calculations on the work of Barrie [24], who empirically observed that in a center-gated mold, the frozen polymer layer is approximately uniform on the mold surface at the instant of mold filling; thus implying that at all instants the melt flow occurs in a cavity of approximately uniform thickness. Thus, if the original cavity has a thickness x, and then a thickness Δx of frozen material forms on the surface, the effective remaining flow path is given by:

$$x_{eff} = x - 2 \, \Delta x \tag{9}$$

It is now assumed that isothermal flow equations can be applied using the reduced, effective cavity thickness x_{eff}, so that an expression for pressure drop in the mold can be written. In deriving this expression, the basic relationship between shear stress vs. shear rate are necessary. Barrie [24] used the conventional power-law model, while Saini and Shenoy [23] used the modified form as obtained from Equation 6:

$$\tau = K(\dot{\gamma}/MFI)^n \tag{10}$$

where K and n are values given in Table 4 as derived from the grade and temperature invarient unified curves of Shenoy et al. [1–6, 8, 12]. The pressure drop expression obtained using Equation 10 in a simplified form can be written as:

$$P_0 = \frac{2KQ^nR_d^{1-n}}{(1-n)MFI^nx^{1+2n}[1 - 2\bar{C}(\pi R_d^2/Qx^2)^{1/3}]^{1+2n}} \tag{11}$$

Differentiating Equation 11 with respect to Q and equating to zero yields the expression for the minimum pressure gradient $P_{0,min}$ for center-gated disc mold cavity filling as:

$$P_{0,min} = \frac{f(n)K\bar{C}^{3n}\pi^nR_d^{1+n}}{MFI^nx^{1+4n}} \tag{12}$$

where $\quad f(n) = \frac{2^{3n+1}}{1-n}\left(\frac{1+5n}{3n}\right)^{3n}\left(\frac{1+5n}{1+2n}\right)^{1+2n} \tag{13}$

and x is the original cavity thickness, R_d the radius of the circular disc cavity, and $\bar{C}$ the proportionality constant, given as:

$$\bar{C} = 2a^{1/2}\left(\frac{T_0 - \theta}{T - \theta}\right) \tag{14}$$

"a" being the heat diffusion coefficient of the melt, θ the mold temperature, T the melt temperature, and T_0 the freeze-off temperature.

For a given polymer type, f(n), $\bar{C}$, K, and n are all constants, and for a given circular type, mold R_d and x are fixed. Hence, the minimum pressure for cavity filling can be estimated from Equation 12 only through the knowledge of the MFI of the polymer at the melt temperature T of mold filling. The MFI determined under standard ASTM test conditions would have to be converted to MFI value at the required temperatures by using either Equation 2 or 3.

Under Equation 12, the minimum clamping force F_{min} can be easily estimated from the following expression:

$$F_{min} = \frac{P_{0,min}\bar{A}}{\bar{B}} \tag{15}$$

where $\bar{A}$ is the effective projected area of the molding given as πR^2 and $\bar{B}$ is a numerical function which depends on n as shown by Barrie [24] for circular, square, and rectangular moldings:

$$\bar{B} = \frac{n+2}{n} \quad \text{(for circular panel with center injection)} \tag{16}$$

$$\bar{B} = \frac{n+1}{n} \quad \text{(for long thin rectangular panel with center injection)} \tag{17}$$

Thus more centrally gated, flat, and symmetrical moldings would show higher values of $\bar{B}$ and hence, a lower clamping force. For engineering design calculations, one could choose Equation 17, which would give the lower estimate of $\bar{B}$. From Table 4 it is clear that some common values of n are 0.33 and 0.44. Thus, a value of $\bar{B} = 4.0$ for $n = 0.33$, $\bar{B} = 3.5$ for $n = 0.44$, and $\bar{B} = 3.0$ for $n \approx 0.50$, could be used as rough estimates.

Compression Molding

Though compression molding is most commonly used for thermosetting materials, there are some specialized materials like ultra high molecular weight polyethylenes (UHMWPE) which are preferentially compression molded rather than injection molded to form the product. Despite the disadvantages in compression molding process of long cycle times, more than 50% of UHMWPE is processed this way because of its characteristic flow behavior, which renders it to be more easily compression molded than injection molded.

The compaction force during the molding operation must be known in order to achieve good control during the process. Following the novel approach through the unified rheological curves, Shenoy and Saini [25] have suggested a simple approach to determine the compaction force during compression molding. Again, using Equation 10 instead of the conventional power-law model, they derived the expressions for compaction force for circular molds and flat strips, respectively, as follows:

For Circular Discs

$$F_{ed} = \frac{2\pi K}{(n+3)} \left(\frac{2n+1}{n} \right)^n \frac{R_{ed}^{n+3}}{(MFI)^n} \left(\frac{-\dot{h}^n}{h_0^{2n+1}} \right) \tag{18}$$

For Flat Strips

$$F_{fs} = \frac{K}{n+2} \left(\frac{2n+1}{n} \right)^n \frac{wL^{n+2}}{(MFI)^n} \left(\frac{-\dot{h}^n}{h_0^{2n+1}} \right) \tag{19}$$

where F_{cd} and F_{fs} = compaction forces required to conduct the squeezing operation
h_0 = initial gap between the plates
$-\dot{h}$ = rate at which the gap is changing with time
R_{cd} = radius
w = width
L = length of the plate
K and n = power-law constants for the modified Ostwald-de Waele model as given by Equation 10, taken as values of 1.66×10^6 g/cm sec^{2-n} and 0.156, respectively, for UHMWPE

Equations 18 and 19 take the following specific form in the case of UHMWPE:

For Circular Disc

$$\frac{F_{cd}h_0(MFI)^{0.156}}{R_{cd}^{3.156}} = 4.6 \times 10^6 \left(\frac{-\dot{h}^{1/2}}{h_0}\right)^{0.312} \tag{20}$$

For Flat Strips

$$\frac{F_{fs}h_0(MFI)^{0.156}}{wL^{2.156}} = 1.07 \times 10^6 \left(\frac{-\dot{h}^{1/2}}{h_0}\right)^{0.312} \tag{21}$$

In a typical compression molding operation, the squeezing rate and the initial separation would be such as to give values of $(-\dot{h}^{1/2}/h_0)$ between 0.01 and 0.1 $(cm\ s)^{-1/2}$. The variation of the left-hand sides of Equations 20 and 21 across this range of $(-\dot{h}^{1/2}/h_0)$ is shown in Figure 6. Knowing the geometrical dimensions of the mold, the compaction force can be easily estimated through the knowledge of the MFI of the polymer at the temperature of molding. The appropriate value of MFI to be used can be calculated by following the procedure discussed earlier.

Calendering

The "calendering" process for shaping of thermoplastic materials into sheets and films by squeezing through a pair of corotating heated rolls has been commonly used for making various polyvinyl

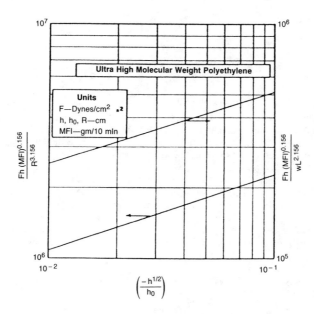

Figure 6. Unified curve showing the variation of the compaction force with the rate of plate separation during compression molding of UHMWPE (from Shenoy and Saini [25]).

chloride (PVC) products. There are a number of critical parameters during such a process. These are, for example, the pressure distribution in the rollers, the torque exerted by each roll, the power input into each roll, and the average temperature rise due to viscous dissipation. Ray and Shenoy [26] have provided a simplified prediction technique based on the novel approach of using the unified master curve for PVC [4]. Their analysis follows the lines of Vlachopoulos and Hrymak [27], but make use of the modified Ostwald-de Waele model given by Equation 10 instead of the conventional power-law form. The expression derived by Ray and Shenoy [26] for the pressure distribution is as follows:

$$P(MFI)^n = C_1 C_2 \int_{x^*}^{\lambda^*} \frac{|\lambda^{*2} - x^{*2}|^{n-1}(\lambda^{*2} - x^{*2})}{(1 + x^{*2})^{2n+1}} dx^* \tag{22}$$

where

$$C_1 = K \left(\frac{2^n + 1}{n} \right)^n \tag{23}$$

$$C_2 = \left(\frac{U}{H_0} \right)^n \left(\frac{2R_0}{H_0} \right)^{1/2} \tag{24}$$

where   P = pressure developed between the rolls
              U = velocity at the roll surface
            H_0 = half the distance between rolls
            R_0 = radius of the roll
          K, n = parameters from Equation 10
λ^* and x^* = dimensionless parameters defined below:

$$x^* = x_0 (2R_0 H_0)^{-1/2} \tag{25}$$

$$\lambda^* = \left[\frac{Q_0}{2UH_0} - 1 \right]^{1/2} \tag{26}$$

where Q_0 is the flow rate of the melt through the rolls.

Numerical integration of Equation 22 gives the pressure distribution vs. the dimensionless distance, x^*, and this was done for two cases: one considering no hydrodynamic slip at the roll surface, and one using the slip condition. The two plots that resulted are unique for PVC formulations and can be used for estimating the pressure distribution merely from the knowledge of the MFI of the formulation. These master curves are shown in Figures 7 and 8. Predictions from these curves using estimated values of MFI were found to give more realistic values than those obtained by Vlachopoulos and Hrymak [27] using complete rheological data of viscosity vs. shear rate. Comparison of the two sets of predictions along with the experimental data used by Vlachopoulos and Hrymak [27] are given in Figures 9 and 10. It can be easily seen that the simple technique of Ray and Shenoy [26] based on the novel approach through the use of master curve gives a closer fit to experimental data.

Ray and Shenoy [26] have also given expressions for the torque exerted by each roll (T) and the power input (φ_p). They are as follows:

$$\Gamma(MFI)^n = C_1(WR_0 H_0 C_2) \int_{-x_0^*}^{\lambda^*} \frac{|\lambda^{*2} - x^{*2}|^{n-1}(\lambda^{*2} - x^{*2})}{(1 + x^{*2})^{2n}} dx^* \tag{27}$$

$$\phi_p(MFI)^n = C_1(WUH_0 C_2) \int_{-x_0^*}^{\lambda^*} \frac{|\lambda^{*2} - x^{*2}|^{n-1}(\lambda^{*2} - x^{*2})}{(1 + x^{*2})^{2n}} dx^* \tag{28}$$

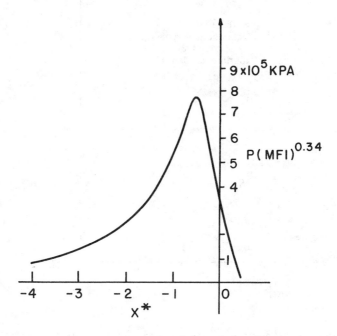

Figure 7. Plot of pressure distribution vs. dimensionless distance—master curve for theory without slip (from Ray and Shenoy [26]).

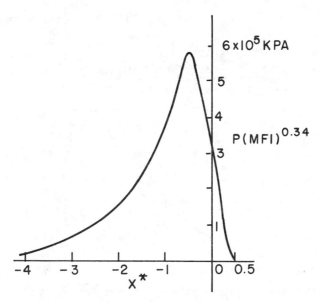

Figure 8. Plot of pressure distribution vs. dimensionless distance—master curve theory with slip (taken from Ray and Shenoy [26]).

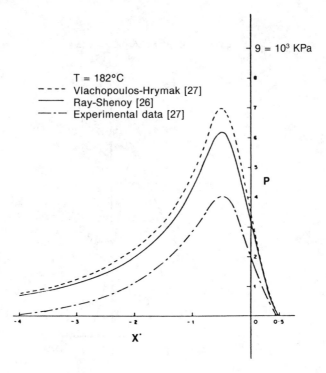

Figure 9. Comparison of predictions made by Ray and Shenoy with the theory and experiment of Vlachopoulos and Hrymak for theory without slip.

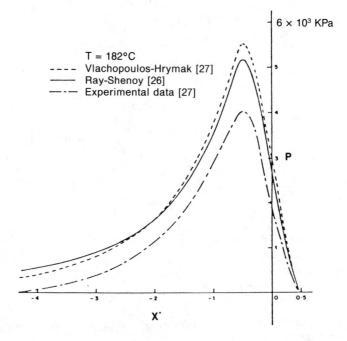

Figure 10. Comparison of predictions made by Ray and Shenoy with the theory and experiment of Vlachopoulos and Hrymak for theory with slip.

Again, the predictions of torque and power input can be done merely through the knowledge of the MFI of the PVC formulation.

Extrusion

Extrusion of polymer melts through dies of complex cross-sectional shapes to form final products is not at all uncommon today. The shape of these dies and the pressure losses through them are important factors in preventing flow defects and controlling the quality of the end product. Shenoy and Saini [28] have given a method for the predictions of pressure losses through dies of complex cross section based on the simple approach of using MFI. They have made use of available simple expressions of Lenk [29–32], but used the modified Ostwald-de Waele power-law model given by Equation 10 instead of the conventional one. The general expression proposed by them is as follows:

$$\frac{\Delta P H_c (MFI)^n}{2L_d} = f_1 f_2 \left(\frac{Q}{H_c^3} \right)^n \tag{29}$$

where f_1 = a function of the geometric variables based on the die shape
         f_2 = a function based on fluid properties, namely, the K and n values as given by Equation 10
         L_d = length of the die
         H_c = characteristic geometric parameter which is specific to each defined die shape

The expressions for f_1 and f_2 for a number of differently-shaped complex dies are given below:

Rectangular Channel Without Taper

$$H_c = H \tag{30}$$

$$f_1 = \frac{\zeta_{WH} + 1}{\zeta_{WH}^{n+1}} \tag{31}$$

$$f_2 = K \left(\frac{4n + 2}{n} \right)^n \tag{32}$$

where ζ_{WH} is the shape factor defined by the ratio of the width W to the height H of the channel. Thus $\zeta_{WH} \to 1$ represents a square, while $\zeta_{WH} \to \infty$ represents a wide slit.

Rectangular Channel of Constant Width and Vertical Taper

$$H_c = H_1 \tag{33}$$

$$f_1 = \frac{1}{\zeta_w^n} \left[\frac{1 - \lambda_1^{2n}}{\lambda_1^{2n}(1 - \lambda_1)} \right] \tag{34}$$

$$f_2 = \frac{K}{2n} \left(\frac{4n + 2}{n} \right)^n \tag{35}$$

where λ_1 is the constant vertical taper factor defined by the ratio of height H_2 at the end of the channel to the length H_1 at the start of the channel, while ζ_w is the shape factor defined by the ratio of the constant width W to the entrance height H_1 of the channel.

Rectangular Channel of Constant Height and Constant Lateral Taper

$$H_c = H \tag{36}$$

$$f_1 = \frac{1}{\zeta_H^n} \left[\frac{1 - \lambda_2^{1-n}}{1 - \lambda^2} \right] \tag{37}$$

$$f_2 = \frac{K}{1 - n} \left(\frac{4n + 2}{n} \right)^n \tag{38}$$

where λ^2 is the constant lateral taper factor defined by the ratio of the width W_2 at the end of the channel to the width W_1 at the start of the channel, and ζ_H is the shape factor defined by the ratio of the entrance width W_1 to the constant height H of the channel.

Rectangular Channel with Constant Vertical Taper as well as Constant Lateral Taper

$$H_c = H_1 \tag{39}$$

$$f_1 = \frac{1}{\zeta^n} \left[\frac{1 - \lambda_1^{2n}}{\lambda_1^{2n}(1 - \lambda_1)} \right] \left\{ 1 + \frac{n(1 - \lambda_2)}{(1 - \lambda_1)} + \frac{2n^2}{(1 - 2n)} \frac{(\lambda_1 - \lambda_1^{2n})(1 - \lambda_2)}{(1 - \lambda_1^{2n})(1 - \lambda_1)} \right\} \tag{40}$$

$$f_2 = \frac{K}{2n} \left(\frac{4n + 2}{n} \right)^n \tag{41}$$

where λ_1 is the constant vertical taper factor defined by the ratio of the height H_2 at the end of the channel to the height H_1 at the start of the channel; λ_2 is the constant lateral taper factor defined by the ratio of the width W_2 at the end of the channel to the width W_1 at the start of the channel; and ζ is the shape factor defined by the ratio of the entrance width W_1 to the entrance height H_1 of the channel.

Rectangular Channel with a Taper such that the Cross-Sectional Shape Factor is Constant

$$H_c = H_1 \tag{42}$$

$$f_i = \left(\frac{\zeta_{WH} + 1}{\zeta_{WH}^{n+1}} \right) \left[\frac{(1 - \lambda_1^{3n})}{\lambda_1^{3n}(1 - \lambda_1)} \right] \tag{43}$$

$$f_2 = \frac{K}{3n} \left(\frac{4n + 2}{n} \right)^n \tag{44}$$

where λ_1 is the taper factor defined by the ratio of the height H_2 at the end of the channel to the height H_1 at the start of the channel; and ζ_{WH} is the shape factor, which is constant such that the tapering channel has a constant cross-sectional rectangular shape.

Cylindrical Channel

$$H_c = R \tag{45}$$

$$f_1 = 1 \tag{46}$$

$$f_2 = K \left(\frac{3n + 1}{\pi n} \right)^n \tag{47}$$

where R is the radius of the channel.

Truncated Right Cone

$$H_c = R_1 \tag{48}$$

$$f_1 = \frac{1 - \lambda_R^{3n}}{\lambda_R^{3n}(1 - \lambda_R)} \tag{49}$$

$$f_2 = \frac{K}{3n}\left(\frac{3n + 1}{\pi n}\right)^n \tag{50}$$

where λ_R is the constant taper factor defined by the ratio of the exit radius R_2 to the entrance radius R_1.

Untapered Polygonal Channel with N_1 Sides

$$H_c = R \tag{51}$$

$$f_1 = \left(\frac{N_1}{\pi} \tan \frac{\pi}{N_1}\right)^{n/2} \tag{52}$$

$$f_2 = K\left(\frac{3n + 1}{\pi n}\right)^n \tag{53}$$

where R is the radius of the circle whose cross-sectional area is equal to the cross-sectional area of the polygon.

Constant Taper Polygonal Channel with N_1 Sides

$$H_c = R_1 \tag{54}$$

$$f_1 = \left(\frac{N_1}{\pi} \tan \frac{\pi}{N_1}\right)^{n/2}\left[\frac{1 - \lambda_R^{3n}}{\lambda_R^{3n}(1 - \lambda_R)}\right] \tag{55}$$

$$f_2 = \frac{K}{3n}\left(\frac{3n + 1}{\pi n}\right)^n \tag{56}$$

where R_1 is the radius of the circle whose cross-sectional area is equal to the cross-sectional area of the entrance of the polygon, and λ_R is equal to R_2/R_1 where R_2 is the radius of the circle whose cross-sectional area is equal to the cross-sectional area of the exit of the polygon.

From Table 4, appropriate values of K and n for the polymer of interest can be chosen and the value of f_2 determined from the above equations for any typical die shape. In all cases, f_1 can be easily estimated from the geometry of the die. Thus, the relationship between $\Delta PH_c/2L$ and Q/H^3 for flow of polymer melt through typical dies can be established through the knowledge of MFI of the polymer at the temperature of flow using Equation 29.

Figure 11 shows a plot of $\Delta PH/2L$ vs. Q/H^3 for flow of polypropylene melt through a rectangular die. The data points correspond to the experimental values of White and Huang [33], the solid line is based on the predictions of Shenoy and Saini [28] using the above simple approach, and the dashed line gives the predictions of Lenk [32] using the rheological data given by White and Huang [33]. Figure 11 gives evidence of the effectiveness of the simple novel approach based on MFI in comparison to the other cumbersome approach through the knowledge of the entire flow curve.

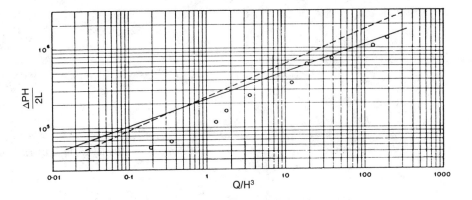

Figure 11. Pressure drop vs. flow rate through a rectangular die for polypropylene (taken from Shenoy and Saini [28]).

Viscous Heat Dissipation and Flow Activation Energy

In all polymer processes, the molten polymer is subjected to a wide range of shear rate and temperature, during which viscous heat gets generated purely because of the friction between the viscous melt and the parts of the processing equipment that it comes in contact with. The viscous heat dissipation results in a temperature rise which offsets the extruder temperature profile settings with respect to throughput rate or screw speed. An estimate of the magnitude of the viscous heat generated during a process is certainly helpful in controlling the temperature rise by a priori changing the processing conditions or altering the screw design. Viscous heat determination also assumes importance when handling heat-sensitive polymers so that appropriate design and process modifications can be made so as to maintain the melt temperature well below the degradation temperature of the polymer.

Shenoy and Saini [34] have shown that plots made in terms of ϕ/MFI vs. $\dot{\gamma}/\text{MFI}$ for viscous heat dissipation factor ϕ are unique with respect to each generic type of polymers. Figure 12 shows a typical unified curve for polypropylene. Shenoy and Saini [34] fitted each of the unique plots by a straight line of the form given below:

$$\frac{\phi}{\text{MFI}} = \alpha_1 \left(\frac{\dot{\gamma}}{\text{MFI}}\right)^{\beta_1} \tag{57}$$

The values of α_1 and β_1 for each generic type of polymer are given in Table 5. Following the procedure for getting the appropriate value of MFI at the temperature of interest as discussed earlier, the viscous heat at the shear rate of concern can be estimated easily from Equation 57.

Once the rate of generation of heat ϕ is known at the shear rate of relevance, then the maximum adiabatic temperature rise can be estimated through an analysis of the temperature profiles developed due to viscous heating by solving the energy equation. The simple equation of Cox and Macosko [35] could be used for calculating the maximum adiabatic temperature rise as follows:

$$\rho C_p \frac{dT}{dt_{\text{res}}} = \phi \tag{58}$$

where ρ = density in g/cc
C_p = specific heat in cal/g °C
t_{res} = residence time in seconds

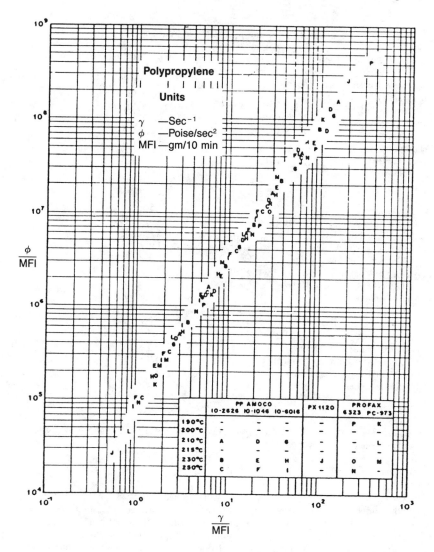

Figure 12. Unified curve for viscous dissipation factor vs. shear rate for polypropylene at 2.16 kg test load condition for MFI measurement (taken from Shenoy and Saini [34]).

The temperature-residence time relationship is extremely useful in order to maintain conditions below excessive thermal degradation during processing.

An understanding of the mechanism of the polymer melt flow processes in relation to the nature and composition of the material can be elucidated by a study of the temperature dependency of the melt viscosity, namely, the flow activation energy. Saini and Shenoy [13] recently proposed the concept of using MFI at two different temperatures within the range of interest to evaluate the activation energy for viscous flow. Equation 3 suggested by them for this evaluation was shown

Table 5
Values of α_1 and β_1 Needed in Equation (57)

Polymer Type	$\alpha_1(\text{g/cm s}^{2-n} \text{ (g/10 min)}^n)$	β_1
Linear Low Density Polyethylenes	8.0×10^4	1.78
High Density Polyethylenes	9.0×10^4	1.54
Low Density Polyethylenes	1.3×10^5	1.46
Polypropylenes	1.4×10^5	1.34
Polystyrenes	3.5×10^5	1.39
Cellulose Esters	3.2×10^5	1.47
Cellulose Ethers	1.1×10^5	1.38
Acrylics	3.2×10^5	1.44
Nylons	2.8×10^5	1.44
Polyesters	5.0×10^4	1.43
Polycarbonates	1.5×10^5	1.52
Poly(vinyl chloride)s	4.6×10^5	1.36
Poly(vinylidene fluoride)s	9.5×10^5	1.40
Poly(phenylene oxide)s	1.0×10^6	1.25
Poly(phenylene sulfide)s	3.0×10^5	1.44
Poly(ether sulfone)s	3.0×10^5	1.60
Poly(ether ether ketone)s	6.0×10^5	1.32
Poly(ether imide)s	1.0×10^6	1.34
Polyarylates	2.2×10^5	1.85
Styrene-butadiene-styrenes	8.0×10^5	1.30
Styrene-acrylonitriles	3.0×10^5	1.33
Acrylonitrile-butadiene styrenes	3.5×10^5	1.38
Vinyl chloride-vinyl acetate copolymer	4.0×10^5	1.33
Ethylene-vinyl acetate copolymer	1.0×10^5	1.58
Polyester elastomer	2.5×10^5	1.47

to give a standard and meaningful value of E. The activation energies calculated by this technique for some polymers are given in Table 6.

Polyblending

Polyblending—modification of one polymer with another—involves the critical steps of selection of the component polymers, their appropriate grades, and their composition based on property requirements, as well as the proper choice of compounding method and conditions. The component grade selection and choice of compounding process parameters are often done arbitrarily based on evaluation of end properties. This involves a sort of trial-and-error procedure before finalizing the appropriate grades of the components and the compounding conditions. Synergistic property advantages cannot be achieved even in thermodynamically miscible polymers, if they are mechanically incompatible due to large differences in melt viscosities at the conditions of compounding. A simple approach of getting quantitative estimation of compounding conditions or grade selection of blend components through MFI has been suggested by Shenoy [36]. A methodology is developed for specifying the temperature and shear rate conditions for melt blending two component polymers whose grades have already been selected based on other considerations. The temperature of compounding in order to achieve maximum mechanical compatibility as suggested by Shenoy [36] is as follows:

$$T_c = \frac{E_{P_2} - E_{P_1}}{R \ln(MFI_{P_2,T_2}/MFI_{P_1,T_1} + E_{P_2}/T_2 - E_{P_1}/T_1)} \tag{59}$$

Table 6
Flow Activation Energies at a Constant Shear Stress Based on Melt Flow Index for a
Number of Common Polymers

Polymer Type	E (Kcal/mole)	Temperature Range of Validity (°C)	ASTM Test Load Condition Used (kg)
Linear Low Density Polyethylenes	3.20	175–205	2.16
High Density Polyethylenes	6.83	175–220	2.16
Low Density Polyethylenes	7.25	175–205	2.16
Polypropylenes	9.87	200–250	2.16
Polystyrenes	25.5	210–250	5.00
Cellulose Esters	34.2	190–230	2.16
Cellulose Ethers	23.2	170–230	2.16
Acrylics	38.5	170–260	3.80
Nylons	18.6	230–300	2.16
Polyesters	20.1	265–285	2.16
Polycarbonates	21.9	250–290	1.20
Poly(vinylidene fluoride)s	8.0	190–290	12.50
Poly(phenylene oxide)s	33.0	260–320	5.00
Poly(phenylene sulfide)s	4.6	280–316	5.00
Poly(ether sulfone)s	36.0	320–370	5.00
Poly(ether ether ketone)s	12.0	360–395	5.00
Poly(ether imide)s	30.0	355–395	5.00
Polyarylates	35.0	288–329	5.00
Styrene-acrylonitriles	30.7	200–250	3.80

where MFI_{P_1,T_1} and MFI_{P_2,T_2} represent the MFI values of the two component polymers, E_{P_1} and E_{P_2} are their respective activation energies, and T_1 and T_2 are the respective temperatures of MFI measurement.

The compounding temperature calculated through Equation 59 graphically represents the inter-section point of the two curves shown in Figure 13 for polymers P_1 and P_2. Thus, if the grades of the two component polymers have been done a priori, the compounding temperature as deter-mined from the intersection of the two curves is automatically fixed. The value of T_c as obtained through Equation 59 may not always result in a meaningful value for the selected grades. For example, the intersection points in Figures 13(b), 13(c), and 13(d) could be respectively too low (even below the melting temperature), too high (even above the degradation temperature), or none at all if the activation energy of the two components are equal. When such is the case, the value of T_c does not have actual relevance for use but is certainly an indication of the incompatibility of the component polymers.

The method for determining the shear rate level in a compounding operation for achieving me-chanical compatibility has also been given by Shenoy [36] through a simple equation, as follows:

$$\dot{\gamma}_c = MFI_{B,T_c} \left(\frac{K_1}{K_2} \right)^{1/(n_2 - n_1)} \tag{60}$$

where MFI_{B,T_c} is the melt flow index value of either component, i.e., of the blend at the temperature of compounding T_c. K_1 and K_2, as well as n_1 and n_2, correspond to the parameters of Equation 10 and those given in Table 4 for the two component polymers. The determination of the above shear rate condition is based on the intersection of the master curves of Shenoy and Saini [2, 5, 7, 8, 12, 14]. Figure 14 shows that when $n_1 = n_2$, the curves do not intersect, and hence, no shear rate condition can be specified for achieving mechanical compatibility. For the case when K and

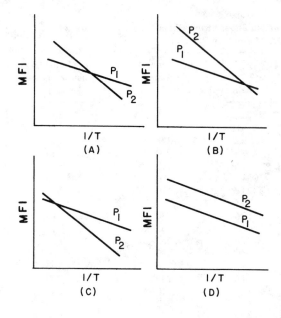

Figure 13. Four possible ways in which curves of melt flow index vs. reciprocal temperature on a semi logarithmic plot would exist for two given component polymers (taken from Shenoy [36]).

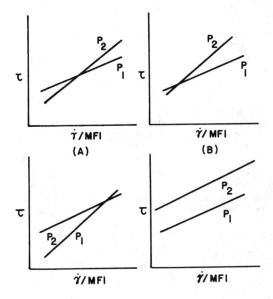

Figure 14. Four possible ways in which curves of shear stress vs. shear rate normalized by MFI on a log-log would exist for two given component polymers (taken from Shenoy [36]).

n values of the component polymers are nearly equal, the blending shear rate does not have much significance, as the two components will be obviously compatible at the blending temperature determined by Equation 59. Shenoy [36] has discussed a number of case studies to illustrate the ability of the above two equations for determining compounding conditions and for selecting appropriate grades of component polymers once the compounding process parameters are fixed.

Degradation

During any type of polymer processing operation, the material is exposed to thermal and oxidative as well as shear degradation, causing molecular scission and hence, a reduction in molecular weight. The decrease or breakdown in molecular weight is generally characterized by changes in MFI of the polymer [37–40]. It is obvious that if this recycled material is to be processed to form a product, then the processing conditions will have to be set different from that for the virgin material in such cases. These conditions can be predicted if the entire rheogram for the recycled material is known. Shenoy et al. [41] have extended their idea of obtaining rheograms from MFI even for recycled material. Such processing rheograms can be superimposed on the master curve of the virgin polymer, as in Figure 2. In this manner, all curves proposed by Shenoy et al. [41] for virgin polymers can be used to obtain estimates of the rheogram for recycled material and thus provide guidelines for reprocessing.

CONCLUSION

The complexities involved in various polymer processing operations are certainly difficult to understand, and true predictions of the flow behavior of the polymer melt in such a situation is a formidable task. The novel approach suggested herein for getting estimates of various important processing parameters, such as the minimum pressure drop during cavity filling and the minimum clamping force to prevent mold opening during injection molding, the compaction force during compression molding, the pressure losses through complex-shaped dies during extrusion, the viscous heat dissipation, flow activation energy, and the reprocessing characteristics, gives a handy tool to the processor. It would, therefore, be an acceptable compromise between the very complex mathematical approaches needed to simulate various flow situations and the simple thumb-rule approach of the common processor.

In the present chapter, the major emphasis was on shear viscosity and its potential for use in processing based on the simple idea of utilizing MFI rather than any other measure of viscosity. However, it is known that the deformations in any polymer process are of both shear and elongational type. It is not just the shear viscosity that is important, but in certain situations the elasticity of the polymer plays a dominant role, whereas in other cases, it is the elongational viscosity that takes the frontline. Estimates of the variation of elasticity and elongational viscosity with shear rate then become necessary if calculations are to be made with respect to the processing parameters of relevance. Shenoy and Saini [42–46] have provided a method for obtaining unified curves of normal stress difference vs. shear rate, as well as elongational viscosity vs. shear rate. In processing operations, where these rheological parameters achieve significance, an approach similar to that followed in this chapter could be attempted in order to obtain estimates of processing parameters that predominantly get affected by changes in elasticity. This chapter would then serve as a foundation for further in-depth analysis in order to demonstrate the practical applications of rheology in polymer processing.

NOTATION

a   heat diffusion coefficient of the melt (cm^2/s) in Equation 14

$\bar{A}$ effective projected area of the molding in Equation 15

$\bar{B}$ numerical function dependent on n for different geometries appearing in Equations 15–17

C_p specific heat of polymer (Kcal/mole) in Equation 58

C_1 proportionality constant in Equations 22, 27, and 28, defined in Equation 23

C_2 proportionality constant in Equations 22, 27, and 28, defined in Equation 24

$\bar{C}$ proportionality constant in Equations 11 and 12, defined in Equation 14

E   activation energy for viscous flow (Kcal/mole $°K$) in Equation 3

E_{P_1} — activation energy for viscous flow of polymer 1 (Kcal/mole °K) in Equation 59

E_{P_2} — activation energy for viscous flow of polymer 2 (Kcal/mole °K) in Equation 59

f_1 — function of geometric parameters based on the shape of the die as given in Equations 31, 34, 37, 40, 43, 46, 49, 52, and 55

f_2 — function of fluid properties as given in Equations 32, 35, 38, 41, 44, 47, 50, 53, and 56

f_{cd} — compaction force required for squeezing operation of circular disc component (dynes) defined in Equations 18 and 20

F_{fs} — compaction force required for squeezing operation of flat strip component (dynes) defined in Equations 19 and 21

F_{min} — minimum clamping force to prevent mold opening as given by Equation 15

h_θ — initial gap between plates (cm) appearing in Equations 18–21

$\dot{h}$ — rate of plate separation with time (cm/s) in Equations 18–21

H_0 — half distance between calendering rolls (cm) in Equations 24, 25, and 26

H_c — characteristic geometric parameter specific to geometric shape (cm) in Equations 30, 33, 36, 39, 42, 45, 48, 51, and 54

K — consistency index of the power-law model (g/cm s^{2-n}) in Equations 6, 10, 11, 12, 18, 19, 23, 32, 35, 38, 41, 44, 47, 50, 53, and 56

K_1, K_2 — consistency index for polymers 1 and 2 (g/cm sec^{2-n}), respectively, in Equation 60

L — length of plate (cm) in Equations 19 and 21

L_1 — test load at condition 1 (kg) in Equation 1

L_2 — test load at condition 2 (kg) in Equation 1

$\bar{M}_n$ — number average molecular weight in Equation 8

$\bar{M}_w$ — weight average molecular weight in Equations 7 and 8

$\bar{M}_z$ — average molecular weight in Equations 7 and 8

$\bar{M}_{z+1}$ — (z + 1) average molecular weight in Equation 8

MFI — melt flow index (g/10 min) in Equations 4–7, 10–12, 18–22, 27–29, and 57

MFI_{B,T_c} — melt flow index at compounding temperature for polymer blend (g/10 min) in Equation 60

MFI_{L_1} — melt flow index at load condition 1 (g/10 min) in Equation 1

MFI_{L_2} — melt flow index at load condition 2 (g/10 min) in Equation 1

MFI_{P_1,T_1} — melt flow index at temperature condition 1 for polymer 1 (g/10 min) in Equation 59

MFI_{P_2,T_2} — melt flow index at temperature condition 2 for polymer 2 (g/10 min) in Equation 59

n — power-law index

n_1 — power-law index for polymer 1 in Equation 60

n_2 — power-law index for polymer 2 in Equation 60

N — Carreau model parameter in Equations 4 and 7

N_1 — number of sides of polygonal channel in Equations 52 and 55

P — pressure developed between calender rolls (dynes/cm²) in Equation 22

$P_{0,min}$ — minimum pressure for mold filling (dynes/cm²) in Equation 11

P_0 — pressure loss through the die (dynes/cm²) in Equation 29

ΔP — pressure loss through the die (dynes/cm²) in Equation 29

Q — flow rate of polymer melt (cm³/s) in Equations 11 and 29

$\bar{Q}$ — correlating factor for various molecular weight distribution expression as given in Equation 8

R — gas constant = 1.9874 Kcal/mol in Equations 3 and 59

R_0 — radius of calender rolls (cm) in Equations 24, 25, and 27

R_d — radius of circular disc mold cavity (cm) in Equations 11 and 12

R_{cd} — radius of circular disc plate (cm) in Equations 18 and 20

t_{res} — residence time (s) in Equation 58

T — polymer melt temperature (°K) in Equations 14 and 58

T_0 — freeze-off temperature in mold (°K) in Equation 14

T_1 ASTM test temperature (°K) in Equations 2 and 59

T_2 temperature of interest (°K) in Equations 2 and 59

T_c compounding temperature (°K) in Equation 59

T_g glass transition temperature (°K) of polymer

T_s standard reference temperature (°K) equal to $T_g + 50$ in Equation 2

U velocity at calender roll surface (cm/s) in Equations 24, 26, and 28

w width of plate (cm) in Equations 19 and 21

W width of calender roll (cm) in Equations 27 and 28

x original cavity thickness (cm) in Equation 9

x^* dimensionless parameter in Equations 24, 27, and 28, defined in Equation 25

x_{eff} effective remaining flow path after material of Δx thickness has frozen in mold cavity, defined in Equation 9

Greek Symbols

α Ellis model parameter in Equation 5

α_1 proportionality constant in Equation 57

β_1 power-index in Equation 57

$\dot{\gamma}$ shear rate (s⁻¹) in Equations 4, 6, 7, 10, and 57

$\dot{\gamma}_c$ compounding shear rate (s⁻¹) in Equation 60

Γ torque exerted on each calender roll (dyne-cm) in Equation 27

η apparent viscosity in Equations 4–7

η_0 zero shear viscosity in Equations 4, 5, and 7

θ mold temperature in Equation 14

λ time constant in Equations 4 and 7

λ_1 vertical taper factor in Equations 34, 40, and 43

λ_2 lateral taper factor in Equations 37 and 40

λ_R taper factor in Equations 49 and 55

λ^* dimensionless parameter in Equations 22 and 26–28

$\xi, \xi_H, \xi_W, \xi_{WH}$ shape factors in Equations 31, 34, 37, 40, and 43

ρ polymer melt density (g/cc) in Equation 58

τ shear stress (dynes/cm²) in Equations 5 and 10

$\tau_{1/2}$ special value of shear stress (dynes/cm²) when apparent viscosity is half the zero shear viscosity given in Equation 5

ϕ viscous heat dissipation (dynes/cm² s) in Equation 57

ϕ_P power input to calender roll (ergs) in Equation 28

REFERENCES

1. Shenoy, A. V., Chattopadhyay, S., and Nadkarni, V. M., "From Melt Flow Index to Rheogram," *Rheol. Acta*, Vol. 22, 1983, pp. 90–101.
2. Saini, D. R., and Shenoy, A. V., "Viscoelastic Properties of Linear Low Density Polyethylene," *Eur. Polym. J.*, Vol. 19, 1983, pp. 811–816.
3. Shenoy, A. V., Saini, D. R., and Nadkarni, V. M., "Rheograms of Cellulosic Polymers from Melt Flow Index," *J. Appl. Polym. Sci.*, Vol. 27, 1982, pp. 4399–4408.
4. Shenoy, A. V., Saini, D. R., and Nadkarni, V. M., "Rheology of Poly(vinyl chloride) Formulations from Melt Flow Index Measurements," *J. Vinyl Tech.*, Vol. 5, 1983, pp. 192–197.
5. Saini, D. R., and Shenoy, A. V., "Deformation Behavior of Poly(vinylidene fluoride)," *Ind. Eng. Chem. Prod. Res. Dev.*, Vol. 25, 1986, pp. 277–282.
6. Shenoy, A. V., Saini, D. R., and Nadkarni, V. M., "Rheograms for Engineering Thermoplastics from Melt Flow Index," *Rheol. Acta*, Vol. 22, 1983, pp. 209–222.
7. Shenoy, A. V., and Saini, D. R., "Melt Rheology of Liquid Crystalline Polymer," *Mol. Crys. Liq. Crys.*, Vol. 135, 1986, pp. 343–354.

8. Saini, D. R., and Shenoy, A. V., "Melt Rheology of Some Specialty Polymers," *J. Elast. Plastics*, Vol. 17, 1985, pp. 189–217.

9. Shenoy, A. V., Saini, D. R., and Nadkarni, V. M., "Rheograms of Filled Polymers from Melt Flow Index," *Polym. Composites*, Vol. 4, 1983, pp. 53–63.

10. Shenoy, A. V., Saini, D. R., and Nadkarni, V. M., "Rheology of Nylon 6 Containing Metal Halides," *J. Mat. Sci.*, Vol. 18, 1983, pp. 2149–2155.

11. Shenoy, A. V., Saini, D. R., and Nadkarni, V. M., "Melt Rheology of Polymer Blends from Melt Flow Index," *Int. J. Polym. Mat.*, Vol. 10, 1984, pp. 213–235.

12. Shenoy, A. V., and Saini, D. R., "Copolymer Melt Rheograms from Melt Flow Index," *Br. Polym. J.*, Vol. 17, 1985, pp. 314–322.

13. Saini, D. R., and Shenoy, A. V., "A New Method for the Determination of Flow Activation Energy of Polymer Melts," *J. Macromol. Sci.*, Vol. B22, 1983, pp. 437–449.

14. Shenoy, A. V., and Saini, D. R., "Rheological Models for Unified Curves for Simplified Design Calculations in Polymer Processing," *Rheol. Acta*, Vol. 23, 1984, pp. 368–377.

15. Smith, D. J., "The Correlation of Melt Index and Extrusion Coating Resin Performance," *TAPPI*, Vol. 60, 1977, pp. 131–133.

16. Borzenskii, F. J., "An Approach to the Use of Rheology in Post Reactor Processing," *Plast. Compounding*, Sept./Oct., 1978, pp. 25–28.

17. Shida, M., Shroff, R. N., and Cancio, L. V., "Correlation of Low Density Polyethylene Rheological Measurements with Optical and Processing Properties," *Polym. Eng. Sci.*, Vol. 17, 1977, pp. 769–774.

18. Boenig, H. V., *Polyolefins*, Chapter 8, Elsevier, Amsterdam, 1966, p. 262.

19. Busse, W. F., "Mechanical Structures in Polymer Melts I. Measurements of Melt Strength and Elasticity," *J. Polym. Sci.*, Vol. A-2, No. 5, 1967, pp. 1249–1259.

20. Dutta, A., "On Viscosity-Melt Flow Index Relationship," *Rheol. Acta*, Vol. 23, 1984, pp. 565–569.

21. Shenoy, A. V., and Saini, D. R., "Upgrading the Melt Flow Index to Rheogram Approach in the Low Shear Rate Region," *J. Appl. Polym. Sci.*, Vol. 29, 1984, pp. 1581–1593.

22. Van Krevelan, D. W., Goedhar, D. J., and Hoftijzer, P. J., "Correlations in the Molecular Weight Distribution of Polymers," *Polymer*, Vol. 18, 1977, pp. 750–751.

23. Saini, D. R., and Shenoy, A. V., "Simplified Calculations for Mould Filling During Non-Isothermal Flow of Polymer Melts," *Plast. Rubber Proc. Appl.*, Vol. 3, 1983, pp. 175–180.

24. Barrie, I. T., "An Application of Rheology to the Injection Moulding of Large-Area Articles," *Plastics and Polymers*, Vol. 38, 1970, pp. 47–51.

25. Shenoy, A. V., and Saini, D. R., "Compression Moulding of Ultra High Molecular Weight Polyethylene," *Plast. Rubber Proc. Appl.*, Vol. 5, 1985, pp. 313–317.

26. Ray, A., and Shenoy, A. V., "PVC Calendering: A Simplified Prediction Technique," *J. Appl. Polym. Sci.*, Vol. 30, 1985, pp. 1–18.

27. Vlachopoulos, J., and Hrymak, A. N., "Calendering Poly(vinyl chloride): Theory and Experiment," *Polym. Eng. Sci.*, Vol. 20, 1980, pp. 725–731.

28. Shenoy, A. V., and Saini, D. R., "Prediction of Pressure Losses Through Typical Die Shapes Based in a Simple Novel Approach," *Polym. Plast. Technol. Eng.*, Vol. 23, 1984, pp. 169–183.

29. Lenk, R. S., "Pressure Drop Through Tapered Dies," *J. Appl. Polym. Sci.*, Vol. 22, 1978, pp. 1775–1779.

30. Lenk, R. S., and Frenkel, R. A., "Pressure Drop Through Tapered Wide-Slit Dies—A Revised Version," *J. Appl. Polym. Sci.*, Vol. 26, 1981, pp. 2801–2804.

31. Lenk, R. S., "Flow in Elliptical Channels," *J. Appl. Polym. Sci.*, Vol. 26, 1981, pp. 3171–3173.

32. Frenkel, R. A., and Lenk, R. A., "Flow Through Rectangular Polygonal Channels," *J. Appl. Polym. Sci.*, Vol. 26, 1981, pp. 3939–3944.

33. White, J. L., and Huang, D., "Extrudate Swell and Extrusion Pressure Loss of Polymer Melts Flowing Through Rectangular and Trapezoidal Dies," *Polym. Eng. Sci.*, Vol. 21, 1981, pp. 1101–1107.

34. Shenoy, A. V., and Saini, D. R., "A Simplistic Route to Viscous Heat Estimations in Polymer Processing," *Polym. Plast. Technol. Eng.*, Vol. 23, 1984, pp. 34–68.

35. Cox, H. W., and Macosko, C. W., "Viscous Dissipation in Die Flows," *AIChE J.*, Vol. 20, 1974, pp. 785–795.
36. Shenoy, A. V., "Estimation of Compounding Conditions and Grade Selections in the Preparation of Thermoplastic Melt Blends," *Polym. Plast. Technol. Eng.*, Vol. 24, 1985, pp. 27–41.
37. Mitterhofer, F., "Processing Stability of Polyolefins," *Polym. Eng. Sci.*, Vol. 20, 1980, pp. 692–695.
38. Rokudai, M., Mihara, S., and Fujiki, T., "Influence of Shear History in the Rheological Properties and Processibility of Branched Polymers. II Optical Properties of Low Density Polyethylene Blown Films," *J. Appl. Polym. Sci.*, Vol. 23, 1979, pp. 3289–3294.
39. Rideal, G. R., and Padget, J. C., "The Thermal-Mechanical Degradation of High Density Polyethylene," *J. Polym. Sci. Symp.*, No. 57, 1976, pp. 1–15.
40. Cuspor, I., and Toth, T., "Study of the Reprocessing of Polypropylene," *Int. Polym. Sci. Technol.*, Vol. 7, 1980, pp. T16–T19.
41. Shenoy, A. V., Saini, D. R., and Nadkarni, V. M., "Estimation of the Melt Rheology of Polymer Waste from Melt Flow Index," *Polymer*, Vol. 24, 1983, pp. 722–728.
42. Shenoy, A. V., and Saini, D. R., "An Approach to the Estimation of Polymer Melt Elasticity," *Rheol. Acta*, Vol. 23, 1984, pp. 608–616.
43. Shenoy, A. V., and Saini, D. R., "A Simplified Approach to the Prediction of Primary Normal Stress Differences in Polymer Melts," *Chem. Eng. Commun.*, Vol. 28, 1984, pp. 1–27.
44. Shenoy, A. V., and Saini, D. R., "Estimation of Melt Elasticity of Degraded Polymer from Melt Flow Index," *Polym. Degrad. Stability*, Vol. 11, 1985, pp. 297–307.
45. Shenoy, A. V., and Saini, D. R., "Re-Analysis of Extensional Flow Data of Polymer Melts," *Die Ange. Makro. Chemie*, Vol. 137, 1985, pp. 77–81.
46. Shenoy, A. V., and Saini, D. R., "A New Shift Factor for Coalescing Dynamic Viscoelastic Data of Polymer Melts, "*Acta Polymerica*, Vol, 37, 1986, pp. 504–507.

CHAPTER 32

RHEOLOGICAL CHARACTERIZATION AND PROCESSABILITY TESTING

Nicholas P. Cheremisinoff

Exxon Chemical Co.
Linden, New Jersey, USA

CONTENTS

INTRODUCTION, 991

INTRODUCTION

This chapter provides an overview of industrial viscometric techniques and laboratory testing methods for characterizing the rheological and processing properties of non-Newtonian materials. Discussions are largely aimed at polymer melt characterization and polymer processing applications. It should be noted, however, that many unit processing operations overlap between industries and therefore, many of the techniques described are adaptable to other applications such as food processing, coatings and paint technology, and ink technology.

DEVELOPMENT OF CONSTITUTIVE EQUATIONS AND FLUID CHARACTERIZATION

Rheology is a subject that addresses the deformation of fluid and fluid-like materials. When surface forces, or stresses, are applied to a fluid body, that body deforms or flows. The reactive behavior can be mathematically described by means of a set of constitutive equations. A constitutive equation defines the cause and effect relationships in terms of the properties or characteristics of the material. To develop such relationships, balance equations must be derived. A balance equation is a mathematical statement of the universal laws of conservation of mass, energy, and momentum that are specific to the system of interest. By way of a simple example found in many fluid dynamic textbooks (see [1, 2]), consider a shearing force applied to a rectangular body of incompressible fluid as illustrated in Figure 1. For steady-state, isothermal flow conditions, we may write the following mass balance (continuity equation) and momentum balance (equation of motion):

Mass Balance

$$\frac{d}{dx} V_x = 0 = \frac{dV_x}{dx} \tag{1a}$$

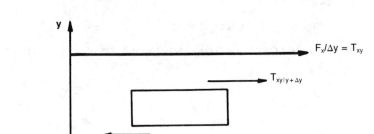

Figure 1. Fluid body subjected to constant force.

and if the body undergoes deformation:

$$V_x \neq f(x) \tag{1b}$$

Momentum Balance

$$-\frac{d\tau_{xy}}{dy} = 0 \tag{2}$$

and $\tau_{xy} = C$ for any body, where C is the applied stress.

A limiting case is that of a *Hookean elastic solid*. The constitutive equation for this system is:

$$\tau_{xy} = G\dot{\gamma}_{xy} \tag{3}$$

where $\dot{\gamma} = C/G$, and G is the shear modulus. The coordinate system for this model is defined in Figure 2.

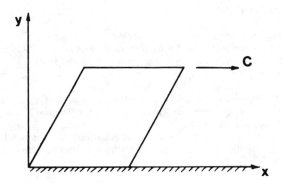

Figure 2. Body undergoing deformation.

The above examples are representations of a fluid's behavior when it is subjected to a force. A material's ability to undergo changes in shape or movement can be characterized by measuring its resistance to undergo deformation. The quantity that provides a measure of deformation is the shear strain γ_{xy}. When $G = G(\gamma_{xy})$, a solid body is non-Hookean, and is described as being elastic. The shear modulus G is a rheological constant characterizing the material. Similarly, $G(\gamma_{xy})$ is a material rheological function.

For a Newtonian fluid, the constitutive equation is Newton's law of viscosity:

$$\tau_{xy} = -\mu \frac{dV_x}{dy} = -\mu \frac{d\gamma_{xy}}{dt} = -\mu \dot{\gamma}_{xy} \tag{4}$$

The system is defined as shown in Figure 3, where:

$$\frac{dV_x}{dy} = -C/\mu \tag{5}$$

Integrating this expression gives:

$$V_x(y) = -\frac{C}{\mu} y + C_1 \tag{6a}$$

where $C_1 = 0$, and hence:

$$V_x(y) = -\frac{C}{\mu} y \tag{6b}$$

or $\quad V = -\frac{C}{\mu} \cdot H \tag{6c}$

and $\quad C = -\left(\frac{V}{H}\right)\mu = \tau_{xy} = -\mu\dot{\gamma} \tag{7}$

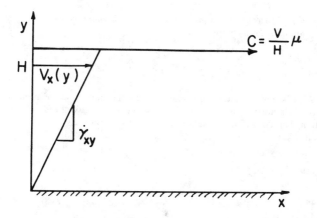

Figure 3. Coordinate system for developing constitutive equation for generalized Newtonian fluid.

The variables in the above relationships and Figure 3 are:

μ = Newtonian viscosity (i.e., resistance to flow)

$\dot{\gamma}_{xy}$ = shear rate (i.e., measure of flow)

fv = material rheological constant

$fu(\dot{\gamma})$ = material rheological function

Constitutive equations can be generalized into two categories: linear and non-linear. For a Newtonian material, Equation 4 is the governing expression, and it is noted that $\mu \neq \mu(\dot{\gamma})$. In this case, the resistance to deformation (viscosity) depends only on those property characteristics of the material that effect the intermolecular forces of the fluid. These property characteristics include the chemical structures of the fluid, temperature, and pressure. From thermodynamic principles, the viscosity of a Newtonian fluid can be approximately defined by:

$$\mu(T, P) = \mu_0 \exp\left\{\frac{\Delta E}{R}\left(\frac{T - T_0}{T_0 T}\right)\right\} \exp\left\{\beta(P - P_0)\right\} \qquad (8)$$

where   T and P = absolute temperature and pressure
          ΔE = flow activation energy
          β = viscosity pressure coefficient
          R = universal gas-law constant.

In contrast, a non-linear form of the constitutive equation is:

$$\tau = f(mf_i \cdots mf_{nj}\dot{\gamma}) \qquad (9)$$

Non-Newtonian materials are described by non-linear constitutive equations, where the most general statement is:

$$\tau = -\eta(\dot{\gamma}) \cdot \dot{\gamma} \qquad (10)$$

Equation 10 is referred to as the *Generalized Newtonian Fluid equation*, where η is a scalar quantity. Restating Equation 4 for an incompressible fluid:

$$\tau_{xy} = -\frac{\mu}{\rho}\frac{d(V_x\rho)}{dy} \qquad (11)$$

The quantity $V_x\rho$ is a momentum concentration, since it has units of momentum per unit volume. Since $d(V_x\rho)/dy$ is a gradient, we may regard this quantity as a flux of the x-directed momentum in the y-direction. This constitutive equation is analogous to Fourier's law of heat conduction and Fick's law of diffusion.

Fourier's Law

$$q/A = -k\frac{d\theta}{dy} \qquad (12a)$$

$$q/A = \frac{-k}{C_p\rho}\frac{d(\theta C_p\rho)}{dy} = -\alpha\frac{d(\theta C_p\rho)}{dy} \qquad (12b)$$

Fick's Law

$$\frac{N_A}{A} = -D_{AB}\frac{dC_A}{dy} \tag{13}$$

where   A = area
q = heat flow
θ = temperature
k = thermal conductivity
α = thermal diffusivity
C_p = specific heat
C_A = concentration of component A
D_{AB} = binary molecular diffusivity for the system A + B.

Equation 12b is Fourier's law for an incompressible fluid, and the quantities $\theta C_p\rho$, $d(\theta C_p\rho)/dy$ are the volumetric thermal concentration and thermal concentration gradient, respectively. Fick's law (Equation 13) is stated for steady-state, equimolal counterdiffusion of components A and B. The analogies between Equations 4, 12 and 13 are striking: μ/ρ, α, and D_{AB} all have the same primary units of length^2/temperature.

The quantity μ/ρ can be thought of as momentum diffusivity. Standard texts on transport phenomenon (see [3]) conventionally term μ/ρ the kinematic viscosity.

Equation 4 is a linear expression, and a plot of τ_{xy} vs. $\dot{\gamma}$ results in a straight line passing through the origin and having slope μ.

Fluid materials that display non-linear behavior through the origin at a given temperature and pressure are non-Newtonian (see Figure 4A). The broad classifications of non-Newtonian fluids are time-independent fluids, time-dependent fluids, and viscoelastic fluids. The first category comprises fluids for which the shear rate at any point is a function of only the instantaneous shear stress. In contrast, time-dependent fluids are those for which shear rate depends on both the magnitude and duration of shear. Some fluids in this second class also show a relationship between shear rate and the time lapse between consecutive applications of shear stress. Less common viscoelastic fluids display the behavior of partial elastic recovery upon the removal of a deforming shear stress.

Time-dependent non-Newtonian fluids can exhibit the property of a yield stress. The yield stress, τ_y, is a minimum stress value that must be exceeded in order for deformation to occur; i.e., when $\tau_{xy} < \tau_y$ the fluid's internal structure remains intact, and when $\tau_{xy} > \tau_y$, shearing movement occurs.

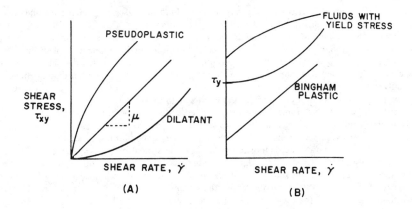

Figure 4. Flow curves for non-Newtonian, time-independent fluids.

Flow curves for these type materials are illustrated in Figure 4B. An idealistic fluid is the Bingham plastic, which models non-Newtonian behavior via a linear constitutive equation.

The rheological flow curve in Figure 4B for this fluid is:

$$\mu_a = \eta + \tau_y/\dot{\gamma} \tag{14}$$

where μ_a is the fluid's *apparent viscosity* and is analogous with the Newtonian apparent viscosity as restated from Equation 4:

$$\mu_a = \tau_{xy}/\dot{\gamma} \tag{15}$$

The Bingham plastic constitutive equation contains a yield stress τ_y and a term η referred to as the *plastic viscosity*. Equation 14 states that the apparent viscosity decreases with increasing shear rate. In practical terms, this means that a value of the apparent viscosity can only be related as a flow property with a corresponding shear rate. Although the Bingham plastic fluid itself is idealistic, it can be applied to modeling a portion of a non-Newtonian's flow curve. Many materials show only small departure from exact Bingham plasticity, and therefore can be approximately described by Equation 14.

A large variety of industrial fluid-like materials can be described as being *pseudoplastic* in nature. The flow curve is illustrated in Figure 4A. Examining this curve, note that it is characterized by linearity at very low and very high shear rates. The slope of the linear region of the curve at the high shear rate range is referred to as the *viscosity at infinite shear* (μ_∞), whereas the slope in the linear portion near the origin is the *viscosity at zero shear rate* (μ_0). A logarithmic plot of τ_{xy} vs. $\dot{\gamma}$ is found to be linear over a relatively wide shear rate range and hence, may be described by a power law expression (known as the Ostwald-de Waele model):

$$\tau_{xy} = K\dot{\gamma}^n \tag{16}$$

The slope n and intercept K are referred to as the flow behavior index (or pseudoplasticity index) and consistency index, respectively. The power law exponent ranges from unity to zero with increasing plasticity (i.e., at n = 1, the expression reduces to the Newtonian constitutive equation). The value of the consistency index is obtained from the intercept on the τ_{xy} axis and hence, represents the viscosity at unit shear rate. As shown later for a variety of polymers, K is very sensitive to temperature, whereas n is much less sensitive. By analogy to Newton's law, the apparent viscosity of a power law fluid is:

$$\mu_a = K\dot{\gamma}^{n-1} \tag{17}$$

Since n < 1, the apparent viscosity of a pseudoplastic fluid decreases with increasing shear rate, and hence, these materials are often referred to as *shear-thinning*.

Another class of time-independent fluids are *dilatant* materials. Volumetric dilatancy refers to the phenomenon whereby an increase in the total fluid volume under application of shear occurs. Rheological dilatancy refers to an increase in apparent viscosity with increasing shear rate. The flow curve is illustrated in Figure 4A. As in the case of a pseudoplastic fluid, a dilatant material is usually characterized by zero yield stress. Hence, the power law model may also be used to describe this fluid behavior, but with n-values greater than unity.

Time-dependent non-Newtonian fluids are classified as thixotropic and rheopectic. Thixotropic fluids display a reversible decrease in shear stress with time at a constant shear rate and temperature. The shear stress of such a material usually approaches some limiting value. Both thixotropic and rheopectic fluids show a characteristic hysteresis, as illustrated by the flow curves in Figure 5. The flow curves are constructed from data generated by a single experiment, in which the shear rate is steadily increased from zero to some maximum value and then immediately decreased toward zero. The arrows on the curves denote the chronological progress of the experiment. An interesting complexity of these materials is that the hysteresis is time history dependent. In other words, changing the rate at which $\dot{\gamma}$ is increased or decreased in the experiment alters the hysteresis loop. For this reason, generalized approaches to defining an index of thixotropy have not met with much success.

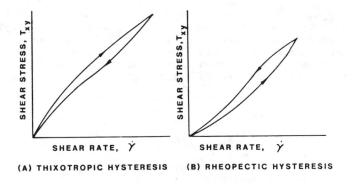

Figure 5. Hysteresis loops for time-dependent fluids.

Rheopectic fluids are sometimes referred to as antithixotropic fluids because they exhibit a reversible increase in shear stress over time at a constant rate of shear under isothermal conditions. The location of the hysteresis loop shown in Figure 5B is also dependent on the material's time history, including the rate at which $\dot{\gamma}$ is changed.

An additional classification of non-Newtonians is viscoelastic fluids, which are materials exhibiting both viscous and elastic properties. For purely Hookean elastic solids the stress corresponding to a given strain is time-independent, but with viscoelastic materials, the stress dissipates over time. Viscoelastic fluids undergo deformation when subjected to stress; however, part of their deformation is gradually recovered when the stress is removed. These materials are sometimes described as fluids that have memory. Viscoelasticity is frequently observed in the processing of various polymers and plastics. For example, in the production of synthetic fibers such as nylon for ultrafine cable, material is extruded through a die consisting of fine perforations. In these examples, the cross section of the fiber or cable may be considerably larger than that of the perforation through which it was extruded. This behavior is a result of the partial elastic recovery of the material.

In this chapter, an overview of techniques aimed at relating rheological characteristics observed from laboratory studies to commercial processing of polymers is presented. The materials largely discussed are polymer melts and solutions. These materials show the properties of pseudoplasticity, exhibit normal forces in excess of hydrostatic pressure in simple shear flow, and often display viscoelastic behavior (i.e., stress relaxation, creep recovery, and stress overshoot). It should be noted that many polymers show all three characteristics. Engineering practices have not yet advanced to the point where we can develop a single generalized constitutive equation to describe the entire range of rheological features. Clearly, the more features that are incorporated into a constitutive equation, the more complex it becomes and hence, the more difficult it is to apply its use in a balance expression needed to address a problem in fluid mechanics.

The use and interpretation of rheological flow curves are heavily relied upon to understand and project the processing characteristics of polymers and other non-Newtonian materials. It should be noted that the flow curves for many types of polymers display a Newtonian plateau or region, then a transition to non-Newtonian, and finally a power law region. The upper limit of shear rate of the Newtonian plateau depends on the polymer's molecular weight and temperature. This upper limit for many polymers is typically 10^{-2} sec^{-1} (Nylon and PET are exceptions). This limit decreases with molecular weight and molecular weight distribution, as well as decreasing temperature. The onset of the transition region between the Newtonian plateau and power law can be related through the dimensionless Debora number:

$$D_b = \lambda/\text{temp} = \lambda\dot{\gamma} \tag{18}$$

where λ is the material's relaxation time.

The transition region is usually quite distinct for monodispersed polymeric melts, and broad for polydisperse melts. The magnitude of viscosity for each of the regions depends on both material and state variables. Another characteristic of pseudoplastic flow curves to keep in mind is that the power law index n in fact is not an absolute constant for a specific material. For many materials, however, it often reaches some constant value for a reasonably wide range of conditions.

The constitutive equation for a power-law fluid was stated in Equation 17, where apparent viscosity depends on two parameters, K and n. The consistency index K has units of $(N-s^n/m^2)$. K is temperature-sensitive and is found to follow the Arrhenius relationship:

$$K = K_0 \exp\left\{\frac{\Delta E}{R_G}\left(\frac{1}{T} - \frac{1}{T_0}\right)\right\} \tag{19}$$

where ΔE = activation energy of flow per mole
R_G = gas constant per mole
T, T_0 = absolute and reference temperatures
K_0 = constant, characteristic of the material

For relatively small temperature ranges, Equation 19 can be approximated by:

$$K = K_0 \exp[-a(T - T_0)] \tag{20}$$

It should be noted that from thermodynamic considerations, K also depends exponentially on pressure.

The apparent viscosity of a power law fluid is a function of all the velocity gradients in non-simple shearing flows. However, from a practical standpoint, most laboratory viscometric techniques measure viscosity in only one velocity gradient.

An important point to realize is that the power law expression is an empirical model, and should therefore not be used for extrapolation of viscosity data. It does not level off to a Newtonian plateau, but instead keeps on increasing.

The so-called Carreau model provides a constitutive expression which in fact does level off to a limiting viscosity η_0, which is either measured or estimated. It is however, a more complex equation having additional model parameters:

$$\frac{\eta(\dot\gamma) - \eta_\infty}{\eta_0 - \eta_\infty} = [1 + (\lambda\dot\gamma)^2]^{(n-1)/2} \tag{21}$$

η_∞ is the solvent viscosity for solutions. For polymer melts it is common practice for $\eta_\infty = 0$. Note that we have changed the notation for apparent viscosity to the more conventional symbol η.

Another model which also incorporates the Newtonian plateau viscosity (η_0) is the Ellis model:

$$\frac{\eta}{\eta(\tau)} = 1 + (\tau/\tau_{1/2})^{\alpha-1} \tag{22}$$

where $\eta_{\tau=\tau_{1/2}} = \eta_0/2 \tag{23}$

The exponent $(\alpha - 1)$ is the slope obtained from a plot of $((\eta_0/\eta) - 1)$ vs. $\log(\tau/\tau_{1/2})$.

The Ellis model can also be expressed as:

$$\tau_{xy} = \frac{1}{A + B\tau_{xy}^{\alpha-1}}\dot\gamma \tag{24}$$

where coefficients A and B have units of $L^2\tau^{-1}F^{-1}$ and $L^{2\alpha}\tau^{-1}F^{-\alpha}$, respectively. Term α is dimensionless. Figure 6 provides a comparison of the power law and Ellis models for ABS at two temperatures. Note that the power law model provides an adequate fit of the data for a large portion of the shear rate range, but departs from the measured values at the low shear rates.

Later in this chapter, the principles used in obtaining viscosity measurements are described. The instruments used are viscometers, which are devices that enable determination of the relationships

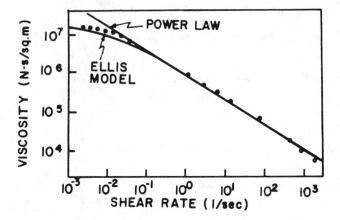

Figure 6. Comparison of power law and Ellis model for ABS polymer melt (data from Cox and Mocosko (4)).

between τ_{xy} and $\dot{\gamma}$. Viscoelastic materials require measurement of both normal and shearing stresses as functions of shear rate, and consequently require more sophisticated measurement techniques. We must first consider a general problem of fluid mechanics which will help to understand the operational principles of standard viscometers.

Consider the classic problem of fluid rod climbing in Couette flow, as illustrated in Figure 7. The mass balance for this system is:

$$\partial V_\theta / \partial \theta = 0 \tag{25}$$

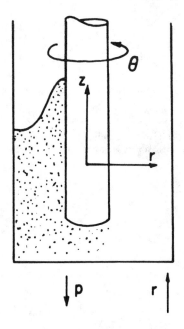

Figure 7. Couette flow system.

and for the θ-momentum:

$$-\frac{1}{r^2}\frac{\partial}{\partial r}(r^2\tau_{r\theta}) = 0 \tag{26}$$

For a generalized Newtonian fluid we may write:

$$\tau_{r\theta} = -\eta(\dot{\gamma}_{r\theta}) \cdot \dot{\gamma}_{r\theta}$$

$$\dot{\gamma}_{r\theta} = r\frac{d}{dr}\left(\frac{V_\theta}{r}\right) \tag{27}$$

Combining the above expressions gives:

$$\frac{1}{r^2}\frac{d}{dr}\left[r^3 \cdot \eta \cdot \frac{d}{dr}\left(\frac{V_\theta}{r}\right)\right] = 0 \tag{28}$$

This expression can be solved by specifying $(\dot{\gamma}_{r\theta})$. Additionally, a torque balance on the rotating rod is:

$$T = R_iH2\pi R_i\tau_{r\theta}|_{r=R_i} \tag{29}$$

The above set of constitutive equations describes a generalized Newtonian fluid, showing that only a torque T is needed in order to sustain Couette-type flow. In contrast, a non-Newtonian such as polymer melt flowing in Couette flow shows $p = p(r)$. That is, a non-zero dP/dr term exists. Consequently, the above analysis does not adequately relate to non-Newtonian behavior.

To understand what happens with a polymer melt or similar material in this type of flow, we must examine the r-component momentum equation and keep track of all the stress terms that can be non-zero. This results in:

$$-\rho\frac{V_\theta^2}{r} = -\frac{dP}{dr} - \frac{1}{r}\frac{d}{dr}(r\tau_{rr}) + \frac{\tau_{\theta\theta}}{r} \tag{30}$$

In creeping Couette flows, it is observed that:

$$\rho\frac{V_\theta^2}{r} \simeq (10^{-1} \sim 10^{-2})\frac{dP}{dr}$$

This condition would result in a depression of the liquid level nearest the rod and not a climbing effect. We can therefore neglect this term (which is the centrifugal force). Hence, the model simplifies to:

$$\frac{dP}{dr} = -\frac{1}{r}\left(r\frac{d}{dr}\tau_{rr} + \tau_{rr}\right) + \frac{\tau_{\theta\theta}}{r}$$

$$\frac{d}{dr}(P + \tau_{rr}) = \frac{\tau_{\theta\theta} - \tau_{rr}}{r}$$

And solving:

$$(P + \tau_{rr})|_{R_o} - (P + \tau_{rr})|_{R_i} = \int_{R_i}^{R_o}\left(\frac{\tau_{\theta\theta} - \tau_{rr}}{r}\right)dr \tag{31}$$

Experimentally it is observed that the integral term is less than zero, and hence:

$$\tau_{\theta\theta} - \tau_{rr} < 0 \tag{32}$$

The analysis reduces to attempting to define which stress component $\tau_{r\theta}$ and $(\tau_{\theta\theta} - \tau_{rr})$ contributes to shearing Couette flow.

An appropriate rheological constitutive equation must be introduced in order to make this assessment. One approach is to use the Criminale-Ericksen-Filby [5] equation which is general for steady shearing flows with one gradient.

$$\tau = -\eta(\dot\gamma) \cdot \dot\gamma - \left[\frac{1}{2}\Psi_1(\dot\gamma) + \Psi_2(\dot\gamma)\right]\dot\gamma \cdot \dot\gamma + \frac{1}{2}\Psi_1\frac{\mathscr{D}\dot\gamma}{\mathscr{D}t} \tag{33}$$

where $\mathscr{D}\dot\gamma/\mathscr{D}t$ is the corotational time derivative defined as:

$$\frac{\mathscr{D}\dot\gamma}{\mathscr{D}t} = \frac{D\dot\gamma}{Dt} + \frac{1}{2}[\omega \cdot \dot\gamma - \dot\gamma \cdot \omega] \tag{34}$$

and ω = vorticity tensor
    $\eta(\dot\gamma)$ = viscosity function
    $\Psi_1(\dot\gamma)$ = first normal stress difference coefficient function
    $\Psi_2(\dot\gamma)$ = second normal stress difference coefficient function

Applying the condition of Couette flow:

$$\dot\gamma = \begin{vmatrix} 0 & \dot\gamma_{\theta r} & 0 \\ \dot\gamma_{r\theta} & 0 & 0 \\ 0 & 0 & 0 \end{vmatrix}$$

Equation 33 can be solved to give:

$$\tau_{r\theta} = -\eta(\dot\gamma) \cdot \dot\gamma_{\theta r}$$

$$\tau_{\theta\theta} - \tau_{rr} = -\Psi_1(\dot\gamma) - \dot\gamma_{\theta r}^2 \tag{35}$$

$$\tau_{rr} - \tau_{zz} = -\Psi_2(\dot\gamma) \cdot \dot\gamma_{\theta r}^2$$

The fluid modeled in this approach exhibits shear as well as normal stresses over and above P_{hyd} in Couette flow. Furthermore, we may note that:

$$\dot\gamma = \begin{vmatrix} 0 & \dot\gamma_{12} & 0 \\ \dot\gamma_{12} & 0 & 0 \\ 0 & 0 & 0 \end{vmatrix}$$

and hence

$$\tau_{12} = -\eta \cdot \dot\gamma_{12}$$

$$\tau_{11} - \tau_{12} = -\Psi_1 \cdot \dot\gamma_{12}^2 \tag{36}$$

$$\tau_{22} - \tau_{33} = -\Psi_2 \cdot \dot\gamma_{12}^2$$

It can be concluded that the proper application of rheometry must be directed at evaluating all three functions: η, Ψ_1 and Ψ_2. From the standpoint of expediency, as is often the case in industrial environments, the tools of rheology (i.e., viscometers) do not always measure all the appropriate

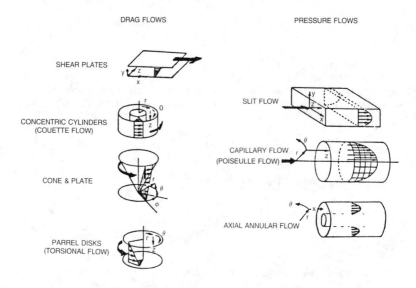

DRAG FLOWS   PRESSURE FLOWS

SHEAR PLATES

CONCENTRIC CYLINDERS
(COUETTE FLOW)

SLIT FLOW

CONE & PLATE

CAPILLARY FLOW
(POISEULLE FLOW)

PARREL DISKS
(TORSIONAL FLOW)

AXIAL ANNULAR FLOW

Figure 8. Common shear flow geometries.

functions. Consequently, many viscometers are applied in a very limited fashion as crude quality control devices and generally do not provide suitable scientific or engineering data applicable to projecting end-use material processability. In later discussions, some of these shortcomings are noted. For now, Figure 8 provides a summary of the types of shear flow geometries non-Newtonian fluids can be subjected to in order to evaluate the appropriate rheological functions.

INDUSTRIAL RHEOMETERS

There are a variety of viscometers used for characterizing non-Newtonian materials. These devices fall into two general categories: scientific instruments designed to make basic measurement of rheological properties, and instruments that are primarily employed for industrial quality-control purposes. The most widely used techniques/instruments in industrial labs are described in this subsection, for polymer characterization as well as other materials.

The capillary tube viscometer is one of the simplest and most widely used instruments for rheological characterization. Before describing its operation, we first consider the problem of capillary flow. Consider the system in Figure 9, where a fluid is forced at a steady rate from a large reservoir into a small diameter capillary tube of length L. Assume steady, isothermal flow of an incompressible fluid and $L/R \gg 1$. The coordinate system is defined along the r, θ, and z axes. Ignoring entrance and exit losses in the capillary tube:

$$V_\theta = 0; \quad V_r = 0$$
$$V_z \neq 0; \quad V_z \neq f(\theta) \quad \text{(axisymmetry)} \tag{37}$$

Writing the continuity equation:

$$\frac{\partial P}{\partial t} + \frac{1}{r}\frac{\partial}{\partial r}(\rho r V_r) + \frac{1}{r}\frac{\partial}{\partial \theta}(\rho V_\theta) + \frac{\partial}{\partial z}(\rho V_z) = 0 \tag{38}$$

where density ρ is assumed to be constant.

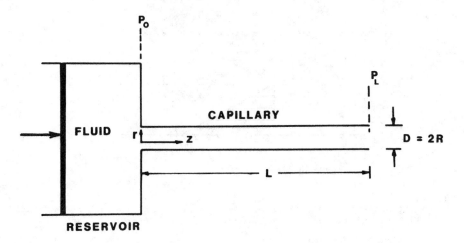

Figure 9. Capillary tube flow.

At steady-state $\partial P/\partial t = 0$, and since $V_r = 0$ and $V_\theta = 0$, the second and third terms on the left-hand side of Equation 38 drop out as well, leaving:

$$\frac{dV_z}{dz} = 0 \tag{39}$$

The momentum equation for the z-component is:

$$\rho\left[\frac{\partial V_z}{\partial t} + V_r\frac{\partial V_z}{\partial r} + \frac{V_\theta}{r}\frac{\partial V_z}{\partial \theta} + V_z\frac{\partial V_z}{\partial z}\right] = -\frac{\partial P}{\partial z} - \left(\frac{1}{r}\frac{\partial}{\partial r}(r\tau_{rz}) + \frac{1}{r}\frac{\partial \tau_{\theta z}}{\partial \theta} + \frac{\partial \tau_{zz}}{\partial z}\right) + \rho g_z \tag{40}$$

From the constraints of the system imposed, the z-component momentum equation reduces to:

$$\frac{dP}{dz} = -\frac{1}{r}\frac{d}{dr}(r\tau_{rz}) \tag{41}$$

Both sides of this expression are a function of r (i.e., $f(r)$) and both sides are constant. We can therefore assume that $dP/dz \simeq \Delta P/L$ (note that $dP/dz < 0$), and can therefore integrate Equation 41.

$$r\tau_{zz} = \frac{\Delta P}{L}r^2 + C_1$$

$$\tau_{rz} = -\frac{\Delta P}{L}r + C_1/r \tag{42}$$

At $r = 0$, $\tau_{zr} \neq \infty$, therefore $C_1 = 0$, and hence:

$$\tau_{zr} = -(\Delta P/2L)r \tag{43}$$

Equation 43 describes the shear stress profile for any incompressible fluid, and the profile across the capillary tube will have the form shown in Figure 10.

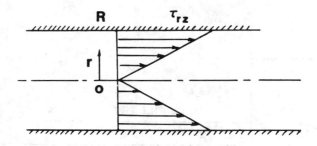

Figure 10. Shear stress profile in tube flow.

Now, if the fluid's rheological properties follow that of a power law constitutive equation, i.e., $\tau = -K|\dot{\gamma}|^{n-1}\dot{\gamma}$, where we note that $\tau = \tau_{zr}$ and $\dot{\gamma} = dV_z/dr$, and K and n are constants, then:

$$-K\left|\frac{dV_z}{dr}\right|^{n-1} \cdot \frac{dV_z}{dr} = -\left(\frac{\Delta P}{2L}\right)r \tag{44}$$

Note that $|(dV_z)/dr| = -(dV_z/dr)$, since $dV_z/dr < 0$.
Integrating this expression and invoking the "no-slip" at the wall condition (i.e., $V_z(r = R) = 0$).

$$V_z(r) = \left(\frac{nR}{n+1}\right)\left[\frac{\Delta PR}{2KL}\right]^{1/n}[1 - (r/R)^{(n+1)/n}] \tag{45}$$

Equation 45 is the velocity profile of a power-law fluid in tube flow.
For a Newtonian fluid (i.e., $n = 1$, $K = \mu$) the velocity profile of Equation 45 reduces to the parabolic velocity profile expression:

$$V_z(r) = \frac{\Delta PR^2}{4\mu L}[1 - (r/R)^2] \tag{46}$$

The theoretical velocity profiles computed from Equation 45 have the shapes shown in Figure 11. For $n = 1$, the parabolic shape (Newtonian, i.e., Equation 46); for $n > 1$, a dilatant fluid; for $n < 1$, a pseudoplastic fluid. For polymer melts and solutions $n < 1$, and hence, velocity profiles are typi-

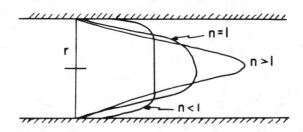

Figure 11. Velocity profiles generated by Equation 9: $n = 1$ Newtonian fluid; $n \gg 1$ dilatant fluid; $n \gg 1$ pseudoplastic fluid.

cally "plug-like." This means that there are very high velocity gradients in the vicinity of the tube wall, as shown in Figure 11.

The volumetric flow rate of the fluid through the tube is:

$$Q = 2\pi \int_0^R V_z(r) r \, dr \tag{47}$$

Substituting in the velocity profile expression (Equation 45) and integrating:

$$Q = \frac{\pi n R^3}{3n + 1} \left[\frac{R \, \Delta P}{2KL} \right]^{1/2} \tag{48}$$

Equation 48 can be written in a linear form as:

$$\log Q = \log \left(\frac{n\pi R^3}{3n + 1} \right) + \frac{1}{n} \log \left(\frac{R}{2KL} \right) + \frac{1}{n} \log \Delta P \tag{49}$$

Note that the first two sets of expressions on the right-hand side are constant. Hence, $Q = f(\Delta P)$, and a logarithmic plot of Q vs. P results in a straight line. Flow data for real pseudoplastic materials tend to be non-linear, as shown in Figure 12.

Orienting the capillary tube so that the flow is vertically downward, a force balance gives:

$$\frac{\pi D^2}{4} \Delta P = \pi D L \tau_w$$

or $\quad (\tau_{rx})_{r=R} = \tau_w = \dfrac{D \, \Delta P}{4L} \tag{50}$

Consider the flow in a slice of fluid to constitute an annulus between r and r + dr:

$$dQ = V 2\pi r \, dr$$

where V is the linear velocity at r. Hence:

$$Q = \pi \int_0^R V 2r \, dr = \pi \int_0^{R^2} V d(r^2)$$

Using no-slip (V = 0, r = R), the expression becomes:

$$\frac{Q}{\pi R^3} = \frac{8Q}{\pi D^3} = \frac{1}{\tau_w^3} \int_0^{\tau_w} \tau_{rx}^2 f(\tau_{rx}) \, d\tau_{rx} \tag{51}$$

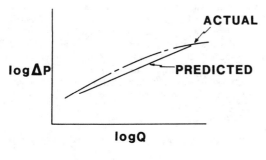

Figure 12. Comparison of actual to theoretical flow curve prediction.

where $f(\tau_{rx}) = -dV/dr$. By appropriate manipulation and replacing τ_w with $D \, \Delta P/4L$, the Rabino-witsch-Mooney equation of shear rate at the tube wall for steady, laminar flow of a time-independent fluid results in:

$$3\left(\frac{8Q}{\pi D^3}\right) + \frac{D \, \Delta P}{4L} \frac{d(8Q/\pi D^3)}{d(D \, \Delta P/4L)} = \left(-\frac{dV}{dr}\right)_w \tag{52}$$

Since $Q = VA = \frac{1}{4}\pi D^2 V$, Equation 52 can be rearranged to:

$$3\left(\frac{8Q}{\pi D^3}\right) = \left(-\frac{dV}{dr}\right)_w = \frac{3}{4}\left(\frac{8V}{D}\right) + \left(\frac{8V}{D}\right) \frac{d[\frac{1}{4}(8V/D)]/(8V/D)}{d(D \, \Delta P/4L)/(D \, \Delta P/4L)}$$

or $\quad -\dot{\gamma}_w = \left(-\frac{dV}{dr}\right)_w = \frac{8V}{D}\left[\frac{3}{4} + \frac{1}{4n}\right] = \frac{3n+1}{4n} \cdot \frac{8V}{D}$ $\tag{53a}$

where $\quad n = \dfrac{d \ln(D \, \Delta P/L)}{d \ln(8V/D)}$

We may also state this expression as:

$$-\dot{\gamma}_w = \frac{3}{4}\Gamma + \frac{\tau_w}{4}\frac{d\Gamma}{d\tau_w} \tag{53b}$$

where $\quad \Gamma = 4Q/\pi R^3$ is the shear rate for a Newtonian fluid.

The Poiseuille equation for a Newtonian fluid [3] is:

$$\Delta P = \frac{8\mu LV}{R^2} = \frac{32\mu LV}{D^2}$$

which can also be written as:

$$\ln(D \, \Delta P/4L) = \ln(8V/D) + \ln(\mu)$$

Since μ is constant, then:

$$\frac{d \ln(D \, \Delta P/4L)}{d \ln(8V/D)} = n = 1.0$$

Substituting this expression into Equation 53 shows that $(-dV/dr)_w = 8V/D$ (see [6] for details). This is only true for a Newtonian fluid, since viscosity is a constant. In the case of a non-Newtonian fluid, n varies along the log-log plot of $D \, \Delta P/4L$ vs. $8V/D$. To apply a capillary tube viscometer then to develop a non-Newtonian fluid's flow curve, data must be converted into a logarithmic plot of $DP/4L$ vs. $8V/D$, where n is determined as the slope of the curve at a particular value of the wall shear stress (i.e., $\tau_w = D \, \Delta P/4L$). The shear rate corresponding to this wall shear stress value is determined from Equation 53. It is important to note that Equation 53 is derived for laminar flow, and hence, one must ensure that capillary tube flow is in this regime by checking the Reynolds number. Metzner and Reed [7] have derived the generalized Reynolds number for a power-law fluid as:

$$Re_{gen} = \frac{D^n V^{2-n} \rho}{\dot{\gamma}} \tag{54}$$

or $\quad Re_{gen} = \dfrac{D^n V^{2-n} \rho}{K 8^{n-1}}$ \hfill (55)

This expression applies to all fluids which are not time-dependent.

Metzner and Reed [7] have shown that such non-Newtonian fluids obey the conventional Newtonian friction factor vs. Reynolds number. Therefore, laminar flow prevails for $Re_{gen} < 2,100$.

Data generated in any capillary tube viscometer will require corrections for four contributions to frictional losses: (a) the head of fluid above the tube exit; (b) kinetic energy effects; (c) tube entrance effects; (d) effective slip near the tube wall. The last effect is not always present, and can generally be detected as explained later.

The first three corrections can be made through application of the total mechanical energy balance. Skelland [6] outlines a correction approach and provides an illustrative example. An alternative approach, which generally gives good results, is the Bagley [8] shear stress correction method. This method was originally developed using a variety of polyethylenes. The resulting flow curve is independent of the capillary's L/D ratio; however, the procedure requires the assumptions of zero slip at the tube walls and time-independency of the fluid material. The method uses a fictitious length of tubing, $N_f R$, that is added to the actual length of tube, L, such that the measured total ΔP across L is that which would be obtained in fully developed flow over the length $(L + N_f R)$ at the flow rate used in the experiment. The procedure is analogous to the application of an effective length in estimating kinetic resistances in pipe flow problems [1, 2]. The shear stress at the wall for fully developed flow over the length $(L + N_f R)$ is then:

$$\tau_w = R\,\Delta P / 2(L + N_f R) \hfill (56)$$

If the fluid is time-independent and there is no slip at the tube wall, then τ_w is a unique function of $4Q/\pi R^3$ $(\simeq \Gamma)$ in laminar flow (see [6] for derivation). Hence:

$$\tau_w = \frac{R}{2}\left(\frac{\Delta P}{L + N_f R}\right) = f\left(\frac{4Q}{\pi R^3}\right) \hfill (57)$$

from which $\quad \dfrac{L}{R} = -N_f + \dfrac{\Delta P}{2f\left(\dfrac{4Q}{\pi R^3}\right)}$ \hfill (58)

The procedure involves obtaining a series of ΔP measurements made on several tubes of various L/R (or L/D) ratios, while maintaining $4Q/\pi R^3$ constant. From this data a plot of L/R vs. ΔP, as shown in Figure 13, for different shear rates can be constructed. Equation 58 is a straight line and hence, the intercept on the L/R ordinate at $\Delta P = 0$ gives $-N_f$. A non-linear plot as shown by the data for 3.6 and 10.8 sec^{-1} would suggest one of our model assumptions is incorrect (i.e., the presence of time dependence or effective slip).

From a linear regression of each of the plots in Figure 13, the correction term N_f (intercept) can be derived.

A plot of N_f vs. Γ $(\equiv 4Q/\pi R^3)$ is constructed in Figure 14 and further regressed to provide an analytical solution to Equation 57. That is, substitution in the expression $\tau_w = R\,\Delta P/2\,(L + N_f R)$ allows calculation of τ_w free from end effects, and should lead to a flow curve that is independent of the L/D ratio used in the capillary viscometer. Illustrations of the results are shown in Figures 15 and 16. Figure 15 shows a plot of τ_w vs. Γ using the raw data obtained from the capillary tube.

Figure 16A shows τ_w data for L/D ratios of 2, 5, and 10 collapsed to a single correlation. The data for L/D = 0.25 are in closer agreement for the high shear rate range $(\Gamma > 36\ sec^{-1})$ but data points fall away from the average curve at the low shear range. Since the resulting flow curve is linear, we may assume there is no time dependency for the material and hence, the lack of agreement in τ_w data obtained at L/D = 0.25 is likely due to slippage. The power-law coefficients K and n can be readily regressed from the single line in Figure 16A $(\tau_w = K\Gamma^n)$. The corrected shear rate

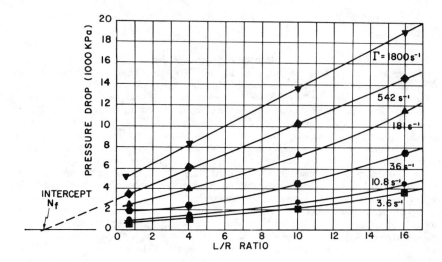

Figure 13. Plot of L/R vs. $\triangle$P for evaluation of Bagley correction term.

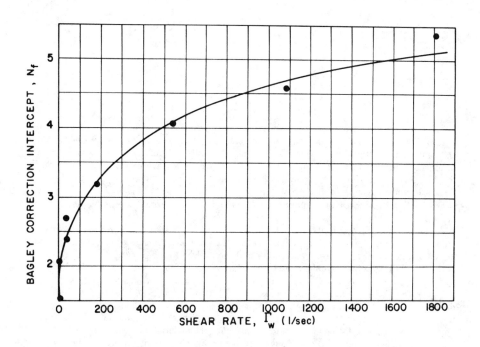

Figure 14. Plot of Bagley correction term vs. Newtonian shear rate Γ.

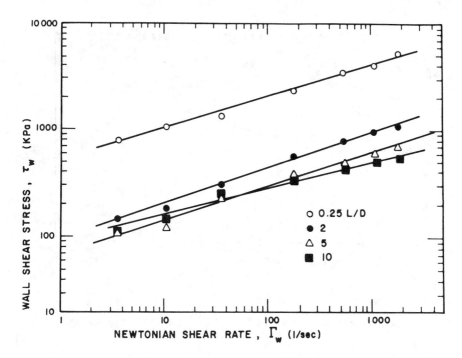

Figure 15. Plot of uncorrected flow curve data.

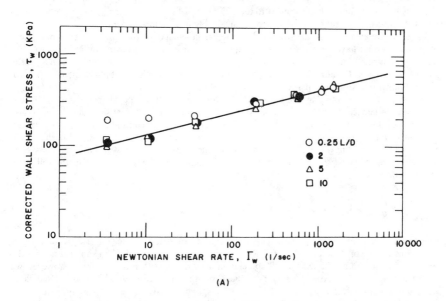

(A)

Figure 16A. Plot of corrected flow curve data using Newtonian shear rate.

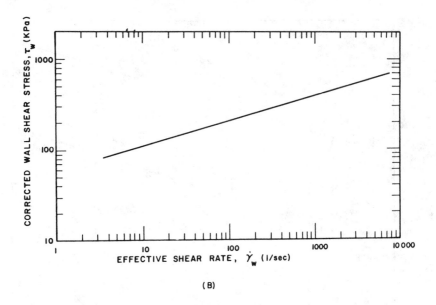

(B)

Figure 16B. Plot of corrected flow curve data using effective shear rate data.

at the wall can now be computed using Equation 53. A plot of τ_w vs. the effective shear rate $\dot{\gamma}$ computed from Equation 53 is shown in Figure 16B. To minimize entrance losses and therefore minimize lengthy correction calculations, the L/D ratio should be made as large as is practically possible. Thomas [9], for example, had to resort to an L/D ratio of 1,000 in work on suspensions. At excessive L/D ratios, frictional corrections become negligible in viscometric data.

In the above example, the data resulted in a linear flow curve. If the data showed a non-linear response it would have been necessary to employ standard tangent-drawing procedures. By constructing tangents to the curve on Figure 16A, we would obtain corresponding values of n from the tangent slopes, and K-values from the tangent intercept at $\Gamma = 1$. We may then recalculate $\dot{\gamma}_w$ from the Rabinowitsch-Mooney equation.

It is important to note that some non-Newtonian fluids display a peculiar orientation of their molecules in the vicinity of the tube walls. In the case of an aqueous suspension, the discrete phase may actually move away from the wall, leaving a thin layer of the continuum phase in the immediate proximity of the wall. In this situation there is a reduction in the apparent viscosity in the vicinity of the wall, known as the phenomenon of "effective slip" at the wall. For a capillary tube viscometer, an effective slip coefficient β can be evaluated as a function τ_w using the following relationship:

$$\frac{Q}{\pi R^3 \tau_w} = \frac{\beta}{R} + \frac{1}{\tau_w^4} \int_0^{\tau_w} \tau_{rx}^2 f(\tau_{rx}) \, d\tau_{rx} \tag{59}$$

A series of capillary tube measurements is needed in order to evaluate β. For a range of tubes of various R but constant L, a plot of $Q/R^3 \tau_w$ vs. τ_w can be constructed. If no slip occurs with the material (i.e., $\beta = 0$) all the curves will coincide in accordance with Equation 59. If, however, we obtain a family of curves, then β has some value. From the family of curves, select some fixed value of τ_w and obtain values of $Q/\pi R^3 \tau_w$ for each corresponding R-value curve. Now prepare a plot of $Q/\pi R^3 \tau_w$ vs. 1/R. The slope of this curve provides a β-value for the selected τ_w, according to Equation 59. By repeating this procedure for different τ_w values, a relationship between τ_w and β

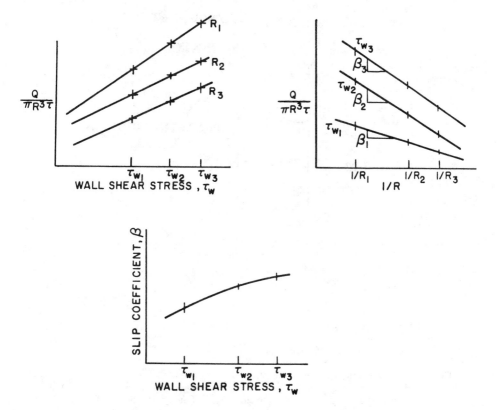

Figure 17. Procedure for correcting for effective wall slip.

can be established. Figure 17 illustrates this method. Once a relationship between the effective slip coefficient and τ_w is established, the measured volumetric flow rate from the capillary tube can be corrected for slippage:

$$Q' = Q_{measured} - \beta \tau_w \pi R^2 \qquad (60)$$

where Q' is the volumetric flow rate corrected for slippage and $\tau_w = D\,\Delta P/4L$ corresponding to $Q_{measured}$.

Concentric cylinder rotary and rotating cylinder viscometers are most often applied to solution viscosity measurements and are usually limited to shear rates of less than 100 s^{-1}.

The basic elements of the concentric cylinder rotary viscometer are shown in Figure 18. The unit operates by applying shear to a fluid located in the annulus between the concentric cylinders. One cylinder (usually the cup) rotates while the other is fixed in space. From a series of measurements of the angular speed of the rotating cup and of the torque applied to the stationary cylinder, a flow curve for the fluid under shear can be derived.

The development of the constitutive equations for this type of viscometer is as follows. A torque balance about the surface of the fixed bob while the cup revolves at a steady angular velocity is:

$$\tau_b(2\pi R_b l)R_b = 2\pi R_b^2 l \tau_b = T \qquad (61)$$

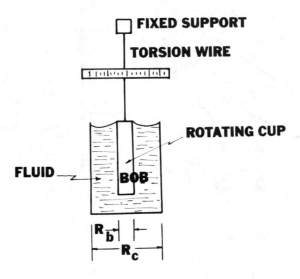

Figure 18. Basic elements of concentric cylinder rotary viscometer.

where T = torque
        R_b = bob radius
        τ_b = shearing stress at the bob surface

The balance equation neglects end effects at the base of the bob and assumes that shear occurs only at the cylindrical surface of the bob. In practice, however, end effects are important and can be accounted for by including an effective bob length, l_{eff}, in Equation 61. Solving Equation 61 for the bob surface shear stress:

$$\tau_b = \frac{T}{2\pi R_b^2 l}$$

The shear rate at the bob surface is a complex relationship, which for brevity is not included here. An approximate relationship proposed by Calderbank and Moo-Young [10] based on the analytical derivation of Kreiger and Maron [11] is as follows:

$$\left(\frac{dV}{dr}\right)_b = \frac{4\pi N}{1 - (R_c/R_b)^2} C_R \tag{62}$$

Equation 62 is applicable for cup-to-bob radii ratios < 1.75. The term C_R represents a series expansion of the shear rate-geometric relationship developed by Kreiger and Maron for time-independent power-law fluids. Table 1 provides values of C_R that can be used in Equation 62. The rheological flow curve can be developed by a logarithmic plot of τ_b vs. $(dv/dr)_b$. By employing different bob or cup sizes, the different ranges of shear rates can be studied. In the extreme, for very small annular gaps (i.e., $R_c/R_b \to 1.0$), the shear rate approaches a constant value across the annulus and can be approximated simply by:

$$\frac{dv}{dr} = \frac{2\pi R N}{R_c - R_b} \tag{63}$$

Table 1
Values of Calderbank—Moo-Young Shear Rate Term (Cr)

n'	Rc/Rb RATIO					
	1.070	1.150	1.166	1.250	1.400	1.746
0.050	2.722	4.999	5.435			
0.100	1.708	2.617	2.801	3.735	5.184	
0.200	1.287	1.622	1.689	2.031	2.593	3.615
0.300	1.162	1.342	1.377	1.554	1.843	2.382
0.400	1.102	1.213	1.234	1.340	1.511	1.826
0.500	1.068	1.139	1.153	1.220	1.327	1.522
0.600	1.045	1.091	1.100	1.144	1.212	1.335
0.700	1.029	1.058	1.064	1.091	1.134	1.209
0.800	1.017	1.034	1.037	1.053	1.077	1.119
0.900	1.007	1.015	1.016	1.023	1.034	1.052
1.000	1.000	1.000	1.000	1.000	1.000	1.000
1.250			0.971		0.941	0.910
1.500			0.952		0.903	0.853
1.750			0.939		0.877	0.814
2.000			0.929		0.857	0.785
2.250			0.921		0.842	0.763
2.500			0.915		0.830	0.746
2.750			0.910		0.820	0.732
3.000			0.906		0.812	0.720
3.250			0.902		0.806	0.711
3.500			0.899		0.800	0.702
3.750			0.897		0.795	0.695
4.000			0.894		0.791	0.689
coefficient (A)	0.903	0.861	1.144	0.898	1.169	1.155
exponent (B)	−0.304	−0.505	−0.320	−0.547	−0.418	−0.485
coef. of fit (r*)	0.946	0.963	0.891	0.974	0.928	0.957

Each set of R_c/R_b data sets has been regressed using the least squares to a power-law expression. For approximate C_R-values apply above model coefficient: $C_R = A (n')^B$

It should be noted that close clearance viscometers such as this are not suitable for use with suspensions where particle sizes are comparable to the annular gap.

End effects can be corrected for by substituting an effective length l_{eff} for the true bob length 1 in Equation 61. The effective length can be determined by calibrating the viscometer using a Newtonian fluid of known viscosity μ and applying the following formula:

$$l_{eff} = \frac{T}{2\pi R_b^2 \mu (dv/dr)_b} \qquad (64)$$

To correct for effective slip in rotary viscometers, the correction method of Mooney [12] can be used. The method involves obtaining measurements using three different R_c/R_b ratios. For R_1, R_2, R_3 radii, such that $R_1 < R_2 < R_3$, three radii ratios can be defined: $S_a = R_2/R_1$, $S_b = R_3/R_2$, $S_c = R_3/R_1$. The rotational speed of the cup required to obtain the same torque for each of these cases can be measured as N_{12}, N_{23} and N_{13}. The effective slip coefficient corresponding to the stress at the surface $2\pi R_2 l$ is:

$$\beta_2 = \frac{2\pi^2 R_2^2}{T} (N_{12} + N_{23} - N_{13}) \tag{65}$$

Repeating this procedure for different torque values provides a correlation between β_2 and the surface shear stress τ_2. To correct for slippage, for a given torque value, τ_b can be computed from Equation 61. The corresponding expression for wall shear stress at the cup surface is:

$$\tau_c = \frac{T}{2\pi R_c^2 l} \tag{66}$$

The effective slip velocities at the bob and cup surfaces are $V_{s,b} = \beta_b \tau_b$ and $V_{s,c} = \beta_c \tau_c$, respectively. The effective velocity of the fluid at the rotating cup surface will be less than that of the cup by the amount $V_{s,c}$. The effective velocity of the fluid at the stationary bob surface is $V_{s,b}$. The true shear rate corresponding to τ_b can be calculated by multiplying either Equation 62 or 63 by the ratio of the actual velocity difference (i.e., from cup to bob) to the velocity difference without slip (i.e., $(V_{sc} - V_{sb})/V_{meas}$).

A modification of the concentric cylinder viscometer is the *Brookfield viscometer*, in which the cup radius is effectively extended to infinity. Flow curves are generated from measurements of the torque needed to rotate a cylindrical rod at various speeds when immersed in the fluid of 'infinite' volume. Basically, the fluid is contained in a cup whose radius is much larger than the rod. With this arrangement, the walls of the retaining cup do not influence the shearing movement of the fluid. Equation 61 defines the shearing stress at the rod surface ($R_b =$ radius of the cylindrical rod, $l =$ length of rod immersed in the fluid). As before, an effective rod immersion length, l_{eff}, can be developed to correct for end effects. The shear rate at the surface of the rotating rod for any time-independent fluid is given by:

$$\left(-\frac{dV}{dr} \right)_b = \frac{4\pi N}{n''} \tag{67}$$

where n'' is the slope of a logarithmic plot of torque vs. rotational speed N, evaluated at the particular N for which T was measured. A plot of τ_b vs. $(-dV/dr)_b$ provides the flow curve. With either device, we may also generate a plot of $D \Delta P/4L$ vs. $8V/D$ (Γ – Newtonian shear rate) for laminar tube flow. In general, both devices enable studies over a very limited shear rate range. Commercial units are usually equipped with an electrical heating jacket and appropriate heat exchange to remove heat generated by friction in the fluid.

The cone-and-plate viscometer is a widely used instrument for shear flow rheological properties studies. The device can be used to measure both viscosity and normal stresses. Applications and analysis of this type of viscometer for studying polymer melts are covered by Lee and White [13, 14], Lobe and White [15], Chapman and Lee [16], Minagawa and White [17], King [18], Meissner [19], and Weissenberg [20]. The principal features of this viscometer are illustrated in Figure 19, consisting essentially of a flat, horizontal plate and an inverted cone, the apex of which is in near contact with the plate. The angle between the plate and cone surface is small (typically $<2°$). The fluid sample is placed in this small gap between the cone and plate. A flow curve is developed from measurements of the torque needed to rotate the cone at different speeds. For a constant speed N, the linear velocity at r is $2\pi r N$. The gap height at r is $r \tan \phi$. Hence, the magnitude of the shear rate at r is:

$$\frac{2\pi r N}{r \tan \phi} = \frac{2\pi N}{\tan \phi} \tag{68}$$

The shear rate is constant between $0 > r > R$, which means that τ_{yx} is also constant over this range. For small ϕ, $\tan \phi \simeq \phi$, and hence, the magnitude of the shear rate $\simeq 2\pi N/\phi$. The following

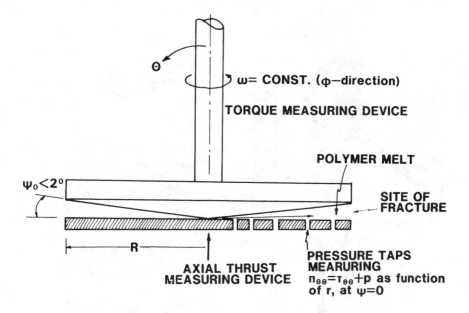

Figure 19. Schematic of cone-and-plate viscometer.

expression defines the relationship between measured torque and shear stress:

$$T = 2\pi\tau_{yx} \int_0^R r^2\, dr = \frac{2}{3}\pi R^3 \tau_{yx}$$

or $\tau_{yx} = \dfrac{3T}{2\pi R^3}$ (69)

Equation 69 enables τ_{yx} to be obtained at different measured torque values. Shear rate can be obtained from Equation 68, and hence, τ_{yx} can be plotted against shear rate for the flow curve.

Commercial instruments that are capable of measuring normal stresses as well as the shear stress are the Weissenberg Rheogoniometer (manufactured by Sangamo Controls, Bognor Regis, U.K.) and the *Mechanical Spectrometer* (manufactured by Rheometrics Inc., Union, NJ, U.S.A.).

Another type of shear flow instrument primarily used for polymer melts is the *sandwich viscometer* (also known as the *parallel-plate viscometer*). The measurement principle is illustrated in Figure 20. A viscous material such as an elastomer is sheared between two parallel steel plates or, as in Figure 20, in a sandwich between three plates. The shear rate is:

$$\dot{\gamma} = V/H$$ (70)

where H = interplate distance.

The applied force can be determined as a function of time, which after normalization with area provides shear stress data as a function of time:

$$\tau = F/2A$$ (71)

It is possible to measure transient start-up stresses of the material with this device. After a sufficiently long time and if the material is stable, the steady-state stress can be measured, at which point the

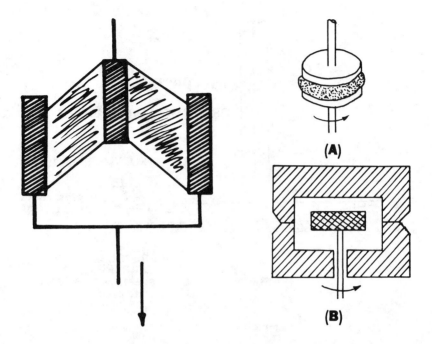

Figure 20. Schematic of sandwich viscometer.   **Figure 21.** (A) Parallel disk viscometer. (B) Mooney shearing disk viscometer.

viscosity can be determined as a function of shear rate. With many materials such as elastomers, both large times and equipment strains are needed. These conditions often result in slippage. To minimize slippage, contact surfaces are usually knurled.

This type of viscometer is capable of making measurements at very low shear rates, on materials which usually exhibit slippage in non-pressurized rotational devices (e.g., cone-and-plate type viscometers). The instrument is described in detail in [21–24].

A *parallel disk viscometer* (also known as a "shearing disk" viscometer) measures viscosity in torsional flow between a stationary and a rotating disk. Design variations are illustrated in Figure 21. The operation involves the use of a serrated disk which is rotated in a sample fixed in a pressurized cavity. This system was developed for rubber applications, where both pressurization and the use of serrated surfaces are intended to avoid slippage. Properties are measured based on the shear rate at the outer radius of the disk, where:

$$Y_a = a\omega/H \tag{72}$$

Shear stress and normal stress differences are given by the following relationships:

$$\tau|_a = \frac{3T}{2\pi a^3}\left[1 + \frac{1}{3}\frac{d \ln T}{d \ln \gamma_a}\right] \tag{73}$$

$$P_{11} - 2P_{22} + P_{33}|_a = \frac{2F'}{\pi a^2}\left[1 + \frac{1}{2}\frac{d \ln F'}{d \ln \gamma_a}\right] \tag{74}$$

where F' = normal thrust. The parallel disk apparatus is limited to low shear rates.

The Mooney viscometer consists of a rotating disk in a cylindrical cavity. This instrument has become the standard quality control instrument of the rubber industry. The American Society for Testing Materials (ASTM) specifies the diameter of the disk to be 19.05 mm and thickness 5.54 mm. A single-point viscosity measurement is made at a standardized rotor speed of 2 rpm., after a period of 4 minutes and 100°C. In the elastomers industry some manufacturers still report measurements at 8 minutes and 127°C; however, considerable effort is underway to standardize to the ASTM guidelines. Measurements are reported in terms of a calibrated torque measurement on a standard dial (referred to as ML-4 reading). The designation ML-4 means: M—Mooney viscometer, L—large disk size (a smaller diameter disk, S, is used for vulcanization scorch tests), and 4—four minutes of test.

ML-4 readings can be converted to torque, shear stress, and viscosity values. Nakajima and Harrel [25] provide the following correlations:

$$T = 8.30 \times 10^{-2} D_R \tag{75a}$$

$$\tau_a = 0.382(D_R)f' \times 10^4 \tag{75b}$$

where D_R = Mooney unit dial reading

T and τ_a have units of N/m and Pa, respectively. f' is a function defined by the following relationship for shear stress at the disk's outer radius:

$$\tau|_a = \frac{T}{\pi a^3} f' \tag{76}$$

$$f' = \frac{n'+3}{4}\left[1 + \frac{[(2/n')^{n'}(n'+3)hH^{n'}]}{2a^{n'+1}\left[1-\left(\frac{a}{a+\delta}\right)^{2/n'}\right]^{n'}}\right]^{-1} \tag{77}$$

where δ = distance between the outer disk radius and cavity
         h = disk thickness

$$n' = \text{power law exponent} \left(\simeq \frac{d\ln T}{d\ln \dot{\gamma}_a}\right)$$

Function f' typically has a value of around 0.55 for the standard measurement conditions.

A *slit rheometer* is an analogous instrument to the capillary viscometer. The primary difference between the devices is the orifice cross-section. Han [26–28] and Wales et al. [29] describe the use of this instrument in the study of polymer melts. The device makes use of a series of flush mounted transducers located along the flow tube. These transducers measure the pressure gradients along the direction of flow, which can then be converted to wall shear stress values via:

$$\tau_w = \delta_c \frac{dP}{dz} \tag{78}$$

where δ_c = half thickness of the channel.

Han [26] gives the following expression for the shear rate at the channel wall:

$$\dot{\gamma}_w = \frac{3Q}{4ab^2}\left[\frac{2}{3} + \frac{1}{3}\frac{d(\ln(3Q/4ab^2))}{d(\ln \tau_w)}\right] \tag{79}$$

where a = half width.

In general, the instrument is capable of operating over comparable shear rate ranges to the capillary viscometer.

The *melt indexer* is widely accepted as a standard quality control instrument in the plastics industry. The device, developed by DuPont, is typically used to specify polyethylenes, polypropylene, and polystyrene. It is essentially an extrusion rheometer, that is in fact similar to a capillary rheometer. The instrument employs a single capillary (diameter of 0.655 mm and L/D ratio of 12) in which extrusion of material is accomplished due to pressure applied by a dead weight. The melt index is given as a measure of the weight in grams extruded for a ten minute test.

The ASTM specifies a series of test conditions involving temperature and applied dead load settings. These conditions are designations A through K, and they cover the following ranges: for temperature, 125–275°C; for applied dead load, 325–21,600 grams (or in terms of pressures, 0.5–29.5 atmospheres). Specifications are selected so that melt indices lie between the values of 0.15 and 25 grams per 10 minute test. The most frequently used condition in the industry is specification E (190°C, 2.95 atm).

Although this is a widely used instrument, its value is that of a quality control tester, which can only empirically relate to end-use processability of products. The melt index (MI) is related to the inverse of viscosity; however, no end loss corrections have been developed, nor can the MI be easily related to the Weissenberg-Rabinowitsch shear rate expression.

Up to this point, instruments based on shear flow have been discussed. However, there are numerous polymer processing operations that involve *uniaxial elongational flows*. An example in processing where elongational flow occurs is in the entrance die region of an extruder. This phenomenon can be studied in a capillary die. Pressure losses through such dies can be used to determine elongational viscosity in polymer melts (see [30, 31] for example). For this reason, a variety of laboratory test devices and techniques have been devised over the years in order to conduct rheological investigations and/or quality control testing in this type of flow. In general, measurements of elongational viscosity are complex to interpret and more difficult than measurements made in shear flow. To make elongational viscosity measurements requires maintaining a constant elongation rate or stress while reaching steady-state conditions. These types of tests are typically applied to polymer melts that include high molecular weight polyolefins, styrenics, elastomers, and their compounds. A few of the most frequently used tests are briefly described below.

The most common method of measuring elongational viscosity is to stretch a filament of the material. The fluid obviously must have a sufficiently high viscosity to be maintained under controllable deformation. Materials suitable for this type of testing are elastomers and polyolefins where melt viscosities are typically 10,000 Pa-s or greater. These types of test measurements are limited to deformation rates below 5 sec^{-1}. Ballman [32], Vinogradov et al. [33], and Stevenson [34] describe different types of filament stretching methods. A very simple arrangement involves clamping both ends of a vertical thermostated filament, which is then stretched at a rate dl/dt in such a manner as to maintain a constant rate of deformation. In this manner, the rate of deformation ϕ' is:

$$\phi' = \frac{1}{l}\frac{dl}{dt} \tag{80}$$

and $\quad l = l(0)e^{Et}$ (81)

In other words, the length of a material undergoing stretching follows an exponential law. The test is illustrated in Figure 22A.

Another approach, illustrated in Figure 22B, involves supporting a horizontal filament on the surface of a hot immiscible oil. The polymer filament is held at both ends, between pairs of toothed or serrated wheels that turn at linear velocity V/2. The filament is drawn at both ends through the wheels. One of these wheels contains a tension-sensing instrument so that deformation rate is proportional to the velocity ($\phi' = (V/2)/(L/2) = V/L$).

Different variations of the filament stretching technique for the measurement of elongational viscosity are described in [35–38].

Stress relaxation and small strain measurements are a class of rheological measurements carried out on bulk polymers, and are usually aimed at obtaining information on the material's response

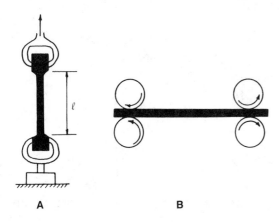

Figure 22. (A) Vertical method of elongational viscosity measurement at constant elongation rate. (B) Horizontal filament stretching test.

A   B

to small strains. Strain can be applied as a step function, and the stress relaxation that takes place after its application is measured.

Stress relaxation measurements are routinely made on elastomers. This test involves application of a strain to a polymer sample that is in either extension, shear, or compression. The measurable parameter is the force response over time, F(t), to the applied strain. Some investigators report the material property in terms of a relaxation modulus defined by:

$$E(t) = \lim_{\Delta l \to 0} \left[\frac{F(t)/A_0}{\Delta l/l_0} \right] \tag{82}$$

where A_0 = initial cross section of sample
         l_0 = initial length of sample
         Δl = amount sample is stretched in extension

For measurements made under shear, a surface of the sample is subjected to a displacement in a direction normal to its thickness. The shear modulus is given by:

$$G(t) = \lim_{\Delta l \to 0} \left[\frac{F(t)/A}{\Delta l/H} \right] \tag{83}$$

where H = sample thickness.

These types of tests are normally coupled with mechanical properties testing. A variety of polymers, particularly elastomers, are widely used in consumer and industrial related products because of their good mechanical properties. Tensile measurements at several strain rates are often made as a quality control check of the polymer's integrity, even though their behavior in compound states may be quite different. The stress-strain curve provides information on both the rheological and mechanical behaviors of the polymer. Figure 23 illustrates typical features of tensile stress-strain curves for polymers. The classification of curves in Figure 23 shows that polymers can be classified in general terms as rubbery, glassy, or variations in between. Compounding can greatly change the stress-strain response curve of a given polymer.

Tensile testing in rubber labs is normally done on a tensile testing machine such as an Instron, and performed according to ASTM standard methods (ASTM D638, ASTM D882). As a product quality control test, many elastomer manufacturers are no longer using tensile testing of neat rubber, but rely more heavily on rheometer-cure-response data. In product development work, however, tensile testing is an integral part of polymer characterization work. A minimal testing scheme involves obtaining a stress-strain curve at room temperature conditions and at perhaps three or

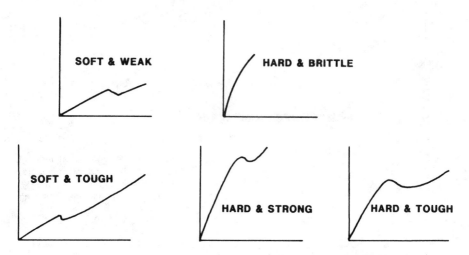

Figure 23. Typical tensile stress-strain curves for polymers.

more strain rates. From each curve, various quantities related to the mechanical and rheological properties or the sample can be derived. Figure 24 shows the generalized tensile stress-strain curve for plastics and the various parameters of interest. The principal information obtained from these curves are:

1. The modulus of elasticity (the initial slope of the curve).
2. The yield stress (peak stress in the early portion of the curve).
3. The stress at failure.

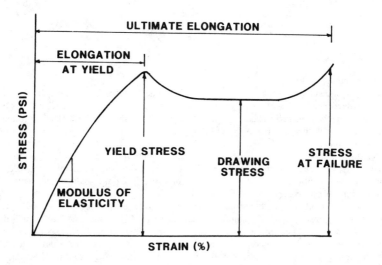

Figure 24. Tensile stress-strain curve for plastics.

4. The elongation (or strain) at yield. This value is also called the yield strength.
5. The ultimate elongation or strain at failure (also referred to as the "elongation at break").
6. The energy to break; measured by the area under the stress-strain curve up to the point of failure. The last feature, the energy to break, is truly a measure of sample toughness.

An important class of experiments originally introduced by Philippoff [39] involves the determination of stress response to an imposed sinusoidal oscillation. Results are analyzed in terms of the dynamic viscosity function η' (not to be confused with the dynamic viscosity of classical fluid mechanics) and the dynamic rigidity function G'. In oscillatory shear flow, we may represent the velocity field using rectangular Cartesian coordinates as follows:

$$V_1 = \epsilon \omega x_2 e^{i\omega t}, \qquad V_2 = V_3 = 0 \tag{84}$$

where ϵ is small enough for second and higher order terms to be neglected, and ω is frequency. The corresponding stress field is:

$$P_{12} = \eta^*(\omega)\epsilon\omega e^{i\omega t}, \qquad P_{11} - P_{12} = P_{22} - P_{33} = 0 \tag{85}$$

where η^* = complex dynamic viscosity, expressed by convention as:

$$\eta^* = \eta' - i\frac{G'}{\omega} \tag{86}$$

Other functions typically defined are:

$$\eta'' = G'/\omega \tag{87a}$$

$$G'' = \omega\eta' \tag{87b}$$

The most widely used method for measuring $G'(\omega)$ and $G''(\omega)$ on polymer melts systems involves placing the melt in the gap between a cone and plate and oscillating one of the elements relative to the other with a shear strain. Figure 25 illustrates this technique.

Another arrangement, illustrated in Figure 26, involves rotating two parallel eccentric disks. The polymer sample undergoes periodic sinusoidal deformation. The forces exerted on the disk are interpreted as $G'(\omega)$ and $G''(\omega)$.

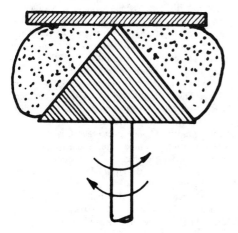

Figure 25. Oscillatory shear in a cone-and-plate device.

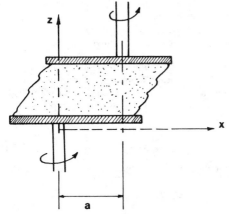

z

x

a

Figure 26. Principle of orthogonal rheometer.

Many industrial research laboratories use the *Weissenberg Rheogoniometer* and *Rheometrics Mechanical Spectrometer* for cone-and-plate sinusoidal oscillation measurements of G'(ω) and G''(ω). Refer to [15, 40–47] for discussions of sinusoidal experiments.

Determination of birefringence during flow is a rheological property measurement technique applied almost exclusively to homogeneous systems of flexible polymer chains. This technique is based on a relationship between flow birefringent behavior and stresses and is determined by Rheo-Optical laws. (see Van Wazer el al. [48] and Dexter, Miller and Philippoff [49]). Basically, the law relates the difference in the principal refractive indices to the difference in the principal stresses as developed during flow. The principal stresses represent the magnitudes of the principle axes of the ellipsoid of the stress tensor. The technique has been applied in purely scientific studies on flexible chain polymer melts such as polyolefin, polystyrene, and elastomers. The major difficulty in its application is that the technique is limited to amorphous polymers. Even trace amounts of crystallinity have a dramatic effect on measurements. Measurements can be performed on polymer solutions using a coaxial cylinder viscometer, whereas polymer melt measurements are normally taken on parallel plate slit extrusion devices. These instruments seek to use flow birefringence to measure shear flow properties.

Measurement of birefringence is accomplished by studying the transmission of a polarized monochromatic light beam that is passed through the fluid medium to some depth. Since the medium in the plane perpendicular to the transmitted wave has different refractive indices in different directions, the wave splits into two parts. Each refracted wave has a different velocity which corresponds to the two refractive indices. The waves are out of phase with each other, and the beam exiting the instrument passes through a polarizer crossed normal with the initial direction of polarization. Birefringence is determined either through the reduction in intensity of the exiting beam, through the use of compensators, or through characterization of the fringe patterns produced by the external polarizer. The fringes indicate conditions where the contributions of the two waves to the direction allowed passage by the analyzer cancel. The method based on the use of compensators is described by Van Wazer et al. [48] and Brydson [50]. Theory and application of flow birefringence measurements of rheological properties are treated in [43, 49, 51–61].

Another rheological test more often used for product quality control is *measurement of the elastic recovery* in polymer melts and their compounds. This is usually done by measuring the *swell* (or *shrinkage*) of materials undergoing extrusion. The tendency of polymers, whether thermoplastic or rubber, to enlarge when emerging from an extruder die is called "die swell." Die swell normally refers to the ratio of extruded size to die size. This behavior is a measure of the relative elasticity in the flowing polymer stream. Die swell is caused by the release of the residual stresses when the sample emerges from the die. Measurement of this behavior has become widely recognized in the rubber and plastics industries as an important indication of polymer processability.

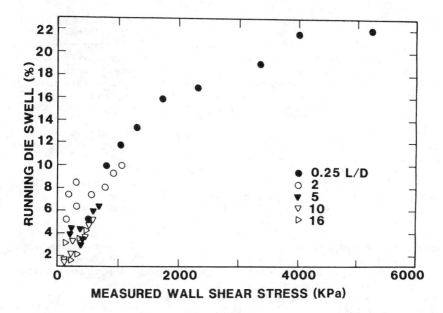

Figure 27. MPT data on running die swell.

Traditional measurements reported by various investigators have been made on extrudates with either a micrometer or by weight per unit length. The Monsanto Industrial Chemicals Co. (Akron, Ohio) has introduced an automated capillary rheometer (called the Monsanto Processability Tester), which employs an extrudate swell detector based on interaction with a scanning laser beam positioned immediately below the capillary die exit. This enables measurement of the running die swell measurements. Figure 27 shows running die swell data for a compound correlated against wall shear for different L/D dies. It's important to note that with some materials, a distinction between running die swells and relaxed die swells should be made. Highly elastic materials will tend to swell more over time, depending on their elastic recovery energy.

C. W. Brabender Instruments, Inc. (Hackensack, NJ) markets an optical-electronic die swell measuring system that can be used for continuous control/monitoring of extruders and plasticorders. The basic design features are illustrated in Figure 28. An infrared, long-life diode (A) emits homogeneous infrared light through a filter (B), diffuser (C), and lens (D); then through a window

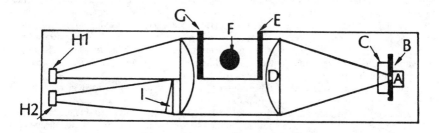

Figure 28. Schematic of opto-electrical die swell tester.

(E). The light impinging on the object (F) is scattered. Only that light reaching ambient light filter (G) is measured by photodetector H1. Light reaching photodetector H2 is diverted through the prism (I) and is uninterrupted. This acts as a reference beam. The electronic instrumentation measures the differences between photodetector H1 and H2 and calculates the object thickness to an accuracy of 0.2% of full scale. The object to be measured must be located vertically within the measuring area. The maximum permissible deviation from vertical is 2.5°. Operation at angles greater than 2.5° from vertical will yield greater errors than 0.1%. If the measuring angle is more than 2.5° from vertical, the measurement will be increased by the factor $1/\cos a$ where "a" is deviation from vertical.

While the upper collimated light serves as the measuring beam, the lower portion impacts on the second photodetector and acts as the reference beam. Thus, the temperature and age affected by drift which occurs on all semi-conductor elements is negated.

In some applications, such as hose and tubing manufacturing, it is important to know both the extrudate diameter and cross section. The device described above can provide two diameter measurements, which provide an out-of-round indication (eccentricity).

Experimental studies are reported in the literature using various methods of swell measurement [15, 62–64].

There are a variety of other instruments employed by various industries for either product developement work or product quality control. Although we shall review these methods in relationship to the industries and products they are most frequently applied to, these devices are by no means restricted to those applications. The fact that one type of instrument has become a standard tool for a particular industry has arisen largely through an evolution of preference, and in some cases convenience, rather than primarily for technical reasons. Most of these techniques can be applied to any fluid characterization; however, the techniques can vary greatly in terms of the specific information they provide.

One industry where rheological characterization has been applied for many years in a subjective manner is in the manufacture of liquid detergents. Consumer applications for these products include dishwashing, hard surface cleaning liquid scourers for walls and floors, fabric softeners, thickened bleaches, liquid abrasive cleaners, combination liquid detergent/wax products for cars, and liquid detergents for washing fabrics. Other examples include personal washing products, such as hair shampoos and conditioners, body shampoos, shower gels, toothpaste, and skin cleansers. The particular rheological properties imparted to these various products is governed in a number of cases by consumer preference or attitudes, as well as by technical benefits derived from certain flow properties. The consumer often makes his or her own rheological assessment through sensory perception of the product. From touch and sight, the consumer describes different products as watery, thin, thick, jelly-like, paste-like, etc. It is the rheologists job, in part, to be able to quantify these subjective terminology so that product development can proceed.

Among the most frequently used viscometers in this industry are the U-tube viscometer, the rolling ball (or Hoeppler) viscometer, the Ford Cup, and the Brookfield viscometer. These basic devices are illustrated in Figure 29. The first three devices have often been used in a totally empirical manner for quality control purposes. For example, in each of these cases, the time for the material to flow through the tube or from a vessel, or for a ball to roll between two points, would be measured over some conveniently specified time interval. With some devices, a scale might be included to display a reading of variables, as in the case of the Brookfield, showing readings between say 10% and 90% of full scale deflection. As such, many devices have been adopted, not just in this industry, based on convenience and expediency rather than on a scientific or engineering basis. The disadvantage with many of the simpler instruments is their inability to generate more than one value to characterize a fluid. Often, this reading is converted into a viscosity value based on a Newtonian calibration.

Barnes [65] describes several modifications to the various techniques used in characterizing detergents. The first of these modifications concerns the Hoeppler viscometer, which normally operates using a fixed tube angle and several balls. He proposes to use variable angle of rolling. By altering the angles, the average stress in the fluid varies due to the change in magnitude of the gravitational force on the ball in the tube direction. For this arrangement, viscosity data can be

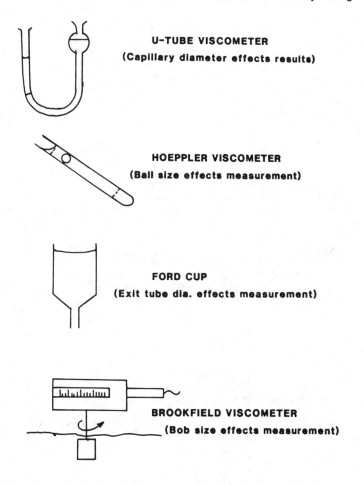

U-TUBE VISCOMETER
(Capillary diameter effects results)

HOEPPLER VISCOMETER
(Ball size effects measurement)

FORD CUP
(Exit tube dia. effects measurement)

BROOKFIELD VISCOMETER
(Bob size effects measurement)

Figure 29. Various viscometers used in the detergents industry.

fitted to a relation:

$$\eta = k_1(\sin \alpha')\theta(A + Bn) \tag{88}$$

where α' = angle of the tube from the horizontal
θ = time for ball to roll between two fixed points
n = slope of curve generated by plotting ln $(\sin \alpha')$ vs. $\ln(1/\theta)$

Note that shear rate in this experiment is $\dot{\gamma} = k_2/\theta$, and A, B, k_1, and k_2 are constants. Also, $A + B = 1$. Usually two experiments (i.e., test at two angles) provide sufficient information such that a power law relation can be derived from η-values.

The Ford cup provides a measure of the time for a fixed volume of fluid (e.g., 50 mls) to flow from the cup into a graduated cylinder. One problem in using this technique with such materials as detergents is the formation of foam, which can make accurate flow-time determinations difficult.

This can be overcome by employing electroresistivity probes along the inside walls of the cup (see Figure 30). This provides accurate measurement of the flow times involved (see [66] for a discussion of electroresistivity probes). A sharp edge orifice fitted to the outlet tube provides steady calibrated flow conditions. Barnes [65] gives the following expressions for viscosity and average shear rate using this technique:

$$\eta = \mu \left(\frac{1+n}{2} \right), \quad \text{N-s/m}^2 \tag{89}$$

$$\dot{\gamma}_{ij} = \frac{2(h_i - h_j)}{\theta_{ij}} \frac{R^2}{r^2}, \quad \text{sec}^{-1} \tag{90}$$

where i, j refer to different heights $(h_1, h_2, h_3, \ldots, \text{etc.})$.

Measurements using a modified Ford cup are quite comparable to those obtained with concentric cylinder viscometers. Materials that are highly thixotropic generate flow times that can be much longer than predicted if steady-state concentric cylinder data are used [65] for comparison, because the total shear in the Ford cup is small compared with the steady-state rotational data. The Ford cup is not applicable to materials where elongational viscosity is much greater than shear flow at the same shear rates. Many detergents show anomalous elastic effects, and hence the Ford cup is not suitable for viscosity measurement in all cases.

Viscosity measurements in shear flow of detergent products can be made in commercial rheometers based on cone-and-plate instruments or concentric cylinder viscometers. Typical commercial

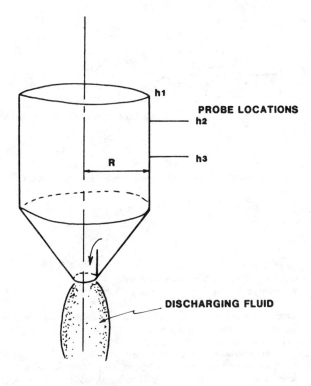

Figure 30. Operation of the Ford cup.

units employed are the Haake Rotovisko, the Ferranti-Shirley viscometers, and the Contraves Rotary viscometer. These instruments cover shear rates typically between 1 to over 1,000 sec[1]. Other instruments employed to a lesser extent are the Deer rheometer and the Weissenberg Rheogoniometer.

The Deer rheometer is designed to subject the sample to a constant stress, whereby the subsequent deformation is measured. This instrument uses a frictionless air bearing so that it is capable of applying a variety of stress patterns with variable time of application and rate of application of stress. Other variations of this instrument are capable of applying oscillatory stress to the fluid sample. Deformation can be studied to measure several parameters: creep, steady-state shear rate, recoverable shear, and various oscillatory parameters. Through geometry changes, the instrument can cover a range of applied stresses. Barnes [65] describes a modified Deer rheometer employed in the study of soap rheology. The system is illustrated in Figure 31, where the rheometer has been modified to measure the extensional properties by simple bending performed at very small deformation. Torque is applied to two vertically mounted rods of soap, which are fixed at both ends. Torque is applied to the samples through the sample end retaining sleeves by magnetic knife edges mounted on radial arms. The knife edges ensure that no twisting of the rods takes place during bending. The extensional compliance is calculated from bending beam theory analysis.

The Weissenberg Rheogoniometer, as noted earlier, can be used to measure G' and G'' as functions of frequency and deformation. These parameters can also be measured for a range of superimposed values of steady shear rate. It is most often applied in industrial laboratories to measure for a range of shear rates, and as a function of shear/time at initiation or cessation of shear.

Other frequently-used viscometers in the detergents manufacturing industry include capillary and orifice viscometers and penetrometers. As noted earlier in this chapter, a capillary viscometer operates by forcing the fluid through a straight circular tube. This instrument is capable of shear rates up to 10^5 sec^{-1}. For fluids obeying power law behavior, the Mooney-Rabinowitz correction enables a definition of the average viscosity/average shear rate parameters. Orifice viscometers are often used in the plastics industry to measure parameters important in pumping fluids through circular orifices. The detergents industry has applied such devices to handle very viscous semi-solid materials such as soap. The last noteworthy device is the penetrometer, which monitors the movement of a weighted penetrator into the surface of a very viscous sample. The penetrometer is most often used for testing such materials as butter or bitumen, in which the penetrator is a sharp truncated pin. Within the detergents industry, this device has proven useful for semi-solid soaps.

There are a variety of other instruments and/or variations of devices described above that are applied in lubrication technology. Lubricating oils are manufactured from the distillation of crude oil. Primary distillation is performed at atmospheric pressure to remove the lighter gasoline, kerosine, and gas oil fractions, and the lubricating oils remain in the residue that boils above about

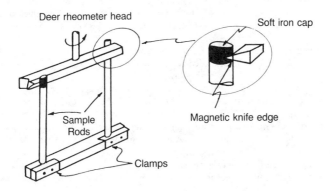

Figure 31. Modified Deer Rheometer used by Barnes [65].

370C. The residue must be distilled under high-vacuum conditions, resulting in several lubricating-oil fractions and an asphaltic bitumen. The second stage residue from those crudes low in asphalt is also a source of lubricating oils. These fractions are referred to as "residual oils" to distinguish them from "distillate oils" that are boiled off in a high-vacuum still. Lubricating-oil fractions can constitute up to 5% of the total crude, depending on the crude source. A further refinement step of the lubricating oils is usually performed with acid or solvents, to remove a variety of unwanted constituents such as sulfur compounds. Hydrotreating at moderate temperatures and pressures saturates the unsaturated hydrocarbons and removes sulfur-bound molecules. Paraffinic constituents separate out as wax at low temperatures. These are removed by chilling and filtering or by a solvent treatment process. Polar compounds and dark coloring constituents are removed from the oil in a final treatment stage using active clays. The refinery streams in these processes are referred to as "base oils" in the petroleum and allied industries. Base oils are characterized by the origin of the crude, the specific refining process used, viscosity, their Viscosity Index (VI), and various other properties. The VI is a measure of the variation of viscosity with temperature, and in general, the higher the VI the smaller the variation.

An important class of products is mineral oils, examples of which are paraffins and aromatics. Oil additives are usually supplied as concentrates in mineral oil, and are readily added during blending operations. Additives can have a variety of purposes for the end-use product; e.g., oxidation inhibitors, additives to neutralize acids, surface-active agents to disperse and maintain other additives in suspension, and ultra-high pressure lubricating additives. Polymers are also added to oils in order to modify rheological properties at extreme temperature conditions (e.g., for motor oils to increase pourability at very low temperatures). A general example of a pour-point depressant is an additive which inhibits the formation of a wax-crystal network at low temperatures. This type of product extends the liquid property range of the lubricant. In lubrication technology, the Navier-Stokes equations for incompressible, viscous, inelastic fluids are often applied to engineering problems. Information on viscosity and proper application of these equations is usually sufficient to estimate oil film thickness and the friction. These equations are usually solved isothermally for computation simplicity, and do not account for viscous heating effects. Hence it is necessary to fully define the viscosity-temperature dependence of these products in order to correct engineering formulations from the Navier-Stokes equations. This is done, as noted earlier, through the use of the VI (Viscosity Index), in which standardized procedures are described in "Kinematic Viscosity," ISO Method 3104, IP Method 71, ASTM Method D445; and "Industrial Liquid Lubricants," ISO Viscosity Classification, ISO 3448.

The capillary viscometer is the standard instrument used for these measurements. Temperature conditions are standardized in these test methods in order to compare oils on a relative basis (e.g., 40C and 100C). In the ISO Viscosity Classification system, a 10-grade oil has a viscosity between 90 and 110 cST at 40C. In all there are six grades for each decade in viscosity.

Many commercial oils contain polymeric additives. Adding small amounts of polymer to an oil reduces the rate of decrease in viscosity with increasing temperature. Examples of the types of polymers used are polyisobutene, polyalkylmethacrylates, and copolymers such as styrene-butadiene and styrene-isoprene.

Molecular weights of these additives range from about 50,000 to several hundred thousand. In an automobile engine, motor oil is exposed to effective shear rates ranging from 10^4 to 10^6 sec^{-1} over wide temperature ranges. Considerably lower shear rates are involved during engine starting. In starting an engine, the cranking speed must be high enough to enable a cylinder to fire. Furthermore, the power the engine delivers when it does fire and the assistance of the starter motor is disengaged during this process. Both these actions depend on the viscosity of the motor oil. One important industry test, a low-temperature, high-shear test method, is the Cold-Cranking Simulator (ASTM Method D2602). The U.S. Society of Automotive Engineers (SAE) provides a classification of engine oil viscosity based on this test method. It should be noted that the industry is in the process of revising test methods and the classification system. Current evolution is leaning towards a high-shear, Cold Cranking Simulator (CCS) viscosity and a yield stress value to be obtained in terms of specified temperatures.

The design of motor oil products requires detailed knowledge of the rheological demands of the oil made by the engine. For example, high temperatures normally achieved in an automobile engine (e.g., 100–150C) cause shear-thinning which can result in increased wear. Also, though, at low temperatures shear-thinning provides the advantage of easier starting conditions. It was noted earlier that base oils are dewaxed in order to remove paraffinics which crystallize out of solution at low temperatures. However, engine oils are never completely dewaxed because of prohibitive refining costs. Consequently, commercial oils can encounter temperatures in which residual waxes will separate out. This important property is tested for by the so-called *Cloud Point*, based on ISO Method 3015, IP Method 219, ASTM Method D2500. The Cloud Point is the temperature at which wax first begins to separate. Another rheological test of motor oil products is the *Pour Point* (ISO Method 3016, IP Method 15, ASTM Method D97). At lower temperatures, oils acquire a yield stress due to the network structure formed by the wax crystals. Considerable research effort has gone into the developement of pour-point depressants, which are additives that interfere with the formation of wax crystal structure.

Illustration of viscometric instruments used in this industry are given in Figures 32 through 35. Figure 32 shows a reverse-flow capillary viscometer. This instrument is used for dark, opaque oils. For this device, the oil flows upward past a set of "timing marks." In this manner, the position of the fluid meniscus is not obscured by oil left behind on the glass wall. Figure 32B illustrates a suspended level viscometer.

Viscosity measurements at low temperatures for transmission and gear oils are usually made with a Brookfield viscometer (methods IP/267 and ASTM D.2983). Other devices equally applicable

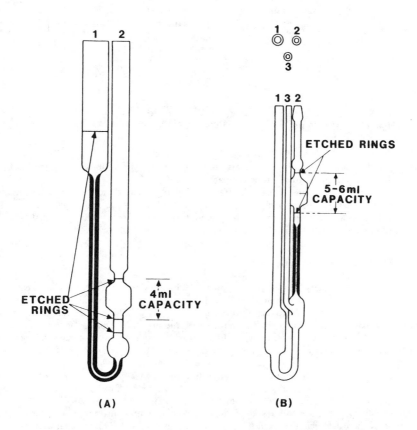

Figure 32. (A) Reverse-Flow capillary viscometer. (B) Suspended level viscometer.

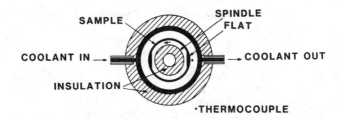

Figure 33. Schematic of cold cranking simulator viscometric cell.

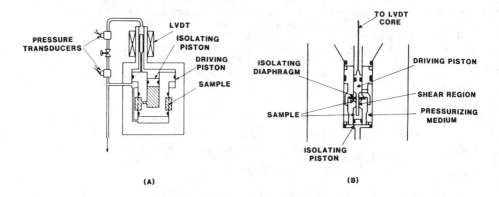

(A)   (B)

Figure 34. (A) High pressure shear stress apparatus described by Bair and Winer [76].

are the Haake Rotovisko RV2 (i.e., constant speed, concentric cylinder instrument), the Hoeppler rolling ball viscometer, and the U-tube capillary viscometer.

The cold-cranking viscometric cell is illustrated in Figure 33. This device consists of a concentric cylinder viscometer. A constant temperature bath is controlled to $-18C$ and oil sample is injected into the viscometer volume via a syringe. Several other viscometers specifically developed for lubrication research are illustrated in Figures 34, 35 and 36.

PROCESSABILITY TESTING

The term "processability" has evolved in polymer technology and refers to the relative ease with which neat or compounded polymers can be handled in production operations and equipment. The most frequently applied production operations are mixing, milling, extrusion, molding, and curing. The end-user manufacturer is concerned with the processing quality or processability of the polymer-based article and is sensitive to factors that may affect the material's behavior and variability during the various manufacturing stages. In the rubber industry, terms such as plasticity and recovery are used heavily as relative ratings of material processability. Plasticity is generally associated with the relative ease of deformation (i.e., the inverse of effective viscosity). In other words, a highly-plastic elastomer or rubber is one that deforms or flows readily. Devices used to test for plasticity, such as the Mooney viscometer, attempt to measure the resistance to deformation.

The specific type of laboratory test depends on the manufacturing operation or operations that will process the elastomer. For example, if the interest lies with the mixing characteristics of a polymer, then the laboratory processability test might be directed at assessing the ease with which

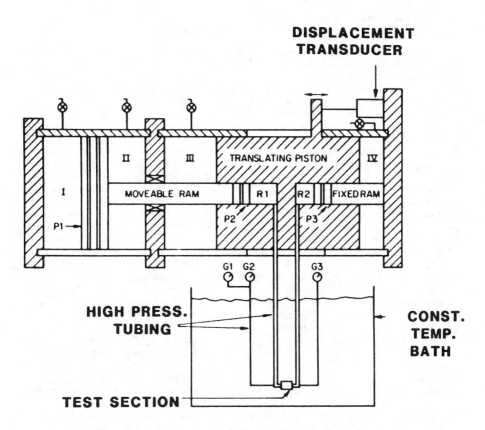

Figure 35. Schematic of high pressure capillary viscometer described by Novak and Winer [77].

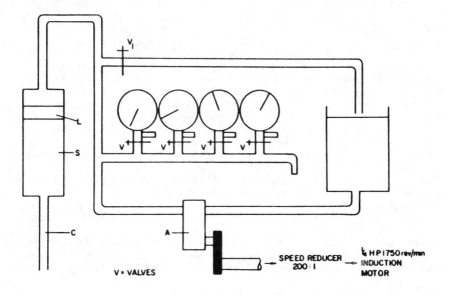

Figure 36. Grease viscometer system based on ASTM Method 1092.

the compounding ingredients can be incorporated and dispersed in the polymer. If, on the other hand, extrusion is of interest, tests might be directed at evaluating the ease by which the compound can be fluxed, transported by the screw, and extruded, and/or the dimensional stability of the extrudate. In applications of injection molding, interest may be in the relative ease of flow of the material, the absence of excessive heat build-up in the runners and gates, the speed of vulcanization, and degree of mold shrinkage. Operations such as calendering, milling, and various other processes can each have their own individual requirements.

A major obstacle in material testing is the ability to scale-up laboratory characterization data to full-scale processing equipment. This, in fact, is a formidable task that is further complicated by economic constraints of manufacturing. Manufacturing operations are manpower intensive and costly. These factors often mandate that processability tests be made simple, fast, and inexpensive, especially when implemented in plant operations for product quality control purposes. Unfortunately, the simpler the test, very often the less correlation it has with processability in full scale equipment. Another serious problem that plagues even the more sophisticated processability testing labs is the scale of equipment and geometric differences which may exist between small-scale apparatuses and commercial equipment. The classical approach to scale-up makes use of the principles of dimensional analysis. The method of similitude requires two fundamental criteria in order to scale up properties or equipment: geometric similitude and dynamic similitude. Very often, lab scale equipment such as mixers or extruders have significantly different geometries than their commercial counterparts. In addition, to minimize experimental efforts and cost, testing is often limited to a very narrow range of conditions. When the laws of similitude are in fact ignored, efforts in laboratory scale processability testing can be wasted and projections as to a product's performance in a commercial operation can be misleading.

The importance of processability testing is that it provides a basis for projecting polymer behavior in commercial operations. If adequate correlations can be developed between full-scale processing operations and the lab, then a basis for product quality testing can be established. In most commercial operations, there are several stages of processing, and hence, laboratory testing must often be implemented in steps to address each stage, in order to regulate product performance. The principal areas evaluated in processability testing are raw material characterization, control of mixing, characterization after mixing, regulation during article shaping, and properties prior to and during vulcanization. The importance of each of these areas is discussed next.

As noted earlier, processability testing must be performed in separate stages in order to be effective in regulating an entire processing operation. The first obvious step is to characterize the neat polymer properties that are most relevant to the behavior in the ensuing processing operations such as mixing, molding, extrusion, etc. As an initial step, the material's viscosity and elasticity, as well as its response to temperature and shear, should be examined in a mixing cycle similar to that of its intended operation. Failure characteristics in terms of such properties as elongation at break and gum green strength provide insight to the material's behavior when subjected to shearing forces on a mill or internal mixer. In conjunction with this, characterization of the molecular weight and molecular weight distribution, as well as detecting the presence of long chain branching, should be conducted using gel permeation chromatography (GPC). The use of GPC and high speed solution viscosity testing on polymer samples represent invaluable tools for controlling the polymerization process so that polymers can be tailor-made for specific processing operations. Also, stress relaxation, which affects properties such as die swell, depends on the molecular weight distribution (MWD). The most pronounced effects of MWD can be observed in the early stages of processing. Batch-to-batch variations in MWD can be one of the most significant causes of problems in mixing; hence, measurements related to MWD are important. One cannot realistically implement processability testing without a characterization of molecular weight and MWD.

Neat polymer characterization should be followed by studying the parameters that affect the mixing process. Conventional approaches to controlling mixing have used the criteria of time and temperature to establish when individual batches should be dumped. With stricter product specifications emerging in new consumer products, more precise and reproducible control techniques of mixing cycles are being imposed. One approach to controlling mixing cycles that requires further study is considering the energy input at different stages in the cycle. It should be noted that most processability testing is conducted at the termination of mixing. One of the most important tests performed involves measuring/rating filler dispersion. The degree of mixedness is important to end-product properties such as tensile strength, elongation or shrinkage, stress relaxation, heat aging characteristics, and the behavior of the mix during the forming operation. Both mix viscosity and elasticity should be measured at this stage.

During the forming or shaping operation, temperature and shear rate must be controlled. Both these parameters affect the flow through the apparatus and during extrusion. The types of tests usually conducted relate to machine capacity, die swell, and the appearance and reproducibility of the extrudate.

Tests are also usually conducted both before and during the vulcanization process. Prior to vulcanization, measurements of the curing rate and/or scorch sensitivity can be made. During vulcanization the heat history of the polymer is a critical parameter to monitor. In the ideal case, thermal history should be homogeneous throughout the product so that the degree of cure and absolute cure state is the same throughout.

In any of the processing operations, polymer flow through the apparatus depends on the vis-coelastic properties of shear and elongational flow. In addition, flow or deformation is affected by the degree of adhesion or friction between the surfaces of the processing approaches and the polymer itself. This latter factor is often overlooked in processability testing because of differences between full-scale equipment and laboratory prototypes. In some applications, however, it can be an important factor that may account for inability to scale-up processing behavior.

Polymer processability is related to the polymer type, molecular-weight, and molecular weight distribution. In addition, it also can be a function of the degree and type of branching, the physical form of the polymer (e.g., granules, powder, slats, strips), the nature of the downstream processes, and the temperature and shear history of the process. Another area is that the mixing process and final physical properties of the material depend also on compounding ingredients. In particular, parameters such as filler type, filler concentration, the degree of polymer/filler interaction, extent of bound rubber, the addition of oils and various process aids, and prevulcanization or scorch can alter processability and final product properties.

As noted earlier, what is often ignored in processability testing for the sake of convenience is the condition of hydrodynamic similarity. Figure 37 shows typical shear rate ranges for different

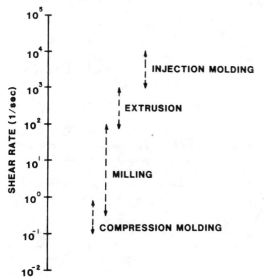

Figure 37. Typical shear rate ranges for commercial processing equipment.

commercial processing operations. With most conventional processability testers (e.g., the Mooney viscometer), testing is done at shear rates far below actual conditions (typically 2.5 sec^{-1}). Although shear rate itself should not be considered the governing criterion for dynamic similitude (a better basis would be a modified Reynolds number or Euler number), it does illustrate that interpretation and extrapolation of laboratory scale processing evaluations is risky, and is almost entirely empirical as practiced by industry today. Nonetheless, testing does provide some guidance, and since there is a wide range of processability tests that have evolved through the years, some latitude exists in selecting a technique or method which at least approaches one or more of the processing operations.

In conjunction with this, one must realize that the viscoelastic properties of polymers and their mixes are not constants. They, in fact, will change with time both in a reversible manner and in an irreversible manner. Samples stored for some period of time may have to be milled and/or premolded into a test piece, and even this can be dangerous as it can alter the processability of the specimen. Sample preparation therefore also enters as a variable, and it is important to establish a standard procedure early on so that data generation can at least be performed on a normalized basis. The ASTM for rubber testing notes that the preparation of specimens for processability measurements should be controlled carefully if reproducible results are to be obtained without modifying the properties to be measured. This is especially the case when performing tests on neat elastomers. The ASTM D1646 provides recommended procedures for sample specimen preparation of rubbers. Some of these procedures involve milling practices. In some cases, it may be necessary for a degree of nonpermanent structure to be broken down either by pretreatment or during the test itself.

Processability primarily depends on the viscoelastic properties of the polymer. It is important, therefore, to understand the characterization terminology used to distinguish viscous and viscoelastic properties. By way of review, one can establish relationships of fundamental rheological properties to processing behavior through the use of processability testing instruments such as rotational, oscillatory, and capillary viscometers. The practical problem of interest is to establish relationships between the fundamental viscoelastic properties and the theories of polymer processing (i.e., milling, extrusion, calendering, building, and performing operations). White [67, 68] provides a review of the fundamental viscoelastic property relationships to polymer processing theory.

Viscoelastic properties of an elastomer at small deformations can be explained by a modulus such as the shear modulus:

$$G^* = G' + iG'' \qquad (91)$$

where G' = inphase, elastic or storage modulus
         G'' = out of phase or loss modulus

Parameters G' and G'' are both temperature and frequency dependent. A parameter known as the frequency factor relates measurements over a temperature range, i.e.:

$$\ln \alpha_T = C_1(T - T_0)/(C_2 + T - T_0) \qquad (92)$$

where T_0 is a reference temperature. In rubber applications, the reference temperature is usually chosen to be about 50°C above the glass transition temperature of the polymer, in which case the constants C_1 and C_2 correspond to the values 8.86 and 101.6°C, respectively. Equation 92 relates the material's response at one shear rate and temperature to a different shear rate through an appropriate change in temperature. The limitation of Equation 92 is that it applies only to small deformations. In contrast, the response of viscoelastic materials at large deformations is highly nonlinear. Nakajima and Collins [69, 70] review large deformation theory. Most textbooks refer to the classical model of viscoelasticity, which uses the spring and dashpot explanation. The Voight and Maxwell models are most often used to describe only the extreme or very limited behavior of elastomeric materials. More sophisticated models are basically extensions of the simple Maxwell spring model and are based on two or more parallel Maxwell elements such that the dashpots are simulated by power law viscosities (see [71] for example).

Using Newton's law of viscosity as the starting point for describing viscoelastic response:

$$\eta = \tau/\dot{\gamma} \tag{93}$$

where η = dynamic viscosity
τ = shear stress
$\dot{\gamma}$ = shear rate

However, polymer melts are non-Newtonian, and hence, a plot of τ vs. $\dot{\gamma}$ results in a curve, not a straight line, even on logarithmic coordinates (see Figure 38). In practice, however, we overlook this and attempt to approximate response at least over a limited range of strain rates by using the empirical power law relationship:

$$\tau = k\dot{\gamma}^n \tag{94a}$$

$$\eta_a = \tau/\dot{\gamma} = k(\dot{\gamma})^{n-1} \tag{94b}$$

It is important to note that the flow curves of different elastomers may cross-over; that is, each material can actually have a different n-value at a given shear rate. As such, a single point viscosity measurement for the purposes of relative comparisons or rankings of polymer behavior may be meaningless. Again, molecular weight distribution can play a dominant role in establishing the pseudoplasticity of an elastomer. For example, in general, very narrow MWD polymers tend to be more Newtonian in their flow response curves (i.e., n ~ 1) over a wide range of shear stress. Most rubbers that are broader in MWD, showing the most probable distribution (i.e., Mw/Mn > 2 − 3) in gum state, display an n-value of about 0.3. Another factor to consider is that many materials, particularly mixtures of different MWD polymers, can in fact show substantial Newtonian response at low shear stresses, but become distinctly non-Newtonian at higher stresses.

In addition to capillary flow, the problem of elongational or extensional flow is of importance to processability testing. In practice, extensional flow occurs at the die entrance of an extruder and in the approach to a nip of a two roll mill. Cotter and Thiel [72] have noted that much of the pressure drop observed at the head of an extruder may be related to extensional flow, particularly with short dies, which are often favored in rubber applications.

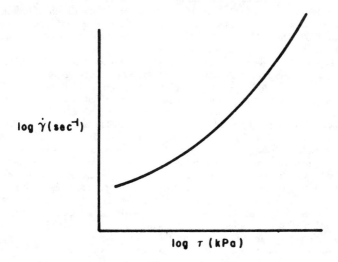

Figure 38. Non-linear flow curve.

The strain rate of a polymer is:

$$\dot{\epsilon} = (1/l_t) \, dl_t/dt \tag{95}$$

where l_t = length of a given element at time t.

Stress/strain testing is a standard characterization tool used in elastomer applications, but there is an important principle to be kept in mind. In normal testing, l_t is in fact not a constant over the experiment. With a purely elastic material, the stresses that develop are related to the deformation and do not depend on the rate at which this deformation is applied. In contrast, a Newtonian material develops stress that is proportional to the rate of deformation. Hence, a measurement of the extensional viscosity of a polymeric material can only be made under the condition of constant deformation rate during a stress-strain experiment. If the strain rate is constant, then:

$$\dot{\epsilon} = [\ln(l_t/l_0)]/t \tag{96}$$

where l_0 = initial length of test specimen. The total strain is thus:

$$\epsilon = \ln(l_t/l_0) \tag{97}$$

The extensional viscosity is normally defined as the ratio of stress to extensional rate, i.e.:

$$\eta_\epsilon = \tau/\dot{\epsilon} \tag{98}$$

Furthermore, from Equation 95 we can deduce the following exponential relationship:

$$l_t = l_0 \, \exp(\dot{\epsilon}t) \tag{99}$$

Equation 99 states that in order for the experiment to be performed at a constant extensional rate, the separation of any two molecules within the bulk elastomer must grow exponentially. In conventional tensile testing machines, this condition is likely never reached. With filled rubbers (e.g., carbon-black filled elastomers), specimens never actually reach steady-state viscosity. Instead, the stress continues to grow with increasing strain up to a rupture point. Rupturing occurs due to rapid orientation of the molecular chains during extensional flow.

The most widely used instruments in elastomers processability and rheological characterization studies are those based on rotary shear. These include the Couette viscometer, cone-and-plate viscometers, the Weissenberg Rheogoniometer, the Mooney viscometer, and similar instruments. These devices have already been discussed.

A few comments on the Mooney viscometer, however, are made because of its relative industry dependence to rubber applications. The Mooney viscometer is a shearing disc viscometer in which a flat, serrated disc rotates in the elastomer sample in a flat grooved or serrated cavity. This creates an element of Couette flow along with rotary shear opposing flat surfaces. However, the flow geometry is more complex, and it's likely there are transition flow patterns in the intermediate regions of the rubber sample. As noted earlier, there are two standard rotor sizes: the larger one, used most frequently, and a smaller one used for highly viscous, stiffer rubbers. The most commonly reported measurement is designated ML 1 + 4 (100°C), meaning the Mooney viscosity measured at 100°C after 1 minute preheat and 4 minutes rotor rotation. Typical Mooney viscosity curves for different rubber samples are shown in Figure 39. There are several inherent problems with the Mooney viscometer, most of which are associated with improper maintenance. Rotor disc wear, negligence in cleaning, poor temperature and rotor speed control, and entrapment of air pockets in rubber samples can effect the accuracy and reproducibility of measurements. As with any heavily used instrument, particularly if applied in frequent quality control testing, it is advisable to run periodic calibration checks and to control chart the measurements.

Another potential problem with the Mooney viscometer is slippage. Instabilities in Mooney viscometer curves for EPDMs have been reported by Market [73] at short times and at rubber temperatures below 100°C. The explanation for this is likely due to shear breakdown of the polymer

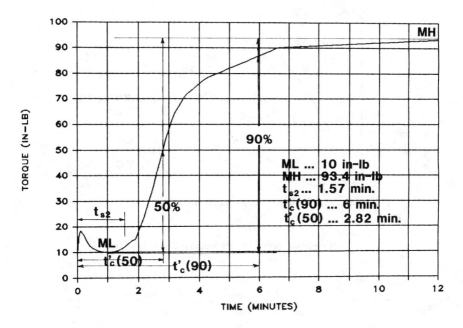

Figure 39. Typical Mooney viscosity curves for rubber samples.

when a critical stress was exceeded. Similar observations have been made by the author for very stiff (very high Mooney) polymers.

A final note on the Mooney viscometer is that the instrument is most often not utilized to its full capabilities in industrial laboratory environments. Measurements are normally restricted to a fixed, very low rotor speed; however, the instrument is capable of performing tests over a relatively wide range of shear rates. The commercially available instrument can be run at shear rates close to 100 sec^{-1}. Depending on the polymer sample, however, heat generation may become a problem, along with the potential for regimes of slip to be encountered. It does, however, offer the potential to be used in a similar fashion as a capillary rheometer.

Another commonly used type of instrument is based on the principle of an eccentric rotating disc, of which the most well known is the Rheometrics Mechanical Spectrometer. The instrument can conduct experiments over a variety of oscillatory and continuous shear modes and test conditions. The device is highly versatile in that it can be used to characterize a wide range of properties and materials ranging from solutions to solids. The instrument is equipped with a variety of adaptors of different geometries, such as cone-and-plate, parallel plate, biconical, concentric cylinder, and an eccentric rotating disc. The last adaption is known as the ERD system (also called the orthogonal rheometer). Rubber is positioned between two parallel, but not coaxial, discs which rotate at the same speed and in the same direction. This action subjects the rubber specimen to sinusoidal oscillations. By measuring the forces on the anvils along the principal axes, one can calculate the real and imaginary components of the shear modulus which forms the basis for determining the normal stress effects. Mocosco and Davis [74] and Willey, et al. [76] provide detailed discussions on this instrument.

Figure 40 illustrates the types of stress-strain relationships that characterize various polymer materials. From dynamic mechanical spectroscopy, the amount of energy dissipated from a block of material subjected to stress is:

$$E'' = E' \tan \delta \tag{100}$$

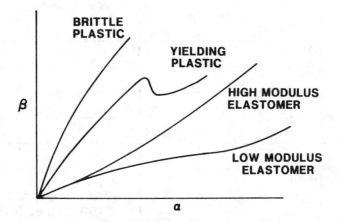

Figure 40. Stress-strain properties of polymers.

where E'' = loss modulus (i.e., energy dissipated)
        E' = storage modulus (i.e., energy stored elastically)
        δ = phase angle between the applied stress and resulting strain

Phase angle δ is analogous to the power factor in basic electricity. The relationship between loss modulus and storage modulus to temperature is shown in Figure 41.

In the processing of polymers, the material is subjected to stresses that invoke physical extension or strain on the molecular structure. The simple dynamic shear experiment shown in Figure 42 shows that when a force F is applied to a block, stress is induced, causing deformation or strain.

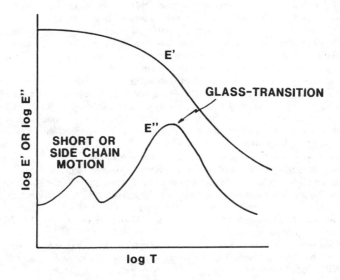

Figure 41. Relationships for storage and loss moduli.

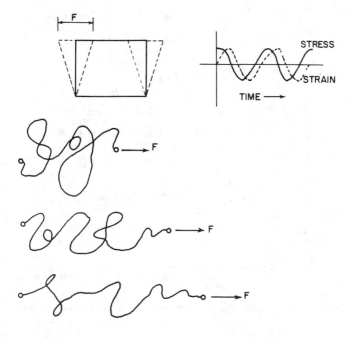

Figure 42. Applications of force to polymer molecules.

On a molecular scale, this means an extension, or rather un-entanglement, of the long polymer molecules. This deformation results in an increase in interatomic distance, and there is a transformation in volume and shape of the material. From thermodynamic principles, the change in free energy upon extension is:

$$\Delta F = \Delta H - T \, \Delta S \tag{101}$$

Enthalpy, ΔH, can be thought of in terms of the familiar spring model described in numerous textbooks. For elastomeric materials it is representative of the increase in interatomic distances. The entropy term denotes the loss in the number of possible chain configurations during the deformation.

Time and temperature dependence of the stress-strain properties of elastomers play an important role in their processability. With elastomers it is possible to identify a failure envelope which characterizes the physical and rheological nature of the material (see Figure 43). From the viewpoint of engineering applications, the tensile strength of elastomers is of great significance in determining end-uses. The tensile strength of elastomeric materials depends on a number of factors, the most critical ones being the extension rate and temperature the material is subjected to, the type of elastomer (i.e., single-phase non-crystallizable, crystallizable, polymers containing domains such as glass domains or ionic domains), the type of crosslinking, and of course, the molecular network.

Elastomers gain their strength properties largely by the incorporation of filler material; however, there are more complex contributions. The various sources of strength include the material's viscoelastic properties, molecular network perfection, the orientation of chains, the degree of energy dissipation by fillers, the ability of fillers to deflect and stop the propagation of microcracks, various polymeric domains which serve as fillers, the deformation of domains, and various interactions among the above. Figure 44 summarizes the various mechanisms contributing to tensile strength.

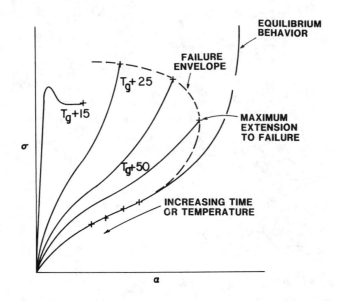

Figure 43. Time and temperature dependence of stress-strain properties.

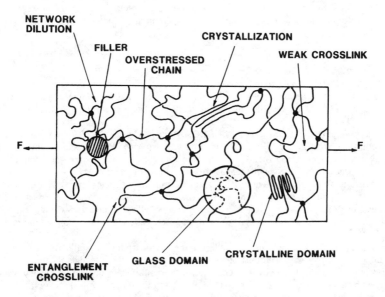

Figure 44. Tensile strength mechanisms.

It is worthwhile reviewing some basic concepts on the principles of vulcanization for elastomers before discussing processability further. Figure 45 presents a simplified picture of the molecular structure of an unvulcanized and sulfur-cured vulcanized rubber network. The sulfur molecule in this case forms a crosslink network by bonding between the rubber molecules. The properties of

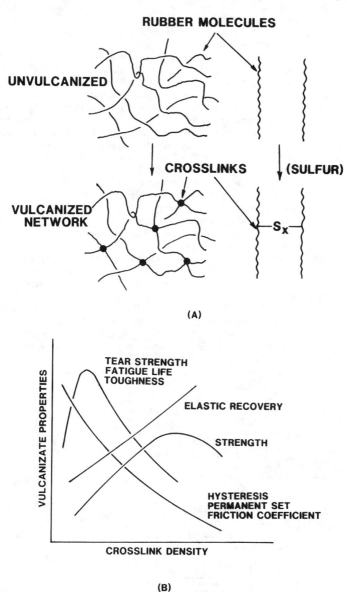

(A)

(B)

Figure 45. (A) Effect of vulcanization on rubber matrix. (B) How vulcanization properties are affected.

the vulcanizate will depend on the crosslink density. The properties of engineering interest are tear strength, fatigue life, material toughness, stiffness, tensile strength, set properties, hysteresis, and others (see Figure 21). There are a battery of testing procedures to assess each of these properties, but in conventional rubber applications, the starting place is usually with the cure response of the vulcanizate. To assess this a device called an oscillating disc rheometer is used, a simplified diagram of which is shown in Figure 46. Typical torque response curves are shown in Figure 47.

Important parameters related to the vulcanization process are the time elapsed before it begins, the rate at which it occurs, and the extent to which it occurs.

The multitude of rubber products used throughout the world cannot be manufactured without the step of vulcanization. The process of vulcanization is the cross-linking of the chain-like rubber molecules which are transformed into an elastic network. There are a variety of cross-linking agents, the most predominant of which are sulfur, organic peroxides, and various poly-functional coupling agents. In conventional cured rubber applications, sulfur is predominantly used because of high vulcanizate properties, wide latitude offered in compounding, and its low cost. An important advantage of a sulfur package curing system is that it provides delayed action which is needed in the processing, shaping, and forming stages of the rubber article prior to its becoming an intractable vulcanized network. Accelerators coupled with sulfur can, in addition, be used to increase the rates of cross-link formation after the delay period.

Elastomeric materials are characterized by their ability to forcibly retract to their approximate original configuration after being subjected to deformation. The forces responsible for retraction can be increased, and the degree of permanent deformation remaining after being removed from the deforming force can be reduced by vulcanization. In other words, vulcanization contributes to enhancing the property of elasticity, and therefore, is responsible for reducing plasticity. A very simple viewpoint of an elastomer is that on a molecular scale it is made up of a network of linear polymer chains that are joined together by cross-links. It is the relative number of network-supporting polymer chains per unit volume of elastomer that establishes the magnitude of retractive force capable of resisting deformation. The number of supporting chains can be increased by raising the number of junctures. The process of vulcanization is a chemical means of producing network junctures. In does this by inserting cross-links between polymer chains. In practice, sulfur vulcanization is performed by heating the elastomer and vulcanizing agents together in a mold.

As noted earlier, properties such as fatigue life, tear strength, and toughness can be characterized by the energy needed to break. A measure of the deformation energy is hysteresis, which is a rate-dependent property. Hysteresis is practically defined as the ratio of the viscous component to the elastic component of deformation resistance.

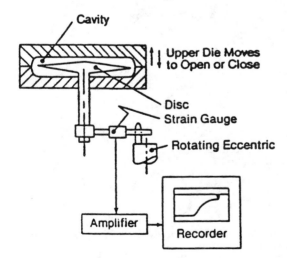

Figure 46. Oscillating disc rheometer.

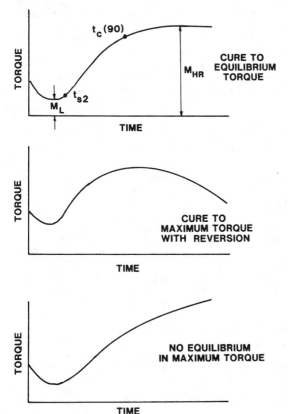

Figure 47. Vulcanization properties characterized on an oscillating disc curemeter.

A practical processing problem is to prevent or minimize the risk of premature vulcanization. This is referred to as scorch. For an elastomeric material to be of engineering/consumer interest, it must have sufficient scorch resistance; i.e., it must be capable of having sufficient time delay in vulcanization to enable processing (mixing/milling/forming/molding/etc.) of the final article. In other words, the process of cross-link formation must be controllable within the limits of the processing requirements of the application. One key requirement, then, in selecting a polymer-compound system for a particular end-use application is that processing time and scorch resistance be compatible.

Scorch resistance can be studied on the laboratory scale, and should be measured at the intended processing temperature. It is measured as the time required for the onset of cross-linking. By using a Mooney viscometer, one can detect this time from a sharp increase in viscosity. A rheometer (or cure meter) such as shown in Figure 16 can supplement this evaluation by providing a measure of the extent of cure.

The curemeter shown in Figure 46 is based on the principle of oscillating disks whereby a sample of rubber is cured in a cavity while a disk, embedded in the sample, is in oscillatory rotation covering an arc-like motion. The resistance to the disk's oscillation is measured as a function of time, producing the curemeter response curve shown in Figure 47. This type of curemeter (rheometer) chart characterizes both the induction time and the rate of cure (i.e., the vulcanization rate). Mooney viscosity measurements over time provide the processing safety guideline in terms of scorch resistance. This latter measurement is usually reported as time in units of minutes for a pre-specified change in Mooney units. In the rubber industry, scorch times are typically reported as minutes for a 5-point rise in Mooney viscosity, or over a 3-point rise. The oscillating disk rheometer is then used to characterize the vulcanization kinetics at a temperature typifying full-scale processing.

Mixing and extrusion constitute two of the most widely used processing operations for elastomeric products. It is critical, therefore, that representative laboratory testing procedures be used to characterize and project the polymer's performance prior to manufacturing finished articles. Small scale internal mixers (midget and B-Banbury size) mixers capable of neat rubber capacities ranging from a 50-or-more grams of rubber to kilogram charges are usually standard equipment in a rubber processing laboratory. As a minimum test, the work input to the machine may be used with some success to assess the state of mixedness during a mix cycle and to determine when to dump the batch. A laboratory scale Banbury or similar type mixer can serve as a processability tester to obtain data on the changes in resistance to deformation during mixing, the times to specific properties of the power trace being used as indexes of processability of the neat polymer or of the degree of dispersibility of carbon black, mineral fillers, or other additives in a given polymer.

More advanced processing laboratories are equipped with instrumented miniature mixers called torque rheometers, which enable measurement of the torque on the rotors. This can provide a basis for developing quantitative indexes of processability as a function of the time of mixing. Companies such as Haake-Buchler and Brabender also provide an adaptable screw mixer section that is a miniature extruder. The torque rheometer is equipped with dual temperature and pressure sensors, as well as a torque meter, and hence provides a measure of the work accomplished in the process material during mixing or extrusion under controlled conditions of temperature, shear, and time. Thus, the device is capable of detecting changes in state, viscosity, or chemical reactions on a real-time basis. It is important to note that the torque rheometer's data can be interpreted in terms of shear force (dyne/cm^2), shear rate (sec^{-1}) and viscosity. The data can be interpreted in terms of work and power. Torque data are a measure of power requirements by adding shaft rotation rate to the torque balance expression.

Conventional polymer processing is comprised of several types: polymerization (i.e., resin cooking); internal mixers (master blending); roll mill/calendering (i.e., preparation for processing and mixing); grinding/cutting (preparation for extrusion); extrusion (melting and pumping); (pelletizing) preparation for final processing; final process of extrusion, injection molding, blow molding, etc. In practical terms, each of these operations is handled in a batch mode, with intermediate product conveyed from one step to another. At each staged operation, a specific shear stress and shear rate are required and are often quite different from the shear rate/shear stress of the next process step. This means that the material could be transferred faster or slower to a successive processing step than the following stage requires for feeding. In addition, the polymer will undergo continuous shear stress and varying temperature stress, which can in fact alter the chemical structure. From the standpoint of processability testing, one must provide a wide latitude of testing in order to keep track of the polymer's viscosity during all the process phases.

Torque is related to the concept of shear stress, and the speed of the rheometer is related to shear rate. The relation of shear stress to shear rate is the apparent viscosity. For this reason, the torque rheometer can be considered a hybrid device between that of a viscometer and a scaled-down processability tester. A basic torque rheometer comprises a drive, a torque (viscosity) measuring system, a sensor, a temperature control unit, and a data recorder. The fundamental work in the area of torque rheometry has been based on using a mixer as a sensor on the basic measuring instrument. As noted earlier, the various processing steps such as mixing, extrusion, calendering, and molding subject the polymer to different shear rates. Thus any polymer can behave differently in these various processes. In fact, any two materials may be perfectly suitable in one process but not suitable in another. Figure 48 provides an example of the influence of shear rate on the stress of two rheologically different polymers. Since apparent viscosity is defined as the ratio of shear stress to shear rate, it is obvious from Figure 48 that no apparent viscosity varies as a function of shear rate, but that the polymers have different viscosities relative to each other. In processing operations involving conditions of low shear rate, these two polymers might be used interchangeably; however, there would be significant differences in operations involving higher shear rates. It is important then that the materials be tested in the same range of shear as anticipated in the actual processing to form a basis for selection.

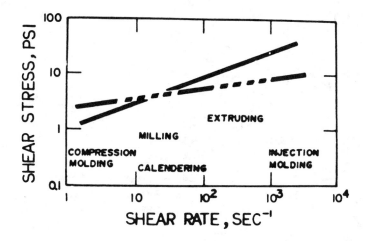

Figure 48. Example flow curves of two polymers.

Plastics-processing operations usually subject the polymer to very high shear rates and temperatures for a period of time. With increased utilization of plastics and elastomers, production rates have increased, meaning that the capacities of processing equipment have increased, exposing new polymers to even higher shear rate conditions. Many of these processing operations require close tolerances on extruded and molded articles. Both the high production rates and close manufacturing tolerances require that the feedstock polymer have exact and duplicate properties from production-to-production. Prediction of material processability cannot be based on only a knowledge of the polymer's solution viscosity or average molecular weight as determined in low shear rate tests. Extrapolation of viscosity data obtained under low shear rate conditions such as a melt index can lead to erroneous conclusions. Two resins or elastomers can have greatly different flow responses as a function of shear rate and hence, have significantly different apparent viscosities in regions of high shear rate. This discussion becomes clearer by diagnosing a typical flow response curve for a polymer. Figure 49A illustrates the generalized flow properties in terms of a plot of shear stress vs shear rate on linear coordinates. Figure 49B shows the same plot on logarithmic coordinates. In examining these plots we note the following: First, at very low shear rates, the response of the polymer is Newtonian in the vicinity of the so-called zero shear viscosity. In the intermediate region, the polymer is pseudoplastic over a wide range (several decades) of shear rate. Finally, at very high shear rates, the polymer is again observed to approach that of Newtonian behavior.

These characteristics can be attributed to the molecular structure of the polymer. Under low shear rate conditions, the thermal motion of the polymer chain segments dominates and overcomes any tendency toward molecular alignment. In this case, the molecules are random and exist in a highly entangled state. In this state, there is the greatest resistance to deformation.

When the material is subjected to higher shear rates, molecules begin to untangle and align. In this state, the resistance to polymer chain slippage past one another is reduced. At very high shear rates, the polymer molecules are nearly totally untangled and aligned, and eventually reach a state of minimum flow resistance.

The pseudoplastic region of the plot in Figure 49B is approximated by the power law model. Figure 50 shows a plot of viscosity vs. shear rate for several polymers. Different rheometers discussed cover the various shear rates in polymer characterization. Note that the low density polyethylene (LDPE) in Figure 50 shows Newtonian flow behavior in the low shear rate region. The values for MI in Figure 50 represent melt index, which is a low shear rate test. Since MI is obtained at low shear, it has a higher correlation with molecular weight and zero shear viscosity. On the other hand, it should

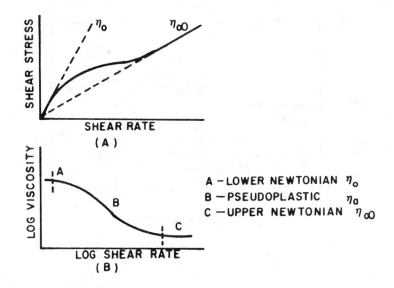

Figure 49. Generalized flow curves for polymers.

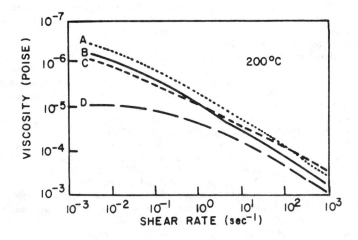

Figure 50. Viscosity vs. shear rate curves for several polymers: Curve A—HDPE (MI = 0.2, $\overline{Mw}$ = 1.7 × 10⁵); Curve B—HDPE (MI = 0.2, $\overline{Mw}$ = 1.4 × 10⁴); Curve C—HDPE (MI = 0.08, $\overline{Mw}$ = 2.0 × 10⁴), Curve D—LDPE (MI = 3.5, $\overline{Mw}$ = 2.0 × 10⁴).

not be expected to correlate with polymer flow response in the shear rate regions normally imposed by commercial processing operations.

Rheological measurements depend on the test specimen, shear rate, temperature, pressure, and the specimen's prior history. Each of these parameters must be carefully controlled during testing in order to obtain reproducible data.

Conventional rheological testing considers the polymer only in the melt state as a function of shear rate and temperature. From a processor's viewpoint, however, there are many potential difficulties caused by the effects of work done to the polymer prior to, and in transition to, the melt state. Thermosetting plastics also present processing problems related to the rate of cure and its effect on polymer rheology.

Extrusion can be considered a typical operation. When dealing with plastics, the resin powder in the feed hopper must be free-flowing, to provide uniform feed, then must be conveyed and compacted in the cool feed zone. The lubricity of the compound must be controlled so the initiation of fusion is neither too fast (high torque) nor too slow (poor melting). The rate of fusion, the apparent viscosity at the hot end of the extruder, and the high temperature-high shear stability in the forming zone must all be considered. Furthermore, the viscoelastic character of the compound also influences extrusion throughout the entire operation.

The basis for processability testing and projection of results from small-scale testing can be established in the following manner: When polymer samples known to provide good processing performance in large scale equipment are compared with samples known to cause processing problems, the operating conditions of shear rate and temperature can be optimized in the lab scale apparatus to provide a correlation with a given factory process.

With a torque rheometer, work energy is measured, which in turn reflects the flow behavior (or viscosity) of the polymer sample under shear and thermal stress. This, in turn, is a function of the rotor speed (i.e., process speed) and temperature during the various viscous stages the polymer undergoes. It is important, then, that the torque rheometer not only measure torque, but also temperature and rpm. It is important to note also that in comparing several stocks, no measurable torque differences may be apparent; however, significant temperature differences may exist. A torque rheometer, then, is capable of providing real-time data on torque and melt temperature under specific set temperature and process speed conditions. Information on the amount of work needed to bring a polymer from its solid state to a homogeneous melt, as well as the time required for processing, can be obtained. In addition, the instrument can be used much like a Mooney viscometer to ascertain scorch time, but at shear conditions more closely approximating the factory operation. In plastics handling, it is possible to ascertain under what conditions the polymer will chemically break down or establish the elasticity of the resin. On this last point, polymers can be "finger-printed" in terms of the bandwidth of the torque response curve. As an example of a processability-product quality test, one could establish an "ideal" curve based on an acceptable, well-processing polymer under specified conditions in actual process equipment. A bandwidth can be established within which the polymer's torque curve must lie in order to be acceptable for the process under consideration. Deviation outside the bandwidth would indicate an unacceptable polymer, or that process conditions must be altered. Although this is strictly an empirical approach, with experience it can form the basis of an acceptable method of product quality control.

The torque rheometer can be compiled with a mixer, as described earlier, to provide a pilot device for mixer/processability studies. In this fashion, a mix can be prepared under different conditions, and the optimum operating range defined and scaled up to production levels. A torque rheometer/mixer arrangement enables different samples to be homogenized to a uniform viscosity, or it can be used to stage identical power inputs to provide repetitive samples in a uniform manner to a standard viscosity and temperature. One advantage of carefully controlled mixing is that it can also provide the basis for specimen preparation for other physical testing such as rubber cure time, tensile strength, and modulus testing.

Another use for the mixer arrangement is in the study of compatibilizers. For example, one can study different ratios of polymer blends with compatibilizers. Properties in this case are highly dependent on particle size and dispersion qualities. The effect of mixing different polymer systems in various ratios with different amounts of "couples" can be carried out. Such a test can be conducted by subjecting the formulation to varying mixing times and speeds. The objective is to maximize physical properties and minimize the amount of compatibilizer, therefore reducing cost.

Figure 51 provides an example where SBR polymers may require different black incorporation times and have different average torque levels. Note that the torque response curves show different amounts of mixing work (i.e., work being the area under the torque curve). It is important to note also that the torque level also provides an indication of the degree of reinforcement. The time re-

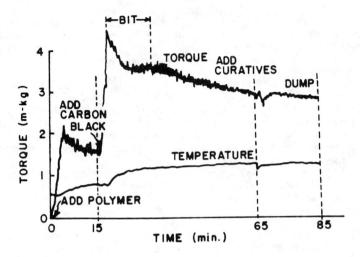

Figure 51. Effects of carbon black and curatives in rubber as measured in a torque-rheometer.

quired for reinforcing or extruding fillers to be incorporated into a polymer is a compounding parameter that can also be readily measured.

Chemical reactions such as rubber scorching, polymer crosslinking, gel formation, and thermosetting of resins can be readily studied in a torque-rheometer-mixer arrangement. By proper selection of the mixer configuration and rotor speed, the shear input can be prespecified. Changes in

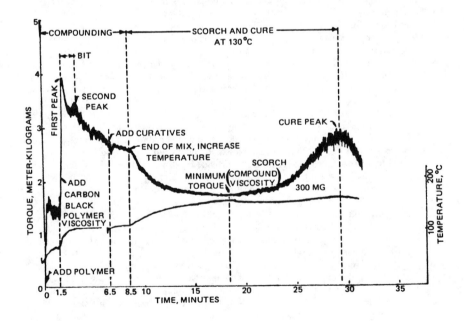

Figure 52. Rubber testing in a torque-recording internal mixer.

torque level can be monitored as the reaction takes place. In other applications, accurate temperature control may be the most critical parameter. Figure 52 provides an example of the effect of compounding ingredients in rubber on the reaction.

An example of a torque response for a typical thermoset is shown in Figure 53. In this example, the measurable variables are the loading peak, the point of maximum flow (i.e., minimum viscosity), the point of maximum cure (the second peak), the time to maximum flow, and time to maximum cure.

An example of rubber scorch evaluated in a mixer-torque rheometer is shown in Figure 54. The curves shown are for two rubber compounds which differ in their accelerator concentration. The specimen having the lower amount of accelerator shows a greater scorch safety, but also has a slower rate of cure. Other example studies where a torque rheometer can be applied are in studying the crosslinking characteristics of polyethylene and in testing the thermal gelling of plastisols.

Mixer-sensor torque rheometry studies can separate out phenomena that take place successively and/or concurrently during processing. For example, extrusion involves several stages (solid flow, fusion/melting rates, viscosity levels, viscosity changes). Each of these regimes can be readily identified on a torque curve equipped with a mixer-sensor. A torque curve derived from an extruder sensor arrangement provides data on the overall combined effect.

The important features of a typical mixer-sensor torque rheometer rheogram are summarized in Figure 55. Phase I of the rheogram denotes a change of state for the material (e.g., the melting of a thermoplastic resin), or structural change occurring in a liquid such as the gellation of a plastisol. Phase II typifies the beginning of viscous flow, and the effects of temperature and shear can be observed in this region. Phase III denotes the region where possible reactions take place, such as the curing of an elastomer. The reaction region would also denote undesirable phenomena such as the degradation of polymers, or scorch, in which case a torque increase would be observed.

It is also possible to correlate torque measurements with some finished product properties. For example, with thermoplastics, one can mix the formulation until achieving a stable viscosity level. After leaving the rotors off for some brief time period to allow the compound to rest, the drive can be turned on again. The initial shock torque that is measured will often be higher than the last recorded torque prior to stopping the drive. This observation exemplifies the recovery of viscosity or structure of a thixotropic material during testing. The ratio of shock torque to former torque of a

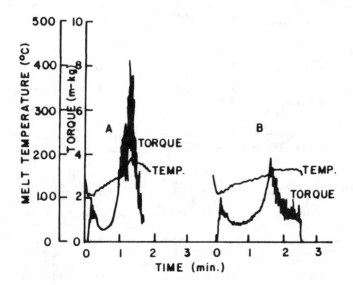

Figure 53. Study of the cure of two thermosetting plastics.

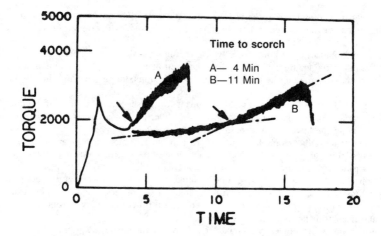

Figure 54. Study of rubber scorch and cure in a mixer-sensor torque rheometer.

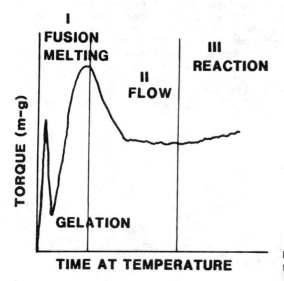

Figure 55. Important features of a torque rheogram.

molding compound can be found to correlate with the property of impact resistance with some blow-molded articles.

Another example of the use of a torque-rheometer-mixer system aimed at processability/product quality testing is given by the rheograms shown in Figure 56. In this example, two production lots of the same EPDM of an extrusion-grade masterbatch were tested in a Banbury-style mixer attachment (system used was a Rheocord System 40, Haake-Buchler). A customer reported that the two materials processed differently; however, both gum and compound Mooney viscosity measurements were the same for the two samples. A comparison of the torque response curves for the two compound samples is shown in Figure 56. The polymer that reportedly processed well displayed a

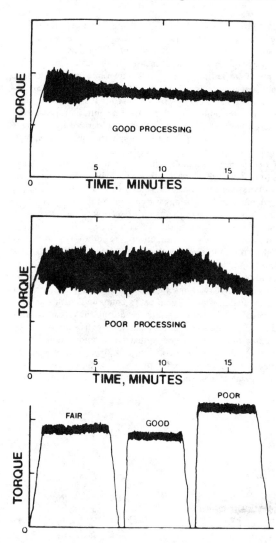

Figure 56. Example on use of torque rheometry to distinguish processing characteristics between polymer samples.

unique torque pattern at an average level. The bandwidth decreased slightly during the first five minutes of mixing; however, the minimum torque level was constant throughout the experiment. The poor processing sample required a much longer mixing time before the same steady bandwidth was achieved. A higher average torque was observed for the poor processing compound, which indicated that a greater amount of energy was needed to process the material. The wider bandwidth also indicated that the sample was more nervy and had greater elasticity. The transition from a rough elastic state to a smoother, more plastic property is likely indicative of improved carbon black/mineral filler dispersion.

Another processing experiment readily conducted in a torque/mixer rheometer is a fusion test. The *time of fusion* of a polymer refers to the time period from the loading of solid polymer into a mixer cavity to the point at which it melts into a plastic-like mass. This time span depends on the base residue and its compounding ingredients (e.g., plasticizers, peptizers, stabilizers) as well as the polymer itself. The test is most often associated with the characterizing of PVC resins, but applies to virtually all types of polymers. The test essentially is aimed at measuring the fusion time, which can be observed by the peak torque required at the time of fusion, as shown in Figure 57. Fusion or melting characteristics of a polymer can be related to processing conditions, for example, the compression zone in a plastics extruder. The amount of energy or work involved in fusion and the time to fusion establish both the degree of fusion and the point where it occurs in a continuous processing operation such as extrusion. The torque response curve shown in Figure 57, derived by mixing a polymer at a constant rotor speed, can be related to an extrusion operation in the following manner: If the material is a plastic resin, for example, the high shear melt viscosity of the polymer is the most important property in the compression and metering sections. The rheogram in Figure 57 shows the material charging and fusion peaks to be relatively close together, after which the material decreases in torque to some constant viscosity level. In the extruder, similar behavior takes place; i.e., the solid polymer is subjected to a shearing force, which brings it to a point of fusion, after which it achieves a constant viscosity and is transported through the metering section of the extruder.

In many rubber and plastics processing problems, it is also of interest to characterize mixing behavior beyond the fusion peak. For example, in rigid PVC formulations, the addition of lubricants is often made. The purpose of a lubricant is to promote proper flow of the plastic melt. The effects of lubricants on melt viscosity and material stability can be simulated over a range of temperatures and shear rates which simulate the feed end of an extruder. Figure 58 illustrates a typical rheogram, noting the important features. A resin or polymer having insufficient lubricity is typically characterized by a high loading peak and a short fusion time. In contrast, a compound with excessive lubrication will experience slippage and usually a slow temperature rise during the mix as characterized by a resulting long fusion time. This can create a serious problem in the extrusion of plastics, as the resin could pass through the extruder without being properly fluxed. It should be noted, however, that proper polymer lubrication and optimization of the fusion peak depend in part on the equipment geometry and flow conditions. Scale-up of processing observation can be risky in this area, and it is a more prudent policy to implement a series of tests on different compounds to de-

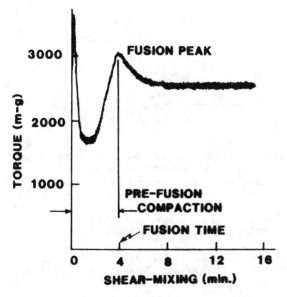

Figure 57. Fusion peak and time as measured in a torque/mixer rheometer.

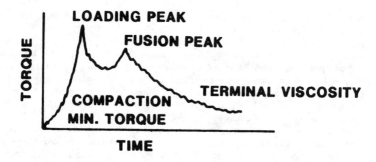

Figure 58. Use of mixer/torque rheometer in characterizing the viscosity of an elastomer.

velop relative processability ratings. As noted, a lubricant is used to promote flow. In the extrusion of rigid plastic materials (e.g., PVC pipe) lubrication reduces frictional heat generation, as well as affecting polymer/metal and polymer/polymer interfacial action. Lubricants will also have an affect on the fusion rate. This is a strong function of the particular stabilizer ingredient used in the compound.

All of the torque curves described are essentially viscosity-sensitive signals that can be related to shear stress via conventional viscometry. The speed setting on a torque rheometer is related to shear rate. This means that if several polymers are evaluated independently at some identical rotor speed and temperature, any variation in torque among the specimens is indicative of viscosity differences. A simple experiment to characterize the viscosity of elastomer samples involves running the torque rheometer at a constant speed to achieve a stable torque response. By running a succession of different speeds, polymer samples can be evaluated over a range of shear rates, as is accomplished in a convential capillary rheometer. A problem, however, is that the geometry of a torque rheometer is complex, and hence, it is extremely difficult to interpret rheograms in terms of fundamental rheological parameters. This means that from the standpoint of processability testing, the instrument is most useful in providing a relative index of processability, and that scale-up to full-size processing machines should be done cautiously. It is possible to relate rotor torque and speed through a power-law relation, as is done with shear stress and shear strain, i.e.:

$$T = C(n)Ks^n \qquad (102)$$

where   T = torque
         n = power-law index
      C(n) = function which depends on n and machine geometry
         K = constant in the power-law shear stress/shear rate, relationship
         s = rotor speed

The power-law index n obtained in a torque rheometer will agree with the value derived from data obtained from a capillary rheometer. This means that from capillary rheometer-derived K and n values, one can calibrate a torque rheometer, in which case C(n) can be deduced as an explicit function of the machine's geometry and the value of n.

To summarize, the rheogram derived from a mixer torque rheometer provides processing information in three general areas: First, it can detect the times at which peaks and troughs occur in torque-time or power-time curves, which in turn are representative of the interactions between polymer rheology and various processing/mixing steps. The second area is that the total work performed by the mixer on the elastomer or polymer can be measured. This is important for two reasons:

Mixing energy is an identifiable index of processing in itself, and can be compared with different polymer samples when experiments are conducted over identical mixing times, rotor speeds, and temperatures. These data, in turn, can form a basis for scaling-up or projecting processing behavior to full-scale equipment. Also, in some processes, it may be more desirable from the standpoint of dispersion and polyblending to dump a masterbatch on the basis of totalized mixer power or torque, rather than using the conventional criteria of mixing to a pre-specified time and temperature. This is an option that needs to be explored for the particular polymers and processing operations under consideration. A third area of information is that the mix cycle history in the initial stages and even the end of the first stage mixing, at least with rubber, are often characterized by the magnitude of short-period-variations in power or torque, as shown by the width of the torque response band on a rheogram (refer back to Figure 56). This can form a basis for fingerprinting a polymer's rheological/processing characteristics and could provide the basis for product quality testing in some instances.

The torque rheometer can be adapted with a screw mixer section to perform extrusion experiments. The use of Garvey dies, slit dies, or capillary dies can provide information on extrudate dimensions/stability, appearance ratings, and swell. The standard rating for extrusion through a Garvey die is shown in Figure 59. Systems such as the Haake-Buchler-Rheocard System 40 or Brabender Plasticorder have drives that can adapt several types of mixer cavity/rotor configurations and screw mixer chambers. Figure 60 illustrates some of the capabilities of the Rheocord System 40 in extrusion experiments on several EPDM samples. The extruder retrofitted with dual temperature and pressure sensors along the axis of the barrel can simultaneously record pressure/temperature/torque responses as a function of experiment time. Through the use of a microprocessor and a control monitor, the operator can pre-program a set of extrusion conditions. For example, the extrusion characteristics of a polymer compound can be studied by automating the experiment such that the drive automatically changes to different screw speeds or temperatures as step or ramp functions (see Figure 61). Thus, a large data base on the extrudability of different compounds or polymer candidates can be generated in a rather short time by running continuous extrusion tests preprogrammed on the instrument. The investigator can then post analyze cross-correlation plots of torque vs. screw speed or torque vs. head/upstream pressure, etc., to obtain relative process ratings between samples. The references cited at the end of this chapter provide more detailed readings on the uses and theory of torque rheometry to polymer processing studies.

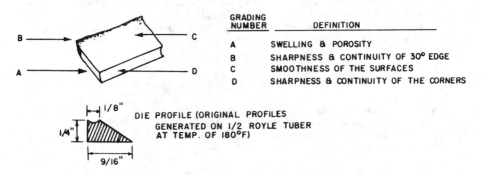

GRADING NUMBER	DEFINITION
A	SWELLING & POROSITY
B	SHARPNESS & CONTINUITY OF 30° EDGE
C	SMOOTHNESS OF THE SURFACES
D	SHARPNESS & CONTINUITY OF THE CORNERS

DIE PROFILE (ORIGINAL PROFILES GENERATED ON 1/2 ROYLE TUBER AT TEMP. OF 180°F)

EXTRUSION RATING BASED ON FOUR SEPARATE GRADINGS, EACH RANGING FROM I = VERY POOR TO 4 = EXCELLENT. THE PERFECT RATING IS 16, AND 12 IS SATISFACTORY FOR MOST PRODUCTION EXTRUSIONS PROVIDED THE 30° EDGE RATES AT LEAST 3.

Figure 59. Garvey die rating system. (Test is described in Vol. 34, 1942 *Industrial and Engineering Chemistry*, and is a method for evaluating the extrudability of rubber stocks. The extrusion strip has two corners, a 150° edge and a 30° edge.

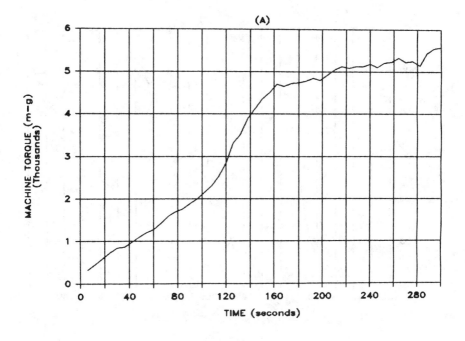

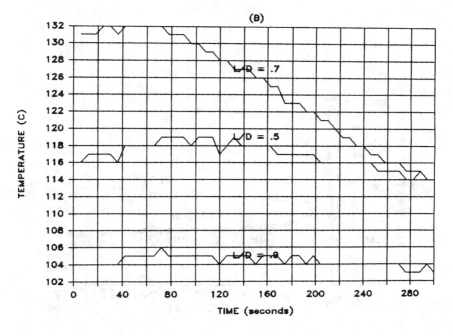

Figure 60. Torque/temperature/pressure response at several locations along extruder can be recorded simultaneously for an extrusion test in the Rheocord-System 40.

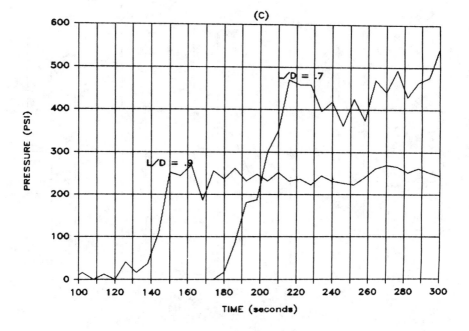

Figure 4 (Continued)

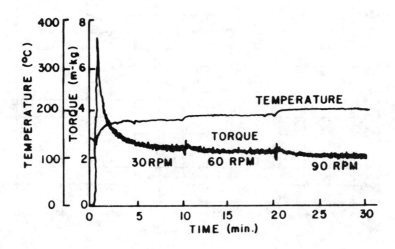

Figure 61. Rheocord can be preprogrammed to provide step or ramp changes in extruder operating conditions such as screw speed and temperature.

NOTATION

A	area	k	thermal conductivity
A, B	coefficients in Ellis model	k_1, k_2	constants
a	constant	L	length
C	applied stress	l	length
C_A	concentration of species A	N	rotational speed
C_p	specific heat	N_f	Bagley correction length term
D	diameter	n	power law exponent
D_{AB}	molecular diffusivity	N''	slope of torque vs. rotational speed
D_b	Debora number	P	pressure
E	activation energy	Q	volumetric flow rate
E'	storage modulus	q	heat flow
E''	loss modulus	R	radius
F'	normal thrust	R_G	universal gas law constant
F(t)	force response	Re_{gen}	generalized Reynolds number
f_v	material rheological constant	r	radius
f'	function	s	rotor speed
G	shear modulus	T	temperature
G(t)	shear modulus	T_0	reference temperature
G'	storage modulus	t	time
G''	loss modulus	V_x	velocity
H	separation distance	x	linear distance
h	thickness	y	distance
K	flow behavior index	z	distance
K_0	constant		

Greek Symbols

α	thermal diffusivity	μ	Newtonian viscosity
α'	angle	μ_a	apparent viscosity
$\dot{\gamma}$	strain or shear rate	ρ	density
δ	distance or phase angle	T	torque
ϵ	strain rate	τ_{xy}	stress
η	viscosity	τ_y	yield stress
η_ϵ	extensional rate	$\tau_{\theta\theta}, \tau_{rr}$	stress components
η^*	complex dynamic viscosity	τ	tensor
θ	temperature	ϕ'	rate of deformation
λ	relaxation time	ω	rotational velocity

REFERENCES

1. Cheremisinoff, N. P., *Fluid Flow Pocket Handbook*, Gulf Pub. Co., Houston, TX (1984).
2. Cheremisinoff, N. P., and Azbel, D., *Fluid Mechanics and Unit Operations*, Ann Arbor Sci., Ann Arbor, Mich. (1983).
3. Bird, R. B., Stewart, W. E., and Lightfoot, E. N., *Transport Phenomena*, John Wiley & Sons (1967).
4. Macoscko, C. W., and Davis, W. M., *Rheol. Acta*, 13, 814 (1974).
5. Criminale, Erickson, and Filby, *Arch. Rat. Mech. Anals.*, 1,410–417 (1956).
6. Skelland, A. H. P., *Non-Newtonian Flow and Heat Transfer*, J. Wiley & Sons, N.Y. (1967).
7. Metzner, A. B., and Reed, J. C., *AIChE J.*, 1 (1955) 434.
8. Bagley, E. B., *J. Appl. Phys.*, 28 (1954) 624–7.
9. Thomas, D. G., *Ind. Eng. Chem.*, 11, 18 (1963) 55.

10. Calderbank, P. H., and Moo-Young, M. B., *Trans. Inst. Ch.E.* (London) 37 (1959) 26–33.
11. Kreiger, I. M., and Maron, S. H., *J. Appl. Phys.*, 25 (1954) 72.
12. Mooney, M., *J. Rheology*, 2 (1931) 231.
13. Lee, M. C. H., *J. Appl. Polym. Sci.*, 29, p. 499, 1984.
14. Lee, B. L., and White, J. L., *Trans. Soc. Rheol.*, 18 (1974) 467.
15. Lobe, V. M., and White, J. L., *Polym. Eng. Sci.*, 19 (1979) 617.
16. Chapman, F. M., and Lee, T. S., *SPE J.*, 26 (1970) 37.
17. Mingawa, N., and White, J. L., *J. Appl. Polym. Sci.*, 20 (1976) 501.
18. King, R. G., *Rheol. Acta*, 5 (1966) 35.
19. Meissner, J., *J. Appl. Polym. Sci.*, 16 (1972) 2877.
20. Weissenberg, K., Proc. 1st Intl. Rheol. Cong. (1948).
21. Zakharenko, N. V., Tolstukhina, F. S., and Bartenev, G. M., *Rubber Chem. Technol.*, 35 (1962) 236.
22. Middleman, S., *Trans. Soc. Rheol.*, 13 (1969) 123.
23. Goldstein, C., *Trans. Soc. Rheol.* 18 (1974) 357.
24. Furuta, I., V. M. Lobe, and White, J. L., *J. Non-Newt. Fluid Mech.*, 1 (1976) 207.
25. Nakajima, N., and Harrel, E. R., *Rubber Chem. Technol.*, 52 (1979) 9.
26. Han, C. D., *Rheology in Polymer Processing*, Academic Press, N.Y. (1976).
27. Han, C. D., *Trans. Soc. Rheology*, 18 (1974) 103.
28. Han, C. D., *J. Appl. Polym. Sci.*, 15 (1971) 2567, 2579, 2591.
29. Wales, J. L. S., den Otter, J. L., and Janeschitz-Krief, H., *Rheol. Acta*, 4 (1965) 146.
30. Cogswell, F. N., *Plastics and Polymers*, 36 (1968) 109.
31. Cogswell, F. N., *J. Non-Newt. Fluid Mech.*, 4 (1978) 9.
32. Ballman, R. L., *Rheol. Acta*, 4 (1965) 137.
33. Vinogradov, G. V., Radushkevich, B. V., and Fikham, V. D., *J. Polym. Sci.*, A-2, 8 (1970) 1.
34. Stevenson, J. F., *AIChE J.*, 18 (1972) 540.
35. Mocosko, C. W., and Lornsten, J. M., SPE Antec. Tech. PAPERS (1973) 461.
36. Ide, Y., and White, J. L., *J. Appl. Polym. Sci.*, 22 (1978) 1061.
37. Cotten, G. R., and Theile, J. L., *Rubber Chem. Technol.* 57 (1979) 749 (1979).
38. Dealy, J. M., Paper Presented at AICHE Meeting, Miami Beach (Nov. 1978).
39. Philippoff, W., *Phys. Zeit*, 35 (1934) 884.
40. Vinogradov, G. V., Malkin, A. Ya., Plotnikova, E. P., Sabsai, O. Yu., and Nikolayeva, N. E., *Intl. J. Polym. Mat.*, 2 (1972) 1 (1972).
41. Munstedt, H., Proc. 7th Int. Rheol. Congr. (1976) 496.
42. Aoki, Y., *J. Soc. Rheol. Japan*, 7 (1979) 20.
43. Andrews, R. D., Hofman-Bang, N., and Tobolsky, A. V., *J. Polym. Sci.*, 3 (1948) 669.
44. Tobolsky, A. V., *Structure and Properties of Polymers*, John Wiley & Sons, New York (1960).
45. Maxwell, B., and Chartoff, R., *Trans. Soc. Rheol.*, 9 (1965) 41.
46. Chen, I. J., and Bogue, D. C., *Trans. Soc. Rheol.*, 16 (1972) 59.
47. Walters, K., *Rheometry*, Chapman and Hall, London (1975).
48. Van Wazer, J. R., Lyons, J. W., Kim, K. Y., and Colwell, R. E., *Viscosity and Flow Measurement*, Interscience, New York, 1963.
49. Dexter, F. D., Miller, J. C., and Philippoff, N., *Trans. Soc. Rheology*, 5 (1961) 193.
50. Brydson, J. A., *Flow Properties of Polymer Melts*, Van Nostrand Reinhold, New York, 1970, Ch. 1.
51. Wales, J. L. S., *Rheol. Acta*, 8 (1969) 38.
52. Han, C. D., and Drexel, L. H., *J. Appl. Polym. Sci.*, 17 (1973) 3429.
53. Brizitsky, V. I., Vinogradov, G. V., Isaev, A. I., and Podolsky, Yu. Ya., *J. Appl. Polym. Sci.*, 22 (1978) 665 (1978).
54. Wales, J. L. S., and Janeschitz-Kriegel, H., *J. Polym. Sci.*, 5 (1967) 781.
55. Gortemaker and Janeschitz-Kriegel (1976).
56. Gortemaker, F. H., Hanson, M. G., de Cindio, B., Laun, H. M., and Janeschitz-Kriegel, H., *Rheol. Acta*, 15 (1976) 256.
57. Meissner, J., *Rheol. Acta*, 8 (1969) 78.
58. Lodge, A. S., *Trans. Faraday Soc.*, 52 (1956) 120.

59-61. Treloar, L. R. G., *Trans. Faraday Soc.*, 36 (1940) 538; ibid. 37 (1941) 84; ibid., 43 (1947) 284.
62. Graessley, W. W., Glasscock, S. D., and Crawley, R. L., *Trans. Soc. Rheology*, 14 (1970) 519.
63. Pliskin, I., *Rubber Chem. Technol.*, 46 (1973) 1218.
64. White, J. L., and Roman, J. F., *J. Appl. Polym. Sci.*, 20 (1976) 1005.
65. Barnes, H. A., Chapt. 2, pp. 31-118 in *Rheometry: Industrial Applications*, ed. K. Walters, J. Wiley, N.Y. (1980).
66. Cheremisinoff, N. P., *Instrumentation for Complex Fluid Flows*, Technomic Publ. Co., Lancaster, PA (1986)
67. White, J. L., *Rubber Chem. Technol.*, 42, 257 (1969).
68. White, J. L., *Rubber Chem. Technol.*, 50, 163 (1977).
69. Nakajima, N., and Collins, E. A., *Polym. Eng. Sci.*, 14, 137 (1974).
70. Nakajima, N., and Collins, E. A., *Trans. Soc. Rheol.* 20, 1 (1976).
71. Turner, D. M., Moore, M. D., and Smith, R. A., in Elastomers: Criteria for *Engineering Design*, Hepburn, C., and Reynolds, R. J., ed., Applied Sci. Pub., London (1979).
72. Cotten, G. R., and Thiele, J. L., *Rubber Chem. Technol.*, 51, 749 (1978).
73. Market, J., Gummi Asbest, Kunstst. 29, 568 (1968).
74. Mocosko, C. W., and Davis, W. M., *Rheol. Acta* 13, 814 (1974).
75. Willey, S. R., Davis, W. M., Mocosko, C. W., and Goldstein, C., *Trans. Soc. Rheol.* 18, 515 (1974).
76. Bair, S., and Winer, W. O., *Trans. ASME* (F) *J. Lub. Technol.*, 101 (1979) 251.
77. Novak, J. D., and Winer, W. O., *Trans. ASME* (F) *J. Lub. Tech.* 90 (1968) 580.

CHAPTER 33

FUNDAMENTALS OF POLYMER MATERIALS

Joo T. Chung

Haake Buchler Instruments, Inc.
Saddle Brook, New Jersey, USA

CONTENTS

INTRODUCTION

Continuous developments of new polymers and improvements of established polymer groups demand versatile instruments that can closely simulate actual productions. As demand increases, the torque rheometer is becoming an industrial standard for fundamental research and development and quality control in polymer industries. Even though the rheometer is widely used, there is no comprehensive reference book to describe the instruments' capabilities.

Chapters 33 and 34 have been prepared to provide a more thorough comprehension of the rheometer, based on the author's experiences.

This chapter will review the fundamental theory of polymers which will be applied to the interpretation of data obtained from the instrument. The following chapter will discuss the torque rheometer and its applications on polymer materials. The torque rheometer with a Miniaturized Internal Mixer (MIM) is used for formulation of multi-component polymer systems, compounding, temperature and shear sensitivity, and flow behavior of polymer materials.

The instrument with a single screw extruder can be used to measure rheological properties, to study extrusion processing characteristics, as well as to provide simulation of actual production lines utilizing various dies in the laboratories. The rheometer with a twin screw extruder allows compounding engineers to develop polymer compounds and alloys. As new and tougher polymer materials are developed, it is necessary for polymer scientists and engineers to test all the materials very close to the fabricated conditions.

The word "polymer" comes from the Greek words poly (many) and mer (small units). In other words, many monomers are chained together to form a polymer. For instance, polyethylene is formed by polymerization of many ethylene monomers.

The latter portion of this volume will primarily deal with torque rheometers. This chapter will briefly review the theoretical fundamentals of polymer materials which will be applied to the application of the rheometers. Since non-Newtonian materials behave differently from Newtonian, understanding of special characteristics of each different material is essential for polymer processing.

Chapter 34 will discuss evolution of torque rheometers, instrumentation and its applications for polymer research and development, as well as quality control in polymer industries.

Detailed mathematical derivations or simulations and polymer theories are beyond the scope of these chapters, and the reader is referred to the bibliography at the end of each chapter.

TYPES OF POLYMERIZATION

Addition Polymerization (Radical Chain Polymerization)

The addition reaction starts with the free radical, which is an initiator for the polymerization reaction. The free radical is usually formed by the decomposition of a relatively unstable component in polymer structures.

In this reaction, repeating units add one at a time to the chain, so monomer concentration decreases steadily throughout the reaction.

$$Mx- + M \longrightarrow Mx + 1$$

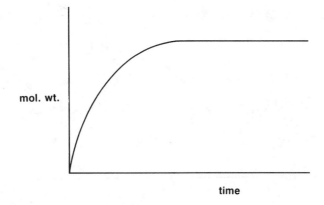

Figure 1. Molecular weight as a function of time in addition reaction.

High polymers can be formed at once by this polymerization. Long reaction times give high yields but do not affect molecular weight (see Figure 1).

Polymers made by chain reaction often contain only carbon atoms in the main backbone chain. These are called "homo chain polymers."

Condensation Polymerization (Step Reaction Polymerization)

This is entirely analogous to the condensation of low molecular weight compounds. In polymer formation, the condensation takes place between two polyfunctional molecules to produce one larger polyfunctional molecule with the possible elimination of a small molecule such as water. The reaction continues until almost all of one of the reagents is used up. The structural units of condensation polymers are usually joined by inter-unit functional groups.

The types of products formed in a condensation reaction are determined by the functionality, i.e., by the average number of reactive functional groups per monomer molecule.

$$Mx + My \longrightarrow Mx + y$$

Generally, mono-functional monomers form low molecular weight products. Bi-functional monomers form linear polymers and poly-functional monomers give branched or cross-linked polymers.

In this polymerization, molecular weight rises steadily throughout the reaction, as shown in Figure 2. Therefore, long reaction time is essential for high molecular weight polymers.

Polymers made by the step reactions may have other atoms, originating in the monomer functional groups as part of the chain. These are called "hetero polymers."

POLYMER STRUCTURE

Linear Polymers

The length of the polymer chain is specified by the number of repeat units in the chain. Polymers with fully extended linear structure are unstable; however, the polymers that have random structure (random coil) are stable. These are illustrated below.

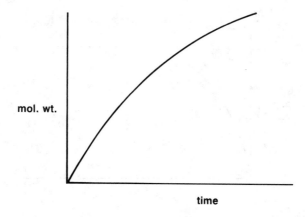

Figure 2. Molecular weight as a function of time in condensation reactions.

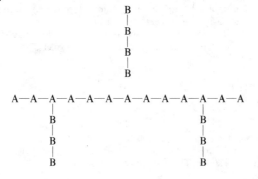

Linear structure (unstable)	Random structure (stable)

1. Random Copolymer   A BBB AA B AAA BB AA BBB
2. Uniform Copolymer   AB AB AB AB AB AB
3. Block Copolymer   AAA BBB AAA BBB AAA BBB
4. Homopolymer   AAAAAAAAA or BBBBBBBBB

Bifunctional monomers in condensation polymerization normally form linear polymers. Linear polymers can be dissolved, melted, molded, and have finite molecular weight.

Branch and Cross-Linked Polymers

Poly-functional monomers in condensation reaction normally form branch polymers or cross-linked polymers.

1. Graft polymer:

```
                        B
                        |
                        B
                        |
                        B
                        |
                        B
                        |
A—A—A—A—A—A—A—A—A—A—A—A—A
    |                   |
    B                   B
    |                   |
    B                   B
    |                   |
    B                   B
```

2. Network polymer:

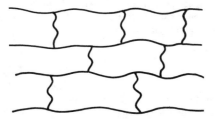

Cross-linked polymers (network) are insoluble, infusible (no melting point), non-moldable, and have infinite molecular weight.

TYPES OF POLYMERS

Thermoplastics

Most linear polymers can be made to soften and take on new shapes by application of heat and pressure. These changes are physical rather than chemical. This type of material is called thermoplastic resin and it is reprocessible.

Thermosets

Thermosets are materials that have undergone a chemical reaction (curing) by application of heat, catalyst, etc. The cross-linked network extending throughout the final article is stable to heat and cannot be made to flow or melt. This type of material is called a thermoset.

Curing of thermosets are described by A, B, and C stages upon degree of curing reaction. "A" stage is the earlier stage, "B" stage is an intermediate stage, and "C" stage is the final stage of the curing reaction [1]. This type of material is not reprocessible.

Rubber (Elastomer)

Rubber deforms upon application of stress and reverts back to its original shape upon elimination of applied stress. It is capable of rapid elastic recovery. It is usually vulcanized by sulfur.

Natural Rubber

Natural rubber is an elastic substance that is obtained by coagulating the milky juice of any of various tropical plants.

Synthetic Rubber

Two or more monomers artificially combined together through chemical reaction form synthetic rubber. Therefore, most rubbers are copolymer.

CRYSTALLINE AND AMORPHOUS POLYMER

Crystalline Polymers

A crystal is an orderly arrangement of atoms in space. Polymer crystallizes under a suitable condition and it is called a crystalline polymer.

Phase transition of the polymer occurs from solid to liquid. The transition temperature of this polymer is called the melting temperature and is often designated as Tm.

These polymers contain non-crystalline portions as well as crystalline portions. There are many polymers which fall into the semi-crystalline region.

Amorphous Polymers

An amorphous polymer does not crystallize under any conditions. Phase transition of this polymer occurs from glassy state to rubbery state. The transition temperature of the polymer is called the glass transition temperature, and is often designated as Tg. Most polymers have both Tg and Tm.

The melting temperature and glass transition temperature can be found by measuring the specific volume or enthalpy of the polymer as a function of temperature. Figures 3 and 4 illustrate Tg and Tm by measuring specific volume and enthalpy as a function of temperature.

Glass transition temperature (Tg) is the temperature of onset of extensive molecular motion. The slope of the curve above the glass transition temperature is characteristic of a rubber, and below the transition temperature is characteristic of a glass [2]. Tg decreases with decreasing amorphous content. Therefore, Tg is sometimes difficult to detect in highly crystalline polymers.

Tables 1 and 2 show glass transition temperature (Tg) and melting temperature (Tm) of commonly used amorphous and crystalline polymers [3].

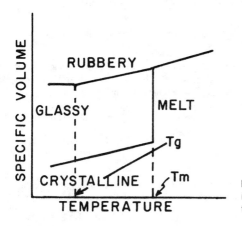

Figure 3. Measurement of Tg and Tm of polymers by measuring specific volume as a function of temperature.

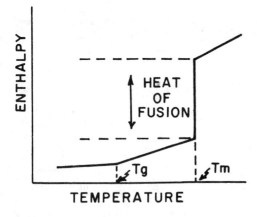

Figure 4. Measurement of Tg and Tm by measuring enthalpy as a function of temperature.

Table 1
Glass-Transition Temperature of Amorphous Polymers

Polymer	Glass Transition Temperature (T_g), °C
Polydimethylsiloxane	−123
Cis-1, 4-polyisoprene	−73
Poly (vinyl acetate)	−72
Polystyrene	100
Poly(methyl methacrylate)	105
Polycarbonate	150
Polysulfone	190
Poly(2,6-dimethyl-1,4-phenylene oxide)	220

Table 2
Thermal Transitions of Crystalline Polymers

Polymer	Glass-Transition Temperature (T_g) °C	Melting Temperature (T_m) °C
Polycaprolactone	−60	61
Polyethylene (high density)	−125	135
Poly(vinylidene fluoride)	−45	172
Poly(oxymethylene)	−85	195
Poly(vinyl alcohol)	85	258
Poly(hexamethylene adipamide)	49	265
Poly(ethylene terephthalate)	69	265
Polytetrafluoroethylene	none	327

CHARACTERIZATION OF MOLECULAR WEIGHT

Molecular weight ($\bar{M}w$) is the sum of the atomic masses of the elements forming the molecule. The structural formula of poly-ethylene is often expressed as:

Ethylene   Ethylene monomer

where n = Degree of polymerization. Therefore, molecular weight of polyethylene can be calculated as n multiplied by the Mw of repeating unit.

Weight Average Molecular Weight ($\bar{M}w$)

Example

Mix 1 g of polymer of 1,000,000 Mol. wt. with 1 g of polymer of 1,000 Mol. wt. What is weight average molecular weight ($\bar{M}w$)?

Solution

Mol. wt. of 2 g of the polymer mix is 1,001,000. Therefore, $\bar{M}w = 500,500$.

Number Average Molecular Weight ($\bar{M}n$)

The number average molecular weight ($\bar{M}n$) is calculated through Avogadro's number.

Example

If two molecules which have a ratio of 1:1,000 molecules of polymer 1,000,000 to polymer 1,000 mixed together, what is Mn?

Solution

$$\begin{array}{l} \text{1 molecule } 1,000,000 \\ \underline{1,000 \text{ molecule } 1,000,000} \\ \text{1,001 molecule } 2,000,000 \end{array}$$

Therefore, $\bar{M}n = 1,998$. Normally, $\bar{M}w > \bar{M}n$

Molecular Weight Distribution

The ratio of $\bar{M}w$ and $\bar{M}n$ is sometimes used as a measure of the breadth of the Molecular Weight Distribution (MWD). The Molecular Weight Distribution range of typical polymers is from $1.5 \sim 2.0$ to $20 \sim 50$.

The MWD of the above examples were discussed earlier and can be simply obtained as follows:

$$MWD = \bar{M}w/\bar{M}n = 25.6$$

POLYMER ADDITIVES

In order to obtain the best mechanical and physical properties from the fabricated products, different additives are often incorporated into polymer resins by formulation engineers. Color pigments are added to get suitable color, impact modifiers are added to improve brittleness, fillers are added to reach desired mechanical properties and reduce production cost, processing aids are added for ease of fabrication, and so on.

Fillers

The primary functions of fillers are cost effectiveness, as well as improving processing and end product properties. They are also used to reduce the thermal expansion coefficient of the base polymer to improve its dielectric properties or to soften polymers. Some examples of fillers are $CaCo_3$, wood dust, talc, clays, silica, and mica.

Lubricants

External Lubricant

External lubricants are incompatible with the polymer and are used at all temperatures. They migrate to the melt-metal interface during processing, promoting some effective slippage of the melt by reducing interfacial viscosity. They can prevent resin from sticking to the hot metal of the processing equipment by reducing friction between the two surfaces. Calcium stearate, zinc stearate, montainic acids, esters, and salts are examples.

Internal Lubricant

These make polymers compatible at processing temperatures. They reduce chain-to-chain intermolecular forces, and thus, melt viscosity. After reducing the cohesive forces between polymer chains, melt viscosity is lowered and flow properties (processing) are improved. Paraffin wax, stearate acid, esters, and polyethylene wax are examples.

Plasticizers

Plasticizers are added to polymers to enhance flexibility, resistancy, and melt flow. Generally, high-boiling organic liquids are used as plasticizers. Their functions are in reducing the glass transition temperature (Tg) or brittleness of the plastics. Phthalates, epoxies, adipates, azelates, trimellitates, phosphates, polyesters, DOP, and DOA are examples.

Stabilizers

Stabilizers are used to protect compounds from chemically breaking down under heat and to prevent discoloring or degrading. Tin and antimony compounds, phenols, epoxy compounds, organotin stabilizer, and barium/cadmium heat stabilizer are examples.

Reinforcement

Reinforcements are used to improve the mechanical properties of the base polymers, mainly their strength and stiffness. Asbestos fiber, short and long glass fiber, graphite fiber, and carbon fiber are examples.

Cross-Linking Agents

Cross-linking agents are used to convert a thermoplastic into a thermoset by increasing such properties as tensile strength and chemical strength. Organic peroxides, Benzoyl peroxide, and MEK peroxides are examples.

Blowing Agents

A blowing agent improves stiffness, lowers labor cost, reduces energy usage, reduces resin consumption, and lightens the weight of the fabricated article.

UV Stabilizers and Antioxidants

The primary function of these additives is to prevent aging. Benzotnazole, hydroxybenzophenones, and benzoates are examples.

Flame Retardants

This additive modifies physical properties. Hydrated alumina and antimonyoxide are examples.

RHEOLOGY

The word rheology originated from the Greek words rheo (flow) and logy (study), i.e., the study of flow behavior of materials. In other words, rheology is the study of the deformation of solid materials and flow of liquid materials.

Much rheological work is concerned directly with polymers because they exhibit such interesting deformation behavior. The simple and traditional linear engineering models are Newton's law for viscous liquids and Hook's law for elastic solids. Most polymer melts and solutions exhibit a combination of viscous and elastic response. These kinds of materials are called viscoelastic.

Basic Rheological Terminology [4]

In order to define the terminology, it is easiest to use a model: two parallel plates which have cross-sectional area A and are filled with material, as shown in Figure 5.

The upper plate moves with velocity of (u + du) and bottom plate moves with velocity of u.

Shear Strain

Shear strain (γ) is the deformation of the material and is defined as:

$$\gamma (\text{shear strain}) = \frac{dx}{dy} \text{ (dimensionless)} \tag{1}$$

Shear Rate

Shear rate ($\dot{\gamma}$) is the rate of deformation and is defined as:

$$\dot{\gamma} \text{ (shear rate)} = \frac{d}{dt}(\gamma) = \frac{du}{dy} (\text{sec}^{-1}) \tag{2}$$

Therefore, shear rate can also be defined as a velocity gradient between the two parallel plates.

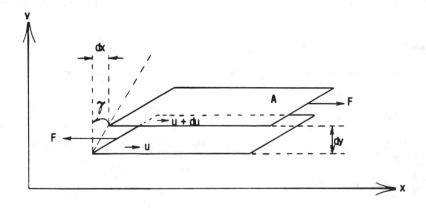

Figure 5. Parallel plate model to define rheology terms.

Shear Stress

Shear stress (τ_{yx}) is the force applied on a plane (which has cross-sectional area A) to shear the material between the two parallel plates and is defined as:

$$\tau_{yx}(\text{shear stress}) = \frac{F}{A} \, (\text{dyne/cm}^2) \tag{3}$$

Relationship Between Shear Stress and Shear Rate or Time

Different materials can be classified depending upon shear stress as a function of shear rate or as a function of time at a constant shear rate. The different fluids are described as follows:

Newtonian fluid, where viscosity is independent of shear rate. In other words, the ratio of shear stress and shear rate (viscosity) is constant.

Pseudoplastic fluid, where viscosity is a function of shear rate; that is, viscosity decreases as shear rate increases.

Dilatant. For this type of material, viscosity increases as shear rate increases.

Bingham plastic. This fluid behaves like a pseudoplastic fluid, but it has a yield stress (τ_0), which is the stress required to start the material flowing. It is often described as shear stress at zero shear rate. Figure 6 illustrates the relationship between shear stress and shear rate graphically. It also shows that dissimilar fluids can have the same apparent viscosity; therefore, it is important to measure rheological properties at the shear rates that are used in actual production.

Thixotropic fluid. The viscosity of this fluid is dependent upon the variable of time; i.e., viscosity decreases as time increases at a constant shear rate.

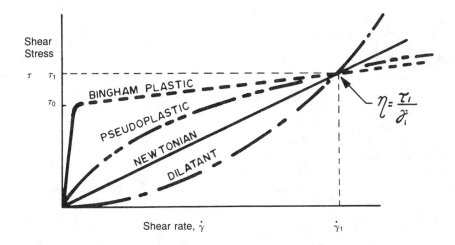

Figure 6. Relationship between shear stress and shear rate for different materials.

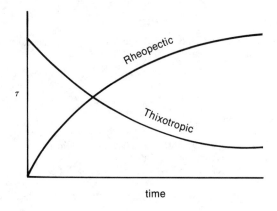

Figure 7. Relationship between shear stress and time.

time

Rheopectic fluid. For this fluid, viscosity increases as time increases at a constant shear rate. Figure 7 shows the relationship between shear stress and time for both thixotropic and rheopectic materials.

Rheological Properties

There are four major rheological properties that are closely related to polymer processing, design, formulation, compounding, and polymer alloying. They are viscosity, elasticity, shear sensitivity, and temperature sensitivity.

Viscosity

Viscosity (η) is the internal resistance of a fluid to flow under defined shear rate and resultant shear stress. It is defined as the ratio of shear stress (τ) and shear rate ($\dot{\gamma}$). A purely viscous fluid is called a Newtonian or an ideally viscous material. It is governed by Newton's law:

$$\tau = \eta\dot{\gamma} \tag{4}$$

Units of viscosity can be used in either CGS or SI units, as shown below:

CGS Unit	SI Unit
$\tau = $ dyne/cm^2	$\tau = $ Newton/m^2
	$= $ Pa
$\eta = \tau/\dot{\gamma}$	
$= $ dyne/cm^2 sec^{-1}	$\eta = \tau/\dot{\gamma}$
$= $ dyne sec/cm^2	$= $ Pa-sec
$= $ poise $= 100$ cp	$= 1{,}000$ m Pa-sec
	$= 1{,}000$ cp
	$= 10$ poise

Elasticity

Elasticity is the property of a material by virtue of which it tends to recover its original size and shape after deformation. If the strain is proportional to the applied stress, the material is said to exhibit Hookean or ideal elastic behavior. It is governed by Hookean's law:

$$\tau = G\gamma \tag{5}$$

where   G = elastic modulus

Viscoelasticity

This is a characteristic mechanical behavior of materials which have both viscous and elastic properties. It is neither truly solid nor truly liquid. A viscoelastic solid remembers for all its subsequent history some "original" shape. A viscoelastic liquid ultimately forgets any original shape. This viscoelastic response is dramatically illustrated by "silly putty" (a silicon polymer). When bounced, it is highly elastic, recovering most of the potential energy it had before being dropped. If stuck on a wall, however, it will slowly flow down the wall and will show little tendency to recover any deformation.

Shear Sensitivity

A good knowledge of the shear sensitivity of the material being processed is particularly important in polymer processing, because excess shear to the polymer in the system might result in structural break down, which in turn, has an affect on the mechanical properties of the final end product.

The power law model, which is a widely used constitutive equation, is often used to characterize the shear sensitivity of polymer materials. The equation is expressed as follows:

$$\tau = m\dot{\gamma}^n \tag{6}$$

where   m = viscous constant
         n = power law index

The power law index, n, is the parameter that indicates the shear sensitivity of the polymer.

A fluid that follows the power law equation is called a power law fluid, and the index (n) is obtained by the slope of either log τ vs. log $\dot{\gamma}$ or log η vs. log $\dot{\gamma}$.

Equation 6 can be expressed in "log" by taking the logarithm in both terms, i.e., log τ = log m + n log $\dot{\gamma}$. Therefore:

$$n = \frac{d \log \tau}{d \log \dot{\gamma}} \tag{7}$$

It also can be calculated using viscosity terms, as follows:

$$\eta = m\dot{\gamma}^{n-1}$$

$$\log \eta = \log m + (n-1) \log \dot{\gamma} \tag{8}$$

Therefore

$$n = 1 + \frac{d \log \eta}{d \log \dot{\gamma}} \tag{9}$$

The constitutive relation changes the flow field for non-Newtonian flows as follows [5]:

n = 0   Ductile yielding material

n = 1   Newtonian fluid

n < 1   Pseudoplastic material

n > 1   Dilatant material

Therefore, if the value of n approaches 1, it is less shear sensitive, and if n approaches 0, it is more shear sensitive.

The velocity profile of a polymer also changes upon the relation, as is illustrated in Figure 8.

Temperature Sensitivity

In general, liquid viscosities decrease and gas viscosities increase with increasing temperature, indicating that there is an essential difference in the flow mechanisms of liquids and gases.

Knowing the temperature sensitivity of the material being processed is helpful in processing the polymer better. If a temperature-sensitive material is exposed to prolonged heat in the system, it results in thermal degradation of the material. Therefore, choosing an optimum temperature profile on the processing equipment and monitoring melt temperature on a continuous basis are desirable for processing heat sensitive materials.

Temperature sensitivity is expressed in terms of apparent flow activation energy. The most commonly used expression relating viscosity to temperature is the Arrhenius equation:

$$\eta = Ae^{\Delta E/RT} \tag{10}$$

where η = viscosity
         E = activation energy
         R = universal constant
         T = Kelvin degree (°K)

Figure 9 illustrates temperature effect on viscosity. Activation energy can be calculated from the slope of the curve. The larger the value of the activation energy in a certain range of temperature, the more temperature sensitive the polymer is.

n = 0: plug flow

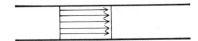

n = 1: parabola

0 < n < 1: "blunt" flow

Figure 8. Typical velocity profiles of polymer melt flow.

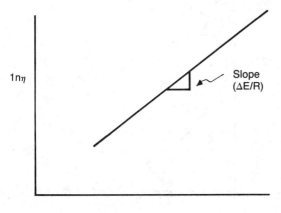

$1n\eta$

Slope
($\Delta E/R$)

$1/T$

Figure 9. Viscosity as a function of temperature.

Most polymer melts dissipate viscosity into heat and increase melt temperature. This frictional heat build-up by polymer melts depends on the shear rate used in the system [5]. The frictional heat (Φ_V) can be calculated as follows:

$$\Phi_V = \tau \dot{\gamma}^{1+n} \qquad \text{for non-Newtonian} \tag{11}$$

$$\Phi_V = \tau \times \dot{\gamma}^2 \qquad \text{for Newtonian} \tag{12}$$

Therefore, the adiabatic rate of temperature rise in a polymer material which is subject to shear stress and shear rate is obtained as [°C/sec] [7].

$$\frac{dT}{dt} = \Phi_V \times \frac{\rho}{Cp} \tag{13}$$

where ρ = melt density
Cp = specific heat

Hence the selection of proper speed in processing equipment is also important for processing heat sensitive material.

FLOW PHENOMENA OF POLYMER FLUIDS

Tube Flow

Consider four identical vertical tubes, the bottoms of which are covered by a flat plate. Two of the tubes contain a fluid which exhibits Newtonian flow properties, while the other two hold a polymer fluid that is pseudoplastic in nature.

Two identical large steel balls are placed in a tube containing a Newtonian fluid and a tube containing the polymer fluid. Two similar but smaller balls are placed in the remaining tubes.

The large and the small balls placed in the Newtonian fluids will fall at the same rate because of its constant viscosity. The large ball placed in the polymer fluid, however, will fall faster than the smaller ball, because the large ball generates higher force than the small ball due to its heavier weight, which in turn increases the shear rate so there is a decrease in viscosity.

When the plate is suddenly removed from the bottom of the tubes and the fluids are allowed to flow out due to gravity, the following phenomena is observed: The level of the tube containing

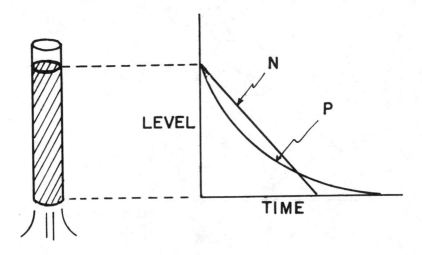

Figure 10. Comparison of tube flow between Newtonian (N) and polymer (P) fluids.

the polymer fluid will initially decrease at a faster rate than the Newtonian fluid, but as the level continues to decrease, the level in the tube containing Newtonian material will decrease faster. Figure 10 illustrates the decrease in level of Newtonian and polymer fluid in the tubes as a function of time.

The polymer fluid initially flows out from the tube faster than the Newtonian due to higher hydrostatic force, which results in an increase in shear rate; however, the polymer material flows slower as the level decreases due to decreasing hydrostatic force, which results in a decrease in shear rate, hence an increase in viscosity. On the other hand, the Newtonian fluid flows out at a constant rate because its viscosity is independent of shear rate. Therefore, the Newtonian fluid flows out faster than the polymer fluid.

Figure 11. Newtonian fluid shows a vortex and polymer solution climbs the rotating inner cylinder.

Flow in a Rotating Cylinder

Two identical cylinders with rotating inner cylinders are filled with a Newtonian fluid and a polymer solution. In the flow of a Newtonian fluid between rotating cylinders, a higher normal stress is exerted on the outer cylinder wall than on the inner wall, due to centrifugal forces [8]. Therefore, the characteristic dip in the liquid surface near the center of the beaker can be seen. For the polymer solution, just the opposite is observed. As illustrated in Figure 11, the highest normal stress is exerted at the center and climbs up the inner cylinder. This phenomenon is sometimes called the Weissenberg effect.

Pressure Hole Error

The pressure measured at the bottom of the pressure hole P_M is the same as the true pressure at the wall P for Newtonian fluids. On the other hand, $(P + \tau_{zz})_M$ is lower than $(P + \tau_{zz})$ for polymer solutions, no matter how small the hole is made. We call this difference a pressure hole error, $P_H = (P + \tau_{zz})_M - (P + \tau_{zz})$ [8]. The system is illustrated in Figure 12.

Die Swell

Another example where there is a dramatic difference between the behavior of the Newtonian fluid and a polymer solution is in the flow through an orifice (see Figure 13). The jet of polymer fluid has a considerably greater diameter than the orifice through which it has been forced, whereas the jet of the Newtonian fluid has a smaller diameter than the orifice. When plastic articles are to be made by an extrusion process, this effect must be considered.

If longer tubes are used, the ratio of extrudate diameter to tube diameter (De/D) should ultimately approach unity. The swell ratio indeed decreases with longer tubes, but is found to reach a limiting value greater than unity as L/D approaches infinity.

Flow in the Parallel Plate

Flow differences between Newtonian and polymer fluids in the parallel plate system are shown in Figure 14. The difference arises due to a similar situation as has been seen in the flow in a rotating cylinder, discussed earlier.

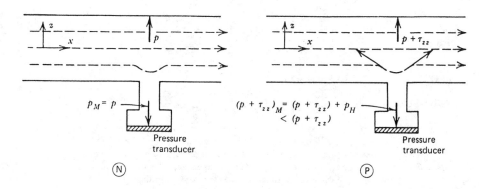

Figure 12. For Newtonian fluid a wall pressure measurement at the bottom of a pressure hole gives the desired result (N). The arrow in (P) indicates how an extra tension along a streamline lifts out of the hole, resulting in a low reading.

D. Die swell

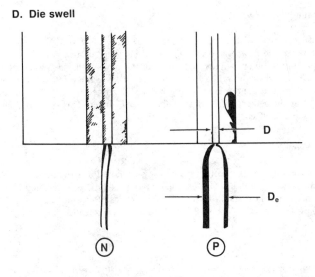

Figure 13. Flow behavior of Newtonian and polymer fluids in flow through an orifice.

F. Flow in the parallel plate

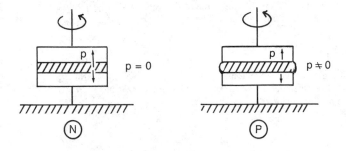

Figure 14. The difference in flow behavior of Newtonian and polymer materials for the parallel plate case.

EFFECT OF Mw AND MWD ON VISCOSITY

Structural Change of Polymers in Shear Field

Polymers undergoing shear field change their structures, which has an affect on viscosity. Figure 15 illustrates structure change in different ranges of shear rates [6].

There is not enough shear stress generated at the low shear rate ranges to reduce entanglement of the polymer structure. Therefore, the viscosity of the material at this range is relatively constant. This range is called the first Newtonian range, or lower Newtonian range. The material structure, however, starts to orient at the medium shear rate ranges, because resultant shear stress in this shear rate range starts to influence structural change. Therefore, the viscosity of the material starts to decrease as orientation of molecules increases. At the high shear rate ranges, the structure is

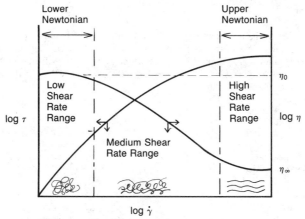

Effect of polymer structural change on viscosity.

Figure 15. The effect of polymer structural change on shear rate.

fully oriented so it is no longer affected, even at higher resultant shear stress. Therefore, the viscosity of the material at this range again reaches relatively constant viscosity. This range is called the second Newtonian range or upper Newtonian range.

In summary, as the shear rate is increased, the number of entanglements between chains is reduced, and hence the dependence of viscosity on molecular weight decreases.

Effect of MWD on Shear Heating and Shear Sensitivity

In general, broad MWD polymers are more shear sensitive than narrow MWD polymers. This is illustrated in Figure 16. In other words, the viscosity of broad MWD polymers decrease more rapidly than narrow MWD polymers in the same shear rate range. This means the broad MWD polymer is more shear sensitive than the narrow MWD polymer.

Therefore, a narrow MWD material generates more viscous dissipation heat in processing than the wide MWD material, since the frictional heat is a function of τ and $\dot{\gamma}$ as discussed earlier.

The theory briefly reviewed in this chapter will be applied to the instruments discussed in Chapter 34.

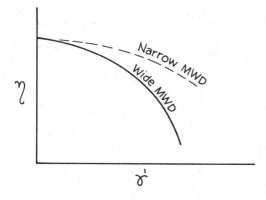

Figure 16. Difference in viscosity changes between broad MWD and narrow MWD polymers.

Acknowledgment

The author wishes to thank Haake Buchler Instruments, Inc. for permission to publish this and the subsequent chapter. He also thanks the HBI Staff and Applications Engineers for their direct and indirect contributions. He thanks Mr. Randy Byrne for his personal support and encouragement. Ms. Mary Greenway, especially, deserves many thanks for her dedicated work in assisting with the preparation of art and manuscript.

NOTATION

A	cross-sectional area	MWD	molecular weight distribution
C_p	specific heat	n	power law index
D	diameter of orifice	P	pressure
De	diameter of extrudate	P_H	pressure hole error
ΔE	activation energy	T	Kelvin temperature
e	exponent	Tg	glass transition temperature
F	force	Tm	melting temperature
G	elastic modulus	t	time
K	constant	U	velocity
$\bar{M}w$	average molecular weight	X, Y	distance
$\bar{M}_n$	number average molecular weight		

Greek Symbols

γ	deformation	η	viscosity
$\dot{\gamma}$	rate of deformation	ρ	melt density
τ_0	yield stress	Φ_V	viscous dissipation heat
τ	shear stress	η_0	viscosity at zero shear rate
τ_{zz}	normal stress	η_∞	viscosity at infinite shear rate

REFERENCES

1. Hayren, C. A., *Handbook of Plastics and Elastomers*, McGraw-Hill Book Co., 1975.
2. Vollmert, B., *Polymer Chemistry*, Springer Verlag, NY, Inc.
3. Fired, J. R., "Polymer properties in the Solid State," *Plastics Eng.*, July, 1982.
4. Schramm, G., *Introduction to Practical Viscometry*, Gebruder Haake Gmbh, 1981.
5. McKelvey, J., *Polymer Processing*, John Wiley & Sons, Inc., 1982.
6. Rosen, S. L., *Fundamental Principals of Polymeric Materials for Practicing Engineers*, Barnes and Noble, Inc., 1971.
7. Gerrarr, J. E., Steidler, F. E., and Appeldoorn, J. K., "Viscous Heating in Capillaries," *I & EC Fundamentals*, Vol. 4, No. 3, Aug., 1965.
8. Bird, R. B., Armstrong, R. C., and Hassager, O., *Dynamics of Polymer Liquids*, Vol. 1, *Fluid Mechanics*, John Wiley & Sons, Inc., 1977.

CHAPTER 34

TORQUE RHEOMETER TECHNOLOGY AND INSTRUMENTATION

Joo T. Chung

Haake Buchler Instruments, Inc.
Saddle Brook, New Jersey, USA

CONTENTS

INTRODUCTION

Torque rheometers with miniaturized internal mixers (MIM) are multipurpose instruments that are well suited for formulating multi-component polymer systems, and studying flow behavior, thermal sensitivity, shear sensitivity, batch compounding, etc. The instrument is applicable to thermoplastics, rubber (compounding, cure, scorch tests), thermoset materials, and also to liquid materials.

The rheometer with a single screw extruder allows one to measure rheological properties and extrusion processing characteristics to differentiate lot-to-lot variance of the materials. It also enables the process engineer to simulate a production line in the laboratory and to develop processing guidelines. Since all the measurements can be done by simulating production, it is much easier to solve problems which the engineer might be facing.

The torque rheometer with a twin screw extruder is considered a scaled-down continuous compounder. It allows the compounding engineer to develop polymer compounds and alloys. It also permits the formulation engineer to ensure his formulation is the optimum one.

Since the instruments are very versatile, low viscosity (liquid) and high viscosity materials, high temperature engineering thermoplastics, rubber, and thermoset materials can be tested. Therefore, they are widely used in quality control and research and development areas in the polymer industries.

DEFINITION OF THE TORQUE RHEOMETER

A torque rheometer is an instrument which is widely used in studying formulations, developing compounds, and characterizing the polymer flow behavior by measuring viscosity-related torque caused by the resistance of the material to the shearing action of the plasticating process.

Relationship Between Torque and Power

Torque is the effectiveness of a force to produce rotation. It is defined as the product of the force and the perpendicular distance from its line of action to the instantaneous center of rotation. By the definition, torque can be expressed as:

$$M = F \times R \tag{1}$$

Units of torque are (g-m), (dyne-cm) or (ft-lb).

Power is the time rate at which work is done, and it can be expressed as:

$$P = F \times V \tag{2}$$

Units of power are (hp), (watt), and (ft-lb/sec).

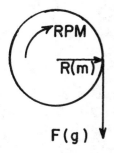

F (g)   **Figure 1.** Definition of torque.

We now can derive the relationship between torque and power using the above definition and Figure 1:

$$M(g\text{-}m) = 725,995 \times \frac{hp}{rpm} \tag{3}$$

History and Progress of the Torque Rheometer

Torque rheometers were developed over fifty years ago. They were utilized in the baking industry to help characterize the mixing of flour doughs. The rheometer is now being widely used in the plastics industries and in research organizations to study the consistency, processability, and rheological properties of polymer melts subjected to various processing conditions.

Mechanical Torque Rheometer

The first torque rheometers were "mechanical" instruments as shown in Figure 2. The mechanical Torque Rheometer consisted of a dynamometer system with lever arm, weight, and dashpot. The lever arm and weight mechanically operated the torque-sensing system of the instrument. Therefore, the calibration of the mechanical torque rheometer was done by manually adjusting the levers and weights, making the calibration procedure very cumbersome. In addition to the awkwardness of calibrating the rheometer, the instrument consisted of several modular systems for temperature controlling and parameter recording. Although it was an excellent instrument, its two largest disadvantages were the amount of time required for calibration and the large space needed for the unit and auxiliary systems. Only one parameter could be recorded on the chart paper, and the chart paper was curvilinear as shown in Figure 3. Therefore, it was inconvenient to analyze the data.

Electronic Torque Rheometer

The second generation of the torque rheometers were "electronic" instruments as shown in Figure 4, and were developed to overcome the inconveniences and limitations of the mechanical torque rheometer. This rheometer is a semi-automatic, compact system in which almost every necessary module is built into the unit.

Figure 5 illustrates the torque measuring principle with the electronic torque rheometer. The torque pick-up system is very different from the mechanical torque rheometer. In this system, the power is transmitted from the input to the output gears of a gearbox through an idle gear. One is mounted on an output gear shaft and the other is suspended on a gearbox housing. A transducer is mounted between the swing arm and the gearbox housing. When a load is applied against the gearbox output shaft, it causes a resistance to the power transmitting parts. The resistance on the output gear shaft, along with a driving force on the input gear shaft, forces an idler gear downward. This downward pull on the idler produces the strain in the transducer. The strain is converted into an electrical signal, which is registered by the torque circuit in the electronic torque rheometer.

Figure 2. Mechanical torque rheometer with temperature controllers.

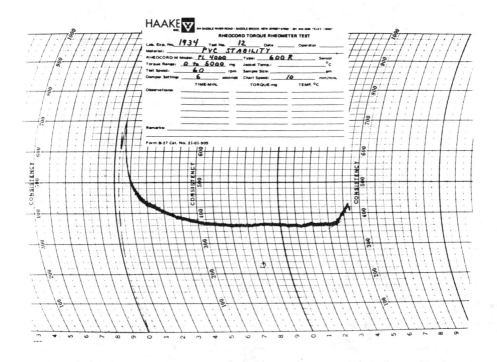

Figure 3. Typical torque curve obtained from a mechanical torque rheometer.

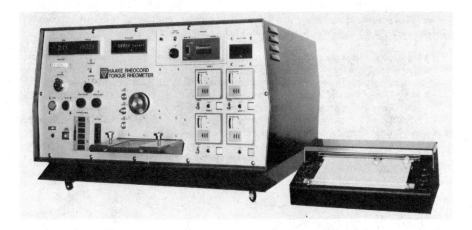

Figure 4. Electronic torque rheometer (EU Model).

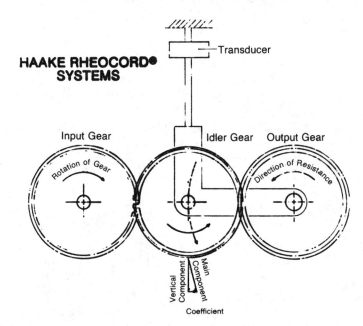

Figure 5. Torque measuring principle on an electronic torque rheometer.

The electronic torque rheometer is more versatile than the mechanical torque rheometer. Advantages over the mechanical torque rheometer are as follows:

1. Torque, melt temperature, totalized torque, or pressure can be recorded continuously and simultaneously on the same chart throughout the test with an electronic torque rheometer as shown in Figure 6. However, only torque can be recorded with mechanical torque rheometers.
2. Chart paper of the electronic torque rheometer is linear and easily read, but the mechanical torque rheometer is curved and develops upside down, making it more difficult to read.
3. The electronic torque rheometer is a compact system, but the mechanical torque rheometer needs several separate modules; therefore, it requires more space.
4. Calibration of the torque rheometer is a lot simpler than of the mechanical torque rheometer because it has an advanced torque measuring system and it can be done electronically.
5. It is much easier and faster for engineers or scientists to analyze data.

Microprocessor-Controlled Torque Rheometer

As the plastic industries continue to grow, there is an increasing demand for accurate and automatic instrumentation for their research, development, and quality control. In 1982, HBI, Inc. introduced to the market a new microprocessor-controlled torque rheometer to meet increasing market demands. The microprocessor-controlled torque rheometer is a very unique system, and

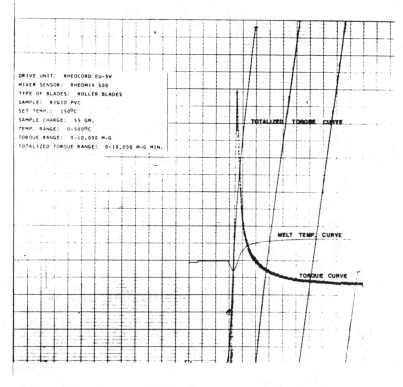

Figure 6. Temperature, torque, and totalized torque curves obtained from the electronic model.

Figure 7. Rheocord System 40 microprocessor-controlled torque rheometer.

offers much more versatility than the electronic model. The rheometer (Figure 7) consists of two basic units: the electro-mechanical drive unit, and the microprocessor Unit. Advantages over the electronic torque rheometer are listed below:

1. The microprocessor-based torque rheometer can control two pieces of equipment simultaneously. An example of this would be a feeder, or post-extrusion system. It allows the user to regulate feed rate or down-stream equipment.
2. The system can drive equipment, control and monitor parameters, and has the additional feature of data acquisition capabilities.
3. The unit displays all parameters graphically or numerically on-line during testing.
4. The rheometer also has capabilities to plot any parameter vs. any parameter in the off-line mode.
5. One can make his own program using either on-line or off-line BASIC languages.
6. The unit has a safety cut-off system when the torque or totalized torque exceeds maximum values.
7. All data can be printed on a printer on-line or off-line.
8. The rheometer will monitor and record three pressures and three melt temperatures, as well as torque, totalized torque, and speed(s).
9. The rheometer is able to program two speeds and four temperatures for studying shear sensitivity or temperature sensitivity.
10. The system allows one to magnify specific portions of the test data, to better differentiate small differences between data.
11. The system allows one to store data on a diskette and to retrieve the data later on.
12. There is a built in RS-232C interface so that another computer can be adapted to the system to on-line testing.
13. The system has automatic calibration capabilities for the torque load cell and pressure transducers in any range.
14. Every parameter measured is recorded for later reference.
15. Makes data analysis automatic when using application software.

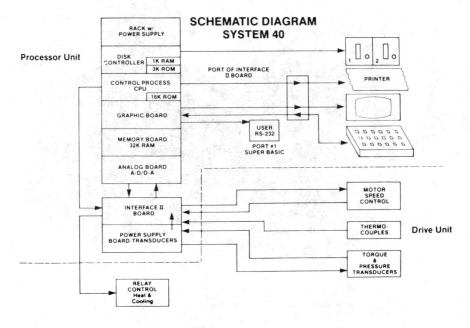

Figure 8. Schematic block diagram of microprocessor-controlled torque rheometer rheocord System 40.

As the torque rheometer is getting more sophisticated and automated, technology in the torque-sensing system is also becoming more advanced. A new torque measuring technology developed by HBI, Inc., is introduced in the microprocessor-controlled torque rheometer. The new system eliminates friction generated between the gears by installing strain gauges directly to a modified output shaft, making more accurate and sensitive measurements possible.

Figure 8 illustrates a block diagram of the microprocessor-controlled torque rheometer.

MINIATURIZED INTERNAL MIXER (MIM)

Most plastic products are not pure polymers, but mixtures of the basic polymer with a variety of additives, such as pigments, lubricants, stabilizers, antioxidants, flame retardants, antiblock agents, cross-linking agents, fillers, reinforcement agents, plasticizers, UV absorbants, and foaming agents. All these additives must be incorporated into the polymer prior to fabrication. Some of the additives take a significant portion of the mixture; others only minute amounts. Some are compatible; others are not.

Depending on the quality of resin and additives and homogenization of the mixtures, the quality of the final product will be varied. Therefore, developing a quality resin and additives which meet with desired physical and mechanical properties of the product and quality control associated with them play an important role in the plastic industry.

Design Concept, Internal Flow, and Mixing Action

The mixer consists of a mixing chamber shaped like a figure eight, with a spiral lobed rotor in each chamber. A totally enclosed mixing chamber contains two fluted mixing rotors that revolve in opposite directions and at different speeds to achieve a shear action similar to a two-roll mill.

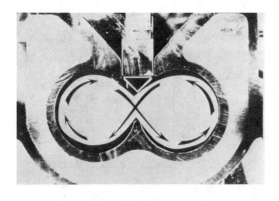

Figure 9. Illustrates material flow patterns in the mixing chamber.

In the chamber, the rotors rotate in order to effect a shearing action on the material mostly by shearing the material repeatedly against the walls of the mixing chamber, as shown in Figure 9. The rotors have cheverons (helical projections), which perform additional mixing functions by churning the material and moving it back and forth through the mixing chamber. The mixture is fed to the mixing chamber through a vertical chute with a ram. The lower face of the ram is part of the mixing chamber.

There is a small clearance between the rotors, which usually rotate at different speeds (eg., gear ratio 3:2, 2:3, and 7:6 for different mixers) at the chamber wall. In these clearances, dispersive mixing takes place. The shape of the rotors and the motion of the ram during operation ensure that all particles undergo high intensive shearing flow in the gaps (clearances).

There are three sets of interchangeable rotors available on the market. They are roller, cam, and sigma rotors, shown in Figure 10. Normally, roller rotors are used for thermoplastics and thermosets, cam rotors for rubber and elastomers, and sigma rotors for liquid materials. Banbury rotors are used with a miniaturized Banbury mixer for rubber compounding and formulation.

Figure 11 provides a schematic diagram of the MIM mixer.

Temperature Control

Temperature is the most important factor in measuring rheological properties and/or flow behavior of the polymer materials, because one can get different results with the same material by changing the temperature even by a few degrees.

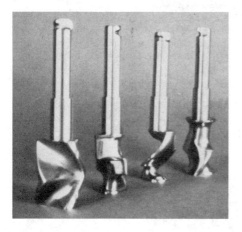

Figure 10. Roller, Cam, Sigma, and Banbury rotors from left.

1. **Back Section**
2. **Center Bowl**
3. **Front Plate**
4. **Rotor Shafts**
5. **Rotors**
6. **Air Cooling Channels cast in aluminum**
7. **Heaters cast in aluminum**
8. **Melt Thermocouple**
9. **Air Valve and Metering Plate**
10. **Air Exhaust**
11. **Bushings**
12. **Ram**

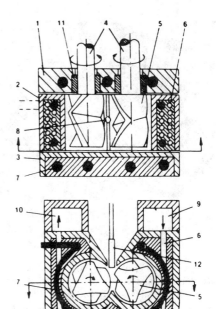

Figure 11. (A) Schematic diagram of MIM Mixer.

The mixer consists of three sections, and each section is heated and controlled by its own heater and temperature controller (see Figure 12). It is designed as such to maintain very accurate and uniform temperature profiles throughout the mixer.

Since mechanical dissipation heat is developed in the small gap between rotors and chamber, the heat conducts to the center bowl and raises the set temperature. In this case, the heater at the center bowl is automatically shut off, and the cooling solenoid valve is automatically energized to circulate cold air through the center section; the heaters in the back and front sections remain energized to maintain their own set temperature throughout the test.

If the mixer was to consist of two sections with one heater and temperature controller only at the bowl, when the heat is shut off due to the conduction heat from the material, there is virtually no heating at that time; therefore, the back section gets cold. This temperature control problem causes a non-uniform temperature profile throughout the mixer. Additionally, heating takes longer than that of the mixer with 3 heaters.

The loading chute is also designed for quick loading, and the chute can be removed from the mixer after the material is fed into the mixer. If the cold chute is not removed, the chute will draw the heat out of the mixer and the set temperature will be disturbed. This will not allow the measurement of flow behavior at the desired temperature. Additionally, if the chute cannot be removed after loading, the chute will be hot; it will cause problems in loading for the test which is to follow.

Mixing

It is well known that plastic materials with two or more components being processed should be well mixed, so that the compounded material would provide best physical properties desired for the final product.

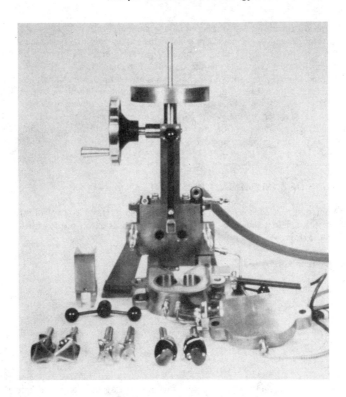

Figure 12. Three-section MIM mixer with three sets of interchangeable rotors.

There are distinctive types of mixing processes. The first is the spreading of particles over positions in space (distributive mixing) and the second is shearing and spreading of available energy of a system between the particles themselves (dispersive mixing) as shown in Figure 13.

In other words, distributive mixing is used for any operation employed to increase the randomness of the spacial distribution of particles without reducing their sizes. This mixing depends on the flow and the total strain, which is the product of shear rate and residence time or time duration. Therefore, the more random the arrangement of the flow pattern, the higher the shear rate; and the longer the residence time, the better the mixing will be.

A dispersive mixing process is similar to that of a simple mixing process, except that the nature and magnitude of forces required to rupture the particles to an ultimate size must be considered [1].

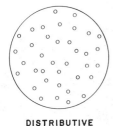

DISTRIBUTIVE

DISPERSIVE

Figure 13. Distributive and dispersive mixing.

A more important function of the intensive mixing is incorporation of the pigments, fillers, and other minor components into the matrix polymer. This mixing is a function of shear stress, which is calculated as a product of shear rate and material viscosity. Breaking up of an agglomerate will occur only when the shear stress exceeds the strength of the particle.

Commonly used mixing procedures in the industries are dump mixing, where all ingredients are added to the mixer at once; upside down mixing, where solid additives are added first, followed by the polymer; seeding mixing, where a small amount of previously well-mixed batch is added to the new batch; and sandwich mixing, where part of the major component is added first, then minor components, followed by the rest of the major component. As a rule of thumb, hard additives are added as early as possible in the mixing cycle. Dilutes, on the other hand, are added as late in the cycle as possible.

APPLICATIONS OF MIM (MINIATURIZED INTERNAL MIXER)

A series of different tests can be performed with the microprocessor-controlled torque rheometer in conjunction with different sensor systems. This section discusses various tests with Miniaturized Internal Mixers (MIM).

Relationship Between Torque and Shear Stress/rpm and Shear Rate

Over a limited shear rate range, the flow behavior can be governed by the power law equation:

$$\tau = m\dot{\gamma}^n$$

The temperature dependence of consistency is given by:

$$m = m_0 e^{\Delta E/RT} \tag{4}$$

Due to the complex geometry of the mixer rotors, and since rotors turn at different speeds, the local wall shear rate varies throughout the chamber [3]. However, we can write:

$$\bar{\dot{\gamma}} = C_1 N \tag{5}$$

$$\bar{\tau} = C_2 M \tag{6}$$

where   M = torque
         N = rpm
C_1 and C_2 = constants. $\bar{\dot{\gamma}}$ and $\bar{\tau}$, and are mean shear rate and mean shear stress averaged over the surface of the chamber.

From the above relationship, the following relationship between torque and rpm can be obtained:

$$M = Ke^{E/RT}N^n \tag{7}$$

where $K = \dfrac{m_0 C_1^n}{C_2}$

Calculation of the actual activation energy and the power law index are possible with a software program. This will be discussed in detail in the section on Temperature Compensated Torque.

Shear Sensitivity

Shear sensitivity of the test material can be obtained from Figures 14 and 15. In order to obtain the data, the power law constitutive equation is adopted.

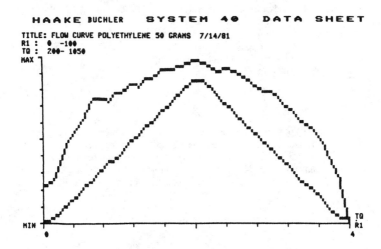

Figure 14. Actual data obtained using speed programming to test the shear sensitivity of the material.

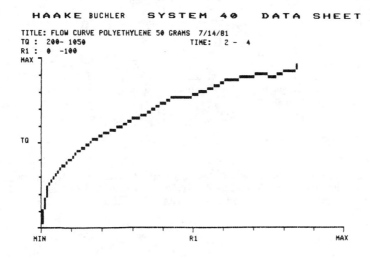

Figure 15. Plot of torque vs. rpm (replotted from data of Figure 14).

Since torque is proportional to shear stress and rpm is proportional to shear rate, as discussed earlier, the following relationship between torque and rpm may be obtained:

$$\log(M) = \log m' + n \log N \tag{8}$$

Therefore, $n = \dfrac{d \log M}{d \log N}$

Figure 14 illustrates the study of polyethylene using speed programming: (0–80 rpm) ramp time with 2 min. up and down. The data obtained are presented as a plot of torque, rpm vs. time curve.

Figure 15 shows a flow curve of the polyethylene, re-plotted (torque vs. rpm) from the data shown in Figure 14. This test is used to obtain the flow behavior of the material as a function of speed.

Shear sensitivity calculation can be obtained using software. This will be discussed in detail in "Temperature-Compensated Torque."

Temperature Dependency of Viscosity

Generally, the viscosity of a polymer decreases as temperature increases, and vice versa. Properties of the material also change depending on temperature. Knowing the temperature dependency of viscosity is important for process engineers. Large variations of viscosity for a certain range of temperatures means that the material is thermally unstable (i.e., requires large activation energy). This kind of material has to be processed with accurate temperature control of the processing equipment.

Figure 16 shows the torque vs. temperature curve obtained from the microprocessor-controlled torque rheometer to see the temperature dependency of viscosity-related torque on PVC material. This data can be applied to the Ahreninus equation described in the previous chapter:

$$\ln \eta = \ln A + \frac{\Delta E}{R} \frac{1}{T} \tag{9}$$

Since viscosity is proportional to the ratio of torque and rpm, the following relationship may be obtained:

$$\ln\left(\frac{M}{N}\right) = \ln A' + \frac{\Delta E}{R} \frac{1}{T} \tag{10}$$

Figure 16 presents data obtained from the torque rheometer, in conjunction with MIM mixer utilizing temperature programming and plotted in the form of torque vs. temperature to find temperature sensitivity of the material.

Temperature Compensated Torque

It is often difficult to explain flow behaviors of materials obtained from the torque rheometer due to melt temperature changes induced by frictional heat while the material is being mixed. Therefore, it is necessary to compensate for the temperature effect of the material.

Temperature compensated torque can be obtained from an integrated form of the Arrhenuius equation [4]:

$$\log \frac{M}{M'} = \frac{E}{4.576}\left(\frac{1}{T} - \frac{1}{T'}\right) \tag{11}$$

where   M = measured torque at T (°K)
          M' = calculated torque at reference temperature T' (°K)

Induction Time

Induction time is defined as the time at which a testing material starts to oxidize. Induction time of a material can be obtained from torque rheometer data. It can be seen as decreasing or increasing torque on the torque curves, depending on structural breakdown or network formation due to oxidation at constant temperature, respectively.

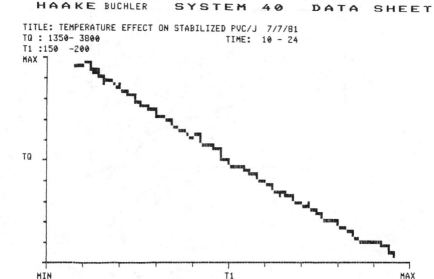

HAAKE BUCHLER   SYSTEM 40   DATA SHEET

TITLE: TEMPERATURE EFFECT ON STABILIZED PVC/J 7/7/81
TQ : 1350- 3800   TIME: 10 - 24
T1 :150 -200

Figure 16. Torque vs. temperature (°C) curve obtained directly from the torque rheometer.

The data can be obtained using temperature compensated torque described above (Table 1), and Figure 17 shows data obtained from the torque rheometer utilizing temperature compensated torque software.

Induction time of the polypropylene at a temperature of 200°C can be obtained by extrapolating the stable torque and sharp decreasing torque regions as shown in Figure 17. The data also can be obtained using torque curves directly obtained from the rheometer.

Figures 18 and 19 are data obtained for the material Torlon from two different lots. They show two different flow characteristics with two different induction times. The lot No. 310042 has longer processibility time than the lot No. 311082.

The induction time of the Torlon can be noted by the increase in torque, which is attributed to formation of network structures due to oxidation.

Table 1
Activation Energy and Power Law Index Data of
Polypropylene from Computer Program

MULTIVARIATE CORRELATION:

LOG TORQUE VS. LOG RPM VS. RECIPROCAL ABS. TEMPERATURE

TITLE: SHEAR TEST LDPE (SHEAR1)   DATE: 3/5/85
FILENAME: PE120R

COEFF. OF MULTIPLE CORRELATION, R = 0.985608
    STD. ERROR OF ESTIMATE, SEOE = 0.03762144

ENERGY OF ACTIVATION, E = 6633 CAL/GRAM MOLE
POWER LAW EXPONENT, N = 0.5078

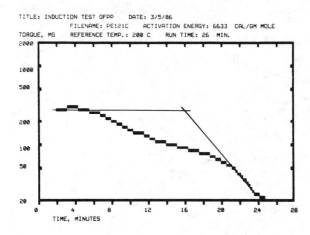

Figure 17. Effect of temperature on degradation of polypropylene with rotor speed 60 RPM and reference temperature 200°C.

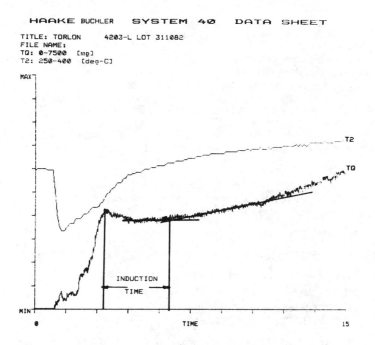

Figure 18. Flow behavior of Torlon at 340°C obtained from Rheomix 600 with roller rotors for lot No. 311082.

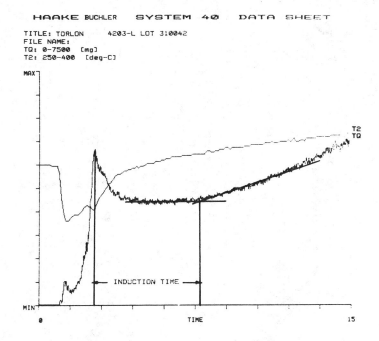

HAAKE BUCHLER   SYSTEM 40   DATA SHEET

TITLE: TORLON   4203-L LOT 3:0042
FILE NAME:
TQ: 0-7500 [mg]
T2: 250-400 [deg-C]

Figure 19. Flow behavior of Torlon at 340°C obtained from Rheomix 600 with roller blades for Lot No. 310042.

Unit Work (Wu)

The unit work is defined as the work energy required to process the unit volume or unit mass of material. This can be calculated from the totalized torque, which is obtained from the rheometer directly. Totalized torque is defined as the energy required to process a certain material for a certain period of time at given conditions, and simply as the area under the torque curve. The totalized torque can be converted to work energy:

$$
\begin{aligned}
Wu &= \frac{Wt}{Vb} \\
&= \frac{2\pi N \int_{t_1}^{t_2} M(t)\, dt}{V_b} \\
&= \frac{61.588 \times N \times TTQ}{V_b}
\end{aligned}
\tag{12}
$$

Unit of unit work $= [\text{Joule/cm}^3]$.

where   Wt = total work energy
         M(t) = torque
         N = rpm
         Vb = charged sample volume
         TTQ = totalized torque

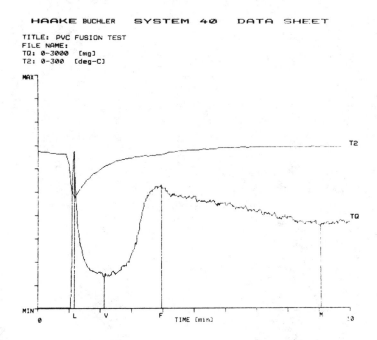

Figure 20. Fusion characteristics of PVC. Fusion time is considered from the loading peak (point L) to the fusion peak (point F).

Fusion Characteristics

Lubricants play an important role in the processing and in the properties of the final product. The lubricants also affect the fusion of the polymer materials. That is, internal lubricants reduce melt viscosity, while external lubricants reduce friction between the melt and the hot metal parts of the processing equipment and prevent sticking, controlling the fusion of the resin [5].

Figure 20 illustrates the fusion characteristics of PVC. The level of external lubricant used in the formulation affects fusion time between point L and point F on the curve [6]. The higher the level of external lubricant in the formulation, the longer the fusion time will be.

If an unnecessarily high level of external lubricant is used in the formulation, it will take a longer period of time to melt the material in processing, which results in reducing production, increasing energy consumption, and poor products. Meanwhile, if too low a level of external lubricant is used, the material will melt too early in the processing equipment, which may result in degradation in the final product. Therefore, selecting the optimum amount of external lubricant is a must for improvement of processing and for good quality of products.

Stability and Processibility of Material

Stability testing of materials enables formulation engineers to select the best stabilizer, and enables process engineers to choose optimum processing parameters [7] which, in turn, reduces scrap. Figure 21 shows the material degradation indicated by the rise in torque due to a cross-linking reaction such as PVC, rubber, and thermoset curing. It also gives the information of processability of the material under testing. Processibility time is determined by the time from loading (point L)

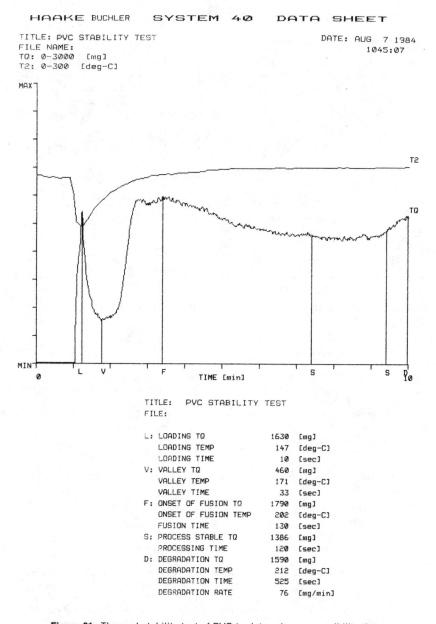

HAAKE BUCHLER   SYSTEM 40   DATA SHEET

TITLE: PVC STABILITY TEST
FILE NAME:
TQ: 0-3000 [mg]
T2: 0-300 [deg-C]

DATE: AUG 7 1984
      1045:07

TITLE: PVC STABILITY TEST
FILE:

L: LOADING TQ	1630	[mg]
LOADING TEMP	147	[deg-C]
LOADING TIME	10	[sec]
V: VALLEY TQ	460	[mg]
VALLEY TEMP	171	[deg-C]
VALLEY TIME	33	[sec]
F: ONSET OF FUSION TQ	1790	[mg]
ONSET OF FUSION TEMP	202	[deg-C]
FUSION TIME	130	[sec]
S: PROCESS STABLE TQ	1386	[mg]
PROCESSING TIME	120	[sec]
D: DEGRADATION TQ	1590	[mg]
DEGRADATION TEMP	212	[deg-C]
DEGRADATION TIME	525	[sec]
DEGRADATION RATE	76	[mg/min]

Figure 21. Thermal stability test of PVC to determine processibility time.

to the onset of degradation (second point S in figure) of the matrial. The longer the time, the better the processibility.

If the material does not cross-link when it degrades, the torque values keep decreasing due to structural break down [8], such as polyolefins.

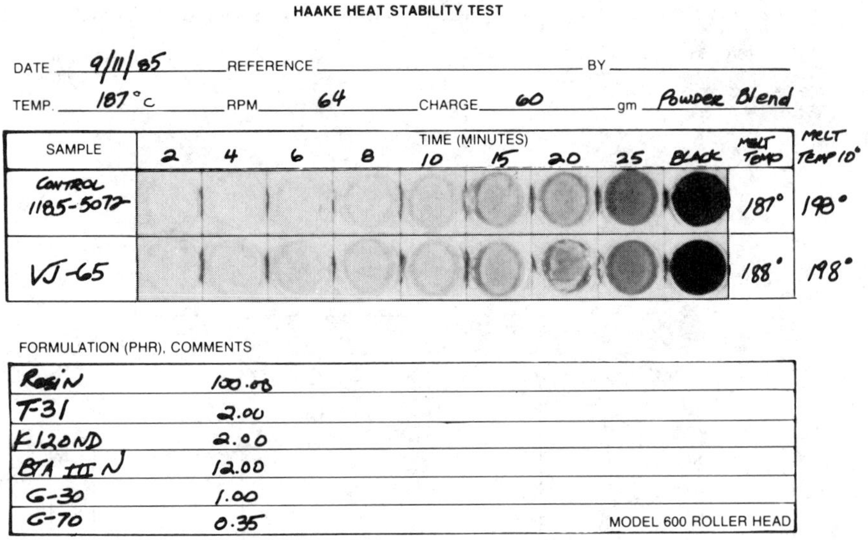

HAAKE HEAT STABILITY TEST

DATE __9/11/85__ REFERENCE _____ BY _____

TEMP. __187°C__ RPM __64__ CHARGE __60__ gm __Powder Blend__

SAMPLE	2	4	6	8	TIME (MINUTES) 10	15	20	25	BLACK	MELT TEMP	MELT TEMP 10°
CONTROL 1185-5072										187°	198°
VJ-65										188°	198°

FORMULATION (PHR), COMMENTS

Resin	100.00
T-31	2.00
E120ND	2.00
BTA III N	12.00
G-30	1.00
G-70	0.35

MODEL 600 ROLLER HEAD

Figure 22. Comparison between color stability of materials with same formulations and control material.

Color Stability (Heat Stability)

Usually heat sensitive polymer materials will degrade if they are exposed to heat for prolonged periods of time. The signs of degradation can be easily detected by color changes of the material and odors of the material.

Determining color stability of materials is helpful to see how stable the material is in processing and how long the processing time (residence time) should be to obtain a quality product which has the best mechanical properties.

Figure 22 shows the changes in color of PVC compounds as degradation proceeds. The control material starts to change color at 4 minutes, and the sample D changes at 2 minutes after exposure to heat. The difference can be attributed to a non-homogeneous dryblend when the material was formulated.

Gelation of Plastisol

Plastisols are dispersions of homopolymers or copolymers of vinyl chloride in PVC plasticizers; i.e., the very small particles are kept in suspension by swelling of the polymer particles from the solving action of the plasticizer. Upon heating, the plastisol particles swell with plasticizer to become a gel. Further heating fuses the ingredients into a homogeneous melt, which becomes a continuous solid upon cooling.

Figure 23 shows the gelation reaction of a plastisol and the amount of gas evolved from a blowing agent used in the plastisol formulation at an elevated temperature. The test was conducted with a programming temperature scan rate at 3°C/min with an MIM mixer (Rheomix 600) and sigma rotors.

Torque value increases rapidly in the first gelation due to the high rate of gelation reaction of the plastisol under heat. The reaction rate is getting slower in the second gelation because most of the reaction has been completed at this stage. After the second gelation, the material turns into a homogeneous melt. The torque value decreases because of increasing temperature.

H A A K E BUCHLER   S Y S T E M 4 0   D A T A S H E E T
TITLE: SAMPLE A (A)
FILE NAME.   A
:0: 0-600
P1: 0-5000

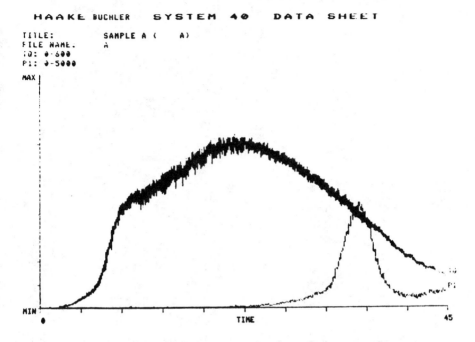

Figure 23. Gelation and gas evolution from blowing agent in the plastisol formulation. Programming temperature at 3°C/min.

Selection of Blowing Agent for Foam Products

Foam products can be produced by adding chemical blowing agents to the formulation. The blowing agents are inorganic or organic materials that decompose under heat to yield gaseous product.

Selection of a blowing agent is very important in foam products. If the proper blowing agent is not chosen, it might react with other ingredients used in the formulation, which results in retarding the blowing agent from activation.

The level of blowing agent used in the formulation is also important. If the level of the agent used is too high, too many unnecessary cells form in the foam product and it will collapse easily. If the level is too low, the product will not have enough cells, and so it will decrease cushionability of the product.

Figures 24 and 25 illustrate evolution of gas from the activation of blowing agents used in rubber. Figure 24 gives information on the temperatures the two blowing agents start to activate at. Figure 25 provides an idea of torque levels when they activate.

One can study how good a blowing agent the processor chooses for formulation and determine if it reacts to any other ingredients in the formulation processing.

Formulation

Most polymers are used with additives such as fillers, lubricants, flame retardants, stabilizers, color pigments, plasticizers, impact modifiers, and so on improve processability, physical and mechanical properties, uniformity, flexibility, and reduce production cost.

HAAKE BUCHLER   SYSTEM 40   DATA SHEET

TITLE: PRODUCTS INC 29-1-0 (291)   DATE: AUG 18 1983
FILE NAME: 291   1059:26
P1: 0-4000 Gas Flow (SCCM)
T2: 0-300 Melt Temperature (°C)

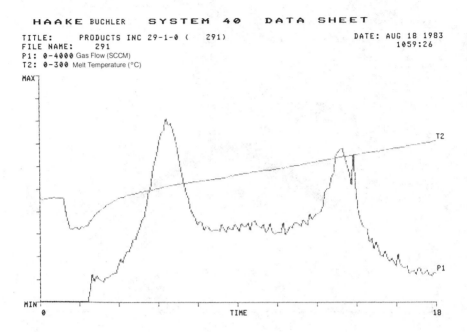

Figure 24. Activation of blowing agent used in rubber formulation as a function of temperature.

HAAKE BUCHLER   SYSTEM 40   DATA SHEET

TITLE: GAS EVOLUTION TEST   DATE: APR 18 1983
P1 :   0- 3800   0628:57
TQ :   0- 650
MAX

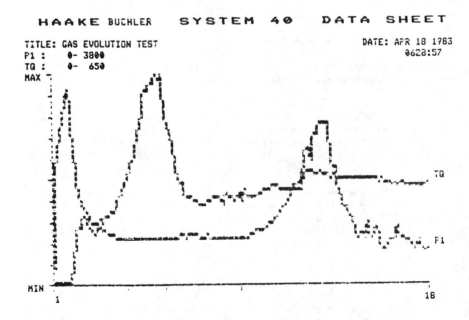

Figure 25. Torque level when blowing agents in the rubber compound activate.

In order to achieve the best properties of the final product, additives have to be added to the resin and homogeneously dry blended. This is called formulation. This application can be performed with an ASTM standard sigma mixer.

Figure 26 illustrates a powder dry blend for PVC based on ASTM D 2396. When the plasticizer is added to the resin, the torque value increases as the plasticizer is absorbed by the resin. The torque value sharply drops when the plasticizer is completely absorbed by the resin. Completely blended powder can be used for further study of material flow behavior.

The sigma mixer also can be applicable to formulating thermoset BMC molding compound by titrating polyester and fiber into the system.

Computer Aided Polymer Formulation

Plastics and rubber formulators have historically used an experimental method often called the "one variable at a time, trial-and-error method." The method involves setting up a starting point formulation based on the formulator's own experience or the experience of others, chosen on the basis of meeting certain key processing requirements and physical property specifications. Processing and property tests are conducted, and if requirements are not met, small incremental changes are made, one variable at a time, until the desired properties are achieved.

After obtaining experience with this technique, many formulators become surprisingly skilled and can quickly develop formulations with acceptable processing and physical properties. However, the method does suffer from a number of shortcomings:

1. Retrieval of information depends on the formulator's memory, his notes, or a tedious review of the test data.

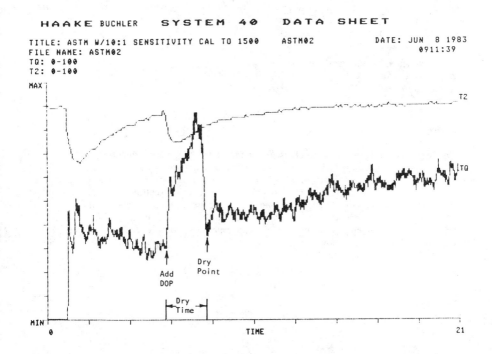

Figure 26. PVC formulation based on ASTM D2396.

2. Interactions between additives can make previous experience invalid. For example, when one solid Ba-Cd stabilizer was substituted for another in a PVC formulation, the extrudate became rough and extremely brittle. It was necessary to make a complete substitution of the lubrication system in order to achieve satisfactory results.
3. Some formulations must be abandoned, since no combination of the initial additives selected can yield the combination of properties desired. The formulation is often abandoned after frustrating results where properties are often approached but never achieved.
4. The formulation accepted is often not the optimum from a processing, property, or cost standpoint.
5. Unless the experiments are carefully designed, it is difficult to apply statistical tests to determine the suitability of the data.
6. New additives with no history of usage often show unexpected interactions and responses which seem to be a violation of principles developed from previous experience.

These objections can be overcome by the application of computer aided polymer formulation. Although the statistical techniques have been available for many years, it was not until the development of computers that we saw it applied to formulating problems, due to the lengthy, complex computations involved. Plasticizer manufacturers were probably among the earliest to employ the statistical analysis, since it is common to use two or three plasticizers in a vinyl formulation in order to comply with property and cost requirements. Prior to the advent of microcomputers, studies of this sort were limited to those with access to main frame or minicomputers. Today we find the use of microcomputers such as the **HBI RHEOCORD SYSTEM 40** in applications involving instrument control as well as in data analysis.

This program allows the RHEOCORD SYSTEM 40 and RHEOMIX-Mixer to design experiments, analyze data statistically, and to store, retrieve, and display processing data in the form of contour plots. By molding plaques and making various physical property tests, physical properties as well as processing properties can be correlated with formulation variables.

The program consists of three parts [9]:

1. Experimental Design Program
2. Regression Analysis Program
3. Plotting Program

Experimental Design Program

The Experimental Design Program must be used to design a set of experiments so that the other two programs can be used. The first step is to consider what formulation variables you wish to study and to set up a base formulation. If you are dealing with unfamiliar formulating ingredients, it is advisable to conduct a few experiments to help you select concentration levels. Two to five formulation variables can be studied at the same time. This provides a more efficient approach than the "one variable at a time, trial and error method," and in addition allows the measurement of interaction effects between ingredients. The following example shows how the base formulation and 5 variable ingredients are set up:

BASE FORMULATION PHR	VARIABLE RANGE PHR
PVC Resin 100	
Additive 1	0.50 to 2.50
Additive 2	0.40 to 1.40
Additive 3	0.00 to 1.60
Additive 4	0.00 to 1.60
Additive 5	42.00 to 50.00

The number of experiments to be conducted depends on the number of variables to be studied, as indicated table below:

VARIABLES	NO. OF EXPERIMENTS
2	13
3	20
4	30
5	33

After the entry of data requested by screen prompts, the computer prints a table of formulations based on a central composite statistical design (see Table 2). Since the base formulation is constant, only the variable ingredients are listed. Note that there are several replicate formulations. It is important that these be treated individually and be weighed and mixed just as any of the other formulations, rather than mixing one large batch and dividing to form the replicates.

RESIN CHARGE WEIGHT

FORMULA NO./COMPONENT WEIGHT, GM

COMPONENT	1	2	3	4	5	6	7
1. ADD1	1.00	2.00	1.00	2.00	1.00	2.00	1.00
2. ADD2	0.65	0.65	1.15	1.15	0.65	0.65	1.15
3. ADD3	0.40	0.40	0.40	0.40	1.20	1.20	1.20
4. ADD4	0.40	0.40	0.40	0.40	0.40	0.40	0.40
5. ADD5	48.00	44.00	44.00	48.00	44.00	48.00	48.00

FORMULA NO./COMPONENT WEIGHT, GM

COMPONENT	8	9	10	11	12	13	14
1. ADD1	2.00	1.00	2.00	1.00	2.00	1.00	2.00
2. ADD2	1.15	0.65	0.65	1.15	1.15	0.65	0.65
3. ADD3	1.20	0.40	0.40	0.40	0.40	1.20	1.20
4. ADD4	0.40	1.20	1.20	1.20	1.20	1.20	1.20
5. ADD5	44.00	44.00	48.00	48.00	44.00	48.00	44.00

FORMULA NO./COMPONENT WEIGHT, GM

COMPONENT	15	16	17	18	19	20	21
1. ADD1	1.00	2.00	0.50	2.50	1.50	1.50	1.50
2. ADD2	1.15	1.15	0.90	0.90	0.40	1.40	0.90
3. ADD3	1.20	1.20	0.80	0.80	0.80	0.80	0.00
4. ADD4	1.20	1.20	0.80	0.80	0.80	0.80	0.80
5. ADD5	44.00	48.00	46.00	46.00	46.00	46.00	46.00

FORMULA NO./COMPONENT WEIGHT, GM

COMPONENT	22	23	24	25	26	27	28
1. ADD1	1.50	1.50	1.50	1.50	1.50	1.50	1.50
2. ADD2	0.90	0.90	0.90	0.90	0.90	0.90	0.90
3. ADD3	1.60	0.80	0.80	0.80	0.80	0.80	0.80
4. ADD4	0.80	0.00	1.80	0.80	0.80	0.80	0.80
5. ADD5	46.00	46.00	46.00	42.00	50.00	46.00	46.00

FORMULA NO./COMPONENT WEIGHT, GM

COMPONENT	29	30	31	32	33
1. ADD1	1.50	1.50	1.50	1.50	1.50
2. ADD2	0.90	0.90	0.90	0.90	0.90
3. ADD3	0.80	0.80	0.80	0.80	0.80
4. ADD4	0.80	0.80	0.80	0.80	0.80
5. ADD5	46.00	46.00	46.00	46.00	46.00

Table 2
List of Possible Combinations of Formulations by Weight

Multivariate Statistical Correlation
Experimental Design, Version 1.0

DATE: 4/6/84
FORMULATIONS: 1314/1   VARIABLES: 5
              TO: 1314/33   FORMULATIONS: 33

COMPONENT	RANGE. PHR	
1. ADD1	0.50	2.50
2. ADD2	0.40	1.40
3. ADD3	0.00	1.60
4. ADD4	0.00	1.60
5. ADD5	42.00	50.00

A random sequence for weighing, mixing, and testing is printed. It is important to follow this procedure in order to randomize any effect that may be caused by testing sequence (Table 3). It is also good practice to have one person conduct the entire sequence of experiments, rather than having one operator starting the experiments and another completing them. After printing the random sequence, data used in the regression program are stored on disk.

Regression Analysis Program

This program is used after conducting processing and physical property tests. It utilizes data generated by Experimental Design Program and requires the input of the experimental data generated (Table 4). A regression analysis is conducted and coefficients computed for a polynomial equation with interaction terms. The following information is printed in the order shown (Tables 4 and 5):

1. Tabulated property data
2. Individual coefficients for the polynomial equation
3. Standard deviation of replicate samples
4. "F" significance test data

Table 3
Random Testing Sequence

DATE: 4/6/84
FORMULATIONS: 1314/1 to 1314/33

TEST THE FORMULATIONS IN THE FOLLOWING RANDOM ORDER:

1. 1214/11	2. 1314/17	3. 1314/30	4. 1314/33	5. 1314/4
6. 1314/26	7. 1314/13	8. 1314/31	9. 1314/22	10. 1314/9
11. 1314/28	12. 1314/8	13. 1314/23	14. 1314/14	15. 1314/1
16. 1314/6	17. 1314/21	18. 1314/18	19. 1314/25	20. 1314/29
21. 1314/2	22. 1314/19	23. 1314/12	24. 1314/27	25. 1314/5
26. 1314/7	27. 1314/20	28. 1314/24	29. 1314/16	30. 1314/3
31. 1314/32	32. 1314/15	33. 1314/10		

Table 4
Input Material Properties and Regression Coefficients

Multivariate Statistical Correlation
Regression Analysis Program

DATE: 4/6/84
FORMULATIONS: 1314/1   VARIABLES: 5
         TO: 1314/33   FORMULATIONS: 33

COMPONENT	RANGE, PHR	
1. ADD1	0.50	2.50
2. ADD2	0.40	1.40
3. ADD3	0.00	1.60
4. ADD4	0.00	1.60
5. ADD5	42.00	50.00

PROPERTY: FUSION TIME, MIN.   DESIGNATION: FT

$Y1 = 1.25$	$Y2 = 1.75$	$Y3 = 2.2$	$Y4 = 0.9$
$Y5 = 2.2$	$Y6 = 0.95$	$Y7 = 1.55$	$Y8 = 1.4$
$Y9 = 1.7$	$Y10 = 1$	$Y11 = 1.3$	$Y12 = 1.4$
$Y13 = 1.4$	$Y14 = 1.15$	$Y15 = 1.7$	$Y16 = 1$
$Y17 = 2.15$	$Y18 = 1.05$	$Y19 = 1.15$	$Y21 = 1.45$
$Y21 = 1.25$	$Y22 = 1.4$	$Y23 = 1.55$	$Y24 = 1.15$
$Y25 = 1.8$	$Y26 = 1.05$	$Y27 = 1.25$	$Y28 = 1.2$
$Y29 = 1.25$	$Y30 = 1.25$	$Y31 = 1.35$	$Y32 = 1.4$
$Y33 = 1.4$			

REGRESSION COEFFICIENTS:

$A(0, 0) = 1.29950979$	$A(0, 1) = -0.247916666$	$A(0, 2) = 0.0270833333$
$A(0, 3) = 0.00625$	$A(0, 4) = -0.0979166666$	$A(0, 5) = -0.235416666$
$A(1, 1) = 0.0755514709$	$A(1, 2) = -0.021875$	$A(1, 3) = -0.059375$
$A(1, 4) = 0.040625$	$A(1, 5) = 0.028125$	$A(2, 2) = 0.0005514774$
$A(2, 3) = -0.009375$	$A(2, 4) = 0.015625$	$A(2, 5) = 0.015625$
$A(3, 3) = 0.0068014864$	$A(3, 4) = -0.009375$	$A(3, 5) = 0.065625$
$A(4, 4) = 0.0130514788$	$A(4, 5) = 0.103125$	$A(5, 5) = 0.03180140$

5. The standard error of estimate (SEDE)
6. The coefficient of multiple correlation (R)

Item 1: Allows checking for data entry errors
Item 2: Gives an indication as to which variables have a strong effect.
Item 3: Provides a measure of reproducibility. This should be watched carefully as an increase in the standard deviation can be causes by change in laboratory procedure.
Item 4: The "F" significance test (Table 5) measures the significance of each individual coefficient in relation to the scatter in the data. A 1% lack of fit is excellent, while a 5% lack of fit is generally considered acceptable. If the coefficient shows a lack of fit exceeding 5%, this means that the coefficient does not have a strong effect on the property being studied. However, the coefficient is not dropped from the equation.
Item 5: The standard error of estimate is an overall measure of scatter in the data.
Item 6: The coefficient of a multiple correlation is a measure of the degree of fit of the data to the equation. A perfect fit yields a value of 1.0, with a value of 0.9 considered excellent. Experiments carefully conducted often yield values of 0.97 to 0.98.
After printing is completed, data are stored on disk to be used in the plotting program.

1108   Polymer Rheology and Processing

Table 5
Haake Buchler System 40 Data Sheet

"F" Analysis For Significance of "A" Coefficients

DATE: 4/6/84   FORMULATIONS; 1314/1 TO 1314/33
PROPERTY: DESIGNATION:

REPLICATE STD. DEV. = 0.08164965   F(5%) = 5.99   F(1%) = 13.74

COEFF.	"F" RATIO	LACK OF FIT	COEFF.	"F" RATIO	LACK OF FIT
(0, 0)	1845.536	< 1%	A(0, 1)	221.266	< 1%
A(0, 2)	2.641	> 5%	A(0, 3)	0.141	> 5%
A(0, 4)	34.516	< 1%	A(0, 5)	199.516	< 1%
A(1, 1)	13.699	< 5%	A(1, 2)	1.148	> 5%
A(1, 3)	8.461	< 5%	A(1, 4)	3.961	> 5%
A(1, 5)	1.898	> 5%	A(2, 2)	0.001	> 5%
A(2, 3)	0.211	> 5%	A(2, 4)	0.568	> 5%
A(2, 5)	0.568	> 5%	A(3, 3)	0.111	> 5%
A(3, 4)	0.398	> 5%	A(3, 5)	19.523	< 1%
A(4, 4)	0.772	> 5%	A(4, 5)	48.211	< 1%
A(5, 5)	4.585	> 5%			

STD ERROR OF ESTIMATE (SEOE) = 0.06013537
CORRELATION COEFFICIENT (R) = 0.9843258

Plotting Program

The Program can be either loaded directly or called from a menu. If more than two formulation variables are used, levels of the other variables are fixed and a contour plot of a property vs. levels of each ingredient (Figure 27) is displayed on the screen. This allows the formulator to choose the proper values of each ingredient to optimize processing or physical properties. Hard copies of the plots can be obtained by a menu in the lower left corner of the screen.

Additive Incorporation and Compounding

All of the additives used in a formulation have to be incorporated to the major component, and the components should be in a stable molecular arrangement. Figure 28 is a test result for incorporation of minor components to the major component, as well as a homogeneous compound after the additives are incorporated. The test was performed with SBR rubber and preblended additives based on ASTM D 3185.

Stadiene Butadiene Rubber (SBR) was loaded into the mixer and mixed for 30 seconds. Preblended additives (carbon black, zinc oxide, sulphur, and stearic acid) were added at 30 seconds. Torque values sharply dropped immediately and increased as the additives incorporated, when the ingredients were fully incorporated, it generated the second peak, and torque values stabilized when the material was homogeneously compounded. The second peak is called the "incorporation peak."

If hard fillers are added to the polymer, torque increases sharply and generates the second peak. This can be seen when carbon black is incorporated.

The time from minor components added to the major component to the point of the "incorporation peak" is called "incorporation time."

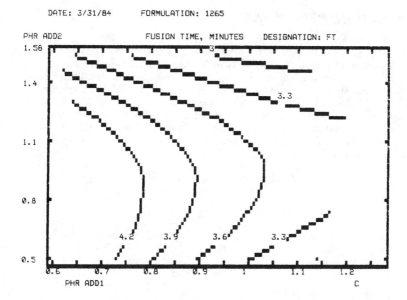

DATE: 3/31/84   FORMULATION: 1265

PHR ADD2   FUSION TIME, MINUTES   DESIGNATION: FT

Figure 27. Contour plot of additive 5 (ADD 5) vs. additive 1 (ADD 1) with control property fusion time.

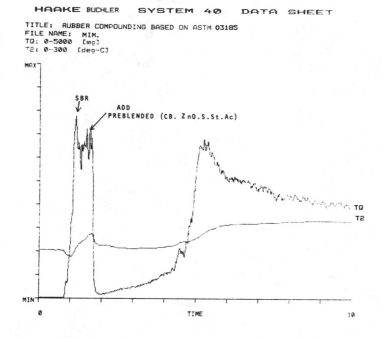

HAAKE BUCHLER   SYSTEM 40   DATA SHEET

TITLE: RUBBER COMPOUNDING BASED ON ASTM 03185
FILE NAME: MIM.
TQ: 0-5000   [mg]
T2: 0-300   [deg-C]

Figure 28. Incorporation of additives to SBR rubber in rubber formulation and compounding.

Scorch and Cure Characteristics of Rubber

Cross-linkable thermoplastics, rubber, and thermoset materials change their physical properties, usually from liquid to solid (cure) by chemical reaction, by heat, or by catalyst during processing.

It is important for process engineers to know how long it takes to cure, how high a torque is generated, and how long it will be in stable flow. This information would help the engineers predict how the material should be processed to provide the best processability and properties.

Figure 29 illustrates test results of cure characteristics of rubber obtained from the Rheomix 600 and cam-type rotors. Once the rubber is introduced to the heated mixer, it generates a sharp increase in torque called the "loading peak." After it is loaded, the material starts to soften, which results in decreasing torque. It reaches minimum torque (maximum flow) and starts to scorch prior to the curing reaction taking place.

When it cures, the torque value increases and torque decreases after the curing reaction is over. The cycle time is considered the time from loading to cure peak.

Cure Characteristics of Thermoset Material

The same test described earlier can be performed for thermoset materials. Figure 30 shows the cure test performed for urea formaldehyde. The time from point L to point C is considered the cycle time of the material at the test condition.

SINGLE SCREW EXTRUDER

Solids conveying, melting, mixing, and pumping are the major functions of polymer processing extruders. The single screw extruder is the machine most widely used to perform these functions.

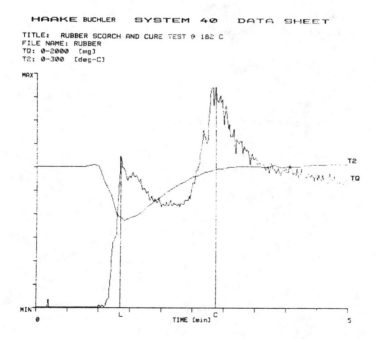

Figure 29. Scorch and cure characteristics of rubber.

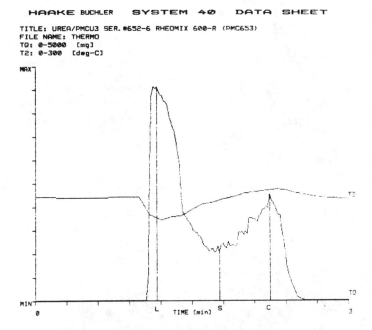

Figure 30. Cure characteristic of urea formaldehyde.

The plasticating extruder has three distinct regions: solids-conveying zone, transition (melting) zone, and pumping zone (shown in Figure 31). It is fed by polymer in the particulate solids form. The solids (usually in pellet or powder form) in the hopper, flow by gravity into the screw channel where they are conveyed through the solids-conveying section. They are compressed by a drag induced mechanism, then melted by a drag induced melt removal mechanism in the transition section. In other words, melting is accomplished by heat transfer from the heated barrel surface and by mechanical shear heating.

Mixing can be carried out either in solid state or in molten state, and is achieved through the application of shear to the material. Pumping is to force the molten polymer through a die to shape the commercial product or for further processing.

Solids Conveying

Solids conveying is one of the basic functions in the screw extruder. The polymer particles in the solids-conveying zone exert an increasing force on each other as the material moves forward, and voids between the pellets are gradually reduced. As the particles move toward the transition section, they are packed closely together to reach a void-free state, and form a solid bed which slides along the helical channels.

The solids-conveying mechanism is based on the internal resistance of a solid body sliding over another (friction) generated between the plug and barrel surfaces and the screw. This type of flow is known as a drag induced plug flow. The frictional force between the barrel surface and the solid plug is the driving force for the movement of the plug; the forces between the screw and the plug retard the motion of the plug in the forward direction.

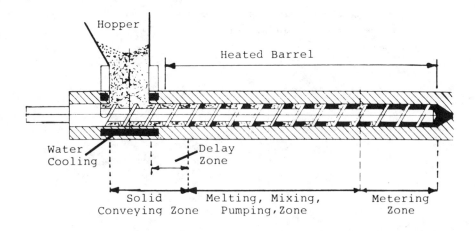

Figure 31. (A) Schematic of single-screw extruder. (B) System 40 with Rheomex $254\frac{3}{4}$-inch extruder sensor.

Melting

Figure 32 illustrates the melting mechanism of material in the extruder. Melting is taking place due to mechanical and thermal energy transformed into heat. The plug which is formed in the solids-conveying zone generates friction in contact with the heated barrel surface, and in contact with the screw. Both of these frictional processes result in frictional heat generation which raises the material temperature, which in turn, exceeds the melting temperature or softening point of the polymer. This will convert the frictional drag into a viscous drag mechanism. This creates a melt film between the hot metal and solid bed.

As the plug moves forward, the melt portion increases and forms a melt pool, which gets larger and larger. The conveying mechanism in this zone is one of viscous drag at the barrel surface, determined by the shear stresses in the melt film and frictional (retarding) drag on the rest of the screw and the flights [2].

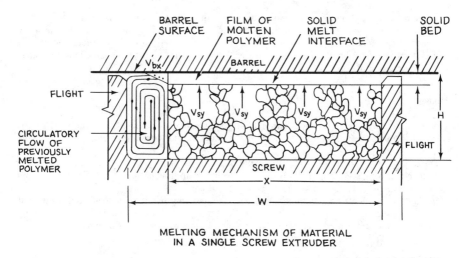

Figure 32. Melting mechanism of material in a single-screw extruder.

Solid and molten material coexist in the melting zone of the extruder. Figure 33 shows melting procedure in the single screw extruders. In this figure, the sequence of events is as follows:

1. Solids conveying section (Delay Zone)
2. Beginning of the transition (Formation of melt film)
3. Formation of melt pool
4. Melting continues and the width of the solid bed decreases, as the channel depth continues to decrease as it progresses down the transition.
5. The solid bed break-up
6. The plastic continues down the metering section to the discharge.

An ideally designed screw gives zero solid bed profile at the end of screw:

$$\text{Solid Bed Profile} = \frac{X}{W} = 0$$

Pumping

Melt conveying occurs in two distinctive regions. One is downstream of the melting zone (after the completion of melting) and the other is in the melt pool, which is an extension of the solid bed profile.

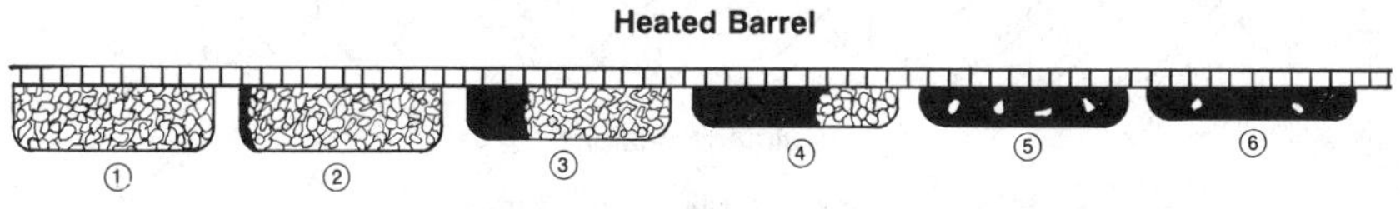

Heated Barrel

Figure 33. Melting progression in a single-screw extruder.

In the metering section or at the end of the screw, the polymer transforms totally into a melt. At this point, the solid bed profile, which is the ratio of the length of the solid bed to the screw lead length, has to reach zero so that only melted polymer comes out of the extruder and die.

In order to create a homogenous melt, mixing screws, barrier screws, and sometimes two stage screws are often used.

Mixing

A standard single screw extruder can exhibit good mixing properties within limits. Mixing is achieved through the application of shear to the material, and constant orientation of the flow pattern.

The screw can be modified to improve mixing by adding a mixing section following the metering section. The mixing section is specially designed to break up flow patterns [10]. Figure 34 shows some of the mixing devices used frequently in screw design.

Mixing sections have no pumping action, and the metering section behind it pumps the melt through this section. Mixing always results in heating the melt by mechanical work, so many polymer melts would degrade. Therefore, the amount of mixing often must be limited.

Screw Design Considerations

Materials (Alloys) for Screw

It is important to select proper materials for construction of a screw. Machine-ability, material strength, abrasion resistance, and corrosion resistance are major factors in the selection of materials.

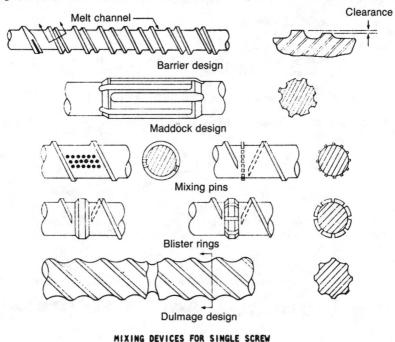

MIXING DEVICES FOR SINGLE SCREW

Figure 34. Different mixing sections often used in a single screw.

Screws made of stainless steel 4140 with chrome (or nickel) plating and flame hardened are widely used. Screws made of duranickel or Hastelloy C are used for corrosion resistance. X-alloy barrels are considered for abrasion resistance, and Hastelloy barrels are used for corrosion resistance.

Solids-Conveying Section

This section determines the effectiveness of solids feeding or conveying. The depth of the feed section should be determined based on the bulk density of the material and the strength of the remaining screw diameter to withstand the maximum torque of the drive.

It is desirable to take the maximum flight depth possible while maintaining the mechanical strength of the screw, especially for low bulk density material. A flight land of one tenth of the screw diameter is normally used. If the tip of the flight is too narrow, the flight may crack during use due to weakness caused by erosional force.

The length of any zone (solids conveying, melting, melt conveying) depends on operating conditions, screw geometry, and physical properties of the polymer being processed. Longer feed sections are usually desirable for a material that has a higher melting point. Long feed sections are favorable for crystalline materials because the solid bed is rigid, and compressibility is low. Shorter feed sections can be utilized for amorphous polymers, because these materials do not have a heat of fusion and have higher compressibility.

Additional flights (only in the feed section) or grooving the barrel in the feed section would be helpful for efficient solids conveying.

Transition Section

Melting takes place and high pressures can be developed in this section. The compression ratio (ratio of feed depth to metering depth) is commonly used terminology for describing the transition of the screw from the feed section to the metering section. The higher rate of compression in the transition section can increase the rate of melting due to higher pressure. The length of the transition section is affected by the length of the feed section. If the screw has a long feed section, there will be more molten polymer in the feed section; therefore, the solid polymer will be at a higher temperature by the time it reaches the transition section. Consequently, the polymer is more easily deformed, and a shorter transition section, or greater compression ratio, can be used.

Metering Section

In this section, melting continues to take place and pumping also occurs. It is ideal that the solid bed profile (amount of solids present in the screw channel at the end of this section) reaches zero. Homogenous melt can be obtained in such a way. The more solids that exist near the end of the metering section, the less homogenous the extrudate will be.

The depth of the metering section is determined by the melt viscosity of the resin. The higher the viscosity, the greater the flight depth should be in order to reduce viscous shear heating. When a deep flight depth is used, a long metering section should be employed to ensure complete melting of the material.

Venting Section

It is difficult to balance the first stage output with the second stage output. If the first stage delivers more than the second stage pumps through the die, the result is vent flow. If the second stage tends to pump more than the first stage delivers, the result is surging of output and pressure. This can be adjusted by controlling the feed or by valving the output.

In this section, maintaining zero pressure drop is the most important factor. A flight depth similar to the feed depth or approximately 15% greater than the first metering section is usually adequate. A multiple flighted configuration can be used for the vent section to increase the amount of surface exposure and the efficiency of devolatilization. The vent section should have at least three flights, or more if possible.

Rule of Thumb for Selection of Screws in Polymer Processing

It is important for the process engineer to choose a proper ratio of length and diameter of screw (L/D ratio of screw) and ratio of flight depth in the feed section and in the metering section of screw (compression ratio) for the polymer to be processed optimally.

Normally short L/D ratio screws may be chosen for heat sensitive materials in order to lessen the chance of degradation by shortening the residence time.

High compression ratio screws can be chosen for high percentage of regrind, powders, and other low bulk density materials. Low compression ratio screws can be used for engineering and heat sensitive materials. The compression ratio of such screws should be made less by deepening the metering section, and not by making the feed section shallower.

APPLICATION OF SINGLE SCREW EXTRUDERS

Production simulations, rheological property measurements, and processing characteristics will be discussed in this section. Above applications using a single screw extruder are widely acknowledged in polymer industries and research organizations because the production line can be closely simulated in the laboratories.

Simulations of Production Line

Simulation of the extrusion process in the laboratory is one of the most important applications of the torque rheometer in conjunction with single screw extruders. Figure 35 illustrates simulations of widely used extrusion processes in the industries.

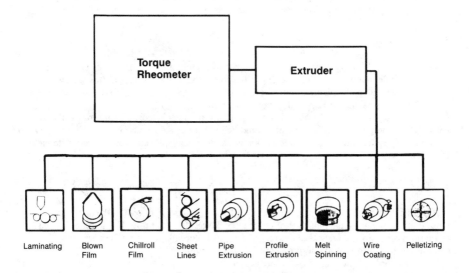

Figure 35. Simulations of various extrusion processes.

Rheological Property Measurement

It is very important for a process engineer to know the rheological properties of a material, since the properties dominate the flow of the material in extrusion processes and also dominate physical and mechanical properties of the extrudates. Therefore, it is also important to measure the properties utilizing a similar miniaturized extruder in the laboratory, so that a process engineer knows the flow properties in the system by simulating the production line. This will enable engineers to develop processing, to see lot-to-lot variances of materials for better quality control of the resins.

It is desirable to know flow properties of a material to be processed in the range of shear rates of equipments to be used. Figure 36 illustrates approximate shear rate ranges processed in different processing equipments. The figure also shows that rheological properties measured at lower shear rate ranges cannot be applicable to high shear rate ranges, and vice versa, because the viscosity of material A is lower than that of material B at low shear rate ranges (1 to 10 sec^{-1}), but it is the opposite at the high shear rate ranges (above 100 sec^{-1}).

Capillary Rheometry

We will discuss rheological property measurements using capillary die and slit die directly attached to the miniaturized single screw extruder, since the capillary and slit rheometers are applicable from low-to-high shear rate and shear stress ranges.

Figure 37 provides a schematic diagram of the extrusion capillary rheometer.

The discussion here is limited primarily to steady isothermal flow through a straight capillary having circular cross sections.

Pressure drop in the capillary. A pressure drop occurs at the entrance of the capillary because fluid particles entering the tube from the reservoir are accelerated to their final steady flow velocity, since the cross section of a capillary is generally much smaller than that of a reservoir section. The energy consumed in this process causes the pressure to drop more rapidly in this region than in the steady flow region refer to Figure 38. The pressure drop is usually considerably greater for viscoelastic polymer melts than for Newtonian fluids.

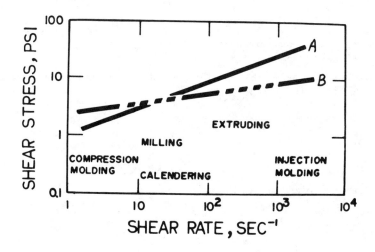

Figure 36. Approximate shear rate ranges for different processing equipment.

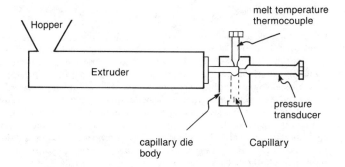

Figure 37. Schematic of extrusion capillary rheometer.

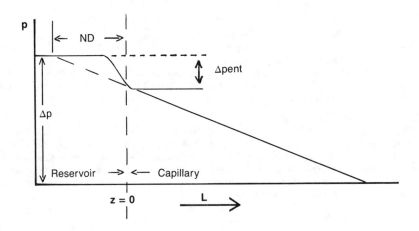

Figure 38. Correction of tube length L by addition of length ND (fictitious length) in order to calculate the pressure gradient in the steady flow region.

Apparent Viscosity. Apparent shear rate (Γ_w) at the wall and resultant apparent shear stress (τ_w) can be obtained by using the following equations:

$$\Gamma_w = \frac{4Q}{\pi R^3} \tag{13}$$

$$\tau_w = \frac{R\,\Delta P}{2L} \tag{14}$$

Therefore, apparent viscosity (η_{app}) may be calculated as:

$$\eta_{app} = \frac{\tau_w}{\Gamma_w} \tag{15}$$

where   Q = vol. flowrate (cc/sec)
           R = radius of capillary (cm)

L = length of capillary (cm)

ΔP = Pressure Drop (dyne/cm^2)

True viscosity. True shear stress (τ_w^*) and true shear rate ($\dot\gamma_w^*$) can be obtained with correction of entrance effect in the capillary.

$$\tau_w^* = \frac{R\,\Delta P}{2(L + ND)} \tag{16}$$

$$\dot\gamma_w^* = \frac{3}{4}\,\Gamma_w + \frac{\tau_w^*}{4}\frac{d\Gamma_w}{d\tau_w^*} \tag{17}$$

$$\eta^* = \tau_w^*/\dot\gamma_w^* \tag{18}$$

where ND = fictitious length (see Figure 39).

Table 6 tabulates numerical rheological properties of polypropylene obtained from the computer software.

Figures 39 and 40 show shear stress vs. shear rate and viscosity vs. shear rate, respectively.

Slit Rheometry

In order to obtain viscosity data, a slit die with three pressure transducers along the die can be used. Since the slope of pressure drop vs. length of die (L) curve in the fully developed region is used to calculate shear stress, entrance effect correction is not necessary in slit rheometry.

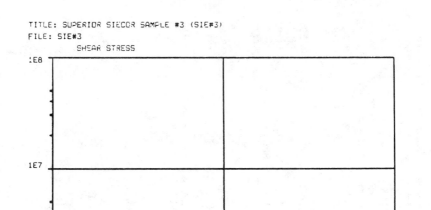

Figure 39. Shear stress vs. shear rate data from capillary software program.

Table 6

Rheological Properties of Polypropylene from Extrusion Capillary Rheometry Software Program

RPM [1/MIN] =	10	RPM [1/MIN] =	60
PRESS. DROP [PSI] =	3239.30	PRESS. DROP [PSI] =	7013.30
APP. SHEAR RATE [1/SEC] =	288.49	APP. SHEAR RATE [1/SEC] =	1648.81
SHEAR STRESS [DYNE/CM2] =	1395874.02	SHEAR STRESS [DYNE/CM2] =	3022161.48
TRUE SHEAR RATE [1/SEC] =	405.89	TRUE SHEAR RATE [1/SEC] =	2317.41
VISCOSITY [POISE] =	3438.97	VISCOSITY [POISE] =	1304.10
RPM [1/MIN] =	20	RPM [1/MIN] =	70
PRESS. DROP [PSI] =	4612.29	PRESS. DROP [PSI] =	7310.29
APP. SHEAR RATE [1/SEC] =	561.26	APP. SHEAR RATE [1/SEC] =	1940.80
SHEAR STRESS [DYNE/CM2] =	1987525.93	SHEAR STRESS [DYNE/CM2] =	3150145.53
TRUE SHEAR RATE [1/SEC] =	789.29	TRUE SHEAR RATE [1/SEC] =	2727.66
VISCOSITY [POISE] =	2518.11	VISCOSITY [POISE] =	1154.88
RPM [1/MIN] =	30	RPM [1/MIN] =	80
PRESS. DROP [PSI] =	5550.30	PRESS. DROP [PSI] =	7477.29
APP. SHEAR RATE [1/SEC] =	865.49	APP. SHEAR RATE [1/SEC] =	2300.99
SHEAR STRESS [DYNE/CM2] =	2391727.44	SHEAR STRESS [DYNE/CM2] =	3222106.93
TRUE SHEAR RATE [1/SEC] =	1216.83	TRUE SHEAR RATE [1/SEC] =	3233.78
VISCOSITY [POISE] =	1965.53	VISCOSITY [POISE] =	996.38
RPM [1/MIN] =	40	RPM [1/MIN] =	90
PRESS. DROP [PSI] =	6108.30	PRESS. DROP [PSI] =	7528.30
APP. SHEAR RATE [1/SEC] =	1119.02	APP. SHEAR RATE [1/SEC] =	2675.16
SHEAR STRESS [DYNE/CM2] =	2632181.16	SHEAR STRESS [DYNE/CM2] =	3244082.45
TRUE SHEAR RATE [1/SEC] =	1573.08	TRUE SHEAR RATE [1/SEC] =	3759.61
VISCOSITY [POISE] =	1673.26	VISCOSITY [POISE] =	862.87
RPM [1/MIN] =	50	RPM [1/MIN] =	100
PRESS. DROP [PSI] =	6559.30	PRESS. DROP [PSI] =	7668.30
APP. SHEAR RATE [1/SEC] =	1369.05	APP. SHEAR RATE [1/SEC] =	2958.41
SHEAR STRESS [DYNE/CM2] =	2826524.73	SHEAR STRESS [DYNE/CM2] =	3304411.88
TRUE SHEAR RATE [1/SEC] =	1924.38	TRUE SHEAR RATE [A/SEC] =	4157.59
VISCOSITY [POISE] =	1468.79	VISCOSITY [POISE] =	794.79

HAAKE BUCHLER SYSTEM 40 DATA SHEET

TITLE: SUPERIOR SIECOR SAMPLE #3 (SIE#3) DATE: MAY 18 1984
FILE: SIE#3 0832:34

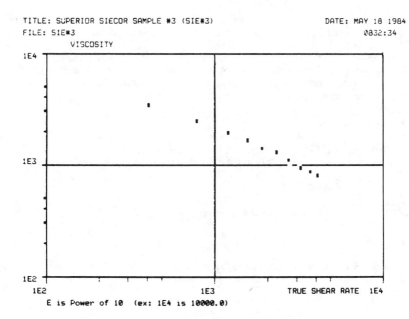

E is Power of 10 (ex: 1E4 is 10000.0)

Figure 40. Viscosity vs. shear rate curve from capillary software program.

The viscosity of materials can be calculated as follows:

Apparent shear rate (Γ_w):

$$\Gamma_w = \frac{6Q}{wh^2} \tag{19}$$

True shear rate ($\dot{\gamma}_w^*$) with Rabinowitch corrections:

$$\dot{\gamma}^* = \frac{\Gamma_w}{3}\left(2 + \frac{d \ln \Gamma_w}{d \ln \tau_w^*}\right) \tag{20}$$

True shear stress (τ_w^*)

$$\tau_w^* = \frac{h}{2L}(\Delta p) \tag{21}$$

where   h = opening of slot (cm)
        w = width of slot (cm)
        L = length of slit die (cm)
        Q = vol. flow rate (cc/sec)
        p = pressure drop (dyne/cm^2)

Polymer Processing Characteristics (Lot-to-Lot Variances)

Even though they are the same polymer materials, often they show variances lot-to-lot in processing and in product quality. The reasons the variance occurs are difficult to detect in the production line because they are dealt with in mass.

The processing characteristics can be easily tested in the laboratory by simulating the production
line and analyzing the data microscopically. A miniaturized single screw extruder (Rheomex) in
conjunction with the Rheocord System 40 can characterize the processing by measuring total shear
energy (mechanical energy), specific energy, residence time, shear rate, and specific output.

Total Shear Energy (TE)

Total shear energy (TE) is the energy introduced to the polymer material by the motor drive
during processing. This is calculated from the measured torque multiplied by screw speed (N).

$$TE = \text{Torque} \times N \times 9.807 \times 10^{-3} \tag{22}$$

These data give information about total mechanical energy required to process the material.

Specific Energy (SE)

Specific energy (SE) is defined as an energy required to process a unit mass of material. This is
calculated from total shear energy divided by the total mass flow rate.

$$SE = \frac{0.0167 \, TE}{\dot{m}} \tag{23}$$

where $\dot{m}$ = total mass flow rate. These data give information about viscous dissipation heat built
up in the system based on screw speeds.

Residence Time (t)

Residence time is the time required for a material to reside in the extruder before it comes out
of the die. It can be obtained from volume of screw (V) divided by volumetric flow rate (Q), or
length of screw (L) divided by angular velocity of screw (πDN):

$$t = \frac{V}{Q} \quad \text{or} \quad t = \frac{L}{\pi DN} \tag{24}$$

Maintaining uniform residence time is important to obtain quality product. If it is not maintained,
sometimes the material will degrade because of excess exposure to heat.

Shear Rate ($\dot{\gamma}$)

Shear rate in the metering section of the screw can be obtained as follows:

$$\dot{\gamma} = \frac{\pi DN}{h} \tag{25}$$

where   D = Diameter of screw
         N = rpm
         h = Gap between screw and barrel

Specific Output

Specific output (SO) is defined as mass flow rate per unit rpm of screw and is calculated from total mass flow rate (m) divided by RPM (N) used.

$$SO = \frac{\dot{m}}{N} \tag{26}$$

This information provides uniformity of solids conveying, melting, and pumping mechanisms of the screw being used.

The following data have been obtained using fiber-graded polypropylene from different lots. Sample A is standard control material, and B and C are from different batches. The test was performed using an instrumented single screw extruder (HBI RHEOMEX252, L/D = 25, D = 3/4″), with a two-stage screw and capillary die (L/D = 40), in conjunction with a microprocessor-controlled torque rheometer (RHEOCORD SYSTEM 40).

Temperature profile on the extruder barrel was 220°C at zone 1, 200°C at zone 2, 190°C at zone 3, and 190°C at the die. The melt temperature was measured with an exposed thermocouple, and entrance pressure was directly measured at the entrance to the capillary.

This test gives a microscopic viewpoint of the polymer's processing characteristics, showing differences which normally would not be seen individually in the overall macroscopic view seen in the production line. Figure 41 shows normalized output (grams of material extruded per screw revolution) vs. rpm. Normalized output tends to decrease as screw speed increases, even though overall output increases as screw speed increases because of melt limitations of the material in the system. Figure 42 illustrates specific energy (energy needed to process one gram of material) vs. rpm. The specific energy increases steadily as screw speed increases because the overall viscosity of the material in the system increases due to decreasing residence time as screw speed increases.

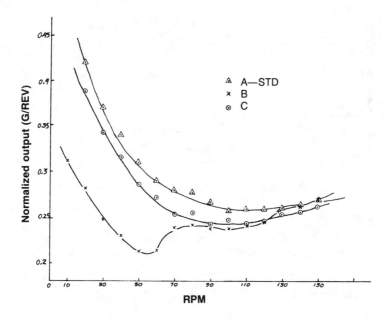

Figure 41. Normalized output as a function of rpm.

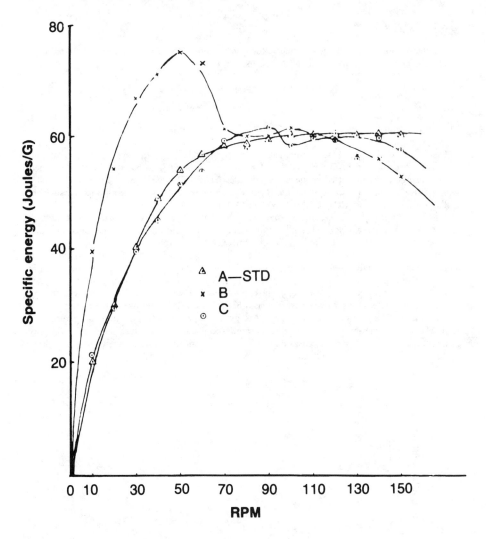

Figure 42. Specific energy as a function of rpm.

Figure 43 denotes viscosity vs. shear rate. The viscosities of samples B and C show much similarity, but the specific output and energy still show big differences.

The test concludes that the same material from different lots show different processing characteristics.

TWIN SCREW EXTRUDER

Although a single screw plasticating extruder is satisfactory for melting and extrusion, its mixing capabilities are limited. Tougher, specialized thermoplastic materials developed for new applications must be processed at conditions requiring very accurate temperature control, uniform resi-

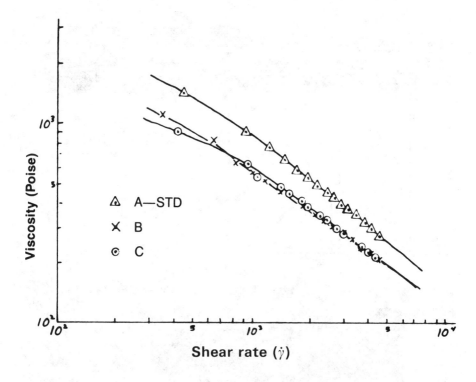

Figure 43. Viscosity vs. shear rate.

dence time distribution, better dispersion of fillers and additives, positive venting, and surge-free extrusion of homogeneous melt for high-quality products.

Twin-screw extruders are widely used for such applications, and overcome limitations of the single-screw extruder and the intensive batch mixer. The twin-screw unit comes in a variety of configurations: they can be non-, partially, or fully intermeshing; they can be conical or cylindrical.

This section discusses the basic principles of solids conveying, melting, mixing, degassing, energy, and residence time of the counterrotating, partially intermeshing, conical twin-screw extruder. Figure 44 shows a schematic diagram of a twin screw extruder. Figure 45 shows the flow exchange in partially intermeshed twin screws and in fully intermeshed twin screws.

Feeding and Solids Conveying

Material feeding is important in extrusion. Starved feeding is a common practice to avoid drive and thrust bearing overload, but forced feeding has application as well. Two types of feeding devices—that is, the force feeding (crammer feeder) and the screw-metering feeder—are commonly used to regulate and control the feed rate. Figure 46 illustrates schematic diagrams of a force feeder and a volumetric metering feeder.

When low-bulk-density material (granulate or powder) with low-bulk-weight fillers such as fumed silica or wood dust are processed, the air in the feed is forced out in the intake zone, and can impede the smooth intake of the inflowing material. Since throughput rate of the extruder is limited by the volumetric-conveying rate, the extruder will tend to surge. Therefore, precompressing the

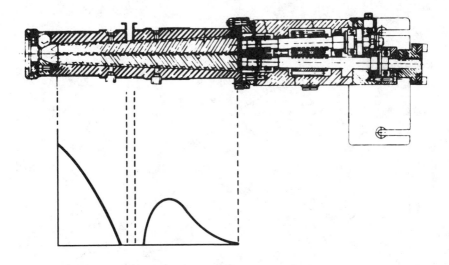

Figure 44. Schematic of conical, counter-rotating, partially intermeshing twin-screw extruder along with pressure profile in the devolatilizing extruder (top). System 40 with Rheomex TW-100 twin screw extruder (bottom).

feed material is required to increase the output rate, and it can be done by means of force-feeding devices at the throat.

High bulk-density material with high-bulk-density filler, such as high-temperature engineering plastics with carbon blacks, on the other hand, cannot be force fed due to rheological and physical properties of the material. In this case, starve feeding, utilizing the gravimetric or volumetric metering feeder to control the feed rate and to avoid thrust-bearing overloading, is a common practice. Desired output rate can be obtained by maintaining optimal processing conditions and by controlling the feed rate.

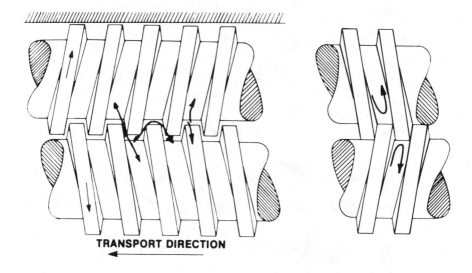

TRANSPORT DIRECTION

Figure 45. Flow interchange in a partially intermeshed twin screw (left) and in a fully intermeshed twin screw (right).

Figure 47 shows the cross section of the feed zone in a counterrotating-screw system. In order to feed as much material as possible, utilizing the largest conveying volume, the screws turn outward on top and inward at the bottom. To obtain more material conveying, a different screw geometry just underneath the hopper often uses a greater pitch and multiple thread starts. The positive displacement of such a filling zone is greater than that of the rest of the extruder. Polymer enters the screw in the intake zone, and is compressed and conveyed toward the downstream into the melting zone, where transition from solids to melt occurs.

In single screw extruders, a continuous solids bed is generally present through which pressure is generated continuously. In a twin-screw extruder, the solids bed is broken up into discontinuous lengths by the interruption of the screw channels by the flights of intermeshing screws. Effective compaction of material can be achieved by making the screws and barrels conical, progressively decreasing barrel and screw diameters and increasing crest.

Melting Mechanism

The inflowing material is compacted in the solids-conveying zone to form a solids bed, to minimize air pockets, and convey material to the downstream melting zone, where it is first heated by direct contact with the barrel surface and then developed into a melt film.

Meanwhile, at the edge of the solids bed, a melt pool is created that draws in solid particles and softens them, and the plasticated mass is taken in by a calender gap. Inflowing unmelted polymer goes into the melt stream by kneading action in the zone where the melting starts to accelerate the melting process. Melt can be conveyed while the trapped air can leak back. The melt will eventually reach a point at which pressure build up commences as a result of the flow of melt back through the various leakage gaps.

In a single screw extruder, the solids bed steadily diminishes along the melting zone. In a twin screw extruder, however, a complete melting sequence can be found in each chamber where the solids bed and melt interface move from the diverging side to the converging side of the screws

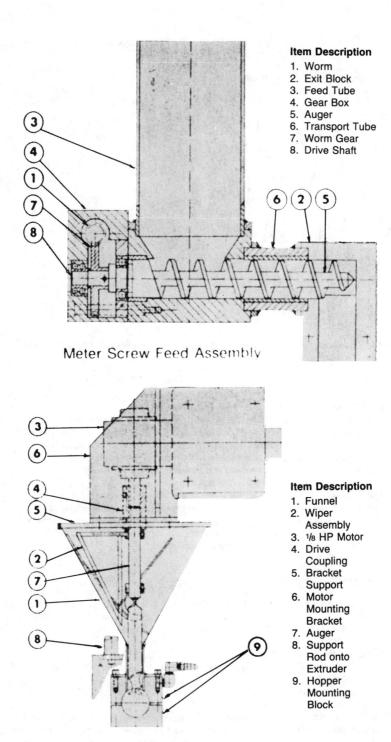

Item Description
1. Worm
2. Exit Block
3. Feed Tube
4. Gear Box
5. Auger
6. Transport Tube
7. Worm Gear
8. Drive Shaft

Meter Screw Feed Assembly

Item Description
1. Funnel
2. Wiper Assembly
3. 1/8 HP Motor
4. Drive Coupling
5. Bracket Support
6. Motor Mounting Bracket
7. Auger
8. Support Rod onto Extruder
9. Hopper Mounting Block

Figure 46. Volumetric metering feeder (top) and schematic of force feeder (bottom).

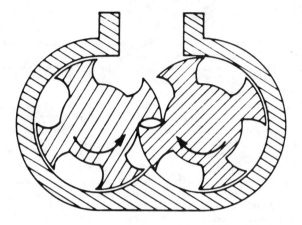

Figure 47. Cross section of the feed zone in the counter-rotating screw system.

while the chambers move through the extruder. L. Janssen [11] has extensively studied the melting mechanism in the twin screws.

Figure 48 shows unwound chambers to illustrate the melting process. The melting mechanism at low backpressure is also different from that at high backpressure. At low backpressure, the melting process takes place at the barrel wall so that heat transfer plays an important role. With high backpressure, however, the fully filled length of the extruder reaches back to the melting zone, and considerable leakage flows take place. In this case, melting starts at the solids/melt interface. Therefore, head pressure affects the melting inside the system.

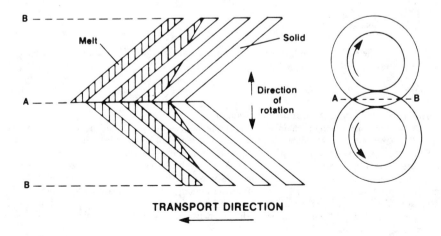

Figure 48. Unwound chamber to illustrate melting process.

Mixing

It is well-known that compounds with two or more components should be mixed well to provide optimum properties in the final product.

There are two distinct types of mixing processes: the spreading of particles over positions in space (distributive mixing), and the sharing or spreading of the available energy of a system between the particles themselves (dispersive mixing).

Distributive mixing is used for any operation employed to increase the randomness of the spatial distribution of particles without reducing their sizes [1]. This mixing depends on the orientation of flow and the total strain, which is the product of shear rate and residence time. Therefore, the more random the arrangement of flow pattern, the higher the shear rate; and the longer the residence time, the better the mixing will be.

Dispersive mixing is similar to that of a simple mixing process, except that the nature and magnitude of forces required to rupture the particles to an ultimate size must be considered [1]. An important application of such intensive mixing is incorporation of pigments, fillers, and other minor components into the matrix polymer. This mixing is a function of shear stress, which is the product of shear rate and material viscosity. Breaking up of an agglomerate will occur only when shear stress exceeds strength of the particle.

If the screws are fully intermeshed so that they are closed lengthwise and crosswise, effective mixing cannot be accomplished because there will be hardly any exchange of material between screws. The only thing that will occur will be positive pumping action. Figure 45 shows material flows in the fully intermeshed and partially intermeshed twin screws. If the screws are partially intermeshed, on the other hand, so that they are open lengthwise and crosswise, there will be a clearance that the melts can exchange between screws allowing various leakage flows.

Figure 49 illustrates the various leakage flows studied in depth by Janssen [11] and others. The magnitude of these leakage flows is dependent on the level of pressure differences between the chambers, but since there is communication between chambers all the way to the die, the leakage flows become a function of the die pressure.

The leakage flows between chambers, although reducing the output rate, can bring about much intensive mixing, which is of great importance in the twin screw extruder. Idealized theoretical output (Qth) from a twin screw extruder can be calculated as:

$$Qth = 2mNV \tag{27}$$

where   m = number of thread starts per screw
         N = screw speed
         V = chamber volume

In practice, the output rate (Qpr) is less than theoretical throughput because of the presence of leakage flows within the extruder [11].

$$Qpr = d \, Qth \tag{28}$$

where the empirical constant d is between 1 and 0.

Such interaction between the chambers generates high shear at points where the screws intermesh, since the material encounters highest shear rates in this region of the machine. Figure 50 shows the different flow patterns of corotating and counterrotating screws. When the screws are rotating in opposite directions, material is forced and milled in the calendar gap and is subjected to extremely high shear. These high shear rates contribute to dispersive mixing. Figure 51 shows pressure buildup in counterrotating and corotating screws. Pressure buildup allows this material to compress and expand so that vigorous mixing can be achieved. Meanwhile, at the intermeshing point, material is also being exchanged from one screw to the other. In this way, distributive mixing is also being affected because of rearrangement of flow patterns.

When the screws rotate in the same direction, they are essential in preventing the material from entering the gap between the screws, because as one screw tries to pull the material into the gap,

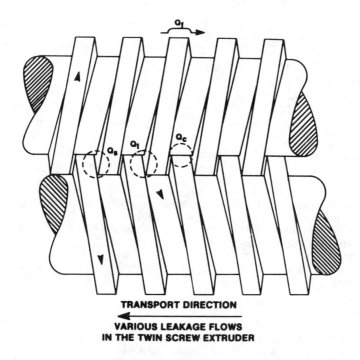

Figure 49. Various leakage flows in the partially intermeshed twin screws.

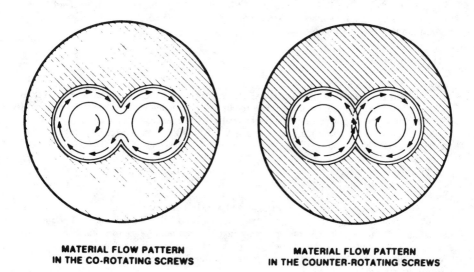

Figure 50. Chamber-to-chamber material-flow pattern in corotating twin screws (left) and in counter-rotating twin screws (right).

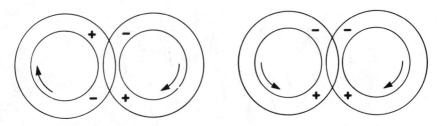

Figure 51. Pressure buildup in a corotating (left) and in a counter-rotating (right) extruder.

the other screw pushes it out. Therefore, the material is not subject to high shear, and dispersive mixing will not be as thorough as in the counterrotating screws. A better distributive mixing, however, can be accomplished with corotating screws because of the frequent reorientation of the material as it passes from one screw to the other.

Adjustment of pressure buildup in the system with the conical twin screws is also versatile to a certain degree, simply by changing the converging section in the barrel, depending on the applications.

Heat Effect

Polymer processing includes the introduction and some removal of mechanical and thermal energies. The temperature change of a fluid element in a flowing-fluid system is determined by the sum of heat gain or loss by conduction to the element and the rate of viscous dissipation within the element. In a thermodynamic sense, the fluid element is a closed system, and the energy balance requires that its rate of increase of internal energy be equal to the rate at which heat is transferred to it and work is done on it. In the process of converting the polymer system from a solid state to a molten state in the twin screw extruder under steady-state conditions, the integral energy balance can be written as follows:

$$\iint_A (\vec{V} \cdot \vec{q}) \, \partial A + \iiint_V (\vec{\tau} : \vec{V}\vec{u}) \, dV = Q \left(\int_{T_1}^{T_2} \bar{C}\rho \, dT + \lambda \right) \tag{29}$$

The first term represents the conducted heat integrated through the entire heat-transfer surface A. This includes heating and cooling through the barrel. The second term denotes the mechanical heat dissipation that is generated by the mechanical work introduced to the material through the rotating rotors over the entire working volume [2, 12]. It is the heat delivered by the motor. In the region where the plastic is still in the solid state, the work is manifested by friction between the particles and the metal wall.

In the extrusion system, the mechanical heat dissipation is always positive; conduction heat may be positive or negative. The specific heat and the fusion heat should be the average value of a multicomponent system.

The counterrotating, partially intermeshing, conical twin-screw extruder allows the best utilization of mechanical energy because of its mixing action, which distributes the unmelted polymer into the melt stream, and its kneading action, which provides homogeneous melt. Since the flow-streamline in the twin screws provides a high shear input, more shearing surface is generated, high pressure is developed, which can be transmitted throughout the system; and very effective heat transport can be achieved.

Practical considerations in mixing equipment usually require maintaining a relatively low temperature. These requirements originate from the temperature-sensitive nature of polymers and the large shear stress required for dispersive mixing.

Degassing

Most polymer systems require venting in order to remove volatiles. This degassing, via a vent port, takes place only when volatiles migrate from the core of the material to the free surface [12], and could be influenced by the material temperature, the pressure, and the material thickness.

These requirements can be met by concial, counterrotating twin screws. Due to intensive kneading and mixing, mechanical energy delivered by drive raises the material temperature of the melt. Pressure influence can be adjusted by changing the converging section and by changing processing parameters in order to maintain zero pressure in the vent-port area. Since the screws rotate outward on top, the material is being pulled away from the center and pushed down into the barrel along the wall; therefore, material would partially fill the screws in this region. Figure 52 shows the material flow at the vent port, and Figure 44 illustrates the pressure profile in the devolatilizing twin-screw extruder.

If the screws rotate inward on top, there will be a pressure buildup along the top of the barrel, because material from each screw is being forced into the nip between them. Thus, there would be pressure at the vent-port area where zero pressure has to be maintained.

Residence Time

Control of the residence time is of great importance for heat-sensitive polymers, because prolonged exposure to high temperature may result in thermal degradation. The degree of degradation depends on the time/temperature history of the polymers; therefore, in order to contain the maximum uniform material quality, the residence time has to be short and uniform. This can be achieved by constantly controlling the feed rate and by maintaining accurate processing control. Residence-time distribution can be determined from the velocity profile directly, if the velocity profile is known at all locations. The mean residence time ($\bar{t}$) equals the volume of the system (V) divided by the throughput (Q); that is:

$$\bar{t} = \frac{V}{Q} \tag{30}$$

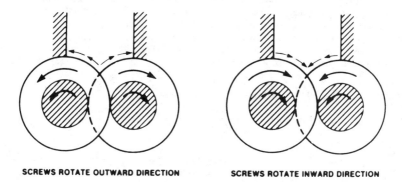

SCREWS ROTATE OUTWARD DIRECTION   SCREWS ROTATE INWARD DIRECTION

**MATERIAL FLOW IN THE
VENT PORT AREA**

Figure 52. Material flow at the vent port in twin screws, rotating outward direction on top (left) and inward direction on top (right).

APPLICATION OF TWIN SCREW EXTRUDER

Polymer Alloy

Metallurgically speaking, an alloy is a substance composed of two or more metals, or of a metal and a non-metal, which are intimately united by fusion and dissolved in each other when they are molten. These alloys will provide durability, corrosion resistance, and other desired properties that cannot be obtained from a single component metal. The same can be applicable to the polymer materials that are called polymer alloys (i.e., blending and mixing multi-component polymer systems in molten state).

As the applications of plastics become more varied, materials that yield specific properties required for a particular application are needed. Research and development of polymer alloys is now very active; it is an inexpensive way to develop new materials with superior properties by blending existing polymers rather than developing new polymers.

Compatibility and Miscibility

Polymer alloys are physical mixtures of structurally different polymers adhered together through intermolecular forces such as Van der Waals forces, hydrogen bonding, or dipole interaction. Therefore, polymer-polymer compatibility and/or miscibility are important factors in polymer alloys. There are two types of alloys, compatible and miscible. Compatible alloys form a homogeneous mixture that neither separates nor is altered by chemical interaction. This is a multi-phase system that shows multiple glass transition temperature and phase morphologies. Miscible alloys mix in any ratio without phase separation, forming a one phase system that shows a single glass transition temperature. In other words, "compatible" is a multi-phase alloy and "miscible" is a single phase alloy. Table 7 is a partial list of compatible and miscible polymer systems and Table 8 shows a partial list of alloys with possible improvement of particular properties.

Polymer Alloy Processing Equipment

Although the single screw extruder, the most widely used machine in polymer processing, gives satisfactory performance in melting and extrusion, its mixing capability is rather limited. Most of the time, polymer alloys can only be achieved by melt mixing. Batch mixers or twin screw extruders are widely used for multi-component polymer system blendings.

Twin screw extruders are a more popular type of processing equipment than batch mixers because the twin-screw extrusion process is continuous, whereas alloying with a batch mixer requires several steps to produce a final product.

Disadvantages of Batch Mixing Process for Alloying

1. Granulate size and shape are non-uniform and irregular, thus making uniform feeding in the extruder difficult.

Table 7
Compatible and Miscible Polymer Systems

Compatible Polymer Systems	Miscible Polymer Systems
PC/ABS	PVC/PMMA
PVC/ABS	PVC/EVA
PPO/HIPS	PVC/CPA
PMMA/ABS	PEO/PS
	CPE/SAN
	PMMA/SAN

Table 8
Alloys and Possible Improvements of Properties

Alloy	Properties
ABS/PC	Improve Impact Strength Easier to Process High Heat Resistance
PVC/PMMA ABS/PVC (Rigid)	Increase Flame Retardancy
ABS/PS	High Heat Resistance Dimension Stability Improve Processing Characteristics
PVC/NBR	Improve Ozone/Weather Resistance, Oil Resisting
SHORT FIBER REINFORCEMENT/ POLYETHER-ETHER KETONE	Improve Strength, Modulus, and Toughness
PPO/HIPS	Processing Latitude
ABS/OLEFIN HIPS/OLEFIN NYLON/OLEFIN	Improve Strength
PU/BISMUTH or PU/BASO4	Improve X-Ray Detection Properties
ETHYLENE/PROPYLENE	Resistance to Ozone, Weather, Heat and Chemicals, High Dielectric Strength

2. Unnecessary steps are required as compared to the twin screw extrusion process.
3. Increased energy and labor costs are required, which results in an increase in production cost.
4. Heat and shear histories accumulate in each step, which might give structural change.

Alloying with a twin-screw extruder can replace the batch mixer, granulator, and single-screw extruder required in the batch process.

Advantages of Twin-Screw Extruder Process for Alloying

1. Continuous process.
2. Simplifies alloying process.
3. Enables the material to maintain uniform residence time.
4. Imposes less heat and shear history than batch process.
5. Saves processing time, energy, and labor costs which are important factors in the reduction of production costs.
6. Mass production is possible.

Figure 53 illustrates the morphology of polyether-ether ketone alloy with short fiber reinforcement, which is obtained from a scanning electron microscope (SEM). The rod shapes represent fiber. This alloy was produced utilizing HBI's TW-100 conical, partially intermeshing, counter-rotating twin screw extruder in conjunction with the HBI System 40 microprocessor-controlled torque rheometer. Figure 54 shows actual data obtained from the rheometer by compounding high impact polystyrene with 17% of flame retardant with the twin screw extruder. Figure 55 illustrates

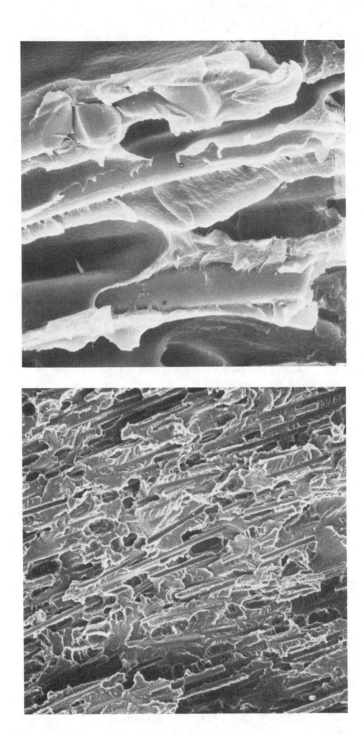

Figure 53. Shows compound of 30% short fibers and 70% PEEK (top: 1,000 × Mag; bottom: 100 × Mag).

HAAKE BUCHLER   SYSTEM 40   DATA SHEET

TITLE: 17% F.R. +   HIPS/83 (TW-100)
FILE NAME:
TQ: 0-7500 [mg]
P3: 0-1000 [psi]

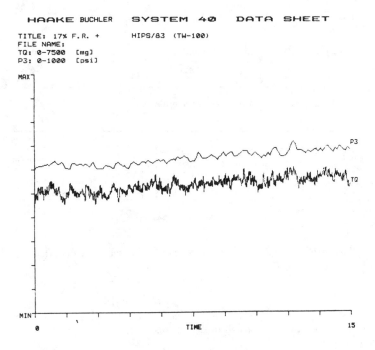

Figure 54. High-impact polystyrene compound with 17% flame retardant using twin-screw extrusion.

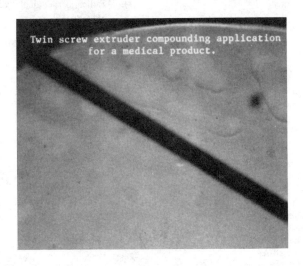

Figure 55. Compound of BASO$_4$ with polyurethane for a medical application.

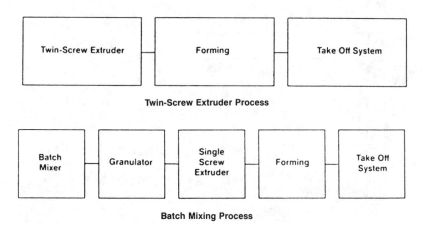

Figure 56. Compares twin-screw extruder process and batch mixing.

a compound of $BaSO_4$ with polyurethane for a medical application. Finally, Figure 56 illustrates, how these compounds can be prepared by a comparison of batch and continuous twin-screw operations.

NOTATION

A	constant, area	ΔP	pressure drop
d	empirical constant	Q	volumetric flow rate
h	opening of slit	R	radius, perpendicular distance, universal constant
K	constant		
L	length	T	temperature (°C)
M	torque	T'	reference temperature (°C)
M'	calculate torque at reference temperature	TTQ	totalized torque
		$\bar{t}$	mean resistance time
m	viscous constant, no. of thread starts	Vb	sample volume
m_0	constant	W	lead length of screw, width of slit
$\dot{m}$	mass flow rate	Wt	total work energy
N	rpm	Wu	unit work
ND	fictitious length	X	length of solid bed
P	power		

Greek Symbols

Γ_w	apparent shear rate	η_{app}	apparent viscosity
$\bar{\dot{\gamma}}$	mean shear rate	η^*	true viscosity
$\dot{\gamma}_w^*$	true shear rate	∇	Del
$\bar{\tau}$	mean shear stress	$\dot{q}$	heat flux vector
τ_w	true shear stress	$\bar{\upsilon}$	velocity vector
t_w	apparent shear stress	λ	heat of fusion

REFERENCES

1. McKelvey, J., *Polymer Processing*, John Wiley & Sons, Inc., 1962.
2. Tadmor, Z., C. G. Gogos, *Principles of Polymer Processing* John Wiley & Sons, Inc., 1979.
3. Geodrich, J. E., and Porter, R. S.; "A Rheological Interpretation of Torque Rheometer Data," *Polymer Engineering and Science*, Jan., 1967.
4. Goodrich, J. E., "Torque Rheometer Evaluation of Poly Propylene Process Stability," *Polymer Eng. Sci.*, July, 1970, Vol. 10 No. 4.
5. Hartitz, E. J., "The effect of Lubricants on Fusion time of Rigid Poly (Vinyl Chloride)," SPE 31st ANTEC, May, 1973.
6. Marx, F. M., "A Torque Rheometer Fusion-Point Test for Evaluating Polyvinyl Chloride Extrudability," *The Western Electric Engr.*, Vol. XI, No. 3, Oct., 1968.
7. King, L. F., and Noel, F., "Thermal Stability of Poly (Vinyl Chloride) During Processing," *SPE Vinyl Tech. News letter* Vol. 5, No. 2, Dec., 1968.
8. Gilfillan, E. G., and O'Leary, P. G., "Accelerated Test for Processing Stability of Poly Propylene," SPE 26th ANTEC, May, 1968.
9. Hatt, B. W., "Formulation for Rigid PVC using Multivariate Analysis," Elkem Chemical, Ltd., England.
10. Cheng, C. Y., "Extruder Screw Design for Compounding," *Plastic Compounding*, March/April, 1981.
11. Janssen, L., *Twin Screw Extrusion*, Elsevier Scientific Publishing Co., 1978.
12. Cheng, C. Y., " High Speed Mixing and Extrusion using the Transfer Mix," SPE 36th ANTEC, April, 1976.

CHAPTER 35

COATING USING PSEUDOPLASTIC LIQUIDS

Miodrag N. Tekić and Vujadin O. Popadić

Faculty of Technology
University of Novi Sad
Novi Sad, Yugoslavia

CONTENTS

INTRODUCTION

Coating is a process of the entrainment of a liquid film onto a sheet which is continuously withdrawn from a liquid bath. This is a problem of considerable practical interest, for such applications as [1]:

- Coating of an adhesive to paper or paperboard
- Cellulosic film coating with photographic emulsion
- Plastic films
- Coating of textile fibers and fabrics with finishes or backings
- Metal foils or sheets coated with polymers

Industrial significance has stimulated many experimental and theoretical studies, mostly on Newtonian fluids. The non-Newtonian fluids have been somewhat neglected due to complexity of the mathematical treatment, which required "more work than thinking." However, the liquids we deal with in coating are mostly non-Newtonian, and this part is aimed to pseudoplastic liquids.

THE CONSTITUTIVE EQUATION

The constitutive equation of pseudoplastic liquids is the well known power-law equation:

$$\tau_{ij} = -p\delta_{ij} + K \left| \frac{1}{2} I_2 \right|^{(n-1)/2} \dot{\ell}_{ij} \tag{1}$$

where τ_{ij} = components of the stress

I_2 and $\dot{\ell}_{ij}$ = second invariant and components of the rate of strain, respectively

K = consistency factor

n = flow behavior index

δ_{ij} = Kronecker delta

For pseudoplastic liquids, $0 < n < 1$, and for Newtonian liquids $n = 1$.
The second invariant of the rate of strain is given by:

$$I_2 = -(\dot{\ell}_{11}\dot{\ell}_{22} + \dot{\ell}_{22}{}^{2b}\dot{\ell}_{33} + \dot{\ell}_{11}\dot{\ell}_{33} - \dot{\ell}_{12}^2 - \dot{\ell}_{13}^2 - \dot{\ell}_{23}^2) \tag{2}$$

In steady, laminar, shearing flow, the constitutive equation, Equation 1 has the simple form:

$$\tau_{12} = K(\dot{\gamma})^n \tag{3}$$

where $\dot{\gamma}$ is the rate of shear.

THE EQUATION OF MOTION

The flow field of coating operation for the case of viscous, incompressible liquid with constant physical properties is described by the following system of momentum and continuity equation; in terms of the rectangular coordinates, x, y, z, these are written:

$$\rho\left(u\frac{\partial u}{\partial x} + v\frac{\partial u}{\partial y} + w\frac{\partial u}{\partial z} + \frac{\partial u}{\partial t} \right) = -\rho\frac{\partial\Omega}{\partial x} - \frac{\partial p}{\partial x} + \frac{\partial\tau_{xx}}{\partial x} + \frac{\partial\tau_{xy}}{\partial y} + \frac{\partial\tau_{xz}}{\partial z} \tag{4}$$

$$\rho\left(u\frac{\partial v}{\partial x} + v\frac{\partial v}{\partial y} + w\frac{\partial v}{\partial z} + \frac{\partial v}{\partial t} \right) = -\rho\frac{\partial\Omega}{\partial y} - \frac{\partial p}{\partial y} + \frac{\partial\tau_{yx}}{\partial x} + \frac{\partial\tau_{yy}}{\partial y} + \frac{\partial\tau_{yz}}{\partial z} \tag{5}$$

$$\rho\left(u\frac{\partial w}{\partial x} + v\frac{\partial w}{\partial y} + w\frac{\partial w}{\partial z} + \frac{\partial w}{\partial t} \right) = -\rho\frac{\partial\Omega}{\partial z} - \frac{\partial p}{\partial z} + \frac{\partial\tau_{zx}}{\partial x} + \frac{\partial\tau_{zy}}{\partial y} + \frac{\partial\tau_{zz}}{\partial z} \tag{6}$$

$$\frac{\partial u}{\partial x} + \frac{\partial v}{\partial y} + \frac{\partial w}{\partial z} = 0 \tag{7}$$

where u, v, w = velocity components in the x, y, z directions

t = time

ρ = density

τ_{ij} = components of the stress

p = pressure

Ω = potential of the field in which flow occurs

Since only gravity field will be considered here, the negative derivatives of Ω are merely equal to the components of g in the respective direction.

In order to have flow field fully defined, the corresponding boundary conditions should be added to Equations 4–7. Since the boundary conditions depend on the geometry of the coating operation, they will be given for each analyzed geometry.

FREE COATING

Surface coating by withdrawal from the liquid bath is commonly called free coating. The amount of liquid entrained by the surface depends on the physical and rheological properties of the liquid, and on the geometry and speed of withdrawal.

Relatively successful theoretical analysis of free coating is possible only for the simplest flow situations, such as continuous withdrawal of flat and cylindrical surfaces. The simple geometries of these and steadiness of the operation provide the possibility to obtain the solutions.

The coating process itself is mainly dependent on the flow dynamics of the region where solid surface is being separated from the surface of bath liquid, from which is being withdrawn. The curvature of the free surface, i.e., the meniscus existence at the separation region, makes the influence of surface tension substantial for the coating process.

Free Coating onto a Vertical Surface

In experimental and theoretical analyses major attention has been paid to the coating of flat sheets withdrawn vertically upward with constant speed from the liquid bath. The reason is the suitability of this geometry for experiments, and the simplicity provided for otherwise complicated theoretical analysis of the problem.

Profile of a liquid film adhering to a vertical flat surface continuously withdrawn at the speed u_0 from a stationary liquid bath is shown in Figure 1. As is shown in the figure, three major regions of the flow field could be observed:

- Region of the constant film thickness
- Region of the dynamic meniscus
- Region of the static meniscus

When the flow is steady and laminar in the region far from the surface of the liquid (region 1), a dynamic equilibrium between gravity and viscous force leads to a constant coating film thickness a_0. The flow in this region is constant and the relationship between the sheet velocity u_0 and the film thickness a_0 is fixed, and is in fact determined by the previous regions of the flow. In region 2, referred to as the dynamic or thin meniscus region, the film thickness varies with height above the

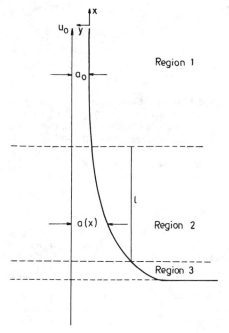

Figure 1. Profile of a liquid film adhering to a vertical moving surface.

bath, x, and it is the result of the interaction of inertial, viscous, gravitational, and interfacial forces. Its extent will be called L, for subsequent analysis. In static or thick meniscus region (region 3) the velocities are small, the viscous and inertial forces are small, and the difference between them must be small compared to the forces of gravity and surface tension. Therefore, this region may be considered as a static condition.

Two major approaches are applied for the analysis of flat surface coating:

- Two-dimensional nonlinear theory, which includes inertial terms of equation of motion
- One-dimensional linearized analysis, which neglects the inertial terms

Boundary Conditions

The boundary conditions should be added to the momentum and continuity equations in order to have the flow field fully defined.

For the free coating, the boundary conditions are as follows:

1. The no-slip condition at the moving sheet yields two boundary conditions:

$$u = u_0, \quad v = 0 \quad \text{at } y = a \tag{8}$$

2. The dynamic balance of stresses at the interface may be expressed by:

$$\frac{1}{2}(\tau_{xx} - \tau_{yy}) \sin 2\theta + \tau_{xy} \cos 2\theta = 0 \quad \text{at } y = 0 \tag{9}$$

$$p + \tau_{xx} \sin^2 \theta + \tau_{yy} \cos^2 \theta + \tau_{xy} \sin^2 \theta = p_0 - \frac{\sigma}{R} \quad \text{at } y = 0 \tag{10}$$

where θ is the angle between the normal to the surface and the y-axis, and R is the radius of curvature of the free surface defined by:

$$R = \frac{d^2a/dx^2}{\left|1 + \left(\dfrac{da}{dx}\right)^2\right|^{3/2}} \tag{11}$$

The conditions in Equations 9 and 10 represent the tangential and the normal stress at the air-liquid interface. The stresses on the atmospheric side of the interface are considered negligible compared to those in the fluid. In industrial operations, however, the air flow is often used to control the coating thickness. In that case, the pressure and shear forces exerted by air on the surface should be considered.

It is also necessary to add the kinematic surface condition, which expresses the fact that the free surface is a streamline:

$$Q = \int_0^a u \, dy = \text{const} \tag{12}$$

For the liquid physical and rheological properties known, and for the given withdrawal speed u_0, Equations 4–7, together with boundary conditions (Equations 8, 9, 10, 12) leads to a family of curves corresponding to various possible film thickness. In order to determine the correct film thickness and its associated curve for the particular complete set of conditions, some additional physical constraints have to be imposed.

Additional conditions can be determined from flow and flow parameters across two fictive horizontal planes placed at the boundaries of the dynamic region. Therefore, one of two boundary conditions is the flow across a horizontal plane through the beginning of the constant thickness region.

Velocities across the horizontal plane passing through the stagnation point are the second set of boundary conditions. Since those velocities are unknown, the boundary condition across the horizontal plane passing through the stagnation point reduces to a relationship between the characteristic of the interface curve at the stagnation point and the flow parameters.

In other words, boundary conditions at the stagnation point preserve the continuity of the slope and curvature of the interface along the entire meniscus. As a static meniscus condition the following equation can be obtained, which describes the equilibrium of gravitational and capillary forces in the thick meniscus region [3]:

$$\frac{\sigma \dfrac{d^2a}{dx^2}}{\left|1 + \left(\dfrac{da}{dx}\right)^2\right|^{3/2}} = \rho gx \tag{13}$$

or [4]:

$$\frac{\sigma}{2\rho g}\left(\frac{d^2a}{dx^2}\right)^2 - \frac{da}{dx} = 1, \tag{14}$$

which may be derived for the static meniscus near the top of the free surface.

Nonlinear Theory

Although the system of Equations 4–7, together with the boundary conditions in Equations 8, 9, 10, and 12, defines fully the flow of a liquid in free coating of flat surfaces, it is necessary to introduce some assumptions and approximations in order to simplify the problem and obtain a solution.

It is clear from physical considerations that the length of dynamic meniscus, L, is significantly larger than the constant film thickness, a_0, so that the condition $\varepsilon = a_0/1 \ll 1$ can be applied. This condition enables the order of magnitude estimation of terms in the system of Equations 4–7 and boundary conditions 8, 9, 10, and 12. Also, by introducing a characteristic vertical speed $u \sim u_0$, through the continuity equation, an expression $v \sim \varepsilon u_0$ can be obtained for the characteristic horizontal speed.

Neglecting the terms of order (ε^2) and assuming steady, laminar, no wave two-dimensional flow, Equations 4–7 and boundary conditions 8, 9, 10, and 12 reduce to the following system [4]:

$$u\frac{\partial u}{\partial x} + v\frac{\partial u}{\partial y} = -\frac{1}{\rho}\frac{\partial p}{\partial x} + \frac{Kn}{\rho}\left|\frac{\partial u^{n-1}}{\partial y}\frac{\partial^2 u}{\partial y^2}\right| - g \tag{15}$$

$$\frac{\partial p}{\partial y} = 0 \tag{16}$$

$$\frac{\partial u}{\partial x} + \frac{\partial y}{\partial y} = 0 \tag{17}$$

$$u = u_0 \qquad v = 0 \qquad \text{at} \quad y = a$$
$$\tag{18}$$
$$\tau_{xy} = 0 \qquad \text{at} \quad y = 0$$

$$(p - p_0) + \sigma\frac{d^2a}{dx^2} - \tau_{yy} = 0 \qquad \text{at} \quad y = 0 \tag{19}$$

Note that a standard approximation [5]:

$$\left|\left(\frac{\partial u}{\partial x}\right)^{n-1}\frac{\partial^2 u}{\partial x^2}\right| \ll \left|\left(\frac{\partial u}{\partial y}\right)^{n-1}\frac{\partial^2 u}{\partial y^2}\right| \tag{20}$$

is applied here. For Newtonian films this is justified, but for pseudoplastic films, when $n \ll 1$ it is clear that the inequality (Equation 20) is not satisfied.

The Equations 12, 15–19 may be replaced by equations integrated with respect to y. This requires knowledge of the velocity profile in the film. It will be assumed here that the local velocity coincides with the exact solution for the laminar constant thickness film. For pseudoplastic liquids this gives:

$$u(x, y) = \frac{2n+1}{n+1} U(x)\left|\left(\frac{y}{a}\right)^{(n+1)/n} - 1\right| + u_0 \tag{21}$$

and, from continuity:

$$v(x, y) = \frac{2n+1}{n+1} y \frac{dU}{dx} - \frac{n}{n+1}\frac{y^{(2n+1)/n}}{a^{(n+1)/n}}\frac{dU}{dx} + \left(\frac{y}{a}\right)^{(2n+1)/n} U \frac{da}{dx} \tag{22}$$

where U(x) is the average velocity over the local film cross section.

After substituting Equations 21 and 22 into Equation 15, making use of the boundary conditions, and integrating over film thickness, Equation 15 becomes:

$$\rho \left|\frac{4(2n+1)}{3n+2} aU \frac{dU}{dx} + \frac{2(2n+1)}{3n+2} U^2 \frac{da}{dx} - u_0 a \frac{dU}{dx} - u_0 U \frac{da}{dx}\right|$$

$$= \sigma a \frac{d^3 a}{dx^3} + K\left(\frac{2n+1}{n}\right)\left(\frac{U}{a}\right)^n - 2Kn\left(\frac{2n+1}{n+1}\right)\left(\frac{dU}{dx}\right)^{n-1}\frac{d^2 U}{dx^2} a - \rho g a \tag{23}$$

By using Equation 21, the constant flux condition along the meniscus can be expressed as:

$$Q = \int_0^a u\, dy = a(x)|u_0 - U(x)| \tag{24}$$

By Equation 24, the function U(x) can be substituted in Equation 23 with function a(x) and by introducing the dimensionless variables:

$$L = \frac{a}{a_0} \qquad \xi = \frac{x}{a_0} \tag{25}$$

Equation 23 becomes:

$$\frac{L^3}{Ca}\frac{dL^3}{d\xi^3} - Re\left|\frac{n}{3n+2} L^2 - \frac{2}{(3n+2)(2n+1)} L_s^2\right|\frac{dL}{d\xi}$$

$$- \frac{2n(2n+1)^n}{(n+1)^n} L^{3-2n}\left(\frac{dL}{d\xi}\right)^{n-1}\frac{d^2 L}{d\xi^2}\left|1 - n + \frac{L_s}{2n+1}\right|$$

$$+ \frac{4n(2n+1)}{(n+1)^n} L^{2-2n}\left(\frac{dL}{d\xi}\right)^{n+1}\left|\frac{nL_s}{2n+1} + 1 - n\right|$$

$$+ \left|\frac{2n+1}{n} L - \frac{L_s}{n}\right|^n L^{2-2n} - T^{2n}L^3 = 0 \tag{26}$$

where $\quad T = \left(\dfrac{\rho g}{K u_0^n}\right)^{1/2n} a_0^{(n+1)/2n}$ $\qquad Ca = \dfrac{a_0^{1-n} u_0^n K}{\sigma}$

$Re = \dfrac{a_0^n u_0^{2-n} \rho}{K}$ $\qquad\qquad\qquad L_s = (2n+1) - nT^2$

$\gamma = \dfrac{\sigma}{\rho} \left| g^{3n-2} \left(\dfrac{K}{\rho}\right)^4 \right|^{-1/(2+n)}$

$Re = T^{3n-2} (Ca\gamma)^{(2+n)/2n}$

Equation 26 is integrated over the thin meniscus region from the beginning of the constant thickness film down to the stagnation point. The integration is done numerically by using the initial conditions at the beginning of the constant film thickness:

$$L = 1 + \varepsilon$$

$$L' = \varepsilon \tag{27}$$

$$L'' = \varepsilon$$

where ε is a small parameter.

By using a simple iteration method, the solution of the numerical integration was adjusted to condition 14 at the stagnation point.

One-Dimensional Theory

One-dimensional treatment of the free coating of flat surfaces by neglecting inertial forces leads to the following analysis of the process:

Region 1: Region of the constant film thickness. The equations of motion for a Power-law liquid reduce to:

$$Kn \left(\dfrac{du}{dy}\right)^{n-1} \dfrac{d^2 u}{dy^2} - \rho g = 0 \tag{28}$$

The appropriate boundary conditions are:

$$u = u_0 \quad \text{at} \quad y = a_0 \quad \text{(no slip)} \tag{29}$$

$$\dfrac{du}{dy} = 0 \quad \text{at} \quad y = 0 \quad \text{(no shear exerted by air)} \tag{30}$$

Corresponding liquid velocity distribution can be written as:

$$u = u_0 + \dfrac{n}{1+n} \left(\dfrac{\rho g}{K}\right)^{1/n} \left(y^{(1+n)/n} - a_0^{(1+n)/n}\right) \tag{31}$$

The value of a_0 is not known, and consequently the solution is not complete. The velocity distribution $u(y)$ for region 2 should be found, and by matching the solutions according to the continuity of the two regions, the addition condition for a_0 obtained.

Region 2: Dynamic meniscus region. In this region, the equation of motion includes pressure and takes the form:

$$Kn\left(\frac{\partial u}{\partial y}\right)^{n-1}\frac{\partial^2 u}{\partial y^2} - \rho g - \frac{\partial p}{\partial x} = 0 \tag{32}$$

Assuming that the curvature of the liquid surfaces is sufficiently small, i.e., $(da/dx) \ll 1$, the free surface is almost vertical, so that the shear stress is well approximated by τ_{xy}, and boundary conditions of Equation 9 take the form

$$\tau_{xy} = 0 \quad \text{at } y = 0 \quad \text{(no shear)} \tag{33}$$

For the same reason, term $1/R$ in Equation 10 can be replaced by d^2a/dx^2, and $\tau \cdot n$ (n — unit vector normal to the free surface) can be approximated by τ_{yy}. Since the y-component of velocity is neglected, it follows that $\tau_{yy} = 0$. However, from the continuity equation for two-dimensional flow, $\tau_{yy} = -\tau_{xx}$, so that the boundary condition in Equation 10 becomes:

$$p + 2K\left(\frac{\partial u}{\partial x}\right)^n = -\sigma\frac{d^2a}{dx^2} \quad \text{at } y = 0 \quad \text{(continuity of normal stress)} \tag{34}$$

Integrating Equation 32, with the no-shear condition of Equation 33 and no slip condition:

$$u = u_0 \quad \text{at } y = a \tag{35}$$

the expression for velocity profile in the region of the dynamic meniscus is obtained:

$$u = u_0 + \left(\frac{\rho g + dp/dx}{K}\right)^{1/n}\frac{n}{1+n}(y^{(1+n)/n} - a^{(1+n)/n}) \tag{36}$$

From equation (36) it follows:

$$\frac{dp}{dx} = K\left|\frac{1+2n}{n}\frac{1}{a^{(1+2n)/n}}(u_0 a - Q)\right|^n - \rho g \tag{37}$$

where $\quad Q = \int_0^a u\,dy \tag{38}$

Note that equation 37 cannot be solved for $p(x)$, because the function $a(x)$ is not known.

By differentiating Equation 34 on (x), using Equation 37 to eliminate dp/dx and Equation 36 to eliminate d^2u/dx^2, an equation for $a(x)$ is obtained:

$$\sigma\frac{d^3a}{dx^3} - 2K\left(\frac{1+2n}{1+n}\right)^n\frac{\partial}{\partial x}\left(\frac{Q\,da}{a^2\,dx}\right)^n + K\left|\frac{1+2n}{n}\cdot\frac{1}{a^{(1+2n)/n}}(u_0 a - Q)\right|^n - \rho g = 0 \tag{39}$$

Or, in dimensionless form:

$$\frac{d^3 L}{d\xi^3} - \left(\frac{n}{1+n}\right)^n 2\left|1 - \frac{n}{1+2n}T_0^{(1+n)/n}\right|^n\left(\frac{1+2n}{n}\right)^{n(1+n)/3}Ca^{(1+n)/3}\frac{d}{d\xi}\left|\frac{1}{L^2}\frac{dL}{d\xi}\right|^n$$

$$+ \left|\frac{1}{L^{(1+2n)/n}}\left(L - 1 + \frac{n}{1+2n}T_0^{(1+n)/n}\right)\right|^n - \left(\frac{n}{1+2n}\right)^n T_0^{1+n} = 0 \tag{40}$$

where $\quad L = \dfrac{a}{a_0} \qquad \xi = \dfrac{x}{a_0}\left|\left(\dfrac{1+2n}{n}\right)^n\dfrac{Ku_0^n}{\sigma a_0^{n-1}}\right|^{1/3}$

$$Ca = \frac{Ku_0^n}{\sigma a_0^{n-1}} \qquad T_0 = a_0\left(\frac{\rho g}{Ku_0}\right)^{1/(n+1)}$$

In Equation 40, value of parameter Q is replaced by a_0 using the solution for region 1, Equation 31, from which follows:

$$Q = u_0 a_0 \left| 1 - \frac{n}{1 + 2n} \left(\frac{\rho g}{K}\right)^{1/n} \frac{a_0^{(1+n)/n}}{u_0} \right| \tag{41}$$

Since a_0, i.e. T_0, is not known, four constraints are needed to solve Equation 40: three boundary conditions for a third other differential equation and a fourth condition to find T_0.

Matching conditions for the regions are used to obtain boundary conditions. Region 1, in terms of L, is specified by:

$$L = 1 \tag{42}$$

$$\frac{dL}{d\xi} = 0 \tag{43}$$

$$\frac{d^2L}{d\xi^2} = 0 \tag{44}$$

Equation 42 follows from the definitions of L and a_0, and Equations 43 and 44 describe the fact that film thickness in region 1 is uniform and that the surface is flat.

The fourth constraint can be obtained by matching the curvatures at the boundary of region 2 and region 3.

Region 3: Static meniscus region. Integrating Equation 13 with the boundary condition:

$$da/dx \longrightarrow -\infty \qquad \text{at} \quad x = 0 \tag{45}$$

an expression for the slope is obtained:

$$\frac{da/dx}{|1 + (da/dx)^2|^{1/2}} = \frac{\rho g x^2}{2\sigma} - 1 \tag{46}$$

At the height x_∞ above the surface of the liquid bath, which is defined as:

$$x_\infty = \left(\frac{2\sigma}{\rho g}\right)^{1/2} \tag{47}$$

the slope disappears. The curvature in that plane is:

$$\left.\frac{d^2a}{dx^2}\right|_{x_\infty} = \left(\frac{2\rho g}{\sigma}\right)^{1/2} \tag{48}$$

or in dimensionless form:

$$\left.\frac{d^2a}{d\chi^2}\right|_{\chi_\infty} = \frac{2^{1/2}}{\left(\dfrac{1 + 2n}{n}\right)^{2n/3}} Ca^{-1/6} T_0^{(1+n)/2} \tag{49}$$

The problem in equating curvatures at the boundary of region 2 and region 3 lies in the behavior of Equation 40. For small values of ξ, $\xi \to 0$; from Equation 40 it follows:

$$L \xrightarrow{\text{lim}} \infty$$

$$\frac{d^3L}{d\xi^3} = \left(\frac{n}{1 + 2n}\right)^n T_0^{1+n}$$

and hence:

$$\frac{d^2L}{d\xi^2} \longrightarrow \infty$$

This disaccords with the curvature value of the upper end of static meniscus (Equation 49). By introducing $L = 1 + \varepsilon$, where ε is a small parameter, it's possible to write Equation 40 in the form:

$$\frac{d^3L}{d\xi^3} - C\left|\frac{n}{L^{2n}}\left|\frac{dL}{d\xi}\right|^{n-1}\frac{d^2L}{d\xi^2} - \frac{2n}{L^{1+2n}}\left|\frac{dL}{d\xi}\right|^{1+n}\right.$$

$$\left. + \left|\frac{1}{L^{(1+2n)/n}}(L-1)(1 - T_0^{(1+n)/n}) + \frac{n}{1+2n}T_0^{(1+n)/n}\right|^n - \left(\frac{n}{1+2n}\right)^n T_0^{1+n} = 0 \right. \tag{50}$$

where:

$$C = 2\left(\frac{n}{1+n}\right)^n \left|\left(\frac{1+2n}{n}\right)^n Ca\right|^{(1+n)/3}\left(1 - \frac{n}{1+2n}T_0^{(1+n)/n}\right)^n$$

Absolute values of the first derivative provide the possibility to avoid taking the root of a negative number and just follows the deviation from Newtonian liquid. Since the third term of Equation 50 is valid only for $L = 1$, it is necessary to check the behavior of the equation for large L. If $C = 0$, we have:

$$\frac{d^3L}{d\xi^3} = 0 \quad \text{as} \quad L \gg 1 \tag{51}$$

or $\quad \dfrac{d^2L}{d\xi^2} = \text{const} \quad \text{as} \quad \xi \longrightarrow 0$

Hence, the curvature becomes constant. Now, a matching procedure to complete the analysis of the problem can be applied. Equation 50 is solved subject to:

$$L = 1$$

$$\frac{dL}{d\xi} = 0 \quad \text{at} \quad \xi \longrightarrow 0$$

$$\frac{d^2L}{d\xi^2} = 0$$

Numerical solution of Equation 50 shows that $d^2L/d\xi^2 = \alpha$ becomes constant for small ξ (large L). However, we note that α will be found to be a function of Ca, T_0, and n. We then solve for T_0 as a function of Ca and n by solving Equation 50 for a pair of values (Ca, T_0, n) and then requiring that the pair also satisfies:

$$T_0 = \left|\left(\frac{1+2n}{n}\right)^{2n/3}\frac{\alpha(Ca, T_0, n)}{2}Ca^{1/6}\right|^{2/(n+1)} \tag{52}$$

A trial-and-error procedure yields $T_0(Ca, n)$.

From the above-shown general solution, some of the theories of free coating on flat surfaces can be obtained as special cases.

Wilkinson's [6] Power-Law Theory

If the normal stress boundary conditions are simplified by omitting the second term on the left-hand side of Equation 34, second term in Equation 50 disappears and the equation becomes:

$$\frac{d^3L}{d\xi^3} + \left. \frac{1}{L^{(1+2n)/n}} (L-1)(1-T_0^{(1+n)/n}) + \frac{n}{1+2n} T_0^{(1+n)/n} \right|^n - \left(\frac{n}{1+2n}\right)^n T_0^{1-n} = 0 \tag{53}$$

Matching the numerical solution of this equation with Equation 52 as described above, gives $T_0(Ca, n)$. Note that in this case, the curvature is a function of T_0 and n, according to Equation 53.

Zero Gravity Theory [7]

If the gravity effects in Equation 53 are neglected, one obtains:

$$\frac{d^3L}{d\xi^3} + \frac{(L-1)^n}{L^{1+2n}} = 0 \tag{54}$$

Numerical solution of Equation 54 gives the curvature for small ξ like Equations 50 and 53, with the difference that α is a function of flow index n only. This makes matching of Equations 54 and 52 using trial and error procedure unnecessary. Value of T_0 is calculated from the expression:

$$T_0 = \left| \left(\frac{1+2n}{n}\right)^{(2n)/3} \frac{\alpha(n)}{2^{1/2}} Ca^{1/6} \right|^{2/(n+1)} \tag{55}$$

Results and Discussion

Film thickness calculated by one-dimensional theories as a function of Ca for various values of flow index n is shown in the Table 1.

A comparison of the predictions of Equation 26 with experimental data and theoretical results obtained by Wilkinson is given in Figure 2. It is evident from Figure 2 that all rheological properties of the liquid, incorporated in the γ parameter, affect the film flow. For that reason the two-dimensional theory has an advantage over one-dimensional theories. This is particularly the case for higher Ca when the significance of inertial terms increases.

Roll Coating

One of the most frequently applied pieces of equipment in coating processes is the device with a roll, which provides the application of uniform liquid film to the moving belt. For design purposes and for equipment operation it is necessary to know the connection of the coating thickness and the process parameters, including rheological and physical properties of the liquid.

The analysis presented here follows the work of Greener and Middleman [8], and it is illustrated by an example given in Figure 3, with the roll and belt moving in the same direction with the same speed. Similar analysis is applicable to cases where speeds and directions are different, as well.

Assuming that the process is mostly determined by the event in the region of the smallest distance between roll and belt, and that in most cases this distance is much smaller than roll diameter, i.e., $a_0 \ll R$, it is reasonable to accept that the surfaces of the roll and belt (and so the flow) are approximately parallel, so that:

$$u \ll v \tag{56}$$

and $\quad \dfrac{\partial}{\partial x} \ll \dfrac{\partial}{\partial y} \tag{57}$

Table 1
Comparison of One-Dimensional Theories for Various Values of Flow Index n

	n = 0.9			n = 0.6			n = 0.3		
Ca	T_0^1	T_0^2	T_0^3	T_0^1	T_0^2	T_0^3	T_0^1	T_0^2	T_0^3
0.0001	0.1890	0.1888	0.1994	0.1599	0.1593	0.1874	0.1289	0.1277	0.1735
0.0004	0.2359	0.2352	0.2543	0.2034	0.2018	0.2501	0.1699	0.1666	0.2475
0.0007	0.2576	0.2565	0.2805	0.2235	0.2211	0.2811	0.1896	0.1845	0.2857
0.001	0.2722	0.2708	0.2986	0.2372	0.2342	0.3027	0.2031	0.1966	0.3130
0.004	0.3358	0.3320	0.3808	0.2976	0.2897	0.4041	0.2644	0.2480	0.4467
0.007	0.3649	0.3592	0.4201	0.3257	0.3143	0.4541	0.2939	0.2707	0.5156
0.01	0.3845	0.3772	0.4473	0.3451	0.3306	0.4891	0.3146	0.2857	0.5650
0.04	0.4704	0.4513	0.5704	0.4333	0.3999	0.6529	0.4124	0.3474	0.8061
0.07	0.5102	0.4826	0.6292	0.4765	0.4266	0.7336	0.4625	0.3736	0.9305
0.1	0.5373	0.5029	0.6699	0.5068	0.4453	0.7902	0.4987	0.3906	1.0200
0.4	0.6573	0.5821	0.8543	0.6487	0.5194	1.0548	0.6785	0.4579	1.4548
0.7	0.7115	0.6136	0.9424	0.7149	0.5496	1.1852		0.4854	1.6793
1	0.7466	0.6333	1.0033	0.7585	0.5689	1.2766		0.5030	1.8401
2	0.8139	0.6707	1.1330	0.8397	0.6059	1.4749		0.5370	2.1980
3	0.8504	0.6918	1.2166	0.8822	0.6272	1.6049		0.5567	2.4388
4	0.8737	0.7063	1.2796	0.9082	0.6421	1.7041		0.5707	2.6255
6	0.9038	0.7261	1.3739		0.6627	1.8543		0.5901	2.9132
8	0.9225	0.7397	1.4450		0.6771	1.9688		0.6038	3.1362
10	0.9346	0.7500	1.5027		0.6880	2.0625		0.6143	3.3209

[1] *Present power-law theory*
[2] *Wilkinson power-law theory [6]*
[3] *zero gravity theory [7]*

Accordingly, for a steady operation, and neglecting the inertial forces, the momentum equations, Equations 4 and 5, become:

$$0 = \frac{\partial p}{\partial x} + K \frac{\partial}{\partial y} \left\{ \left| \left(\frac{\partial u}{\partial y} \right)^2 \right|^{(n-1)/2} \frac{\partial u}{\partial y} \right\} \tag{58}$$

$$\frac{\partial p}{\partial y} = 0 \tag{59}$$

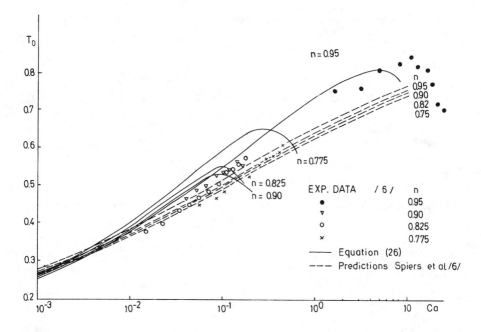

Figure 2. Comparasion of the nonlinear theory with experimental data and theoretical results obtained by Spiers et al. [6].

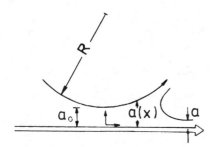

Figure 3. Definition sketch for analysis of roll coating.

When the peripheral speed of the roll is equal to the belt speed u_0, then appropriate boundary conditions are:

$$u = u_0 \quad \text{at} \quad y = 0 \tag{60}$$

$$u = u_0 \quad \text{at} \quad y = a(x) \tag{61}$$

where $a(x)$ is the equation of roll surface. The second term at the right-hand side of Equation 58 is written in the form given because by squaring the shear rate, $(\partial u/\partial y)$, before taking the fractional root indicated, it is possible to avoid taking a fractional root of a negative number. Such a "crisis" arises in this flow since there are regions where $\partial u/\partial y$ is negative.

For the given geometry and limiting the analysis to the case $x \ll R$, the equation of the surface might be approximated by the expression:

$$a(x) = a_0 \left(1 + \frac{x^2}{2a_0 R} \right) \tag{62}$$

It is convenient for later operations to make the problem dimensionless by defining:

$$\xi = \frac{x}{(a_0 R)^{1/2}} \qquad u_x = \frac{u}{u_0}$$

$$\eta = \frac{y}{a_0} \qquad p = \left(\frac{a_0}{u_0} \right)^n \left(\frac{a_0}{R} \right)^{1/2} \frac{p}{K} \tag{63}$$

In terms of the new variables, Equation 58 and boundary conditions 60 and 61 take the form:

$$0 = -\frac{\partial p}{\partial \xi} + \frac{\partial'}{\partial \eta} \left\{ \left| \left(\frac{\partial u_x}{\partial \eta} \right)^2 \right|^{(n-1)/2} \frac{\partial u_x}{\partial \eta} \right\} \tag{64}$$

$$u_x = 1 \qquad \text{at} \quad \eta = 0 \tag{65}$$

$$u_x = 1 \qquad \text{at} \quad \eta = \bar{a}(\xi) \tag{66}$$

$$\text{where} \quad \bar{a}(\xi) = \frac{a(x)}{a_0} = 1 + \frac{1}{2} \xi^2 \tag{67}$$

From Equation 59, it follows that P is a function of ξ only, so that it's possible to integrate Equation 64, and using boundary conditions 65 and 66, obtain an expression for the velocity distribution:

$$u_x = 1 + \frac{n}{n+1} \left(\frac{\partial P}{\partial \eta} \right)^{1/n} \left| \eta^{(1+n)/n} - \eta^{1/n} \bar{a}(\xi) \right| \tag{68}$$

This equation gives u_x as an explicit function of η and as an implicit function of ξ through $\bar{a}(\xi)$ and $\partial P/\partial \xi$.

From continuity, by introducing Q, volume flow rate per coating width, the following is obtained:

$$Q = \int_0^{a(x)} u \, dy \tag{69}$$

or in dimensionless form:

$$\lambda = \frac{Q}{u_0 a_0} = \int_0^{a(x)} u_x \, d\eta. \tag{70}$$

By applying Equation 68 and integrating, the expression for $P(\xi)$ is written:

$$P(\xi) = A \int_{-\xi_0}^{\xi} \frac{|(\bar{a} - \lambda)^2|^{(n-1/2)}(a - \lambda)}{\bar{a}^{1+2n}} \tag{71}$$

$$\text{where} \quad A = \left(\frac{1 + 2n}{n} \right)^n 2^{1+n} \tag{72}$$

and ξ_0 is the value of ξ for which $P = 0$. Equation 71 is integrated so that it is assumed (in the absence of any other information) that $-\xi_0$ is practically $-\infty$.

$$Q = 2u_0a \tag{73}$$

and

$$\lambda = \frac{2a}{a_0} \tag{74}$$

In order to evaluate λ, the geometry and the dynamics of the separation region should be considered. Let us assume that the film equally separates, as shown in Figure 3. Then the separation point is $(\xi_1, \frac{1}{2}\bar{a}_1)$.

At the separation point the velocity vanishes, so that:

$$0 = 1 - \frac{1 + 2n}{1 + n} \frac{\bar{a}_1 - \lambda}{\bar{a}_1} \tag{75}$$

and

$$\bar{a}_1 = 1 + \frac{1}{2}\xi_1^2 = \frac{1 + 2n}{n}\lambda \tag{76}$$

The constraint $P(\xi_1) = 0$, gives (by setting the upper limit at ξ_1 in Equation 71) an integral equation for λ, which has to be solved by trial-and-error.

The calculations presented in Figure 4 show that λ is moderately increased by non-Newtonian shear behavior.

The influence of flow index n on the pressure distribution is shown in Figure 5. It is seen that p increases with decreasing n. When comparing, one should keep in mind that the dimensionless pressure is analyzed.

It does not necessarily follow that the actual pressure p for a non-Newtonian fluid is always higher than that of a Newtonian fluid, without considering the basis for comparison.

Once the pressure distribution is known, it is possible, using Equation 68, to calculate velocity distribution and so the stresses. From these, the roll sheet separating force and forces required to tear the roll and pull the sheet can be obtained; hence, the roll/sheet separating force is:

$$F = WK\left(\frac{u_0}{a_0}\right)^n Rf(n) \tag{77}$$

The function f(n) is given in Figure 6.

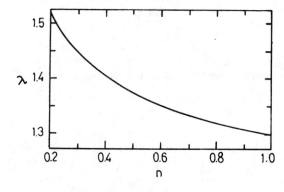

Figure 4. Nondimensional coating thickness λ as a function of n.

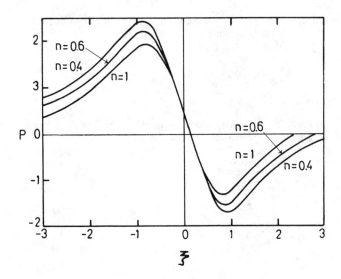

Figure 5. Pressure profiles for Newtonian and power law fluids.

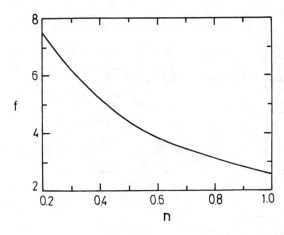

Figure 6. Nondimensional roll-separating force as a function of n.

Wire Coating

The analysis presented here follows fully the work of Roy, S. C. and Dutt, D. K. [9], whose theory is derived also by dividing the entire film thickness profile into three regions, as shown in Figure 7.

Assuming one-dimensional flow of a pseudoplastic liquid, the equation of motion for the x-component (Figure 7) reduces to the following form:

$$\frac{d}{dx}\left|\sigma\left(C_V^P - C_R^P\right)\right| - \rho g - \frac{K}{r}\frac{d}{dr}\left|r\left(-\frac{du}{dr}\right)^n\right| = 0 \qquad (78)$$

In the surface tension term of Equation 78, C_R^P is the principal curvature, radial direction, and C_V^P the principal curvature, vertical plane.

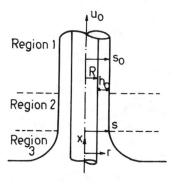

Figure 7. Definition sketch for analysis of wire coating.

This equation is valid for all three regions, and the flow equations for the specific region can be obtained from it by introducing assumptions applicable to the region.

Region 1: Region of the constant film thickness. This region occurs at a distance approximately eight times the constant film thickness above the stagnation point. In this region the surface tension effects do not enter the flow equation, and the flow equation becomes:

$$-\rho g - \frac{K}{r}\frac{d}{dr}\left| r\left(-\frac{du}{dr}\right)^n \right| = 0 \tag{79}$$

The wall and air-liquid interface boundary conditions are:

$$u = u_0 \qquad \text{at} \quad r = R$$

$$\tau_{rx} = 0 \qquad \text{at} \quad r = s_0$$

Equation 79 is integrated to get the velocity profile and the flow rate Q, as:

$$Q_1 = 2\pi u_0 \int_R^{s_0} r \, dr - 2\pi \left(\frac{\rho g}{2K}\right)^{(1/n)} s_0^{(1+1/n)} \int_R^{s_0} r \, dr \int_{(R/s_0)}^{r} \left(\frac{1}{r} - r\right)^{1/n} dr \tag{80}$$

By introducing:

$$F(S_0) = \int_1^{S_0} \left(1 - \frac{1}{r^2}\right)^{(1+1/n)} r^{(1/n)-2} \, dr \tag{81}$$

where $S_0 = s_0/R$, Equation 80 simplifies to:

$$Q_1 = \pi u_0 R^2 S_0^2 - \pi u_0 R^2 - \pi \left(\frac{\rho g}{2K}\right)^{(1/n)} (S_0 R)^{(3+1/n)} F(S_0) \tag{82}$$

Equation 82 can be used to calculate the film thickness knowing the values of wire diameter, withdrawal speed, flow rate, and liquid properties. The film thickness so calculated will represent the true film thickness if the operation conditions satisfy the assumptions made earlier in this work.

Region 2: Dynamic meniscus region. Equation 78 for this region becomes:

$$\sigma \frac{d}{dx}\left(\frac{d^2s}{dx^2}\right) - \rho g - \frac{K}{r}\frac{d}{dr}\left| r\left(-\frac{du}{dr}\right)^n \right| = 0 \tag{83}$$

The wall and interface boundary conditions are:

$$u = u_0 \quad \text{at} \quad r = R$$

$$\tau_{rx} = 0 \quad \text{at} \quad r = s$$

By applying the usual procedure to obtain velocity profile and flow rate from Equation 83, the expression for flow rate, Q_z, was obtained:

$$Q_2 = \pi u_0 (s^2 - R^2) - \pi \left(\frac{\rho g}{2K} - \frac{\sigma}{2K} \frac{d^3 s}{dx^3} \right)^{(1/n)} s^{(3 + 1/n)} F(S) \tag{84}$$

where $\quad S = \dfrac{s}{R}$

$$F(S) = \int_1^s \left(1 - \frac{1}{r^2} \right)^{(1 + 1/n)} r^{(1/n) - 2} \, dr \tag{85}$$

Flow Matching for Regions 1 and Region 2

Matching flow for these two regions by continuity and simplification, one obtains:

$$\left(\frac{\rho g}{2K} - \frac{\sigma}{2K} \frac{d^3 s}{dx^3} \right)^{(1/n)} s^{(3 + 1/n)} F(S) = u_0 (s^2 - s_0^2) + \left(\frac{\rho g}{2K} \right)^{(1/n)} s_0^{(3 + 1/n)} F(S_0) \tag{86}$$

This equation is transfered into dimensionless form as:

$$\left(D_1^{(n + 1)} + \frac{d^3 L}{dB_1^3} \right)^{(1/n)} F(LS_0) = \frac{(L^2 - 1) + D_1^{(1 + 1/n)} F(S_0)}{L^{(3 + 1/n)}} \tag{87}$$

Appropriate initial conditions are:

$$L = 1$$

$$\frac{dL}{dB_1} = 0 \tag{88}$$

$$\frac{dL}{dB_1} = 0 \quad \text{at} \quad B_1 = 0$$

where $\quad \dfrac{d^2 L}{dB_1^2} = 0$

$L = \dfrac{s}{s_0} \quad$ relative coated radius, dimensionless coordinate

$D_1 = s_0 \left(\dfrac{\rho g}{2K u_0^n} \right)^{(1/(n + 1))} \quad$ dimensionless coated radius

$B_1 = - \left| \dfrac{2K}{\sigma} \dfrac{u_0^n}{s_0^{n + 2}} \right|^{1/3} \cdot x \quad$ dimensionless coordinate

Equations 87 and 88 represent the most general one-dimensional problem for power-law liquids.

Region 3: Static meniscus region. Equation 78 for the static meniscus reduces to the following equation:

$$\sigma \frac{d}{dx}(C_V^P - C_R^P) - \rho g = 0 \qquad (89)$$

Evidently, Equation 89 is the same for both Newtonian and non-Newtonian fluids. The curvature at the top of region 3 was calculated by White and Tallmadge [10]. In the range of practical interest, the curvature is given by:

$$\lim_{s \to s_0} \frac{d^2s}{dx^2} = \frac{2}{a_i} \left| \frac{3.36\,(S_0 G_0)}{1 + 3,36\,(S_0 G_0)} + \frac{0.5}{S_0 G_0} \right| \qquad (90)$$

where $\quad a_1 = \left(\dfrac{2\sigma}{\rho g}\right)^{1/2} \qquad$ capillary length

$\qquad G_0 = R\left(\dfrac{\rho g}{2\sigma}\right)^{1/2} \qquad$ dimensionless wire radius, Goucher number

The curvature values of Equation 90 were compared with experimental data on Newtonian liquids. The accuracy was within 0.5% for all G_0^{11}.

Curvature Matching for Regions 2 and 3.

The matching condition of equal radii of curvature can be stated in dimensionless form as:

$$\lim_{L \to 1} \frac{d^2L}{dB_1^2} = \lim_{L \to \infty} \frac{d^2L}{dB_1^2}. \qquad (91)$$

The general solution of Equation 87 with initial conditions 88 appears to be very difficult.

However, an approximate solution of Equation 87 can be obtained by putting $L = 1 + \varepsilon$, using binomial series and Taylor series, and neglecting terms of order ε^2 and above:

$$\frac{d^3\varepsilon}{dB_1^3} = \left\{ \frac{2nD_1^{(n-1/n)}}{F(S_0)} - \frac{nS_0 F'(S_0)}{F(S_0)} D_1^{n+1} - (3n+1)D_1^{n+1} \right\} \frac{\varepsilon}{(1+\varepsilon)^{3n+1}} \qquad (92)$$

where $\quad F'(S_0) = \frac{d}{dS_0} \left| \int_1^{S_0} \left(1 - \frac{1}{r^2}\right)^{(1+1/n)} r^{(1/n)-2}\,dr \right|$

$$= \left(1 - \frac{1}{S_0^2}\right)^{(1+1/n)} S_0^{(1/n)-2} \qquad (93)$$

Introducing a new independent variable:

$$B_2 = \left\{ \frac{2nD_1^{(n-1/n)}}{F(S_0)} - \frac{nS_0 F'(S_0)}{F(S_0)} D_1^{n+1} - (3n+1)D_1^{n+1} \right\}^{1/3} B_1 \qquad (94)$$

one obtains:

$$\frac{d^3L}{dB_2^3} = \frac{L-1}{L^{3n+1}} \qquad (95)$$

Table 2
Effect of n on α

n	α	n	α
0.3	1.8619	0.7	0.6174
0.4	1.2194	0.8	0.5317
0.5	0.9165	0.9	0.4671
0.6	0.7371	1.0	0.4166

Equation 95 was solved numerically to obtain the values of:

$$\alpha = \lim_{L \to \infty} \frac{d^2 L}{dB_2^2} \tag{96}$$

The values of α so calculated are given in Table 2.
From Equations 91, 94 and 96:

$$u_0 = \frac{\left\{ \left[(3n+1) + \frac{nS_0 F'(S_0)}{F(S_0)} \right] \left(\frac{\rho g}{\sigma} \right) + \left(\frac{2C_m}{a_1 S_0 R \alpha} \right)^{3/2} (S_0 R) \right\} (S_0 R)^{(1 + 1/n)} \left(\frac{\rho g}{2K} \right)^{1/n} F(S_0)}{2n \left(\frac{\rho g}{\sigma} \right)} \tag{97}$$

where $\quad C_m = \frac{3.36 (S_0 G_0)}{1 + 3.36 (S_0 G_0)} + \frac{0.5}{S_0 G_0}.$ $\tag{98}$

Equation 97 serves for prediction of the cylinder withdrawal speed needed to obtain required constant film thickness a_0, when cylinder radius R and liquid properties (ρ, σ, K, n) are known.

Elastic effects of liquids are not considered, so that equation is not expected to hold for the withdrawal of viscoelastic liquids.

Comparison with Experiments

The experimental data available are very restricted. The authors compared their theory with the experimental data of Middleman [12] and Roy [13].

Physical properties of the liquids studied are given in Table 3, and the comparison of data with theory is given in Table 4.

Table 3
Physical Properties of Fluids

Author	Fluid	μ Ns/m²	ρ kg/m³	σ mN/m	γ_1	$\dfrac{K}{\dfrac{Ns^n}{m^2}}$	n
Middleman [12]	80% Glycerine	0.061	1.210	70.7	0.133	—	1.0
Roy [14]	Mineral oil	0.02205	0.876	28.4	0.104	—	1.0
Middleman [12]	0.5% Poly-ox 301	0.11	1.000	62.4	0.089	0.108	0.73
Roy [14]	0.5% Carbopol 941	0.894*	1.000	69.0	1.49	4.518**	0.523

* Low shear viscosity.
** Calculated from Pseudo consistency index

Table 4
Comparison of Measured Withdrawal Speed with Predicted Speed

Fluid	Wire Radius R, cm.	Film thickness h_0, cm.	Experimental u_0 cm./sec.	Predicted u_0 |Eq. (97)| cm./sec.	G_0	Ca_1
0.5% Polyox 301	0.0262	0.0175	11.9	12.7	0.073	0.21
do	0.0262	0.0214	17.6	19.2	0.073	0.31
do	0.0262	0.0252	22.7	28.3	0.073	0.4
do	0.0262	0.0272	28.9	34.6	0.073	0.51
do	0.0262	0.0328	35.2	51.4	0.073	0.62
do	0.0262	0.0404	45.4	78.9	0.073	0.8
do	0.0262	0.0454	56.7	98.5	0.073	1.0
do	0.0262	0.0510	61.3	127.8	0.073	1.08
Mineral oil	0.0445	0.0270†	17.2	16.02	0.173	0.134
do	0.0445	0.0651†	87.3	90.6	0.173	0.678
do	0.0445	0.0840†	125.4	145.8	0.173	0.974
do	0.0317	0.00715†	10.6	13.7	0.123	0.082
do	0.0317	0.0435†	61.7	59.7	0.123	0.479
do	0.0317	0.0541†	87.3	87.01	0.123	0.678
do	0.0187	0.0214†	36.3	32.6	0.073	0.282

† *Photographic thickness reported by Roy [13]*
* *Calculated from experimental flow rate data reported by Roy [14] by using Equation 82.*

NOTATION

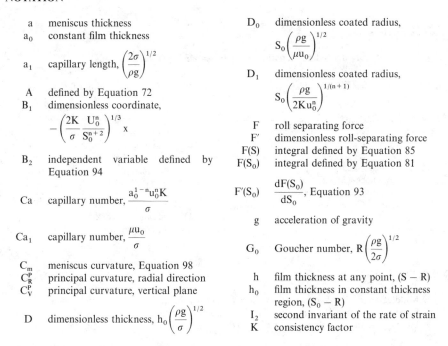

a	meniscus thickness
a_0	constant film thickness
a_1	capillary length, $\left(\dfrac{2\sigma}{\rho g}\right)^{1/2}$
A	defined by Equation 72
B_1	dimensionless coordinate, $-\left(\dfrac{2K}{\sigma}\dfrac{U_0^n}{S_0^{n+2}}\right)^{1/3}x$
B_2	independent variable defined by Equation 94
Ca	capillary number, $\dfrac{a_0^{1-n}u_0^n K}{\sigma}$
Ca_1	capillary number, $\dfrac{\mu u_0}{\sigma}$
C_m	meniscus curvature, Equation 98
C_R^P	principal curvature, radial direction
C_V^P	principal curvature, vertical plane
D	dimensionless thickness, $h_0\left(\dfrac{\rho g}{\sigma}\right)^{1/2}$

D_0	dimensionless coated radius, $S_0\left(\dfrac{\rho g}{\mu u_0}\right)^{1/2}$
D_1	dimensionless coated radius, $S_0\left(\dfrac{\rho g}{2Ku_0^n}\right)^{1/(n+1)}$
F	roll separating force
F′	dimensionless roll-separating force
F(S)	integral defined by Equation 85
$F(S_0)$	integral defined by Equation 81
$F'(S_0)$	$\dfrac{dF(S_0)}{dS_0}$, Equation 93
g	acceleration of gravity
G_0	Goucher number, $R\left(\dfrac{\rho g}{2\sigma}\right)^{1/2}$
h	film thickness at any point, $(S - R)$
h_0	film thickness in constant thickness region, $(S_0 - R)$
I_2	second invariant of the rate of strain
K	consistency factor

l   extent of thin meniscus

$\dot{\ell}_{ij}$ components of the rate of strain

L   dimensionless meniscus thickness, $\dfrac{a}{a_0}$

L_S dimensionless thickness at stagnation point

n   flow behavior index

p   hydrostatic pressure

p_0 static pressure of air

P   dimensionless pressure,

$$\left(\frac{a_0}{u_0}\right)^n \left(\frac{a_0}{R}\right)^{1/2} \frac{p}{K}$$

Q   liquid flux

Q_1 volume flow rate of liquid in Region 1

Q_2 volume flow rate of liquid in Region 2

r   radial coordinate

R   radius curvature, roll diameter, wire radius

Re   Reynolds number, $\dfrac{a_0^n u_0^{2-n}\rho}{K}$

s   radius of coated wire at any point

s_0 radius of coated wire in Region 1

S   dimensionless coated radius, $\dfrac{s}{R}$

S_0 dimensionless coated radius, $\dfrac{s_0}{R}$

t   time

T   dimensionless film thickness,

$$a_0^{(n+1)/2n}\left(\frac{\rho g}{K u_0^n}\right)^{1/(n+1)}$$

T_0 dimensionless film thickness,

$$a_0\left(\frac{\rho g}{K u_0^n}\right)^{1/(n+1)}$$

u, v, w   velocity of liquid in x, y, and z directions, respectively

u   vertical velocity of liquid

u_0 withdrawal speed

u_x dimensionless vertical velocity, $\dfrac{u}{u_0}$

U   average velocity over local film cross section

v   horizontal velocity of liquid

W   width of the roll

x, y, z   rectangular coordinates

x   vertical coordinate

y   horizontal coordinate

Greek Symbols

α   curvature defined by Equation 96

γ   dimensionless parameter,

$$\frac{\sigma}{\rho}\left|g^{3n-2}\left(\frac{K}{\rho}\right)^4\right|^{-1/(2+n)}$$

γ_1 dimensionless parameter,

$$K\left(\frac{\rho g^3}{\sigma}\right)^{n/4}\Big/(\rho g\sigma)^{1/2}$$

$\dot{\gamma}$ rate of shear

δ_{ij} Kronecker delta

ε   ratio a_0/ℓ, small parameter

η   dimensionless horizontal coordinate, $\dfrac{y}{a_0}$

μ   viscosity of liquid

λ   dimensionless liquid flux, $\dfrac{Q}{u_0 a_0}$, dimensionless film thickness

σ   surface tension

τ_{ij} components of the stress

θ   angle between the normal to the surface and the y-axis

ζ   dimensionless vertical coordinate,

$$\frac{x}{a_0},\ \frac{x}{a_0}\left|\left(\frac{1+2^n}{n}\right)^n\cdot\frac{K u_0^n}{\sigma a_0^{n-1}}\right|\frac{x}{(a_0 R)^{1/2}}$$

Ω   potential of the field

ρ   liquid density

REFERENCES

1. Middleman, S., *Fundamentals of Polymer Processing*, McGraw-Hill, Inc., 1977, New York.
2. Esmail, M. N., and Hummel, R. L., AIChE J., 1975 *21*, 958.
3. Landau, L., and Levich, B., *Acta Phys. URS*, 1942 *17*, 41.

4. Deryaqin, B. V., and Levi, S. M., *Film Coating Theory*, Focal Press, New York, 1964.
5. Tekić, M. N., and Popadić, V. O., *Chem. Engng. Sci.*, 1983 *38*, 285.
6. Spiers, R. P., Subbaraman, C. V., and Wilkinson, W. L., *Chem. Engng. Sci.* 1975 *30*, 379.
7. Gutfinger, C., and Tallmadge, J. A., *AIChE J.* 1965 *11*, 403.
8. Greener, J., and Middleman S., *Polymer Engng. Sci.* 1975 *15*, 1.
9. Roy, S. C., and Dutt, D. K., *Chem. Engng. Sci.* 1981 *36*, 1933.
10. White, D. A., and Tallmadge, J. A., *Chem. Engng.. Sci.* 1965 *20*, 33.
11. Tallmadge, J. A., *AIChE J.*, 1966 *12*.
12. Middleman, S., *Polymer Engng. Sci.* 1978 *18*, 355.
13. Roy, S. C., *Can. J. Chem. Engng.* 1971 *49*, 583.
14. Roy, S. C., Thesis, M. S., Illinois Inst. Technol., January 1967.

INDEX